Authors

3rd EDITION AUTHORS

Susan A. Brown, *Mathematics Department Chair*
York High School, Elmhurst, IL

R. James Breunlin, *Mathematics Department Chair*
Schaumburg High School, Schaumburg, IL

Mary Helen Wiltjer, *Mathematics Teacher*
Oak Park and River Forest High School, Oak Park, IL

Katherine M. Degner, *Mathematics Teacher*
Williamsburg Comm. High School, Williamsburg, IA

Susan K. Eddins, *Mathematics Teacher (retired)*
IL Mathematics & Science Academy, Aurora, IL

Michael Todd Edwards, *Assistant Professor of Mathematics Education*
Miami University, Ohio, Oxford, OH

Neva A. Metcalf, *Mathematics Teacher*
Evanston Township High School, Evanston, IL

Natalie Jakucyn, *Mathematics Teacher*
Glenbrook South High School, Glenview, IL

Zalman Usiskin, *Professor of Education*
The University of Chicago

AUTHORS OF EARLIER EDITIONS

John W. McConnell, *Instructional Supervisor of Mathematics*
Glenbrook South High School, Glenview, IL

Sharon Senk, *Professor of Mathematics*
Michigan State University, East Lansing, MI

Ted Widerski, *Mathematics Teacher*
Waterloo High School, Waterloo, WI

Cathy Hynes Feldman, *Mathematics Teacher*
The University of Chicago Laboratory Schools

James Flanders, UCSMP

Margaret Hackworth, *Mathematics Supervisor*
Pinellas County Schools, Largo, FL

Daniel Hirschhorn, UCSMP

Lydia Polonsky, UCSMP

Leroy Sachs, *Mathematics Teacher (retired)*
Clayton High School, Clayton, MO

Ernest Woodward, *Professor of Mathematics*
Austin Peay State University, Clarksville, TN

www.WrightGroup.com

Copyright © 2008 by Wright Group/McGraw-Hill.

Printed in the United States of America.

Send all inquiries to:
Wright Group/McGraw-Hill
P.O. Box 812960
Chicago, IL 60681

ISBN 978-0-07-611012-4
MHID 0-07-611012-5

2 3 4 5 6 7 8 9 VHP 13 12 11 10 09 08 07

The University of Chicago School Mathematics Project

ALGEBRA

Teacher's Edition

VOLUME 2 • CHAPTERS 7–13

Authors

Susan A. Brown
R. James Breunlin
Mary Helen Wiltjer
Katherine M. Degner
Susan K. Eddins
Michael Todd Edwards
Neva A. Metcalf
Natalie Jakucyn
Zalman Usiskin

Director of Evaluation

Denisse R. Thompson

Mc Graw Hill **Wright Group**

The **McGraw·Hill** Companies

Since the first two editions of *Algebra* were published, millions of students and thousands of teachers have used the materials. Prior to the publication of this third edition, the materials were again revised, and the following teachers and schools participated in evaluations of the trial version during 2005–2006:

Shannon Johnson, *Junction City Middle School*
Junction City, KS

Julie Pellman, *Hyman Brand Hebrew Academy*
Overland Park, KS

Dan Kramer, *Highlands High School-Ft. Thomas*
Fort Thomas, KY

Craig Davelis, Megan Mehilos,
Sue Nolte, Lynette TeVault, *York High School*
Elmhurst, IL

Jan Boudreau, *Rosemont Middle School*
La Crescenta, CA

Tammy Anderson, *Ashland High School*
Ashland, OR

Dennis Massoglia, *Washington Middle School*
Calumet, MI

Erica Cheung, *Stone Scholastic Academy*
Chicago, IL

The following schools participated in field studies in 1992–1993, 1987–1988, or 1986–1987 as part of the first edition or the second edition research.

Rancho San Joaquin Middle School
Lakeside Middle School
Irvine High School
Irvine, CA

D.W. Griffith Jr. High School
Los Angeles, CA

Mendocino High School
Mendocino, CA

Chaffey High School
Ontario, CA

Eagleview Middle School
Colorado Springs, CO

Lincoln Junior High School
Lesher Junior High School
Blevins Junior High School
Fort Collins, CO

Bacon Academy
Colchester, CT

Rogers Park Jr. High School
Danbury, CT

Clearwater High School
Clearwater, FL

Safety Harbor Middle School
Safety Harbor, FL

Aptakisic Junior High School
Buffalo Grove, IL

Austin Academy
Bogan High School
Disney Magnet School
Hyde Park Career Academy
Von Steuben Metropolitan Science Center
Washington High School
Chicago, IL

Morton East High School
Cicero, IL

O'Neill Middle School
Downers Grove, IL

Elk Grove High School
Elk Grove Village, IL

Glenbrook South High School
John H. Springman School
Glenview, IL

Mendota High School
Mendota, IL

Carl Sandburg Jr. High School
Winston Park Jr. High School
Palatine, IL

Grant Middle School
Springfield, IL

McClure Junior High School
Western Springs, IL

Hubble Middle School
Wheaton, IL

Central Junior High School
Lawrence, KS

Old Rochester High School
Mattapoisett, MA

Fruitport High School
Fruitport, MI

Sauk Rapids-Rice Schools
Sauk Rapids, MN

Parkway West Middle School
Chesterfield, MO

Taylor Middle School
Van Buren Middle School
Albuquerque, NM

Crest Hills Middle School
Shroder Paideia Middle School
Walnut Hills High School
Cincinnati, OH

Lake Oswego Sr. High School
Lake Oswego, OR

Springfield High School
Springfield, PA

R.C. Edwards Jr. High School
Central, SC

Easley Junior High School
Easley, SC

Liberty Middle School
Liberty, SC

Northeast High School
Clarksville, TN

Hanks High School
El Paso, TX

Robinson Middle School
Maple Dale Middle School
Fox Point, WI

Glen Hills Middle School
Glendale, WI

▷ Contents

VOLUME 1

VOLUME 2

 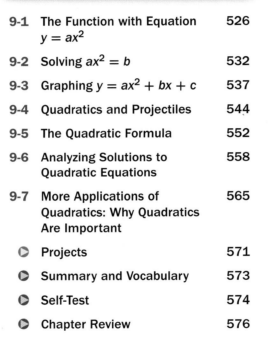

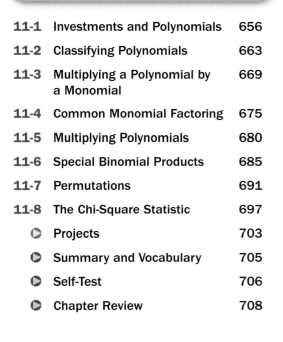
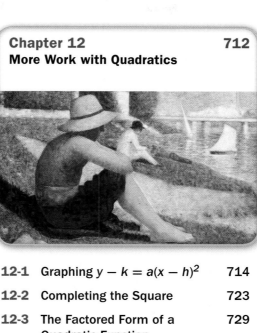

Chapter 7

Using Algebra to Describe Patterns of Change

Chapter Overview		Local Standards	Pacing (in days)		
			Average	Advanced	Block
7-1	**Compound Interest** **D** Calculate compound interest.		1	1	0.5
7-2	**Exponential Growth** **E** Solve problems involving exponential growth and decay. **H** Graph exponential relationships.		1	1	0.5
7-3	**Exponential Decay** **E** Solve problems involving exponential growth and decay. **H** Graph exponential relationships.		1	1	0.75
	QUIZ 1		0.5	0.5	0.25
7-4	**Modeling Exponential Growth and Decay** **E** Solve problems involving exponential growth and decay. **F** Determine whether a situation is constant increase, constant decrease, exponential growth, exponential decay, or a nonconstant change.		1	0.5	0.5
7-5	**The Language of Functions** **C** Use the language of functions. **I** Graph functions.		1	1	0.5
7-6	**Function Notation** **A** Evaluate functions. **C** Use the language of functions. **I** Graph functions.		1	0.5	0.75
	QUIZ 2		0.5	0.5	0.25
7-7	**Comparing Linear Increase and Exponential Growth** **B** Calculate function values in spreadsheets. **G** Compare linear increase with exponential growth.		1	1	0.5
	Self-Test		1	1	0.5
	Chapter Review		2	2	1
	Test		1	1	0.5
	TOTAL		**12**	**11**	**6.5**

Technology Resources

Teacher's Assessment Assistant, Ch. 7

Electronic Teacher's Edition, Ch. 7

Differentiated Options Universal Access

	Accommodating the Learner	Vocabulary Development	Ongoing Assessment	Materials
7-1	pp. 400, 402		written, p. 403	scientific or graphing calculator
7-2	pp. 406, 407	p. 405	oral, p. 410	graphing calculator or graphing software
7-3	pp. 412, 413	p. 415	group, p. 418	graphing calculator
7-4	pp. 421, 422		written, p. 424	graphing calculator
7-5	pp. 427, 428		group, p. 431	
7-6	pp. 434, 435		written, p. 438	Computer Algebra System (CAS)
7-7	pp. 441, 442		oral, p. 446	graphing calculator or computer with spreadsheet software

Objectives

		Lessons	Self-Test Questions	Chapter Review Questions
Skills				
A	Evaluate functions.	7-6	1–4, 11–14	1–8
B	Calculate function values in spreadsheets.	7-7	25	9, 10
Properties				
C	Use the language of functions.	7-5, 7-6	9, 15, 16	11–13
Uses				
D	Calculate compound interest.	7-1	5	14–17
E	Solve problems involving exponential growth and decay.	7-2, 7-3, 7-4	8, 10	18–20
F	Determine whether a situation is constant increase, constant decrease, exponential growth, exponential decay, or a nonconstant change.	7-4	24	21–26
G	Compare linear increase with exponential growth.	7-7	6, 7, 18, 19	27, 28
Representations				
H	Graph exponential relationships.	7-2, 7-3	20, 21, 23	29–33
I	Graph functions.	7-5, 7-6	17, 22	34–40

Resource Masters Chapter 7

Resource Master 1, Graph Paper (page 2), can be used with Lessons 7-1 through 7-7. **Resource Master 2, Four-Quadrant Graph Paper** (page 3), can be used with Lessons 7-2 through 7-5, and 7-7. **Resource Master 4, Graphing Equations** (page 5), can be used with Lessons 7-2 and 7-4. **Resource Master 5, Spreadsheet** (page 6), can be used with Lesson 7-7.

Resource Master 98 Lesson 7-1

Warm-Up

In the following table, P_1, P_2, and P_3 stand for the three population estimates on page 397 and x stands for the number of years from now. Complete the table. Then discuss the results and describe trends in the data.

x	P_1	P_2	P_3
0			
1			
2			
3			
10			
20			
40			
60			

Additional Examples

1. Suppose you deposit P dollars in a savings account upon which the bank pays an annual yield of 3.5%. If the account is left alone, how much money will be in it at the end of a year?

2. Suppose you deposit $200 in a savings account upon which the bank pays an annual yield of 3.5%.
   a. If the account is left alone, how much money will be in it at the end of three years?
   b. How much interest did you earn in the three years?

Resource Master for Lesson 7-1

Resource Master 99 Lesson 7-1

Additional Example

3. When the twins were born, their parents put $3,000 into an account for college. What will be the total amount of money in the account after 19 years at an annual yield of 5.9%?

Questions 17–19

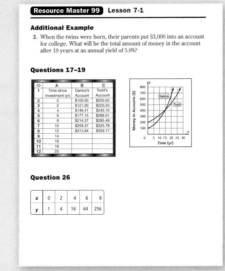

Question 26

x	0	2	4	6	8
y	1	4	16	64	256

Resource Master for Lesson 7-1

Resource Master 100 Lesson 7-2

Warm-Up

1. Calculate 2^x, for $x = 0, 1, 2, \ldots, 28$.

Additional Examples

1. Thirty deer are introduced to a forest preserve. Assume that the deer population doubles every year. How many deer would there be after 25 years?

2. Graph the equation $y = 1.1 \cdot 2.1^x$, when x is 0, 1, 2, 3, 4.

Exponential Population Growth

Year	Population
1930	5,677,251
1940	6,907,387
1950	10,586,223
1960	15,717,204
1970	19,971,069
1980	23,667,764
1990	29,760,021
2000	33,871,648

Source: U.S. Census Bureau

Resource Master for Lesson 7-2

Resource Master 101 Lesson 7-2

Question 12

Time Intervals from Now	Time (min)	Number of Mold Spores
0	0	3,000
1	20	12,000
2	40	48,000
3	60	192,000

Question 13

Source: Bureau of the Census

Question 14

Stage of Gossip	0	1	2	3	4	5	6	7	8	9	10
New Friends Informed	1	2	4								
Total Number of Friends Informed	1	3	7								

Resource Master for Lesson 7-2

Resource Master 102 Lesson 7-3

Warm-Up

In 1–3, graph the equation with a graphing utility. Idenfity:
   a. the y-intercept of each graph.
   b. three points on the graph.
   c. the line that the graph approaches as x becomes very large.

1. $y = 100(0.80)^x$
2. $y = 21,000(0.85)^x$
3. $y = 10(0.97)^x$

Additional Example

1. Assume that each day after cramming, a student forgets 15% of the words known the day before. A student crams for a Spanish test on Thursday by learning 120 vocabulary words on Wednesday night. But the test is delayed from Thursday to Monday. If the student does not study more, how many words is he or she likely to remember on Monday?

Resource Master for Lesson 7-3

Resource Master 104 Lesson 7-3
Resource Master 103 Lesson 7-3

Additional Examples

2. In June 1953, the first Chevrolet Corvette rolled off the assembly line with a sticker price of approximately $3,000. Suppose its value depreciated by 9% each year after production.
   a. Find an equation that gives the car's value y when it is x years old.
   b. What was the predicted value of the car in 1960? How close is this to the actual price of a 1953 Corvette, which was $1,640, in 1960?
   c. Graph the car's value for the interval $0 \leq x \leq 5$.
   d. What was the predicted value of the car in 2006? How close is this to the actual price of a 1953 Corvette, which was $59,900 in 2006?

3. Caffeine is a drug found in a wide variety of food products consumed by Americans. In fact, more than half of all adult Americans consume at least 300 milligrams of caffeine every day. Once in the body, it takes about 6 hours for half of the caffeine to be eliminated. Suppose the pattern of eliminating caffeine from the body continues after it is ingested at one time; that is, half of the remaining caffeine is eliminated every 6 hours.
   a. Write an equation to describe y, the amount of caffeine in the bloodstream after x six-hour periods have passed.
   b. Make a calculator table for the equation from Part a. Use the table to find when approximately 1 milligram of caffeine remains in the body.
   c. How much caffeine remains after 108 hours?
   d. According to the equation, when will the amount of caffeine in the body be zero?

Resource Masters for Lesson 7-3

Resource Master for Lesson 7-4

Resource Master 105 Lesson 7-4

Warm-Up

In 1–4, tell whether the situation is constant increase, constant decrease, exponential growth, exponential decay, or nonconstant examples of these.

1. There were originally 400 bacteria in a dish, and the number of bacteria has been doubling every 20 minutes.
2. The population of bears has been decreasing by 15 each year.
3. The population of zebras has been decreasing by 15% each year.
4. Each day the young heifer gains between 2 and 5 pounds.

Resource Masters for Lesson 7-4

Resource Master 107 Lesson 7-4
Resource Master 106 Lesson 7-4

Additional Example

The diagram and table below show the world's population at various points in time.

1. Write an equation to model the data.
2. Find the deviation between the actual value for the year 2000 and the predicted value.
3. Use the model to predict the world's population in 2050.

Year	Years since 1900	World's Population (in billions)
1900	0	1.6
1950	50	2.55
1960	60	3
1970	70	3.7
1980	80	4.5
1990	90	5.3
2000	100	6.1
2006	106	6.5

Resource Master for Lesson 7-5

Resource Master 108 Lesson 7-5

Warm-Up

In 1–4, find the value of y when $x = 8$.

1. $y = 3 \cdot 2^x$
2. $y = 6x^2$
3. $y = 17 - (8 - x)$
4. $y = 7 + \sqrt{\frac{x+1}{4}}$

Additional Examples

1. Consider the square root function $y = \sqrt{x}$, which pairs nonnegative real numbers with their square roots.
   a. Give the domain.
   b. Find the value of the function when $x = 9$.
2. What are the domain and range of the function described by the equation $y = -2x + 7$?
3. In Lesson 7-2, the equation $y = 5,000 \cdot 1.04^x$ describes a function that models the total amount of money y in a savings account after x years. If $5,000 is invested at an annual yield of 4%, what is the range of this function?

Resource Master for Lesson 7-5

Resource Master 109 Lesson 7-5

The Domain and Range of a Function

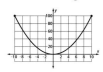

Question 10

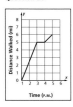

Resource Master for Lesson 7-5

Resource Master 110 Lesson 7-5

Question 13

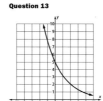

Questions 16–18

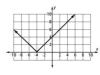

Resource Master for Lesson 7-6

Resource Master 111 Lesson 7-6

Warm-Up

In 1–4, suppose $f(x) = 3(x + 12)$.

1. Calculate $f(5)$.
2. Calculate $f(-2.5)$.
3. Calculate $f(0) + f(1)$.
4. For what value of x does $f(x) = 15$?

In 5–9, suppose $g(x) = 2^x - x$.

5. Calculate $g(0)$.
6. Calculate $g(1)$.
7. Calculate $g(2)$.
8. Calculate $g(3)$.
9. Calculate $g(10)$.

Additional Examples

1. Given a function with equation $f(x) = -3x - 1$, find $f(3)$.
2. Use the three functions given on pages 432 and 433 for population models to find $E(15)$, $L(15)$, and $C(15)$. Explain what the results mean in the context of the population situation.
3. Possibility 2, on page 432, used the linear function $L(x) = 100,000 + 3,000x$ to model the population of a town x years in the future. According to this model, in how many years will the population reach 170,000?

Resource Master for Lesson 7-6

Resource Master 112 Lesson 7-6

Additional Example

4. For the exponential model $E(x) = 100,000(1.02)^x$, use the graph to find when the population reaches 200,000.

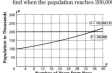

Question 11

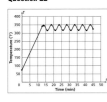

Resource Master for Lesson 7-7

Resource Master 113 Lesson 7-7

Warm-Up

Let $E(x) = 1.1^x$ and $L(x) = 1,000x$.

1. Which is greater, $E(0)$ or $L(0)$?
2. Which is greater, $E(10)$ or $L(10)$?
3. Which is greater, $E(100)$ or $L(100)$?
4. Which is greater, $E(1,000)$ or $L(1,000)$?

Comparing Using a Graph

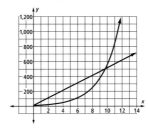

Resource Master for Lesson 7-7

Resource Master 114 Lesson 7-7

A Summary of Constant Increase and Exponential Growth

Constant Increase	Exponential Growth
• Begin with an amount b.	• Begin with an amount b.
• Add m (the slope) in each of the x time periods.	• Multiply by g (the growth factor) in each of the x time periods.
• After x time periods, the amount: $L(x) = mx + b$.	• After x time periods, the amount: $E(x) = b \cdot g^x$.
$L(x) = mx + b, \ m > 0$	$E(x) = b \cdot g^x, \ g > 1$

Chapter 7 **Using Algebra to Describe Patterns of Change**

Pacing

Each lesson in this chapter is designed to be covered in one day. At the end of the chapter, you should plan to spend 1 day to review the Self-Test, 1 to 2 days for the Chapter Review, and 1 day for a test. You may wish to spend a day on projects and possibly a day is needed for quizzes. This chapter should therefore take 10 to 13 days. We strongly advise you to not spend more than 14 days on this chapter; there is ample opportunity to review ideas in later chapters.

Chapter 7 Projects

At the end of each chapter, you will find projects related to the chapter. At this time, you might want to have students look over the projects on pages 447 and 448. You might want to have students tentatively select a project on which to work. Then, as students read and progress through the chapter, they can finalize their project choices.

Sometimes students might work alone; at other times, you might let them collaborate with classmates for a presentation and discussion. We recommend that you allow for diversity and encourage students to use their imaginations when presenting their projects. As students work on projects throughout the year, they should see the many uses of mathematics in the real world.

Contents

A small city of 100,000 people has been growing. School planners want to know how many classrooms the city might need during the next 50 years. They consider three possibilities.

1. The population stays the same.

2. The population increases by 3,000 people per year (increasing by a constant amount).

3. The population grows by 2% a year (increasing at a constant growth rate).

The graph on the next page shows what would happen under the three possibilities. P is the population x years from now.

Chapter 7 Overview

This chapter introduces two topics, exponential growth and functions. These topics have made their way into introductory algebra courses because of their importance and because technology has made them easily accessible. Scientific calculators allow students to obtain values of exponential functions that before would often require logarithms. Graphing calculators make it possible to see functions more easily and more clearly than with hand graphing.

The first examples of nonlinear graphs to examine are exponential functions, not quadratic functions. Exponential growth and exponential decay are among the most used mathematical concepts in modern business, finance, biology, physics, and sociology. The graphs of quadratics are studied in Chapter 9.

(continued on next page)

Possibility 3 is often considered the most reasonable. Under this assumption, $P = 100{,}000(1.02)^x$. Because the variable x is an exponent, this equation is said to represent *exponential growth.* This chapter discusses the important applications of exponential growth and compares them with the constant-increase and constant-decrease situations you studied in Chapter 6.

397

Lesson 7-1 introduces a topic—compound interest—that all students will encounter whether or not they take algebra. Compound interest is an example of exponential growth that is studied in Lesson 7-2. This is contrasted with exponential decay in Lessons 7-3 and 7-4.

Lessons 7-5 and 7-6 introduce the language and notation of functions. Rather than making the discussion more abstract, the language of functions makes it easier to discuss the broad issue of change.

In these lessons, we speak of the change in the dependent variable as the independent variable changes. For many students, this is the first time that they encounter the idea of a variable *varying,* the idea from which "variable" gets its name. With this language, it is easier to discuss different types of functions and to compare linear and exponential functions, as is done in Lesson 7-7.

Lesson 7-1

GOAL

Review the meaning of powers as repeated multiplication and introduce students to compound interest.

SPUR Objective

(The SPUR Objectives for all of Chapter 7 are found in the Chapter Review on pages 452–455.)

D Calculate compound interest.

Materials/Resources

- Lesson Masters 7-1A or 7-1B
- Resource Masters 1, 98, and 99
- Scientific or graphing calculator

HOMEWORK

Suggestions for Assignment
- Questions 1–27
- Question 28 (extra credit)
- Reading Lesson 7-2
- Covering the Ideas 7-2

Local Standards

---

1 Warm-Up

In the following table, P_1, P_2, and P_3 stand for the three population estimates on page 397 and x stands for the number of years from now. Complete the table. Then discuss the results and describe trends in the data.

x	P_1	P_2	P_3
0	(100,000)	(100,000)	(100,000)
2	(100,000)	(106,000)	(104,040)
10	(100,000)	(130,000)	(121,899)
60	(100,000)	(280,000)	(328,103)

P_1 is constant. P_2 increases steadily. P_3 grows slower than P_2 initially, but after 20 years starts growing faster and produces a larger estimated population after 40 years.

Lesson 7-1 Compound Interest

> ▶ **BIG IDEA** Compound interest is the way most banks and other savings institutions pay savers who put their money into their accounts.

Powers and Repeated Multiplication

A number having the form x^n is called a **power.** When n is a positive integer, x^n describes repeated multiplication. For example, $10^3 = 10 \cdot 10 \cdot 10 = 1{,}000$ and $3^5 = 3 \cdot 3 \cdot 3 \cdot 3 \cdot 3 = 243$. These are examples of the following property.

> **Repeated Multiplication Property of Powers**
>
> When n is a positive integer, $x^n = \underbrace{x \cdot x \cdot \ldots \cdot x}_{n \text{ factors}}$.

The number x^n is called the **nth power** of x and is read "x to the nth power" or just "x to the n." In the expression x^n, x is the **base** and n is the **exponent.** Thus, 3^5 is read "3 to the 5th power," or "3 to the 5th," where 3 is the base and 5 is the exponent. In the expression $100{,}000(1.02)^x$ found on page 397, 1.02 is the base and x is the exponent. The number 100,000 is the coefficient of the power 1.02^x.

How Is Interest Calculated?

An important application of exponents and powers occurs with savings accounts. When you save money, you can choose where to put it. Of course, you can keep it at home, but banks, savings and loan associations, and credit unions will pay you to let them hold your money for you. The amount you give them at the start is called the **principal.** The amount they pay you is called **interest.**

Interest is always a percent of the principal. The percent that the money earns per year is called the **annual yield.**

Background

Compound interest is very important for students to understand. Savings accounts, loans, and investments all involve compound interest. As consumers, it is probably accurate to say that the Compound Interest Formula $I = P(1 + r)^n$ is more important for students to know than the Pythagorean Theorem.

Another reason is pedagogical: compound interest naturally deals with powering as repeated multiplication, and easily brings one into exponents greater than 2 or 3.

If you invest money at 6% for 10 years, your investment is repeatedly multiplied by 1.06 ten times; that is, it is multiplied by 1.06^{10}.

A third reason is that our studies have shown that students who have not studied compound interest score lower than on multiple-choice items involving this topic, which means that misconceptions overcome any correct ideas they might have. For such a major consumer topic, it is important to remove these misconceptions.

(continued on next page)

Example 1

Suppose you deposit *P* dollars in a savings account upon which the bank pays an annual yield of 4%. If the account is left alone, how much money will be in it at the end of a year?

Solution

Total = principal + interest (4% of principal)

$= P + 0.04P$

$= (1 + 0.04)P = 1.04P$

You will have 1.04P, or 104% of the principal.

 QY1

Compound Interest and How It Is Calculated

When the year is up, the account will have extra money in it because of the interest it earned. If that money is left in the account, then at the end of second year, the bank will pay interest on all the money that is now in the account (the original principal and the first year's interest). This leads to **compound interest,** which means that the interest earns interest.

Example 2

Suppose you deposit $100 in a savings account upon which the bank pays an annual yield of 4%. Assume the account is left alone in Parts a and b.

a. How much money will be in the account at the end of 4 years?

b. How much interest would you earn in the 4 years?

Solution

a. Refer to Example 1. Each year the amount in the bank is multiplied by $1 + 0.04 = 1.04$.

End of first year: $100(1.04) = 100(1.04)^1 = 104.00$

End of second year: $100(1.04)(1.04) = 100(1.04)^2 = 108.16$

End of third year:

$100(1.04)(1.04)(1.04) = 100(1.04)^3 = 112.4864 \approx 112.48$

End of fourth year:

$100(1.04)(1.04)(1.04)(1.04) = 100(1.04)^4 \approx 116.9858 \approx 116.98$

At the end of 4 years there will be $116.98 in the account.

b. Because you started with $100, you earned $116.98 − $100 = $16.98 in the 4 years.

> **QY1**
>
> If you deposited $1,000 in a savings account with an annual yield of 4%, what would you have at the end of a year?

Compound Interest   **399**

2 Teaching

Notes on the Lesson

Compound interest and how it is calculated. The Compound Interest Formula need not be learned by rote if compounding is thought of as a scale change of $1 + r$ repeated *n* times. Two ideas are fundamental to having students see this. One is the Distributive Property, as shown in Example 1. The other is expressing repeated products as powers, as in Example 2.

Additional Examples

Example 1 Suppose you deposit *P* dollars in a savings account upon which the bank pays an annual yield of 3.5%. If the account is left alone, how much money will be in it at the end of a year? **1.035P**

Example 2 Suppose you deposit $200 in a savings account upon which the bank pays an annual yield of 3.5%.

a. If the account is left alone, how much money will be in it at the end of three years? **$221.74**

b. How much interest did you earn in the 3 years? **$21.74**

How is interest calculated? According to federal law, investment advertisements must state both the interest rate and the annual yield. The difference between annual *rate* and annual *yield* is as follows: the interest rate determines the multiplier used when interest is calculated for each compounding period. The annual yield is the result of doing this over one year.

For example, suppose an investment has an 8.25% *annual rate* compounded daily. We would expect the *annual yield* to be slightly higher. Each day the account would earn $\frac{1}{365}$ of 8.25%, so the amount is multiplied by $1 + \frac{0.0825}{365}$. When compounded 365 times, the multiplier is $\left(1 + \frac{0.0825}{365}\right)^{365} \approx 1.0860 = 108.60\%$. In effect, the account has grown by 8.60%. Thus, the annual rate of 8.25% compounded daily equals a rate of about 8.60% yearly, and 8.60% is the annual yield.

7-1

Notes on the Lesson

Even though they have used the $\boxed{\wedge}$ key on their calculators before, some students will need additional instruction and practice in its use. Because we often use long time periods and sometimes use nonintegral values for r and for n, the calculator is indispensable here. Instead of using the key sequence shown in Example 3, students may find it easier to evaluate $P(1 + r)^n$ by keying in $(1 + r)^n$ first and then multiplying by P. Parentheses are needed either way, unless the student mentally adds 1 to the rate.

Note-Taking Tips

Students should define all of the variables involved in the Compound Interest Formula when they write the formula in their notebooks. They often confuse A with P and vice versa. Make sure they include examples along with the definition.

Additional Example

Example 3 When the twins were born, their parents put $3,000 into an account for college. What will be the total amount of money in the account after 19 years at an annual yield of 5.9%? **$8,915.47**

Examine the pattern in the solution to Example 2. At the end of t years there will be $100(1.04)^t$ dollars in the account. By replacing 100 by P for principal, and 0.04 by r for the *annual yield,* we obtain a general formula for compound interest.

> **Compound Interest Formula**
>
> If a principal P earns an annual yield of r, then after t years there will be a total amount A, where $A = P(1 + r)^t$.

The compound interest formula is read "*A* equals *P* times the quantity 1 plus *r*, that quantity to the *t*th power."

> **GUIDED**
>
> ### Example 3
>
> When Jewel was born, her parents put $2,000 into an account for college. What will be the total amount of money in the account after 18 years at an annual yield of 5.4%?
>
> **Solution** Here $P =$ $2,000, $r = 5.4\%$, and $t = 18$. Substitute the values into the Compound Interest Formula. Use $5.4\% = 0.054$.
>
> $A = P(1 + r)^t$
>
> $\quad = \underline{\ ?\ } (1 + \underline{\ ?\ })^{\underline{\ ?\ }}$ 2,000; 0.054; 18
>
> To evaluate this expression, use a calculator key sequence such as the following.
>
> $\underline{\ ?\ }$ $\boxed{\times}$ $\underline{\ ?\ }$ $\boxed{\wedge}$ $\underline{\ ?\ }$ $\boxed{\text{ENTER}}$ 2000; 1.054; 18
>
> Your display shows $\underline{\ ?\ }$, which rounded down to the nearest cent is $\underline{\ ?\ }$. 5154.196734; $5,154.19
>
> In 18 years, at an annual yield of 5.4%, $2,000 will increase to $\underline{\ ?\ }$. $5,154.19

STOP **QY2**

Eighteen years may seem like a long time, but it is not an unusually long amount of time for money to be in college accounts or retirement accounts.

Why Do You Receive Interest on Savings?

Banks and other savings institutions pay you interest because they want money to lend to other people. The bank earns money by charging a higher rate of interest on the money they lend than the rate they pay customers who deposit money.

Tuition fees at public four-year colleges increased 35% between 2001 and 2006.

Source: The College Board

> ▸ **QY2**
>
> Suppose you invest $6,240 in an account at 6.3% annual yield for 10 years. How much will be in the account at the end of the 10 years?

400 Using Algebra to Describe Patterns of Change

> **Accommodating the Learner** ⬆
>
> Most financial institutions compound interest on investments more than once a year. The formula for compound interest given in this lesson can be modified to take this into account. Explain to the students that if a financial institution compounds interest more often, the formula would be $A = P\left(1 + \frac{r}{n}\right)^{nt}$ where n is the number of times interest is compounded each year. Have students compare the changes in interest earned for different values of n. Some suggestions would be letting n be 1 for annually, 2 for semi-annually, 4 for quarterly, and 12 for monthly.

Thus, if the bank could loan the $1,000 you deposited at 4% (perhaps to someone buying a car) at 12% a year, the bank would receive 0.12($1,000), or $120 from that person. So the bank would earn $120 − $40 = $80 in that year on your money. Part of that $80 goes for salaries to the people who work at the bank, part for other bank costs, and part for profit to the owners of the bank.

Questions

COVERING THE IDEAS

1. How is the expression 4^{10} read?
   "4 to the 10th power" or "4 to the 10th"
2. Consider the expression $10x^9$. Name each of the following.
   a. base x b. power x^9 c. exponent 9 d. coefficient 10

3. a. Calculate 7^3 without a calculator. 343
   b. Calculate 7^3 with a calculator. Show your key sequence.
      343; 7 [^] 3 [ENTER]

In 4–6, rewrite the following expressions using exponents.

4. $\underbrace{\frac{5}{9} \cdot \frac{5}{9} \cdot \ldots \cdot \frac{5}{9}}_{t \text{ times}}$ $\left(\frac{5}{9}\right)^t$

5. $18 \cdot -3 \cdot -3 \cdot -3 \cdot -3$ $18 \cdot (-3)^4$

6. $21 \cdot x \cdot x \cdot x \cdot x \cdot x \cdot x \cdot x \cdot x \cdot x \cdot x$ $21x^{10}$

7. On page 397, three possibilities are offered for the growth of a population. What is the predicted population in 50 years using the indicated possibility?
   a. Possibility 1 100,000 people
   b. Possibility 2 250,000 people
   c. Possibility 3 about 269,159 people

8. **Matching** Match each term with its description.
   a. money you deposit iii   i. annual yield
   b. interest paid on interest ii   ii. compound interest
   c. yearly percentage paid i   iii. principal

In 9 and 10, write an expression for the amount in the bank after 1 year if P dollars are in an account with the annual yield given.

9. 2% 1.02P   10. 3.25% 1.0325P

11. a. Write the Compound Interest Formula. $A = P(1 + r)^t$
    b. What does A represent? total amount including interest
    c. What does P stand for? starting principal
    d. What is r? annual yield
    e. What does t represent? number of years

Compound Interest   **401**

Extension

Before calculators became common, the Rule of 72 was used to approximate an answer to two questions:

What interest rate will double my investment in Y years?

The answer to this question is approximated by dividing the number 72 by the number of years you wish to invest the money. For example if you invest your money for 6 years, divide 72 by 6 to get 12%.

How long will it take me to double my money if I invest my money at P% per year?

The answer to this question is approximated by dividing the number 72 by the rate of return. For example, if you invest your money at 5%, divide 72 by 5 to get 14.4 years.

Recommended Assignment
- Questions 1–27
- Question 28 (extra credit)
- Reading Lesson 7-2
- Covering the Ideas 7-2

Notes on the Questions

Question 2 Go over this question carefully to ensure that students are familiar with the vocabulary of powers.

Question 8 Go over this question carefully for the language of compound interest.

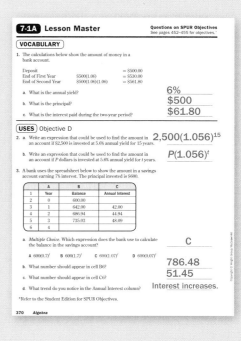

7-1

Notes on the Questions

Question 15 Some students are surprised that after several years the interest from 8% annual yield is not exactly twice that earned from 4% annual yield. Extend this situation to investigate what happens to each investment after 6 years.

Question 16 The answer to this question also surprises students. The lesser rate compounded more often yields more money. Have students verify this by comparing 1.10^{30} with 1.05^{60}.

Question 20 Students are expected to solve this problem by using *trial and error*. Another way to answer this question is to use the *Rule of 72*. If money is invested at x% annual yield, it will double in about $\frac{72}{x}$ years. Your class can test this rule with several interest rates.

Question 28 Newspaper ads often give the annual rate, the number of times per year the interest is compounded, and the annual yield. Use local interest rates as a source for Warm-Up problems. You can also extend the work in the text to study the General Compound Interest Formula $T = P\left(1 + \frac{i}{t}\right)^{nt}$, where t = the number of times per year interest is compounded.

Additional Answers

16. (a) because $P(1.05)^6 \approx 1.34P$,
    $P(1.1)^3 \approx 1.33P$ and $1.34 > 1.33$

17b., 18b.

Time since investment (yr)	Danica's Account	Todd's Account
0	$100.00	$200.00
2	$121.00	$220.50
4	$146.41	$243.10
6	$177.16	$268.02
8	$214.36	$295.49
10	$259.37	$325.78
12	$313.84	$359.17
14	$379.74	$395.98
16	$459.49	$436.57
18	$555.99	$481.32
20	$672.74	$530.66

In 12–14, assume the interest is compounded annually.

12. Suppose you deposit $300 in a new savings account paying an annual yield of 2.5%. If no deposits or withdrawals are made, how much money will be in the account at the end of 5 years? **$339.42**

13. A bank advertises an annual yield of 4.81% on a 5-year CD (certificate of deposit). If the CD's original amount was $2,000, how much will it be worth after 5 years? **$2,529.55**

14. How much interest will be earned in 7 years on a principal of $1,000 at an annual yield of 5.125%? **$418.86**

APPLYING THE MATHEMATICS

In 15 and 16, assume the interest is compounded annually.

15. Susana invests $250 at an annual yield of 4%. Jake invests $250 at an annual yield of 8%. They leave the money in the bank for 2 years. **15a: Susana earns $20.40; Jake earns $41.60**
    a. How much interest does each person earn?
    b. Jake's interest rate is twice Susana's. Does Jake earn twice the interest that Susana does? Why or why not?

15b. No. After the first year, he has more money on which to earn interest than Susana does.

16. Which yields more money, (a) an amount invested for 6 years at an annual yield of 5%, or (b) the same amount invested for 3 years at an annual yield of 10%? Explain your answer. **See margin.**

In 17–19 on the next page, use the following: Danica invested $100 in an account that earns an annual yield of 10%. On the same day, Todd deposited $200 in an account earning 5% annually. Below are a graph and a spreadsheet that compare the amount in Danica's and Todd's accounts.

◇	A	B	C
1	Time since Investment (yr)	Danica's Account	Todd's Account
2	0	$100.00	$200.00
3	2	$121.00	$220.50
4	4	$146.41	$243.10
5	6	$177.15	$268.01
6	8	$214.37	$295.49
7	10	$259.37	$325.78
8	12	$313.84	$359.17
9	14		
10	16		
11	18		
12	20		

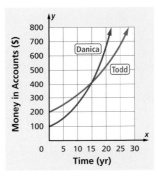

Accommodating the Learner ⬇

Students do not really understand why it is important to look for the best interest rate. Have students experiment with a fixed amount of money. Students should build a table similar to the one below and look at the effect of changing the interest rate.

Students also do not really understand how long it actually takes for their money to grow. Have students experiment with a fixed but reasonable interest rate. Students should build a table similar to the one below and look at the effect of time on an investment.

Interest Rate	2%	4%	6%	10%	12%
Interest Earned					

Years Invested	1	5	10	15	25
Total $ in Account					

17. **a.** What formula will show the amount in Danica's account after t years? $A = 100 \cdot 1.1^t$

   b. Complete the column indicating the amounts in Danica's account. **See margin.**

18. Repeat Question 17 for Todd's account. **18a.** $A = 200 \cdot 1.05^t$
   18b. See margin.

19. In what year will Danica and Todd have the same amount in their accounts? **around year 15**

20. Use your calculator to make a table. If a principal of $1,000 is saved at an annual yield of 5% compounded annually and nothing is withdrawn from the account, in how many years will it double in value? **about 3rd month in year 14; See margin for table.**

REVIEW

21. In World Cup Soccer, a team gets 3 points for a win and 1 point for a tie. Let W be the number of wins and T the number of ties. **(Lessons 6-9, 3-7)**

   a. If a team has more than 3 points, what inequality must W and T satisfy? $3W + T > 3$

   b. Graph all possible pairs (W, T) for a team that has played 3 games and has more than 3 points. **See margin.**

22. Miho puts $6.00 into her piggy bank. Each week thereafter she puts in $2.50. (The piggy bank pays no interest.)

   a. Write an equation showing the total amount of dollars Y after X weeks. $Y = 2.5X + 6$

   b. Graph the equation. **(Lesson 6-2) See margin.**

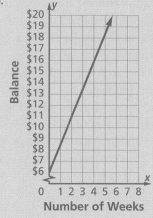

Ecuador's Ulises De La Cruz, left, and England's Joe Cole battle for the ball during a 2006 World Cup soccer match between England and Ecuador.

23. Find the probability of getting a number that is a factor of 12 in one toss of a fair die. **(Lesson 5-6)** $\frac{5}{6}$

In 24 and 25, solve the sentence. (Lessons 4-5, 4-4)

24. $38c - 14 = 6(c - 3) + 4$ **24.** $c = 0$

25. $8(2 + \frac{1}{8}u) > 2u + 1 - u$ **25.** all real numbers

26. **Multiple Choice** Which formula describes the numbers in the table at the right? **(Lesson 1-2)** C

   A $y = x + (x + 1)$ **B** $y = 2x$

   C $y = 2^x$ **D** $y = x^2$

x	0	2	4	6	8
y	1	4	16	64	256

27. Find t if $2^t = 32$. **(Previous Course)** $t = 5$

EXPLORATION

28. Find out the yield for a savings account in a bank or other savings institution near where you live. (Often these yields are in newspaper ads.) **Answers vary. Sample answer: 1.50% APY**

QY ANSWERS

1. $1,040

2. $11,495.20

---

4 Wrap-Up

Ongoing Assessment

Ask students to find the total amount of money they would have in their account if they invest $500 at 4% for 5 years. **$608.32** Students should compare this to the total amount of money they would have in their account if they had invested the same $500 at 8% for 5 years. **$734.66**

Project Update

If you have not had students look over the projects on pages 447 and 448, you might want to do so now. Project 3, Richter Scale, on page 447, relates to the content of this lesson.

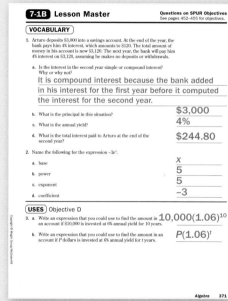

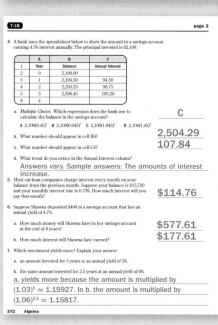

Additional Answers

20.

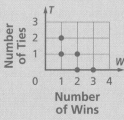

21b.

22b.

Lesson 7-2

Lesson 7-2

Exponential Growth

GOAL

Help students understand how some situations lead to exponential growth and introduce them to graphs associated with such growth.

SPUR Objectives

E Solve problems involving exponential growth and decay.

H Graph exponential relationships.

Materials/Resources

· Lesson Masters 7-2A or 7-2B

· Resource Masters 1, 2, 4, 100, and 101

· Graphing calculator or graphing software

HOMEWORK

Suggestions for Assignment

• Questions 1–20

• Question 21 (extra credit)

• Reading Lesson 7-3

• Covering the Ideas 7-3

Local Standards

1 Warm-Up

Calculate 2^x, for $x = 0, 1, 2, ..., 28$. (The last value can be multiplied by 26 to give the answer to Example 1. Multiplying the values by 1.5 gives the y-coordinates for Example 2. Either can be used to ease into the reading.) $2^0 = 1$; $2^1 = 2$; $2^2 = 4$; . . .; $2^{28} = 268{,}435{,}456$

▶ **BIG IDEA** Growth at a constant percentage rate can be described by an expression of the form bg^x, where $g > 1$ and the variable is in the exponent.

Powering and Population Growth

An important application of powers is in population growth situations. As an example, consider rabbit populations, which can grow quickly. In 1859, 24 rabbits were imported to Australia from Europe as a new source of food. Rabbits are not native to Australia, but conditions there were ideal for rabbits and so they flourished. Soon, there were so many rabbits that they damaged grazing land. By 1887, the government was offering a reward for a way to control the rabbit population. How many rabbits might there have been in 1887? Example 1 provides an estimate.

Example 1

Twenty-six rabbits are introduced to another area. Assume that the rabbit population doubles every year. How many rabbits would there be after 28 years?

Solution Since the population doubles every year, in 28 years it will double 28 times. The number of rabbits will be

$$26 \cdot \underbrace{2 \cdot 2 \cdot 2 \cdot \ldots \cdot 2}_{\text{28 factors}}$$

To evaluate this expression on a calculator, rewrite it as $26 \cdot 2^{28}$. Use the $\boxed{y^x}$ or $\boxed{\wedge}$ key. There would be 6,979,321,856, or about 7 billion rabbits after 28 years.

What Is Exponential Growth?

The rabbit population in Example 1 is said to grow exponentially. In **exponential growth**, the original amount is repeatedly *multiplied* by a positive number called the **growth factor**.

A pet rabbit's diet should be made up of good quality pellets, fresh hay (alfalfa, timothy, or oat), water, and fresh vegetables.

Source: House Rabbit Society

Background

What is exponential growth? The Growth Model for Powering is similar to the models students have seen for addition, subtraction, multiplication, and division. That is, it indicates a class of applications of the operation, and in so doing, it gives a way of thinking about what the operation of powering means. We identify the base by the letter g to emphasize that it is the growth factor. In the Compound Interest Formula, $I = P(1 + r)^x$, $g = 1 + r$.

Even though we use integer values for the variables g and x in Examples 1 and 2, the Growth Model for Powering holds for any positive real value of g and any value of x. However, in this lesson g is always greater than 1 because we are dealing with growth. In Lesson 7-3 we introduce values of g with $0 < g < 1$, the result being exponential decay.

What happens if the exponent is zero? When the only definition that students have for powering is "repeated multiplication," a zero

(continued on next page)

Growth Model for Powering

If a quantity is multiplied by a positive number g (the growth factor) in each of x time periods, then, after the x periods, the quantity will be multiplied by g^x.

In Example 1, the population doubles (is multiplied by 2) every year, so $g = 2$. There are 28 time periods, so $x = 28$. The original number of rabbits, 26, is multiplied by g^x, or 2^{28}. So the population y of rabbits after x years is given by the formula $y = 26 \cdot 2^x$.

In general, if the amount at the beginning of the growth period is b, the growth factor is g, and y is the amount after x time periods, then $y = b \cdot g^x$. We call this the **exponential growth equation.**

The compound interest formula $A = P(1 + r)^t$ is another example of an exponential growth equation. Suppose \$5,000 is invested at an annual yield of 4%. Using the variable names of the exponential growth equation, $b = 5,000$ and $g = 1.04$. So y, the value of the investment after x years, is given by $y = 5,000 \cdot 1.04^x$.

If the money is kept invested for 11 years, then $x = 11$, and the total amount will be $5,000 \cdot 1.04^{11}$, which is \$7,697.27.

What Happens If the Exponent Is Zero?

In the exponential growth equation $y = b \cdot g^x$, x can be any real number. Consider the situation when $x = 0$. In 0 time periods no time has elapsed. The starting amount b has not grown at all and so it remains the same. It can remain the same only if it is multiplied by 1. This means that $g^0 = 1$, regardless of the value of the growth factor g. This property applies also when g is a negative number.

Zero Exponent Property

If x is any nonzero real number, then $x^0 = 1$.

In words, the zero power of any nonzero number equals 1. For example, $4^0 = 1$, $(-2)^0 = 1$, and $\left(\frac{5}{7}\right)^0 = 1$. The zero power of 0, which would be written 0^0, is undefined.

What Does a Graph of Exponential Growth Look Like?

An equation of the form $y = b \cdot g^x$, where g is a number greater than 1, can describe exponential growth. Graphs of such equations are not lines. They are *exponential growth curves.*

Vocabulary Development

exponent is not meaningful because you cannot repeat something 0 times. However, the idea of "zero time periods from now," namely the present, is meaningful. Thus, when $x = 0$, it is natural that $b \cdot g^x = b$, which implies that $g^x = 1$ for all nonzero g.

What does a graph of exponential growth look like? We use the letter b for the coefficient in $y = b \cdot g^x$ because in Lesson 7-7 we compare $y = b \cdot g^x$ to $y = b + mx$. In both cases, b is the y-intercept, the starting point for the situation.

Students need to associate exponential growth with a graph rising from left to right. Be sure to point out that just because the graph of a function rises from left to right, that does not necessarily mean the graph represents exponential growth. Have students explain the difference between the graph of $y = 2x + 1$ and the graph of the exponential growth equation $y = 2^x$. The graph of $y = 2x + 1$ is a line rising to the right. The graph of $y = 2^x$ is a curve rising to the right.

---

2   Teaching

Notes on the Lesson

If your students have read the lesson on their own, ask them for the main ideas. There are four:

1. the growth model, and its application here to rabbits;
2. the use of the growth model to explain why $g^0 = 1$ when $g \neq 0$;
3. the graphing of equations of the form $y = b \cdot g^x$ and why they are not linear;
4. the fact that such equations model real population growth in some situations.

Each of these ideas is covered again in later lessons in the chapter, so if students are unsure about them, it is still reasonable to proceed to the next lesson.

Powering and population growth. The rabbit example is a true story. Some sources give 24 for the number of rabbits introduced in 1859. But no one knows how many rabbits there were in Australia in 1887. The estimate here is reasonable. By 1907, the problem was so acute that an anti-rabbit fence 1,833 km (over 1,000 miles) long was constructed in Western Australia to keep rabbits out of the territory.

What does a graph of exponential growth look like? Have students graph $y = 1.5 \cdot 2^x$ using a graphing utility so they can see the continuity of the graph through the points whose coordinates they can calculate.

Additional Example

Example 1 Thirty deer are introduced to a forest preserve. Assume that the deer population doubles every year. How many deer would there be after 25 years? 1,006,632,960

7-2

Additional Example

Example 2 Graph the equation $y = 1.1 \cdot 2.1^x$, when x is 0, 1, 2, 3, 4.

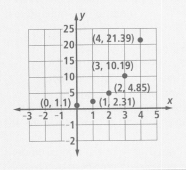

Notes on the Lesson

The Now/Next method. The use of iteration to obtain successive integer values of the exponential function is powerful and will be used later in the chapter. So you should make certain that students see how they can quickly determine values on their calculators. This iteration can be done on a spreadsheet program as well.

Example 2

Graph the equation $y = 1.5 \cdot 2^x$, when x is 0, 1, 2, 3, and 4.

Solution Substitute $x = 0, 1, 2, 3,$ and 4 into the formula $y = 1.5 \cdot 2^x$. Below we show the computation and the results listed as (x, y) pairs.

Computation	(x, y)
$1.5 \cdot 2^0 = 1.5 \cdot 1 = 1.5$	(0, 1.5)
$1.5 \cdot 2^1 = 1.5 \cdot 2 = 3$	(1, 3)
$1.5 \cdot 2^2 = 1.5 \cdot 4 = 6$	(2, 6)
$1.5 \cdot 2^3 = 1.5 \cdot 8 = 12$	(3, 12)
$1.5 \cdot 2^4 = 1.5 \cdot 16 = 24$	(4, 24)

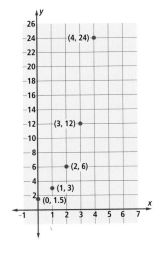

Notice that the y-intercept of the graph in Example 2 is 1.5. Also, the graph does not have a constant rate of change. When something grows exponentially, its rate of change is continually increasing.

Now/Next Method

Example 2 showed how to compute y-values. In an exponential growth equation, $y = b \cdot g^x$, you can compute the y-values by substituting for x. However, that method might not always be the fastest.

Numbers in an exponential growth pattern can be displayed on the homescreen of a graphing calculator using the Now/Next method.

Step 1 Type the starting value 48 (the Now) and press ENTER.

Step 2 Multiply by the growth factor 1.5. The calculator represents the Now by Ans (for "answer"). The calculator at the right is now programmed for Now/Next. By pressing ENTER, it automatically performs Now • 1.5 to get the Next term.

Try this on a calculator. Notice how quickly the table values can be displayed by repeatedly pressing ENTER.

STOP QY

Exponential Population Growth

Other than money calculated using compound interest, few things in the real world grow exactly exponentially. However, exponential growth curves can be used to approximate changes in population. For example, consider the population of California from 1930 to 2000 shown in the table on the next page.

► **QY**

A Now/Next table is shown below.

x	y
0	4
1	?
2	?
3	?

• 2.5
• 2.5
• 2.5

a. What are the three numbers that fill in the missing cells if the growth factor is 2.5?

b. Write an equation of the form $y = b \cdot g^x$ for the ordered pairs (x, y).

406   Using Algebra to Describe Patterns of Change

Accommodating the Learner ↑

Present the students with the following scenario. Suppose 18 deer are introduced to a 100-acre forest preserve located just outside of town. According to the exponential growth model, if the deer population doubles every year, there would be 18,874,368 deer in the preserve after 20 years. Ask students if this makes sense. Introduce them to the idea of limiting factors. Students need to begin to understand that in the real world, the environment plays a role in limiting

exponential growth. Ask students to identify as many limiting factors as possible. Students should explain why each of these is a limiting factor. There are 4,356,000 square feet in 100 acres. The answer would require that there be over 4 deer per square foot. Other limiting factors include availability of food and water, the increased spread of diseases due to density, and the deer death rate.

California's population is graphed below. The curve is the graph of the exponential growth model $y = 5.68(1.29)^x$, where y is the population (in millions) x decades after 1930. The growth factor 1.29 was chosen because it is an "average" growth factor for California for the six decades shown. The points lie quite close to the curve, indicating that California's population since 1930 has grown about 29% per decade.

Year	Population
1930	5,677,251
1940	6,907,387
1950	10,586,223
1960	15,717,204
1970	19,971,069
1980	23,667,764
1990	29,760,021
2000	33,871,648

Source: U.S. Census Bureau

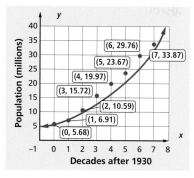

1a. $y = 11 \cdot 3^x$, where y is the population and x is the number of years after 1995

1c. 2,673 round gobies

Questions

COVERING THE IDEAS

1. A round goby is a bottom-dwelling fish native to Eastern Europe. In 1995, it was found in the Great Lakes, where it is expected to be harmful to already existing habitats. The round goby is known to spawn several times during the summer, and biologists are tracking the growth of its population. Suppose 11 round gobies were in the Great Lakes in 1995 and that their population triples in size each year.

   a. Write an exponential growth equation to describe this situation.

   b. How many round gobies were in the Great Lakes after 2 years? **99 round gobies**

   c. How many round gobies were in the Great Lakes in 2000?

   d. How many round gobies will there be in the Great Lakes in 2025? **about 2,265 trillion round gobies**

Round gobies have a well-developed sensory system that allows them to feed in complete darkness.

Source: University of Wisconsin Sea Grant

2. Copy the table at the right and complete it to make a Now/Next table for $y = 50 \cdot 1.2^x$.

3. Suppose that $3,000 is invested in an account with a 4.5% annual yield.

   a. What is the growth factor? **1.045**

   b. What will be the value of the account after two years? **$3,276.07**

x	y	
0	?	50
1	?	60
2	?	72
3	?	86.4

Exponential Growth　　**407**

Accommodating the Learner ⬇

Some students may have difficulty understanding the difference between continually doubling a quantity and continually adding 2 to the same quantity. Ask students to complete the table on the right so they can see the difference. Next, ask students to write an equation that models the linear growth in column 1 and one that models the exponential growth in column 2. Students should then find the value of each equation for an arbitrary large number in the domain of both of the functions. $3 + 2N$, $3 \cdot 2^N$, Answers vary.

Adding 2	Multiplying by 2
3	3
$3 + 2 = 5$	$3 \cdot 2 = 6$
$3 + 2 + 2 = \underline{7}$	$3 \cdot 2 \cdot 2 = \underline{12}$
$3 + 2 + 2 + 2 = \underline{9}$	$3 \cdot 2 \cdot 2 \cdot 2 = \underline{24}$
$3 + 2 + 2 + 2 + 2 = \underline{11}$	$3 \cdot 2 \cdot 2 \cdot 2 \cdot 2 = \underline{48}$

7-2

3 Assignment

Recommended Assignment

- Questions 1–20
- Question 21 (extra credit)
- Reading Lesson 7-3
- Covering the Ideas 7-3

Notes on the Questions

Question 12 Describing a pattern with the variable in the exponent is important to understanding this chapter. Ask students to explain how they obtained their answer to Part c.

Additional Answers

9a.

x	y
0	0.5
1	1
2	2
3	4
4	8

9b.

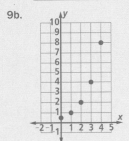

7-2A Lesson Master

Questions on SPUR Objectives
See pages 452–455 for objectives.

USES Objective D

In 1–3, match the scenario to the correct formula listed below.

A $P = 7(1.02)^t$ B $P = 7(2)^t$ C $P = 7(1.2)^t$

1. A colony of bacteria doubles every hour. If a scientist started with 7 cells, how many cells would there be in t hours? **B**

2. Scientists introduced 7 sea turtles into the ocean. They hope the sea turtle population grows by 2% each year. How many sea turtles will there be in t years? **A**

3. When Pricy Pants Company opens a new store, they charge $7 for a pair of pants. Each year their cost of pants increases by 20%. How much will it cost to buy a pair of pants t years from the opening year? **C**

4. Anya has started a new job paying $8.00 per hour. Assuming that her work is excellent, she will get a 5% raise every 4 months.

a. After 3 years, how many raises will she have gotten? **9 raises**

b. What will her pay rate be after 3 years? **$12.41/hr**

c. If her employer kept giving her pay raises this way, what would her pay rate be after she had been working for 10 years? **$34.58/hr**

REPRESENTATIONS Objective H

5. The president of Acme Industries predicts that the sales of a new product will grow by 35% every year for the next 5 years. This year's sales were $40,000.

a. Make a table of values showing the amount of sales 0, 1, 2, 3, 4 and 5 years from now.

Years	Sales ($)
0	40,000
1	54,000
2	72,900
3	98,415
4	132,860.25
5	179,361.34

b. Graph the sales for the first five years.

Algebra   373

---

4. **True or False** An amount is multiplied by 10 in each of 12 time periods. After the 12 time periods, the original amount will be multiplied by 120. **false**

In 5 and 6, evaluate the expression when $x = 17$, $y = 1.05$, and $z = 1.04$.

5. a. x^0 **1**   b. $x \cdot x^0$ **17**   c. $(x + x)^0$ **1**

6. a. y^0 **1**   b. $y^0 - z^0$ **0**   c. $(z - y)^0$ **1**

7. Explain why $(-5)^0$ and -5^0 are not equal.

8. Explain how $g^0 = 1$ applies to exponential growth.

9. Let $y = 0.5 \cdot 2^x$. **9a–b. See margin.**
   a. Make a table for $x = 0, 1, 2, 3, 4$.
   b. Graph the values from Part a.

10. Write an equation of the form $y = b \cdot g^x$ to fit the numbers in the calculator display at the right. $y = 18 \cdot 4^x$

11. Consider the exponential growth model $y = 5.68(1.29)^x$ for California's population on page 407.
   a. How much does the model's value for 1990 deviate from the actual population? **by about 3.585 million people**
   b. What does the model predict for the population of California in 2020? **about 56.190 million people**

7. $(-5)^0 = 1$, but $-5^0 = -1$, by the order of operations

8. The amount at $x = 0$ will be $y = b \cdot g^0 = b \cdot 1 = b$.

APPLYING THE MATHEMATICS

12. Alexander Fleming discovered penicillin by observing mold growing on Petri dishes. Suppose you are biochemist studying a type of mold that has grown from 3,000 spores to 192,000 spores in one hour. You record the following information.

Time Intervals from Now	Time (min)	Number of Mold Spores
0	0	3,000
1	20	12,000
2	40	48,000
3	60	192,000

a. What is the growth factor as the time interval increases by 1? **4**
b. How many mold spores would there be after 2 hours? Explain how you found your answer.
c. If this growth rate continues, how many mold spores will there be after x hours have passed? $y = 3,000 \cdot 4^{3x}$

Before tossing away some old Petri dishes in 1928, Alexander Fleming accidentally discovered a blue mold growing on the culture of a harmful bacteria.

Source: San Jose State University

12b. 12,288,000 spores;
Answers vary.
Sample answer:
$3,000 \cdot 4^6 = 12,288,000$

408   Using Algebra to Describe Patterns of Change

Extension

Have students go online to find data that seem to model exponential growth. If students have trouble finding data, suggest they look at population growth rates in some of our fastest growing states, or the number of cell phone subscribers. There are a lot of data available within these topics. Students should enter a representative amount of their data (5 to 7 points) into their graphing calculators and create a scatterplot of the data points. Once they have successfully completed this part of the task, have students use the STAT, CALC, and ExpREG commands to produce a regression equation to model the data points. Then have them graph the regression equation and the scatterplot in the same viewing window.

13. The equation $y = 34{,}277 \cdot 1.04^x$ can be used to model the population y of Colorado x years after 1860. This graph shows Colorado's actual population.

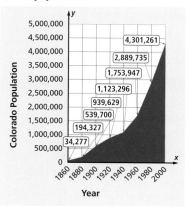

Year

Source: Bureau of the Census

a. What do 1.04 and 34,277 in the equation represent?

b. What does the equation predict for the population of Colorado in 1960? By how much did the actual population deviate from the prediction?

c. Use the model to predict the population of Colorado in 2030.

13a. 1.04 is the growth rate; 34,277 is the 1860 population.

13b. 1,731,158 people; 22,789 people

13c. about 26,956,933 people

14. Gossip can be spread quickly in a school. Suppose one person begins spreading the gossip by telling 2 friends. Each friend then tells 2 of his or her different friends. Each person who hears the gossip continues to tell 2 more different friends.

three girls sharing a secret

a. Complete the table below showing the number of new friends and total number of people who have heard the gossip if the pattern continues. **14a–c. See margin.**

Stage of Gossip	0	1	2	3	4	5	6	7	8	9	10
New Friends Informed	1	2	4	?	?	?	?	?	?	?	?
Total Number of Friends Informed	1	3	7	?	?	?	?	?	?	?	?

b. Make ordered pairs (x, y) from the first two rows of the table and plot the points on a graph.

c. Make ordered pairs (x, y) from the first and third rows of the table and plot the points on a graph.

d. How many stages of gossip will be needed before 800 people in all hear the gossip? **9 stages**

Exponential Growth **409**

Additional Answers

14b.

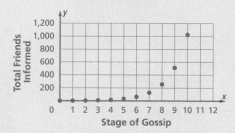

14c.

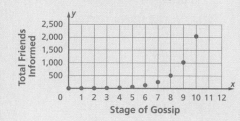

Additional Answers

14a.

Stage of Gossip	0	1	2	3	4	5	6	7	8	9	10
New Friends Informed	1	2	4	8	16	32	64	128	256	512	1,024
Total Friends Informed	1	3	7	15	31	63	127	255	511	1,023	2,047

7-2

Notes on the Questions

Question 16 Some students may use the pattern $b \cdot g^x$ rather than the Compound Interest Formula.

4 Wrap-Up

Ongoing Assessment

Call on a student to explain the meaning of each of the variables in the equation $y = b \cdot g^x$. Students should be able to explain that b represents the beginning amount, g is the growth factor, and y is the amount after x growth periods. Ask the student to give an example of an equation representing exponential growth.

---

15. **a.** Graph $y = 2.5^x$ for $x = 0, 1, 2, 3, 4,$ and 5. **See margin.**
    b. Calculate the rate of change on the graph from $x = 0$ to $x = 1$. **1.5**
    c. Calculate the rate of change on the graph from $x = 4$ to $x = 5$. **58.59375**
    d. What do the answers to Parts b and c tell you about this graph? **This graph is not a line. Its rate of change increases as x increases.**

REVIEW

16. Ashley deposits $3,400 in a savings account with an annual yield of 5%. What will be the total amount of money in the account after 8 years? (**Lesson 7-1**) **$5,023.34**

17. **a.** Suppose a person's birthday is in July. What is the probability that it is on July 4th? $\frac{1}{31}$
    b. Suppose a person's birthday is in March. What is the probability that it is before the 10th? (**Lesson 5-6**) $\frac{9}{31}$

18. At one time, the exchange rate for Swiss francs per U.S. dollar was 1.305, meaning that 1 dollar would buy 1.305 francs. With this exchange rate, how many U.S. dollars would 1 Swiss franc buy? (**Lesson 5-4**) **approximately $0.76**

19. In the triangle at the right, side $\overline{AC}$ is 20% longer than side $\overline{AB}$ and side $\overline{BC}$ is 45% shorter than side $\overline{AC}$. If $AB = 9$, find the perimeter of the triangle. (**Lesson 4-1**) **25.74**

20. **Multiple Choice** Which expression does *not* equal $-(3x - 3y)$? (**Lessons 2-4, 2-1**) **B**

    A $3(y - x)$ B $3y + 3x$ C $-3x + 3y$ D $-3(x - y)$

EXPLORATION

21. This exploration will help to explain why 0^0 is undefined. You will examine values of x^0 and 0^x when x is close to 0.
    a. Use your calculator to give values of x^0 for $x = 1, 0.1, 0.01, 0.001,$ and so on. What does this suggest for the value of 0^0?
    b. Use your calculator to give values of 0^x for $x = 1, 0.1, 0.01, 0.001,$ and so on. What does this suggest for the value of 0^0?
    c. What does your calculator display when you try to evaluate 0^0? Why do you think it gives that display? **Depending on the calculator used, it will either display a domain error or give an answer of 1 with a warning. This is because, as in Parts a and b, there is no obvious value for 0^0, so 0^0 is undefined.**

21a. 1, 1, 1, 1, ... This suggests a value of 1.

21b. 0, 0, 0, 0, ... This suggests a value of 0.

QY ANSWERS

a. 10; 25; 62.5

b. $y = 4 \cdot 2.5^x$

Additional Answers

15a.

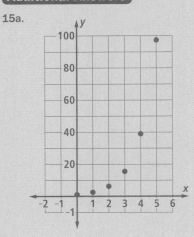

Lesson 7-3 Exponential Decay

Vocabulary

exponential decay
half-life

▶ **BIG IDEA** Decay at a constant percentage rate can be described by an expression of the form bg^x, where $0 < g < 1$ and the variable is in the exponent.

The Growth Factor and the Type of Exponential Change

Three children were arguing. Tammy said, "If you multiply 5 by a positive number, the answer is always greater than 5." Nancy said, "No, you're wrong! I can multiply 5 by something and get an answer less than 5." Leon said, "I can multiply 5 by something and get 5 for an answer."

In the children's arguments, what matters is how the multiplier compares to 1. If Nancy chooses a multiplier between 0 and 1, multiplying by 5 gives a result that is less than 5. For example, $5 \cdot \frac{1}{10} = \frac{1}{2}$. Of course, Leon can do $5 \cdot 1$ and get 5 for an answer.

This relates to exponential equations of the form $y = b \cdot g^x$ because the growth factor g can be greater than, equal to, or less than 1. In the last lesson, you saw only situations in which the growth factor was greater than 1, so there was an increase over time in each case. While a growth factor always has to be positive, it can be less than 1. When this is true, there is a decrease over time. This happens in situations of **exponential decay.**

Examples of Exponential Decay

Psychologists use exponential decay models to describe learning and memory loss. In Example 1, the growth factor is less than 1 so the amount remembered decreases.

Example 1

Assume that each day after cramming, a student forgets 20% of the vocabulary words learned the day before. A student crams for a French test on Friday by learning 100 vocabulary words Thursday night. But the test is delayed from Friday to Monday. If the student does not study over the weekend, how many words is he or she likely to remember on Monday?

(continued on next page)

Mental Math

Find the number.

a. 7 less than 4 times the number is 13. **5**

b. –10 times the number, plus 80, is 10. **7**

c. 14 minus 3 times the number is 121. $-\frac{107}{3}$

Background

In the preceding lessons, the growth factor g has been greater than 1. This lesson deals with the exponential growth model $y = b \cdot g^x$ where g is a positive number less than 1. The result is exponential decay. Students should realize that the growth factor affects whether there is growth or decay, just as slope of a line determines increase or decrease.

Linear increase/decrease and exponential growth/decay are mathematically *isomorphic;* that is, they have the same structure. Linear is related to addition and exponential is related to multiplication. For example, the additive identity 0 is pivotal in linear increase/decrease; a slope greater than 0 means increase, whereas a slope less than 0 means decrease. Similarly, the multiplicative identity 1 is pivotal in exponential growth/decay; a growth factor greater than 1 means growth whereas a growth factor less than 1 signals decay.

GOAL

Extend the growth model of powering to situations where the growth factor is less than 1 (but positive, as always)—that is, to situations of decay.

SPUR Objectives

E Solve problems involving exponential growth and decay.

H Graph exponential relationships.

Materials/Resources

· Lesson Masters 7-3A or 7-3B
· Resource Masters 1, 2, and 102–104
· Graphing calculator
· Quiz 1

HOMEWORK

Suggestions for Assignment
• Questions 1–20
• Question 21 (extra credit)
• Reading Lesson 7-4
• Covering the Ideas 7-4

Local Standards

1 Warm-Up

In 1–3, graph the equation with a graphing utility. Identify:
a. the *y*-intercept of each graph.
b. three points on the graph.
c. the line that the graph approaches as *x* becomes very large.
1. $y = 100(0.80)^x$
2. $y = 21,000(0.85)^x$
3. $y = 10(0.97)^x$
Check students' graphs.

1a. 100; b. Answers vary. Sample answer: (1, 80), (2, 64), (3, 51.2); c. *x*-axis

2a. 21,000; b. Answers vary. Sample answer: (1, 17,850), (2, 15,172.5), (3, 12,896.63); c. *x*-axis

3a. 10; b. Answers vary. Sample answer: (10, 7.3742) (11, 7.153) (12, 6.9384); c. *x*-axis

2 Teaching

Notes on the Lesson

Examples of exponential decay. In all three examples, students are limited by their knowledge of powers to restricting the domain of x to be the set of nonnegative integers, even though the situations have meaning when x is not an integer. When students graph the equations in the Warm-Up, they will see that the graphs of the equations have values when x is not an integer. You could mention to students that they can calculate such values with any scientific or graphing calculator and that they will learn how to calculate some values by hand in their next algebra course.

Graphs of exponential decay do not have a constant slope. In decay situations, as x increases, the slope decreases but remains positive. You can pick any small number, say 0.01, and find a place on the x-axis beyond which the slope connecting any two points will be less than 0.01. This is a way of saying that the limit of the slope is 0. The line connecting the two points looks more and more horizontal.

Students are often intrigued by the fact that the graph of an exponential decrease situation approaches the x-axis (as an asymptote) but never touches it. The graph of the equation in any of the examples may be examined with a graphing utility and shown to get closer and closer to the x-axis without reaching it until the limit of the utility is reached.

Solution If 20% of the words are forgotten each day, 80% are remembered.

Day	Day Number	Number of Words Remembered
Thursday	0	100
Friday	1	$100(0.80) = 80$
Saturday	2	$100(0.80)(0.80) = 100(0.80)^2 = 64$
Sunday	3	$100(0.80)(0.80)(0.80) = 100(0.80)^3 = 51.2 \approx 51$
Monday	4	$100(0.80)(0.80)(0.80)(0.80) = 100(0.80)^4 = 40.96 \approx 41$

On Monday the student is likely to remember about 41 vocabulary words.

STOP QY1

> ▸ QY1
>
> If the student does not study between now (Thursday) and the test, how many words will be remembered x days from Thursday?

As they get old, cars and other manufactured items often wear out. Therefore, their value decreases over time. This decrease, called *depreciation,* is often described by giving the percent of the value that is lost each year. If the item is worth r percent less each year, then it keeps $(1 - r)$ percent of its previous value. This is the growth factor. (The word "growth" is used even though the value is shrinking.)

Example 2

In 1998, a new car cost $21,000. Suppose its value depreciates 15% each year.

a. Find an equation that gives the car's value y when it is x years old.

b. What was the predicted value of the car in 2005? How close is this to the actual price of a 1998 car, which was $7,050 in 2005?

c. Graph the car's value for the interval $0 \leq x \leq 8$.

About 35% of the cost of owning and operating a car comes from depreciation.

Source: Federal Highway Administration

Solutions

a. If the car loses 15% of its value each year, it keeps 85%, so the growth factor is $1 - 0.15 = 0.85$. In the exponential growth equation $y = b \cdot g^x$, b is 21,000, the new car's price, and g is 0.85. An equation that gives the value of the car is $y = 21,000 \cdot (0.85)^x$.

b. The year 2005 is 7 years after 1998, so $x = 7$.
$21,000(0.85)^7 \approx 6,732.12$. The predicted value was $6,732.12. The deviation between the actual price and the predicted price was $7,050 - 6,732.12 = 317.88$, so the model gives a fairly accurate prediction.

Accommodating the Learner ⬆

Carbon-14 dating is a way to determine the age of artifacts of a biological origin up to about 60,000 years old. How does it work? When a living organism dies, the ratio of carbon-12 and carbon-14 in the organism is the same as in every other living organism. While the carbon-12 does not dissipate, the carbon-14 has a half-life of 5,730 years. This means that every 5,730 years, half of the remaining carbon-14 in the organism decays and is not replaced. By comparing the amount of carbon-12 to the remaining carbon-14, the age of the organism can be determined. The equation $\left(\frac{1}{2}\right)^{\frac{t}{5,730}} = c$ relates the percent of carbon c remaining t years after the organism died. King Tutankamen's coffin currently has about 66.7% of its carbon-14 remaining. Using their graphing calculators and its table features, ask students to estimate how many years ago King Tutankamen died. The answer should be approximately 3,330 years ago.

c. The table below shows the value of the car each year. The initial value, $21,000, is the *y*-intercept of the graph. In the table, to move from one *y* value to the next, you can multiply by 0.85. The decrease is seen in the graph by the fact that the curve goes downward as you go to the right.

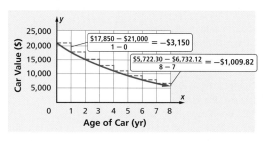

x	y (dollars)
0	21,000.00
1	17,850.00
2	15,172.50
3	12,896.63
4	10,962.13
5	9,317.81
6	7,920.14
7	6,732.12
8	5,722.30

As with graphs of exponential growth, the points of an exponential decay relationship lie on a curve rather than a straight line. Another graph of the car value is shown below, with segments showing the rate of change between points. Notice that as you go from one year to the next, the amount of decrease is decreasing. For example, in going from new ($x = 0$) to 1 year old ($x = 1$), the value of the car dropped $3,150. But between $x = 7$ and $x = 8$, the value lost was only about $1,000.

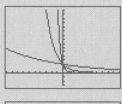

In each case, 15% of the value is lost. But as time passes, this is 15% of a smaller number.

 QY2

In Example 3 on the next page, the "population" is the amount of medication in a person's body.

> **QY2**
>
> A new boat costs $32,000. Its value depreciates by 8% each year. Give an equation for *y*, the value of the boat, when it is *x* years old.

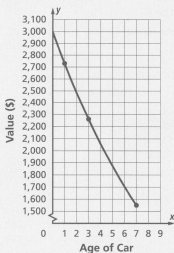

Additional Examples

Example 1 Assume that each day after cramming, a student forgets 15% of the words known the day before. A student crams for a Spanish test on Thursday by learning 120 vocabulary words on Wednesday night. But the test is delayed from Thursday to Monday. If the student does not study more, how many words is he or she likely to remember on Monday? **53**

Example 2 In June 1953, the first Chevrolet Corvette rolled off the assembly line with a sticker price of approximately $3,000. Suppose its value depreciated by 9% each year after production.

a Find an equation that gives the car's value *y* when it is *x* years old. $y = 3,000 \cdot (0.91)^x$

What was the predicted value of the car in 1960? How close is this to the actual price of a 1953 Corvette, which was $1,640, in 1960? **$1,550.28, $89.72**

Graph the car's value for the interval $0 \leq x \leq 7$.

What was the predicted value of the car in 2006? How close is this to the actual price of a 1953 Corvette, which was $59,900 in 2006? **$20.25, $59,879.75**

Accommodating the Learner ⬇

Have students graph equations of the form $y = 2 \cdot g^x$ for the following values of *g*: 0.1, 0.5, and 0.9 using their graphing calculators. Have students write a paragraph describing the differences and similarities of the graphs. When they are done, ask students to share their findings with one another. To extend this idea, have students graph equations of the form $y = b \cdot 0.5^x$ for the following values of *b*: –2, 2, 5.

7-3

Additional Example

Example 3 Caffeine is a drug found in a wide variety of food products consumed by Americans. In fact, more than half of all adult Americans consume at least 300 milligrams of caffeine every day. Once in the body, it takes about 6 hours for half of the caffeine to be eliminated. Suppose the pattern of eliminating caffeine from the body continues after it is ingested at one time; that is, half of the remaining caffeine is eliminated every 6 hours.

a. Write an equation to describe y, the amount of caffeine in the bloodstream after x six-hour periods have passed.

b. Make a calculator table for the equation from Part a. Use the table to find when approximately 1 milligram of caffeine remains in the body.

c. How much caffeine remains after 108 hours?

d. According to the equation, when will the amount of caffeine in the body be zero?

Solutions

a. The amount of caffeine starts at __?__. Because 50% of the caffeine is lost each six-hour period, the growth factor is __?__. The exponential equation is $y =$ __?__ · __?__ __?__. 300 mg, 0.5, 300, 0.5

b.
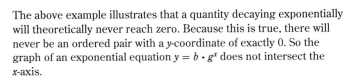

This table shows the starting value of 300 milligrams, with x increasing by 1 for each row. Scroll down the table to find where y is close to 1 milligram. This happens at $x =$ __?__. So 1 milligram of caffeine remains after about __?__ six-hour periods. 8, 8

c. First change 108 hours into __?__ six-hour periods. When $x =$ __?__ six-hour periods, then $y =$ __?__ · __?__ __?__ ≈ 0.001. So after 18 six-hour periods, there is almost no caffeine left. 18, 18, 300, 0.5, 18

d. Using this equation, the amount of caffeine in the body will never be zero. No matter how large the value of x becomes, y will always be greater than zero.

Example 3

A common medicine for people with diabetes is insulin. Insulin breaks down in the bloodstream quickly, with the rate varying for different types of the medication. Suppose that initially there are 10 units of insulin in a person's bloodstream and that the amount decreases by 3% each minute.

a. Write an equation to describe y, the amount of insulin in the bloodstream, after x minutes have passed.

b. Make a calculator table for the equation from Part a. Use the table to find when 5 units of insulin remain in the bloodstream. (This is half of the initial amount. The amount of time it takes half the quantity to decay is called the **half-life.**)

c. How much insulin remains after 4 hours?

d. According to the equation, when will the amount of insulin in the body be zero?

Solutions

a. The amount of insulin starts at __?__ units. Because 3% of the insulin is lost each minute, the growth factor is __?__. The exponential equation is $y =$ __?__ · __?__ ^{x}. 10; 0.97; 10; 0.97

b. The screen at the right shows the starting value of 10 units, with x increasing by 1 for each row. Scroll down the table to find where y is close to 5 units. This happens at $x =$ __?__. So 5 units of insulin remain after about __?__ minutes. 23; 23

c. First change 4 hours into __?__ minutes. When $x =$ __?__ minutes, then $y =$ __?__ · __?__ __?__ ≈ 0.007 unit of insulin remain. So after 4 hours, there is almost no insulin left. 240; 240; 10; 0.97; 240

d. Using this equation, the amount of insulin in the body will never be zero. No matter how great the value of x becomes, y will always be greater than zero.

The above example illustrates that a quantity decaying exponentially will theoretically never reach zero. Because this is true, there will never be an ordered pair with a y-coordinate of exactly 0. So the graph of an exponential equation $y = b \cdot g^x$ does not intersect the x-axis.

Graphs and Growth Factors

Exponential growth and exponential decay are both described by an equation of the same form, $y = b \cdot g^x$.

The value of g determines whether the equation describes growth or decay. A third situation happens when there is no change. The three possibilities are graphed below.

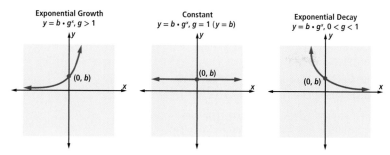

Exponential Growth
$y = b \cdot g^x, g > 1$

Constant
$y = b \cdot g^x, g = 1$ ($y = b$)

Exponential Decay
$y = b \cdot g^x, 0 < g < 1$

(0, b)

(0, b)

(0, b)

The growth factor can be given in words like "double," "triple," or "half," which indicate a factor of 2, 3, or $\frac{1}{2}$, respectively. But it is also common to describe the growth factor by using percent. If the quantity is growing by a percent r, the value of growth factor g is greater than 1 and the exponential equation is $y = b(1 + r)^x$. If the quantity is shrinking, g is less than 1 and the equation is $y = b(1 - r)^x$. Recall that the graph of equation $y = k$ is a horizontal line, like that shown in the middle graph above. In this situation, in which the original quantity remains constant, there is neither growth nor decay. It can be described by an exponential equation where g is 1. For example, the horizontal line $y = 5$ is also the graph of $y = 5 \cdot 1^x$, since $1^x = 1$.

Questions

COVERING THE IDEAS

In 1–3, give the growth factor for a quantity with the given characteristic.

1. decreases exponentially by 17% **0.83**

2. increases exponentially by 2.5% **1.025**

3. does not change **1**

4. Many teachers have policies about late work that lower a student's grade for each day that it is late. Suppose a teacher lowers the grade of a 50-point assignment by 20% for every day late.
   a. Let x = the number of days late an assignment is and y = the number of points the assignment would earn. Make a table of values using x = 0, 1, 2, 3, 4, and 5.
   b. Write an equation to describe the relationship. $y = 50 \cdot 0.8^x$

4a.

x	y
0	50
1	40
2	32
3	25.6
4	20.48
5	16.38

Notes on the Lesson

Graphs and growth factors. Ensure that students realize that the growth factor, not the coefficient, determines whether the situation is of exponential growth or exponential decay.

ENGLISH LEARNERS
Vocabulary Development

Students need to associate exponential decay with a graph falling from left to right. Be sure to point out that just because the graph of a function falls from left to right that does not necessarily mean the graph represents exponential decay. Have students consider the graph of the equation $y = -2x + 2$. Ask them to explain the difference between its graph and the graph of the exponential decay equation $y = 2(0.5)^x$.

The graph of $y = -2x + 1$ is a line falling to the right. The graph of $y = 2(0.5)^x$ is a curve falling to the right.

7-3

3 Assignment

Recommended Assignment

- Questions 1–20
- Question 21 (extra credit)
- Reading Lesson 7-4
- Covering the Ideas 7-4

Notes on the Questions

For most classes, review Questions 1–12 in order to ensure that the basic ideas of the lesson are clear to students.

Question 13 Being able to predict future school population is an important task for school districts in determining if there is enough classroom space. Here population growth ideas are used to modify school attendance. In the near future, because school does not begin until age 4 or 5, knowing the ages of children in a community provides another way to predict future school attendance.

5. Suppose a new car costs $32,000 in 2006. Find the value of the car in one year if the following is true.
   a. The car is worth 85% of its purchase price. **$27,200**
   b. The car depreciated 20% of its value. **$25,600**
   c. The value of the car depreciated $d\%$. $32,200 \cdot (1 - 0.01d)$ dollars

6. A new piece of industrial machinery costs $2,470,000 and depreciates at a rate of 12% per year.
   a. Find the value of the machine after 15 years. **$363,025.42**
   b. Find the value of the machine after t years. $2,470,000 \cdot 0.88^t$ dollars

7. A person with diabetes requires a dose of 15 units of insulin. Assume that 3% of the insulin is lost from the bloodstream each minute. How much insulin remains in the bloodstream after 30 minutes? After x minutes? about 6 units; $15 \cdot 0.97^x$ units

8. a. Complete the table for the exponential decay situation at the right.
   b. Write an equation to describe the relationship.
   $y = 160 \cdot 0.75^x$

x	y
0	160
1	?
2	?
3	?

120, 90, 67.5 · 0.75

In 9–11, classify the pattern in the table as exponential growth, exponential decay, or constant.

9.
x	y
0	35
1	?
2	?

· 1, · 1 **constant**

10.
x	y
0	0.26
1	?
2	?

· 1.13, · 1.13 **growth**

11.
x	y
0	458
1	?
2	?

· 0.32, · 0.32 **decay**

12. **Fill in the Blank** Fill in each blank with "decay" or "growth."
   a. $\frac{2}{3}$ can be the growth factor in an exponential ___?___ situation. **decay**
   b. $\frac{3}{2}$ can be the growth factor in an exponential ___?___ situation. **growth**

APPLYING THE MATHEMATICS

13. Suppose a school has 2,500 students and the number of students is decreasing by 2% each year.
   a. If this rate continues, write an equation for the number of students after x years. $y = 2,500 \cdot 0.98^x$
   b. If this rate continues, how many students will the school have 10 years from now? about 2,043 students

416   Using Algebra to Describe Patterns of Change

---

14. Imagine that you begin with a cutout of an equilateral triangle. If you fold on the dotted lines as shown below, each vertex will touch the midpoint of the opposite side. Four regions will be formed.

Before folding   **Fold each vertex like this.**   **After 1 set of folds**

If you repeat this process, you will get a sequence of successively smaller equilateral triangles. Suppose the original triangle has an area of 100 square centimeters.

a. Complete the chart below.

Set of folds	0	1	2	3
Regions	1	4	?16	? 64
Area of a Region (cm²)	100	?	?	?

                                      25 6.25 1.5625

b. Write an equation to describe the number of regions y after x sets of folds. $y = 4^x$

c. Write an equation to describe the area of each region y after x sets of folds. $A = 100 \cdot 0.25^x$

15. Suppose one plate of tinted glass allows only 60% of light to pass through. The amount of light y that will pass through x panes of glass can then be described by the exponential decay equation $y = 0.6^x$.

a. Plot and label 5 points on a graph of this equation.

b. If enough panes of glass are put together, will the amount of light passing through the panes ever be zero according to this model? No, it will get infinitely close to zero.

16. The amount of a radioactive substance decreases over time. The *half-life* of a substance is the amount of time it takes half of the material to decay. Strontium-90 has a half-life of 29 years. This means that in each 29-year period, one half of the strontium-90 decays and one half remains. Suppose you have 2,000 grams of strontium-90. 16a. 62.5 g; 16b. about 1.95 g; 16c. 290 yr

a. How much strontium-90 will remain after 5 half-life periods?

b. How much strontium-90 will remain after 10 half-life periods?

c. How many years equal 10 half-life periods of strontium-90?

15a.

Light-Panes Relation

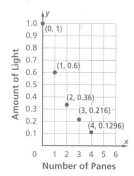

Colored light patterns reflect on the floor of the Old Louisiana State Capitol in Baton Rouge during the building's restoration in the early 1990s.

Exponential Decay   **417**

Notes on the Questions

Question 14 This question should be discussed because in Chapter 8, paper folding will be used as a way to give meaning to negative exponents.

Question 15 The same idea can be used to calculate the amount of light that reaches various underwater depths.

7-3

Notes on the Questions

Question 18 The rule of 72 works because if $(1 + r)^t = 2$, then

$t \cdot \log(1 + r) = \log 2$, so $t = \dfrac{\log 2}{\log(1 + r)}$.

Graphing $t = \dfrac{72}{r}$ and $t = \dfrac{\log 2}{\log(1 + r)}$ on the same axes indicates how good an approximation the rule of 72 gives.

4 Wrap-Up

Ongoing Assessment

Divide students into pairs. Ask them to write four equations on a piece of paper. Three equations should model exponential decay, exponential growth, and linear behavior. The fourth equation should model none of the previous behaviors. Have students exchange papers with their partners and identify which behavior each equation models.

Project Update

Project 4, Powers of Ten, on page 448, relates to the content of this lesson.

---

17. Consider the equation $y = \left(\frac{1}{2}\right)^x$.
    a. Make a table of values giving y as both a fraction and a decimal when $x = 0, 1, 2, 3, 10,$ and 20. **See margin.**
    b. Find all solutions to the equation $\left(\frac{1}{2}\right)^x = 0$. **no solutions**

REVIEW

18. The rule of 72 is a simple finance method that can be used to estimate the number of periods that it will take an investment to double in value. The method is to divide 72 by the growth rate expressed as a percent, and the result will be the approximate number of periods. For example, if \$50 is invested at 6% per year, then the rule of 72 says that after $\frac{72}{6} = 12$ years, a \$50 investment will be worth $50 \cdot 2 = \$100$. Calculation shows that after 12 years, this investment is worth \$100.61. **(Lessons 7-2, 7-1)**
    a. Use the rule of 72 to estimate the time it will take for \$250 invested at 9% to double in value. **8 yr**
    b. Use the compound interest formula to give an exact value of a \$250 investment after the number of periods found in Part a. **\$498.14**

19. Refer to the table at the right that shows the average consumption of bottled water per person in the United States. **(Lesson 6-7, 6-4)**
    a. Draw a scatterplot with *year* on the *x*-axis and *gallons per person* on the *y*-axis.
    b. Find an equation of an eyeballed line to the data.
    c. Write the slope-intercept form of your equation for the line of fit from Part b.
    d. Use your equation to predict the consumption of bottled water in the United States in 2007.

20. Solve $4.8q + 9.1 < 12.3q - 7.4$. **(Lessons 4-5, 3-8)** $q > 2.2$

EXPLORATION

21. Archaeologists use radioactivity to determine the age of ancient objects. Carbon-14 is a radioactive element that is often used to date fossils. Find the half-life of carbon-14 and describe how it is used to help date fossils. **See margin.**

19a.

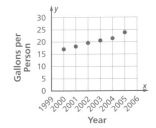

19b. Answers vary.
Sample answer:
$y = 1.7x - 3,359.8$

19c. Answers vary.
Sample answer:
$y = 1.7x - 3,359.8$

19d. about 29.1 gal of bottled water per person

Year	Bottled Water (gal/person)
2000	17.3
2001	18.8
2002	20.9
2003	22.4
2004	24.0
2005	25.7

Source: www.beveragemarketing.com

QY ANSWERS

1. $100(0.80)^x$

2. $y = 32,000 \cdot (0.92)^x$

7-3B **Lesson Master**

Questions on SPUR Objectives
See pages 452–455 for objectives.

(USES) Objective E

In 1–4, use the table to answer the questions.

The following table represents the answers given by an online car-depreciation calculator.

	A	B	C	
	Age of Car	**Value of Car**	**Depreciation Rate**	
	0	22,000	n/a	row 1: C1=32%
	1	15,000		row 2: C2=13%
	2	13,050		row 3: C3=13%
	3	11,354		row 4: C4=13%
	4	9,878		

1. Calculate cells C1, C2, C3, and C4 of the table.

   value = 15,000(0.87)^t

2. Use the pattern to write the formula for the value of the car *t* years after its first "birthday."

3. By this pattern, how much will the car be worth when it is 8 years old? Round to the nearest dollar. **\$5,659**

4. By this pattern, at what age will the car be worth less than \$4,000? **11 yr**

5. *Multiple Choice.* Which equation represents a starting amount *b* depreciating at a rate of 40% each year? **C**

   A $y = b(1.60)^t$ B $y = b(1.4)^t$
   C $y = b(0.6)^t$ D $y = b(0.40)^t$

6. Write an equation in the form $y = b \cdot g^x$ to describe the numbers in the calculator display below.

   y = 572 · (0.84)^x

   572
   Ans*.84   572
   480.48
   403.6032
   339.026688
   284.7824179

Algebra 377

Additional Answers

17a.

x	Decimals	Fractions
0	1	1
1	0.5	$\frac{1}{2}$
2	0.25	$\frac{1}{4}$
3	0.125	$\frac{1}{8}$
10	0.000976563	$\frac{1}{1,024}$
20	0.0000009537	$\frac{1}{1,048,576}$

21. Half-life: 5,730 years. By measuring the proportion of carbon-14 to its more common isotope, carbon-12, scientists know how many half-lives have passed since the carbon-14 was created in the upper atmosphere.

Modeling Exponential Growth and Decay

Vocabulary

exponential regression

▶ **BIG IDEA** Situations of exponential growth and decay can be modeled by equations of the form $y = bg^x$.

As you saw with the population of California in Lesson 7-2, sometimes a scatterplot shows a data trend that can be approximated by an exponential equation. Similar to linear regression, your calculator can use a method called **exponential regression** to determine an equation of the form $y = b \cdot g^x$ to model a set of ordered pairs.

Modeling Exponential Decay

In the Activity below, exponential regression models how high a ball bounces.

Mental Math

Each product is an integer. Write the integer.

a. $\frac{1}{4} \cdot 360$ 90

b. $\frac{2}{3} \cdot 45$ 30

c. $\frac{4}{5} \cdot 135$ 108

d. $\frac{5}{12} \cdot 228$ 95

Activity

Each group of 5 or 6 students needs at least 3 different types of balls (kickball, softball, and so on), a ruler, markers or chalk, and large paper with at least 25 parallel lines that are 3 inches apart.

Step 1 Tape the paper to a wall or door so the horizontal lines can be used to measure height above the floor. To make measuring easier, number every fourth line (12 in., 24 in., 36 in., and so on).

Step 2 One student will drop each ball from the highest horizontal line and the other students will act as spotters to see how high the ball bounces. The 1st spotter will mark the height to which the ball rebounds after the 1st bounce. The 2nd spotter will mark the rebound height after the 2nd bounce, and so on, until the ball is too low to mark.

Step 3 Make a table similar to the one at the right and record the rebound heights after each bounce. See margin.

Step 4 For each ball, enter the data in a list and create a scatterplot on your calculator. See margin.

Step 5a. Use the linear regression capability of your calculator to find the line of best fit for the data. Graph this line on the same screen as your scatterplot. Sketch a copy of the graph. See margin.

(continued on next page)

Bounce	Ball Height (in.)
0 (drop height)	?
1	?
2	?
3	?
?	?

Background

Exponential regression is usually done in the following way. If $y = b \cdot g^x$, then $\log y = \log b + x(\log g)$. The second equation is of the form $y = mx + b$, with $y = \log y$ and $m = \log g$. So, in calculating exponential regression for a set of data, the computer applies linear regression to the logarithms of the second coordinates, and then takes the equation of that line, looks at its slope, and uses the inverse logarithm of the slope to obtain the base in the exponential equation of best fit.

Additional Answers

Activity Step 3: Answers vary.

Step 4:

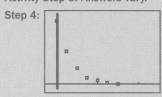

Step 5a: $y = -10.68x + 52.46$

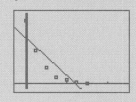

GOAL

Model situations that might be exponential.

SPUR Objectives

E Solve problems involving exponential growth and decay.

F Determine whether a situation is constant increase, constant decrease, exponential growth, exponential decay, or a nonconstant change.

Materials/Resources

· Lesson Master 7-4A or 7-4B
· Resource Masters 1, 2, 4, and 105–107
· Graphing calculator

HOMEWORK

Suggestions for Assignment
• Questions 1–20
• Questions 21–22 (extra credit)
• Reading Lesson 7-5
• Covering the Ideas 7-5

Local Standards

1 Warm-Up

In 1–4, tell whether the situation is constant increase, constant decrease, exponential growth, exponential decay, or nonconstant examples of these.

1. There were originally 400 bacteria in a dish, and the number of bacteria has been doubling every 20 minutes. exponential growth

2. The population of bears has been decreasing by 15 each year. constant decrease

3. The population of zebras has been decreasing by 15% each year. exponential decay

4. Each day the young heifer gains between 2 and 5 pounds. nonconstant increase

7-4

2 Teaching

Notes on the Lesson

Activity. We encourage doing the Ball Activity. Spotters and recording heights will be repeated in the discussion of graphs of quadratic functions later when a ball will be thrown from one person to another and quadratic regression will be used to fit a parabola to the path.

Notes on the Activity

This activity will require that each group of students have enough room. Consider moving this activity to the hallway or even outdoors if weather permits. If more than one class period is necessary, consider a stopping point to keep all groups on track.

Additional Example

Example

The diagram and table below show the world's population at various times.

1. Write an equation to model the data.

2. Find the deviation between the actual value for the year 2000 and the predicted value.

3. Use the model to predict the world's population in 2050.

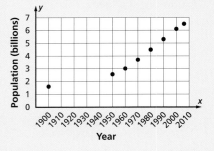

Year	Years since 1900	World's Population (in billions)
1900	0	1.6
1950	50	2.55
1960	60	3
1970	70	3.7
1980	80	4.5
1990	90	5.3
2000	100	6.1
2006	106	6.5

b. Find the deviation between the actual and predicted height of the ball after the 3rd bounce. 12.42 in.

c. Use your linear regression model to predict the height of the ball after the 8th bounce. −32.98 in.

Step 6a. Use the exponential regression capability of your calculator to find an exponential curve to fit the data. Graph this equation on the same screen as your scatterplot. Sketch a copy of the scatterplot and curve. **See margin.**

b. Find the deviation between the actual and predicted height of the ball after the 3rd bounce. 0.71 in.

c. Use your exponential regression model to predict the height of the ball after the 8th bounce. 0.25 in.

Step 7 Which seems to be the better model of the data the linear equation or the exponential equation? Explain how you made your decision. **See margin.**

Step 8 Repeat Step 6 to find exponential regression equations that fit the bounces of the other balls. **Answers vary.**

Step 9 Write a paragraph comparing the "bounciness" of the balls you tested. The balls should bounce with rebound percentages similar to the bar graph for Questions 2–4 in Covering the Ideas.

STOP QY

Modeling Exponential Growth

Advances in technology change rapidly. Some people say that if you purchase a computer today it will be out of date by tomorrow. When computers were first introduced to the public, they ran much more slowly. As computers have advanced over the years, the speed has increased greatly. On the next page is an example of data that a person collected to show the advancement in computer technology. The processing speed of a computer is measured in megahertz (MHz).

GUIDED

Example

The table and graph on the next page show the average speed of a computer and the year it was made.

a. Write an equation to model the data.

b. Find the deviation between the actual speed for the year 2000 and the predicted speed.

c. Use the model to predict the processing speed of a computer made in 2020.

▶ QY

A student dropped a ball from a height of 0.912 meter and used a motion detector to get the data below.

Bounce	Rebound Height (m)
0	0.912
1	0.759
2	0.603
3	0.496
4	0.411
5	0.328
6	0.271

a. Write an exponential equation to fit the data.
b. After the 8th bounce, how high will the ball rebound?

Additional Answers

Step 6a: $y = 74.02(0.49)^x$

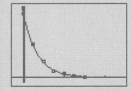

Step 7: The exponential model seems a better fit for the data. Answers vary. Sample answer: The deviation after the 3rd bounce is much less, and the exponential model will not predict negative heights for the bounce of a ball.

Year	Years since 1976	Speed (MHz)
1976	0	2
1978	2	4
1980	4	5
1982	6	8
1984	8	13
1986	10	16
1988	12	20
1990	14	35
1992	16	48
1994	18	60
1996	20	85
1998	22	180
2000	24	420

Source: Microprocessor Quick Reference Guide

Guided Example

a. $2.241 \cdot 1.218^x$

b. $2.241 \cdot 1.218^{24} \approx 255$; 255; 165; 165 MHz

Solutions

a. First enter the data into your calculator lists. Instead of letting years be the x-values, let $x =$ the years since 1976. So for 1976 itself, $x = 0$ and for 1978, $x = 2$. Next, use exponential regression on your calculator to find an exponential equation to fit the data. For $y = b \cdot g^x$, the calculator gives $b \approx 2.241$ and $g \approx 1.218$. (Your calculator may call this equation $y = ab^x$.)
The exponential equation that best fits the data is $y = \underline{\quad?\quad}$.

b. For 2000, $x = 24$ and the actual speed was 420 MHz. Substitute 24 into the equation to find the predicted value. **The predicted speed is** $y = \underline{\quad?\quad}$ **MHz. The deviation is** $420 - \underline{\quad?\quad} = \underline{\quad?\quad}$. **The actual processing speed in 2000 was** $\underline{\quad?\quad}$ **more than the predicted speed.**

c. The year 2020 is $2020 - 1976$, or 44 years after 1976, so substitute 44 for x in your exponential equation. $y = \underline{\quad?\quad} (\underline{\quad?\quad})^{\underline{?}}$, so the predicted processor speed for the year 2020 is $\underline{\quad?\quad}$ MHz.
2.241; 1.218; 44; 13,148.9

Questions

COVERING THE IDEAS

1. Suppose a ball is dropped and it rebounds to a height of y feet after bouncing x times, where $y = 6(0.55)^x$. Use the equation to
   a. give the height from which the ball was dropped, and
   b. give the percent the ball rebounds in relation to its previous height.   a. 6 ft; b. 55%

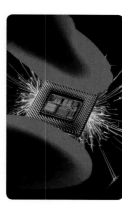

On April 25, 1961, the patent office awarded the first patent for an integrated circuit to Robert Noyce while Jack Kilby's application was still being analyzed. Today, both men are acknowledged as having independently conceived of the idea.

Source: PBS

Solution

1. Enter the data into your calculator lists. For convenience, let $x =$ the years since 1900. Next, use exponential regression on your calculator to find an exponential equation to fit the data. For $y = b \cdot g^x$, the calculator gives $b \approx 1.44$ and $g \approx 1.014$. (Your calculator may call this equation $y = ab^x$.)
   The exponential equation that best fits the data is $y = \underline{\quad?\quad}$.
   $1.44(1.014)^x$

2. For 2000, $x = 100$ and the actual population was 6.1 billion people. Substitute 100 into the equation to find the predicted population. The predicted population is $y = 5.8$ billion people. The deviation is $6.1 - \underline{\quad?\quad} = \underline{\quad?\quad}$. The actual population in 2000 was 0.3 billion more people than the predicted population. 5.8, 0.3

3. The year 2050 is 150 years after 1900, so use 150 for x in your exponential equation. $y = \underline{\quad?\quad}(\underline{\quad?\quad})^{\underline{?}}$. So the predicted world population in the year 2050 is $\underline{\quad?\quad}$ billion people.
   1.44, 1.014, 150, 11.6

3 **Assignment**

Recommended Assignment

- Questions 1–20
- Questions 21–22 (extra credit)
- Reading Lesson 7-5
- Covering the Ideas 7-5

7-4A Lesson Master

Questions on SPUR Objectives
See pages 452–455 for objectives.

USES Objectives E and F

In 1–5, multiple choice. Tell if the situation described is:

A exponential growth B exponential decay
C constant increase D constant decrease

1. Every year, there are 5% fewer patients with the disease.   B
2. With better techniques, farmers are able to increase their output 3% each year.   A
3. Each year, there are 30 fewer students in the school.   D
4. In a single-elimination tournament, half of the teams are eliminated in each round of play.   B
5. Every time Joan took the test her score increased points.   C
6. Amalgamated Industries receives hundreds of applications for each job opening. Their selection process is to review applications and discard 50% of them. This is repeated until only one applicant is left. Let $n =$ the number of times that half the applications are discarded.
   a. Write an expression of the form $b \cdot g^n$ to describe the number of people left after the applications have been reviewed n times. $b \cdot 0.5^n$
   b. If 512 people apply for a job, how many are left when $n = 4$?   32 people

REPRESENTATIONS Objective H

7. It seems like there are coffee stores on every corner in some neighborhoods. At the right is a table that shows the total number of coffee stores each year since 1987.
   a. Create a scatterplot on your calculator. Does the data appear to be linear or exponential?   exponential
   b. Using regression, find an equation to fit the data. Let $x =$ the number of years since 1987. $y = 27.4(1.44)^x$
   c. Use your equation from Part b to predict how many stores there will be in 2013.   359,067 stores
   d. In what year will there be more than 20,000 stores?   2006

Year	Number of Stores
1987	17
1988	33
1989	55
1990	84
1991	116
1992	165
1993	272
1994	425
1995	676
1996	1,015
1997	1,412
1998	1,886
1999	2,135
2000	3,501
2001	4,709
2002	5,886
2003	7,225
2004	8,337

Algebra   379

Accommodating the Learner

Some students may still be having trouble recognizing equations that model exponential growth and decay. Ask students to consider the following six equations. Tell them to identify which equations represent growth, which ones represent decay, and which ones are linear. If the equation is not growth, decay, or linear, have students indicate so.

1. $q = 3.1 \left(\frac{2}{3}\right)^x$ decay
2. $3x - 5y = 1$ linear
3. $a = \frac{1}{4}(2.1)^x$ growth
4. $m = 0.0002(0.5)^x$ decay
5. $y = 3x^2 + 2x - 5$ not growth, decay, or linear
6. $u = \frac{7}{8}(11)^v$ growth

7-4

6a. Answers vary. Sample answer: No, the data appear linear.

6b. Answers vary. Sample answer: Yes, the data appear to grow exponentially.

6c. Answers vary. Sample answer: Yes, the data appear to decay exponentially.

6d. Answers vary. Sample answer: No, the data do not appear to grow or decay exponentially.

In 2–4, use the graph to answer the questions. The percent written above each bar represents the percent of the previous height to which each type of ball will rebound.

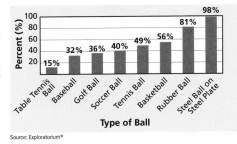

Source: Exploratorium®

2. Which ball's rebound height could be modeled by the equation $y = 10(0.49)^x$? **tennis ball**

3. If a basketball is dropped from a height of 15 feet above the ground, how high will it rebound after the 1st bounce? After the 5th bounce? **8.4 ft; about 0.83 ft**

4. Find and compare the rebound percentages in the Activity on page 419 to those in the graph. Are they similar or different? **Answers vary. Sample answer: They are similar.**

5. A computer's memory is measured in terms of megabytes (MB). The table at the right shows how much memory an average computer had, based on the number of years it was made after 1977. Use exponential regression to predict the amount of memory for a computer made in 2020. **about 80,817 MB**

Years After 1977	Memory (MB)
0	0.0625
2	1.125
3	8
6	16
7	30
9	32
13	40
17	88
21	250
27	512

6. For each scatterplot, tell whether you would expect exponential regression to produce a good model for the data. Explain your reasoning. **6a–d. See margin.**

a.
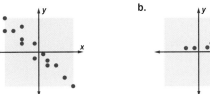

b.

c.
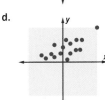

d.

Accommodating the Learner

When students use the regression features of their graphing calculators it would be nice to have some idea how well the regression equation models the given data. When using the ExpReg command (note that diagnostics need to be turned on with the "Diagnostics On" feature of the calculator) the calculator gives an idea of how closely the data fit the regression equation by giving a value of r^2 between 0 and 1. The closer r^2 is to 1, the better the regression equation models the data. Have students use the ExpReg command on the following three sets of data to determine which set of data is modeled best by an exponential regression. Graph each set of data and the regression curve.

x	0	1	2	3	4	5
y	2	2.7	2.9	3.8	4.2	5
y_2	5	7.1	17.2	71.3	102	111.2
y_3	0.1	5.2	6.8	12.3	19.5	25.1

APPLYING THE MATHEMATICS

Matching In 7–9, the graphs relate the bounce height of a ball to the number of times that it has bounced. Match a graph to the equation.

a. $y = 5.1(0.90)^x$ b. $y = 8.7(0.90)^x$ c. $y = 8.7(0.42)^x$

7.
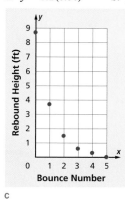
Bounce Number
c

8.
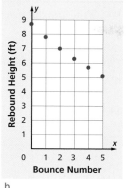
Bounce Number
b

9.
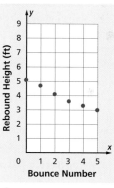
Bounce Number
a

10. The table at the right shows the number of weeks a movie had played in theaters, how it ranked, and how much money it grossed each weekend. (Note that $x = 0$ is the weekend the movie opened.)

  a. Create a scatterplot with y = gross sales after x weeks in theaters. Why is the exponential model a better model for these data than a linear model? **See margin.**

  b. Use exponential regression to find an equation to fit the data.

  c. What gross sales are predicted for the weekend of the 20th week?

Weeks in Theaters	Rank	Weekend Gross ($)
0	1	114,844,116
1	1	71,417,527
2	2	45,036,912
3	2	28,508,104
4	3	14,317,411
5	5	10,311,062
6	7	7,515,984
7	11	4,555,932
8	13	3,130,214
9	18	2,204,636
10	22	890,372
11	25	403,186

10b. $y = 118,976,118 \cdot 0.618^x$

10c. about $7,856.50

11. Lydia and Raul started with 2 pennies in a cup, shook them out onto the table, and added a penny for each coin that showed a head. They continued to repeat this process and their data are recorded in the table at the right. **11a. See margin.**

  a. Create a scatterplot of their data.

  b. Use exponential regression to derive an equation relating the trial number to the number of pennies they will have on the table.

Trial Number	Number of Pennies
0	2
1	2
2	3
3	5
4	8
5	13
6	17
7	25
8	38
9	60

11b. Let p be the number of pennies and t be the trial number.
$p = 1.57 \cdot 1.49^t$

Notes on the Questions

Question 10 Many data like these seem to decrease exponentially from a peak. Another example might be the prevalence of a communicable disease in a particular outbreak.

Question 11 The expected values of numbers of pennies in the trials is in theory very close to an exponential function. The pattern is like that in the Fibonacci sequence. The Fibonacci sequence is as close to exponential as one can get with an integer-value sequence.

Additional Answers

10a.
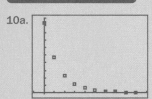

The data seem to curve down, and the y-axis (gross sales) must always be nonnegative.

11a.
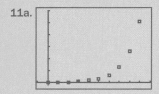

Notes on the Questions

Question 21 The key to the exponential decay of the heights is that the height does *not* affect the percent of rebound. If the height did affect the percent, then there would not be a constant exponential decay factor.

4 ▶ Wrap-Up

Ongoing Assessment

Using separate coordinate systems have students draw a scatterplot that represents exponential growth, exponential decay, and a line. Ask them to explain in writing why the points they graphed model each idea.

Project Update

Project 2, A Famous Snowflake, on page 447, relates to the content of this lesson.

For 12 and 13, create a real-world problem that could be modeled by the given equation.

12. $y = 72(1.08)^x$

13. $y = 14(0.65)^x$

REVIEW

14. The population of a city is 1,250,000. Write an expression for the population y years from now under each assumption. **(Lessons 7-3, 7-2, 6-1)**

   a. The population grows 2.5% per year. $1{,}250{,}000 \cdot 1.025^y$

   b. The population decreases 3% per year. $1{,}250{,}000 \cdot 0.97^y$

   c. The population decreases by 1,500 people per year. $1{,}250{,}000 - 1{,}500y$

15. Graph $y = 125\left(\frac{2}{5}\right)^x$ for integer values of x from 0 to 5. **(Lesson 7-3)** See margin.

16. Rewrite x^3y^4 using the Repeated Multiplication Property of Powers. **(Lesson 7-1)** $x \cdot x \cdot x \cdot y \cdot y \cdot y \cdot y$

17. An art store buys a package of 40 bristle paintbrushes for $80.00 and a package of 30 sable paintbrushes for $150. If they plan to sell an art kit with 4 bristle paintbrushes and 3 sable paintbrushes, how much should they charge for the kit to break even on their costs? **(Lesson 5-3)** $23

18. **Skill Sequence** Divide and simplify each expression. **(Lesson 5-2)**

   a. $\frac{4}{x} \div \frac{5}{x}$ $\frac{4}{5}$

   b. $\frac{4}{x} \div \frac{5}{2x}$ $\frac{8}{5}$

   c. $\frac{4}{x} \div \frac{5}{x^2}$ $\frac{4x}{5}$

19. Recall that if an item is discounted x%, you pay $(100 - x)$% of the original price. Calculate in your head the amount you pay for a camera that originally cost $300 and is discounted each indicated amount. **(Lesson 4-1)**

   a. 10% $270

   b. 25% $225

   c. $33\frac{1}{3}$% $200

20. Evaluate $(3a)^3(4b)^2$ when $a = -2$ and $b = 6$. **(Lesson 1-1)** $-124{,}416$

EXPLORATION

21. In the ball-drop activity on pages 419–420 and Questions 2–4 on page 422, you explored the rebound height of a ball as a percent of its previous height. Different types of balls have different percents. Does the height from which the ball is dropped affect the percent a ball will rebound? Explain your answer.

22. Do the activity described in Question 11 on page 423. How close is your exponential model to the one in that question?

a young artist at work

---

12. Answers vary. Sample answer: Hannibal has $72 in a CD earning 8% per year. How much money, y, does he have after x years?

13. Answers vary. Sample answer: If 35% of a 14-kg block of ice melts every day, how much ice, y, remains after x weeks?

21. No, the percent of rebound height is affected by the composition of the ball and not by the height from which it is dropped.

22. Answers vary. Sample answer: Our model is similar: $y = 2 \cdot 1.5^x$.

Additional Answers

15.

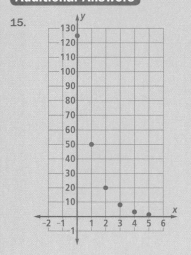

Lesson 7-5
The Language of Functions

▶ **BIG IDEA** A function is a relationship between two variables in which the value of the first variable is associated with, or determines, a unique value of the second variable.

In this course, you have seen many situations that involve two variables. In an investment situation, the length of time that money has been invested determines the value of the investment. In temperatures, the Fahrenheit temperature determines the Celsius temperature or vice versa. In a sequence of dot patterns, the term number determines the number of dots. When the value of a first variable determines the value of a second variable, we call the relationship between the variables a *function*.

A Squaring Function

Consider the squares of the integers from 1 to 10. There are two variables. The first is the integer. The second is its square. We can describe the relationship between these integers and their squares in many ways.

Table or List

Integer	Square
1	1
2	4
3	9
4	16
5	25
6	36
7	49
8	64
9	81
10	100

Graph

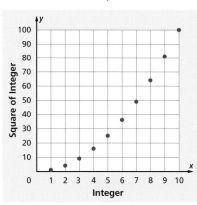

Equation $y = x^2$, where x is an integer from 1 to 10

Words The square of an integer from 1 to 10 is the result of multiplying the integer by itself.

The Language of Functions **425**

Vocabulary

function
input
output
value of the function
squaring function
independent variable
dependent variable
domain of a function
range of a function
relation

Mental Math

To the nearest mile per gallon, estimate the mpg of a car that went

a. 300 miles on 11 gallons of gas. **27 mpg**

b. 250 miles on 9 gallons of gas. **28 mpg**

c. 400 miles on 14 gallons of gas. **29 mpg**

Lesson 7-5

GOAL

Introduce the basic terminology and ideas of functions.

SPUR Objectives

C Use the language of functions.
I Graph functions.

Materials/Resources

· Lesson Masters 7-5A or 7-5B
· Resource Masters 1, 2, and 108–110

HOMEWORK

Suggestions for Assignment
• Questions 1–25
• Question 26 (extra credit)
• Reading Lesson 7-6
• Covering the Ideas 7-6

Local Standards

1 Warm-Up

In 1–4, find the value of y when $x = 8$.

1. $y = 3 \cdot 2^x$. **768**
2. $y = 6x^2$ **384**
3. $y = 17 - (8 - x)$ **17**
4. $y = 7 + \sqrt{\dfrac{x+1}{4}}$ **8.5**

Background

We have delayed the formal introduction of the idea of function until this lesson because we wanted to have many examples to illustrate the concept. All of the situations in the preceding lessons of the chapter have described functions and can be used as examples of the key ideas.

The idea of function. Two definitions of *function* are common in school mathematics. One definition is static: a **function** is a set of ordered pairs in which no two ordered pairs

have the same *x* component. The static definition of a function is quite useful when there is no formula relating the independent and dependent variables. Such situations are quite common in the real world, where the independent variable is time and data (such as amount of crime, water level, Consumer Price Index) are collected over time. We may search for a formula that comes close to the relationship, but do not expect any exact fit.

(continued on next page)

Notes on the Lesson

A squaring function. Students have been dealing with pairs of values and their graphs since the beginning of the school year. Now we want them to think of the set of ordered pairs as having properties. This is one of the reasons we begin with a function with a simple name: the squaring function. Also, we can naturally distinguish different squaring functions by their domains. The sequence 1, 4, 9, 16, ..., n^2, ... is a squaring function with a domain of the set of positive integers; the function that maps the length of a side of a square onto its area is a squaring function with a domain of the set of positive real numbers; the parabola with equation $y = x^2$ is the graph of a squaring function with a domain of the set of all real numbers.

The domain and range of a function. Experience with graphing utilities helps to explain domain and range. The domain is the set of values that needs to be covered by the horizontal dimensions of the window if you want to see all of the graph. The range is the set of values that the vertical dimension reaches. They are in alphabetical order: horizontal before vertical; *x* before *y*; domain before range.

In general, you can think of functions either as special kinds of correspondences or as special sets of ordered pairs. A **function** is a correspondence in which each value of the first variable (the **input**) corresponds to *exactly one* value of the second variable (the **output**), which is called a **value of the function.** We think of the first variable as determining the value of the second variable. The table, graph, equation, and words on page 425 describe a **squaring function.** The value of a number determines the value of its square. For example, when $x = 3$, the value of the squaring function is 9.

STOP QY1

The graph on page 425 shows the squaring function as a set of ordered pairs. A function is a set of ordered pairs in which each first coordinate appears with *exactly one* second coordinate. That is, once you know the value of the first variable (often called *x*), then there is only one value for the second variable (often called *y*). For this reason, the first variable is called the **independent variable** and the second variable is called the **dependent variable.**

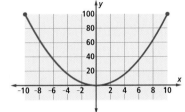

▶ **QY1**

What is the value of the squaring function when $x = 7$?

The Domain and Range of a Function

Suppose in the squaring function that *x* can be any real number from –10 to 10. You cannot list all the ordered pairs of the function, but the function still can be described by the equation $y = x^2$, where *x* is a real number from –10 to 10. The function can still be described in words: The square of any real number from –10 to 10 is the result of multiplying the number by itself. And the function can still be described by a graph, as shown at the right.

The difference between this squaring function and the one on page 425 is in the *domain of the function*. The **domain of a function** is the set of allowable inputs in the function, that is, the set of possible values of the first (independent) variable. In the squaring function on page 425, the domain is {1, 2, 3, 4, 5, 6, 7, 8, 9, 10}. In the squaring function on this page, the domain is the set of real numbers from –10 to 10.

If a function has a graph, you can read its domain from the graph. The domain is the set of *x*-coordinates of the points of the graph.

Corresponding to the domain of a function is its **range,** the set of possible values of the second (dependent) variable. The range is the set of possible values of the function. In the squaring function on page 425, the range is {1, 4, 9, 16, 25, 36, 49, 64, 81, 100}. In the squaring function on this page, the range is the set of real numbers from 0 to 100.

The other definition is dynamic: a **function** is a correspondence between two variables such that each value of the first (independent) variable corresponds to (or is mapped on, or determines) exactly one value of the second (dependent) variable. When the dynamic definition is in use, the set of ordered pairs is sometimes defined to be the **graph of the function**.

In this lesson, we use *x* to stand for the independent variable and *y* to stand for the dependent variable. In the next lesson, $f(x)$

notation will be used, and we will name the function *f*.

The domain and range of a function. The set of possible values of the independent variable is both the domain of that variable and the domain of the function. The set of possible values of the dependent variable can often be difficult to determine, but an accurate graph can often provide a picture.

STOP QY2

When a set of numbers is not specifically given for the domain of a function, you should assume that the domain is the set of all numbers possible in the situation.

Example 1

Consider the reciprocal function $y = \frac{1}{x}$, which pairs real numbers with their reciprocals.

a. Give the domain.

b. Find the value of the function when $x = 4$.

Solution

a. The domain is the set of all values that can replace x, the independent variable. Any number except 0 can be used. (Because $\frac{1}{0}$ is undefined, 0 has no reciprocal.) **So the domain is all real numbers except 0.**

b. Substitute 4 for x. The value of the function is $\frac{1}{4}$.

GUIDED

Example 2

What are the domain and range of the function described by the equation $y = 4x - 3$?

Solution The domain is the set of allowable values of x. Because no situation is given for x, you should assume that its domain is ___?___.
all real numbers

The range is the set of possible values of y. The graph of $y = 4x - 3$ is an oblique line. So any value of y is possible, and the range is ___?___.
all real numbers

In many places in this book, you have seen one function modeling another.

Example 3

In Lesson 7-3, the equation $y = 21,000(0.85)^x$ describes a function that models a car's value y when it is x years old if it was purchased for $21,000 and depreciates 15% a year. What is the range of this function?

Solution You can think of the car's value as decreasing constantly even though you have not yet studied values of powers when the exponent is not an integer. Refer to the graph in Lesson 7-3 on page 413. According to the model, the value of the car keeps decreasing but never reaches 0. So the range of the function is the set of real numbers y with $0 < y \leq 21,000$ which is written in set-builder notation as $\{y: 0 < y \leq 21,000\}$.

STOP QY3

> **QY2**
>
> A third squaring function is graphed below. What is its domain? What is its range?
>
>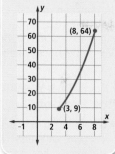

> **QY3**
>
> Use a calculator to estimate the value of $21,000(0.85)^x$ to the nearest penny when $x = 25, 25.3,$ and 26.

Note-Taking Tips

This lesson has a large number of new vocabulary words such as *function, input, output, domain, range, independent, dependent,* and *relation.* When presenting these ideas, be sure to provide the students with clear and concise examples of each. Insist that students write the terms, definitions, and examples in their notebooks. Consider a graphic organizer to help students visualize how all of these terms are related.

Additional Examples

Example 1 Consider the square root function $y = \sqrt{x}$, which pairs nonnegative real numbers with their square roots.

a. Give the domain. nonnegative real numbers

b. Find the value of the function when $x = 9$. 3

Example 2 What are the domain and range of the function described by the equation $y = -2x + 7$?

Solution
The domain is the set of allowable values of x. Because no situation is given for x, you should assume that its domain is __?__. all real numbers

The range is the set of possible values of y. The graph of $y = -2x + 7$ is an oblique line. So any value of y is possible, and the range is __?__. all real numbers

Example 3 In Lesson 7-2, the equation $y = 5,000 \cdot 1.04^x$ describes a function that models the total amount of money y in a savings account after x years. If $5,000 is invested at an annual yield of 4%. What is the range of this function? $y \geq 5,000$

Accommodating the Learner

Students may get the idea that the domain and range of all lines is the set of real numbers. Ask students to graph the line $y = 3$ and the line $x = -2$ on the same coordinate system. Ask students to identify the domain and range of each line. Discuss with them the idea that while the domain may be the set of real numbers for some lines it may only be a single value for others. The same can be said for the range. Ask students to generalize what they have just learned from these two examples.

$y = 3$: domain, all real numbers; range, 3

$x = -2$: domain, -2; range, all real numbers

Notes on the Lesson

Relations that are not functions. In some books one of the first things that students learn about functions is that there are sets of ordered pairs that are not functions. This is nice to know, but at this point it is not critical.

Functions whose domains or ranges are not sets of numbers. In contrast to the preceding paragraph, it is useful for students to realize that functions do not have to involve numbers. One of our favorite types of functions is one found by identifying relatives. For example, one function without any numbers is the function m that maps a person onto his or her mother.

Relations That Are Not Functions

The word **relation** describes any set of ordered pairs. It is possible to have relations between variables that are not functions. This happens when the first variable x in a relation corresponds to more than one value of the second variable y. For example, the relation described by the equation $x = y^2$ does *not* describe a function. When $x = 4$, then $y = 2$ or $y = -2$. So the value $x = 4$ corresponds to two different values for y, 2 and -2. Because a value of x does not always determine exactly one value of y, the relation is not a function.

Functions Whose Domains or Ranges Are Not Sets of Numbers

It is possible to have functions whose domains and ranges are not sets of real numbers, or even that have little to do with mathematics. For example, every person on Earth has a unique blood type. So there is a function whose domain is the set of all living people on Earth and whose range is the set of all blood types. Each ordered pair of this function is of the form (a person, that person's blood type). This function has no equation and cannot be graphed, but it is still a function with a domain (the set of all people) and a range (the set of all blood types).

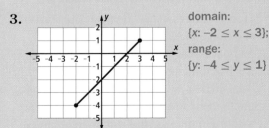

Everybody has a blood type. The most common blood-type classification system is the ABO system discovered by Karl Landsteiner in the early 1900s.

Source: University of Utah

Questions

COVERING THE IDEAS

1. Consider the function described by $y = x^2$ with domain the set of integers from 1 to 5.
   a. What is the value of this function when $x = 3$? 9
   b. The point (4, 16) is on the graph of this function. Which of these coordinates is the input and which is the output?
   c. Which variable is the independent variable and which is the dependent variable?
   d. What is the range of this function? {1, 4, 9, 16, 25}

2. Consider a cubing function described by $y = x^3$ with domain the set of real numbers from -50 to 50. Find the value of this function when
   a. $x = 36$. 46,656   b. $x = -36$. $-46,656$ c. $x = 0$. 0

3. a. What is the value of the reciprocal function when $x = -1$? -1
   b. What is the value of the reciprocal function when $x = 3.5$? $\frac{2}{7}$

4. Give the two definitions of *function* stated in this lesson.

1b. 4 is the input and 16 is the output.

1c. 4 is the independent variable and 16 is the dependent variable.

4. a correspondence in which each value of the first variable corresponds to exactly one value of the second variable; a set of ordered pairs in which each first coordinate appears with exactly one second coordinate

428   Using Algebra to Describe Patterns of Change

Accommodating the Learner ⬇

Students will need practice identifying the domain and range of functions. Present them with the following examples of functions. Have them identify the domain and range of each of them.

1.

x	-3	0	6	9	23
y	14	3	-9	0	2

domain: {-3, 0, 6, 9, 23}, range: {-9, 0, 2, 3, 14};

2. $3x - 6y = -12$ domain: the set of all real numbers; range: the set of all real numbers

3.

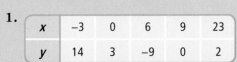

domain: {$x: -2 \leq x \leq 3$}; range: {$y: -4 \leq y \leq 1$}

4. $y = -5$ domain: the set of all real numbers; range: {-5}

5. Explain why 0 is not in the range of the reciprocal function.

In 6 and 7, the graph of a function is given.

a. From the graph, determine the domain of the function.

b. From the graph, determine the range of the function.

6.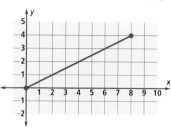

7.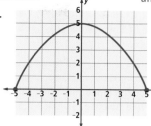

5. No real number has 0 as its reciprocal because if $0 = \frac{1}{x}$, then $x = \frac{1}{0}$, which is undefined.

8. Determine if the following statement is *always, sometimes but not always,* or *never* true. The graph of a function may contain both points (6, 5) and (6, 7). never

6a. $\{x: 0 \le x \le 8\}$
6b. $\{y: 0 \le y \le 4\}$
7a. $\{x: -5 \le x \le 5\}$
7b. $\{y: 0 \le y \le 5\}$

9. **Multiple Choice** Which table does *not* describe a function? C

A
x	y
1	6
2	53
3	8

B
x	y
1	6
2	6
3	6

C
x	y
6	1
6	2
6	3

D
x	y
6	6
6	6
6	6

APPLYING THE MATHEMATICS

10. The graph at the right is of a function showing the distance walked by a hiker over time.

a. Find the value of the function when x = 2 P.M. 2.5 mi

b. Find the value of the function when x = 3:30 P.M. 5 mi

c. Find x for which the value of the function is 5.5 miles. 4:30 P.M.

d. Use inequalities to describe the domain and range of this function. domain: $1 \le x \le 5$; range: $0 \le y \le 6$

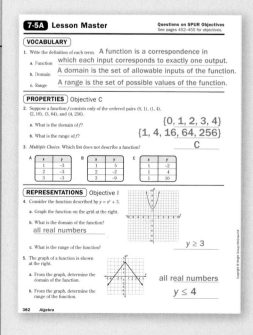

Time (P.M.)

In 11 and 12, determine if the graph of ordered pairs (x, y) is that of a function. Justify your answer. 11–12. See margin.

11.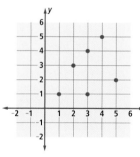

12.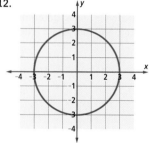

The Language of Functions **429**

Extension

Suppose the number of people entering a football stadium each minute can be modeled by the equation $p = 54m$ where p is the number of people having entered after m minutes. Ask the students to identify the domain and range for this equation. Ask them to graph the equation. Based on their experience, most students will indicate the domain and range to be the nonnegative real numbers, and the graph is a ray starting at the point (0, 0) with a slope of 54. Ask students to identify five or six points on the ray. Have students find the value of p when $m = 1.3$ or 2.11. Now ask students if it is possible to have 70.2 or 113.94 people in the stadium. Discuss with your students the idea of *discrete* data. Ask them to identify other examples where the domain and or range would be discrete.

3 Assignment

Recommended Assignment

• Questions 1–25

• Question 26 (extra credit)

• Reading Lesson 7-6

• Covering the Ideas 7-6

Notes on the Questions

Notice the variety of functions in this question set.

1. squaring function

2. cubing function

3. reciprocal function

6. function whose graph is a line segment

7. function whose graph is part of a parabola

10. function with a broken line graph

13. function of exponential decay

16. absolute value function

Emphasize that functions are among the most important ideas in all of mathematics because they bring together such a variety of ideas.

Additional Answers

11. No; The input x = 3 corresponds to both outputs y = 1 and y = 4.

12. No; Answers vary. Sample answer: The input x = 0 corresponds to both outputs y = 3 and y = −3.

7-5A Lesson Master

Questions on SPUR Objectives
See pages 452–455 for objectives.

VOCABULARY

1. Write the definition of each term. **A function is a correspondence in which each input corresponds to exactly one output.**

a. Function

b. Domain **A domain is the set of allowable inputs of the function.**

c. Range **A range is the set of possible values of the function.**

PROPERTIES Objective C

2. Suppose a function f consists only of the ordered pairs (0, 1), (1, 4), (2, 16), (3, 64), and (4, 256).

a. What is the domain of f? **{0, 1, 2, 3, 4}**

b. What is the range of f? **{1, 4, 16, 64, 256}**

3. *Multiple Choice.* Which list does not describe a function? **C**

A
x	y
1	−3
2	−3
3	−3

B
x	y
1	5
2	−2
3	−9

C
x	y
1	−2
1	4
1	10

REPRESENTATIONS Objective I

4. Consider the function described by $y = x^2 + 3$.

a. Graph the function on the grid at the right.

b. What is the domain of the function? **all real numbers**

c. What is the range of the function? **$y \ge 3$**

5. The graph of a function is shown at the right.

a. From the graph, determine the domain of the function. **all real numbers**

b. From the graph, determine the range of the function. **$y \le 4$**

382 Algebra

7-5

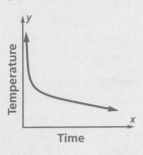
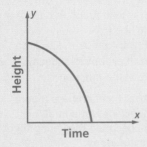
13. The function $y = 5 \cdot 0.8^x$ is graphed at the right.

   a. **True or False** Zero is in the range of this function. false
   b. What is the value of this function when $x = 0$? 5
   c. What is the domain of the function that is graphed?
   d. What is the range of the function that is graphed?
   e. Suppose x can be any positive integer. What is the greatest possible value of y? 4

In 14 and 15, a situation is described in which one quantity can be used to predict values of the second quantity. Tell which quantity you wish to be the input and which should be the output in order to have a function. Sketch a reasonable graph. Do not mark numbers on the axes. Think only about the basic shape of the graph.

14. the amount of time since a cup of hot coffee was poured and its temperature See margin.

15. the height of a skydiver who has jumped from an airplane See margin.

In 16–18, use the graph of an absolute value function below. Find the range for the part of the function whose domain is given.

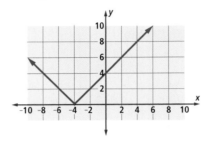

16. domain $= \{x: x \geq 1\}$ $\{y: y \geq 5\}$

17. domain $= \{x: -6 \leq x \leq -2\}$ $\{y: 0 \leq y \leq 2\}$

18. domain $= \{x: x \leq 0\}$ $\{y: y \geq 0\}$

In 19 and 20, an equation for a function is given. Determine the domain and the range of the function. You may use a graphing calculator to help you.

19. $y = \frac{1}{75}x - 3$

20. $y = 100 \cdot \left(\frac{1}{2}\right)^x$, when $x \geq 0$ domain: $\{x: x \geq 0\}$; range: $\{y: 0 < y \leq 100\}$

13c. the set of all real numbers

13d. $\{y: y > 0\}$

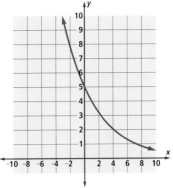

People have been using parachutes for hundreds of years, even during the 1100s in China.

Source: United States Parachute Association

19. domain: the set of all real numbers; range: the set of all real numbers

430   Using Algebra to Describe Patterns of Change

21. Since 1980, world records in the men's marathon have been set many times.

Date	Record-Setter	Country	Time	Location of Race
Dec. 6, 1981	Robert de Castella	Australia	2 hr, 8 min, 18 sec	Fukuoka, Japan
Oct. 21, 1984	Steve Jones	Britain	2 hr, 8 min, 5 sec	Chicago, USA
Apr. 20, 1985	Carlos Lopes	Portugal	2 hr, 7 min, 12 sec	Rotterdam, Netherlands
Apr. 17, 1988	Belayneh Dinsamo	Ethiopia	2 hr, 6 min, 50 sec	Rotterdam, Netherlands
Sept. 20, 1998	Ronaldo de Costa	Brazil	2 hr, 6 min, 5 sec	Berlin, Germany
Oct. 24, 1999	Khalid Khannouchi	Morocco	2 hr, 5 min, 42 sec	Chicago, USA
Apr. 14, 2002	Khalid Khannouchi	USA	2 hr, 5 min, 38 sec	London, England
Sept. 28, 2003	Paul Tergat	Kenya	2 hr, 4 min, 55 sec	Berlin, Germany

Source: www.marathonguide.com

a. Consider the function using the pairs (date, time). This function is an example of a *decreasing function*. Why do you think it is called a decreasing function?

b. Consider the eight ordered pairs (record-setter, time). By examining the definition of function, explain why these eight ordered pairs do *not* make up a function.

REVIEW

22. In China, most families are allowed to have only one child. This policy was implemented to reduce the population, with a goal of reaching 700 million citizens by 2050. Suppose the 2005 population of 1.3 billion decreases by 1% each year. (**Lesson 7-3**)

a. Write an expression for the population of China x years after 2005.

b. Will the goal of having 700 million citizens or less in the year 2050 be met? **no**

23. Find the slope of the line given by the equation $\frac{7}{20}(x + 18) = \frac{8}{3}(y - 11)$. (**Lessons 6-2, 4-4, 3-8**) $\frac{21}{160}$

24. Triangle 1 has an area of 12 cm² and is similar to Triangle 2, which has an area of 108 cm². What is the ratio of similitude of Triangle 1 to Triangle 2? (**Lesson 5-10**) **3**

25. The maximum number p of people allowed on a certain elevator times the average weight w of an adult should not exceed 1,500 pounds. Write an inequality describing the rule and solve for p. (**Lesson 3-6**)

EXPLORATION

26. Find equations for two different functions with the same domain that contain both the ordered pairs (1, 1) and (2, 6).

21a. Answers vary. Sample answer: As the value of the input increases, that of the output decreases.

21b. Khalid Khannouchi is associated with two record-setting times; that is, one input produces two outputs.

22a. Let y be the population in millions, and let x be the number of years after 2005. $y = 1,300 \cdot 0.99^x$

25. $pw \leq 1,500$; $p \leq \dfrac{1,500}{w}$

26. Answers vary. Sample answer: $y = (x + 1)^2 - 3$ and $y = 5x - 4$

1. 49

2. domain: {x: $3 \leq x \leq 8$}; range: {y: $9 \leq y \leq 64$}

3. $361.15; $343.97; $306.98

---

4 Wrap-Up

Ongoing Assessment

Form groups of three students. Ask students to illustrate the concept of a function in many ways. Students should provide examples, graphs, and diagrams. Ask students to define at least two functions that are not numerical. Have each group share their ideas with the class.

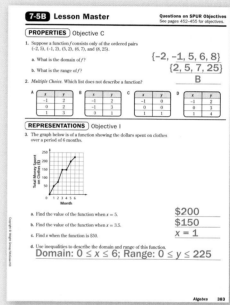

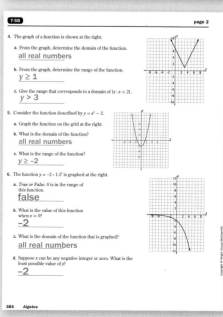

Lesson 7-6

Function Notation

$f(x)$ notation

function notation

GOAL

Introduce $f(x)$ function notation.

SPUR Objectives

A Evaluate functions.

C Use the language of functions.

I Graph functions.

Materials/Resources

· Lesson Masters 7-6A or 7-6B
· Resource Masters 1, 111, and 112
· Computer Algebra System (CAS)
· Quiz 2

HOMEWORK

Suggestions for Assignment

• Questions 1–16
• Questions 17–18 (extra credit)
• Reading Lesson 7-7
• Covering the Ideas 7-7

Local Standards

---

1 Warm-Up

In 1–4, suppose $f(x) = 3(x + 12)$.

1. Calculate $f(5)$. **51**

2. Calculate $f(-2.5)$. **28.5**

3. Calculate $f(0) + f(1)$. **75**

4. For what value of x does $f(x) = 15$? **−7**

In 5–9, suppose $g(x) = 2^x - x$.

5. Calculate $g(0)$. **1**

6. Calculate $g(1)$. **1**

7. Calculate $g(2)$. **2**

8. Calculate $g(3)$. **5**

9. Calculate $g(10)$. **1,014**

▶ **BIG IDEA** When a function f contains the ordered pair (x, y), then y is the value of the function at x, and we may write $y = f(x)$.

Refer to the graph on page 397. Recall that each equation represents a different prediction of the population of a town x years in the future. Each model describes a function. The functions are of three types.

Possibility 1 $P = 100,000$ describes a *constant function* where the population does not change.

Possibility 2 $P = 100,000 + 3,000x$ describes a *linear function* with 3,000 new people per year.

Possibility 3 $P = 100,000(1.02)^x$ describes an *exponential function* with a growth rate of 2% per year.

It is important to see these functions on the same axes because we want to compare them. But in talking about three functions, we might easily get confused. If we say the letter P, which P are we talking about? It would be nice to be able to name a function in a simple and useful manner.

$f(x)$ Notation

Conveniently, mathematics does have another way to name functions. With this method, Possibility 3 can be written $E(x) = 100,000(1.02)^x$.

We chose the letter E as a name for the function as a reminder of exponential growth. The symbol $E(x)$ shows that x is the input variable. It is read "E of x." What is the purpose of using this new symbol? It allows us to show the correspondence between specific pairs of values for the input (number of years x) and output (population predicted by the exponential growth model). For example, when $x = 3$, the output is $E(3) = 100,000(1.02)^3 = 106,120.8$. So $E(3) = 106,120.8 \approx 106,121$ people. When $x = 20$, the output is $E(20) = 100,000(1.02)^{20} \approx 148,595$ people.

The other population models can be written in function notation as well.

Give the coordinates of a solution to the inequality.

a. $y \le -22x + 6$ $(0, 6)$

b. $5m - 4n > 3$ $(0, -1)$

c. $-b + 3 < a - 4.5$ $(8, 0)$

Background

$f(x)$ notation. The $f(x)$ function notation is not completely new to students. They have seen it in calculator or computer commands such as EXPAND( ) and SOLVE( ). They have seen $P(E)$ used to describe the probability of an event.

Students have graphed $y = 100,000 + 3,000x$, and it seems that $f(x) = 100,000 + 3,000x$ is just a more complicated way of saying the same thing. The notation clearly tells about the dependence of the second value on the first value—that is, $E(x)$ depends on x—and the use of $f(x)$ rather than y allows the use of a letter that describes the situation. So, by using E, L, and C for "exponential," "linear," and "constant," we can identify the relationship easily. When two or more quantities depend on x, they can be distinguished.

Some calculators and computers identify a function as $f(x)$, but we are careful to distinguish the function f from the value $f(x)$ of the function at x.

Possibility 2 could be written $L(x) = 100,000 + 3,000x$.
Possibility 1 could be written $C(x) = 100,000$.
Now each model has a different name.

It is important to know that $E(x)$ *does not* denote the multiplication of E and x. The parentheses indicate the input of a function.

Example 1

Given a function with equation $f(x) = 5x - 19$, find $f(2)$.

Solution $f(x) = 5x - 19$ is a general formula that tells how to find the output for any input. The symbol $f(2)$ stands for "the output of function f when the input is 2." So substitute 2 for x and evaluate the expression on the right side.

$$f(2) = 5(2) - 19$$
$$= 10 - 19 = \text{-}9$$

So $f(2) = \text{-}9$.

In Example 1, we say that –9 is the *value of the function* when $x = 2$.

GUIDED

Example 2

Use the three functions given earlier for population models to find $E(10)$, $L(10)$, and $C(10)$. Explain what the results mean in the context of the population situation.

Solution

$E(x) = 100,000(1.02)^x$

$E(10) = 100,000(1.02)^{\underline{?}\ 10}$

After 10 years, the population based on the exponential model is predicted to be about __?__ people. **121,899**

$L(x) = 100,000 + 3,000x$

$L(10) = \underline{\ ?\ } + \underline{\ ?\ } (\underline{\ ?\ }) = \underline{\ ?\ }$ **100,000; 3,000; 10; 130,000**

After 10 years, the population based on the linear model is predicted to be __?__ people. **130,000**

$C(x) = 100,000$

$C(10) = 100,000$

After __?__ years, the population based on the _____?_____ model is predicted to be __?__ people. **10; constant; 100,000**

Notes on the Lesson

Although students have seen $P(E)$ and other examples of directives in $f(\ )$ notation, $f(x)$ can be more difficult for students to grasp because both f and x are variables. Also, f stands for a relationship, not just a number. Emphasize that f signifies a correspondence of a certain type, and $f(x)$ is the number that belongs to x under that correspondence.

You may find it helpful to introduce letters to name certain relationships. For example, you could introduce $s(x)$ or $SQR(x)$ for the square of x, so that $s(x) = SQR(x) = x^2$; $SQRT(x)$ for the square root of x, so that $SQRT(x) = \sqrt{x}$ (a good function for examining domain and range); $A(x)$ for the area of a polygon x, and so on.

Additional Examples

Example 1 Given a function with equation $f(x) = -3x - 1$, find $f(3)$. **−10**

Example 2 Use the three functions given earlier for population models to find $E(15)$, $L(15)$, and $C(15)$. Explain what the results mean in the context of the population situation.

Solution

$E(x) = 100,000(1.02)^x$

$E(15) = 100,000(1.02)^{\underline{?}\ 15}$

After 15 years, the population based on the exponential model is predicted to be about __?__ people. **134,587**

$L(x) = 100,000 + 3,000x$

$L(15) = \underline{?}\ 100,000 + 3,000(15)$

$= \underline{?}\ 145,000$

After 15 years, the population based on the linear model is predicted to be __?__ people. **145,000**

$C(x) = 100,000$

$C(15) = 100,000$

After __?__ years, the population based on the __?__ model is predicted to be __?__ people. **15; constant function; 100,000**

7-6

Additional Examples

Example 3 Possibility (2) used the linear function $L(x) = 100{,}000 + 3{,}000x$ to model the population of a town x years in the future. According to this model, in how many years will the population reach 170,000? **23.33**

Example 4 For the exponential model $E(x) = 100{,}000(1.02)^x$, use the graph to find when the population reaches 200,000. **about 35 years from now**

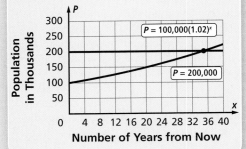

In working with functions, questions arise in which you are given the value of one variable and are asked to find the value of the other variable. In Example 1, you were given the *input* value. You substituted to find the output value. In the next two examples, you are given the value of the *output*. This results in an equation to solve. When you have a formula for a function, symbolic methods may be used to solve the equation to find the input value.

Example 3

Possibility 2 used the linear function $L(x) = 100{,}000 + 3{,}000x$ to model the population of a town x years in the future. According to this model, in how many years will the population reach 150,000?

Solution In $L(x) = 100{,}000 + 3{,}000x$, replace $L(x)$ with 150,000. Then solve for x.

$$150{,}000 = 100{,}000 + 3{,}000x$$
$$50{,}000 = 3{,}000x$$
$$16.67 \approx x$$

The linear model predicts that in about 17 years the population will be 150,000. So $L(x) = 150{,}000$ when $x \approx 17$.

Because functions can also be described with tables and graphs, tables and graphs are useful in solving problems in which you are given the output and need to find the input.

Example 4

For $E(x) = 100{,}000(1.02)^x$, use the graph to find when the population reaches 150,000.

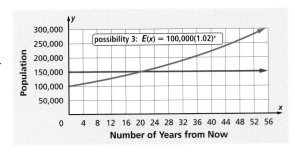

Solution Graph $y = 100{,}000(1.02)^x$. To help you see the point on this graph whose y-coordinate is 150,000, also graph the horizontal line $y = 150{,}000$. Trace on the graph to find where these two graphs intersect. When x is between 20 and 21 years, $E(x)$ is approximately 150,000.

Check Substitute 20 and 21 for x in the equation $E(x) = 100{,}000(1.02)^x$.

Using $x = 20$, $E(x) = E(20) = 100{,}000(1.02)^{20} \approx 148{,}595$.

Using $x = 21$, $E(x) = E(21) = 100{,}000(1.02)^{21} \approx 151{,}567$.

$148{,}595 < 150{,}000 < 151{,}567$, so the answer is reasonable.

434 Using Algebra to Describe Patterns of Change

Accommodating the Learner ⬇

Students may need practice evaluating functions. Have students evaluate each of the following functions. Let $x = 3$.

1. $c(x) = -2x + 4$ **-2**

2. $d(x) = x^2 + 4x + 1$ **22**

3. $f(x) = 12 \cdot 5^x$ **1,500**

4. $g(x) = -(x + 4)(1 - x)$ **14**

If students continue to struggle, change the value of x or introduce a few more equations.

Unless the situation suggests a better letter, the most common letter used to name a function is f. That is, instead of writing $y = 3x + 5$, we might write $f(x) = 3x + 5$. Then f is the linear function with slope 3 and y-intercept 5. It is read "f of x equals 3 times x plus 5." This way of writing a function is called **$f(x)$ notation** or **function notation**. The symbol $f(x)$ is attributed to the great Swiss mathematician Leonhard Euler (1707–1783).

Activity

The CAS allows you to work with functions.

1. **a.** Use the DEFINE command to define $f(x) = 3x^2 + 2x + 10$ in your CAS.
   b. Find $f(2)$. **26**
   c. Find $f(3) + f(-6)$. **149**
   d. Find $f(2006) - f(2005)$. **12,035**
   e. Find $f(a)$. $3a^2 + 2a + 10$
   f. Find $f(y)$. $3y^2 + 2y + 10$
   g. Find $f(\text{math})$. (Do not type in multiplication symbols between the letters. CAS sees *math* as just one big variable called a string variable.)
   h. Find $f(\text{your name})$. $3\text{yourname}^2 + 2\text{yourname} + 10$
2. **a.** Define $g(x) = \frac{x^3 + 999}{8x - 1}$.
   b. Find $g(7)$, $g(\pi)$, $g(t)$, and $g(\text{mom})$.
3. Explain the relationships between function notation and substitution.
4. Without using a CAS, find $h(4)$ and $h(\text{algebra})$ if $h(x) = 5x + 2x^2 + 1$. $h(4) = 53$; $h(\text{algebra}) = 5\text{algebra} + 2\text{algebra}^2 + 1$

Activity
1g. $3\text{math}^2 + 2\text{math} + 10$

Activity 2b.
$g(7) = \frac{122}{5}$;

$g(\pi) = \frac{\pi^3 + 999}{8\pi - 1}$;

$g(t) = \frac{t^3 + 999}{8t - 1}$;

$g(\text{mom}) = \frac{\text{mom}^3 + 999}{8\text{mom} - 1}$

Activity 3.
Answers vary. Sample answer: Function notation allows you to "substitute" for the input to find the output.

Questions

COVERING THE IDEAS

1. How is the symbol $f(x)$ read? **f of x**

In 2 and 3, let $E(x) = 100{,}000(1.02)^x$, $L(x) = 100{,}000 + 3{,}000x$, and $C(x) = 100{,}000$.

2. **a.** Without a calculator, find the values of $E(1)$, $L(1)$, and $C(1)$.
   b. What do these values mean in the population projection situation?

3. **a.** With a calculator if necessary, find the values of $E(25)$, $L(25)$, and $C(25)$. $E(25) \approx 164{,}061$; $L(25) = 175{,}000$; $C(25) = 100{,}000$
   b. What do these values mean in the population projection situation?

4. If $f(x) = 4 \cdot 0.12^x$, find each value.
   a. $f(1)$ **0.48**   **b.** $f(3)$ **0.006912**   **c.** $f(5)$ **about 0.0001**

2a. $E(1) = 102{,}000$;
$L(1) = 103{,}000$;
$C(1) = 100{,}000$

2b. They are the population estimates for 1 yr from the present.

3b. They are the population estimates for 25 yr from the present.

Notes on the Lesson

Activity. This activity brings home the point that a CAS deals with a symbol or string of symbols as just that. It acts, as David Hilbert viewed mathematics, as symbols without meaning. Of course, Hilbert knew that mathematics does have meaning, but what he meant was that one can operate with algebraic symbols without having any meaning for those symbols. This is both the power of algebra and, for students who are looking to know why they have to study algebra, its weakness.

Notes on the Activity

Some steps of the activity may be confusing for students. Single variables may even be difficult. In the context of algebra, students do not always think of a variable as a number. Now, using a CAS, variables can be more than one letter as in Step 1h. Reinforce with students that a CAS sees the variable x as being no different than the variable *your name*.

7-6

3 Assignment

Recommended Assignment
- Questions 1–16
- Questions 17–18 (extra credit)
- Reading Lesson 7-7
- Covering the Ideas 7-7

Notes on the Questions

It is useful to go over all the questions in this lesson.

Question 8 Here we have the halving function. Some other possibilities of this type are $d(x) = 2x$ for the doubling function and $t(x) = 3x$ for the tripling function.

Question 9 Point out how much simpler it is in Part a to write $W(4)$ than to write "the value of y when $x = 4$."

Additional Answers

9b.

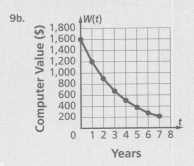

7-6A Lesson Master

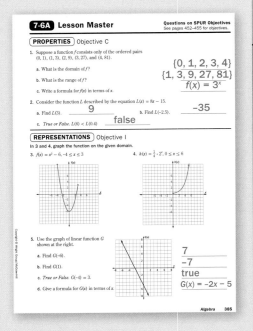

---

5. Let p be a function with $p(n) = 100 \cdot 2^n$. Find the value of $p(n)$ when $n = 7$. **12,800**

6. Determine if the statement is *always true, sometimes but not always true,* or *never true.* If $g(x) = 4x^2$ and $g(x) > 0$, then $x > 0$. **sometimes, but not always**

APPLYING THE MATHEMATICS

7. The table below shows the amount of money earned by a person who worked x hours.

Hours Worked x	Total Amount Earned $f(x)$
5	$45
10	$90
15	$135
20	$180
25	$225
30	$270

  a. What is the value of $f(5)$? **$45**

  b. What is the value of $f(15)$? **$135**

  c. Find x if $f(x) = \$180$. **20**

8. Let $h(n) = 0.5n$.

  a. Calculate $h(0)$, $h(1)$, and $h(2)$. **$h(0) = 0$; $h(1) = 0.5$; $h(2) = 1$**

  b. Calculate $h(-1) + h(-2)$. **−1.5**

  c. Why do you think the letter h was chosen for this function?

9. A computer purchased for $1,600 is estimated to depreciate at a rate of 25% per year. The computer's value after t years is given by $W(t) = 1,600(0.75)^t$. **9b. See margin.**

  a. Evaluate $W(4)$ and explain what the value means.

  b. Graph the function W for values of t with $0 \le t \le 7$.

  c. Use your graph to estimate the solutions to $W(t) < 1,000$ and explain what your answer means.

10. Suppose $L(x) = 12x - 18$.

  a. Calculate $L(5)$. **42**

  b. Calculate $L(3)$. **18**

  c. Evaluate $\dfrac{L(5) - L(3)}{5 - 3}$. **12**

  d. What is the meaning of your calculation in Part c?
  The rate of change of $L(x)$ between $x = 3$ and $x = 5$ is 12.

8c. Answers vary. Sample answer: because 0.5 is equal to one-half

9a. 506.25; It is the estimated value of the computer in 4 years.

9c. $t > 1.63$; This means after about 1.63 years the computer's value is less than $1,000.

In 2005, approximately 89% of U.S. public middle and junior high schools had the use of computers in the classroom.

Source: Quality Education Data, Inc.

436 Using Algebra to Describe Patterns of Change

Extension

Introduce the ideas of *inverse* and *composition of functions* on a limited basis. Students will readily see that $p(q(x)) = x$ when $p(x) = 2x$ and $q(x) = \frac{1}{2}x$. If you don't want to use composition notation, consider using the idea presented in the diagram below.

If you carefully select your functions, the students will understand them. This can lead to a discussion on how this idea is used, such as in the areas of coding and decoding.

$p(x) = 2x \qquad q(x) = \frac{1}{2}x$

$q(6) \qquad\qquad p(3)$

6 → 3 → 6

11. Oven temperature T varies with the length of time t the oven has been on. An oven, whose initial temperature was 80°, was set for 325°. The actual temperature was measured and then graphed over a 45-minute interval. Below is the graph of the function f where $T = f(t)$.

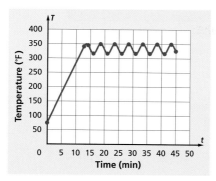

a. Estimate $f(25)$. about 325°
b. What is the meaning of $f(25)$?
c. Estimate the solution to the equation $f(t) = 200$. $t \approx 6$
d. What is the meaning of the solution in Part c?
   The oven reached 200° after being on for about 6 min.

11b. The temperature of the oven after it was on for 25 min was 325°.

REVIEW

In 12 and 13, could the table of values represent a function with x as the independent variable and y as the dependent variable? Why or why not? (Lesson 7-5)

12.

x	-3	-2	-1	0	1	2	3
y	0	1	5	1	6	0	2

Yes, each x value results in only one y value.

13.

x	0	1	5	1	6	0	2
y	-3	-2	-1	0	1	2	3

No. Answers vary. Sample answer: $x = 1$ results in both $y = -2$ and $y = 0$.

14. Consider the relation described by the equation $x^2 + 3y^2 = 31$. (Lesson 7-5)

a. Is $(2, 3)$ a solution? yes
b. Is $(2, -3)$ a solution? yes
c. Is $x^2 + 3y^2 = 31$ the equation of a function? Explain.

14c. No; the input $x = 2$ corresponds to both outputs $y = 3$ and $y = -3$.

15. Rewrite $8y - 4x + 1 = 25 + 6x$ in each form. (Lessons 6-8, 6-4)

a. standard form
   $5x - 4y = -12$

b. slope-intercept form
   $y = \frac{5}{4}x + 3$

Function Notation   **437**

4 Wrap-Up

Ongoing Assessment

On the board or on the overhead write the following:

Evaluate each function in Column 1 for $x = 4$ and match the value of each function with numbers in Column 2.

$f(4) = 13$, $g(4) = -10$, $h(4) = 48$

Column 1	Column 2
$f(x) = x^2 - 3$	48
$g(x) = 2 - 3x$	13
$h(x) = 3 \cdot 2^x$	–10

Project Update

Project 1, Reciprocal Functions, on page 447, relates to the content of this lesson.

7-6B Lesson Master

Questions on SPUR Objectives
See pages 452–455 for objectives.

PROPERTIES Objective C

1. Suppose a function f consists only of the ordered pairs (0, 1), (1, -2), (2, 4), (3, -8), (4, 16), and (5, -32).
   a. What is the domain of f? {0, 1, 2, 3, 4, 5}
   b. What is the range of f? {-32, -8, -2, 1, 4, 16}
   c. Write a formula for $f(x)$ in terms of x. $f(x) = (-2)^x$
2. Consider the function J described by the equation $J(x) = -5x + 2$.
   a. Find $J(2)$. -8
   b. Find $J(-3.2)$. 18
   c. *True or False.* $J(4) < J(5)$ false
3. If $g(x) = 2 \cdot 1.3^x$, find $g(-3.3)$. Round to the nearest hundredth. 0.84
4. Suppose $L(x) = -2x - 3$.
   a. Calculate $L(4)$. -11
   b. Calculate $L(2)$. -7
   c. Evaluate $\frac{L(4) - L(2)}{4 - 2}$. -2
   d. What have you calculated in Part c? the slope of line L
5. The table below shows the centimeters of rainfall in a given town on day x of the month.

x	$R(x)$
1	2
2	4
3	0
4	10

   a. What is the value of $R(2)$? 4
   b. On what day did they have 10 centimeters of rainfall? day 4
   c. Find x if $R(x) = 2$. $x = 1$

REPRESENTATIONS Objective I

In 6–8, graph the function on the given domain.

6. $f(x) = -x^2 + 3, -1 \le x \le 3$
7. $d(x) = 0.6 \cdot 2^x, 0 \le x \le 4$
8. $h(x) = 2x^2 - 5, -2 \le x \le 2$

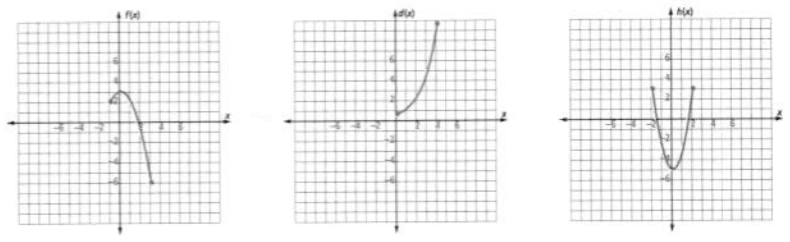

9. Use the graph of a linear function L.

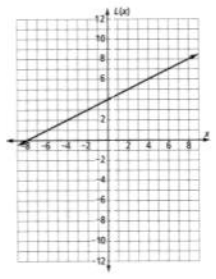

   a. Find $L(-4)$. 2
   b. *True or False.* $L(-2) = 5$ false
   c. Give a formula for $L(x)$ in terms of x. $L(x) = 0.5x + 4$

10. Use the graph of an exponential function E.

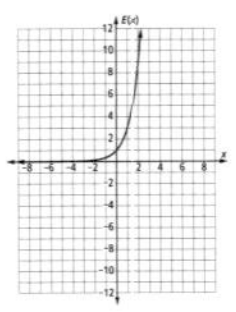

   a. Find $E(0)$. 1
   b. Find $E(1)$. 3
   c. Give a formula for $E(x)$ in terms of x. $E(x) = 3^x$

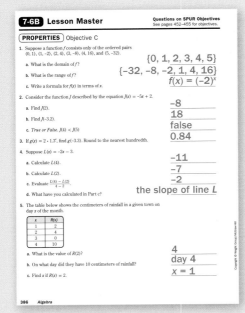

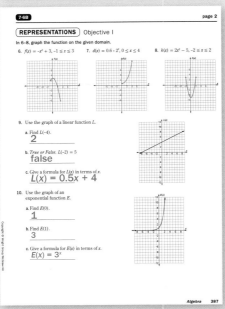

16. ***Skill Sequence*** (Lessons 4-4, 2-2, 2-1)
    a. Simplify $3(5 - 2m)$. $15 - 6m$
    b. Simplify $3(5 - 2m) - 2(7m + 1)$. $13 - 20m$
    c. Solve $3(5 - 2m) - 2(7m + 1) = 43$. $m = -\frac{3}{2}$

EXPLORATION

17. Some functions involve more than one input variable. The chart below shows wind chill as a function of the wind speed and the temperature. For wind speed V and temperature T, let $W(V, T)$ = wind chill and let $F(V, T)$ = frostbite time.

Temperature (°F)

Wind (mph) / Calm	40	35	30	25	20	15	10	5	0	–5	–10	–15	–20	–25	–30	–35	–40	–45
5	36	31	25	19	13	7	1	–5	–11	–16	–22	–28	–34	–40	–46	–52	–57	–63
10	34	27	21	15	9	3	–4	–10	–16	–22	–28	–35	–41	–47	–53	–59	–66	–72
15	32	25	19	13	6	0	–7	–13	–19	–26	–32	–39	–45	–51	–58	–64	–71	–77
20	30	24	17	11	4	–2	–9	–15	–22	–29	–35	–42	–48	–55	–61	–68	–74	–81
25	29	23	16	9	3	–4	–11	–17	–24	–31	–37	–44	–51	–58	–64	–71	–78	–84
30	28	22	15	8	1	–5	–12	–19	–26	–33	–39	–46	–53	–60	–67	–73	–80	–87
35	28	21	14	7	0	–7	–14	–21	–27	–34	–41	–48	–55	–62	–69	–76	–82	–89
40	27	20	13	6	–1	–8	–15	–22	–29	–36	–43	–50	–57	–64	–71	–78	–84	–91
45	26	19	12	5	–2	–9	–16	–23	–30	–37	–44	–51	–58	–65	–72	–79	–86	–93
50	26	19	12	4	–3	–10	–17	–24	–31	–38	–45	–52	–60	–67	–74	–81	–88	–95
55	25	18	11	4	–3	–11	–18	–25	–32	–39	–46	–54	–61	–68	–75	–82	–89	–97
60	25	17	10	3	–4	–11	–19	–26	–33	–40	–48	–55	–62	–69	–76	–84	–91	–98

Frostbite Times: 30 minutes, 10 minutes, 5 minutes

Source: National Weather Service

a. Pick three (V, T) pairs and find $W(V, T)$ and $F(V, T)$.
b. Find two solutions for the equation $W(V, T) = -55$.
c. Find two solutions for $W(V, T) = -39$ that have different values for $F(V, T)$. Answers vary. Sample answer: (55, –5) and (15, –15)

17a. Answers vary. Sample answer: $W(5, -10) = -22$, $F(5, -10) = 30$; $W(10, -40) = -66$, $F(10, -40) = 10$; $W(60, -45) = -98$, $F(60, -45) = 5$

17b. Three possible answers: (60, –15), (35, –20), (20, –25)

18. Let $m(x)$ = the mother of person x and $f(x)$ = the father of person x. Using yourself for x, find $m(f(x))$ and $f(f(x))$. (*Hint:* Start with the inner-most parentheses.) What are simpler descriptions for each of these two functions? $m(f(x))$ = mother of your father; $f(f(x))$ = father of your father. Simpler descriptions are paternal grandmother and paternal grandfather.

Lesson 7-7

Comparing Linear Increase and Exponential Growth

> **BIG IDEA** In the long run, exponential growth always overtakes linear (constant) increase.

In the patterns that are constant increase/decrease situations, a number is repeatedly *added*. In exponential growth/decay situations, a number is repeatedly *multiplied*. In this lesson, we compare what happens as a result.

Mental Math

What is the date of the *x*th day of the year in a nonleap year when

a. $x = 100$? **April 10**

b. $x = 200$? **July 19**

c. $x = 300$? **October 27**

GUIDED

Example

Suppose you have $10. For two weeks, your rich uncle agrees to do one of the following.
Option 1: Increase what you had the previous day by $50.
Option 2: Increase what you had the previous day by 50%.
Which option will give you more money?

Solution Make a table to compare the two options for the first week. Use the Now/Next method to fill in the table. The exponential growth factor is 1.50.

Start = $10
Next = Now + $50

Day	Option 1: Add $50.
0	$10
1	? $60
2	? $110

+ $50

Start = $10
Next = Now · 1.50

Day	Option 2: Multiply by 1.50.
0	$10
1	? $15
2	? $22.50

· 1.50

Continue the table until day 14. You should find that at first, you get more money from Option 1. But the table shows that starting on day __?__, Option 2 gives more money. **In the long run, Option 2, increasing by 50% each day, is the better choice. 10**

Above, the two options were described by telling how the amounts changed each day. In that situation, the Now/Next method works well. But to graph the situation on your calculator, you need equations for these functions.

Comparing Linear Increase and Exponential Growth **439**

Background

This is an activity lesson in which students are expected to use a computer or calculator with spreadsheet capability.

The word "rate" is often used in discussing both constant increase and exponential growth. With constant increase, it is a rate of change; with exponential growth, it is a growth rate. This dual use of "rate" can be very confusing. We try to avoid confusion by using the words *growth* and *decay* when referring to change under exponential

growth and the words *increase* and *decrease* when referring to linear change. So we contrast "constant growth rate" from "constant increase."

The reason that we use spreadsheets rather than lists for Activities 1 and 2 is that many lists do not have recursive definition capability. All spreadsheets carry that capability.

(continued on next page)

Lesson 7-7

GOAL

Utilize tables and recursion to show the difference between linear increase and exponential growth. Introduce the idea of recursion through the use of Now/Next statements as they are manifested in spreadsheets.

SPUR Objectives

B Calculate function values in spreadsheets.

G Compare linear increase with exponential growth.

Materials/Resources

· Lesson Masters 7-7A or 7-7B
· Resource Masters 1, 2, 5, 113, and 114
· Graphing calculator or computer with spreadsheet software

HOMEWORK

Suggestions for Assignment
• Questions 1–24
• Question 25 (extra credit)
• Reading Lesson 8-1
• Covering the Ideas 8-1

Local Standards

1 Warm-Up

Let $E(x) = 1.1^x$ and $L(x) = 1,000x$.

1. Which is greater, $E(0)$ or $L(0)$? $E(0)$
2. Which is greater, $E(10)$ or $L(10)$? $L(10)$
3. Which is greater, $E(100)$ or $L(100)$? $L(100)$
4. Which is greater, $E(1,000)$ or $L(1,000)$? $E(1,000)$

7-7

Notes on the Lesson

With $E(x)$ for exponential growth and $L(x)$ for linear increase, notice how much easier it is to compare values. For example, in the Warm-Up, by using $E(0)$, $L(0)$, etc., we avoid 8 separate uses of y. However, many graphing utilities will only allow Y_1, Y_2, etc., for values of the function.

You may wish to make a table with the analogies between linear and exponential functions.

Linear	Exponential
$L(x) = mx + b$	$E(x) = b \cdot g^x$
contains $(0, b)$	contains $(0, b)$
y-intercept b	y-intercept b
Add m in each of x time periods.	Multiply by g in each of x time periods.
contains $(1, m + b)$, $(2, 2m + b)$, etc.	contains $(1, bg)$, $(2, bg^2)$, etc.
slope m	growth rate g
$m > 0$ means increase.	$g > 1$ means growth.
$m < 0$ means decrease.	$0 < g < 1$ means decay.
$m = 0$ means constant function.	$g = 1$ means constant function.

To emphasize that $E(x)$ always overtakes $L(x)$ when x is sufficiently large, notice for Example 1, in the short term the linear increase brings in more money, but ultimately the exponential growth overtakes the linear increase.

Here is another example. Suppose a town has 10,000 people. Would a 2% yearly growth ever overcome a yearly increase of 10,000 people? Surely not in the first year, because under the 2% growth, the town would grow only by 200 people. But after 286 years, the compounding of the annual 2% growth rate overcomes the linear increase of 10,000.

Comparing Using a Graph

To find the equations for the functions in the Guided Example, you can make a table to compare the two options during the first week. The exponential growth factor is 1.50. Let $L(x) =$ the amount given to you under Option 1, and let $E(x) =$ the amount given to you under Option 2.

Day	Option 1: Add $50.	Option 2: Multiply by 1.50.
0	$L(0) = 10 = \$10.00$	$E(0) = 10 = \$10.00$
1	$L(1) = 10 + 50 \cdot 1 = \$60.00$	$E(1) = 10 \cdot 1.50^1 = \$15.00$
2	$L(2) = 10 + 50 \cdot 2 = \$110.00$	$E(2) = 10 \cdot 1.50^2 = \$22.50$
3	$L(3) = 10 + 50 \cdot 3 = \$160.00$	$E(3) = 10 \cdot 1.50^3 = \$33.75$
4	$L(4) = 10 + 50 \cdot 4 = \$210.00$	$E(4) = 10 \cdot 1.50^4 = \$50.63$
5	$L(5) = 10 + 50 \cdot 5 = \$260.00$	$E(5) = 10 \cdot 1.50^5 = \$75.94$
x	$L(x) = 10 + 50x$	$E(x) = 10 \cdot 1.50^x$

We see how the values compare by graphing the two functions E and L. The graphs of $L(x) = 10 + 50x$ and $E(x) = 10 \cdot 1.5^x$ are shown at the right.

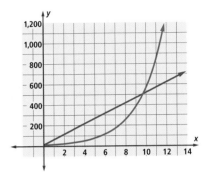

The line $L(x) = 10 + 50x$ has a constant rate of change. The graph of $y = 10 \cdot 1.5^x$ is a curve that gets steeper and steeper as you move to the right. Notice that at first the exponential curve is below the line. But toward the middle of the graph, it intersects the line and passes above it. On later days, the graph of the curve rises farther and farther above the line.

The longer your uncle gives you money, the better Option 2 is compared to Option 1.

Comparing Using Spreadsheets

Activity 1 shows how to use a spreadsheet to confirm the results of Guided Example 1.

Activity 1

Step 1 Create a spreadsheet similar to the one at the right. Be sure to have titles in row 1. In cells A2 through A16 enter the numbers 0 to 14.

◇	A	B	C
1	Day x	Option 1	Option 2
2	0	10	10
3	1	=B2+50	

Comparing using spreadsheets. It is very possible that students are already familiar with spreadsheets. The algebra of spreadsheets is an exceedingly common language in homes and in the workplace. The names of the variables are A1, A2, A3, ..., B1, B2, ... Each time we ask the spreadsheet to calculate something and put it in another cell, we are writing an algebraic formula. For example, if in cell C1 we type "$= A1 + B1$," then we are naming the variable C1. The spreadsheet does the calculation for us. Each time that we copy a formula to other cells, we are creating a function. The function may be explicitly defined or it may be an iterative sequence, but it is a function either way. Most spreadsheet programs allow us to graph the explicitly defined functions. Either with the graph or by successive approximation, we can solve many equations.

(continued on next page)

Step 2 Type =B2+50 in cell B3. Press [ENTER]. What appears in cell B3? **60**

Step 3 Type the formula for Option 2 into cell C3. (*Hint*: What is the Now/ Next formula for Option 2?) **C2*1.5**

An advantage of spreadsheets is that you don't have to type a formula into each cell. When you type the formula =B2+50 into cell B3, the spreadsheet remembers this as: "Into this cell put 50 plus the number that is in cell B2 above." For example, if you copy cell B3 to cell D5, the formula copied will change to =D4+50 because one cell above D5 is D4. This way of copying in spreadsheets is called *replication*.

Step 4 Replicate the formula in cell B3 into cells B4 through B16.

Step 5 Replicate the formula in cell C3 into cells C4 through C16.

Step 6 Compare your spreadsheet to the table on page 440. Experiment by changing the starting amount of $10 to other values. Then go back to the original starting amount of $10 before doing the next step.

Step 7 Add two more columns to your spreadsheet.

◇	A	B	C	D	E
1	Day x	Option 1	Option 2	$L(x) = 10 + 50x$	$E(x) = 10 \cdot 1.5^x$
2	0	10	10		
3	1	=B2+50			

Step 8 Type =10+50*A2 in cell D2. This puts into D2 the value of the function L for the domain value in cell A2.

Step 9 Replicate the formula in cell D2 into cells D3 through D16.

Step 10 Compare the values in columns B and D. If they are the same, then you know that you have done the previous steps correctly.

Step 11 Type =10*1.5^A2 into cell E2. This puts into E2 the value of the function E for the domain value in cell A2.

Step 12 Replicate the formula in cell E2 into cells E3 through E16. What should happen? Have you done the previous steps correctly? **The values in column E should be equal to the values in column C.**

Comparing Linear Increase and Exponential Growth **441**

Also, almost all spreadsheet programs have a form of summation notation that makes for a very easy transition to traditional Σ-notation. Sum(A1:A5) is similar to $\sum_{i=1}^{5} A_i$. Thus algebra capability is in most every computer and on virtually every business desk. People who think they don't know algebra are using this capability.

Accommodating the Learner ⬆

Ask students to write a letter to those students who are having a difficult time understanding the difference between constant growth and exponential growth. Students should use language that makes sense to them. The letter should include a definition of both types of growth. It should include algebraic examples of both. It should include real-world examples of both. In the case of each real-world example, students should explain why it fits the growth model it is supposed to represent. Tables and graphs should be included.

Notes on the Activity

If you don't have access to spreadsheets, this activity can be done using the students' graphing calculators. Let $Y1 = 10 + 50x$ and $Y2 = 10 \cdot 1.5^x$. Use the TBLSET command to set TblStart to 1 and ΔTbl to 1. Then use the TABLE command to compare the values of the two functions. If you have access to spreadsheets, consider doing this activity as intended even if using the calculator seems easier. Many students have never used a spreadsheet, and working with formulas and replication will be a good learning experience.

Notes on the Lesson

Below are some hints for creating spreadsheets with Microsoft Excel.

- The normal view of a spreadsheet is the one pictured in this lesson. If this view is not what students have on their screen, you may want to ask students to change their view by choosing NORMAL from the VIEW menu.

- Throughout the lesson activities, we right justify all of the input data. Once again, you may want to make sure that students do this by highlighting the desired column, going to the FORMATTING toolbar and choosing the ALIGN RIGHT icon.

- An alternative way to copy a formula from one cell to another is to highlight the cell with the formula, grab the small square at the lower right of the highlighted box, and drag the box to the desired new cell.

- To begin Activity 2, you may want to have students start a new worksheet by choosing NEW from the FILE menu.

- To change the width of a column, simply move the cursor to the top label of that column until you see a double-arrowed cursor. Then drag the column line until the desired width is achieved.

7-7

Notes on the Activity

If students don't seem to grasp the effect of not having limiting factors on growth, suggest they research the introduction of the nonnative rabbit to the continent of Australia. With just a little research, students will quickly understand the impact of uninhibited growth, the impact on the environment, and how difficult it is to stop growth once it has gotten out of hand. This is a great use of mathematics for real-world experience.

Additional Answers

Activity 2 Step 4: for 1993–2015

Year	Option 1	Option 2	$L(x) = 19 + 2(x - 1993)$	$E(x) = 19(1.06)^{(x - 1993)}$
1993	19	19.00	19	19
1994	21	20.14	21	20.14
1995	23	21.35	23	21.35
1996	25	22.63	25	22.63
1997	27	23.99	27	23.99
1998	29	25.43	29	25.43
1999	31	26.95	31	26.95
2000	33	28.57	33	28.57
2001	35	30.28	35	30.28
2002	37	32.10	37	32.10
2003	39	34.03	39	34.03
2004	41	36.07	41	36.07
2005	43	38.23	43	38.23
2006	45	40.53	45	40.53
2007	47	42.96	47	42.96
2008	49	45.53	49	45.53
2009	51	48.27	51	48.27
2010	53	51.16	53	51.16
2011	55	54.23	55	54.23
2012	57	57.49	57	57.49
2013	59	60.94	59	60.94
2014	61	64.59	61	64.59
2015	63	68.47	63	68.47

Step 5: **Mountain Lion Population**

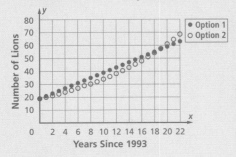

Activity 2

In 1993, Florida introduced 19 mountain lions into its northern region. With animals in the wild, there are two scenarios. If there are no limiting factors, the population of animals tends to grow exponentially. However, if limiting factors are established, the population growth tends to be linear. Limiting factors can be things such as climate, availability of food, predators, and hunting.

Suppose the scientists who introduced the mountain lions into northern Florida used one of the following options to model the population growth.

Option 1: There are limiting factors so that 2 more mountain lions appear each year.

Option 2: There are no limiting factors so that the population grows by 6% each year.

Step 1 First, create a spreadsheet similar to the one below.

◇	A	B	C	D	E
1	Year	Option 1	Option 2	$L(x)$	$E(x)$
2	1993	19	19		
3	1994				

Step 2 Enter formulas into B3 and C3 to calculate the population using the Now/Next method.

Step 3 Copy and paste B3 into cells B4 and lower. Also copy and paste C3 into cells C4 and lower. Be sure to gather enough data and compare the populations in column B to those in column C.

Step 4 Enter formulas for $L(x)$ and $E(x)$ in columns D and E and copy these for as many rows as you used in Step 3. **See margin.**

Step 5 Graph each option's population equation on the same axes. Let the x-coordinates be the number of years since 1993. (Let $x = 0$ be 1993.) You can use the chart feature of the spreadsheet to create the graphs. **See margin.**

Step 6 Answer the following questions using the collected data and the graphs.

1. In 2010, which option would provide a larger population of mountain lions? **Option 1**

2. In which year (if ever), would Option 2 create a larger population of mountain lions? **starting in year 2012 and beyond**

A typical male mountain lion patrols 50 to 300 square miles, depending on how plentiful food is.

Source: *USAToday*

Step 2. for B3, use "=B2+2" and for C3, use "=C2*1.06"

Accommodating the Learner ⬇

Students may still need to do some more thinking about the ideas of constant increase and exponential growth. Instruct students to form groups of four. Tell them to brainstorm as many real-world examples of constant increase and exponential growth as they can. If students need some examples, provide them with some. Once students have had enough time to generate a list of their own, ask each group to share with the class.

A Summary of Constant Increase and Exponential Growth

In this lesson, you have seen that differences between linear and exponential models can be seen in the equations that describe them, the tables that list ordered pairs, and the graphs that picture them. You have seen that if the growth factor is greater than 1, exponential growth always overtakes constant increase. Here is a summary of their behavior.

Constant Increase	Exponential Growth
• Begin with an amount b.	• Begin with an amount b.
• Add m (the slope) in each of the x time periods.	• Multiply by g (the growth factor) in each of the x time periods.
• After x time periods, the amount is given by the function $L(x) = mx + b$.	• After x time periods, the amount is given by the function $E(x) = b \cdot g^x$.

$L(x) = mx + b,\ m > 0$

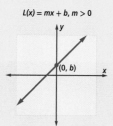

$E(x) = b \cdot g^x,\ g > 1$

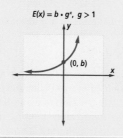

Questions

COVERING THE IDEAS

1. What is the difference between a constant increase situation and an exponential growth situation?

In 2–5, let $L(x) = 20 + 3x$ and $E(x) = 20(1.03)^x$.

2. Calculate $L(5)$ and $E(5)$. $L(5) = 35;\ E(5) \approx 23.185$

3. Sketch a graph of both functions on the same axes.

4. Give an example of a value of x for which $E(x) > L(x)$.
Answers vary. Sample answer: 100

5. What kind of situation could have led to these equations?
See margin.

1. Answers vary. Sample answer: The rate of change varies in an exponential growth situation, but remains constant in a constant increase situation.

3.

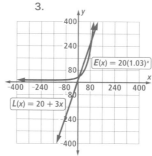

Comparing Linear Increase and Exponential Growth **443**

Additional Answers

5. Answers vary. Sample answer: $E(x)$ could represent the value of a $20 investment in a bank account with an annual yield of 3% after x years. $L(x)$ could represent the amount in a bank account after x years if $20 is initially invested and $3 is added each year.

---

3 Assignment

Recommended Assignment
- Questions 1–24
- Question 25 (extra credit)
- Reading Lesson 8-1
- Covering the Ideas 8-1

Notes on the Questions

We suggest going over Questions 1–7 in order, as they cover the lesson's main points.

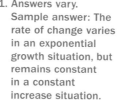

Notes on the Questions

Question 9 One of the reasons deer populations might grow so quickly is that all of their traditional natural predators (bears, lynx, etc.) have been removed from the environment, and the only predator left is man. You should discuss this question because students might have strong opinions on the subject.

Additional Answers

6a.

Years	Alexis ($)	Lynn ($)
Present (0)	50	50
1	57	53.50
2	64	57.25
3	71	61.25
4	78	65.54
5	85	70.13
6	92	75.04
7	99	80.29
8	106	85.91
9	113	91.92
10	120	98.36
11	127	105.24
12	134	112.61
13	141	120.49
14	148	128.93
15	155	137.95
16	162	147.61
17	169	157.94
18	176	169.00
19	183	180.83
20	190	193.48
21	197	207.03
22	204	221.52
23	211	237.03
24	218	253.62
25	225	271.37

6b.

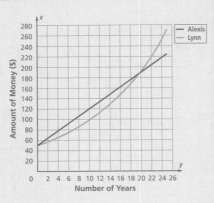

6. Two friends found $100 and split it equally between them. Alexis put her half in a piggy bank and added $7 to it each year. Lynn put her half in a bank with an annual yield of 7%. **6a–b. See margin.**

   a. Make a spreadsheet to illustrate how much money each friend has at the end of each year for the next 25 years. Have one column represent Alexis and one column represent Lynn.

   b. Sketch a graph to represent the amount of money each friend has over the next 25 years.

7. Rochelle started to make the following spreadsheet. She replicated the formula in cell A2 into cells A3 and A4.

   a. Give the formulas that will occur in cells A3 and A4.

   b. What numbers result from the formulas in A3 and A4? **54; 67**

   c. How will the values in A3 and A4 change if Rochelle changes the start value in A1 to −5? **They will decrease to 21 and 34.**

   d. Does column A illustrate constant increase or exponential growth? Explain.

◇	A	B
1	28	6
2	=A1+13	=1.2*B1
3		
4		
5		

7a. A2+13; A3+13

7d. constant increase; The outputs are represented by the linear function $f(x) = 13x + 28$.

8a. 1.2*B2; 1.2*B3

8b. 8.64; 10.368

8c. They will decrease to −7.2 and −8.64.

8d. exponential growth

8. Repeat Question 7 for column B.

9. The number of deer in the state of Massachusetts is a problem. In 1998, the deer population was estimated to be about 85,000. The Massachusetts Division of Fisheries and Wildlife had to decide whether to allow hunting (a limiting factor) or to ban hunting (no limiting factor). If hunting is allowed, they predict the deer population to increase at a constant rate of about 270 deer a year. If hunting is not allowed, the prediction is the deer population would grow exponentially by 15% each year.

   a. Write a Now/Next formula for the deer population if hunting is allowed. **Next = Now + 270**

   b. Write a Now/Next formula for the deer population if hunting is banned. **Next = Now · 1.15**

   c. Let $L(x)$ = the number of deer x years after 1998 if hunting is allowed. Find a formula for $L(x)$. **$L(x) = 85,000 + 270x$**

   d. Let $E(x)$ = the number of deer x years after 1998 if hunting is not allowed. Find a formula for $E(x)$. **$E(x) = 85,000(1.15)^x$**

   e. The state allowed hunting. The 2006 deer population was estimated between 85,000 and 95,000. Was the prediction correct? **See margin.**

In 1906, the U.S. deer population was a sparse 500,000. Today, experts estimate that 20 million deer roam the nation.

Source: Tufts University

Additional Answers

9e. Answers vary. Sample answer:

Yes; $L(8) = 87,160$

APPLYING THE MATHEMATICS

10. Refer to the spreadsheet at the right.
    a. What Now/Next formula could be used to generate the numbers in column A? **Next = 11*Now**
    b. Let $f(x)$ be the value in column A at time x. What is a formula for $f(x)$? $f(x) = 15 \cdot 11^{x-2}$

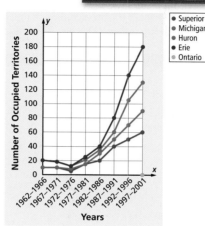

◇	A
1	
2	15
3	165
4	1815
5	19965
6	219615
7	2415765
8	26573415
9	292307565
10	3215383215
11	35369215365

11. Suppose you are reading a 900-page novel at the rate of 25 pages per hour. You are currently at page 67. **11a. See margin.**
    a. Is the number of pages you read in the book an example of constant increase or exponential growth? Explain.
    b. Write an equation to describe the pages finished x hours from now. $f(x) = 67 + 25x$
    c. How many hours will it take you to finish the book? **33.32 hr**

12. The graph at the right shows the number of territories in which bald eagles nest around the five Great Lakes. **12a-b. See margin.**
    a. Would you describe the graphs as constant increase or exponential growth? Explain your answer.
    b. The graph of which lake can be represented by $y = 14.5 \cdot 1.053^x$, where x is the years since 1962? Explain your answer.

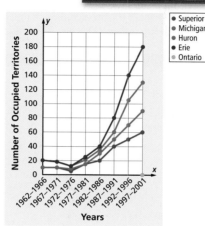

MATCHING In 13–16, each graph is drawn on the window $-2 \le x \le 15$, $0 \le y \le 2{,}000$. Match the graph with its equation.

a. $f(x) = 100 \cdot 1.25^x$ b. $g(x) = 100 + 125x$
c. $h(x) = 100 + 60x$ d. $j(x) = 100 \cdot 1.1^x$

13. 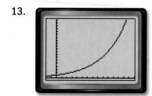 a

14. 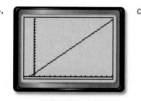 c

15. 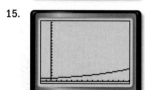 d

16. 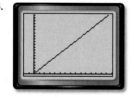 b

Notes on the Questions
Question 10b Discuss the value of $x - 2$ as the exponent. Up until now, our exponent was always x. On spreadsheets it is important to note location of values.

Questions 13–16 It is important that the windows be the same. By changing the window, any linear increase can be made to *look* larger or smaller, and so can any exponential growth.

Question 23 The month in which a person is born can change the probability. For example, for a person born in March, the possibility is $\frac{10}{31}$ but for someone born in September, it changes to $\frac{10}{30}$. So taking the first 10 days of all 12 months, there are 120 days in a total of 365 days a year (excluding leap years). Therefore, the probability of a person being born in the first 10 days of a month equals $\frac{120}{365}$, which reduces to $\frac{24}{73}$.

Additional Answers

11a. Constant increase; Answers vary. Sample answer: Reading at 25 pages per hour is a constant rate of increase.

12a. Exponential growth; A constant increase results in a straight line.

12b. Lake Michigan; Answers vary. Sample answer: In 1997, $y \approx 88.4$. The lake closest to this value is Lake Michigan.

7-7

4 Wrap-Up

Ongoing Assessment

Ask a student to explain the concept of replication as it applies to a spreadsheet. Show the student the following spreadsheet and identify the formulas that would be in cells A3 and A4 if the contents of cell A2 are replicated down. Ask the student to identify the actual number that would appear in cells A2, A3, and A4. **16, 12, 8**

	A
1	20
2	= A1 − 4
3	= A2 − 4
4	= A3 − 4

Project Update

Project 5, The Logistic Function and Growth, on page 448, relates to the content of this lesson.

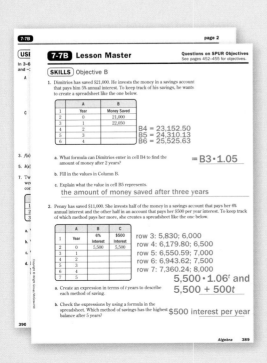

---

17. The principal of a high school is making long-range budget plans. The number of students dropped from 2,410 students to 2,270 in one year. Student enrollment is dropping, as shown in rows 2 and 3 of the spreadsheet. The situation may be modeled by a linear function or an exponential function.

    a. Make a spreadsheet similar to the one at the right. Show the future enrollments in the two possible situations. See margin.

	A	B Constant Decrease	C Exponential Decrease
1			
2	0	2410	2410
3	1	2270	2270

    b. What are the predicted enrollments 5 years from the year shown in row 3? By how much do they differ?
    1,570, approximately 1,683; by 113

    c. What are the predicted enrollments 15 years from year shown in row 3? By how much do they differ?
    170, approximately 925; by 755

The safest way to transport children to and from school and school-related activities is in a school bus.

Source: National Association of State Directors of Pupil Transportation Services

REVIEW

18. Let $M(x) = 13x - 18$. Find the value of x for which $M(x) = -1.2$. **(Lesson 7-6)** approximately **1.292**

19. **True or False** If a is any real number, then a is in the range of the function with equation $y = 3x$. **(Lesson 7-5)** true

20. Write an exponential expression for the number, which, written in base 10, is 7 followed by n zeroes (For example when $n = 3$, this number is 7,000.) **(Lesson 7-2)** $7(10^n)$

21. Write the equation $\frac{y - 3x + 2}{15} - \frac{1}{3} = \frac{7x + 2y}{5}$ in standard form.
    (Lessons 6-8, 3-8, 2-2) $24x + 5y = -3$

22. Do the points $(-1, 3)$, $(5, 4)$, and $(0, -8)$ lie on a line? How can you tell? **(Lesson 6-6)**

23. If you ask a random person the date of his or her birth, what is the probability that it will be one of the first ten days of the month? **(Lesson 5-6)** $\frac{24}{73}$

24. Calculate $5(-5)^5$. **(Lesson 2-4)** $-15,625$

EXPLORATION

25. The statement, "If the growth factor g is greater than 1, exponential growth always overtakes constant increase," was made at the start of this lesson. Write a similar statement that could describe the relationship between exponential decay and constant decrease.

22. No, the slope of the line containing $(-1, 3)$ and $(5, 4)$ is not the same as the slope of the line containing $(5, 4)$ and $(0, -8)$.

25. Answers vary. Sample answer: If the growth factor g is less than 1, constant decrease always ultimately results in more loss than exponential decay.

446   Using Algebra to Describe Patterns of Change

Additional Answers

17a.

	Constant	Exponential		Constant	Exponential
0	2410	2410	9	1150	1406
1	2270	2270	10	1010	1325
2	2130	2138	11	870	1248
3	1990	2014	12	730	1175
4	1850	1897	13	590	1107
5	1710	1787	14	450	1043
6	1570	1683	15	310	982
7	1430	1585	16	170	925
8	1290	1493			

Chapter 7 Projects

1 Reciprocal Functions

For a function f, the function g with $g(x) = \frac{1}{f(x)}$ is called the *reciprocal function* of f.

a. On the same pair of axes, graph the function with equation $y = x$, and its reciprocal, the function with equation $y = \frac{1}{x}$. Do the same for $y = 2$, $y = x^2$, and $y = 2^x$.

b. For each function in Part a, for what values of x is the reciprocal not defined?

c. What is the reciprocal of the reciprocal of the function f?

d. Give an example of a function h that is equal to its reciprocal function. Give an example of a function that is always greater than its reciprocal function and a function that is always less than its reciprocal function.

e. Describe any general patterns you noticed when graphing reciprocal functions.

2 A Famous Snowflake

The drawing below illustrates the construction of a famous shape called the Koch snowflake. In the first stage, you begin with a triangle. At every other stage, you draw a small triangle in the middle of each of the sides of the previous stage.

| Stage 1 | Stage 2 | Stage 3 | Stage 4 |

a. On a large piece of paper, draw the fifth stage of the Koch snowflake.

b. The first stage of the Koch snowflake has three sides. The next stage has 12 sides. The step after that has 48 sides. This number seems to grow exponentially. Explain why this is indeed the case, and find the growth factor and the initial value.

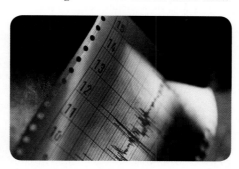

3 Richter Scale

The Richter scale is a scale used to measure the intensity of earthquakes. Look up the meaning of the Richter scale.

a. In 1992, an earthquake in Landers, California, measured 7.5 on the Richter scale. The largest earthquake ever recorded was the Great Chile earthquake of 1960, which measured 9.5 on the Richter scale. How much more powerful was the Chilean earthquake than the Landers earthquake?

b. Suppose a scientist plotted the magnitude of the most powerful annual earthquakes in a certain region over time and found that the measurements on the Richter scale increased linearly. How did the magnitude of the earthquakes increase?

c. Can an earthquake have a negative measure on the Richter scale? What does this mean?

Project Rubric

Advanced	Student correctly provides all of the details asked for in the project as well as additional correct independent conclusions.
Proficient	Student correctly provides all of the details asked for in the project.
Partially proficient	Student correctly provides some of the details asked for in the project or provides all details with some inaccuracies.
Not proficient	Student correctly provides few of the details asked for in the project or provides all details with many inaccuracies.
No attempt	Student makes little or no attempt to complete the project.

Chapter 7

The projects relate to the content of the lessons of this chapter as follows:

Project	Lesson
1	7-6
2	7-4
3	7-1
4	7-3
5	7-7

1 Reciprocal Functions

Students may not have much experience with the asymptotic behavior of curves. The functions $y = \frac{1}{x}$, $y = \frac{1}{x^2}$, $y = 2^x$, and $y = \frac{1}{2^x}$ all exhibit asymptotic behavior. It may be necessary to have some discussion related to exponential decay. Remind students that in decay the domain is $x > 0$. Thus, as the quantity gets smaller, the graph of the curve gets closer to the axis but never touches it.

2 A Famous Snowflake

If students like this project, they should consider doing research on the Sierpinski Triangle. It models ideas being presented in the Koch snowflake and will help to peak student interest in expanding their research. The ideas presented in this project and in the Sierpinski Triangle problem are a small introduction into the branch of mathematics called *fractals*.

3 Richter Scale

Trying to explain the significance of what appear to be small numerical changes on the Richter scale and the devastating impact it has in real life is difficult to do. Most of us have never really experienced an earthquake, let alone a second one of a different magnitude. Students should be encouraged to expand this project to include data from earthquakes around the world. Data should include the magnitude of the quake, number of deaths attributed to the quake, structural damage, and so on.

4 Powers of Ten

Encourage a student who has done this project to share his or her findings. Provide this student with the necessary equipment and class time to model what he or she has learned. If more than one student would like to get involved, encourage students to work together to consolidate what they have learned, and to make a combined presentation. This is a project that ties what students are learning in the chapter with the real world.

5 The Logistic Function and Growth

This project brings the idea of "unbounded" growth in nature into perspective. It reinforces the concept of limiting factors found in this chapter. The equation presented in this project may be a bit intimidating, but with a little help students will get past that. Make sure that students have answered Parts b and c correctly. It is important that they don't miss the point of these two questions.

4 Powers of Ten

In 1977, Charles and Ray Eames created a short documentary movie called *Powers of Ten,* which began with a picture of a picnic, and zoomed out by a factor of ten every ten seconds. (The movie is available on the Internet.) You can create a similar effect yourself. Download a free program that allows you to view satellite images of Earth at different levels of magnification.

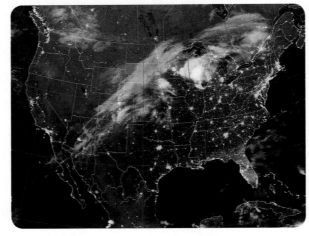

a. Find your school on the software, and zoom in as much as the software allows. Note the altitude from which you are viewing. Zoom out to an altitude ten times as high. Describe what you see. Do this as many times as the program allows.

b. Find out how many times you would have to zoom out before you could see the entire solar system, and how many times you would have to zoom out before you could see the entire galaxy.

c. Describe what you would see in the first three pictures if you zoomed in instead of out.

5 The Logistic Function and Growth

In this chapter you saw exponential growth used as a model for population growth. In nature, it is impossible for a population to continue to grow exponentially. (Otherwise it would overrun the entire Earth and still continue to grow!) When a population reaches a certain size, the resources available do not allow it to grow any larger. One way in which scientists model this kind of growth is called a *logistic function.* This is a function of the form $P(n) = a\frac{1 + b2^{-cn}}{1 + d2^{-cn}}$. This function gives the size of the population after n years.

a. Use a spreadsheet or a calculator to calculate the first 10 values of P, when $a = 200$, $b = 1$, $c = 0.5$, and $d = 20$. Plot the graph of the function and use exponential regression to find the exponential function that best fits the data. Do you think that in the first 10 years the population grows approximately exponentially?

b. For the values given in Part a, graph the first 100 values of the function. Does the population still appear to grow exponentially?

c. Explain why this function gives a better model of population growth than the exponential function.

Notes

Chapter 7 — Summary and Vocabulary

- In Chapter 6, you saw many examples of constant-increase and constant-decrease patterns of change. They give rise to equations of the form $y = mx + b$. The change is called **linear** because the graph is a line. Now in Chapter 7, we turned our attention to patterns of change called **exponential growth** and **exponential decay.** They give rise to equations of the form $y = b \cdot g^x$.

- Graphs of exponential functions are curves. The change is called **exponential** because the independent variable is in the exponent. In exponential change, the number g is the growth factor. If $g > 1$, the situation is **exponential growth.** Among the common applications of exponential growth are compound interest and population growth. In the long run, exponential growth will always overtake a situation of linear increase. If $0 < g < 1$, the situation is **exponential decay.**

- These and other patterns can be described using the mathematical idea of a function. A **function** is a set of ordered pairs in which each first coordinate appears with exactly one second coordinate. Thus, functions exist whenever the value of one variable determines a unique value of another variable.

- A function may be described by a list of ordered pairs, a graph, an equation, or a written rule. If a function f contains the ordered pair (a, b), then we write $f(a) = b$. We say that b is the value of the function at a. If you know a formula for the function, you can obtain values and graphs of functions using calculators, spreadsheets, or paper and pencil.

- Constant-increase or constant-decrease situations are described by **linear functions.** Constant growth or decay situations are described by **exponential functions.** Repeatedly adding a quantity m to an initial value b gives rise to values of the linear function $f(x) = mx + b$. Repeatedly multiplying an initial value b by the growth factor g gives rise to values of the exponential function $f(x) = b \cdot g^x$. Spreadsheets are particularly useful for finding values of functions.

Vocabulary

7-1
power, nth power
base
exponent
principal
interest
annual yield
compound interest

7-2
exponential growth
growth factor
exponential growth equation

7-3
exponential decay
half-life

7-4
exponential regression

7-5
function
input, output
value of the function
squaring function
independent variable
dependent variable
domain of a function
range of a function
relation

7-6
$f(x)$ notation
function notation

Theorems and Properties

Repeated Multiplication Property of Powers (p. 398)
Compound Interest Formula (p. 400)
Growth Model for Powering (p. 405)
Zero Exponent Property (p. 405)

Self-Test

For the development of mathematical competence, feedback and correction, along with the opportunity for practice, are necessary. The Self-Test provides the opportunity for feedback and correction; the Chapter Review provides additional opportunities and practice. We cannot overemphasize the importance of these end-of-chapter materials. It is at this point that the material "gels" for many students, allowing them to solidify skills and understanding. In general, student performance should improve after these pages.

Assign the Self-Test as a one-night assignment. Worked-out solutions for all questions are in the Selected Answers section of the student book. Encourage students to take the Self-Test honestly, grade themselves, and then be prepared to discuss the test in class.

Advise students to pay special attention to those Chapter Review questions (pages 452–455) that correspond to the questions they missed on the Self-Test.

Additional Answers

1. $\left(\frac{1}{5}\right)^2 + \left(\frac{1}{5}\right)^0 = \frac{1}{25} + 1 = \frac{26}{25}$

3. $f(1,729) = 3(1,729)^0 = 3 \cdot 1 = 3$

6. Tyrone will have $400(1.044)^{10} \approx 615.26$ dollars and Oleta will have $400 + 22(10) = 620$ dollars, so Oleta will have more.

7. After 25 years, Tyrone will have $400(1.044)^{25} \approx 1,173.74$ dollars, and Oleta will have $400 + 22(25) = 950$ dollars, so Tyrone will have more money.

8. The value of the car is depreciating 16%, so the growth factor is $1 - 0.16 = 0.84$.

9. $m(x) = 34,975(0.84)^x$, $x \geq 0$. Because x represents years, it cannot be negative.

10. $m(5) = 34,975(0.84)^5 \approx \$14,626.96$

14. $f(12) = |-12 - 3| = |-15| = 15$

15. From the graph and knowledge of the absolute value function, you can see only positive values and 0 are in the range. The range is all nonnegative numbers.

16. From the graph you can see the only values in the range are those greater than or equal to $f(5)$. $f(5) = |5 - 3| = 2$ so the range is all real numbers ≥ 2.

Chapter **7** Self-Test

Take this test as you would take a test in class. You will need a calculator. Then use the Selected Answers section in the back of the book to check your work.

1. Evaluate $x^2 + x^0$ when $x = \frac{1}{5}$. See margin.

2. Write $8 \cdot 8 \cdot 8 \cdot 8 \cdot d \cdot d \cdot d \cdot d \cdot d \cdot d$ using exponents. $8^4 d^6$

3. If $f(x) = 3x^0$, find $f(1,729)$. See margin.

4. If $g(y) = 3y - y^2$, find $g(-2)$.
$g(-2) = 3(-2) - (-2)^2 = -6 - 4 = -10$

In 5–7, Tyrone deposits $400 into a savings account that pays 4.4% interest per year.

5. Write and evaluate an expression for the amount of money Tyrone will have after 7 years, assuming he doesn't deposit or withdraw money from the account.
$400(1.044)^7 \approx 540.70$

6. At the same time that Tyrone makes his deposit, his sister Oleta deposits $400 in a highly unusual savings account. The account pays exactly $22 interest each year. Who will have more money after 10 years? See margin.

7. Who will have more money after 25 years? See margin.

In 8–10, use the following information. A particular new 2006 car costs $34,975. Suppose its value depreciates 16% each year.

8. What is the growth factor of the value of the car? See margin.

9. Write a function $m(x)$ that approximates the car's value in x years. Specify the domain of your function. See margin.

10. Find $m(5)$, the approximate value of the car in 5 years. See margin.

For 11–13, $f(x) = 5 \cdot 0.74^x$. Calculate the value.

11. $f(1)$ $f(1) = 5 \cdot 0.74^1 = 3.7$

12. $f(5)$ $f(5) = 5 \cdot 0.74^5 \approx 1.11$

13. $f(7)$ $f(7) = 5 \cdot 0.74^7 \approx 0.61$

In 14–16, use the absolute value function $f(x) = |x - 3|$ graphed below. Consider the domain as the set of all real numbers. 14–16. See margin.

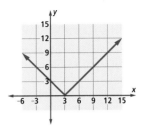

14. Determine $f(-12)$.

15. What is the range of the function f?

16. If the domain is restricted to $\{x: x \geq 5\}$, what is the range?

17–19. See margin.

In 17–19, let $E(x) = 30(1.05)^x$ and $L(x) = 30 + 2x$.

17. Sketch a graph of these functions.

18. Which is greater, $L(9)$ or $E(9)$?

19. Give an example of a value of x when $L(x) < E(x)$.

In 20 and 21, write an equation describing the situation and graph the equation.

20. The population p of a country increases by 2.5% per year. In 1980, it had 76 million residents. Let k be the number of years since 1980. 20–21. See margin.

21. The circulation c of a newspaper has decreased by 1% each month since January 2000, when it was 880,000. Let x be the number of months since January 2000.

Additional Answers

17.

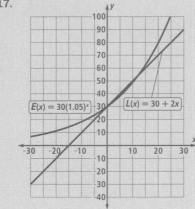

18. $L(9) = 30 + 2 \cdot 9 = 48$, $E(9) = 30(1.05)^9 \approx 46.5$; $L(9)$ is greater

19. Answers vary. Sample answer: $x = 20$; $E(20) \approx 79.60$, $L(20) = 70$, $70 < 79.60$

In 22 and 23, graph the function on the given domain. 22–23. See margin.

22. $h(k) = 1 - 3.5k$, $-10 \leq k \leq 8$

23. $c(x) = 10 \cdot 2^x$, $0 \leq x \leq 5$

24. **Matching** Decide which of the situations the function with the given equation describes.

 i. constant increase

 ii. constant decrease

 iii. exponential growth

 iv. exponential decay

 a. $f(x) = -4x + 18$

 b. $g(x) = 0.4(5)^x$

 c. $h(x) = 5(0.4)^x$

 d. $m(x) = \frac{2}{3}x - 7$

24a. f is a linear function with negative slope, so it describes a constant decrease situation, ii.

24b. g is an exponential function with growth factor 5. Since $5 > 1$, g describes an exponential growth situation, iii.

24c. h is an exponential function with growth factor 0.4. Since $0.4 < 1$, h describes an exponential decay situation, iv.

24d. m is a linear function with positive slope, so it describes a constant increase situation, i.

25. It is estimated that a house purchased in 1990 for \$100,000 has increased in value about 4% a year since that time. Suppose you want to use a spreadsheet to display the estimated value of the house from 1990 to 2010.

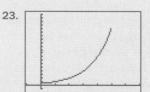

◇	A	B
1	Year	Value of House
2	1990	\$100,000
3		
4		
5		

 a. What formula could you enter in cell A3 to get the appropriate value using cell A2?

 b. Explain the process by which you would obtain appropriate amounts in cells B4 to B22.

25a. The year increases by 1, so add 1 to the value in A2. Input "= A2 + 1".

25b. Answers vary. Sample answer: In cell B3, input "= 1.04*B2", and then replicate the formula from B3 to B4 through B22.

22.

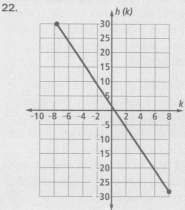

23.

20. An increase of 2.5% tells you that the growth factor is 1.025. The beginning population is 76 million, so the population p, in millions, k years after 1980 is $p(k) = 76(1.025)^k$.

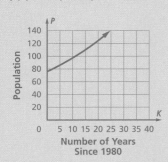

21. A decrease of 1% tells you that the growth factor is 0.99. The beginning circulation is 880,000, so the circulation is $c(x) = 880{,}000(0.99)^x$.

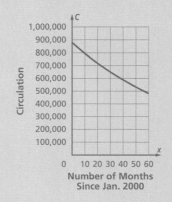

Chapter Review

The main objectives for the chapter are organized in the Chapter Review under the four types of understanding this book promotes—Skills, Properties, Uses, and Representations.

Whereas end-of-chapter material may be considered optional in some texts, in *UCSMP Algebra* we have selected these objectives and questions with the expectation that they will be covered. Students should be able to answer these questions with about 85% accuracy after studying the chapter.

You may assign these questions over a single night to help students prepare for a test the next day, or you may assign the questions over a two-day period. If you work the questions over two days, then we recommend assigning the *evens* for homework the first night so that students get feedback in class the next day, and then assigning the *odds* the night before the test because the answers are provided to the odd-numbered questions in the Selected Answers at the back of the book.

It is effective to ask students which questions they still do not understand and use the day as a total class discussion of the material that the class finds most difficult.

Resources

• Assessment Resources: Chapter 7 Test, Forms A–D; Chapter 7 Test, Cumulative Form

Technology Resources

Teacher's Assessment Assistant, Ch 7
Electronic Teacher's Edition, Ch. 7

Chapter 7 Chapter Review

SKILLS
PROPERTIES
USES
REPRESENTATIONS

SKILLS Procedures used to get answers

OBJECTIVE A Evaluate functions.
(Lesson 7-6)

In 1–4, suppose $f(x) = 10 - 3x$. Evaluate the function.

1. $f(2)$ 4
2. $f(-4)$ 22
3. $f(1) + f(0)$ 17
4. $f(3 + 6)$ −17
5. If $g(x) = \left(\frac{11}{6}\right)^x$, give the value of $g(2)$. $\frac{121}{36}$
6. If $h(x) = 2x^3$, calculate $h(4)$. 128
7. If $f(t) = -8t$ and $g(t) = 6t$, give the value of $f(-1) + g(-2)$. −4
8. If $E(m) = 6^m$ and $L(m) = m + 5$, find a value for m for which $E(m) < L(m)$.
Answers vary. Sample answer: 0

OBJECTIVE B Calculate function values in spreadsheets. (Lesson 7-7)

In 9 and 10, use the spreadsheet below.

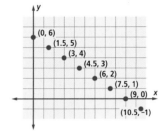

◇	A	B	C
1	x	1000(1.05)^x	1000+50x
2	0	1000	1000
3	1		
4	2		
5	3		

9. Rani wants to put values of the function with equation $y = 1,000(1.05)^x$ in column B of the spreadsheet. 9a–c. See margin.
   a. What formula can she enter in cell B3?
   b. What number will appear in cell B3?
   c. What should she do to get values of y in column B when $x = 2, 3, 4, 5, \ldots, 10$?

10a–c. See margin.
10. Olivia wants to put values of the function with equation $f(x) = 1,000 + 50x$ in column C of the spreadsheet.
   a. What formula can she enter in cell C3?
   b. What number will appear in cell C3?
   c. What should she do to get values of $f(x)$ in column C when $x = 2, 3, 4, 5, \ldots, 10$?

PROPERTIES The principles behind the mathematics

OBJECTIVE C Use the language of functions. (Lessons 7-5, 7-6)

11. Suppose $y = f(x)$.
   a. What letter names the independent variable? x
   b. What letter names the function? f

12. A linear function L is graphed below.
12b. {0, 1.5, 3, 4.5, 6, 7.5, 9, 10.5}

(0, 6)
(1.5, 5)
(3, 4)
(4.5, 3)
(6, 2)
(7.5, 1)
(9, 0)
(10.5, −1)

   a. What is $L(3)$? 4
   b. What is the domain of L?
   c. What is the range of L?
   d. Find a formula for $L(x)$ in terms of x.
   $L(x) = -\frac{2}{3}x + 6$

   12c. {6, 5, 4, 3, 2, 1, 0, −1}

Additional Answers

9a. Answers vary. Sample answer:
   "= B2*1.05"

9b. 1,050

9c. Replicate the formula in B3 down to B12.

10a. Answers vary. Sample answer:
   "= C2 + 50"

10b. 1,050

10c. Replicate the formula in C3 down to C12.

13b. {200, 400, 500, 1,000}

13. Suppose a function f consists of only the ordered pairs (2, 200), (4, 400), (5, 500), and (10, 1,000).

a. What is the domain of f? {2, 4, 5, 10}

b. What is the range of f?

c. Give a formula for $f(x)$ in terms of x. $f(x) = 100x; x = 2, 4, 5, 10$

USES Applications of mathematics in real-world situations

OBJECTIVE D Calculate compound interest. (Lesson 7-1)

14. An advertisement indicated that a 3-year certificate of deposit would yield 4.53% per year. If $2,000 is invested in this certificate, what will it be worth at the end of 3 years? $2,284.29

15. When Brie was born, she received a gift of $500 from her grandparents. Her parents put it into an account at an annual yield of 5.2%. Brie is now 12 years old. How much is this gift worth now? $918.66

16. In 2004, the endowment of Harvard University (the value of the university's assets) was reported to be about $22.14 billion. Suppose the trustees of the university feel they can grow this endowment by 6% a year. What would be the value of the endowment in 2010? about $31.4 billion

17. Which investment yields more money: (a) x dollars for 4 years at an annual yield of 8% or (b) the same amount of money at an annual yield of 4% for 8 years? Explain your reasoning. (b); $1.04^8 > 1.08^4$

OBJECTIVE E Solve problems involving exponential growth and decay. (Lessons 7-2, 7-3, 7-4)

18. In 1990, there were 4.4 million cell phone subscribers in the United States; by 2006, there were 219.4 million subscribers. The table below shows the number of cell phone subscribers for each year from 1990 to 2006.

Year	Cell Phone Subscribers (in thousands)
1990	4,369
1991	3,380
1992	8,893
1993	13,067
1994	19,283
1995	28,154
1996	38,195
1997	48,706
1998	60,831
1999	76,285
2000	97,036
2001	118,398
2002	134,561
2003	148,066
2004	169,467
2005	194,479
2006	219,420

a. Create a scatterplot with y = cell phone subscribers and x = the year since 1990. Why is the exponential model a better model for these data than a linear model? 18a–b. See margin.

b. Use exponential regression to find an equation to fit the data.

c. Use your equation from Part b to predict the number of cell phone subscribers for the year 2013. about 2,056,074,681

Additional Answers

18a. The data is increasing at an exponential rate.

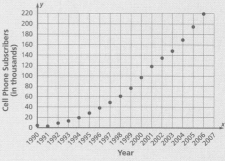

18b. $y = 5,881.33(1.29)^x$

Chapter **7** Review

Chapter Review

Additional Answers

21. constant increase

22. constant decrease

27a. $A(n) = 10,000,000(1.02)^n$

27b. $B(n) = 20,000,000 + 1,000,000n$

27c. country B;

$B(30) = 50,000,000 > A(30) =$
$18,113,616$

28. Answers vary. Sample answer: In an exponential growth situation the rate of change is always increasing, while it remains constant in a linear increase situation. Given enough time, the rate of change will be larger in an exponential growth situation, and given even more time, this means the exponential growth situation will always overtake the linear increase.

29.

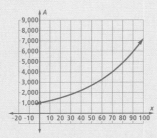

Answers vary. Sample answer: $1,000 is invested at 2% interest per year.

30.

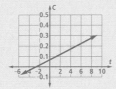

Answers vary. Sample answer: Deposit $0.07 in a piggy bank, and each week add $0.03.

31.

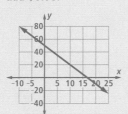

Answers vary. Sample answer: You have $50 in a bank account, and each day you take out $3.

---

19. Twelve fish were introduced into a large lake. In 3 years, the population had multiplied by a factor of 20.

   a. In 15 years, at this growth rate, by how much would the population be multiplied? $20^5 = 3,200,000$

   b. **Multiple Choice** If P is the number of fish t years after introduction, which formula relates P and t? C

   A $P = 12(20)^{\frac{t}{t}}$ **B** $P = 12(20)^{3t}$

   C $P = 12(20)^{\frac{t}{3}}$

20. Suppose a car depreciates 20% in value each year, and its purchase price was $22,000.

   a. What is the growth factor in the situation? 0.8

   b. What is the car's value 1 year after purchase? $17,600

   c. What is its value n years after purchase? $22,000(0.8)^n$

OBJECTIVE F Determine whether a situation is constant increase, constant decrease, exponential growth, exponential decay, or a nonconstant change. (Lesson 7-4)

In 21–24, does the equation describe a situation of constant increase, constant decrease, exponential growth, or exponential decay? 21–22. See margin.

21. $y = \frac{1}{5}x - 10$ 22. $m = -3n + 4$

23. $p = \frac{2}{3}(3)^r$ 24. $y = 3\left(\frac{2}{3}\right)^x$

   exponential growth   exponential decay

25. A store is going out of business. It advertises that it is reducing prices 1% on day 1, then 2% more on day two, then 3% more on day 3, and so on for 100 days. Is this a situation of constant decrease, exponential decay, or neither of these?
   neither

26. Is the sequence: $\frac{1}{12}, \frac{1}{6}, \frac{1}{4}, \frac{1}{3}, \ldots$ one of constant increase, constant decrease, exponential growth, exponential decay, or a different kind of increase or decrease?
   constant increase

OBJECTIVE G Compare linear increase with exponential growth. (Lesson 7-7)

27. Country A has 10 million people and its population is growing by 2% each year. Country B has 20 million people and its population is growing by 1 million people per year. 27a–c. See margin.

   a. Give an equation for the population $A(n)$ of country A, n years from now.

   b. Give an equation for the population $B(n)$ of country B, n years from now.

   c. In 30 years, if these trends continue, which country would have the greater population? Explain why.

   d. In 100 years, if these trends continue, which country would have the greater population? Explain why.
      country B; $B(100) > A(100)$

28. Explain why exponential growth always overtakes linear increase if the time frame is long enough. See margin.

REPRESENTATIONS Pictures, graphs, or objects that illustrate concepts

OBJECTIVE H Graph exponential relationships. (Lessons 7-2, 7-3)

In 29–32, graph the equation and describe a situation that it might represent. 29–32. See margin.

29. $A = 1,000(1.02)^x$

30. $C = 0.07 + 0.03t$

31. $y = 50 - 3x$

32. $V = 10,000(0.90)^t$

33. Graph the function of Question 20 for integer values of the domain from 1 to 10. See margin.

Additional Answers

32.

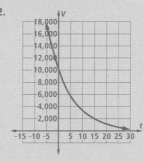

Answers vary. Sample answer: A car is worth $10,000 when it is bought and depreciates in value by 10% per year.

33.

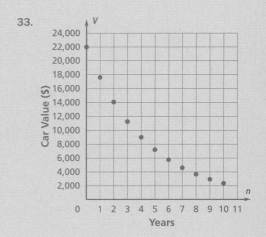

OBJECTIVE I Graph functions.
(Lessons 7-5, 7-6)

In 34–37, graph the function on the domain
$-5 \leq x \leq 5$. 34–37. See margin.

34. $f(x) = 30 - 2x$

35. $g(x) = x^2$

36. $h(x) = 3 \cdot 2^x$

37. $m(x) = x^3 - x$

38. **Multiple Choice** Which is the graph of the function A when $A(x) = \left(\frac{1}{3}\right)^x$? **A**

A

B

C

D

39. Refer to the graph of a linear function L below.

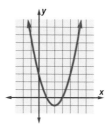

a. What is the value of $L(2)$? **1**
b. What is the value of $L(0)$? **2**
c. What is the domain of L? $\{y: 0 \leq x \leq 4\}$
d. What is the range of L? $\{y: 0 \leq y \leq 2\}$

40. On the grid below, each tick mark is one unit.

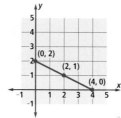

a. What is $f(0)$? **3**
b. What is $f(3)$? **0**
c. What is the domain of f?
d. What is the range of f? $\{y: y > -1\}$

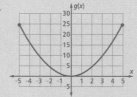
40c. $\{x:$ All real numbers$\}$

Assessment

Evaluation The *Assessment Resources* provide five forms of the Chapter 7 Test. Forms A and B present parallel versions of a short-answer format. Form C consists of four to six short-response questions that cover the SPUR objectives from Chapter 7. Form D offers performance assessment that covers a subset (or even just one) of the SPUR objectives for the chapter. The fifth type of test is a Chapter 7 Test, Cumulative Form. About 50% of this test covers Chapter 7, and the remaining 50% covers the previous 6 chapters evenly.

Feedback After students have taken the test for Chapter 7 and you have scored the results, return the tests to students for discussion. Class discussion on the questions that caused trouble for most students can be very effective in identifying and clarifying misunderstandings. You might want to have them write down the items they missed and work either in groups or at home to correct them. It is important for students to receive feedback on every chapter test, and we recommend that students see and correct their mistakes before proceeding too far into the next chapter.

36.

37.
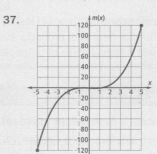

Additional Answers

34.
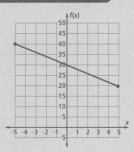

35.

Chapter Overview

	Local Standards	Pacing (in days)		
		Average	Advanced	Block
8-1 The Multiplication Counting Principle H Use powers to count the number of sequences possible for repeated choices.		1	0.5	0.5
8-2 Products and Powers of Powers A Simplify products, quotients, and powers of powers. G Identify properties of powers that justify a simplification, from the following list: Zero Exponent Property (Chapter 7); Negative Exponent Property; Power of a Product Property; Power of a Quotient Property; Product of Powers Property; Quotient of Powers Property; Power of a Power Property.		1	0.5	0.5
8-3 Quotients of Powers A Simplify products, quotients, and powers of powers. G Identify properties of powers that justify a simplification. (See Lesson 8-2 above for list.)		1	0.5	0.75
QUIZ 1		0.5	0.5	0.25
8-4 Negative Exponents A Simplify products, quotients, and powers of powers. B Evaluate negative integer powers of real numbers. G Identify properties of powers that justify a simplification. (See Lesson 8-2 above for list.)		1	1	0.5
8-5 Powers of Products and Quotients A Simplify products, quotients, and powers of powers. B Evaluate negative integer powers of real numbers. C Rewrite powers of products and quotients. G Identify properties of powers that justify a simplification. (See Lesson 8-2 above for list.)		1	1	0.5
8-6 Square Roots and Cube Roots D Simplify square roots. E Evaluate cube roots.		1	1	0.75
QUIZ 2		0.5	0.5	0.25
8-7 Multiplying and Dividing Square Roots D Simplify square roots.		1	1	0.5
8-8 Distance in a Plane I Represent squares, cubes, square roots, and cube roots geometrically. J Calculate distances on the x-y coordinate plane.		1	0.5	0.5
8-9 Remembering Properties of Powers and Roots C Rewrite powers of products and quotients. F Test a special case to determine whether a pattern is true.		1	1	0.5
Self-Test		1	1	0.5
Chapter Review		2	2	1
Test		1	1	0.5
TOTAL		14	12	7.5

Technology Resources

Teacher's Assessment Assistant, Ch. 8

Electronic Teacher's Edition, Ch. 8

Differentiated Options Universal Access

	Accommodating the Learner	Vocabulary Development	Ongoing Assessment	Materials
8-1	pp. 459, 460		oral, p. 463	scientific or graphing calculator
8-2	pp. 465, 466	p. 465	written, p. 468	Computer Algebra System (CAS)
8-3	pp. 470, 471		written, p. 473	scientific or graphing calculator
8-4	pp. 475, 476		group, p. 480	scientific or graphing calculator, Computer Algebra System (CAS)
8-5	pp. 483, 484		oral, p. 487	two pieces of 8.5 in.-by-11 in. paper (per student), tape, scissors, ruler
8-6	pp. 490, 492		written, p. 496	scientific or graphing calculator, graph paper
8-7	pp. 499, 501		written, p. 504	scientific or graphing calculator
8-8	pp. 506, 507		group, p. 510	scientific or graphing calculator
8-9	pp. 512, 514	p. 513	written, p. 516	scientific or graphing calculator

Objectives

		Lessons	Self-Test Questions	Chapter Review Questions
Ⓢkills				
A	Simplify products, quotients, and powers of powers.	8-2, 8-3, 8-4, 8-5	1, 7, 9, 11, 12, 15	1–11
B	Evaluate negative integer powers of real numbers.	8-4, 8-5	2, 3, 18	12–21
C	Rewrite powers of products and quotients.	8-5, 8-9	8, 10, 16	22–29
D	Simplify square roots.	8-6, 8-7	4–6	30–36
E	Evaluate cube roots.	8-6	17	37–42
Ⓟroperties				
F	Test a special case to determine whether a pattern is true.	8-9	20	43–46
G	Identify properties of powers that justify a simplification, from the following list: Zero Exponent Property (Chapter 7); Negative Exponent Property; Power of a Product Property; Power of a Quotient Property; Product of Powers Property; Quotient of Powers Property; Power of a Power Property.	8-2, 8-3, 8-4, 8-5	13, 14, 19	47–54
Ⓤses				
H	Use powers to count the number of sequences possible for repeated choices.	8-1	25	55–58
Ⓡepresentations				
I	Represent squares, cubes, square roots, and cube roots geometrically.	8-8	23, 24	59–64
J	Calculate distances on the x-y coordinate plane.	8-8	21, 22	65–71

Resource Masters Chapter 8

Resource Master 1, Graph Paper (page 2), can be used with Lesson 8-8. **Resource Master 2, Four-Quadrant Graph Paper** (page 3), can be used with Lessons 8-4, 8-6, and 8-8.

Resource Master 115 Lesson 8-1

Warm-Up

1. How many 3-letter acronyms can be formed using only the vowels A, E, I, O, and U?

2. How many of the acronyms in Question 1 begin with the letter A?

3. How many of the acronyms in Question 1 end in the letter O?

4. If Y is considered a vowel, how do the answers to Questions 1–3 change?

Additional Examples

1. In an apartment building, each apartment has a building number from 1 to 9 followed by a letter from A to F. For example, one apartment designation is 9A. How many different apartment designations are possible in this building?

2. A combination lock requires a sequence of three numbers from 0 to 99 to open it. How many different possible codes are there?

3. Suppose a test has 10 true/false questions and 8 multiple-choice questions with 4 choices. What is the probability that a person could guess on each of the 18 questions and answer them all correctly?

Resource Master for Lesson 8-1

Resource Master 116 Lesson 8-2

Warm-Up

1. Write 2^x as a decimal when x is an integer from 1 to 10.

2. Multiply any two of the first five numbers in your list of answers for Question 1. The product will also be in the list. Why is this?

3. Repeat Questions 1 and 2 with 3^x instead of 2^x. Does the same pattern hold?

Additional Examples

1. A collector started with 2 antique pocket watches, and every year his number of pocket watches doubled. Write an expression for the number of pocket watches the collector has after d years, and then after 5 more years.

2. Simplify $w^4 \cdot k^5 \cdot k^3 \cdot w^2 \cdot k$.

3. Write $(3^5)^3$ as a single power.

4. Simplify $2g(g^2)^9$.

Resource Master for Lesson 8-2

Resource Master 117 Lesson 8-3

Warm-Up

Use these integer powers of 3: $\frac{1}{2,187}, \frac{1}{729}, \frac{1}{243}, \frac{1}{81}, \frac{1}{27}, \frac{1}{9}, \frac{1}{3}, 1, 3, 9, 27, 81, 243, 729, 2,187, 6,561$

1. Write the product $\frac{1}{243} \cdot 6,561 = 27$ as a product of powers of 3.

2. Now write the quotient $\frac{2,187}{9} = 243$ as a quotient of powers of 3.

Additional Examples

1. The area of China is 9,596,960 square kilometers. In July 2006, China's population was estimated at 1,313,973,713 people. What is the population density of China in people per square kilometer?

2. Simplify $\frac{40b^6c^5}{8bc^2}$.

Question 28

◇	A	B
1	Time (hours)	Distance (miles)
2	1.0	
3	1.5	97.5
4	2	130
5	2.5	162.5
6	3	
7	3.5	

Resource Master for Lesson 8-3

Resource Master 118 Lesson 8-4

Warm-Up

1. Use a calculator to evaluate 9^n and 9^{-n} when $n = 2$.

2. Multiply the two values in Question 1. What is the product?

3. Evaluate 9^n and 9^{-n} for another value of n of your own choosing, and again multiply the two values. Is your product the same or different than the product in Question 2?

4. Pick a base other than 9 and repeat Questions 1–3.

5. Make a statement about the relationship between b^n and b^{-n}.

Additional Examples

1. Rewrite $c^{-9}d^2$ without negative exponents.

2. Write each expression without negative exponents.
   a. $\left(\frac{3}{2}\right)^{-4}$
   b. $\left(\frac{1}{k^5}\right)^{-5}$

3. Five years ago, Molly bought a 60-month certificate of deposit (CD) that had an annual yield of 5%. If the CD is now worth $1,914.42, what was the amount initially invested?

Resource Master for Lesson 8-4

Resource Master 119 Lesson 8-4

Additional Examples

4. Simplify $\frac{3x^2y}{12x^4y^3z^4}$. Write the answers without negative exponents.

$$\frac{3x^2y}{12x^4y^3z^4} = \frac{3}{12} \cdot \frac{x^2}{x^4} \cdot \frac{y}{y^3} \cdot \frac{z^0}{z^4}$$

$$= \frac{1}{4} \cdot x^{-2} \cdot y^{-2} \cdot z^{-4}$$

$$= \frac{1}{4} \cdot \frac{1}{x^2} \cdot \frac{1}{y^2} \cdot \frac{z^0}{1}$$

$$= \underline{?}$$

5. Simplify $(k^{-3})^4$. Write without negative exponents.

Resource Master for Lesson 8-4

Resource Master 120 Lesson 8-5

Warm-Up

Written as a product of powers, the prime factorization of 1,500 is $2^2 \cdot 3 \cdot 5^3$. The prime factorization of 162 is $2 \cdot 3^4$.

1. What is the prime factorization of $1,500^5$?

2. What is the prime factorization of $1,500 \cdot 162$?

3. What is the prime factorization of $\frac{1,500 \cdot 162}{27}$?

Additional Examples

1. Simplify $(-2y)^4$.

2. Simplify $(-4x^3yz^4)^5$.

   Apply the Power of a Product Property.

   $(-4)^{-5}(x^3)^{-5}(y)^{-5}(z^4)^{-5}$

   Apply the Power of a Power Property.

   $(-4)^{-5}x^{-5}y^{-5}z^{-5}$

   Evaluate the numerical power.

3. Write $\left(\frac{2}{5}\right)^3$ as a simple fraction.

4. Suppose we change the activity on page 483 and 484 so that the tall box has dimensions $\frac{p}{3} \times \frac{p}{3} \times h$ and the short box has dimensions $\frac{2p}{3} \times \frac{2p}{3} \times \frac{h}{2}$.
   a. Find the volume of each box.
   b. Show that the volume of the tall box is always less than or equal to the volume of the short box.
   c. The volume of the short box is how many times the volume of the tall one?

Resource Master for Lesson 8-5

Resource Master 121 — Lesson 8-6

Warm-Up

1. What is the meaning of the word *hypotenuse*?
2. **Multiple Choice** The principal square root of 400 is __?__.
   A 20   B 200
   C 1,600   D 160,000
3. **Multiple Choice** The two square roots of 5 are __?__.
   A 25 and −25
   B 2.5 and −2.5
   C about 2.24 and −2.24
   D nonexistent
4. If the two shorter sides of a right triangle have lengths 8 and 10, what is the length of the longest side of the triangle?
5. **Fill in the Blank.** 6 is a cube root of 216 because __?__.

Additional Examples

1. What are the square roots of each number?
   a. 121
   b. 13.5
2. Use the Pythagorean Theorem to find the length of the missing side.

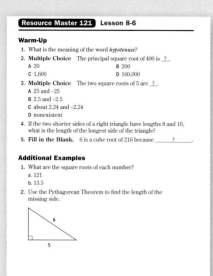

Resource Master for Lesson 8-6

Resource Master 122 — Lesson 8-6

Activity 1

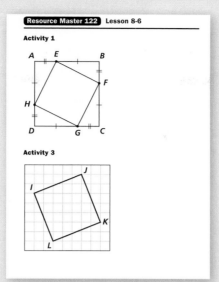

Activity 3

Resource Master for Lesson 8-6

Resource Master 123 — Lesson 8-6

Activity 4

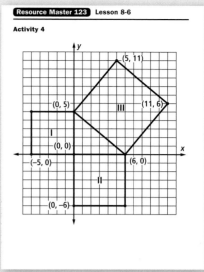

Resource Master for Lesson 8-6

Resource Master 124 — Lesson 8-7

Warm-Up

1. Check that each statement is true by using decimal approximations.
   $\sqrt{3} + \sqrt{12} = \sqrt{27}$
   $\sqrt{5} + \sqrt{20} = \sqrt{45}$
   $\sqrt{6} + \sqrt{24} = \sqrt{54}$
2. Find a similar statement with $\sqrt{7}$ as the first value.
3. What is the general pattern?

Additional Examples

1. Simplify $\sqrt{50}$.
2. A leg of a right triangle is 2 inches long and the hypotenuse is 4 inches long.
   a. Find the exact length of the third side.
   b. Put the exact length in simplified radical form. Now use the Product of Square Roots Property to simplify the result. Note that the perfect square 4 is a factor of 12.

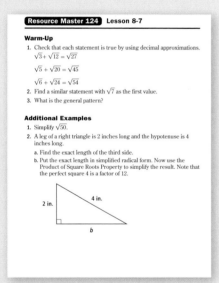

Resource Master for Lesson 8-7

Resource Master 125 — Lesson 8-7

Additional Examples

3. Assume x, y, and z are positive. Simplify $\sqrt{98x^3yz^2}$.
   $\sqrt{98x^3yz^2} = \sqrt{\underline{\ ?\ }} \cdot \sqrt{2} \cdot \sqrt{x^2} \cdot \sqrt{y} \cdot \sqrt{z^2}$
   $= \underline{\ ?\ } \cdot \sqrt{2} \cdot x \cdot \sqrt{y} \cdot z$
   $= \underline{\ ?\ }\, xz\, \sqrt{2} \cdot \sqrt{y}$
   $= \underline{\ ?\ }\, xz\sqrt{2y}$
4. At Fermi National Accelerator Laboratory in Illinois, there is a pendulum hanging from the high ceiling in the atrium of Wilson Hall. The approximate length of the pendulum is 240 feet. What is the time p for one period of the pendulum?

Resource Master for Lesson 8-7

Resource Master 126 — Lesson 8-8

Warm-Up

In 1–3, find the distance between the given points.

1. (0, 0) and (−7, 0)
2. (0, 0) and (0, 13)
3. (−7, 0) and (0, 13)
4. Explain why the distance between (−6, 0) and (1, 13) is equal to the distance calculated in Question 3.
5. Find the distance between (a, b) and $(a + 3, b + 4)$.

Additional Examples

1. Find DE in $\triangle DEF$ below.

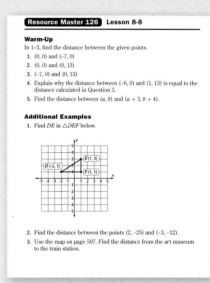

2. Find the distance between the points (2, −25) and (−3, −12).
3. Use the map on page 507. Find the distance from the art museum to the train station.

Resource Master for Lesson 8-8

Resource Master 127 — Lesson 8-8

Questions 14–15

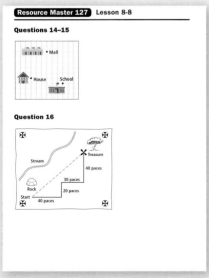

Question 16

Resource Master for Lesson 8-8

Resource Master 128 — Lesson 8-9

Warm-Up

In 1 and 2, show with an example that the indicated equation does *not* describe a general property of powers.

1. $\sqrt{a} + \sqrt{a} = \sqrt{2a}$
2. $(a + b)^5 = a^5 + b^5$
3. **Multiple Choice** For all real numbers b, $\sqrt{b^{100}} = $ __?__.
   a b^{10} b b^{50}
   c $b^{99.5}$ d $\dfrac{b^{100}}{2}$
4. Darla thinks $\sqrt{2} \cdot \sqrt{3} \cdot \sqrt{5} \cdot \sqrt{7} \cdot \sqrt{11} = \sqrt{2{,}310}$. Is she right? If so, why? If not, what is the correct product?

Additional Examples

1. Mark was not sure how to simplify $(x^{23})^6$. He felt the answer could be x^{138} or x^{29}. Which is correct?
2. Notice that $2^2 + 2^2 = 2^3$ because $4 + 4 = 8$, and that $0^2 + 0^2 = 0^3$. Can you conclude that $x^2 + x^2 = x^3$?
3. Using the radii from Example 3 in the text, find the ratio of the surface area of the Earth to the surface area of Jupiter.
4. If $\left(\dfrac{25r^{-4}}{10y^3}\right)^{-5} = ar^n$, what are the values of a and n?

Resource Master for Lesson 8-9

Pacing

Each lesson in this chapter is designed to be covered in one day. At the end of the chapter, you should plan to spend 1 day to review the Self-Test, 1 to 2 days for the Chapter Review, and 1 day for a test. You may wish to spend a day on projects and possibly a day is needed for quizzes. This chapter should therefore take 12 to 15 days. We strongly advise you to not spend more than 16 days on this chapter; there is ample opportunity to review ideas in later chapters.

Using Pages 456–457

As discussed in Chapter 7, the graph of an exponential function $y = a^x$ on a calculator has points on it for values of x that are not positive integers.

1. Ask students to graph $y = 10^x$ on a graphing calculator with the window set for $-2 \leq x \leq 2$. From their knowledge of scientific notation, students should be able to see that the following points are on the graph: $(-2, 0.01)$, $(-1, 0.1)$, $(0, 1)$, $(1, 10)$, $(2, 100)$.
2. How many powers of 2 do they know? Have students multiply each side of $2^2 = 4$ by 2 to get $2^3 = 8$, and then multiply each side of $2^3 = 8$ by 2 to get $2^4 = 16$. Continue this up to 2^{10}.

You can continue this with powers of 3, 4, 5, and 6. It is helpful for students to know the squares and cubes of all the integers from 1 to 10. If students know these squares and cubes they can easily obtain the squares and cubes of integers from -1 to -10.

Chapter 8 Projects

At the end of each chapter, you will find projects related to the chapter. At this time, you might want to have students look over the projects on pages 517 and 518. You might want to have students tentatively select a project on which to work. Then, as students read and progress through the chapter, they can finalize their project choices.

▶ **Contents**

Visible light, infrared and ultraviolet radiation, x-rays, microwaves, and radio waves are all parts of the electromagnetic spectrum. Waves differ only in their wavelengths. Radio waves can be as long as 1,000 meters or longer; x-rays can be as short as one billionth of a meter or less.

To describe these numbers, we use powers of 10. On the scale shown below, each tick mark is 10 *times* the length of the tick mark to its left. You have seen these powers of 10 used in scientific notation.

The Electromagnetic Spectrum

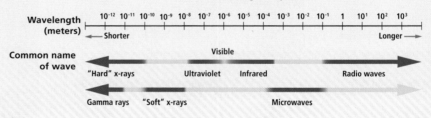

456

Chapter 8 Overview

The work students have done with exponential growth and decay in Chapter 7 and with scientific notation in this and earlier courses means that they are familiar with the calculation of powers of numbers. This knowledge readies them for a discussion of properties of these powers.

This chapter is divided into two parts, as indicated by its title. The first part, about integer powers, runs through Lesson 8-5. Lesson 8-1 begins this part with the application of x^n, where x and n are both positive integers, to permutations with replacement. This application and repeated multiplication help to justify the properties of products and of power of a power in Lesson 8-2. From these properties, we deduce the division of powers with the same base in Lesson 8-3 and the properties of x^n when n is negative in Lesson 8-4. Powers of products and quotients complete this part of the chapter in Lesson 8-5.

(continued on next page)

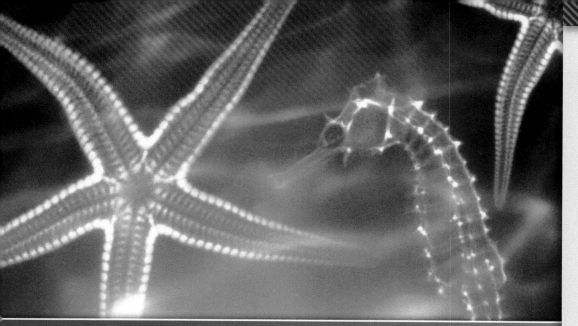

Here is a graph of $y = 10^x$ on the window $-5 \leq x \leq 5$, $-10 \leq y \leq 20$. You can see that as x increases by 1, y is multiplied by 10. The coordinates of some points on this graph are easily found by hand. When $x = 0$, $y = 10^0 = 1$. When $x = 1$, $y = 10^1 = 10$. When $x = 2$, $y = 10^2 = 100$. When $x = 3$, $y = 10^3 = 1,000$, too large to be on the graph. But the graph contains values of the function when x is negative. What is the meaning of 10^{-1}, 10^{-2}, 10^{-3}, and so on?

Also, the graph computes values for y when x is not an integer. Although we do not discuss all the powers of x in this chapter, the meanings of $\frac{1}{2}$ and $\frac{1}{3}$ are discussed and found to be related to square roots and cube roots. Additionally, there is the question of how all these powers and roots are related. For example, how is x^7 related to x^{-7}? Are the 7th powers of different numbers related in any way? The answers to these questions provide additional understanding of some of the applications of powers that you saw in the preceding chapter. They also shed light on some important formulas for lengths, area, and volume found in geometry.

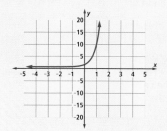

The second part of the chapter deals with square roots and has an excursion into cube roots. Lesson 8-6 connects the two parts of the chapter with the recognition that $\sqrt{x} = x^{\frac{1}{2}}$ when $x \geq 0$. Consequently, the properties of powers can be applied to obtain properties of square roots. These properties are found in Lesson 8-7. The application of the Pythagorean Theorem to derive the formula for the distance between two points is in Lesson 8-8. Lesson 8-9 is a problem-solving lesson that discusses strategies that students can use to help them remember the properties they have seen earlier in the chapter.

Lesson 8-1

The Multiplication Counting Principle

Vocabulary

scientific notation

GOAL

Work from the Multiplication Counting Principle to answer questions regarding the number of permutations with replacement of *n* objects.

SPUR Objective

(The SPUR Objectives for all of Chapter 8 are found in the Chapter Review on pages 521–523.)

H Use powers to count the number of sequences possible for repeated choices.

Materials/Resources

· Lesson Master 8-1A or 8-1B
· Resource Master 115
· Scientific or graphing calculator

HOMEWORK

Suggestions for Assignment
- Questions 1–21
- Questions 22 and 23 (extra credit)
- Reading Lesson 8-2
- Covering the Ideas 8-2

Local Standards

1 Warm-Up

You might write or project the following so that students can do these questions as they enter the classroom.

1. How many 3-letter acronyms can be formed using only the vowels A, E, I, O, and U? $5^3 = 125$
2. How many of the acronyms in Question 1 begin with the letter A? $5^2 = 25$
3. How many of the acronyms in Question 1 end in the letter O? $5^2 = 25$
4. If Y is considered a vowel, how do the answers to Questions 1–3 change? Change the 5 to 6 in all three cases.

▶ **BIG IDEA** Expressions involving powers result from certain counting problems and are used in scientific notation.

The Jaipur Friendship and Knitting Society decided that it would call itself by the 3-letter acronym JFK. (An *acronym*, like USA or NCAA, is a "word" made up of the first letter of each word in a phrase.) They were disappointed to learn that JFK was already a popular acronym. It is the initials of President John Fitzgerald Kennedy and identifies one of the airports in New York City as well as some highways throughout the country. So the society decided to use JFKS.

Members of the society realized that there is only a certain number of 3-letter acronyms. So they wondered, how many 3-letter acronyms are there in the English language?

To answer this question, we apply a very useful problem-solving strategy. We consider a simpler problem we may be able to solve and then apply its solution to the problem we want to solve.

Example 1

How many 2-letter acronyms are there?

Solution Count the acronyms in an organized manner, alphabetically. AA, AB, AC, ..., AZ gives 26. BA, BB, BC, ... BZ gives another 26. There will be 26 groups of 26, so the total number is $26 \cdot 26 = 26^2 = 676$.

Notice that we gave the answer to Example 1 in three forms: as a *product* $26 \cdot 26$, as a *power* 26^2, in our customary *base-10 decimal* system as 676. Each of these forms is useful, so you need to be able to move back and forth from one way of writing a number to another.

Example 1 applies multiplication in a manner that is so important that it has a special name, the *Multiplication Counting Principle*.

Multiplication Counting Principle

If one choice can be made in *m* ways and then a second choice can be made in *n* ways, then there are *mn* ways of making the first choice followed by the second choice.

Mental Math

Simplify $\dfrac{n \cdot 3n \cdot 6n \cdot 9n}{n \cdot 2n \cdot 4n \cdot 6n} \cdot \dfrac{27}{8}$

Knitting was first introduced to Europe in the 5th century CE.

Source: Fine Living TV Network

Background

The Multiplication Counting Principle is sometimes given the name "Fundamental Counting Principle." The name reflects its role as a powerful tool in counting problems. Until recently, this principle was generally not taught until 11th or 12th grade, when it was discussed in connection with permutations and combinations. Because it is important in mathematics and its applications, because it is not a difficult topic, and because computing powers is reasonably easy with calculators, this discussion does not need to be delayed that

long, and more and more texts have started including it in algebra or even earlier.

There are two kinds of permutations: those with replacement (that allow repetition of the symbols) and those without replacement (that do not allow repetition). BB is allowed in a permutation of length 2 of the 26 letters of the alphabet with replacement; BB is not allowed in a permutation without replacement. In Chapter 10, we discuss permutations without replacement.

The Multiplication Counting Principle was applied in Example 1. There were 26 choices for the first letter. After that choice was made, there were 26 choices for the second letter. So $m = 26$ and $n = 26$, and the number of 2-letter acronyms is $26 \cdot 26$, or 676.

Example 2

How many 3-letter acronyms are there?

Solution 1 Apply the Multiplication Counting Principle to the result of Example 1, which found that there are 676 different 2-letter acronyms. For each one, there are 26 possible third letters. So the total number is $676 \cdot 26 = 17{,}576$.

Solution 2 Keep the result from Example 1 in factored form. There are $26 \cdot 26$ different 2-letter acronyms. Now, with 26 possible third letters, the total number is $26 \cdot 26 \cdot 26 = 26^3$. This is also equal to 17,576.

The idea behind the solutions to Example 2 is very powerful and can be continued. To get the number of 4-letter acronyms, you can work from the number of 3-letter acronyms. Each 3-letter acronym is the beginning of 26 4-letter acronyms, so the number of 4-letter acronyms is $26^3 \cdot 26$, or 26^4, and so on. This thinking is much like the Now/Next thinking you used in the spreadsheets of Lesson 7-8.

 QY1

Choosing From *n* Objects Repeatedly

A sequence of two objects is said to have "length" 2; a sequence of three objects has length 3, and so on. In the previous examples you counted ways to make acronyms of length 2 and 3. Order matters with acronyms. President John Fitzgerald Kennedy had initials JFK, but not KFJ. Order also matters with acronyms such as NASA (National Aeronautics and Space Administration) and SCUBA (self-contained underwater breathing apparatus).

The process used to find the number of different acronyms of length 2 or 3 can be generalized, leading to the following result.

> **Arrangements Theorem**
>
> If there are n ways to select each object in a sequence of length L, then n^L different sequences are possible.

 QY2

> ▶ **QY1**
>
> The Russian alphabet has 33 letters. How many 4-letter Russian acronyms are possible?

> ▶ **QY2**
>
> A test has 20 multiple-choice questions with 5 choices each. How many different sets of answers are possible?

The Multiplication Counting Principle **459**

---

2 | Teaching

Notes on the Lesson

Although the Multiplication Counting Principle is quite easy to apply, it is not at all obvious to students. You may wish to show part of a tree diagram for Example 1, with A having 26 branches leading to each of the letters A through Z; B having 26 branches leading to each of the letters A through Z, and so on. (It is tedious to draw all 26 branches, but drawing a few gives the idea.) With 26 letters each having 26 branches, the total number of permutations is $26 \cdot 26$, or 26^2.

Another way to show Example 1 is with a 26×26 matrix in which the rows and columns are each identified by the letters A through Z. Then each element of the matrix can be identified with the 2-letter acronym of its row and column. From the area or array models of multiplication, the number of elements is 26^2.

Example 2 extends Example 1 by introducing a third letter. An easy way to get the answer without going through all the questions is to realize that every 3-letter acronym begins with a 2-letter acronym. Then there are 26 possible choices for the last letter. So the number of 3-letter acronyms is 26 times the number of 2-letter acronyms found in Example 1.

Additional Examples

Example 1 In an apartment building, each apartment has a building number from 1 to 9 followed by a letter from A to F. For example, one apartment designation is 9A. How many different apartment designations are possible in this building? $9 \cdot 6 = 54$

Example 2 A combination lock requires a sequence of three numbers from 0 to 99 to open it. How many different possible codes are there? $100^3 = 1{,}000{,}000$

Accommodating the Learner ⬇

Expand the explanations for the solutions to Examples 1 and 2. Sometimes students mistakenly add m and n rather than multiply them. Make sure students understand the reasoning behind the multiplication. An easier example to understand might be the set of all 2-digit numbers, where 0 is written as 00, 1 is written as 01, and so on. Provide students with a chart of the numbers 00 to 99. Students know there are 100 numbers, and ten possibilities for each digit. Looking at the chart can help them visualize the pattern.

Notes on the Lesson

Example 3 involves three applications of the Multiplication Counting Principle. First is obtaining the number of different possible answer sheets for 20 questions with 4 choices each. Second is obtaining the same information for the 10 questions with 5 choices. Then, if you are sure your work is correct, apply the principle a third time to give the number of combined permutations. The reciprocal of this number is the probability that a person would answer all of the questions correctly. The probability is very small.

Additional Example

Example 3 Suppose a test has 10 true/false questions and 8 multiple-choice questions with 4 choices. What is the probability that a person could guess on each of the 18 questions and answer them all correctly?

Solution

Part 1 This part has 10 questions with choices T and F. We want to know how many sequences m of length 10 there are with these 2 letters. $m = \underline{\ ?\ }\ 2^{10} = 1{,}024$

Part 2 This part has 8 questions with 4 choices. Let n be the number of sequences of length 8 with 4 letters. $n = \underline{\ ?\ }\ 4^8 = 65{,}536$

Now apply the Multiplication Counting Principle and multiply the results from Part 1 and Part 2 to determine how many different test papers are possible. $mn = \underline{\ ?\ }\ 2^{10} \cdot 4^8 = 67{,}108{,}864$

In base 10, this number is 67,108,864. If a person is guessing, then we assume that each one of these test papers is equally likely, and only one of them has all the correct answers. So the probability of having a perfect test is $\frac{1}{mn} = \underline{\ ?\ }$. $\frac{1}{67{,}108{,}864} \approx 0.00000001$

In Example 3, not all of the objects have the same number of choices possible.

Example 3

Suppose a standardized test has 20 questions with 4 choices and 10 questions with 5 choices. What is the probability that a person could guess on every one of the 30 questions and answer them all correctly?

Solution Think of the test as having 2 parts. Count the number of ways each part can be created.

Part 1 This part has 20 questions with 4 choices. We want to know how many sequences m of length 20 there are with these 4 letters.

$$m = \underline{\ ?\ }\ 4^{20}$$

Part 2 This part has 10 questions with 5 choices. Let n be the number of sequences of length 10 with 5 letters.

$$n = \underline{\ ?\ }\ 5^{10}$$

Now apply the Multiplication Counting Principle and multiply the results from Part 1 and Part 2 to determine how many different sets of answers are possible.

$$mn = \underline{\ ?\ }\ (4^{20})(5^{10})$$

In base 10 this number is 10,737,418,240,000,000,000. If a person is guessing, then we assume that each one of these sets of answers is equally likely, and only one of them has all the correct answers. So the probability of having a perfect test is $\frac{1}{mn} = \underline{\ ?\ } \cdot \frac{1}{10{,}737{,}418{,}240{,}000{,}000{,}000}$

The national average mathematics score on The National Assessment of Educational Progress (NAEP) at grade 8 was 16 points higher in 2005 than in 1990.

Source: National Assessment of Educational Progress

Writing Large Numbers in Scientific Notation

Depending on your calculator and the mode it is in, if you enter mn to calculate the answer to Example 3, the result will be displayed either as the long base-10 number or in *scientific notation*. You should try this on your calculator. Presumably you have used scientific notation in other mathematics or science classes. Recall that in **scientific notation,** a number is represented as $x \cdot 10^n$, where n is an integer and $1 \le x < 10$. In scientific notation, $10{,}737{,}418{,}240{,}000{,}000{,}000 \approx 1.0737 \cdot 10^{19}$.

A major advantage of scientific notation is that it quickly tells you the size of a number. The exponent is one less than the number of digits in the whole number. A whole number $x \cdot 10^n$ has $n + 1$ digits. Notice that the exponent is 19 in the scientific notation form of the number above, and the base-10 form has 20 digits.

Accommodating the Learner ⬆

Ask students to write a justification for the Arrangements Theorem. They can do this by giving an example and generalizing or providing a more abstract justification. This is not intended to be a formal proof, but simply a way for them to understand and remember the theorem.

Questions

COVERING THE IDEAS

1. a. Write all the 2-letter acronyms that can be made from the five vowels A, E, I, O, and U.

   b. **Fill in the Blanks** In Part a, you have found the number of sequences of length __?__ of __?__ objects. **2; 5**

   1a. AA, AE, AI, AO, AU, EA, EE, EI, EO, EU, IA, IE, II, IO, IU, OA, OE, OI, OO, OU, UA, UE, UI, UO, UU

2. The Greek alphabet is about 2,750 years old and is used by about 12 million people in Greece and other countries around the world. It contains 24 letters.

   a. How many 2-letter acronyms are there using Greek letters?   **2a. 576**

   b. How many 4-letter acronyms are there using Greek letters?   **2b. 331,776**

3. Write the number 5^6 in base-10 and in scientific notation.   **3. 15,625; $1.5625 \cdot 10^4$**

4. a. Write an example of a 6-letter acronym made from the five letters A, B, C, D, and E. **Answers vary. Sample answer: AABCDE**

   b. How many of these 6-letter acronyms are possible? **15,625**

5. Suppose part of a spreadsheet has 6 columns and 15 rows.

   a. How many cells are in the spreadsheet? **90**

   b. Explain how your answer applies the Multiplication Counting Principle by indicating how choices are involved in finding the number of cells.

   5b. To label each cell, we choose each cell among 15 columns and 6 rows, so there are 6 · 15 choices, thus 90 cells.

6. a. Draw three horizontal lines and four vertical lines. In how many points do these lines intersect? **12**

   6a.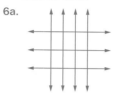

   b. If you drew 30 horizontal lines and 40 vertical lines, in how many points would they intersect? **1,200**

   c. If you drew h horizontal lines and v vertical lines, in how many points would they intersect? **hv**

7. a. A quiz consists of 10 true-or-false questions. How many different sets of answers are possible? Write your answer in exponential form, in base-10, and in scientific notation.

   7a. 2^{10}; 1,024; $1.024 \cdot 10^3$

   b. If you guess on all 10 questions, what is the probability of getting all the questions correct? $\frac{1}{1,024}$

   c. Answer Parts a and b if there are Q true or false questions on the test. 2^Q; $\frac{1}{2^Q}$

8. A test has 5 true-or-false questions and 15 multiple-choice questions with 4 choices each.

   a. How many different sets of answers are possible? Write your answer in exponential form, in base-10, and in scientific notation.

   8a. $2^5 \cdot 4^{15}$; 34,359,738,368; $3.4359738368 \cdot 10^{10}$

   b. If you guessed on every question, what is the probability you would get all 20 questions correct? $\frac{1}{2^5 4^{15}}$

Extension

Ask students to find the total number of different sets of answers that are possible for a test that has two parts, both of which are multiple-choice with 4 answer choices. The first part is 10 questions long and the second part is 8 questions long. Ask students to do the problem two different ways. First ask them to find m and n, and multiply them. For the second method, ask them to condense the problem and simply find the number of different sets of answers that are possible for an 18-question test with four answer choices. Ask students to leave both answers with exponents and to compare the exponents. See if students can identify the pattern of the Product Property of Exponents. $m = 4^{10}$; $n = 4^8$; $4^{10} \cdot 4^8 = 4^{18}$

8-1

3 Assignment

Recommended Assignment

- Questions 1–21
- Questions 22 and 23 (extra credit)
- Reading Lesson 8-2
- Covering the Ideas 8-2

Notes on the Questions

Question 8b You may wish to write the probability as a decimal to emphasize how small it is. (0.0000000003)

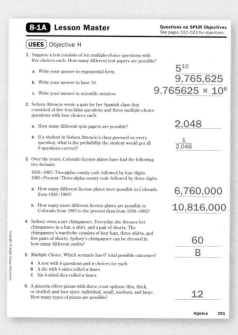

9. Use the information on the electromagnetic spectrum on page 456. Write the number in base-10 notation.

   a. the longest wavelength marked on the spectrum $10^3 = 1,000$

   b. the shortest wavelength marked on the spectrum
   $10^{-12} = 0.000000000001$

APPLYING THE MATHEMATICS

10. Radio station call letters in the United States must start with either W or K.

    a. How many choices are there for the first letter? **2**

    b. How many choices are there for the second letter? **26**

    c. How many different 4-letter station names are possible? **35,152**

11. The Cayuga Indians played a game called *Dish* using 6 peach pits. The pits were blackened on one side and plain on the other. When pits were tossed, they landed on the blackened and plain sides with about the same frequency. When the six pits were tossed, a player scored if either all blackened or all plain sides landed up. What is the probability that a player would score points on one toss of the pits? $\frac{1}{32}$

In June 2005, there were 2,019 commercial U.S. radio stations.

Source: Federal Communications Commission

12. How many 6-digit whole numbers are there? Answer the question in two ways.

    a. by subtracting the least 6-digit number from the greatest 6-digit number and working from that **900,000**

    b. by thinking of the problem as a series of choices: 9 choices for the left digit (because it cannot be zero) and 10 choices for every other **900,000**

13. Assume that everyone in the United States has a first name, a middle name, and a last name. Therefore, everyone has a 3-letter acronym of his or her initials. If your initials are typical, about how many of the 300 million people in the United States have your initials? **17,069 people**

14. How many different sets of answers are possible for each of the following tests?

    a. a group of P true-or-false questions 2^P

    b. a group of Q questions that can be answered "sometimes," "always," or "never" 3^Q

    c. a test made up of two parts: P true or false questions and Q *always, sometimes but not always,* or *never* questions 2^P3^Q

REVIEW

15. Do the ordered pairs (x, y) that satisfy $y < -4x + 8$ describe a function? Why or why not? (**Lesson 7-5**) No, because for each value of x, there are several values of y.

Notes on the Questions

Question 13 You could make this an Exploration problem.

Question 18 This strategy is the capture-recapture strategy that is actually used to determine fish populations.

Question 22 This question, whose answers may be found in an almanac or on the Internet, helps to point out how many acronyms are used in our government and how many of them start with similar letters.

16. Consider these points $(0, -2)$, $(6, 4)$, and $(-10, -12)$.
    (**Lessons 6-6, 3-4**) 16a. $y = x - 2$
    a. Write an equation for the line containing these three points.
    b. If the point $(x, 20)$ lies on this line, find the value of x. 22

17. Refer to the similar triangles at the right. If the ratio of similitude of the smaller triangle to the larger triangle is $\frac{1}{3}$, find the area of the larger triangle. (**Lesson 5-10**) 108 units^2

18. A biologist captured, tagged, and released 40 fish caught in a lake. Three weeks later, the biologist caught 28 fish. Of these, 8 had tags. Based on these findings, estimate the total number of fish in the lake. (**Lesson 5-9**) 140 fish

19. Solve $\frac{1}{5}x - \frac{3}{10} = \frac{9}{10}$. (**Lesson 3-8**) $x = 6$

In 20 and 21, write the number in scientific notation. (Previous Course)
20. seven thousandths $7 \cdot 10^{-3}$ 21. 2.8 billion $2.8 \cdot 10^9$

EXPLORATION

22. Many of the cabinet-level departments in the United States government are identified by acronyms. Tell what department each of these acronyms stands for. As a hint, we have put the departments (not the acronyms) in alphabetical order.

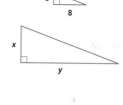

a. USDA	b. DOC	c. DOD	d. ED
e. DOE	f. HHS	g. DHS	h. HUD
i. DOJ	j. DOL	k. DOS	l. DOI
m. DOT	n. VA		22a–n. See margin.

The Pentagon has three times the floor space of the Empire State Building in New York.

Source: Pentagon Tours

23. The Greek alphabet has 24 letters and the Russian alphabet has 33 letters.
    a. Are there more 4-letter Greek acronyms or 3-letter Russian acronyms? 4-letter Greek acronyms
    b. What is the least value of n for which there are *fewer* n-letter Greek acronyms compared to $(n - 1)$-letter Russian acronyms? $n = 11$

QY ANSWERS

1. $33^4 = 1,185,921$

2. $5^{20} =$
   $95,367,431,640,625 \approx$
   $9.5 \cdot 10^{13}$

The Multiplication Counting Principle   **463**

Additional Answers

22a. United States Department of Agriculture

22b. Department of Commerce

22c. Department of Defense

22d. Education Department

22e. Department of Energy

22f. Health and Human Services

22g. Department of Homeland Security

22h. Housing and Urban Development

22i. Department of Justice

22j. Department of Labor

22k. Department of State

22l. Department of the Interior

22m. Department of Transportation

22n. Veterans Affairs

8-1

4 Wrap-Up

Ongoing Assessment

Ask students to describe different situations where they might use the Multiplication Counting Principle and the Arrangements Theorem. Have them discuss what these situations have in common.

Project Update

If you have not had students look over the projects on pages 517 and 518, you might want to do so now. Project 5, Mathematics and Crossword Puzzles, and Project 6, Counting Braille Letters, on page 518, relate to the content of this lesson.

Lesson 8-2

Products and Powers of Powers

GOAL

Introduce and apply the Product of Powers Property: For $b \neq 0$ and all m and n, $b^m \cdot b^n = b^{m+n}$. Examine the Power of a Power Property: For $b \neq 0$ and all m and n, $(b^m)^n = b^{mn}$.

SPUR Objectives

A Simplify products, quotients, and powers of powers.

G Identify properties of powers that justify a simplification. (See page 456B for the list of properties.)

Materials/Resources

- Lesson Master 8-2A or 8-2B
- Resource Master 116
- Computer Algebra System (CAS)

HOMEWORK

Suggestions for Assignment

- Questions 1–28
- Question 29 (extra credit)
- Reading Lesson 8-3
- Covering the Ideas 8-3

Local Standards

1 | Warm-Up

1. Write 2^x as a decimal when x is an integer from 1 to 10. 2; 4; 8; 16; 32; 64; 128; 256; 512; 1,024

2. Multiply any two of the first five numbers in your list of answers for Question 1. The product will also be in the list. Why is this? The product of the powers will also be a result of repeatedly using 2 as a factor.

3. Repeat Questions 1 and 2 with 3^x instead of 2^x. Does the same pattern hold? 3; 9; 27; 81; 243; 729; 2,187; 6,561; 19,683; 59,049; Yes, and for the same reason.

> **BIG IDEA** Because of the relationship between repeated multiplication and powers, products and powers of powers can be themselves written as powers.

Multiplying Powers with the Same Base

When n is a positive integer, $x^n = \underbrace{x \cdot x \cdot \ldots \cdot x}_{n \text{ factors}}$. From this, a number of important properties can be developed. They all involve multiplication in some way because of the relationship between exponents and multiplication. Addition is different. In general, there is no way to simplify the sum of two powers. For example, $3^2 + 3^4 = 9 + 81 = 90$, and 90 is not an integer power of 3. But notice what happens when we multiply powers with the same base.

$$3^2 \cdot 3^4 = \underbrace{(3 \cdot 3)}_{2 \text{ factors}} \cdot \underbrace{(3 \cdot 3 \cdot 3 \cdot 3)}_{4 \text{ factors}} = \underbrace{(3 \cdot 3 \cdot 3 \cdot 3 \cdot 3 \cdot 3)}_{6 \text{ factors}} = 3^6$$

$$1.06^0 \cdot 1.06^3 = 1 \cdot \underbrace{(1.06 \cdot 1.06 \cdot 1.06)}_{3 \text{ factors}} = 1.06^3$$

$$(-6)^5 \cdot (-6)^5 = \underbrace{(-6 \cdot -6 \cdot -6 \cdot -6 \cdot -6)}_{5 \text{ factors}} \cdot \underbrace{(-6 \cdot -6 \cdot -6 \cdot -6 \cdot -6)}_{5 \text{ factors}} = (-6)^{10}$$

These three expressions involved multiplying powers of the same base, where the base was a specific number (3, 1.06, or –6). The same process is used to multiply powers of a variable.

Activity

Step 1 Evaluate each expression.
- a. $z^7 \cdot z^4 \; z^{11}$
- b. $y^6 \cdot y^8 \; y^{14}$
- c. $y^2 \cdot y^4 \cdot y^3 \; y^9$
- d. $x^3 \cdot x \; x^4$
- e. $x^4 \cdot x^2 \cdot x \; x^7$
- f. $t \cdot t \cdot t \; t^3$
- g. $t^3 \cdot t^4 \cdot t \cdot t$
- h. $z^0 \cdot z^5 \cdot z^2 \cdot z^2$

Step 2 Check your answers using a CAS.
- a. When multiplying powers with the same base, how is the exponent of the answer related to the exponents of the original factors?
- b. Some of the variables do not have visible exponents, like $x^3 \cdot x$. Does the relationship you described in Part a apply in this case?
- c. Refer to Part h. What does z^0 equal? How does this fit in with the answer to Part 2a?

Mental Math

Use the circle graph. Give each value in the indicated form.

- **a.** blue sector, decimal 0.4
- **b.** green sector, fraction $\frac{7}{20}$
- **c.** red sector, percent 15%
- **d.** yellow sector, decimal 0.1
- **e.** yellow sector, fraction $\frac{1}{10}$

Activity
1g. t^9
1h. z^9

2a. The exponent of the answer is the sum of the exponents of the factors.

2b. Yes, since $x = x^1$

2c. 1; Multiplication by 1 does not change the answers; neither does addition of 0, so the rule holds.

Background

Lessons 8-2 through 8-5 deal with the formal properties of powers. When expressing these properties, we use the letter b for the base.

We call $b^m \cdot b^n = b^{m+n}$ and $(b^m)^n = b^{mn}$ the "properties of powers" rather than the "laws of exponents" in order to emphasize that these are properties of the operation called powering.

We justify the Product of Powers Property by using the Repeated Multiplication Model

for Powering. Then the Product of Powers Property is used to explain the Power of a Power Property.

Not all algebra students are ready to use the properties of powers. Some must solve these problems by going back to the meaning of powers as repeated multiplication.

The general pattern established in the activity leads us to the *Product of Powers Property*.

Product of Powers Property

For all m and n, and all nonzero b, $b^m \cdot b^n = b^{m+n}$.

The Product of Powers Property can be illustrated with a multiplication fact triangle. Notice that the powers are multiplied, but the exponents are added.

Activity 1
Part 1a:

In general:

Here is a situation leading to multiplying powers with the same base.

Example 1

Suppose you fold an 8.5-inch by 11-inch piece of paper alternating the direction of the folds (fold down, fold to the left, fold down, fold to the left, and so on).

First Fold
(Fold Down)

Second Fold
(Fold Left)

Third Fold
(Fold Down)

Imagine that you keep folding indefinitely. **Write an expression for the number of regions created by first folding the paper n times, and then folding it *three times more*.**

Solution You begin with 1 piece of paper, which is 1 region. Each time you fold the paper, you double the number of regions. After n folds, you have 2^n regions. Folding an additional 3 times doubles the number of regions 3 more times. The number of folds is $2^n \cdot 2 \cdot 2 \cdot 2$ or $2^n \cdot 2^3$. Applying the Product of Powers Property, $2^n \cdot 2^3 = 2^{n+3}$.

Products and Powers of Powers **465**

Vocabulary Development

Ask students to review their exponent vocabulary prior to Lesson 8-2. They should be able to carefully identify and define the *base*, *coefficient*, and *exponent* of an expression.

Accommodating the Learner ⬆

Ask students to write the four multiplication facts for each fact triangle shown above Example 1. Now, ask them to consider the related division facts for the first triangle. These are $\frac{z^{11}}{z^7} = z^4$ and $\frac{z^{11}}{z^4} = z^7$. Now that students have learned the Product of Powers Property, see if they can deduce the Quotient of Powers Property using the second fact triangle.

2 Teaching

Notes on the Lesson

Another way to verify the Product of Powers Property is to use the Multiplication Counting Principle. Consider the following problem: You are taking a quiz on the Civil War, about which you know very little. You are told that part of the quiz will be on the North and part on the South. The teacher says if you can get all the questions on one part right, you will pass. And if you can get all the questions on both parts right, you will get an A. When you see the quiz, you feel there is a chance you might pass even though you know nothing. All the questions are multiple-choice with 4 possibilities. But there are only 3 questions on the North and 7 questions on the South. Let a be the number of different sets of answers that are possible for the North portion and b be the number of different sets of answers that are possible for the South portion. So $a = 4^3$ and $b = 4^7$. From the Multiplication Counting Principle, if there are a ways of doing a first thing and b ways of doing a second independent thing, then there are ab ways of doing both. In this case, because the full test has 10 questions, we know that $ab = 4^{10}$. So we have $4^3 \cdot 4^7 = 4^{10}$. Question 17 applies this idea.

You also could use the Growth Model of Powering to explain the Product of Powers Property. Suppose a population of bacteria quadruples each day. In 3 days, the population is multiplied by 4^3. In 7 days, it is multiplied by 4^7. So if the 7 days followed the 3 days, the population would be multiplied by $4^3 \cdot 4^7$. But 7 days followed by 3 days is 10 days, and we know the population would then be multiplied by 4^{10}. Again we have $4^3 \cdot 4^7 = 4^{10}$. Question 21 applies this idea.

Additional Example

Example 1 A collector started with 2 antique pocket watches, and every year his number of pocket watches doubled. Write an expression for the number of pocket watches the collector has after d years, and then after 5 *more years*. 2^d pocket watches; 2^{d+5} pocket watches

8-2

466

Notes on the Lesson

Example 4 It is critical for students to realize that grouping factors with the same base can be done only because all of the powers are multiplied. The analogy can and should be made with like terms. You can collect terms (multiples of a number) only if they are like terms (multiples of the same number); you can "collect" powers only if they are powers of the same number.

Additional Examples

Example 2 Simplify $w^4 \cdot k^9 \cdot k^3 \cdot w^2 \cdot k$. $w^6 \cdot k^{13}$

Example 3 Write $(3^8)^3$ as a single power. 3^{24}

Example 4 Simplify $2g(g^3)^9$. $2g^{28}$

Note-Taking Tips

Encourage students to carefully justify in their notes the Product of Powers Property and the Power of a Power Property. Rather than just trying to memorize when to add the powers and when to multiply them, students should learn to refer to a simple example they can use to deduce the correct method. Ask students to consider $x^2 \cdot x^3$ and $(x^2)^3$. For the first, they can expand $x^2 \cdot x^3 = (x \cdot x) \cdot (x \cdot x \cdot x)$ to find the result x^5. From this example, students can conclude that $x^n x^m = x^{n+m}$. For the second, $(x^2)^3 = x^2 \cdot x^2 \cdot x^2 = x^6$, so $(x^n)^m = x^{nm}$.

Multiplying Powers with Different Bases

The Product of Powers Property tells how to simplify the product of two powers with the same base. A product with different bases, such as $a^3 \cdot b^4$, usually *cannot* be simplified.

Example 2

Simplify $r^9 \cdot s^5 \cdot r^7 \cdot s^2$.

Solution Use the properties of multiplication to group factors with the same base.

$$r^9 \cdot s^5 \cdot r^7 \cdot s^2 = r^9 \cdot r^7 \cdot s^5 \cdot s^2 \quad \text{Commutative Property of Multiplication}$$
$$= r^{9+7} \cdot s^{5+2} \quad \text{Product of Powers Property}$$
$$= r^{16} \cdot s^7 \quad \text{Simplify.}$$

$r^{16} \cdot s^7$ cannot be simplified further because the bases are different.

Check Perform the multiplication with a CAS.

A CAS indicates that $r^9 \cdot s^5 \cdot r^7 \cdot s^2 = r^{16} \cdot s^7$. It checks.

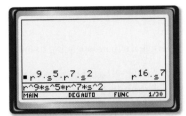

What Happens If We Take a Power of a Power?

When powers of powers are calculated, interesting patterns also emerge.

Example 3

Write $\left(5^2\right)^4$ as a single power.

Solution Think of 5^2 as a number that is raised to the 4th power.

$$\left(5^2\right)^4 = 5^2 \cdot 5^2 \cdot 5^2 \cdot 5^2 \quad \text{Repeated Multiplication Model for Powering.}$$
$$= 5^{2+2+2+2} \quad \text{Product of Powers Property}$$
$$= 5^8 \quad \text{Simplify.}$$

The general pattern is called the *Power of a Power Property*.

> **Power of a Power Property**
>
> For all m and n, and all nonzero b, $\left(b^m\right)^n = b^{mn}$.

Some expressions involve both powers of powers and multiplication.

466   Powers and Roots

Accommodating the Learner

Suggest to struggling students that they group together terms with the same base using the Commutative Property of Multiplication. For instance, in Additional Example 2, students can reorder the problem as $w^4 \cdot w^2 \cdot k^9 \cdot k^3 \cdot k$. Suggest that students group the factors with the same base using parentheses, and that they actually write the exponent 1 for the factor k. These steps yield $(w^4 \cdot w^2) \cdot (k^9 \cdot k^3 \cdot k^1)$, an expression to which it is easier to apply the Product of Powers Property.

Example 4

Simplify $3m(m^4)^2$.

Solution 1 First rewrite $(m^4)^2$ as repeated multiplication.

$$3m(m^4)^2 = 3m^1 \cdot m^4 \cdot m^4 = 3m^9$$

Solution 2 First use the Power of a Power Property with $(m^4)^2$.

$$3m(m^4)^2 = 3m^1 \cdot m^8 = 3m^9$$

Questions

COVERING THE IDEAS

In 1 and 2, write the product as a single power.

1. $18^5 \cdot 18^4$ 18^9

2. $(-7)^3 \cdot (-7)^2$ $(-7)^5$

3. Write $w^4 \cdot w^3$ as a single power and check your answer by substituting 2 for w. w^7; $2^4 \cdot 2^3 = 16 \cdot 8 = 128$; $2^7 = 128$

In 4–6, suppose you fold an 8.5-inch by 11-inch piece of paper as in Example 1. Calculate the number of regions created by folding the paper in the way described.

4. two times, then three more times 2^5

5. three times, then two more times, then two more times 2^7

6. m times, then n more times 2^{m+n}

7. Find the expression that completes the fact triangle at the right. m^8

In 8–10, rewrite the expression as a single power.

8. $(2^3)^4$ 2^{12}

9. $(m^5)^2$ m^{10}

10. $(y^2)^6$ y^{12}

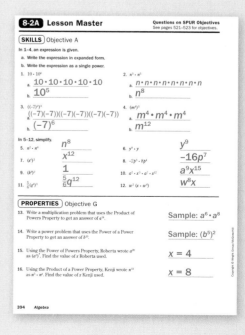

In 11–16, simplify the power.

11. $3a^4 \cdot 5a^2$ $15a^6$

12. $2(k^{10})^7$ $2k^{70}$

13. $d(d^{13})$ d^{14}

14. $m^2 \cdot m^9 \cdot a^0 \cdot m^7 \cdot a^9$ $m^{18}a^9$

15. $a^3(b^3a^5)$ a^8b^3

16. $4k^2(k^3)^5$ $4k^{17}$

APPLYING THE MATHEMATICS

17. A quiz has two parts. The first part has 5 multiple-choice questions. The second part has 3 multiple-choice questions. Each multiple-choice question has 4 choices. How many different sequences of answers are possible on the 8 questions? 65,536 sequences

In 18–20, solve the equation. Show all work.

18. $2^4 \cdot 2^n = 2^{12}$ $n = 8$

19. $(5^6)^x = 5^6$ $x = 1$

20. $(a^7 \cdot a^n)^2 = a^{24}$ $n = 5$

---

3 Assignment

Recommended Assignment

- Questions 1–28
- Question 29 (extra credit)
- Reading Lesson 8-3
- Covering the Ideas 3-3

Notes on the Questions

Questions 4–6 You might ask students if the number of regions is affected by the direction of the fold. (It is not. It is just clearer to picture the problem if the folds are in different directions.)

Question 7 This question emphasizes that the Product of Powers Property is about multiplication. In Lesson 8-3, the Quotient of Powers Property utilizes the same fact triangle.

Question 17 This question is designed to show how the Multiplication Counting Principle can explain $4^5 \cdot 4^3 = 4^8$. See the Notes on the Lesson on page 465.

Question 21 This question is designed to show how the Growth Model of Powering can explain $3^4 \cdot 3^{20} = 3^{24}$. See the Notes on the Lesson on page 465.

Question 29 To find the answers to this question, students could search the Internet for metric prefixes or look in a dictionary. Some dictionaries have a table of the metric prefixes.

8-2

21. Suppose a population P of bacteria triples each day.
    a. Write an expression for the number of bacteria after 4 days. $P \cdot 3^4$
    b. How many days after the 4th day will the bacteria population be $P \cdot 3^{20}$? **16 days**

22. Does the Product of Powers Property work for fractions? Write each expression as a power and a simple fraction.
    a. $\frac{3}{5} \cdot \frac{3}{5} \cdot \frac{3}{5}$ b. $\frac{3}{5} \cdot \frac{3}{5} \cdot \frac{3}{5} \cdot \frac{3}{5}$ c. $\frac{3}{5} \cdot \frac{3}{5} \cdot \frac{3}{5} \cdot \frac{3}{5} \cdot \frac{3}{5} \cdot \frac{3}{5} \cdot \frac{3}{5}$

22a. $\left(\frac{3}{5}\right)^3$; $\frac{27}{125}$

22b. $\left(\frac{3}{5}\right)^4$; $\frac{81}{625}$

22c. $\left(\frac{3}{5}\right)^7$; $\frac{2,187}{78,125}$

REVIEW

23. Abigail is going to buy a new car. She has to choose the body style (sedan, SUV, or convertible), transmission (automatic or standard), and color (white, black, red, blue, or green). **(Lesson 8-1)**
    a. How many different ways can Abigail make her choices? **30 ways**
    b. If another color choice of silver is given to her, how many more choices does she have? **6 more choices**

24. If $f(x) = 3x + 2$ and $g(x) = 3x^2 - 2$, find each value. **(Lesson 7-6)**
    a. $f(3)$ **11**   b. $g(-2)$ **10**   c. $f(5) - g(5)$ **−56**   d. $g(-4) + f(-4)$ **36**

25. A band sold 1,252 tickets for a concert that were priced at $35. The band decided to lower the ticket price to their next concert to $30 in hopes of attracting a larger audience. After lowering the price, 1,510 tickets were sold. **(Lessons 6-6, 3-4)**
    a. Write a linear equation that relates the price of the ticket x and the number of tickets sold y. $y = -51.6x + 3,058$
    b. Use your answer to Part a to predict the number of tickets that will be sold if the price is lowered to $20. **2,026 tickets**

26. Consider the line $y = 4x - 5$. Find **(Lessons 6-4, 6-2)**
    a. its slope. **4**   b. its y-intercept. **−5**   c. its x-intercept. **1.25**

27. Write 0.00324 in scientific notation. **(Previous Course)** 3.24×10^{-3}

28. Write these numbers as decimals. **(Previous Course)**
    a. $9.8 \cdot 10^0$ **9.8**   b. $9.8 \cdot 10^{-1}$ **0.98**
    c. $9.8 \cdot 10^{-2}$ **0.098**   d. $9.8 \cdot 10^{-3}$ **0.0098**

In 2004, there were 4,236,736 passenger cars produced in the United States.

Source: Automotive News Data Center

EXPLORATION

29. There are prefixes in the metric system for some of the powers of 10. For example, the prefix for 10^3 is kilo-, as in kilogram, kilometer, and kilobyte. Give the metric prefix for each power.
    a. 10^6 **mega** b. 10^9 **giga** c. 10^{12} **tera** d. 10^{15} **peta** e. 10^{18} **exa**

Lesson 8-3 Quotients of Powers

> **BIG IDEA** Because of the relationship between multiplication and division, quotients of powers can be themselves written as powers.

As you know, $\frac{24}{3} = 8$ because $8 \cdot 3 = 24$. Similarly, $\frac{24}{3} = \frac{8 \cdot \cancel{3}^1}{1 \cancel{3}} = 8$. Both of these methods can be helpful in understanding quotients of powers.

For example, suppose $\frac{x^{10}}{x^2} = x^?$. By rewriting this statement to read $x^? \cdot x^2 = x^{10}$, we can apply the Product of Powers Property, $x^{?+2} = x^{10}$. You can see that the unknown exponent is 8 because $8 + 2 = 10$. So $\frac{x^{10}}{x^2} = x^8$. Another way of finding the unknown exponent in $\frac{x^{10}}{x^2} = x^?$ is to write both the numerator and denominator in expanded form and simplify the fraction.

$$\frac{x^{10}}{x^2} = \frac{\cancel{1x} \cdot \cancel{1x} \cdot x \cdot x \cdot x \cdot x \cdot x \cdot x \cdot x \cdot x}{1 \cancel{x} \cdot \cancel{x}_1}$$
$$= x \cdot x \cdot x \cdot x \cdot x \cdot x \cdot x \cdot x$$
$$= x^8$$

Activity

1. Simplify each expression.
   a. $\frac{a^7}{a^4}$ a^3
   b. $\frac{m^{14}}{m^5}$ m^9
   c. $\frac{y^{12}}{y}$ y^{11}
   d. $\frac{n^{13}}{n^{13}}$ 1

2. When dividing powers of the same base, how is the exponent of the answer related to the exponents of the original division?

The general pattern established in the Activity is the *Quotient of Powers Property*.

Quotient of Powers Property

For all m and n, and all nonzero b, $\frac{b^m}{b^n} = b^{m-n}$.

 QY

Mental Math

True or false?
a. $x^{100} + x^{101} = x^{201}$ false
b. $x^{100} \cdot x^{101} = x^{201}$ true
c. $x^{100} + x^{101} = 2x^{101}$ false
d. $x^{100} + x^{100} = 2x^{100}$ true

Activity
2. The answer's exponent is the difference of the numerator's exponent and the denominator's exponent.

▶ **QY**

Simplify $\frac{z^{50}}{z^{10}}$.

Background

In this lesson, quotients of powers of the same number are simplified. The approach utilizes the Repeated Multiplication Model for Powering and related facts.

The Quotient of Powers Property can be *proved* from the Product of Powers Property. Here is a proof. The Product of Powers Property indicates that $b^x \cdot b^y = b^{x+y}$ for all x and y, and for all nonzero b. So let $x = n$ and $y = m - n$. Then $x + y = m$. So, substituting for x, y, and $x + y$,

$b^n \cdot b^{m-n} = b^m$. Now, dividing both sides of the equation by b^n, $\frac{b^m}{b^n} = b^{m-n}$.

Some students will do the problems in this lesson by rewriting them as repeated multiplication. Rewriting can be used to explain why the properties hold true. But it does not work if the exponents are large, and it can be time consuming, so try to wean those students away from this technique.

GOAL

Develop and apply the Quotient of Powers Property: If $b \neq 0$, for all m and n, $\frac{b^m}{b^n} = b^{m-n}$.

SPUR Objectives

A Simplify products, quotients, and powers of powers.

G Identify properties of powers that justify a simplification. (See page 456B for the list of properties.)

Materials/Resources

· Lesson Master 8-3A or 8-3B
· Resource Master 117
· Scientific or graphing calculator
· Quiz 1

HOMEWORK

Suggestions for Assignment
• Questions 1–29
• Question 30 (extra credit)
• Reading Lesson 8-4
• Covering the Ideas 8-4

Local Standards

1 Warm-Up

Write this list of integer powers of 3 on the board: $\ldots, \frac{1}{2,187}, \frac{1}{729}, \frac{1}{243}, \frac{1}{81}, \frac{1}{27}, \frac{1}{9}, \frac{1}{3}$, 1, 3, 9, 27, 81, 243, 729, 2,187, 6,561, $\ldots$.

1. Write the product $\frac{1}{243} \cdot 6,561 = 27$ as a product of powers of 3.
   $3^{-5} \cdot 3^8 = 3^3$

2. Now write the quotient $\frac{2,187}{9} = 243$ as a quotient of powers of 3.
   $\frac{3^7}{3^2} = 3^5$

These results verify the Product of Powers Property and the Quotient of Powers Property.

Notes on the Lesson

There is only one new idea in this lesson, but it is applied in a variety of ways: to division of powers of the same real number (Activity), to division of powers of numbers in scientific notation (Example 1), and to division of monomials (Example 2).

Notes on the Activity

Students may ask what happens when the greater power is in the denominator. Suggest that they write the numerator and denominator in expanded form and simplify the fraction. Tell students that in this case, it is acceptable to give the answer as a fraction.

Additional Example

Example 1 The area of China is 9,596,960 square kilometers. In July 2006, China's population was estimated at 1,313,973,713 people. What is the population density of China in people per square kilometer? about 137 people/km^2

Fact triangles are another way of representing the Quotient of Powers Property.

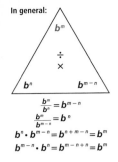

A specific case:

$$\frac{m^8}{m^3} = m^5$$
$$\frac{m^8}{m^5} = m^3$$
$$m^3 \cdot m^5 = m^8$$
$$m^5 \cdot m^3 = m^8$$

In general:

$$\frac{b^m}{b^n} = b^{m-n}$$
$$\frac{b^m}{b^{m-n}} = b^n$$
$$b^n \cdot b^{m-n} = b^{n+m-n} = b^m$$
$$b^{m-n} \cdot b^n = b^{m-n+n} = b^m$$

The Zero Power

In Question 1d of the Activity, you should have seen that $\frac{n^{13}}{n^{13}} = 1$. More generally, consider the fraction $\frac{b^m}{b^m}$. By the Quotient of Powers Property, $\frac{b^m}{b^m} = b^{m-m} = b^0$. But you also know that any nonzero number divided by itself is 1. So $1 = \frac{b^m}{b^m} = b^0$. This is another way of showing why $b^0 = 1$.

An Application of the Quotient of Powers Property

The Quotient of Powers Property is useful in dividing numbers written in scientific notation.

Example 1

The Gross Domestic Product (GDP) of a country is the total value of all the goods and services produced in the country. When the GDP is divided by the population of the country, the result is the GDP per person, often called the *GDP per capita*. In 2006, Denmark had a population of about 5.5 million and a GDP of $243.4 billion. What is Denmark's GDP per capita?

Solution Since GDP per capita is a rate unit, the answer is found by division.

$$\frac{\$243,400,000,000}{5.5 \text{ million people}} = \frac{2.434 \times 10^{11}}{5.5 \times 10^6} \qquad \text{Write in scientific notation.}$$

$$= \frac{2.434}{5.5} \cdot \frac{10^{11}}{10^6} \qquad \text{Multiplying Fractions Property}$$

$$\approx 0.44 \cdot 10^5 \qquad \text{Quotient of Powers Property}$$

$$\approx \$44,000/\text{person} \qquad \text{Write in base 10.}$$

Approximately 5.5 million people live in Denmark, making it one of the most densely populated nations in Northern Europe.

Source: Danish Tourist Board

470 Powers and Roots

Accommodating the Learner ⬇

To help students remember which property of powers uses addition, which uses multiplication, and which uses subtraction, spend some time discussing with students what they are doing when they simplify each expression by first writing the expanded forms of the powers. Also, help students connect *addition* with writing terms out one by one and counting them, *subtraction* with the concept of canceling, and *multiplication* with repeated addition.

Check Change the numbers to decimal notation and simplify the fraction.

$$\frac{243,400,000,000}{5,500,000} = \frac{2,434,000}{55} \approx 44,000$$

Dividing Powers with Different Bases

To use the Quotient of Powers Property, the bases must be the same. For example, $\frac{a^5}{b^2}$ cannot be simplified further. To divide two algebraic expressions that involve different bases, group powers of the same base together and use the Quotient of Powers Property to simplify each fraction.

Example 2

Simplify $\frac{30a^3n^6}{5a^2n}$.

Solution 1

$$\frac{30a^3n^6}{5a^2n} = \frac{30}{5} \cdot \frac{a^3}{a^2} \cdot \frac{n^6}{n} \qquad \text{Multiplying Fractions Property}$$

$$= \frac{30}{5} \cdot a^{3-2} \cdot n^{6-1} \qquad \text{Quotient of Powers Property}$$

$$= 6 \cdot a^1 \cdot n^5 = 6an^5 \qquad \text{Arithmetic}$$

Solution 2

$$\frac{30a^3n^6}{5a^2n} = \frac{30 \cdot a \cdot a \cdot a \cdot n \cdot n \cdot n \cdot n \cdot n \cdot n}{5 \cdot a \cdot a \cdot n} \qquad \begin{array}{l}\text{Repeated Multiplication}\\\text{Property of Powers}\end{array}$$

$$= \frac{6 \cdot a \cdot n \cdot n \cdot n \cdot n \cdot n}{1} \qquad \text{Equal Fractions Property}$$

$$= 6an^5 \qquad \text{Arithmetic}$$

Check Use a CAS to check your answer, as shown below.

Questions

COVERING THE IDEAS

In 1–3, write the quotient as a single power.

1. $\frac{2^7}{2^4}$ 2^3

2. $\frac{8^5}{8^m}$ 8^{5-m}

3. $\frac{3^m}{3^n}$ 3^{m-n}

Additional Example

Example 2 Simplify $\frac{40b^{10}c^3}{8bc^2}$. $5b^9c$

Note-Taking Tips

As students encounter more properties of exponents, suggest that they keep a page in their notebook where they list each of the properties and show an example of each one. Additionally, students should keep examples of problems combining the different properties on that page, with an explanation in their own words of when to use each property.

Accommodating the Learner ⬆

Ask students to solve more complicated problems, including some that require the use of all three properties of powers that they have learned in Lessons 8-2 and 8-3. For example, ask students to simplify the expression $\frac{32x^3(y^2)^4 x^4}{8x^2y}$. $4x^5y^7$ Extend their learning even farther by including negative exponents in the denominator. Though they have not yet learned the meaning of negative exponents, they can still apply the Quotient of Powers Property for a preview of Lesson 8-4.

8-3

3 Assignment

Recommended Assignment

- Questions 1–29
- Question 30 (extra credit)
- Reading Lesson 8-4
- Covering the Ideas 8-4

Notes on the Questions

Question 1 You might ask students to switch the numerator and denominator in the fraction and use the Quotient of Powers Property to write $\frac{2^4}{2^7}$ as a single power (2^{-3}). This will lead you into Lesson 8-4 and illustrate that x^m and x^{-m} are reciprocals.

Question 5 You might generalize this question to ask: If $m = n$, then $\frac{b^m}{b^n} = ?$. Have students note that the answer given by the Quotient of Powers Property is consistent with the answer given by the Zero Exponent Property. Question 13 is related to the same idea.

Question 11 You might want to say that these are "unlike powers." In Lesson 8-4 students will learn that this fraction can be rewritten as a^3b^{-4}, but most students would not think of that as a simpler form.

Question 30 The results of these calculations surprise many students.

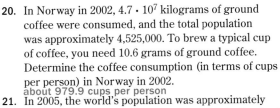

In 4–9, use the Quotient of Powers Property to simplify the fraction.

4. $\frac{x^{12}}{x^2}$ x^{10}

5. $\frac{a^{20}}{a^{20}}$ 1

6. $\frac{6.5 \times 10^{21}}{3.1 \times 10^{19}}$ $\frac{650}{3.1}$

7. $\frac{12a^2b^{12}}{2ab^7}$ $6ab^5$

8. $\frac{2a^5b^9}{8a^3b}$ $\frac{a^2b^8}{4}$

9. $\frac{24a^{10}b^5}{6a^4b^5}$ $4a^6$

10. In 2006, the African country of Burundi had a population of about 8.1 million and a GDP of about \$5.7 billion. What is Burundi's GDP per capita? \$703.70

11. Why can't $\frac{a^3}{b^4}$ be simplified? The bases differ.

12. If $\frac{b^n}{b^m} = 1$, how must m and n be related? $m = n$

APPLYING THE MATHEMATICS

In 13–15, write the quotient as a single power.

13. $\frac{4^3}{2^6}$ 1

14. $\frac{16 \cdot 2^m}{2^6}$ 2^{m-2}

15. $\frac{4^3}{8 \cdot 2^6}$ 2^{-3}

In 16–19, rewrite the expression so that it has no fraction.

16. $\frac{(7m)^5}{(7m)^3}$ $(7m)^2$

17. $\frac{(7+3m)^7}{(7+3m)^6}$

18. $\frac{x^{5a-10}}{x^{3-3a}}$

19. $\frac{2a^6 + 6a^6}{2a^5}$

17. $7 + 3m$

18. x^{8a-13}

19. $4a$

20. In Norway in 2002, $4.7 \cdot 10^7$ kilograms of ground coffee were consumed, and the total population was approximately 4,525,000. To brew a typical cup of coffee, you need 10.6 grams of ground coffee. Determine the coffee consumption (in terms of cups per person) in Norway in 2002. about 979.9 cups per person

21. In 2005, the world's population was approximately $6.446 \cdot 10^9$ people. In the same year, global oil output was approximately $8.0 \cdot 10^7$ million barrels per day. A barrel is equivalent to 35 gallons of oil.

   a. How many barrels of oil was this per person per day?

   b. At this rate, how many gallons of oil were consumed per person during 2005? about 158,547,936 gallons

22. Write an algebraic fraction that can be simplified to $12a^2b$ using the Quotient of Powers Property. Answers vary. Sample answer: $\frac{24a^{35}b^2}{2a^{33}b}$

REVIEW

In 23–26, simplify the expression. (Lesson 8-2)

23. $3x \cdot x^2$ $3x^3$

24. $n \cdot n^2 \cdot n^3$ n^6

25. $2h^3 \cdot 6h^4 + 3h \cdot 4h^6$ $24h^7$

26. $a^x \cdot a^y \cdot a^z$ a^{x+y+z}

The number of cups of coffee consumed per capita per year in the Nordic countries of Norway, Sweden, Denmark, and Finland is among the highest in the world.

Source: nationmaster.com

21a. about 12,410.8 barrels of oil per person per day

8-3A Lesson Master

Questions on SPUR Objectives
See pages 521–523 for objectives.

SKILLS Objective A

In 1 and 2, a fraction is given.

2a. $\frac{21 \cdot a \cdot a \cdot a \cdot a \cdot a \cdot a \cdot b \cdot b \cdot b}{3 \cdot a \cdot a \cdot a \cdot a \cdot b}$

a. Write the numerator and denominator in expanded form.

b. Simplify the fraction.

1. a. $\frac{m \cdot m \cdot m \cdot m \cdot m \cdot m \cdot m}{m \cdot m \cdot m \cdot m}$

b. m^3

2. a.

b. $7a^2b^2$

In 3–10, simplify.

3. $(-9)^{m-n}$

4. $3.01 \cdot 10^4$ or 30,100

5. a^5

6. n^{13}

7. $\frac{r^4}{3}$ $7ab^2$

8. -32

9. $\frac{7}{2}$

10. $14m^4$

PROPERTIES Objective G

11. Write an algebraic fraction to which the Quotient of Powers Property can be applied to simplify to $5a^4$. Answers vary. Sample: $\frac{20n^3}{4n}$

12. Explain how to use the Quotient of Powers Property to find the value of x in $\frac{a^x}{a^7} = m^5$. Think of a number that if 7 is taken away from it, the difference is 5. The number is 12.

13. Marco tried to simplify $\frac{n^8}{n^2}$ and he got n^4. Explain the error he made in simplifying the fraction. Marco divided the exponents instead of subtracting them. The correct answer is n^6.

Algebra 397

27. Suppose each question on a 5-question, multiple-choice quiz has four choices. (**Lesson 8-1**)

 a. Give the probability of guessing all the correct answers as the reciprocal of a power. $\frac{1}{4^5}$

 b. Give the probability of guessing all wrong answers. $\frac{243}{1,024}$

28. Distances after various times when traveling at 65 miles per hour are shown on the spreadsheet below. (**Lesson 6-1**)

◇	A	B
1	Time (hours)	Distance (miles)
2	1.0	65 ?
3	1.5	97.5
4	2	130
5	2.5	162.5
6	3	195 ?
7	3.5	227.5 ?

 a. Complete the spreadsheet.

 b. Name two ways to get the value in cell B7.

29. Calculate the total cost in your head. (**Lesson 2-2**)

 a. 8 cans of tuna fish at $2.99 per can **$23.92**

 b. 5 tickets to a movie at $10.50 per ticket **$52.50**

EXPLORATION

30. The average 14 year old has a volume of about 3 cubic feet.

 a. Consider all the students in your school. Would their total volume be more or less than the volume of one classroom? Assume the classroom is 10 feet high, 30 feet long, and 30 feet wide.

 b. Assume the population of the world to be 6.4 billion people and the average volume of a person to be 4 cubic feet. Is the volume of all the people more or less than 1 cubic mile? How much more or less? (There are $5{,}280^3$ cubic feet in a cubic mile.) **less, by 121,600,000,000 ft^3**

28b. Answers vary.
Sample answer:
$3.5 \cdot 65$ and
$162.5 + 65$

30a. Answers vary.
Sample answer:
Less, if the
school's size is
no greater than
3,000 students.

QY ANSWER

z^{40}

4   Wrap-Up

Ongoing Assessment

Ask students to simplify the expression $\frac{10x^2(x^3)^2}{5x^4}$ by first applying the Product of Powers and Power of a Power Properties, and then finishing the simplification with the Quotient of Powers Property. Students should show all their steps and justify each one. $2x^4$

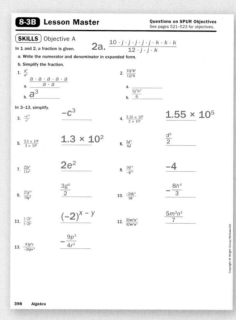

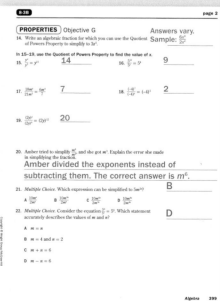

Lesson 8-4

Lesson 8-4 — Negative Exponents

> ▶ **BIG IDEA** The numbers x^{-n} and x^n are reciprocals.

GOAL

Develop the meaning of powers with negative exponents by extending the properties of powers that were presented in Lesson 8-2.

SPUR Objectives

A Simplify products, quotients, and powers of powers.

B Evaluate negative integer powers of real numbers.

G Identify properties of powers that justify a simplification. (See page 456B for the list of properties.)

Materials/Resources

· Lesson Master 8-4A or 8-4B
· Resource Masters 2, 118, and 119
· Scientific or graphing calculator
· Computer Algebra System (CAS)

HOMEWORK

Suggestions for Assignment

• Questions 1–27
• Question 28 (extra credit)
• Reading Lesson 8-5
• Covering the Ideas 8-5

Local Standards

1 Warm-Up

1. Use a calculator to evaluate 9^n and 9^{-n} when $n = 2$. 81; 0.012345679...
2. Multiply the two values in Question 1. What is the product? 1
3. Evaluate 9^n and 9^{-n} for another value of n of your own choosing, and again multiply the two values. Is your product the same as or different than the product in Question 2? the same
4. Pick a base other than 9 and repeat Questions 1–3. Values vary; Products are 1.
5. Make a statement about the relationship between b^n and b^{-n}. The product of b^n and b^{-n} is always 1.

What Is the Value of a Power with a Negative Exponent?

You have used base 10 with a negative exponent to represent small numbers in scientific notation. For example, $10^{-1} = 0.1 = \frac{1}{10^1}$, $10^{-2} = 0.01 = \frac{1}{10^2}$, $10^{-3} = 0.001 = \frac{1}{10^3}$, and so on.

Now we consider other powers with negative exponents. That is, we want to know the meaning of b^n when n is negative. Consider this pattern of the powers of 2.

$$2^4 = 16$$
$$2^3 = 8$$
$$2^2 = 4$$
$$2^1 = 2$$
$$2^0 = 1$$

Each exponent is one less than the one above it. The value of each power is half that of the number above. Continuing the pattern suggests that the following are true.

$$2^{-1} = \frac{1}{2}$$
$$2^{-2} = \frac{1}{4} = \frac{1}{2^2}$$
$$2^{-3} = \frac{1}{8} = \frac{1}{2^3}$$
$$2^{-4} = \frac{1}{16} = \frac{1}{2^4}$$

A general description of the pattern is simple: $2^{-n} = \frac{1}{2^n}$. That is, 2^{-n} is the reciprocal of 2^n. We call the general property the *Negative Exponent Property*.

Negative Exponent Property

For any nonzero b and all n, $b^{-n} = \frac{1}{b^n}$, the reciprocal of b^n.

Give the area of

a. a square with side $\frac{s}{2}$. $\frac{s^2}{4}$

b. a circle with radius $3r$. $9\pi r^2$

c. a rectangle with $\frac{3}{4}x$ and $\frac{8}{3}y$ dimensions. $2xy$

Background

In many books, the Negative Exponent Property, $b^{-n} = \frac{1}{b^n}$, is a definition. We are able to deduce it (in the text after Example 1) because we have assumed the Product of Powers Property for all exponents. The first explanation in the lesson is an inductive argument, because students at this level are more often convinced by patterns than by deduction.

The Growth Model used in Example 3 explains that negative powers of a positive number should be positive because going back in time does not mean that negative values are introduced. This is confirmed by evaluating negative powers. The Growth Model can also confirm the Negative Exponent Property: Suppose quantity Q has been growing with a growth factor g for n time periods. Then n years ago, there was $Q \cdot g^{-n}$. In the n years, it grew by g^n, so there is now $(Q \cdot g^{-n}) \cdot g^n$. But there is now Q. So $Q = (Q \cdot g^{-n}) \cdot g^n$. Divide both sides by Q, and $1 = g^{-n} \cdot g^n$.

(continued on next page)

Notice that even though the exponent in 2^{-4} on the previous page is negative, the number 2^{-4} is still positive. All negative integer powers of positive numbers are positive.

 QY

▶ **QY**

Write 5^{-4} as a simple fraction without a negative exponent.

Example 1

Rewrite $a^7 \cdot b^{-4}$ without negative exponents.

Solution

$a^7 \cdot b^{-4} = a^7 \cdot \dfrac{1}{b^4}$ Substitute $\dfrac{1}{b^4}$ for b^{-4}.

$\phantom{a^7 \cdot b^{-4}} = \dfrac{a^7}{b^4}$

Because the Product of Powers Property applies to all exponents, it applies to negative exponents. Suppose you multiply b^n by b^{-n}.

$b^n \cdot b^{-n} = b^{n \, + \, -n}$ Product of Powers Property

$\phantom{b^n \cdot b^{-n}} = b^0$ Property of Opposites

$\phantom{b^n \cdot b^{-n}} = 1$ Zero Exponent Property

To multiply b^n by b^{-n}, you can also use the Negative Exponent Property.

$b^n \cdot b^{-n} = b^n \cdot \dfrac{1}{b^n}$ Negative Exponent Property

$\phantom{b^n \cdot b^{-n}} = 1$ Definition of reciprocal

In this way, the Product of Powers Property verifies that b^{-n} must be the reciprocal of b^n. In particular, $b^{-1} = \dfrac{1}{b}$. That is, the –1 power (read "negative one" or "negative first" power) of a number is its reciprocal.

Suppose the base b is a fraction, $b = \dfrac{x}{y}$. Then the reciprocal of b is $\dfrac{y}{x}$. Consequently, this gives us a different form of the Negative Exponent Property that is more convenient when the base is a fraction. The simplest way to find the reciprocal of a fraction $\dfrac{a}{b}$ is to invert it, producing $\dfrac{b}{a}$.

Negative Exponent Property for Fractions

For any nonzero x and y and all n, $\left(\dfrac{x}{y}\right)^{-n} = \left(\dfrac{y}{x}\right)^{n}$.

It is also possible to use permutations and probability as examples of negative exponents. Consider the probability that you randomly pick the same 3-letter acronym as someone else. Because there are 26^3 acronyms, the probability that yours is the same as someone else's is 26^{-3}.

We speak of negative exponents rather than negative powers. In a power such as 7^{-8}, the exponent value is negative, but the value of the power is positive.

Accommodating the Learner ⬇

Students often struggle to write a unit fraction such as $\dfrac{1}{32}$ as a power of an integer. This is because they do not recognize common integer powers. Encourage students to learn the integer powers of 2 up to 2^5, of 3 up to 3^4, of 4 up to 4^3, and the perfect squares for all numbers up to 15.

2   Teaching

Notes on the Lesson

Example 1 This example shows a straightforward use of the Negative Exponent Property. Emphasize that any example with variables can be checked by substitution. For example, let $a = 2$ and $b = 10$. Then the question is whether or not the statement

$2^7 \cdot 10^{-4} = \dfrac{2^7}{10^4}$ is true. This can be

verified without a calculator if students know the powers of 10.

Additional Example

Example 1 Rewrite $c^{-8}d^2$ without negative exponents. $\dfrac{d^2}{c^8}$

8-4

Notes on the Lesson

Example 2 In Lesson 8-9, these kinds of expressions are evaluated using the Power of a Power Property. For example, the expression in Part a can be rewritten as $\left(\left(\frac{5}{4}\right)^2\right)^{-1}$ or as $\left(\left(\frac{5}{4}\right)^{-1}\right)^2$. These expressions can be evaluated from the inside out.

Example 3 Notice how negative exponents help in what seems to be a very difficult problem.

Additional Examples

Example 2 Write each expression without negative exponents.

a. $\left(\frac{3}{2}\right)^{-4}\left(\frac{2}{3}\right)^4$

b. $\left(\frac{1}{k^4}\right)^{-5} k^{20}$

Example 3 Five years ago, Molly bought a 60-month certificate of deposit (CD) that had an annual yield of 5%. If the CD is now worth $1,914.42, what was the amount initially invested? Molly invested $1,500.

GUIDED

Example 2

Write each expression without negative exponents.

a. $\left(\frac{5}{4}\right)^{-2}$

b. $\left(\frac{1}{m^2}\right)^{-3}$

Solution

a. Use the Negative Exponent Property for Fractions.

$$\left(\frac{5}{4}\right)^{-2} = \left(\underline{?}\right)\frac{4}{5}$$

$$= \underline{?}\ \frac{16}{25}$$

b. Take the reciprocal to the opposite power.

$$\left(\frac{1}{m^2}\right)^{-3} = \left(\frac{?}{1}\right)^3 m^2$$

$$= (\underline{?})^3\ m^2$$

$$= \underline{?}\ m^6$$

Recall the compound interest formula $A = P(1 + r)^t$. In this formula, negative exponents stand for unit periods going back in time.

Example 3

Ten years ago, Den put money into a college savings account at an annual yield of 6%. If the money is now worth $9,491.49, what was the amount initially invested?

Solution

Here $P = 9,491.49$, $r = 0.06$, and $t = -10$ (for 10 years ago).

So, $A = 9,491.49(1.06)^{-10} \approx 5,300$.

So, Den originally started with approximately $5,300.

Check Use the Compound Interest Formula. If Den invested $5,300, he would have $5,300(1.06)^{10}$, which equals $9,491.49. It checks.

Quotient of Powers and Negative Exponents

The last lesson involved fractions in which two powers of the same base are divided. When the denominator contains the greater power, negative exponents can be used to simplify the expression. For example, $\frac{x^5}{x^9} = x^{5-9} = x^{-4}$.

Accommodating the Learner ⬆

Ask students to explore how many different methods they can find to simplify $\left(\frac{x^3 y^{-2}\, zx}{xz^{-1}}\right)^{-1}$. Which methods do they prefer and why?

$\frac{y^2}{x^3 y^2}$

This can be verified using repeated multiplication.

$$\frac{x^5}{x^9} = \frac{\overset{1}{\cancel{x}}\cdot\overset{1}{\cancel{x}}\cdot\overset{1}{\cancel{x}}\cdot\overset{1}{\cancel{x}}\cdot\overset{1}{\cancel{x}}}{\underset{1}{\cancel{x}}\cdot\underset{1}{\cancel{x}}\cdot\underset{1}{\cancel{x}}\cdot\underset{1}{\cancel{x}}\cdot\underset{1}{\cancel{x}}\cdot x\cdot x\cdot x\cdot x} = \frac{1}{x^4}$$

In this way, you can see again that $b^{-n} = \frac{1}{b^n}$.

GUIDED

Example 4

Simplify $\frac{5a^4b^7c^2}{15a^{11}b^5c^3}$. Write the answer without negative exponents.

Solution

$$\frac{5a^4b^7c^2}{15a^{11}b^5c^3} = \frac{5}{15}\cdot\frac{a^4}{a^{11}}\cdot\frac{b^7}{b^5}\cdot\frac{c^2}{c^3}$$ Group factors with the same base together.

$$= \frac{1}{3}\cdot a^{\underset{-7}{?}}\cdot b^{\overset{2}{?}}\cdot c^{\underset{-1}{?}}$$ Quotient of Powers Property

$$= \frac{1}{3}\cdot\frac{1}{a^{?}}\cdot\frac{b^{?}}{1}\cdot\frac{1}{c^{?}} \quad 7;\ 1$$ Negative Exponent Property

$$= \underline{\ ?\ }\ \frac{b^2}{3a^7c}$$ Multiply the fractions.

Applying the Power of a Power Property with Negative Exponents

Consider $(x^3)^{-2}$, a power of a power. Wanda wondered if the Power of a Power Property would apply with negative exponents. She entered the expression into a CAS and the screen below appeared.

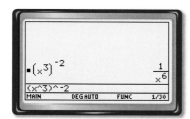

This is the answer that would result from applying the Power of a Power Property.

$$(x^3)^{-2} = x^{3\cdot-2} = x^{-6}$$

Then you can rewrite the power using the Negative Exponent Property.

$$x^{-6} = \frac{1}{x^6}$$

All the properties of powers you have learned can be used with negative exponents. They can translate an expression with a negative exponent into one with only positive exponents.

Negative Exponents   **477**

Notes on the Lesson

Examples 4 and 5 These are important examples, for they show the consistency of the properties of powers. Students should understand that the Quotient of Powers and Power of a Power Properties hold whether the result is a positive or a negative exponent.

As a further example of the consistency of mathematics, you might have students graph $f(x) = 2^x$ for $-5 \le x \le 5$. Verify that $f(-5)$ is the reciprocal of $f(5)$, $f(-4)$ is the reciprocal of $f(4)$, and so on.

Additional Examples

Example 4 Simplify $\frac{3x^2yz^6}{12x^4y^3z^4}$.

Write the answers without negative exponents.

$$\frac{3x^2yz^6}{12x^4y^3z^4} = \frac{3}{12}\cdot\frac{x^2}{x^4}\cdot\frac{y}{y^3}\cdot\frac{z^6}{z^4}$$

$$= \frac{1}{4}\cdot x^{\underline{?}}\cdot y^{\underline{?}}\cdot z^{\underline{?}} \quad -2;\ -2;\ 2$$

$$= \frac{1}{4}\cdot\frac{1}{x^{\underline{?}}}\cdot\frac{1}{y^{\underline{?}}}\cdot\frac{z^{\underline{?}}}{1} \quad 2;\ 2;\ 2$$

$$= \underline{\ ?\ }\ \frac{z^2}{4x^2y^2}$$

Example 5 Simplify $(k^{-3})^4$. Write without negative exponents. $\frac{1}{k^{12}}$

Extension

Ask students to rewrite the expression $\left(\frac{x}{y^{-1}}\right)^{-1}$ without negative exponents. Next, have them rewrite $\left(\left(\frac{x}{y^{-1}}\right)^{-1}\right)^{-1}$ without negative exponents. Then have them rewrite $\left(\left(\left(\frac{x}{y^{-1}}\right)^{-1}\right)^{-1}\right)^{-1}$ without negative exponents. Have them generalize their answers for $\left(\dots\left(\left(\left(\frac{x}{y^{-1}}\right)^{-1}\right)^{-1}\right)^{-1}\dots\right)^{-1}$.

$\frac{1}{xy}$; xy; $\frac{1}{xy}$; If $\frac{x}{y^{-1}}$ is raised to the negative one power an odd number of times, the result is $\frac{1}{xy}$. If $\frac{x}{y^{-1}}$ is raised to the negative one power an even number of times, the result is xy.

8-4

3 Assignment

Recommended Assignment

- Questions 1–27
- Question 28 (extra credit)
- Reading Lesson 8-5
- Covering the Ideas 8-5

Notes on the Questions

Questions 6 and 7 You might extend the idea here and ask students to give $\frac{9}{16}$ and $\frac{625}{81}$ as negative powers of simple fractions.

Example 5

Simplify $(y^{-4})^2$. Write without negative exponents.

Solution

$$(y^{-4})^2 = y^{-8} \qquad \text{Power of a Power Property}$$

$$= \frac{1}{y^8} \qquad \text{Negative Exponent Property}$$

Questions

COVERING THE IDEAS

1. **Fill in the Blanks** Complete the last four equations in the pattern below. Then write the next equation in the pattern. $3^{-5} = \frac{1}{243}$

$$3^4 = 81$$
$$3^3 = 27$$
$$3^2 = 9$$
$$3^1 = 3$$
$$3^0 = 1$$
$$3^{-1} = \underline{\ ?\ } \quad \frac{1}{3}$$
$$3^{-2} = \underline{\ ?\ } \quad \frac{1}{9}$$
$$3^{-3} = \underline{\ ?\ } \quad \frac{1}{27}$$
$$3^{-4} = \underline{\ ?\ } \quad \frac{1}{81}$$

In 2–5, write as a simple fraction.

2. $7^{-2}\ \frac{1}{49}$ 　　3. $5^{-3}\ \frac{1}{125}$ 　　4. $\left(\frac{2}{3}\right)^{-1}\ \frac{3}{2}$ 　　5. $(y^6)^{-4}\ \frac{1}{y^{24}}$

In 6–9, write as a negative power of an integer.

6. $\frac{1}{36}\ 6^{-2}$ 　　7. $\frac{1}{81}\ 3^{-4}$ 　　8. $0.1\ 10^{-1}$ 　　9. $0.0001\ 10^{-4}$

10. Eight years ago, Abuna put money into a college savings account at an annual yield of 5%. If there is now \$7,250 in the account, what amount was initially invested? Round your answer to the nearest penny. **\$4,907.09**

11. Rewrite each expression without negative exponents.
   a. $w^{-1}\ \frac{1}{w}$ 　　b. $w^{-1}x^{-2}\ \frac{1}{wx^2}$ 　　c. $w^{-1}y^3\ \frac{y^3}{w}$ 　　d. $5w^{-1}x^{-2}y^3\ \frac{5y^3}{wx^2}$

In 12–14, write each expression without negative exponents.

12. $9^2 \cdot 9^{-2}\ 1$ 　　13. $n^a \cdot n^{-a}\ 1$ 　　14. $(m^{-5})^3\ \frac{1}{m^{15}}$

15. Simplify $\frac{32a^8bc^3}{8a^6b^4c}$. Write without negative exponents.
   $\frac{4a^2c^2}{b^3}$

478　　Powers and Roots

---

16. **a.** Graph $y = 2^x$ when the domain is $\{-4, -3, -2, -1, 0, 1, 2, 3, 4\}$.

b. Describe what happens to the graph as x decreases.
   It approaches 0.

17. Graph $y = 10^x$ as on page 457. Describe what happens as x goes from 0 to –12. The values of y seem to get extremely close to 0.

16a.

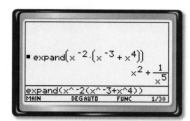

APPLYING THE MATHEMATICS

18. If the reciprocal of $a^{-12}b^5$ is $a^n b^m$, find m and n. $n = 12; m = -5$

19. Use properties of algebra to justify the answer shown on the CAS screen below.

```
▪ expand(x^-2·(x^-3 + x^4))
                          x² + 1/x⁵
expand(x^-2(x^-3+x^4))
MAIN    DEG AUTO    FUNC    1/30
```

19. $x^{-2}(x^{-3} + x^4) =$
$x^{-2}(x^{-3}) + x^{-2}(x^4)$
$= x^{(-2+-3)} +$
$x^{(-2+4)} = x^{-5} +$
$x^2 = x^2 + \frac{1}{x^5}$

20. $a = -9; 7^{-9} \cdot 7^3 =$
$7^{-9+3} = 7^{-6}$

21. $m = -1; 5^{-1} \cdot$
$\frac{1}{25} = 5^{-1} \cdot$
$5^{-2} = 5^{-3}$

In 20 and 21, solve and check each equation.

20. $7^a \cdot 7^3 = 7^{-6}$

21. $5^m \cdot \frac{1}{25} = 5^{-3}$

22. Suppose you draw a square with area 25 square units and connect the midpoints of each side to create a smaller square inside the original. A sequence of successively smaller squares may be created by repeating the process with the most recently created square. The shaded regions show squares in the sequence.

Step 0

Step 1

Step 2

Step 3

Area = 25 units²   Area = _?_   Area = _?_   Area = _?_

Write the area of the shaded square for each step as 25 times a power of 2.

a. Step 1
   $25 \cdot 2^{-1}$

b. Step 2
   $25 \cdot 2^{-2}$

c. Step 10
   $25 \cdot 2^{-10}$

d. Step n
   $25 \cdot 2^{-n}$

Notes on the Questions

Question 22 Ask students to explain why the area of the shaded region in Step 1 is half the area of the shaded region in Step 0. (Split the large square in Step 1 into 4 squares whose side lengths are half that of the large square, and you can see that the shaded region covers half of each of these 4 squares.) Ask if the perimeter of the shaded square in Step 1 is half the perimeter of the shaded square in Step 0. (It is not. It is more than half. This can be seen by rotating the shaded square of Step 1 until its sides are horizontal and vertical. Its sides are more than half the length of the sides of the square in Step 0.)

Notes on the Questions

Question 27 The only reason the teacher gives a number less than 13 is so that Tyra can multiply the number by 8 in her head.

Question 28 A hydrogen atom has a diameter of about $120 \cdot 10^{-12}$ meter.

4 Wrap-Up

Ongoing Assessment

Have students work the following problems individually.

1. Write $(3^2)^{-2}$ as a simple fraction. $\frac{1}{81}$

2. Write $\frac{1}{16}$ as a negative power of an integer. 4^{-2} or 2^{-4}

3. Write $4x^{-2}y^3$ without negative exponents. $\frac{4y^3}{x^2}$

Next, organize students into pairs, and have students exchange papers and informally grade the other student's work. When they are done, give them a chance to discuss any differences in their solutions.

Project Update

Project 2, Fraction Exponents, on page 517, relates to the content of this lesson.

In 23–25 first simplify. Then evaluate when $a = 2$ and $b = 5$.
(Lessons 8-3, 8-2)

23. $\frac{a^2 \cdot a^5 \cdot a^3}{a^4}$ a^6; 64

24. $(b^2 a^{-2})^3$

25. $(2b^3)^a$

24. $a^{-6}b^6$; $\frac{15,625}{64}$

25. $2^a b^{3a}$; 62,500

26. Some people use randomly generated passwords to protect their computer accounts. Suppose a Web site uses random passwords that are six characters long. They allow only lower-case letters and the digits 0 through 9 to be used. (Lessons 8-1, 5-6)

   a. What is the total number of possible passwords?

   b. Jacinta forgot her password. What is the probability that she will guess her password correctly on the first try? $\frac{1}{36^6}$

   c. Myron says there would be more possibilities available if the site switched to passwords four characters long but allowed the use of upper-case letters as well. Is Myron correct? Why or why not? **Myron is wrong because $62^4 < 36^6$.**

27. Tyra is learning addition and multiplication. For practice, Tyra's teacher gives her a whole number less than 13. Tyra then multiplies the number by 8, adds 25, and states her answer. (Lessons 7-6, 7-5) a. $m(x) = 8x + 25$

   a. Describe the situation with function notation, letting x be the number Tyra is given and $m(x)$ the number Tyra states.

   b. What is the domain of the function you wrote?

   c. What are the greatest and least values the function can have? **121 and 25**

28. Objects in the universe can be quite small. Do research to find objects of the following sizes.

   a. 10^{-3} meter

   b. 10^{-6} meter

   c. 10^{-9} meter
   Answers vary.
   Sample answer:
   diameter of a DNA helix

   d. 10^{-12} meter
   Answers vary.
   Sample answer:
   gamma rays

Nearly 49 million laptop computers were sold worldwide in 2004, almost double the number sold in 2000.

Source: *USA Today*

26a. $(26 + 10)^6$
   $= 36^6$, or
   2,176,782,336

27b. whole numbers less than 13

28a. Answers vary.
   Sample answer:
   length of an amoeba

28b. Answers vary.
   Sample answer:
   length of a bacterium

Lesson 8-5

Powers of Products and Quotients

▶ **BIG IDEA** Because of the relationship among multiplication, division, and powers, powers distribute over products and quotients.

The Power of a Product

The expression $(3x)^4$ is an example of a power of a product. It can be rewritten using repeated multiplication.

$$(3x)^4 = (3x) \cdot (3x) \cdot (3x) \cdot (3x) \qquad \text{Repeated Multiplication Model for Powering}$$
$$= 3 \cdot 3 \cdot 3 \cdot 3 \cdot x \cdot x \cdot x \cdot x \qquad \text{Associative and Commutative Properties}$$
$$= 3^4 \cdot x^4 \qquad \text{Repeated Multiplication Model for Powering}$$
$$= 81x^4 \qquad \text{Arithmetic}$$

You can check this answer using a CAS.

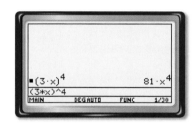

In general, any positive integer power of a product can be rewritten using repeated multiplication.

$$(ab)^n = \underbrace{(ab) \cdot (ab) \cdot \ldots \cdot (ab)}_{n \text{ factors}}$$
$$= \underbrace{a \cdot a \cdot \ldots \cdot a}_{n \text{ factors}} \cdot \underbrace{b \cdot b \cdot \ldots \cdot b}_{n \text{ factors}}$$
$$= a^n \cdot b^n$$

When a and b are nonzero, this result holds for all values of n.

> **Power of a Product Property**
>
> For all nonzero a and b, and for all n, $(ab)^n = a^n b^n$.

Mental Math

Find the slope of the line through

a. (-4.5, 19) and (90, 19). **0**

b. (4, -1.5), (-3.5, -1.5). **0**

c. (0, 0) and $\left(\frac{3}{4}, \frac{7}{4}\right)$. **$\frac{7}{3}$**

Powers of Products and Quotients **481**

GOAL

Introduce and apply the last two of the basic properties of powers: the Power of a Product Property $(ab)^n = a^n b^n$, and the Power of a Quotient Property $\left(\frac{a}{b}\right)^n = \frac{a^n}{b^n}$, both true for all real numbers a, b, and n for which the expressions are defined.

SPUR Objectives

A Simplify products, quotients, and powers of powers.

B Evaluate negative integer powers of real numbers.

C Rewrite powers of products and quotients.

G Identify properties of powers that justify a simplification. (See page 456B for the list of properties.)

Materials/Resources

· Lesson Master 8-5A or 8-5B
· Resource Master 120
· Two pieces of 8.5 in.-by-11 in. paper for each student
· Tape, scissors, ruler

> **HOMEWORK**
>
> **Suggestions for Assignment**
> • Questions 1–23
> • Question 24 (extra credit)
> • Reading Lesson 8-6
> • Covering the Ideas 8-6

> **Local Standards**

1 Warm-Up

Written as a product of powers, the prime factorization of 1,500 is $2^2 \cdot 3 \cdot 5^3$. The prime factorization of 162 is $2 \cdot 3^4$.

1. What is the prime factorization of $1,500^3$? $2^6 \cdot 3^3 \cdot 5^9$

2. What is the prime factorization of $1,500 \cdot 162$? $2^3 \cdot 3^5 \cdot 5^3$

3. What is the prime factorization of $\frac{1,500 \cdot 162}{27}$? $2^3 \cdot 3^2 \cdot 5^3$

Background

The properties of this lesson and Lessons 8-2 and 8-3 have similar names that are derived from the order of operations. The expression $(ab)^n$ is viewed as a power of a product because the product is done first and then the power is taken. In contrast, $2^x \cdot 2^y$ is a product of powers. These distinctions may help students remember the names of properties. Knowing the actual names of the properties is not important; the goal is being able to do the appropriate computation or simplification.

The power of a quotient. An argument deducing the Power of a Quotient Property from the Power of a Product Property is shown on page 482. Another way to think of the Power of a Quotient Property is as the Power of a Product Property in disguise. The Negative Exponent Property is the mask. The unmasking is done by writing the quotient as a product:

$$\left(\frac{a}{b}\right)^n = (ab^{-1})^n$$

(continued on next page)

8-5

Notes on the Lesson

The Warm-Up shows applications of the properties of this lesson to the prime factorizations of whole numbers. There are also uses of these properties in calculating powers of numbers written in scientific notation. For example, the Earth's moon has a radius of approximately $1.738 \cdot 10^3$ kilometers. Using the formula $V = \frac{4}{3}\pi r^3$ for the volume of a sphere, we see that finding the volume of the moon requires the calculation $\frac{4}{3}\pi(1.738 \cdot 10^3)^3$, which gives a volume of about $22 \cdot 10^9$ km^3, or $2.2 \cdot 10^{10}$ km^3.

Although all the examples in this lesson deal with positive integer exponents, point out that the properties work with all nonzero a and b and all n.

The two properties of this lesson are sometimes called the Distributive Properties of Powering over Multiplication and Division. You can see this by writing the properties using the $\cdot$ and $\div$ symbols.

Power of a Product:
$(a \cdot b)^n = (a^n) \cdot (b^n)$

Power of a Quotient:
$(a \div b)^n = (a^n) \div (b^n)$

If in these properties, the exponent is replaced by $\cdot$, $\cdot$ is replaced by $+$, and $\div$ is replaced by $-$, the Distributive Properties of Multiplication over Addition and Subtraction appear.

Additional Examples

Example 1 Simplify $(-2y)^4$. $16y^4$

Example 2 Simplify $(-4x^3\,yz^4)^5$.

Apply the Power of a Product Property.
$(-4)^{\underline{?}}(x^3)^{\underline{?}}(y)^{\underline{?}}(z^4)^{\underline{?}}$ 5; 5; 5; 5

Apply the Power of a Power Property.
$(-4)^{\underline{?}}\, x^{\underline{?}}\, y^{\underline{?}}\, z^{\underline{?}}$ 5; 15; 5; 20

Evaluate the numerical power.
$\underline{?}$ $-1{,}024x^{15}y^5z^{20}$

Note-Taking Tips

Make sure students include the following warning in their notes for this lesson: The Power of a Product Property applies only to products, not to sums. Thus $(ab)^n = a^nb^n$, but $(a + b)^n \neq a^n + b^n$.

This property can be applied to simplify the expression $(3x)^4$ from page 481. The power is applied to each factor of $3x$, so $(3x)^4 = 3^4x^4$, resulting in $81x^4$.

Example 1
Simplify $(-4x)^3$.

Solution Use the Power of a Product Property.

$(-4x)^3 = (-4)^3 \cdot x^3 = -64x^3$

Check Substitute a test value for x and follow order of operations.

Let $x = 1.5$. Does $(-4x)^3 = -64x^3$?
$$(-4 \cdot 1.5)^3 = -64(1.5)^3$$
$$(-6)^3 = -64 \cdot (3.375)$$
$$-6 \cdot -6 \cdot -6 = -216$$
$$-216 = -216 \qquad \text{It checks.}$$

Remember that in the order of operations, powers take precedence over opposites. In $-64x^3$, the power is done before the multiplication. In $(-4x)^3$, the multiplication is inside parentheses so it is done before the power.

STOP QY1

> **▶ QY1**
>
> Simplify $(3xy)^4$.

GUIDED

Example 2
Simplify $(-5x^2y^3z)^3$.

Solution

$(-5x^2y^3z)^3$
$= (-5)^{\underline{?}}(x^2)^{\underline{?}}(y^3)^{\underline{?}}z^{\underline{?}}$ 3; 3; 3; 3   Apply the Power of a Product Property.
$= (-5)^{\underline{?}}x^{\underline{?}}y^{\underline{?}}z^{\underline{?}}$ 3; 6; 9; 3   Apply the Power of a Power Property.
$= \underline{?}$ $-125x^6y^9z^3$ Evaluate the numerical power.

The Power of a Quotient

The expression $\left(\frac{a}{b}\right)^n$ is the power of a quotient. By using the properties of the previous lessons, you can write this without parentheses.

$$\left(\frac{a}{b}\right)^n = \left(a \cdot \frac{1}{b}\right)^n = (a \cdot b^{-1})^n = a^n \cdot (b^{-1})^n = a^n \cdot b^{-n} = \frac{a^n}{b^n}$$

Power of a Quotient Property

For all nonzero a and b, and for all n, $\left(\frac{a}{b}\right)^n = \frac{a^n}{b^n}$.

Activity. At times, algebra simply verifies the obvious. For example, when we use the Distributive Property to explain that 3 times a price plus 5 times that price is 8 times that price ($3p + 5p = 8p$). Using intuition, we are trying to show students that mathematics, looked at logically, makes everything reasonable. But at other times, algebra shows us that what we thought might be reasonable is not. Most people believe that there should be no difference in the volumes of the boxes formed in the activity. We are folding the same piece of paper. Because the lateral surface areas of these 3-dimensional figures are the same, shouldn't their volumes also be the same? This activity shows that the volumes are not. The key reason is that, in the volume formula, one of the dimensions is squared, which makes this dimension, based on the perimeter of the base, more powerful than the height of the prism.

The Power of a Quotient Property enables you to find powers of fractions more quickly.

Example 3

Write $\left(\frac{3}{4}\right)^5$ as a simple fraction.

Solution 1 Use the Power of a Quotient Property.

$$\left(\frac{3}{4}\right)^5 = \frac{3^5}{4^5} = \frac{243}{1,024}$$

Solution 2 Use repeated multiplication.

$$\left(\frac{3}{4}\right)^5 = \frac{3}{4} \cdot \frac{3}{4} \cdot \frac{3}{4} \cdot \frac{3}{4} \cdot \frac{3}{4} = \frac{3^5}{4^5} = \frac{243}{1,024}$$

Check Change the fractions to decimals.

$$\left(\frac{3}{4}\right)^5 = 0.75^5 = 0.2373046875$$

$$\frac{243}{1,024} = 0.2373046875$$

They are equal.

STOP QY2

Powers are found in many formulas for area and volume.

Activity

You will need two pieces of 8.5-in. by 11-in. paper, tape, scissors, and a ruler.

Step 1

Begin with one sheet of paper, positioned so that it is taller than it is wide. Fold it into fourths lengthwise and tape the long edges together to form the sides of a tall box with a square base.

11 in.

8.5 in.

8.5 in.
perimeter of base

(continued on next page)

▶ **QY2**

Rewrite $11 \cdot \left(\frac{2}{m}\right)^6$ as a simple fraction.

Additional Example

Example 3 Write $\left(\frac{2}{5}\right)^3$ as a simple fraction. $\frac{8}{125}$

Notes on the Activity

Students should do this activity in pairs. One person can hold the pieces of paper while the other tapes the specified edges together. You might consider asking different groups of students to work with papers of different sizes (other than 8.5 in.-by-11 in.), and compare the results as a class. This will help students generalize the activity during the discussion following, and will help students recognize that the volumes of the two boxes are consistently in the ratio of 1 to 2.

Accommodating the Learner ⬆

Ask students to discuss the sign of the expression $(-4x^3 z^2)^2$ and the sign of the similar expression $(-4x^3 z^2)^3$. Help them discover that the first expression will be positive for all real numbers, but that the second expression might be positive or negative depending on the value of x. To help them find the pattern, ask students to evaluate each expression if $x = 2$ and $z = 3$. Then ask them to repeat the evaluation using $x = -2$ and $z = 3$, using $x = 2$ and $z = -3$, and finally using $x = -2$ and $z = -3$. Once they find the pattern, discuss the reasoning using the properties of exponents.

82,944 and –23,887,872;
82,944 and 23,887,872;
82,944 and –23,887,872

8-5

Additional Answers

Activity

Step 3: B; Answers vary. Sample answer: The volume of the box will be the product of the area of the square base and the height of the box. Because the area of the base increases as the square of the width of the box, the box will have more volume with a larger base than with a larger height. Therefore, we should expect the short, wide box to have more volume than the tall, skinny box.

Step 2 Cut the other piece of paper in half to create two 8.5-in. by 5.5-in. pieces. Fold each half, as shown by the dotted lines. Tape these pieces together to form a 17-in. by 5.5-in. piece of paper. Tape the short edges together to form the sides of a short box with a square base.

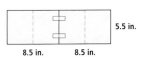

5.5 in.

8.5 in.   8.5 in.

17 in.
perimeter of base

Step 3 **Multiple Choice** Which of the following do you think is true? **B**

A The tall, skinny box has more volume.

B The short, wide box has more volume.

C Both boxes have the same volume.

In several sentences, justify your conjecture with a logical argument. **See margin.**

Step 4 Test your conjecture using the formula $V = s^2h$ for the volume V of a box with height h and a square base whose sides have length s.

a. Calculate the length of the sides of the base of the tall prism.

$s = $ __?__ **2.125 in.**

b. Calculate the volume of the tall prism. $V = $ __?__ **$(2.125)^2 \cdot 11 \approx 49.67$ in^3**

c. Repeat Parts a and b for the short prism. $s = $ __?__ **4.25 in.**, $V = $ __?__ **$(4.25)^2 \cdot 5.5 \approx 99.34$ in^3**

Step 5 According to your calculations, which is the correct answer to Step 3? __?__ **B**

Do you think you would get the same result if you started with a sheet of paper of a different size? Why or why not?

Step 5. Yes, the same result would be obtained with a sheet of paper of a different size because the result shows that a larger s yields a box with greater volume, regardless of the actual dimensions of any particular sheet of paper.

Using Powers of Quotients to Explain the Activity Results

Suppose you begin with a sheet of paper with height h and width p. The shorter box has half the height of the taller box, but the perimeter of its base is twice as long. Each side of the base of the tall box has length $\frac{p}{4}$. Each side of the base of the short box has length $\frac{2p}{4}$. So for the short prism, $2p = $ perimeter and $\frac{h}{2} = $ height.

Tall Box   **Short Box**

h

$\frac{h}{2}$

$\frac{p}{4}$ $\frac{2p}{4}$

Accommodating the Learner

Encourage students to follow along with the section entitled *Using Powers of Quotients to Explain the Activity Results* using the boxes they created. Students can write the dimensions directly on the boxes. Students may need to unfold and untape the shapes to understand why the side lengths are $\frac{p}{4}$ and $\frac{2p}{4}$, respectively.

The volume of a box with a square base is given by the formula $V = s^2h$, where the height is h and the side of the base is s. So, the volume of the tall box $= \left(\frac{p}{4}\right)^2 \cdot h$, and the volume of the short box $= \left(\frac{2p}{4}\right)^2 \cdot \frac{h}{2}$. To compare these volumes, we use properties of powers to simplify the expressions.

Example 4

The tall box has volume $\left(\frac{p}{4}\right)^2 \cdot h$ and the short box has volume $\left(\frac{2p}{4}\right)^2 \cdot \frac{h}{2}$.

a. Show that the volume of the tall box is always less than or equal to the volume of the short box.

b. The volume of the short box is how many times the volume of the tall one?

Solution

a. First apply the Power of a Quotient Property to simplify each volume.

Tall Box

$$V = \left(\frac{p}{4}\right)^2 \cdot h$$

$$= \frac{p^2}{4^2} \cdot h$$

$$= \frac{p^2}{16} \cdot h$$

$$= \frac{p^2h}{16}$$

Short Box

$$V = \left(\frac{2p}{4}\right)^2 \cdot \frac{h}{2}$$

$$= \left(\frac{(2p)^2}{4^2}\right) \cdot \frac{h}{2}$$

$$= \left(\frac{4p^2}{16}\right) \cdot \frac{h}{2}$$

$$= \left(\frac{p^2}{4}\right) \cdot \frac{h}{2} = \frac{p^2h}{8}$$

Volume of the tall box $= \frac{p^2h}{16}$

$$= \frac{1}{2} \cdot \frac{p^2h}{8}$$

$$= \frac{1}{2} \cdot \text{volume of short box}$$

Because the volume of the tall box is half the volume of the short one, the volume of the tall box is less than the volume of the short box.

b. The volume of the short box is 2 times the volume of the tall box.

Questions

COVERING THE IDEAS

1. a. Rewrite $(6x)^3$ without parentheses. $216x^3$
   b. Check your answer by letting $x = 2$.

In 2–5, rewrite the expression without parentheses.

2. $(5t^2)^3$ $125t^6$ 3. $8(-7xy)^3$ 4. $2(x^2y)^4$ $2x^8y^4$ 5. $(-t)^{93}$ $-t^{93}$

1b. $(6 \cdot 2)^3 = 1{,}728$; $216(2)^3 = 1{,}728$

3. $-2{,}744x^3y^3$

Notes on the Lesson

Do not be dismayed if Example 4 is difficult for students. This kind of substitution is known to be difficult even for calculus students. It is presented here not because we expect mastery at this time, but because it is clearly a skill that needs a number of exposures.

Additional Example

Example 4 Suppose we change the activity so that the tall box has dimensions $\frac{p}{3} \times \frac{p}{3} \times h$ and the short box has dimensions $\frac{2p}{3} \times \frac{2p}{3} \times \frac{h}{2}$.

a. Find the volume of each box.

tall box: $\frac{p^2h}{9}$; short box: $\frac{(2p)^2h}{18}$
$$= \frac{2p^2h}{9}$$

b. Show that the volume of the tall box is always less than or equal to the volume of the short box.

Because the volume of the tall box is half the volume of the short one, the volume of the tall box is less than the volume of the short box.

c. The volume of the short box is how many times the volume of the tall one?

The volume of the short box is 2 times the volume of the tall box.

Extension

Ask students to consider the following question. If the length of the edge of one cube is four times the length of the edge of another cube, what is the ratio of their volumes? Students should sketch diagrams of the cubes and choose a variable for the edge length of the smaller cube. Next, ask students to write an expression for the volume of each cube. Finally, ask students to write the ratio as a fraction without simplifying either expression. Ask students

to use the properties of exponents to simplify and find the ratio of the volumes. s^3 and $64s^3$; $\frac{1}{4^3}$; $64 : 1$

Have them generalize their findings to a cube with an edge n times the length of another cube. $\frac{1}{n^3}$; $n^3 : 1$

8-5

3 Assignment

Recommended Assignment
- Questions 1–23
- Question 24 (extra credit)
- Reading Lesson 8-6
- Covering the Ideas 8-6

Notes on the Questions

Question 11 This question involves direct variation but is presented here without the language of variation. The area varies directly as the square of the leg.

Question 12 This question is similar to the Activity. It is the only complex item in this question set; allow time for it to be discussed. Before assigning it, you might ask students which volume they think is greater.

6. Aisha made a common error when she wrote $(3x)^4 = 12x^4$. Show her this is incorrect by substituting 2 in for x. Then, write a note to Aisha explaining what she did wrong.

In 7–9, write as a simple fraction.

7. $\left(\frac{2}{3}\right)^4$ $\frac{16}{81}$

8. $5\left(\frac{n^5}{10}\right)^3$ $\frac{n^{15}}{200}$

9. $\left(\frac{19}{2y}\right)^3$ $\frac{6,859}{8y^3}$

10. What is the area of a square with perimeter p? $\frac{p^2}{16}$

APPLYING THE MATHEMATICS

11. The area A of an isosceles right triangle with leg L can be found using the formula $A = \frac{1}{2}L^2$. If L is multiplied by 6, what happens to the area of the triangle? **The area is multiplied by 36.**

12. Suppose you tape a 3-in. by 5-in. notecard to a pencil widthwise (as shown in Figure 1). Assume that the radius of the round pencil is $\frac{3}{16}$ in.

   a. If you rotate the pencil, what shape is traced by point A? Find the area of the shape.

   b. If you rotate the pencil, the entire notecard in Figure 1 traces a cylinder. Cylinders with height h and a base of radius r have volume $V = \pi r^2 h$. Calculate the volume of this region.   **about 235.62 in³**

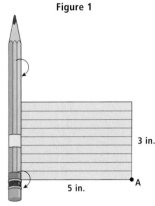

Figure 1

3 in.

5 in.   A

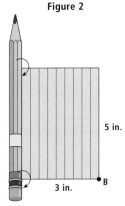

Figure 2

5 in.

3 in.   B

   c. Suppose you tape a 3 in.-by-5 in. notecard to a pencil heightwise, as shown in Figure 2. If you rotate the pencil, what shape is traced by point B? Find the area of the shape.

   d. If you rotate the pencil, what shape is traced by the entire notecard? Calculate the volume of this region.

   e. **True or False** Changing the taping of the notecard does not change the volume of the shape that is traced by the notecard when the pencil is rotated.   **false**

6. $(3 \cdot 2)^4 = 1{,}296$; $12(2)^4 = 192$; Aisha multiplied 3 by 4 to get 12 instead of using the Power of a Product Property properly and taking 3 to the power of 4 and getting 81. The correct answer is $(3x)^4 = 81x^4$.

12a. Point A traces a circle. The area of the circle is about 78.54 in².

12c. Point B traces a circle. The area of the circle is about 31.92 in².

12d. The entire notecard traces a cylinder. The volume of the cylinder is about 159.60 in³.

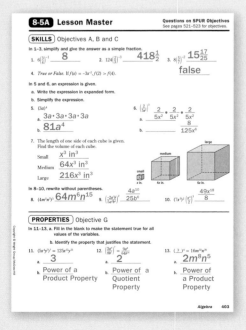

In 13–15, rewrite without parentheses and simplify.

13. $(xy)^2 \left(\frac{x}{y}\right)^3 \frac{x^5}{y}$ 14. $(abc)^0 \cdot \frac{(ab)^2}{abc} \frac{ab}{c}$ 15. $(2w)^4(3w^3)^2$ $144w^{10}$

In 16–18, fill in the blank with an exponent or an expression that makes the statement true for all values of the variables.

16. $(3x^2y)^{\underline{?}} = 27x^6y^3$ 3   17. $(2xy^2)^{\underline{?}} = 1$ 0   18. $(\underline{\ ?\ })^3 = 64x^6y^9$ $(4x^2y^3)$

19. If $x = 5$, what is the value of $\frac{(3x)^9}{(3x)^7}$? 225

REVIEW

In 20 and 21, simplify the expression so that your answer does not contain parentheses or negative exponents. Then evaluate when $r = 1.5$ and $s = 1$. (Lessons 8-4, 8-3)

20. $r^4s^9r^{-3}s^7$ rs^{16}; 1.5   21. $\frac{17s^{-2}}{5^5} \cdot r^{-2}$ $\frac{17}{3{,}125r^2s^2}$; $\frac{17}{7{,}031.25}$

22. On each day (Monday through Friday) this week, Antoine will do one of three activities after school: play tennis, walk his dog, or read. How many different orders of activities are possible? (Lesson 8-1) $3^5 = 243$

23. Solve $9(p - 2) < 47p - 2(5 - p)$ for p. (Lesson 4-5) $-\frac{1}{5} < p$

The World Junior Tennis competition, the international team competition for players aged 14 and under, was started by the International Tennis Federation in 1991.

Source: International Tennis Federation

EXPLORATION

24. A list of some powers of 3 is shown below. Look carefully at the last digit of each number.

$$3^0 = 1 \qquad 3^4 = 81$$
$$3^1 = 3 \qquad 3^5 = 243$$
$$3^2 = 9 \qquad 3^6 = 729$$
$$3^3 = 27$$

a. Predict the last digit of 3^{10}. Check your answer with a calculator. 9

b. Predict the last digit of 3^{20}. Check your answer with a calculator. 1

c. Describe how you can find the last digit of any positive integer power of 3. See margin.

d. Does a similar pattern happen for powers of 4? Why or why not? Yes, a similar pattern happens for powers of 4: for powers greater than 0, if the power is divisible by 2, then the last digit is 6, otherwise the last digit is 4.

QY ANSWERS

1. $81x^4y^4$

2. $\frac{704}{m^6}$

Powers of Products and Quotients   **487**

Additional Answers

24c. One can determine the last digit of any positive integer power p of 3 by dividing p by 4. If the quotient is a whole number, then the last digit is 1. If the quotient has a remainder, the last digit can be determined by the value of the remainder: a remainder of 0.25 implies the last digit is 3, a remainder of 0.5 implies the last digit is 9, and a remainder of 0.75 implies the last digit is 7.

---

4 Wrap-Up

Ongoing Assessment

Ask students to demonstrate their understanding of the properties of exponents by describing how to rewrite without parentheses and simplify the expression below. Encourage students to state the name of the property for each step but remember, at this point, the goal is simplification.

$$\left(\frac{3(x^3 y^2)}{(-y)^3}\right)^2 \ \frac{9x^6}{y^2}$$

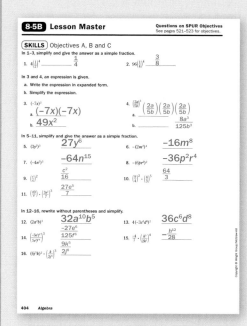

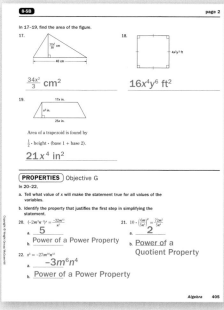

Lesson 8-6

GOAL

Review square roots and the Pythagorean Theorem, and introduce cube roots.

SPUR Objectives

D Simplify square roots.
E Evaluate cube roots.

Materials/Resources

· Lesson Master 8-6A or 8-6B
· Resource Masters 2 and 121–123
· Scientific or graphing calculator
· Quiz 2

HOMEWORK

Suggestions for Assignment
• Questions 1–30
• Question 31 (extra credit)
• Reading Lesson 8-7
• Covering the Ideas 8-7

Local Standards

1 Warm-Up

Use this Warm-Up to see how much of the material in this lesson is new to your students.

1. What is the meaning of the word *hypotenuse*? the longest side of a right triangle

2. **Multiple Choice** The principal square root of 400 is ___?___. A
   A 20   **B** 200
   C 1,600   **D** 160,000

3. **Multiple Choice** The two square roots of 5 are ___?___. C
   A 25 and −25
   B 2.5 and −2.5
   C about 2.24 and −2.24
   D nonexistent

4. If the two shorter sides of a right triangle have lengths 8 and 10, what is the length of the longest side of the triangle? $\sqrt{164}$

5. *Fill in the Blank.* 6 is a cube root of 216 because ___?___ = 216. 6^3

Lesson 8-6 — Square Roots and Cube Roots

Vocabulary

square
squared
square root
radical sign ($\sqrt{}$)
cube
cubed
cube root

▶ **BIG IDEA**   If a first number is the square (or the cube) of a second number, then the second number is a square root (or cube root) of the first.

Areas of Squares and Powers as Squares

The second power x^2 of a number x is called the **square** of x, or x **squared,** because it is the area of a square with side length x. This is not a coincidence. The ancient Greek mathematicians pictured numbers as lengths, and they pictured the square of a number as the area of a square.

It is easy to calculate the area of a square on a grid if the square's sides are horizontal and vertical, but what if the square's sides are slanted?

Activity 1

Follow these steps to determine the area of the square *EFGH*, at the right.

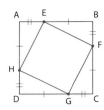

Step 1 Square *ABCD* is 3 units on a side. What is its area? 9 units²

Step 2 Triangle *AEH* is a right triangle with legs of length 1 unit and 2 units. What is the area of △*AEH*? 1 unit²

Step 3 Subtract the areas of the four corner triangles from the area of *ABCD* to get the area of *EFGH*. 5 units²

488   Powers and Roots

Mental Math

In each set, which does not equal the others?
a. $\frac{3x}{5}, \frac{3}{5}x, \frac{3}{5x}, \frac{3}{5x}$
b. $\frac{y}{9}, y \cdot \frac{1}{9}, \frac{1}{9} \cdot \frac{1}{y}, y \div 9, \frac{1}{9} \cdot \frac{1}{y}$

Background

This lesson will take more than a day if students have not previously seen square roots and the Pythagorean Theorem.

The lesson begins with a review of the geometric origin of the words "square" and "square root," and the radical sign. This review includes the geometric definition and basic algebraic property of square roots, namely that $\sqrt{x} \cdot \sqrt{x} = x$ for any nonnegative number x. An interlude notes that for all x, $\sqrt{x} = x^{\frac{1}{2}}$. Then the geometric interpretation of squares and square

roots is used to show a special case of the Pythagorean Theorem. (A more general proof is found in Chapter 13.) The lesson ends with an introduction of what may be the only new material for most students, cube roots.

It is critical to make the distinction between the phrase "square root of x" and the symbol $\sqrt{x}$. When x is positive, the symbol stands for only one of its two square roots—its positive square root.

(continued on next page)

Sides of Squares and Square Roots

You should have found that the area of *EFGH* is 5 square units. If the area of the square *EFGH* is 5 square units, what is the length of one of its sides? The Greek mathematicians could do the previous calculations easily. But now they were stumped. Can *GH* be $2\frac{1}{2}$?

No, because $\left(2\frac{1}{2}\right)^2 = 2.5^2 = 6.25$, which is greater than 5. In fact, the Greeks were able to show that it is impossible to find any simple fraction whose square is exactly 5. So they simply called the length the *square root* of 5. We still do that today. The length of a side of a square whose area is *x* is called a square root of *x*. The length of *GH* is a square root of 5. Similarly, a square root of 9 is 3, because a square with area 9 has side 3.

> **Definition of Square Root**
>
> If $A = s^2$, then s is a **square root** of A.

If two numbers have the same absolute value, such as 3 and –3, then they have the same square, 9. Although –3 cannot be the length of a side of a square, every positive number but 0 has two square roots, one positive and one negative. We denote the square roots of *A* by the symbols $\sqrt{A}$ (the positive root) and $-\sqrt{A}$ (the negative root). So the square roots of 9 are $\sqrt{9} = 3$ and $-\sqrt{9} = -3$. The two square roots of 5 are $\sqrt{5}$ and $-\sqrt{5}$. In the figure on the previous page, $GH = \sqrt{5}$.

The Radical Sign $\sqrt{}$

The **radical sign** $\sqrt{}$ indicates that a square root is being found. The horizontal bar attached to it, called a *vinculum*, acts like parentheses. The order of operations applies, so work is done inside the radical sign before the square root is taken. For example, $\sqrt{16 - 9} = \sqrt{7}$. On the other hand, $\sqrt{16} - \sqrt{9} = 4 - 3 = 1$.

In dealing with square roots, it helps to know the squares of small positive integers: 1, 4, 9, 16, 25, 36, 49, 64, 81, 100, 121, 144, ...

> **Example 1**
>
> What are the square roots of each number?
>
> a. 64
>
> b. 17.3
>
> *(continued on next page)*

Notes on the Lesson

This lesson, though long, is one you may wish to read aloud with your students. Pause for questions after every few sentences.

Notes on the Activity

The idea behind Activities 1 and 3 is that by enclosing a tilted square in a larger square whose sides are horizontal and vertical, the area of the tilted square can be found. The significance of this idea is that if a square has area *A*, then the length of its side is $\sqrt{A}$. This information can be used to obtain the length of a segment that is neither horizontal nor vertical. Students can also use Activity 1 as an opportunity to visualize the area of a right triangle as half the area of a related rectangle. They can picture the four triangles pairing off to form two rectangles. This will also make computation of the area more efficient.

This is the *principal square root of x*. The other square root of *x* is denoted by $-\sqrt{x}$. You may wish to read $\sqrt{x}$ as "the positive square root of *x*" to emphasize that this symbol does not stand for the negative square root of *x*.

Cube roots provide a parallel to square roots, and so they make it easier to see what square roots are about. This parallel comes in their definition, in the analogies between areas of squares and volumes of cubes, and in the Cube of the Cube Root Property: $\sqrt[3]{x} \cdot \sqrt[3]{x} \cdot \sqrt[3]{x} = x$.

After seeing cube roots, students may wonder why we don't write the principal square root of *x* as $\sqrt[2]{x}$. The reason is only because square roots are so much more common than any other roots that to write $\sqrt[2]{x}$ instead of $\sqrt{x}$ would be a waste of time and ink or lead.

8-6

Additional Example

Example 1 What are the square roots of each number?

a. 121 **11 and −11**

b. 13.5 **about 3.67 and about −3.67**

Solutions

a. Because $8^2 = 64$ and $(-8)^2 = 64$, the square roots of 64 are 8 and −8. We can write $\sqrt{64} = 8$ and $-\sqrt{64} = -8$.

b. Because there is no decimal that multiplied by itself equals 17.3, just write $\sqrt{17.3}$ and $-\sqrt{17.3}$. A calculator shows $\sqrt{17.3} \approx 4.1593$ and so $-\sqrt{17.3} \approx -4.1593$.

Square Roots That Are Not Whole Numbers

The Greek mathematician Pythagoras and his followers, the Pythagoreans, were able to prove that numbers like $\sqrt{5}$ are not equal to simple fractions or ratios. Today we know that there is no finite or repeating decimal that equals $\sqrt{5}$. While $\sqrt{5}$ is approximately 2.23606797..., the decimal does not end nor repeat. You should check that the squares of truncated forms of 2.23606797..., are very close to 5. For example, $2.236 \cdot 2.236 = 4.999696$. But only $\sqrt{5}$ and $-\sqrt{5}$ square to be exactly 5, so $\sqrt{5} \cdot \sqrt{5} = 5 = -\sqrt{5} \cdot -\sqrt{5}$.

> **Square of the Square Root Property**
>
> For any nonnegative number x, $\sqrt{x} \cdot \sqrt{x} = \sqrt{x^2} = x$.

You can use this property to simplify or evaluate expressions that are exact, rather than use your calculator to deal with approximations.

STOP QY1

A Positive Square Root of x Is a Power of x

Suppose $m = \frac{1}{2}$ and $n = \frac{1}{2}$ in the Product of Powers Property $x^m \cdot x^n = x^{m+n}$. Then, $x^{\frac{1}{2}} \cdot x^{\frac{1}{2}} = x^{\frac{1}{2} + \frac{1}{2}} = x^1 = x$.

This means that $x^{\frac{1}{2}}$ is a number which, when multiplied by itself, equals x. Thus $x^{\frac{1}{2}}$ is a square root of x, and we identify $x^{\frac{1}{2}}$ as the positive square root of x. So, for any positive number x, $x^{\frac{1}{2}} = \sqrt{x}$.

For example, $100^{\frac{1}{2}} = \sqrt{100} = 10$ and $64.289^{\frac{1}{2}} = \sqrt{64.289} \approx 8.02$.

Activity 2

Use a calculator to verify that $x^{\frac{1}{2}} = \sqrt{x}$.

Step 1a. Enter 16^(1/2). What number results? **4**

b. You have calculated the square root of what number? **16**

▶ **QY1**

Explain why $4\sqrt{10} \cdot 3\sqrt{10} = 120$.

Accommodating the Learner ⬇

Students are sometimes careless with their terminology, using the term squared when they mean square root. This will often carry over to their approach to solving problems in the future. For example, students sometimes try to solve equations such as $\sqrt{x} = 4$ by taking the square root of both sides instead of squaring both sides. Work with students on using appropriate terminology and clearly understanding the difference between the square and the square root of a number.

Step 2a. Enter 8^0.5. What number results? 2.83

   b. You have calculated the square root of what number? 8

Step 3 Enter (−4)^(1/2). What results, and why?
Error; no real number is the square root of a negative number.

Activity 3

Use the idea of Activity 1 to determine the length of a side of square *IJKL* shown below. Show your work.

Activity 3: $\sqrt{29}$ units;
$7^2 - 4(\frac{1}{2})(5 \cdot 2) =$
$49 - 20 = 29$ units^2

Activity 4

Three squares are drawn on a coordinate grid at the right.

1. Use the idea of Activities 1 and 3 to determine the area of square III. Explain your work.

2. What is the area of square I? 25 units^2

3. What is the area of square II? 36 units^2

4. How are the areas of the three squares related to each other? $25 + 36 = 61$ units^2

The Pythagorean Theorem

The result of Activity 4 is one example of the *Pythagorean Theorem*. We state this theorem in terms of area first, and then in terms of powers.

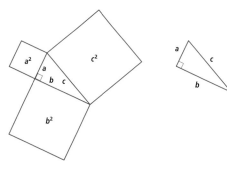

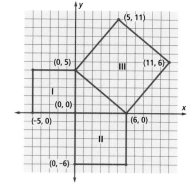

Activity 4
1. 61 units^2; area of square III = area of square with 11 units on a side −4 (area of right triangle with legs of lengths 6 units and 5 units) =
$11^2 - 4(\frac{1}{2} \cdot 6 \cdot 5) =$
$121 - 60 = 61$ units^2

Notes on the Activity

When doing Activity 2, consider including more examples that are similar so students can generalize the concept. For instance, for Steps 1 and 2, ask students to repeat the process with other numbers, including some numbers that are perfect squares and some that are not. For Step 3, ask students to repeat the process with other negative numbers and also with the power 0.5.

Activity 4 shows that the sum of the areas of squares drawn on the shorter sides (the legs) of a particular right triangle equals the area of the square on the longest side (the hypotenuse). We have purposely picked a hypotenuse whose length is not a whole number. Whereas today, we think of the Pythagorean Theorem as being about lengths of sides in a right triangle, the area interpretation of the Pythagorean Theorem in this activity was used by the ancient Greeks. To help students complete this activity, ask them to sketch the squares on their own graph paper. Remind them that they can check their answers using estimation by counting the number of grid squares inside each of the three squares they have drawn.

8-6

Additional Example

Example 2 Use the Pythagorean Theorem to find the length of the missing side. $\sqrt{11} \approx 3.32$

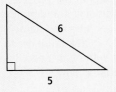

Pythagorean Theorem

(*In terms of area*) In any right triangle, the sum of the areas of the squares on its legs equals the area of the square on its hypotenuse.

(*In terms of length*) In any right triangle with legs of lengths a and b and a hypotenuse of length c, $a^2 + b^2 = c^2$.

For example, in $\triangle GDH$ from Activity 1, $HD^2 + DG^2 = GH^2$.

$$1^2 + 2^2 = GH^2$$
$$1 + 4 = GH^2$$
$$5 = GH^2$$

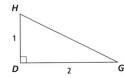

By the definition of square root, $GH = \sqrt{5}$.

The Pythagorean Theorem is perhaps the most famous theorem in all of mathematics. It seems to have been discovered independently in many cultures, for it was known to the Babylonians, Indians, Chinese, and Greeks well over 2,500 years ago. In the United States and Europe, this theorem is known as the Pythagorean Theorem because Pythagoras or one of his students proved it in the 6th century BCE. In China, it is called the Gougu Theorem. In Japan, it is called "The Theorem of the Three Squares."

Example 2

Use the Pythagorean Theorem to find the length of the missing side.

Solution Use the Pythagorean Theorem to write an equation involving the lengths of the three sides of the right triangle.

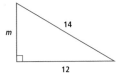

$$m^2 + 12^2 = 14^2$$
$$m^2 + 144 = 196$$
$$m^2 + 144 - 144 = 196 - 144$$
$$m^2 = 52$$
$$m = \sqrt{52}$$
$$m \approx 7.21$$

Check Substitute the solution into the original triangle and apply the Pythagorean Theorem.

Does $\left(\sqrt{52}\right)^2 + 12^2 = 14^2$?
$52 + 144 = 196$ Yes, it checks.

Accommodating the Learner ↑

Connect the Square of the Square Root Property and the Cube of the Cube Root Property to the Power of a Power Property discussed earlier in the chapter. Ask students to find the missing number for each of the following.

a. $\sqrt{x^2} = (x^2)^{\frac{?}{}} = x^{\frac{1}{2}}$

b. $\sqrt[3]{x^3} = (x^3)^{\frac{?}{}} = x^{\frac{1}{3}}$

Help students generalize their results to write $\sqrt[n]{b} = b^{\frac{1}{n}}$.

Cubes and Cube Roots

The third power x^3 of a number x is called the **cube** of x, or x **cubed,** because it is the volume of a cube with edge x. So, for example, the volume of a cube with edge of length 6 inches is $6 \cdot 6 \cdot 6$, or 216 cubic inches. We write $6^3 = 216$, and we say "6 cubed equals 216." Like the square, this is not a coincidence. The ancient Greek mathematicians pictured the cube of a number s as the volume of a cube whose edge is s.

Also, in a manner like that of a square, if the volume of a cube is V, then an edge of the cube is called a **cube root** of V.

> **Definition of Cube Root**
>
> If $V = s^3$, then s is a cube root of V.

Since $6^3 = 216$, 6 is a cube root of 216. Unlike square roots, cube roots do not come in pairs. For example, –6 is not a cube root of 216, since $(-6)^3 = -216$. In the real numbers, all numbers have exactly one cube root.

 QY2

The cube root of V is written using a radical sign as $\sqrt[3]{V}$. For example, $\sqrt[3]{216} = 6$ and $\sqrt[3]{-216} = -6$. Many calculators have a $\sqrt[3]{}$ command, though it may be hidden in a menu. You should try to locate this command on your calculator. However, you will learn an alternate method for calculating cube roots in the next lesson.

> **QY2**
>
> **Fill in the Blanks**
> Since $4^3 = 64$, ___?___ is the cube root of ___?___.

> **Cube of the Cube Root Property**
>
> For any nonnegative number x, $\sqrt[3]{x} \cdot \sqrt[3]{x} \cdot \sqrt[3]{x} = \sqrt[3]{x^3} = x$.

For example, $1.2^3 = 1.2 \cdot 1.2 \cdot 1.2 = 1.728$. This means:

- 1.728 is the cube of 1.2.
- 1.2 is the cube root of 1.728.
- $1.2 = \sqrt[3]{1.728}$

When the value of a square root or cube root is not an integer, your teacher may expect two versions: (1) the exact answer written with a radical sign and (2) a decimal approximation rounded to a certain number of decimal places.

Cubes and cube roots. The following table shows the parallels between square roots and cube roots. The table can help students understand both types of roots, and summarizes the lesson. Suggest that students add this table to their notes for the lesson.

	Square root	Cube root
Geometric origin of phrase	side of square	edge of cube
Definition	If $A = s^2$, then $s = \sqrt{A}$.	If $V = s^3$, then $s = \sqrt[3]{V}$.
Basic property	$\sqrt{A} \cdot \sqrt{A} = A$	$\sqrt[3]{V} \cdot \sqrt[3]{V} \cdot \sqrt[3]{V} = V$
As a power	$\sqrt{A} = A^{\frac{1}{2}}$	$\sqrt[3]{V} = V^{\frac{1}{3}}$

You may wish to make a table of square roots and cube roots, such as the following, and provide copies to your students. Emphasize that the decimal values are approximations. Pick a number (such as 17) and square its square root or cube its cube root to check the values in the table.

x	$x^{\frac{1}{2}}$	$x^{\frac{1}{3}}$
1	1.00000000	1.00000000
2	1.41421356	1.25992105
3	1.73205081	1.44224957
4	2.00000000	1.58740105
5	2.23606798	1.70997595
6	2.44948974	1.81712059
7	2.64575131	1.91293118
8	2.82842713	2.00000000
9	3.00000000	2.08008382
10	3.16227766	2.15443469
11	3.31662479	2.22398009
12	3.46410162	2.28942849
13	3.60555128	2.35133469
14	3.74165739	2.41014226
15	3.87298335	2.46621207
16	4.00000000	2.51984210
17	4.12310563	2.57128159
18	4.24264069	2.62074139
19	4.35889894	2.66840165
20	4.47213596	2.71441762

> **Extension**

Teach students how to approximate square roots without a calculator using the following method. To approximate $\sqrt{58}$, note that 58 is between the perfect squares 49 and 64, so $\sqrt{49} < \sqrt{58} < \sqrt{64}$. Simplify this to show that $7 < \sqrt{58} < 8$. Point out that because 58 is closer to 64 than to 49, $\sqrt{58}$ is closer to 8. Provide students with other similar square roots to approximate. You might wish to challenge students to employ a similar method for approximating a few cube roots.

8-6

3 Assignment

Recommended Assignment
- Questions 1–30
- Question 31 (extra credit)
- Reading Lesson 8-7
- Covering the Ideas 8-7

Notes on the Questions

Question 2 This question emphasizes the two-way relationship between a square and a square root. Discuss student responses in class. You might ask students the corresponding question for volume.

Question 11 The verification that square roots do what they are supposed to do is critical to understanding them.

Questions

COVERING THE IDEAS

1. **a.** A side of a square is 16 units. What is its area? **256 units²**

   b. The area of a square is 16 square units. What is the length of a side? **4 units**

2. Rewrite the following sentences, substituting numbers for x and y to produce a true statement. *A square has a side of length x and an area y. Then y is the square of x, and x is the square root of y.*

   2. Answers vary.
   Sample answer:
   A square has a side of length 5 and an area of 25. Then 25 is the square of 5, and 5 is the square root of 25.

In 3–6, write or approximate the number to two decimal places.

3. $\sqrt{36}$ **6**

4. $\sqrt{121}$ **11**

5. $50^{\frac{1}{2}}$ **7.07**

6. $10^{0.5}$ **3.16**

In 7–10, evaluate the expression to the nearest thousandth.

7. $\sqrt{1,000}$ **31.623**

8. $\sqrt{100 + 100}$ **14.142**

9. $\sqrt{5} \cdot \sqrt{5}$ **5**

10. $2 \cdot \left(\frac{3}{4}\right)^{\frac{1}{2}} \left(\frac{3}{4}\right)^{\frac{1}{2}}$ **1.5**

11. **a.** Approximate $\sqrt{11}$ to the nearest hundred-thousandth. **3.31662**

    b. Multiply your answer to Part a by itself. **11**

    c. What property is validated by Parts a and b? **Square of the Square Root Property**

In 12–14, find the length of the missing side of the right triangle. If the answer is not an integer, give both its exact value and an approximation to the nearest hundredth.

12.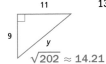

13.

14.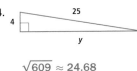

$\sqrt{202} \approx 14.21$

52

$\sqrt{609} \approx 24.68$

15. Write the cubes of the integers from 1 to 10. **1; 8; 27; 64; 125; 216; 343; 512; 729; 1,000**

16. 2 is a cube root of 8 because ___?___. $8 = 2^3$

17. **a.** Write the exact cube root of 1,700. $\sqrt[3]{1,700}$

    b. Estimate the cube root of 1,700 to the nearest thousandth. **11.935**

    c. Check your answer to Part b by multiplying your estimate by itself three times. **1,700.07**

In 18 and 19, evaluate the expression.

18. $\sqrt[3]{2.197}$ **1.3**

19. $\sqrt[3]{45} \cdot \sqrt[3]{45} \cdot \sqrt[3]{45}$ **45**

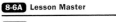

8-6A Lesson Master

Questions on SPUR Objectives
See pages 521–523 for objectives.

SKILLS Objectives D and E

1. Use the triangles at the right.

   a. Calculate AB. $\sqrt{13}$

   b. Express AC as $2 \cdot AB$. $2\sqrt{13}$

   c. Find PQ. $\sqrt{52}$

   d. Does $AC = PQ$? Use decimal approximations to justify your answer. **Yes.** $AC \approx 7.21$, $PQ \approx 7.21$

2. Which of the expressions below are equal to $\sqrt{72}$? **A, B, D**

   A $2\sqrt{18}$ B $3\sqrt{8}$ C $4\sqrt{6}$ D $6\sqrt{2}$

3. If $f(x) = 2\sqrt{x} \cdot \sqrt{x}$, what is $f(5)$? **10**

4. Simplify. Assume the variables are positive numbers.

   a. $\sqrt{5^2 + 12^2}$ **13**

   b. $\sqrt{81a^8b^{20}}$ **$9a^4b^{10}$**

   c. $\sqrt{9w^2 + 7w^2}$ **$4w$**

5. Find the area of the rectangle to the nearest hundredth. **146.64 cm²**

6. *True or False.* Assume a is positive. $\sqrt{5a} \cdot \sqrt{5a} = 25a$ **false**

7. *True or False.* $\sqrt[3]{4m} \cdot \sqrt[3]{4m} \cdot \sqrt[3]{4m} = 4m$ **true**

8. If $g(x) = \sqrt[3]{x}$, what is $g(-27)$? **−3**

9. Order the following numbers from least to greatest. **See below.**

   $2\sqrt{13}$, $\sqrt[3]{43}$, $\sqrt{23}$, $2\sqrt[3]{-8}$

10. Show why 6 is the cube root of 216. $6 \cdot 6 \cdot 6 = 6^3 = 216$

9. $2\sqrt[3]{-8}, \sqrt[3]{43}, \sqrt{23}, 2\sqrt{13}$

406

APPLYING THE MATHEMATICS

20. Suppose p is a positive number.

  a. What is the sum of the square roots of p? 0

  b. What is the product of the square roots of p? $-p$

21. In Chapter 7, the equation $P = 100{,}000(1.02)^x$ gave the population x years from now of a town of 100,000 today with a growth rate of 2% per year. Calculate P when $x = \frac{1}{2}$, and tell what the answer means.

22. A small park is shown below. If you want to go from one corner to the other corner, how many fewer feet will you walk if you go diagonally through the park rather than walk around it? Round your answer to the nearest foot. 229 ft

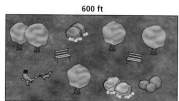

600 ft

300 ft

23. In the movie *The Wizard of Oz,* the scarecrow recites the following after receiving his diploma, "The sum of the square roots of any two sides of an isosceles triangle is equal to the square root of the remaining side." The scarecrow was attempting to recite the Pythagorean Theorem.

  a. Write several sentences explaining how this statement differs from the Pythagorean Theorem.

  b. Is the scarecrow's statement accurate? If not, produce a counterexample.

24. A dog is on a leash that is 10 meters long and attached to a pole 2.5 meters above the the dog's collar. To the nearest tenth of a meter, how far from the pole can the dog roam? 9.7 m

REVIEW

25. As you know, $4 \cdot 9 = 36$. So the square of 2 times the square of 3 equals the square of 6. Determine the general pattern. (**Lesson 8-5**) $(x^2)(y^2) = (xy)^2$

26. Simplify $a^6 \cdot \left(\frac{3}{a}\right)^3$. (**Lesson 8-5**) $27a^3$

In 27 and 28, solve. (**Lessons 8-4, 8-2**)

27. $3^4 \cdot 3^x = 3^{12}$ 8

28. $\frac{1}{512} = 2^a$ -9

21. 100,995; Answers vary. Sample answer: The population 6 months from the original date

23a. Answers vary. Sample answer: The scarecrow's statement is an incorrect statement about isosceles triangles, while the Pythagorean Theorem is a true statement about right triangles. The statement is about the square roots of the sides, while the Pythagorean Theorem is about the squares of the lengths of the sides.

23b. No, Answers vary. Sample answer: Let an isosceles triangle have sides $a = 9$, $b = 9$, and $c = 4$. Then $\sqrt{a} + \sqrt{b} = \sqrt{9} + \sqrt{9} = 3 + 3 = 6$; while $\sqrt{c} = \sqrt{4} = 2$, so $\sqrt{a} + \sqrt{b} \neq \sqrt{c}$.

Notes on the Questions

Question 21 Point out that the population of a town does not increase all at one time, so this estimate of the population at the middle of a year is quite reasonable.

Question 22 This is a classic question to test knowledge of the Pythagorean Theorem.

Question 23 The scarecrow in "The Wizard of Oz" is sad that he doesn't have a brain. His incorrect recitation of the Pythagorean Theorem may have been author L. Frank Baum's way of showing that.

Square Roots and Cube Roots **495**

8-6

4 Wrap-Up

Ongoing Assessment

Ask students to use graph paper to sketch a right triangle. After students have measured and labeled the legs with their lengths, ask them to use the Pythagorean Theorem to find the length of the hypotenuse. Then ask students to measure the hypotenuse to check their answer. Compare different answers as a class, and discuss any triangles that had integer hypotenuse lengths.

Project Update

Project 1, Estimating Square Roots, and Project 3, Interview with Pythagoras, on page 517 relate to the content of this lesson.

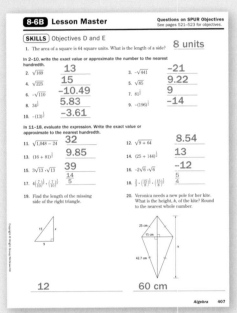

29. Other than the sun, the star nearest to us, Proxima Centauri, is about $4 \cdot 10^{13}$ km away. Earth's moon is about $3.8 \cdot 10^5$ km from us. If it took astronauts about 3 days to get to the moon in 1969, at that speed how long would it take them to get to Proxima Centauri? **(Lesson 8-3)** 865,177 yr

30. **Skill Sequence** Solve each equation for y. Assume $a \neq 0$. **(Lesson 4-7)** 30a.–d. $y = \frac{1}{2} - \frac{3}{4}x$

    a. $3x + 4y = 2$

    b. $6x + 8y = 4$

    c. $9x + 12y = 6$

    d. $3ax + 4ay = 2a$

You would have to circumnavigate Earth $9\frac{1}{2}$ times to equal the distance from Earth to the moon.

EXPLORATION

31. Make a table to evaluate $n^{\frac{1}{3}}$ on your calculator when n is 1, 2, 3, ..., up to 7. What do you think $n^{\frac{1}{3}}$ is equivalent to? Give a reason for your answer.

X	Y₁
1	1
2	1.2599
3	1.4422
4	1.5874
5	1.71
6	1.8171
7	1.9129

X=7

The cube root of n. Answers vary. Sample answer: if $a^{\frac{1}{2}} = \sqrt{a}$, then $a^{\frac{1}{3}} = \sqrt[3]{a}$

QY ANSWERS

1. $4\sqrt{10} \cdot 3\sqrt{10}$
   $= 4 \cdot 3 \cdot \sqrt{10} \cdot \sqrt{10}$
   $= 12 \cdot 10$
   $= 120$

2. 4; 64

496 Powers and Roots

Lesson 8-7

Multiplying and Dividing Square Roots

Vocabulary

radicand

▶ **BIG IDEA** Like powers, square roots distribute over products and quotients.

Activity 1

Step 1 Compute these square roots to the nearest thousandth either individually or using the list capability of a calculator.

$\sqrt{1} = 1.000$ $\sqrt{2} \approx 1.414$ $\sqrt{3} \approx 1.732$ $\sqrt{4} = \underline{\ ?\ }$

$\sqrt{5} \approx \underline{\ ?\ }$ $\sqrt{6} \approx 2.449$ $\sqrt{7} \approx \underline{\ ?\ }$ $\sqrt{8} \approx \underline{\ ?\ }$

$\sqrt{9} = \underline{\ ?\ }$ $\sqrt{10} \approx \underline{\ ?\ }$ $\sqrt{11} \approx \underline{\ ?\ }$ $\sqrt{12} \approx \underline{\ ?\ }$

$\sqrt{13} \approx \underline{\ ?\ }$ $\sqrt{14} \approx \underline{\ ?\ }$ $\sqrt{15} \approx \underline{\ ?\ }$ $\sqrt{16} = \underline{\ ?\ }$

$\sqrt{17} \approx \underline{\ ?\ }$ $\sqrt{18} \approx \underline{\ ?\ }$ $\sqrt{19} \approx \underline{\ ?\ }$ $\sqrt{20} \approx \underline{\ ?\ }$

Step 2 Consider the product $\sqrt{2} \cdot \sqrt{3}$. Find the product of the decimal approximations, rounded to 3 decimal places.

Decimal approximations: $\underline{\ ?\ } \cdot \underline{\ ?\ } \approx 2.449$ 1.414; 1.732

Is the decimal product found in the table above? $\underline{\ ?\ }$ yes

If so, write the equation that relates the product of the square roots.

Square roots: $\underline{\ ?\ } \cdot \underline{\ ?\ } = \underline{\ ?\ }$ $\sqrt{2}; \sqrt{3}; \sqrt{6}$

Step 3 Repeat Step 2 but use a product of two different square roots from the list $\sqrt{2}, \sqrt{3}, \sqrt{4}, \sqrt{5}$.   **Answers vary. Sample answers are given.**

Square roots: $\underline{\ ?\ } \cdot \underline{\ ?\ }$ $\sqrt{2}; \sqrt{4}$

Decimal approximations: $\underline{\ ?\ } \cdot \underline{\ ?\ } \approx \underline{\ ?\ }$ 1.414; 2; 2.828

Is the decimal product found in the table above? $\underline{\ ?\ }$ yes

If so, write the equation that relates the product of the square roots.

Square roots: $\underline{\ ?\ } \cdot \underline{\ ?\ } = \underline{\ ?\ }$ $\sqrt{2}; \sqrt{4}; \sqrt{8}$

Step 4 Multiply another pair of square roots in the table. $\underline{\ ?\ } \cdot \underline{\ ?\ }$ $\sqrt{2}; \sqrt{6}$

Predict what their product will be. $\underline{\ ?\ }$ Is your prediction correct? $\underline{\ ?\ }$ yes $\sqrt{12}$

Mental Math

Given $f(x) = 611x^2 + 492x - 1{,}000$. Calculate the following.

a. $f(0)$ –1,000

b. $f(1)$ 103

Step 1. $\sqrt{4} = 2$,
$\sqrt{5} \approx 2.236$,
$\sqrt{7} \approx 2.646$,
$\sqrt{8} \approx 2.828$,
$\sqrt{9} = 3$,
$\sqrt{10} \approx 3.162$,
$\sqrt{11} \approx 3.317$,
$\sqrt{12} \approx 3.464$,
$\sqrt{13} \approx 3.606$,
$\sqrt{14} \approx 3.742$,
$\sqrt{15} \approx 3.873$,
$\sqrt{16} = 4$,
$\sqrt{17} \approx 4.123$,
$\sqrt{18} \approx 4.243$,
$\sqrt{19} \approx 4.359$,
$\sqrt{20} \approx 4.472$

Lesson 8-7

GOAL

Discuss the uses of the Product of Square Roots Property—for all nonnegative a and b, $\sqrt{a} \cdot \sqrt{b} = \sqrt{ab}$—and its applications to writing square roots with smaller whole numbers under the radicand and to the Quotient of Square Roots Property.

SPUR Objective

D Simplify square roots.

Materials/Resources

· Lesson Master 8-7A or 8-7B
· Resource Masters 124 and 125
· Scientific or graphing calculator

HOMEWORK

Suggestions for Assignment

• Questions 1–34
• Questions 35 and 36 (extra credit)
• Reading Lesson 8-8
• Covering the Ideas 8-8

Local Standards

1 Warm-Up

1. Check that each statement is true by using decimal approximations.
   $\sqrt{3} + \sqrt{12} = \sqrt{27}$
      $1.732 + 3.464 = 5.196$
   $\sqrt{5} + \sqrt{20} = \sqrt{45}$
      $2.236 + 4.472 = 6.708$
   $\sqrt{6} + \sqrt{24} = \sqrt{54}$
      $2.449 + 4.899 = 7.348$

2. Find a similar statement with $\sqrt{7}$ as the first value. $\sqrt{7} + \sqrt{28} = \sqrt{63}$

3. What is the general pattern?
      $\sqrt{x} + \sqrt{4x} = \sqrt{9x}$

You can use the Product of Square Roots Property to show why this pattern is true for all x. Specifically, $\sqrt{x} + \sqrt{4x} = \sqrt{x} + \sqrt{4} \cdot \sqrt{x} = \sqrt{x} + 2\sqrt{x} = 3\sqrt{x} = \sqrt{9} \cdot \sqrt{x} = \sqrt{9x}$.

Background

Activity 1. Some students have a difficult time seeing $\sqrt{x}$ as representing a number. They view the radical sign $\sqrt{\ }$ as an operator (which it is) separate from the radicand. With fractions, some students cannot view $\frac{m}{n}$ as a single number and instead think of m, the fraction bar, and n separately. This activity is designed to help students think of square roots of numbers by dealing with their decimal approximations.

In Step 3, the student is asked to pick from the given list of square roots. The products of larger square roots might not be in the list from Step 1. If the Step 1 list went up to $\sqrt{100}$, then any two different square roots up to $\sqrt{11}$ could be chosen. Step 4 is designed to show that the pattern continues.

(continued on next page)

8 7

2 Teaching

Notes on the Activity

We recommend that Activity 1 be done in pairs even though it is a rather routine activity. One student can work with the calculator while the other records the results. Then, at Step 3, the roles might be reversed. Ask students to think of factoring the radicand. For example, what numbers can be multiplied together to create $\sqrt{16}$? Further, ask them to consider products of perfect squares and imperfect squares. For instance, $\sqrt{8} = \sqrt{4} \cdot \sqrt{2}$ can also be written as $2 \cdot \sqrt{2}$. This will preview simplifying radicals, a topic they will practice later in the lesson.

Notes on the Lesson

Product of Square Roots Property. The equations $\sqrt{a} \cdot \sqrt{b} = \sqrt{ab}$ and $a^{\frac{1}{2}} \cdot b^{\frac{1}{2}} = (ab)^{\frac{1}{2}}$ look different enough to dissuade most students from recognizing that they are the same equation in different notation. To convince students that $x^{\frac{1}{2}}$ is indeed another way of writing $\sqrt{x}$, you can ask students to pick any positive value for x and use a calculator to evaluate the two expressions.

The mathematical reason that they are equal comes from the Product of Powers Property. For all positive values of b and for all m and n, $b^m \cdot b^n = b^{m+n}$, so this property must work when $m = n = \frac{1}{2}$. Consequently, $b^{\frac{1}{2}} \cdot b^{\frac{1}{2}} = b^{\frac{1}{2}+\frac{1}{2}} = b^1 = b$, which means that $b^{\frac{1}{2}}$ must be a square root of b. By convention, we choose $b^{\frac{1}{2}}$ and $\sqrt{b}$ to represent the same square root, namely the principal (or positive) square root.

Notes on the Activity

It may help to discuss the objective of Activity 2 with students before they begin. This activity is a continuation of Activity 1 and you could combine them. Tell them that they are looking for a pattern in the values for $\frac{\sqrt{a}}{\sqrt{b}}$. Explain that 2, 3, and 6 are all factors of 6, 12, and 18, so they are looking at different choices for $\frac{\sqrt{a}}{\sqrt{b}}$ that will yield integers when a is divided by b. Ask them to predict the outcome by using the exponent $\frac{1}{2}$ and the Power of a Quotient Property. Then, have them find evidence supporting their prediction.

In Activity 1, you should have discovered that when the product of two numbers a and b is a third number c, it is also the case that the product of the square root of a and the square root of b is the square root of c. That is, if $ab = c$, then $\sqrt{a} \cdot \sqrt{b} = \sqrt{c} = \sqrt{ab}$. For example, because $5 \cdot 6 = 30$, $\sqrt{5} \cdot \sqrt{6} = \sqrt{30}$. You can check this by using decimal approximations to the square roots.

> **Product of Square Roots Property**
>
> For all nonnegative real numbers a and b, $\sqrt{a} \cdot \sqrt{b} = \sqrt{ab}$.

The Product of Square Roots Property may look unusual when the square roots are written in radical form. But when the square roots are written using the exponent $\frac{1}{2}$, the property takes on a familiar look.

$$a^{\frac{1}{2}} \cdot b^{\frac{1}{2}} = (ab)^{\frac{1}{2}}$$

It is just the Power of a Product Property, with $n = \frac{1}{2}$! This is further evidence of the appropriateness of thinking of the positive square root of a number as its $\frac{1}{2}$ power.

Activity 2

Step 1 Pick a square root from $\sqrt{6}$, $\sqrt{12}$, and $\sqrt{18}$.   Step 1. Answers vary.
Pick a square root from $\sqrt{2}$, $\sqrt{3}$, and $\sqrt{6}$.   Sample answers are given.
Find the quotient of the decimal approximations.

Square roots ___?___ ÷ ___?___ $\sqrt{6}$; $\sqrt{2}$
Decimal approximations ___?___ ÷ ___?___ ≈ ___?___   2.449; 1.414; 1.732
Is the quotient found in the table in Activity 1? ___?___   yes
If so, write the quotient as a square root. ___?___ $\sqrt{3}$
If not, is the quotient close to a number in the table? ___?___
What square root is it closest to? ___?___

Step 2 Repeat the process in Step 1 using a different square root from each group. **Answers vary.**

Step 3 Repeat the process again using a third pair of square roots. **Answers vary.**

In Activity 2, you should have discovered that when the quotient of two numbers c and a is a third number b, it is also the case that the quotient of the square root of c and the square root of a is the square root of b. That is, if $\frac{c}{a} = b$, then $\frac{\sqrt{c}}{\sqrt{a}} = \sqrt{\frac{c}{a}} = \sqrt{b}$. For example, since $\frac{24}{8} = 3$, $\frac{\sqrt{24}}{\sqrt{8}} = \sqrt{\frac{24}{8}} = \sqrt{3}$.

By showing the Product of Square Roots Property with the exponent $\frac{1}{2}$ rather than the radical sign $\sqrt{}$, we see that this is not a new property, but just the Power of a Product Property written in a new form. You might ask students to write the Quotient of Square Roots Property with the exponent $\frac{1}{2}$ rather than the radical sign. There are corresponding properties for cube roots and any other powers. (See Question 35.)

Quotient of Square Roots Property. This property is the special case of $\left(\frac{a}{b}\right)^n = \frac{a^n}{b^n}$, when $n = \frac{1}{2}$. It follows from the Product of Square Roots Property in the same way that the Power of a Quotient Property followed from the Power of a Product Property in Lesson 8-5.

Quotient of Square Roots Property

For all positive real numbers a and c, $\frac{\sqrt{c}}{\sqrt{a}} = \sqrt{\frac{c}{a}}$.

Fact triangles can be used to visualize the Product of Square Roots Property and the Quotient of Square Roots Property. For all positive numbers a, b, and c:

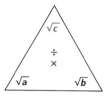

$$a \cdot b = c$$
$$b \cdot a = c$$
$$\frac{c}{a} = b$$
$$\frac{c}{b} = a$$

$$\sqrt{a} \cdot \sqrt{b} = \sqrt{c}$$
$$\sqrt{b} \cdot \sqrt{a} = \sqrt{c}$$
$$\frac{\sqrt{c}}{\sqrt{a}} = \sqrt{b}$$
$$\frac{\sqrt{c}}{\sqrt{b}} = \sqrt{a}$$

 QY1

"Simplifying" Radicals

A radical expression is said to be simplified if the quantity under the radical sign, called the **radicand,** has no perfect square factors other than 1.

Just as you can multiply square roots by using the Product of Square Roots Property, $\sqrt{4} \cdot \sqrt{10} = \sqrt{4 \cdot 10} = \sqrt{40}$, you can rewrite a square root as a product by factoring the radicand.

$$\sqrt{40} = \sqrt{4 \cdot 10}$$
$$= \sqrt{4} \cdot \sqrt{10}$$
$$= 2 \cdot \sqrt{10}$$

Many people consider $2\sqrt{10}$ to be simpler than $\sqrt{40}$ because it has a smaller radicand. This process is called *simplifying a radical*. The key to the process is to find a perfect square factor of the radicand.

Example 1
Simplify $\sqrt{27}$.

Solution Perfect squares larger than 1 are 4, 9, 16, 25, 36, 49,.... . Of these, 9 is a factor of 27.

(continued on next page)

> **QY1**
>
> Use either the Product or Quotient of Square Roots Property to evaluate each expression.
>
> a. $\sqrt{8} \cdot \sqrt{2}$
>
> b. $\frac{\sqrt{45}}{\sqrt{5}}$
>
> c. $\frac{\sqrt{80}}{\sqrt{40}}$

Notes on the Lesson

"Simplifying" Radicals. We put the word "simplifying" in quotes because of the argument that is found after Example 1. Before the advent of calculators, it seemed quite reasonable to think of $2\sqrt{10}$ as being simpler than $\sqrt{40}$, but with calculators, the second expression may be viewed as simpler.

Although $\sqrt{2} + \sqrt{8} = \sqrt{18}$, it is crucial that students realize that there is no general "Sum of Square Roots Property" or "Difference of Square Roots Property." Square roots are defined in terms of multiplication. For this reason, all of their basic properties involve multiplication and division. Only because $\sqrt{8}$ and $\sqrt{18}$ are multiples of $\sqrt{2}$ can the sum $\sqrt{2} + \sqrt{8}$ be simplified.

Additional Example
Example 1 Simplify $\sqrt{50}$. $5\sqrt{2}$

Accommodating the Learner ⬇

Students sometimes feel overwhelmed by simplifying numerical and variable square roots at the same time. Make sure students are comfortable with each method before you begin to combine them. Also, help students recognize when an expression can or cannot be simplified. Before beginning Guided Example 3, give students an opportunity to practice identifying which expressions can be simplified.

8-7

Additional Example

Example 2 A leg of a right triangle is 2 inches long and the hypotenuse is 4 inches long.

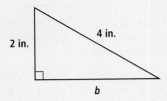

2 in.   4 in.

b

a. Find the exact length of the third side.

By the Pythagorean Theorem,

$\underline{?}^2 + b^2 = \underline{?}^2$ 2; 4

$b^2 = \underline{?}^2 - \underline{?}^2$ 4; 2

$b^2 = 12$

$b = \underline{?}\sqrt{12}$ in.

b. Put the exact length in simplified radical form.

Now use the Product of Square Roots Property to simplify the result. Note that the perfect square 4 is a factor of 12.

$b = \sqrt{\underline{?} \cdot 3}$ 4

$b = \sqrt{\underline{?}} \cdot \sqrt{\underline{?}}$ 4; 3

$b = \underline{?} \cdot \sqrt{3}$ 2

The exact length of the side is $\sqrt{12}$, or $\underline{?}$ inches. $2\sqrt{3}$

$\sqrt{27} = \sqrt{9 \cdot 3}$ Factor 27.

$= \sqrt{9} \cdot \sqrt{3}$ Product of Square Roots Property

$= 3\sqrt{3}$ $\sqrt{9} = 3$

Check Using a calculator we see $\sqrt{27} \approx 5.196152423$ and $3\sqrt{3} \approx 5.196152423$.

Is $3\sqrt{3}$ really simpler than $\sqrt{27}$? It depends. For estimating purposes, $\sqrt{27}$ is simpler since we can easily see it is slightly larger than $\sqrt{25}$ or 5. But for seeing patterns, $3\sqrt{3}$ may be simpler. In the next example, the answer $7\sqrt{2}$ is related to the given information in a useful way that is not served by leaving it in the unsimplified form $\sqrt{98}$.

GUIDED

Example 2

Each leg of the right triangle below is 7 cm long.

7 cm c cm

7 cm

a. Find the exact length of the hypotenuse.

b. Put the exact length in simplified radical form.

Solutions

a. Use the Pythagorean Theorem.

$c^2 = \underline{?}^2 + \underline{?}^2$ Substitute the lengths of the legs. 7; 7

$c^2 = 98$ Add.

$c = \underline{?}$ Use a radical sign to write the exact answer. $\sqrt{98}$

b. Now use the Product of Square Roots Property to simplify the result. Note that the perfect square 49 is a factor of 98.

$c = \sqrt{\underline{?} \cdot 2}$ 49

$c = \sqrt{\underline{?}} \cdot \sqrt{\underline{?}}$ 49; 2

$c = \underline{?}\sqrt{2}$ 7

The exact length of the hypotenuse is $\sqrt{98}$ or $\underline{?}$ cm. $7\sqrt{2}$

The Product of Square Roots Property also applies to expressions containing variables.

GUIDED

Example 3

Assume x and y are positive. Simplify $\sqrt{48x^2y^2}$.

Solution

$$\sqrt{48x^2y^2} = \sqrt{\underline{\;?\;}} \cdot \sqrt{3} \cdot \sqrt{x^2} \cdot \sqrt{y^2}\quad 16$$
$$= \underline{\;?\;} \cdot \sqrt{3} \cdot x \cdot y\quad 4$$
$$= \underline{\;?\;}\, xy\sqrt{3}\quad 4$$

Check Substitute values for x and y. We choose $x = 4$ and $y = 3$.

$$\sqrt{48x^2y^2} = \sqrt{48 \cdot 16 \cdot 9}\qquad\qquad 4xy\sqrt{3} = 4 \cdot 4 \cdot 3\sqrt{3}$$
$$= \sqrt{\underline{\;?\;}}\quad 6{,}912\qquad\qquad\qquad = \underline{\;?\;}\,\sqrt{3}\quad 48$$
$$\approx 83.14\qquad\qquad\qquad\qquad\qquad \approx 83.14$$

It checks.

STOP QY2

Although square roots were first used in connection with geometry, they also have important applications in physical situations. One such application is with the pendulum clock.

In a pendulum clock, a clock hand moves each time the pendulum swings back and forth. The first idea for a pendulum clock came from the great Italian scientist Galileo Galilei in 1581. (At the time of Galileo, there was no accurate way to tell time; watches and clocks did not exist. People used sand timers but they were not very accurate.) Galileo died in 1642, before he could carry out his design. The brilliant Dutch scientist Christiaan Huygens applied Galileo's concept of tracking time with a pendulum swing in 1656.

A very important part of constructing the clock was calculating the time it takes a pendulum to complete one swing back and forth. This is called the *period* of the pendulum. The formula $p = 2\pi\sqrt{\dfrac{L}{32}}$ gives the time p in seconds for one period in terms of the length L (in feet) of the pendulum.

Example 4

A pendulum clock makes one "tick" for each complete swing of the pendulum. If a pendulum is 2 feet long, how many ticks would the clock make in one minute?

Solution First calculate p when $L = 2$.

(*continued on next page*)

▶ **QY2**

a. Assume x and y are positive.
   Simplify $\sqrt{25x^2y}$.

b. Assume x is positive.
   Simplify $\dfrac{\sqrt{24x^2}}{\sqrt{6x^2}}$.

Dutch mathematician, Christiaan Huygens (1629–1695), patented the first pendulum clock, which greatly increased the accuracy of time measurement.
Source: University of St. Andrews

Multiplying and Dividing Square Roots   **501**

Additional Examples

Example 3 Assume x, y, and z are positive. Simplify $\sqrt{98x^2yz^2}$.   49

$$\sqrt{98x^2yz^2} = \sqrt{?} \cdot \sqrt{2} \cdot \sqrt{x^2} \cdot \sqrt{y} \cdot \sqrt{z^2}$$
$$= \underline{\;?\;} \cdot \sqrt{2} \cdot x \cdot \sqrt{y} \cdot z\quad 7$$
$$= \underline{\;?\;}\, xz\sqrt{2} \cdot \sqrt{y}\quad 7$$
$$= \underline{\;?\;}\, xz\sqrt{2y}\quad 7$$

Example 4 At Fermi National Accelerator Laboratory in Illinois there is a pendulum hanging from the high ceiling in the atrium of Wilson Hall. The approximate length of the pendulum is 240 feet. What is the time p for one period of the pendulum? **about 17.2 sec**

8-7

3 Assignment

Recommended Assignment
- Questions 1–34
- Questions 35 and 36 (extra credit)
- Reading Lesson 8-8
- Covering the Ideas 8-8

Notes on the Questions

Questions 9–12 You might write a large perfect square under a radical sign, such as $\sqrt{32,400}$, on the board. Students may be surprised that the Product of Square Roots Property works even when a square root is an integer. Here students might first see 100 as a perfect square factor, then perhaps 4, and then 9. That is, $\sqrt{32,400}$
$= \sqrt{324} \cdot \sqrt{100} = 10\sqrt{324}$
$= 10\sqrt{4} \cdot \sqrt{81} = 10 \cdot 2 \cdot 9 = 180$.

$$p = 2\pi\sqrt{\frac{2}{32}} = 2\pi\sqrt{\frac{1}{16}} = 2\pi\frac{\sqrt{1}}{\sqrt{16}} = 2\pi \cdot \frac{1}{4} = \frac{\pi}{2}$$

It takes $\frac{\pi}{2}$ seconds for the pendulum to go back and forth.

$$\frac{1 \text{ tick}}{\frac{\pi}{2} \text{ s}} \cdot \frac{60 \text{ s}}{1 \text{ min}} = \frac{60}{\frac{\pi}{2}} \frac{\text{tick}}{\text{min}} \approx 38.2 \text{ ticks/min}$$

So the clock makes about 38.2 ticks per minute.

Questions

COVERING THE IDEAS

In 1–4, use the Product or Quotient of Square Roots Property to evaluate the expression.

1. $\sqrt{8} \cdot \sqrt{2}$ 4

2. $\sqrt{36 \cdot 81 \cdot 100}$ 540

3. $\frac{\sqrt{40}}{\sqrt{10}}$ 2

4. $\frac{\sqrt{6^3}}{\sqrt{6}}$ 6

5. If $\sqrt{3} \cdot \sqrt{6} = \sqrt{x} = y\sqrt{z}$, what is x, what is y, and what is z? $x = 18, y = 3, z = 2$

6. If $\frac{\sqrt{63}}{\sqrt{7}} = \sqrt{x} = y$, what is x and what is y? $x = 9, y = 3$

7. **Multiple Choice** Which is *not* equal to $\sqrt{50}$? B
   A $\sqrt{5} \cdot \sqrt{10}$
   B $\sqrt{25} + \sqrt{25}$
   C $\sqrt{2} \cdot \sqrt{25}$
   D $5\sqrt{2}$

8. a. Use the formula $p = 2\pi\sqrt{\frac{L}{32}}$ to calculate the time p for one period of a pendulum of length $L = 8$ feet. $\pi \sec \approx 3.14 \sec$
   b. If the clock makes one tick for each pendulum swing back and forth, how many ticks are there in one minute? about 19 ticks

In 9–12, simplify the square root.

9. $\sqrt{18}$ $3\sqrt{2}$

10. $\sqrt{24}$ $2\sqrt{6}$

11. $\sqrt{50}$ $5\sqrt{2}$

12. $8\sqrt{90}$ $24\sqrt{10}$

13. Assume m and n are positive. Simplify each expression.
   a. $\sqrt{150m^2n}$ $5m\sqrt{6n}$
   b. $\frac{\sqrt{112m^7}}{\sqrt{7m^3}}$ $4m^2$

14. The length of each leg of a right triangle is 8 cm. What is the exact length of the hypotenuse? $8\sqrt{2}$ cm

15. Let $m = \frac{1}{2}$ in the Power of a Quotient Property $\left(\frac{x}{y}\right)^m = \frac{x^m}{y^m}$. What property of this lesson is the result? Quotient of Square Roots Property

---

APPLYING THE MATHEMATICS

In 16–19, write the exact value of the unknown in simplified form. Then approximate the unknown to the nearest hundredth.

16.
10

17.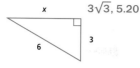
$3\sqrt{3}$, 5.20

18.
$6\sqrt{2}$, 8.49

19.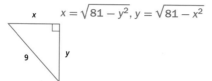
$x = \sqrt{81 - y^2}$, $y = \sqrt{81 - x^2}$

20. Find the area of a triangle with base $\sqrt{18}$ and height $6\sqrt{2}$. **18**

21. The radical $\sqrt{50}$ is equivalent to $5\sqrt{2}$. Explain why it is easier to tell that $\sqrt{50}$ is slightly larger than 7 than it is to tell $5\sqrt{2}$ is slightly larger than 7. Answers vary. Sample answer: Because $\sqrt{49} = 7$

In 22–25, explore adding square roots. You can add square roots using the Distributive Property if their radicands are alike. So, $3\sqrt{11} + 5\sqrt{11} = 8\sqrt{11}$, but $2\sqrt{11} + 4\sqrt{3}$ cannot be simplified. In each expression below, simplify terms if possible, then add or subtract.

22. $2\sqrt{25} + \sqrt{49}$ **17**

23. $\sqrt{12} - 10\sqrt{3}$ **$-8\sqrt{3}$**

24. $\sqrt{45} - \sqrt{20}$ **$\sqrt{5}$**

25. $4\sqrt{50} + 3\sqrt{18}$ **$29\sqrt{2}$**

REVIEW

In 26 and 27, consider the rectangular field pictured here.
(Lesson 8-6, Previous Course)

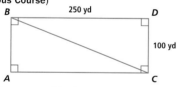

26. How much shorter would it be to walk diagonally across the field as opposed to walking along the sides to get from B to C?
80.742 yd shorter

27. Suppose A is the origin of the coordinate system with the y-axis on $\overleftrightarrow{AB}$ and the x-axis on $\overleftrightarrow{AC}$. Give the coordinates of point D. **(250, 100)**

Notes on the Questions

Questions 22–25 Before doing these questions, check that students realize $3\sqrt{n} + 4\sqrt{n} = 7\sqrt{n}$, and so on.

Questions 26 and 27 These two questions set up the content of the next lesson and should be discussed before moving on to Lesson 8-8.

8-7

4 Wrap-Up

Ongoing Assessment

Ask students to rewrite $\sqrt{75}$ as the product of two powers and as a quotient of two powers.

Answers vary. Sample answer:

$\sqrt{3} \cdot \sqrt{25}$; $\dfrac{\sqrt{150}}{\sqrt{2}}$

Next have them demonstrate that the two expressions are equivalent.

Answers vary. Sample answer:

$\sqrt{3} \cdot \sqrt{25} = \sqrt{3 \cdot 25} = \sqrt{75} =$

$\sqrt{\dfrac{150}{2}} = \dfrac{\sqrt{150}}{\sqrt{2}}$

In 28–30, write the expression as a power of a single number. (Lessons 8-4, 8-3, 8-2)

28. $\dfrac{k^{15}}{k^9}$ k^6

29. $x^4 \cdot x$ x^5

30. $(w^2)^{-3}$ $\dfrac{1}{w^6}$ or w^{-6}

31. Which is greater, $(6^4)^2$, or $6^4 \cdot 6^2$? (Lesson 8-2) $(6^4)^2$

32. In 1995, Ellis invested \$5,000 for 10 years at an annual yield of 8%. In 2005, Mercedes invested \$7,000 for 5 years at 6%. By the end of 2010, who would have more money? Justify your answer. (Lesson 7-1)   Ellis, Answers vary. Sample answer: \$10,794.60 > \$9,367.58

33. After x seconds, an elevator is on floor y, where $y = 46 - 1.5x$. Give the slope and y-intercept of $y = 46 - 1.5x$, and describe what they mean in this situation. (Lesson 6-4)

34. A box with dimensions 30 cm by 60 cm by 90 cm will hold how many times as much as one with dimensions 10 cm by 20 cm by 30 cm? (Lesson 5-10)   27

EXPLORATION

35. Is there a Product of Cube Roots Property like the Product of Square Roots Property? Explore this idea and reach a conclusion. Describe your exploration and defend your conclusion.   Answers vary. Sample answer: Yes, $a^{\frac{1}{3}} b^{\frac{1}{3}} = (ab)^{\frac{1}{3}}$

36. Use the formula $p = 2\pi\sqrt{\dfrac{L}{32}}$ to determine the length of a pendulum that will make 1 tick each second. Answer to the nearest hundredth of an inch.   9.73 in.

Elisha Graves Otis invented the first safety brake for elevators in 1852, kick-starting the elevator industry.

Source: Elevator World, Inc.

33. Slope = –1.5, y-intercept = 46; The slope describes how many floors it descends per second, and the y-intercept is where the elevator is at 0 sec.

QY ANSWERS

1a. 4

1b. 3

1c. $\sqrt{2}$

2a. $5x\sqrt{y}$

2b. 2

Lesson 8-8 Distance in a Plane

> ▶ **BIG IDEA** Using the Pythagorean Theorem, the distance between any points in a plane can be found if you know their coordinates.

Competitions involving small robots (sometimes called Robot Wars™ or BotBashes™) began in the late 1990s as engineering school projects but quickly spread to competitions open to the public. Even television programs have featured the battling 'bots. The competitions take place in an enclosed arena that is laid out in a grid pattern like the one below.

Mental Math

What is 20% of each quantity?

a. 40x 8x

b. 5y y

c. 40x + 5y 8x + y

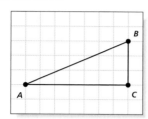

To get from point *A* to point *B* in the arena, robots can be maneuvered manually by their "driver," but because the shortest distance between *A* and *B* is the straight line segment, robot designers like to program direction and distance commands into their robots. The distance traveled is an application of the Pythagorean Theorem because side $\overline{AB}$ is the hypotenuse of a right triangle.

Distances along Vertical and Horizontal Lines

To find the distance between any two points in the coordinate plane, we begin by examining the situation where points are on the same vertical or horizontal line.

You can find the distance between two points on vertical or horizontal lines by thinking of them as being on a number line. The distance can be obtained by counting spaces or by subtracting appropriate coordinates. Consider the rectangle *DEFG* graphed on the next page.

Japan's humanoid robot VisiON NEXTA kicks a ball during a penalty kick competition at the RoboCup 2005 in Osaka, Japan.

Distance in a Plane   **505**

Background

The distance between two points in a plane is one of the most important ideas for later work with coordinate geometry and with the equation for a circle. Finding the distance between two points whose coordinates involve variables also provides wonderful practice in algebra.

Rather than giving students the distance formula at the beginning of the lesson, we have students find the distance between two points by drawing a right triangle whose hypotenuse is the segment connecting

the two points. Students will understand the traditional distance formula better, having worked on problems with such a triangle.

GOAL

Introduce and apply formulas for the distance between two points on the same horizontal or vertical line and for the Pythagorean distance between any two points in a plane.

SPUR Objectives

I Represent squares, cubes, square roots, and cube roots geometrically.

J Calculate distances on the *x-y* coordinate plane.

Materials/Resources

· Lesson Master 8-8A or 8-8B
· Resource Masters 1, 2, 126, and 127
· Scientific or graphing calculator

HOMEWORK

Suggestions for Assignment

• Questions 1–26
• Question 27 (extra credit)
• Reading Lesson 8-9
• Covering the Ideas 8-9

Local Standards

1 Warm-Up

In 1–3, find the distance between the given points.

1. (0, 0) and (−7, 0) 7
2. (0, 0) and (0, 13) 13
3. (−7, 0) and (0, 13) $\sqrt{218}$
4. Explain why the distance between (−6, 0) and (1, 13) is equal to the distance calculated in Question 3. The segment connecting those points is a translation image of the segment connecting the points in Question 3.
5. Find the distance between (a, b) and (a + 3, b + 4). 5

8-8

2 Teaching

Notes on the Lesson

Begin by going through a question like the one posed in Example 1, drawing the right triangle. You should note that two right triangles could be drawn to obtain the distance. In Example 1, the other right triangle has its third vertex at (1, 5).

Additional Example

Example 1 Find DE in $\triangle DEF$ below. $\sqrt{13} \approx 3.61$

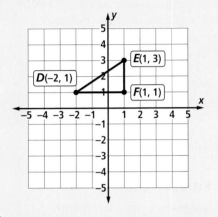

Note-Taking Tips

Encourage students to memorize the distance formula by first learning the formula as $distance^2 = (change\ in\ x)^2 + (change\ in\ y)^2$. If they can see the connection with the Pythagorean Theorem, the formula becomes much easier for many students to remember. Suggest that they include this formula alongside the distance formula in their notes.

Horizontal Distance The distance DE can be found by counting spaces on the number line or it can be calculated by subtracting the x-coordinates and then taking the absolute value.

$$DE = |-2 - 3| = 5$$

Vertical Distance Similarly, the distance EF can be found by counting spaces or it can be calculated by subtracting the y-coordinates and taking the absolute value.

$$EF = |3 - (-1)| = 4$$

STOP QY1

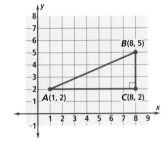

> **QY1**
>
> Find the length of the segment whose endpoints are (50, 21) and (50, 46).

The Distance between Any Two Points in a Plane

The Pythagorean Theorem enables you to find the distance between any two points in the plane.

Example 1

Find AB in $\triangle ABC$ at the right.

Solution $\overline{AB}$ is the hypotenuse of $\triangle ABC$ whose legs, $\overline{AC}$ and $\overline{BC}$, are horizontal and vertical, respectively. The length of the legs can be calculated by subtracting appropriate coordinates.

$$AC = |8 - 1| = 7 \qquad BC = |5 - 2| = 3$$

Now apply the Pythagorean Theorem.

$$(AB)^2 = (AC)^2 + (BC)^2$$
$$(AB)^2 = 7^2 + 3^2$$
$$(AB)^2 = 58$$
$$AB = \sqrt{58} \approx 7.62$$

This method can be generalized to find the distance between any two points on a coordinate grid.

Let point $A = (x_1, y_1)$ and $B = (x_2, y_2)$, as shown at the right. Then a right triangle can be formed with a third vertex at $C = (x_2, y_1)$. Using these coordinates, $AC = |x_2 - x_1|$ and $BC = |y_2 - y_1|$. Now use the Pythagorean Theorem.

$$AB^2 = AC^2 + BC^2 = |x_2 - x_1|^2 + |y_2 - y_1|^2$$

Since a number and its absolute value have the same square, $|x_2 - x_1|^2 = (x_2 - x_1)^2$ and $|y_2 - y_1|^2 = (y_2 - y_1)^2$.

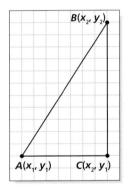

Accommodating the Learner ⬇

When students begin to use the distance formula, they are sometimes confused as to why it does not matter which point is chosen to be (x_1, y_1) and which is used for (x_2, y_2). Take extra time to show students that once the differences $x_2 - x_1$ and $y_2 - y_1$ are squared, either choice yields the same values.

Thus $AB^2 = (x_2 - x_1)^2 + (y_2 - y_1)^2$.

Take the positive square root of each side. The result is a formula for the distance between two points in the coordinate plane.

Formula for the Distance between Two Points in a Coordinate Plane

The distance AB between the points $A = (x_1, y_1)$ and $B = (x_2, y_2)$ in a coordinate plane is $AB = \sqrt{(x_2 - x_1)^2 + (y_2 - y_1)^2}$.

GUIDED

Example 2

Find the distance between the points (23, 16) and (31, −11) to the nearest thousandth.

Solution Using the formula for the distance between two points in a plane, let $A = (x_1, y_1) = (\underline{\ ?\ }, \underline{\ ?\ })$ and $B = (x_2, y_2) = (\underline{\ ?\ }, \underline{\ ?\ })$. 23; 16; 31; −11

$AB = \sqrt{(\underline{\ ?\ } - \underline{\ ?\ })^2 + (\underline{\ ?\ } - \underline{\ ?\ })^2}$ 31; 23; −11; 16

$= \sqrt{(\underline{\ ?\ })^2 + (\underline{\ ?\ })^2}$ 8; −27

$= \sqrt{\underline{\ ?\ } + \underline{\ ?\ }} = \sqrt{\underline{\ ?\ }} \approx \underline{\ ?\ }$ 64; 729; 793; 28.160

Example 3

Use the map at the right. It shows streets and the locations of three buildings in a city. The streets are 1 block apart.

a. Give the coordinates of all three buildings.

b. Find the distance from the train station to the zoo.

Solutions

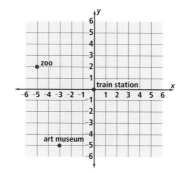

a. The coordinates are as follows.

train station (0, 0)

zoo (−5, 2)

art museum (−3, −5)

b. We need to find the distance from (0, 0) to (−5, 2).

distance $= \sqrt{(0 - -5)^2 + (0 - 2)^2}$

$= \sqrt{(5)^2 + (-2)^2}$

$= \sqrt{25 + 4}$

$= \sqrt{29} \approx 5.39$ blocks

Notes on the Lesson

Example 2 In this example, one point has a negative coordinate, so the substitution into the formula involves subtracting a negative number.

Additional Examples

Example 2 Find the distance between the points (2, −25) and (−3, −12).

Using the formula for the distance between two points in a plane, let $A = (x_1, y_1) = (\underline{\ ?\ }, \underline{\ ?\ })$ and $B = (x_2, y_2) = (\underline{\ ?\ }, \underline{\ ?\ })$. Answers vary. Sample answer: 2; −25; −3; −12

$AB = \sqrt{(\underline{\ ?\ } - \underline{\ ?\ })^2 (\underline{\ ?\ } - \underline{\ ?\ })^2}$

   −3; 2; −12; −25

$= \sqrt{(\underline{\ ?\ })^2 + (\underline{\ ?\ })^2}$ −5; 13

$= \sqrt{\underline{\ ?\ } + \underline{\ ?\ }} = \sqrt{\underline{\ ?\ }} \approx \underline{\ ?\ }$

   25; 169; 194; 13.93

Example 3 Use the map at the left. Find the distance from the art museum to the train station. $\sqrt{34} \approx 5.83$ blocks

Accommodating the Learner ⬆

Use this opportunity to provide students with extra practice manipulating fractions by asking them to find the distance between points with fractional coordinates.

8-8

3 Assignment

Recommended Assignment

- Questions 1–26
- Question 27 (extra credit)
- Reading Lesson 8-9
- Covering the Ideas 8-9

Notes on the Questions

Questions 1–5 These questions cover the idea of finding distances along horizontal or vertical lines. You might cover Questions 2–5 before doing Question 1.

Question 13 If students are bothered by the decimals, point out that they could perform a size change of magnitude 100 on both points to obtain integer coordinates, calculate the distance between the points, and then divide that distance by 100.

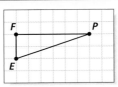 **QY2**

STOP QY2

▶ **QY2**

In Example 3, find the distance from the zoo to the art museum.

Questions

COVERING THE IDEAS

1. Refer to $\triangle EFP$ at the right.

   a. Determine FE. **2**

   b. Determine FP. **6**

   c. Use the Pythagorean Theorem to calculate EP. $\sqrt{40} \approx 6.325$

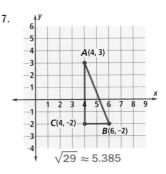

In 2–5, find PT.

2. $P = (3, 4)$ and $T = (3, 9)$ **5**

3. $P = (-3, 4)$ and $T = (4, 4)$ **7**

4. $P = (-\frac{2}{3}, \frac{1}{2})$ and $T = (\frac{5}{3}, \frac{1}{2})$ $\frac{7}{3}$

5. $P = (33, -4)$ and $T = (33, 18)$ **22**

In 6 and 7, find the length of $\overline{AB}$.

6.

$\sqrt{45} \approx 6.708$

7.

$\sqrt{29} \approx 5.385$

In 8–13, find the distance between the two points.

8. $E = (4, 9); D = (8, 6)$ **5**

9. $F = (15, 2); G = (20, -10)$ **13**

10. $H = (5, -1); I = (11, 2.2)$ **6.8**

11. $J = (-6, -7); K = (-2, 0)$ $\sqrt{65} \approx 8.062$

12. $L = (-1, 2); M = (-3, 4)$ $\sqrt{8} \approx 2.828$

13. $N = (-0.43, -0.91); P = (-0.36, -0.63)$ $\sqrt{0.0833} \approx 0.288617$

Extension

One method to determine if three points are collinear is to find the distance between all three pairs of points, and to check to see if the sum of the two smaller distances is exactly equal to the greatest distance. Provide students with a diagram, and lead them through a justification of the method as needed.

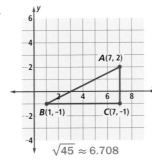

8-8A Lesson Master

Questions on SPUR Objectives
See pages 521–523 for objectives.

REPRESENTATIONS Objectives I and J

1. A square has a diagonal with a length of 18 cm.
   a. Find the length of a side of the square. $9\sqrt{2}$ cm
   b. Find the area of the square.   162 cm²

2. A cube has a volume of 686 cubic inches. Find the exact length of an edge. $7\sqrt[3]{2}$ in.

3. The area of the isosceles triangle ABC at the right is 6 square units. What is the exact value of AB? $\sqrt{13}$ units

4. Give the formula for the distance between two points in a plane. $\sqrt{(x_2-x_1)^2 + (y_2-y_1)^2}$

5. Use the graph at the right to complete the following.
   a. Give the coordinates of points A and B. $A(2, 3)$ $B(7, 5)$
   b. Find the distance between A and B. $\sqrt{29}$

In 6–8, find the distance between the given points. Give the exact simplified value.

6. $(-3, 8)$ and $(5, 6)$ $2\sqrt{17}$

7. $(2, 7)$ and $(7, 2)$ $5\sqrt{2}$

8. $(4, -6)$ and $(-1, 3)$ $\sqrt{106}$

9. Use the graph at the right to complete the following.
   a. Find the length of $\overline{UF}$. $2\sqrt{13}$ units
   b. Find the area of $\triangle FUN$.   12 units²

412   *Algebra*

APPLYING THE MATHEMATICS

In 14 and 15, use the map at the right, which shows the locations of a house, school, and mall. Suppose each square of the grid is a half mile on a side.

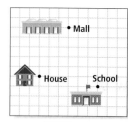

14. **a.** What is the distance from the house to the school?
    b. Which is closer to the house, the mall or the school? the mall

15. How far is it from school to the mall? $\sqrt{11.25} \approx 3.35$ mi

16. Pirate Slopebeard has the treasure map below. How far is the treasure from the start if you travel along a straight path "as the crow flies?" $\sqrt{8,500} \approx 92$ paces

14a. $\sqrt{9.25} \approx 3.04$ mi

17. Write an expression for the distance between the points $(0, 0)$ and (b, d). $\sqrt{b^2 + d^2}$

18. The vertices of a triangle are $(3, 4)$, $(6, 9)$, and $(9, 4)$. Is the triangle equilateral? How do you know?

19. Write the distance formula using a power instead of a radical sign. $[(x_2 - x_1)^2 + (y_2 - y_1)^2]^{\frac{1}{2}}$

20. Does it matter which ordered pair is first when using the distance formula? Choose two ordered pairs. Do the calculation both ways to verify your answer.

18. No; the distance between $(3, 4)$ and $(9, 4)$ is 6. the distance between $(3, 4)$ and $(6, 9)$ is $\sqrt{34}$. Since these distances are not equal, the triangle is not equilateral.

20. no, Answers vary. Sample answer: Consider the distance between $(3, 4)$ and $(10, 12)$.

$[(10 - 3)^2 + (12 - 4)^2]^{\frac{1}{2}}$
$= (113)^{\frac{1}{2}}$

$[(3 - 10)^2 + (4 - 12)^2]^{\frac{1}{2}}$
$= (113)^{\frac{1}{2}}$

REVIEW

21. Evaluate $3^{\frac{1}{2}} \cdot 4^{\frac{1}{2}} \cdot 12^{\frac{1}{2}}$ in your head. **(Lesson 8-7)** 12

22. Consider the function f with $f(x) = 1.5^x$. Find the following values to the nearest hundredth. **(Lessons 8-6, 7-6)**
    a. $f(0)$ 1
    b. $f\left(\frac{1}{2}\right)$ 1.22
    c. $f(1)$ 1.5
    d. $f(2)$ 2.25
    e. $f(-1)$ 0.67
    f. $f(-2)$ 0.44

23. If $d = \sqrt{6}$, find the value of $\frac{d^5}{(3d)^2} \cdot 10d$. **(Lessons 8-6, 8-5)** 40

Notes on the Questions

Questions 14 and 15 Coordinates are not needed to do these questions, but the idea of putting a right triangle on a coordinate system is needed.

Question 16 In this problem, students have to determine their own coordinate system. Point out that the answer is the same no matter where the origin is located, but the computations are easier if the origin is conveniently located.

Question 20 This question is about an important aspect of the distance formula and it should be discussed.

Distance in a Plane **509**

8-8

4) Wrap-Up

Ongoing Assessment

Ask students to choose a partner and have each person write an ordered pair. Then ask the partners to take their two ordered pairs and plot them on a coordinate plane. Next, have them each use the distance formula to find the distance between the points. Once they are both finished with their calculations, the partners should compare their answers and discuss any differences in their work or their solutions.

Project Update

Project 3, Interview with Pythagoras, on page 517, and Project 4, Moving in the Coordinate Plane, on page 518, relate to the content of this lesson.

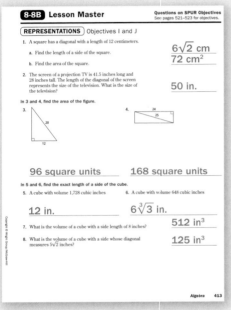

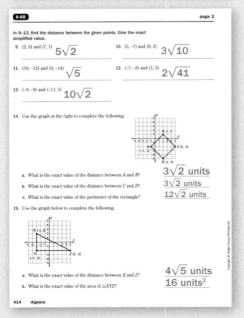

24. Suppose Pythagoras Park is a rectangle 250 meters wide and 420 meters long. There are sidewalks around the edges of the park and a diagonal sidewalk connecting the southeast corner to the northwest corner. Esmeralda and Dory are standing at the southeast corner and want to get to the ice cream stand at the northwest corner. (**Lessons 8-6, 5-3**)

    a. How many meters would Esmeralda and Dory have to walk if they traveled along the diagonal sidewalk? Round your answer to the nearest meter. **489 m**

    b. How many meters would Esmeralda and Dory have to walk if they traveled along the edge sidewalks? **670 m**

    c. Esmeralda walks along the diagonal sidewalk at 60 meters per minute while Dory jogs along the edge sidewalks at 100 meters per minute. Who arrives at the ice cream stand first? **Dory**

25. Suppose the graph of f is a line with slope $\frac{8}{5}$ and $f(7) = 1.2$. Write a formula for $f(x)$. (**Lessons 7-6, 6-2**) $f(x) = \frac{8}{5}x - 10$

26. Suppose $f(x) = 29x - 2$ and $g(x) = 2(34.5x + 17.75)$. For what value of x does $f(x) = g(x)$? (**Lessons 7-6, 4-4**) **−0.9375**

EXPLORATION

27. You may have seen videos showing giant robotic arms maneuvering through space to perform a task. Did you ever wonder how the robot is controlled? One component is calculating how far to move the arm. To do this, designers extend the ideas in this lesson from 2 dimensions (x, y) to 3 dimensions (x, y, z) and calculate the distance between two *ordered triples* that describe locations in space. The distance between two points (x_1, y_1, z_1) and (x_2, y_2, z_2) in space is $\sqrt{(x_2 - x_1)^2 + (y_2 - y_1)^2 + (z_2 - z_1)^2}$. Calculate the distance between $(3, 5, 2)$ and $(-4, 3, -2)$. Draw a picture of the two points and the distance on the graph below. **8.31**

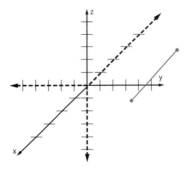

According to the U.N.'s 2004 World Robotics Survey, most industrial robots are used on assembly lines, chiefly in the auto industry.

QY ANSWERS

1. 25

2. $\sqrt{53} \approx 7.28$ blocks

510   Powers and Roots

Remembering Properties of Powers and Roots

▶ **BIG IDEA** If you forget any of the properties of powers, you can recall them by testing special cases, following patterns, and knowing alternate ways of rewriting the same expression.

Here are six properties of powers that were presented in this chapter. They apply to all exponents m and n and nonzero bases a and b.

Properties of Powers

Product of Powers	Negative Exponent
$b^m \cdot b^n = b^{m+n}$	$b^{-n} = \frac{1}{b^n}$
Power of a Power	Quotient of Powers
$(b^m)^n = b^{mn}$	$\frac{b^m}{b^n} = b^{m-n}$
Power of a Product	Power of a Quotient
$(ab)^n = a^n b^n$	$\left(\frac{a}{b}\right)^n = \frac{a^n}{b^n}$

In addition, two properties of square roots were studied. They apply to all nonnegative numbers a and b.

Properties of Square Roots

Product of Square Roots	Quotient of Square Roots
$\sqrt{a} \cdot \sqrt{b} = \sqrt{ab}$	$\frac{\sqrt{a}}{\sqrt{b}} = \sqrt{\frac{a}{b}}, b \neq 0$

With so many properties, some students confuse them. This lesson shows you how to use general problem-solving strategies to remember the properties and to test a special case to verify your reasoning.

Testing a Special Case

Because of calculators, a strategy called *testing a special case* is often possible. You can use this strategy to verify your reasoning.

Mental Math

Evaluate.

a. $|-19 + -42|$ 61

b. $|55.5 - 32| + |-9|$ 32.5

c. $|-10 + 5| - |-30 + 15|$ -10

Background

Of all the concepts that students need to learn in mathematics, there is none more important than the notion of the *consistency* of mathematics. This consistency allows us to use the problem-solving strategy in this lesson, testing special cases. Consistency enables us to generalize, to prove, and to disprove.

Yet students often see properties of powers as distinct independent facts to be memorized.

The purpose of this lesson is to dissuade students from memorizing without understanding.

We have already taken advantage of this powerful strategy in many of the checks of problems in earlier chapters, so it should be familiar to students.

GOAL

Summarize the chapter by providing problem-solving strategies by which students can recall the properties of the chapter.

SPUR Objectives

C Rewrite powers of products and quotients.

F Test a special case to determine whether a pattern is true.

Materials/Resources

· Lesson Master 8-9A or 8-9B
· Resource Master 128
· Scientific or graphing calculator

HOMEWORK

Suggestions for Assignment
• Questions 1–30
• Question 31 (extra credit)
• Reading Lesson 9-1
• Covering the Ideas 9-1

Local Standards

1 Warm-Up

In 1 and 2, show with an example that the indicated equation does *not* describe a general property of powers.

1. $\sqrt{a} + \sqrt{a} = \sqrt{2a}$ Answers vary.
Sample answer: Let $a = 3$.
$\sqrt{3} + \sqrt{3} = 2\sqrt{3} = \sqrt{4} \cdot \sqrt{3} = \sqrt{4 \cdot 3} = \sqrt{12} \neq \sqrt{2 \cdot 3} = \sqrt{6}$

2. $(a + b)^5 = a^5 + b^5$ Answers vary.
Sample answer: Let $a = 2$ and $b = 3$.
$(2 + 3)^5 = 5^5 = 3,125 \neq 275 = 32 + 243 = 2^5 + 3^5$

3. **Multiple Choice** For all real numbers b, $\sqrt{b^{100}} = \underline{?}$. B
A b^{10} **B** b^{50} **C** $b^{99.5}$ **D** $\frac{b^{100}}{2}$

4. Darla thinks $\sqrt{2} \cdot \sqrt{3} \cdot \sqrt{5} \cdot \sqrt{7} \cdot \sqrt{11} = \sqrt{2,310}$. Is she right? If so, why? If not, what is the correct product? Yes, $\sqrt{2} \cdot \sqrt{3} \cdot \sqrt{5} \cdot \sqrt{7} \cdot \sqrt{11} = \sqrt{2 \cdot 3 \cdot 5 \cdot 7 \cdot 11} = \sqrt{2,310}$

8-9

2 Teaching

Notes on the Lesson

You may wish to teach this lesson by going over the reading with students paragraph by paragraph, example by example.

Six of the eight properties at the beginning of the lesson naturally pair with each other: products and quotients of powers, powers of products and quotients, and powers and quotients of square roots. This brings the list to five properties, not eight. The square root properties are special cases of the properties just above them, so it could be argued that there are only three properties from which everything else easily follows: the Product of Powers Property, the Negative Exponent Property, and the Power of a Power Property. Furthermore, the Negative Exponent Property follows from the Product of Powers Property.

Example 1 Emily's three choices might be options on a multiple-choice test. Testing a special case can be used both to verify properties and to find counterexamples.

Example 2 This example shows the use of testing a special case in finding a counterexample. It illustrates that although the numbers 0, 1, and 2 are not good for checking answers to problems involving powers, they may be just the numbers you would want to use in some special situations. For example, Squire Root could have seen that x^4 does not always equal $x^3 + x^3$ by noting that these expressions are not equal when $x = 1$. But there is a true pattern lurking underneath the equation $2^3 + 2^3 = 2^4$. In general, for all integers n, $2^n + 2^n = 2^{n+1}$.

Additional Examples

Example 1 Mark was not sure how to simplify $(x^{23})^6$. He felt the answer could be x^{138} or x^{29}. Which is correct? By testing a special case such as $x = 2$, he can see that the correct answer is x^{138}.

Example 2 Notice that $2^2 + 2^2 = 2^3$ because $4 + 4 = 8$, and that $0^2 + 0^2 = 0^3$. Can you conclude that $x^2 + x^2 = x^3$? $x = 3$ is a counterexample which shows that because $3^2 + 3^2 = 18 \neq 27 = 3^3$, the property is not always true.

Example 1

Emily was not sure how to simplify $x^5 \cdot x^6$. She felt the answer could be x^{30}, $2x^{11}$, or x^{11}. Which is correct?

Solution 1 Use a special case. Let $x = 3$. Now calculate $x^5 \cdot x^6$ (with a calculator) and see if it equals the calculator result for x^{30} or $2x^{11}$ or x^{11}.

$x^5 \cdot x^6 = 3^5 \cdot 3^6 = 177{,}147$
$x^{30} = 3^{30} = 205{,}891{,}132{,}094{,}649 \approx 2.0589 \cdot 10^{14}$
$2x^{11} = 2 \cdot 3^{11} = 354{,}294$
$x^{11} = 3^{11} = 177{,}147$

So, the answer is x^{11}.

Solution 2 Use repeated multiplication to rewrite x^5 and x^6.

$x^5 \cdot x^6 = (x \cdot x \cdot x \cdot x \cdot x) \cdot (x \cdot x \cdot x \cdot x \cdot x \cdot x)$

Notice there are 11 factors of x in the product. So, $x^5 \cdot x^6 = x^{11}$.

Showing That a Pattern Is Not Always True

When testing a special case, you should be careful in choosing numbers. The numbers 0, 1, and 2 are not good for checking answers to problems involving powers, because a pattern may work for a few of these numbers but not for all numbers. Recall that a *counterexample* is a special case for which the answer is false. To show a pattern is not true, it is sufficient to find one counterexample.

Example 2

Sir Lancelot's assistant, Squire Root, noticed $2^3 + 2^3 = 2^4$ since $8 + 8 = 16$. He guessed that in general, there is a property $x^3 + x^3 = x^4$.

He tested a second case by letting $x = 0$ and found $0^3 + 0^3 = 0^4$. He concluded that the property is always true. Is he correct?

Solution Try a different value for x. Let $x = 5$.

Does $5^3 + 5^3 = 5^4$? Does $125 + 125 = 625$? No. $x = 5$ is a counterexample that shows that Squire's property is not always true.

If you have trouble remembering a property or are not certain that you have simplified an expression correctly, try using repeated multiplication or testing a special case.

In Example 3, using the properties of powers, a calculation that is complicated even with a calculator, is reduced to two calculations.

Accommodating the Learner ⬇

Spend extra time teaching struggling students how to check their own work with special cases. Encourage them to test an answer whenever they have time remaining on quizzes or tests.

Example 3

The mean radius of Earth is about $3.96 \cdot 10^3$ miles. The mean radius of Jupiter is about $4.34 \cdot 10^4$ miles. Using the formula $V = \frac{4}{3}\pi r^3$ for the volume V of a sphere with radius r, how many times could Earth fit inside Jupiter?

Solution To answer the question, you need to divide the volume of Jupiter by the volume of Earth. So substitute for r in the formula for the volume of a sphere.

$$\frac{\text{volume of Jupiter}}{\text{volume of Earth}} \approx \frac{\frac{4}{3}\pi(4.34 \cdot 10^4)^3}{\frac{4}{3}\pi(3.96 \cdot 10^3)^3}$$

$$= \frac{(4.34 \cdot 10^4)^3}{(3.96 \cdot 10^3)^3} \qquad \text{Multiplication of Fractions}$$

$$= \left(\frac{4.34 \cdot 10^4}{3.96 \cdot 10^3}\right)^3 \qquad \text{Power of a Quotient Property}$$

$$= \left(\frac{43.4}{3.96}\right)^3 \qquad \text{Quotient of Powers Property}$$

$$\approx 1,316 \qquad \text{Arithmetic}$$

In Example 3, notice that by using the properties, we reduced a complicated calculation to two operations: division of 43.4 by 3.96 and then cubing of the quotient.

Earth could fit inside Jupiter about 1,300 times. (Jupiter is *very* big compared to Earth!)

It is important to realize that the properties of numbers and operations are consistent. If you apply them correctly, you can find many paths to a correct solution. The result you get using some properties will not disagree with the results another person gets by correctly using other properties.

GUIDED

Example 4

If $\left(\frac{9q^{-5}}{6q^{-3}}\right)^{-7} = aq^n$, what are the values of a and n?

Solution 1 This question requires that the expression on the left side be simplified into the form aq^n.

(*continued on next page*)

Notes on the Lesson

Example 3 This example can be done many different ways. After dividing by the common factors in the numerator and denominator, an alternate solution is to take the cube of the expressions first. This yields $\frac{4.34^3 \cdot 10^{12}}{3.96^3 \cdot 10^9}$, or $\approx 1,316$. Jupiter is so big that *all* the other planets of the solar system could fit inside it. (Our sun is so big that about 985 Jupiters could fit inside it!)

Example 4 This example gives two methods for simplifying a fractional expression that involves a negative power. Individual students will likely be more comfortable with one of the methods, but it's important for students to realize that most problems can be approached in more than one way. Emphasize again that negative powers mean reciprocals, not negative numbers. But if students forget this or any other property, they can test a special case.

Additional Example

Example 3 Using the radii from Example 3 in the text, find the ratio of the surface area of Earth to the surface area of Jupiter. 0.08 : 1

ENGLISH LEARNERS
Vocabulary Development

Discuss the terms *counterexample, special case*, and *proof* and how they are related. Show how counterexamples can be used to show that a statement is false, but stress that a special case is not sufficient for proving the validity of a general property.

8-9

Additional Example

Example 4 If $\left(\dfrac{25r^{-3}}{10r^2}\right)^{-5} = ar^n$,

what are the values of a and n?

Solution

This question requires that the expression on the left side be simplified into the form ar^n.

Apply the Power of a Power Property to eliminate the parentheses.

$\left(\dfrac{25r^{-3}}{10r^2}\right)^{-5} = \dfrac{25^{?}\, r^{?}}{10^{?}\, r^{?}}$ −5; 15; −5; −10

Apply the Quotient of Powers Property.

$= \dfrac{25^{?}}{10^{?}}\, r^{?}$ −5; −5; 25

Apply the Negative Exponent Property.

$= \dfrac{10^{?}}{25^{?}}\, r^{?}$ 5; 5; 25

Use the Power of a Quotient Property.

$= \left(\dfrac{10}{25}\right)^{?}\, r^{?}$ 5; 25

Rewrite the fraction in lowest terms.

$= \left(\dfrac{2}{5}\right)^{?}\, r^{?}$ 5; 25

Thus, $a = \left(\dfrac{2}{5}\right)^{?}$ and $n = \underline{\ ?\ }$. 5; 25

$\left(\dfrac{9q^{-5}}{6q^{-3}}\right)^{-7} = \dfrac{9^{\,?}\, q^{\,?}}{6^{\,?}\, q^{\,?}}$ −7; 35 ⁄ −7; 21
Apply the Power of a Power Property to eliminate the parentheses.

$= \dfrac{9^{\,?}}{6^{\,?}}\, q^{\,?}\ ^{14}$ Apply the Quotient of Powers Property. −7; −7

$= \dfrac{6^{\,?}\ ^{7}}{9^{\,?}\ ^{7}}\, q^{\,?}\ ^{14}$ Apply the Negative Exponent Property $\left(b^{-n} = \dfrac{1}{b^n}\right)$.

$= \left(\dfrac{6}{9}\right)^{?}\ ^{7}\, q^{\,?}\ ^{14}$ Use the Power of a Quotient Property.

$= \left(\dfrac{2}{3}\right)^{?}\ ^{7}\, q^{\,?}\ ^{14}$ Rewrite the fraction in lowest terms.

Thus, $a = \left(\dfrac{2}{3}\right)^{?}\ ^{7}$ and $n = \underline{\ ?\ }$. 14

Solution 2 Work with a partner and follow these steps.

1. Apply the Quotient of Powers Property inside the parentheses.

2. Write the fraction in lowest terms.

3. Apply the Power of a Power Property.

You should obtain the same answer as in Solution 1.

Example 4
Solution 2

1. $\left(\dfrac{9g^{-5}}{6g^{-3}}\right)^{-2} = \left(\dfrac{9}{6}g^{-2}\right)^{-7}$

2. $\left(\dfrac{3}{2}g^{-2}\right)^{-7}$

3. $\left(\dfrac{3}{2}\right)^{-7} g^{-2\,\cdot\,-7} = \left(\dfrac{2}{3}\right)^7 \cdot g^{14}$

Questions

COVERING THE IDEAS

1. **Multiple Choice** For all nonzero values of n, $\dfrac{n^{40}}{n^{10}} =$ B

   A n^4.   B n^{30}.   C 1^{30}.   D 1^4.

2. **Multiple Choice** For all nonzero values of s, $\dfrac{s^4}{(2s)^2} =$ C

   A $4s^2$.   B $\dfrac{s^2}{2}$.   C $\dfrac{s^2}{4}$.   D 1.

3. **Multiple Choice** For all nonzero values of v, $\dfrac{v^8 \cdot v^{12}}{(v^8)^{12}} =$ C

   A 1.   B $-v^{76}$.   C v^{-76}.   D v^{76}.

4. **Multiple Choice** For all values of m and n, $(3m)^2 \cdot (2n)^3 =$ C

   A $6m^2n^3$.   B $48m^2n^3$.   C $72m^2n^3$.   D $3{,}125m^2n^3$.

5. What is a counterexample? A special case for which the answer is false

---

Accommodating the Learner ⬆

Create a variety of expressions that require students to apply multiple properties. Initially, lead them through problems step by step, as in Guided Example 4. Gradually, encourage students to become more independent. As there are several approaches to solving most of these problems, ask students to find as many different solution methods as they can and choose the most efficient one.

6. **True or False** If two special cases of a pattern are true, then the pattern is true. false

7. **True or False** If one special case of a pattern is false, then the pattern is false. true

8. Consider the equation $x^4 = 8x$.

   a. Is the equation true for the special case $x = 2$? yes
   b. Is the equation true for the special case $x = 0$? yes
   c. Is the equation true for the special case $x = 3$? no
   d. Is the equation true for all values of x? no

In 9–11, test special cases to decide whether the pattern is always true. Show all work.

9. $(r^3)^{-4} = r^{3-4}$ no   10. $(2n)^3 = 2n^3$ no   11. $5y^3 \cdot 4y^4 = 20y^7$ yes

In 12–15, name the property or properties being used.

12. $\left(\frac{2}{q}\right)^{10} = \frac{2^{10}}{q^{10}}$ Power of a Quotient   13. $(x + 4)(x + 4)^4 = (x + 4)^5$

14. $(2x^2y)^3 = 2^3x^6y^3$ 15. $\left(\frac{2}{41}\right)^{-3} = \left(\frac{1}{\frac{2}{41}}\right)^3$ Negative Exponent

13. **Product of Powers**

14. **Power of a Product and Power of a Power**

In 16–18, write the expression without negative exponents.

16. $\left(\frac{3}{5}\right)^{-1}$ $\frac{5}{3}$ 17. $\left(\frac{3x^2}{y^3}\right)^{-2}$ $\frac{y^6}{9x^4}$ 18. $\left(\frac{2m^{-2}}{12m}\right)^{-40}$ $\frac{6^{40}m^{120}}{1}$

In 19 and 20, refer to Example 3 and use the fact that the mean radius of Mars is about $2.11 \cdot 10^3$ miles.

19. About how many times could Mars fit into Earth? 6

20. About how many times could Mars fit into Jupiter? 8,702

APPLYING THE MATHEMATICS

21. Describe two different ways to simplify $\left(\frac{x^6}{x^3}\right)^{-2}$.

22. Consider the pattern $\frac{2}{x} - \frac{1}{y} = \frac{2y - x}{xy}$.

    a. Is the pattern true when $x = 3$ and $y = 5$? yes
    b. Test the special case when $x = y$. yes
    c. Test another case. Let $x = 6$ and $y = 2$. yes
    d. Do you think the pattern is *always*, *sometimes but not always*, or *never true* for all nonzero x and y? always

21. Answers vary. Sample answer:
$$\left(\frac{x^6}{x^3}\right)^{-2} = \frac{x^{-12}}{x^{-6}} =$$
$$x^{-6} = \frac{1}{x^6}; \left(\frac{x^6}{x^3}\right)^{-2} =$$
$$(x^3)^{-2} = x^{-6} = \frac{1}{x^6}$$

In 23 and 24, use the fact that the prime factorization of 24 is $2^3 \cdot 3$ and the prime factorization of 360 is $2^3 \cdot 3^2 \cdot 5$.

23. Give the prime factorization of 360^{25}. $2^{75}3^{50}5^{25}$

24. Give the prime factorization of $\left(\frac{360}{24}\right)^8$. $5^8 3^8$

Remembering Properties of Powers and Roots **515**

3 Assignment

Recommended Assignment
- Questions 1–30
- Question 31 (extra credit)
- Reading Lesson 9-1
- Covering the Ideas 9-1

Notes on the Questions

Question 8 This equation has two real solutions, 0 and 2.

Questions 16–18 Encourage students to try more than one way to work out these questions.

Question 22 Point out to students that different values are used for x and y when testing the pattern. This is not necessary, but it avoids not detecting an error due to switching the variables.

Question 24 If students realize that $\frac{360}{24} = 15$, they can see that the answer should be $5^8 \cdot 3^8$.

Question 31 We encourage going through at least some part of this question so that students realize that the basic properties of powers are related to multiplication and division, and not to addition and subtraction.

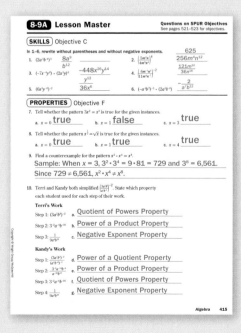

8-9

4 Wrap-Up

Ongoing Assessment

Have students consider the expression $\left(\frac{2x - y}{x}\right)^2$. Then either by testing special cases or by rewriting, have them determine which of the following expressions is equivalent: $\frac{-4y}{x} + \frac{y^2}{x^2} + 4$ or $\frac{4x^2 - y^2}{x^2}$. $\frac{-4y}{x} + \frac{y^2}{x^2} + 4$

REVIEW

25. Find the distance between the points $(-3, -9)$ and $(12, 56)$. Round to the nearest tenth, if necessary. **(Lesson 8-8)** 66.7

26. Let $y = \sqrt{3}$ and $z = \sqrt{5}$. Evaluate $\frac{y}{z} \cdot (2yz)^3$. **(Lesson 8-7)** 360

27. An isosceles right triangle is a right triangle in which both legs have the same length. Lenora says that an isosceles right triangle with legs of length s always has a hypotenuse of length $s \cdot \sqrt{2}$. Is Lenora correct? Why or why not? **(Lesson 8-6)**

28. Three days a week, Rollo rollerblades to work. He rollerblades eight and a half blocks. On each block, there are fourteen houses. Each house has three trees in its front yard. How many trees does Rollo rollerblade by on his way to work each week? **(Lesson 8-1)** 1,071 trees

29. A line has an x-intercept of 12 and a y-intercept of 15. Write an equation of this line. **(Lesson 6-6)** $y = -\frac{5}{4}x + 15$

30. On a regular die, which is more likely: rolling an even number six times in a row, or rolling a number less than 3 four times in a row? **(Lesson 5-7)** rolling an even number

EXPLORATION

31. Six of the eight properties mentioned at the beginning of this lesson involve either multiplication or division. Show that *none* of these six properties is true if every multiplication is replaced by addition and every division is replaced by subtraction.

Let $a = 4$, $b = 5$, $m = 2$, and $n = 3$. Then calculations show that:

$b^m + b^n \neq b^{m+n}$; $(b^m)^n \neq b^{m+n}$; $(a + b)^n \neq a^n + b^n$;

$b^m - b^n \neq b^{m-n}$; $(a - b)^n \neq a^n - b^n$; $\sqrt{a} + \sqrt{b} \neq \sqrt{a + b}$

27. yes, Answers vary. Sample answer: In an isosceles right triangle with legs of length s and a hypotenuse of length h, $h^2 = s^2 + s^2 = 2s^2$. So, $h = \sqrt{2s^2} = \sqrt{2}\sqrt{s^2} = s \cdot \sqrt{2}$.

The first known roller skates were created in the 1760s and possessed a single line of wheels.

Source: National Museum of Roller Skating

Chapter 8 Projects

1 Estimating Square Roots

To estimate a square root without a calculator, you can use an algorithm called the *Babylonian method*. Suppose you want to estimate $\sqrt{r}$.

Step 1 Guess a number a_1 that is reasonably close to $\sqrt{r}$.

Step 2 Replace a_1 with $a_2 = \frac{1}{2}\left(a_1 + \frac{r}{a_1}\right)$.

Step 3 Replace a_2 by $a_3 = \frac{1}{2}\left(a_2 + \frac{r}{a_2}\right)$.

Doing this process again and again will make each a_n closer and closer to the square root. For example, suppose you wanted to estimate $\sqrt{5}$. A good starting guess for a_1, is 2. In Step 2, replace a_1 with $a_2 = \frac{1}{2}\left(2 + \frac{5}{2}\right) = 2.25$.

In Step 3, replace 2.25 with $a_3 = \frac{1}{2}\left(2.25 + \frac{5}{2.25}\right)$ $= 2.23611111\ldots$. Step 3 should already give you a very good approximation of $\sqrt{5}$.

a. Use the Babylonian method to estimate $\sqrt{10}$, $\sqrt{21}$, and $\sqrt{30.235}$. Then find these numbers using your calculator. In each step of the Babylonian method, find the absolute value of the difference between the number a_n and the square root. What do you conclude?

b. Calculate $\sqrt{5}$ again, but this time, in Step 1, choose the inappropriate guess $a_1 = 1,000,000$. Does the method still work?

c. Use the method to calculate $\sqrt{9}$, using the guess $a_1 = 3$. What do you notice?

2 Fraction Exponents

In this chapter you saw both $\frac{1}{2}$ and $-\frac{1}{2}$ used as exponents. In this project you will discover the meaning of exponents that are other fractions.

a. Recall the rule $b^m \cdot b^n = b^{m+n}$. According to this rule, what should the number $b^{\frac{1}{3}} \cdot b^{\frac{1}{3}} \cdot b^{\frac{1}{3}}$ equal? Check this with a calculator.

b. Remember the rule $b^{m \cdot n} = (b^m)^n$. Because $\frac{2}{3} = \frac{1}{3} \cdot 2$, what should $b^{\frac{2}{3}}$ be? Check your answer with a calculator.

c. What should the number $b^{\frac{m}{n}}$ be?

3 Interview with Pythagoras

Who was Pythagoras? Use a library or the Internet to find out about his life, philosophy, mathematics, and the people who followed him. Write an interview with him, as if it were to be printed in a local newspaper. Include responses you think Pythagoras might have given. You may want to perform your interview (with a partner) for your class.

Project Rubric

Advanced	Student correctly provides all of the details asked for in the project as well as additional correct independent conclusions.
Proficient	Student correctly provides all of the details asked for in the project.
Partially proficient	Student correctly provides some of the details asked for in the project or provides all details with some inaccuracies.
Not proficient	Student correctly provides few of the details asked for in the project or provides all details with many inaccuracies.
No attempt	Student makes little or no attempt to complete the project.

Chapter 8

The projects relate to the content of the lessons of this chapter as follows:

Project	Lesson(s)
1	8-6
2	8-2, 8-4
3	8-6, 8-8
4	8-8
5	8-1
6	8-1

1 Estimating Square Roots

If students are unsure of a number to choose that is close to $\sqrt{r}$, tell them to choose between perfect squares on either side of the number. Remind students that for Part b of Step 3, they will need to go through many iterations of the pattern before they formulate a conclusion. If they find that the method still works, ask them to explain why the method's directions are to guess a number close to $\sqrt{r}$. If there is time, ask students to look up and define *recursive* equations.

2 Fraction Exponents

Remind students that $\sqrt[2]{b}$ is written with a fractional exponent as $b^{\frac{1}{2}}$. Ask them how they might rewrite $\sqrt[3]{b}$ with a fractional exponent. You may want to provide extra problems for students to practice before they generalize Part c. In addition, some students may be ready to extend this project to fourth roots and beyond.

Provide extra problems for students to practice with, but you may wish to stay with fractions that will simplify to having either a factor of 2 or a factor of 3 in the denominator. Otherwise, students will be venturing into the concepts of fourth roots and higher, with which they have not worked yet. Also, encourage students to write the square root as $\sqrt[2]{}$ until they have figured out the pattern for $b^{\frac{m}{n}}$. Then they can more easily find the pattern with $b^{\frac{1}{2}}$ and $b^{\frac{1}{3}}$.

3 Interview with Pythagoras

Consider providing a detailed rubric for this project to clarify your expectations. In the rubric, in addition to content points, specify point values for the proper interview format and a conversational style, for a flowing and logical writing style, and for correct grammar and spelling. Provide details as to how much of the paper should include discussion of Pythagoras's mathematical contributions.

4 Moving in the Coordinate Plane

Clarify the question, "How many different possibilities for this are there?" Remind students that the player has only four choices of commands. The player cannot give the command "move up 5 and right 2," because that would count as seven different commands. To help students answer Part d, suggest that they test several different numerical points and see how many commands they need to get there. For example, they could use (1, 2), (2, 3), (3, 4), and (4, 5).

5 Mathematics and Crossword Puzzles

To help students find the relative frequency of real words for each word length, suggest that students create a table with these column headings: Number of Letters, Number of Possible Words, Number of Real Words, Relative Frequency of Real Words. This will help them organize their thoughts. Remind students that they will need to research the number of words of a given length. Be aware that answers will vary somewhat.

6 Counting Braille Letters

To help students answer Part b, suggest that they find the total number of Braille symbols and letters. Then help them realize that they have two choices for each dot—raised and not raised. Ask students to review the Multiplication Counting Principle, and to use that property to justify their answers to Parts b and c. Finally, ask them to explain the reasoning behind the Multiplication Counting Principle, and why it can be applied to this problem.

4 Moving in the Coordinate Plane

In a computer game, a spaceship is in the middle of the screen, which has coordinate (0, 0). The player can give it one of four instructions—up, down, left, or right—that cause the ship to move one unit in the appropriate direction. For example, the right command will cause the spaceship to move to (1, 0).

a. Suppose the player gave the spaceship 5 commands in a row (for example: up, down, right, right, up). How many different possibilities for this are there?

b. Draw all the possible points in the plane that the spaceship can be in at the end of the five commands. How many different points are there?

c. Complete Parts a and b for two commands, three commands, and four commands. What patterns do you notice? Check these patterns for six commands.

d. What is the minimal number of commands necessary for the ship to reach the point (m, n)?

5 Mathematics and Crossword Puzzles

When stumped on a definition in a crossword puzzle for which they are missing a few letters, many people resort to guessing.

a. Suppose you know three letters out of a five letter word. How many possible guesses are there? How many possible guesses are there if you know that the first missing letter is a vowel?

b. Find a dictionary on the Internet that is intended for use with crossword puzzles. These dictionaries often sort words by length, as well as alphabetically. For n from 2 to 10, what is the number of possible words of length n that can be

spelled with the letters of the English alphabet? For each length, how many of these possibilities are actually words? What is the relative frequency of real words, for each word length?

6 Counting Braille Letters

Braille is a system of writing that can be read by people by touch. Each letter consists of six dots, some of which are raised and some are not. For example, the letter J is written ⠚ (the black dots represent raised dots), and the letter M is written ⠍.

a. Look up a table with a list of all Braille symbols and letters.

b. Why do you think Braille has six dots? Would four dots have been enough? Would five?

c. Modern versions of Braille have eight dots. How many different possible letters and symbols can be written with eight dots?

Notes

_____

Chapter 8 — Summary and Vocabulary

◐ In Chapter 7, you saw many applications of the operation of powering to situations of exponential growth and decay. Another important application of powering is to the counting of objects: If there are n ways to select each object in a sequence of length L, then n^L different sequences are possible. **Powers** are also convenient for writing very large and very small numbers and are essential in **scientific notation.**

◐ The operation of taking a number to a power has many properties that connect it with multiplication and division. If two powers of the same number are multiplied or divided, the result is another power of that number: $x^m \cdot x^n = x^{m+n}$ and $\frac{x^m}{x^n} = x^{m-n}$. From these results, we can verify again that when $x \neq 0$, $x^0 = 1$. We can also deduce that $x^{-n} = \frac{1}{x^n}$.

◐ The terms **square root** and **cube root** come from the historical origins of these ideas in geometry. If a square has side s, its area is s^2, "s squared." If its area is A, the length of its side is $\sqrt{A}$, or $A^{\frac{1}{2}}$. If a cube has edge e, then its volume is e^3 or, "e cubed." If a cube has volume V, then each of its edges has length $\sqrt[3]{V}$.

◐ The **nth power** of a product xy is the product of the nth powers: $(xy)^n = x^n \cdot y^n$. Closely related to squares are square roots, and so we have $\sqrt{xy} = \sqrt{x} \cdot \sqrt{y}$. Similarly, the nth power of a quotient is the quotient of the nth powers: $\left(\frac{x}{y}\right)^n = \frac{x^n}{y^n}$ and so $\sqrt{\frac{x}{y}} = \frac{\sqrt{x}}{\sqrt{y}}$. These properties help to simplify and rewrite expressions involving radicals.

◐ Two important applications of squares and square roots are the **Pythagorean Theorem** and the **distance formula** between two points in a coordinate plane, which is derived from that theorem.

Vocabulary

8-1
scientific notation

8-6
square
squared
square root
radical sign ($\sqrt{}$)
cube
cubed
cube root

8-7
radicand

Theorems and Properties

Multiplication Counting Principle (p. 458)	Negative Exponent Property for Fractions (p. 475)	Pythagorean Theorem (p. 492)
Arrangements Theorem (p. 459)	Power of a Product Property (p. 481)	Cube of the Cube Root Property (p. 493)
Product of Powers Property (p. 465)	Power of a Quotient Property (p. 482)	Product of Square Roots Property (p. 498)
Power of a Power Property (p. 466)		
Quotient of Powers Property (p. 469)	Square of the Square Root Property (p. 490)	Quotient of Square Roots Property (p. 499)
Negative Exponent Property (p. 474)		

Summary and Vocabulary **519**

Summary and Vocabulary

The Summary gives an overview of the entire chapter and provides an opportunity for students to consider the material as a whole. Thus, the Summary can be used to help students relate and unify the concepts presented in the chapter.

Terms and symbols are listed by lesson to provide a checklist of concepts that students must know. Emphasize to students that they should read the vocabulary list carefully before starting the Self-Test on the next page. If students do not understand the meaning of a term, they should refer back to the indicated lesson.

Theorems and Properties covered in the chapter are listed below the Summary, with page references included to lead students back to the location in the chapter where the theorem or property is stated.

Additional Answers

Self Test (p. 520)

3. $(-4)(-3) = 12$; $(-3)^4 = 81$; $(-4)^{-3} = \frac{1}{(-4)^3} = -\frac{1}{64}$; so from least to greatest:
$(-4)^{-3}, (-4)(-3), (-3)^4$

4. $\sqrt{600} = \sqrt{100 \cdot 6} = \sqrt{100} \cdot \sqrt{6} = 10\sqrt{6}$

5. $\sqrt{25x} = \sqrt{25 \cdot x} = \sqrt{25} \cdot \sqrt{x} = 5\sqrt{x}$

6. $2^{\frac{1}{2}} \cdot 50^{\frac{1}{2}} = (2 \cdot 50)^{\frac{1}{2}} = 100^{\frac{1}{2}} = 10$

7. $y^4 \cdot y^2 = y^{4+2} = y^6$

8. $(10m^2)^3 = 10^3(m^2)^3 = 10^3 m^6 = 1{,}000m^6$

9. $\frac{a^{15}}{a^3} = a^{15-3} = a^{12}$

10. $\left(\frac{m}{6}\right)^3 = \frac{m^3}{6^3} = \frac{m^3}{216}$

11. $g^4 \cdot g \cdot g^0 = g^{4+1+0} = g^5$

12. $\frac{6n^2}{4n^3 \cdot 2n} = \frac{6n^2}{8n^4} = \frac{3}{4}n^{2-4} = \frac{3}{4}n^{-2} = \frac{3}{4n^2}$

Self-Test

For the development of mathematical competence, feedback and correction, along with the opportunity for practice, are necessary. The Self-Test provides the opportunity for feedback and correction; the Chapter Review provides additional opportunities for practice. We cannot overemphasize the importance of these end-of-chapter materials. It is at this point that the material "gels" for many students, allowing them to solidify skills and understanding. In general, student performance should improve after these pages.

Assign the Self-Test as a one-night assignment. Worked-out solutions for all questions are in the Selected Answers section of the student book. Encourage students to take the Self-Test honestly, grade themselves, and then be prepared to discuss the test in class.

Advise students to pay special attention to those Chapter Review questions (pages 521–523) that correspond to the questions they missed on the Self-Test.

Additional Answers

3–12. See page 519.

14. $\frac{2}{x^2} \cdot \frac{5}{x^5}$

$= \frac{2 \cdot 5}{x^2 x^5}$ Multiplication of fractions

$= \frac{10}{x^{(2+5)}}$ Arithmetic and Product of Powers Property

$= \frac{10}{x^7}$ Arithmetic

15. The prime factorization of $10(288)^2$ is

$2 \cdot 5 \cdot (2^5 \cdot 3^2)^2 = 2 \cdot 5 \cdot (2^5)^2 \cdot (3^2)^2 = 2 \cdot 5 \cdot 2^{10} \cdot 3^4 = 5 \cdot 2^{11} \cdot 3^4$

16. $\left(\frac{3}{y^2}\right)^{-3} = \left(\frac{y^2}{3}\right)^3 = \frac{(y^2)^3}{3^3} = \frac{y^6}{27}$

19a. Power of a Quotient Property

19b. Power of a Power Property

19c. Quotient of Powers Property

19d. Negative Exponent Property

Chapter 8 Self-Test

Take this test as you would take a test in class. You will need a calculator. Then use the Selected Answers section in the back of the book to check your work.

1. Multiple Choice $x^4 \cdot x^7 =$ A: $x^{4+7} = x^{11}$

   A x^{11} B x^{28} C $2x^{11}$ D $2x^{28}$

2. Rewrite 5^{-3} as a simple fraction. $5^{-3} = \frac{1}{5^3} = \frac{1}{125}$

3. Order from least to greatest: $(-4)(-3)$, $(-3)^4$, $(-4)^{-3}$ See margin.

In 4–6, simplify the expression. 4–6. See margin.

4. $\sqrt{600}$ 5. $\sqrt{25x}$ 6. $2^{\frac{1}{2}} \cdot 50^{\frac{1}{2}}$

In 7–12, simplify the expression. 7–12. See margin.

7. $y^4 \cdot y^2$ 8. $(10m^2)^3$ 9. $\frac{a^{15}}{a^3}$

10. $\left(\frac{m}{6}\right)^3$ 11. $g^4 \cdot g \cdot g^0$ 12. $\frac{6n^2}{4n^3 \cdot 2n}$

13. Rewrite $4y^{-3}w^2$ without a negative exponent and justify your answer. $\frac{4w^2}{y^3}$, by the Negative Exponent Property

14. Rewrite $\frac{2}{x^2} \cdot \frac{5}{x^5}$ as a single fraction without negative exponents. Justify your steps. See margin.

15. The prime factorization of 288 is $2^5 \cdot 3^2$. Use this information to find the prime factorization of $10(288)^2$. See margin.

16. Rewrite $\left(\frac{3}{y^2}\right)^{-3}$ without parentheses or negative exponents. See margin.

17. Evaluate $\sqrt[3]{30}$ to the nearest thousandth. 3.107

18. If $f(x) = 1{,}000(1.06)^x$, estimate $f(-3)$ to the nearest integer. $1{,}000(1.06)^{-3} \approx 1{,}000 \cdot 0.84 = 840$

19. State the general property that justifies each step. 19a–d. See margin.

   a. $\left(\frac{x^{-9}}{x^{-5}}\right)^3 = \frac{(x^{-9})^3}{(x^{-5})^3}$ b. $= \frac{x^{-27}}{x^{-15}}$

   c. $= x^{-12}$ d. $= \frac{1}{x^{12}}$

20. Find a value of m for which $m^2 \neq m^{-2}$. Answers vary. Sample answer: $\frac{1}{4}$

21. What is the distance between the points $(9, 5)$ and $(1, -10)$? See margin.

22. Common notebook paper outside the United States is called A4, with dimensions 210 mm by 297 mm. A piece of A4 paper is placed on a grid as shown below. If the paper is cut along a diagonal, how long is the cut line? See margin.

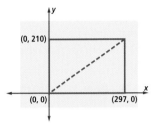

23. The volume of a cube is 30 cubic inches. What is the length of an edge of the cube?

24. A square has a diagonal with length 12 meters. What is the area of the square? See margin.

25. In some states, a license plate consists of 2 letters followed by 4 digits. How many different license plates are possible that fit this description? (Note: There are ten digits: 0, 1, 2, . . ., 9.) $26^2 \cdot 10^4 = (676) \cdot (10{,}000) = 6{,}760{,}000$

23. $V = s^3$, so $s = \sqrt[3]{V}$. Therefore, $s = \sqrt[3]{30} \approx 3.107$ in.

Additional Answers

21. $\sqrt{(1-9)^2 + (-10-5)^2} = \sqrt{289} = 17$

22. The upper right corner of the paper has coordinates (297, 210) and the lower left corner has coordinates (0, 0), so using the distance formula gives

$\sqrt{(297-0)^2 + (210-0)^2} = \sqrt{132{,}309} \approx 363.7$ mm.

24. The diagonal and two consecutive sides of the square form an isosceles triangle. The Pythagorean Theorem gives $s^2 + s^2 = 12^2$, where s is the length of the side of the square. So, $2s^2 = 144$ or $s^2 = 72$. Since the area of the square is s^2, the area is 72 m².

Chapter 8 · Chapter Review

SKILLS
PROPERTIES
USES
REPRESENTATIONS

SKILLS Procedures used to get answers.

OBJECTIVE A Simplify products, quotients, and powers of powers. (Lessons 8-2, 8-3, 8-4, 8-5)

In 1–7, simplify the expression. 1, 6. See margin.

1. $2m^2 \cdot 3m^3 \cdot 4m^4$
2. $\frac{6y^8}{12y^4}$ $\frac{y^4}{2}$
3. $\frac{7xy^2}{3x^2y^{-2}}$ $\frac{7y^4}{3x}$
4. $b^{-2}(4b^5)$ $4b^3$
5. $\left(\frac{v^4}{v^8}\right)^6$ $\frac{1}{v^{24}}$
6. $\frac{7.28 \cdot 10^{115}}{8.3 \cdot 10^{72}}$
7. $a^{10}(3a^3) + 5a^{13}(a^7 - 2)$ $5a^{20} - 7a^{13}$

In 8 and 9, rewrite the expression a. without fractions and b. without negative exponents. 9a. See margin.

8. $\frac{a^{-1}b^4}{b^{-2}c^3}$ a. $a^{-1}b^6c^{-3}$; b. $\frac{b^6}{ac^3}$
9. $\frac{60x^2}{45x^{-2}}$ b. $\frac{4}{3}x^4$
10. Rewrite $-ab^{-1}$ without a negative exponent. $\frac{-a}{b}$
11. Rewrite $(7x^{-7})(6y^{-3})$ without a negative exponent. $\frac{42}{x^7y^3}$

OBJECTIVE B Evaluate negative integer powers of real numbers. (Lessons 8-4, 8-5)

In 12–15, rewrite the expression as a decimal or fraction without an exponent.

12. 4^{-3} $\frac{1}{64}$
13. 6^{-2} $\frac{1}{36}$
14. $\left(\frac{1}{10}\right)^{-2}$ 100
15. $\left(\frac{2}{3}\right)^{-5}$ $\frac{243}{32}$
16. If $f(x) = 2x^{-4}$, what is $f(-3)$? $\frac{2}{81}$
17. The value of a house today is estimated at \$150,000 and has been growing at 3% a year. Its value x years from now will be $150,000(1.03)^x$. What was its value 5 years ago? Round your answer to the nearest thousand dollars. \$129,000
18. Write $603.8 \cdot 10^{-4}$ in decimal form. 0.06038
19. If $0.0051 = 5.1 \cdot 10^n$, what is n? $n = -3$

In 20 and 21, tell whether each expression names a positive number, a negative number, or zero.

20. a. $5^3 + 3^{-5}$ positive
    b. $3^5 - 3^{-5}$ positive
21. a. $\left(-\frac{1}{2}\right)^{-3}$ negative
    b. $-\left(\frac{1}{2}\right)^{-3}$ negative

OBJECTIVE C Rewrite powers of products and quotients. (Lessons 8-5, 8-9)

In 22–29, rewrite the expression without parentheses. 24–29. See margin.

22. $(xy)^5$ x^5y^5
23. $(60m^2n^3)^2$ $3,600m^4n^6$
24. $30\left(\frac{1}{3}u^4v\right)^3$
25. $\left(\frac{3}{4}\right)^{11} \cdot \left(\frac{6}{8}\right)^{-4}$
26. $\frac{1}{2}\left(\frac{1}{v}\right)^3 - (2v)^{-3}$
27. $\left(\frac{-8s}{t^2}\right)^{-4}$
28. $(m^3n^{-2})(m^2n^{-3})^3$
29. $\left(\frac{2y^2z^{-3}}{6y^{-3}z^4}\right)^{-2}$

OBJECTIVE D Simplify square roots. (Lessons 8-6, 8-7) 30–35. See margin.

In 30–36, simplify the expression. Assume the variables stand for positive numbers.

30. $\sqrt{6} \cdot \sqrt{24}$
31. $(4^3 + 4^3)^{\frac{1}{2}}$
32. $\sqrt{3^2 + 4^2}$
33. $5\sqrt{7} \cdot 2\sqrt{3}$
34. $\sqrt{17m} \cdot \sqrt{17m}$
35. $\sqrt{\frac{4x^2}{y^2}}$
36. $\sqrt{36a^{36}b^4}$ $6a^{18}b^2$

OBJECTIVE E Evaluate cube roots. (Lesson 8-6)

In 37–40, give the exact cube root of the number, or the cube root rounded to the nearest thousandth.

37. -8 -2
38. 1 1
39. 200 5.848
40. $1,330$ 10.997

Chapter Review

The main objectives for the chapter are organized in the Chapter Review under the four types of understanding this book promotes—Skills, Properties, Uses, and Representations.

Whereas end-of-chapter material may be considered optional in some texts, in *UCSMP Algebra* we have selected these objectives and questions with the expectation that they will be covered. Students should be able to answer these questions with about 85% accuracy after studying the chapter.

You may assign these questions over a single night to help students prepare for a test the next day, or you may assign the questions over a two-day period. If you work the questions over two days, then we recommend assigning the *evens* for homework the first night so that students get feedback in class the next day, and then assigning the *odds* the night before the test because the answers are provided to the odd-numbered questions in the Selected Answers at the back of the book.

It is effective to ask students which questions they still do not understand and use the day as a total class discussion of the material that the class finds most difficult.

Resources

• Assessment Resources: Chapter 8 Test, Forms A–D; Chapter 8 Test, Cumulative Form

Technology Resources

Teacher's Assessment Assistant, Ch 8
Electronic Teacher's Edition, Ch. 8

Additional Answers

1. $24m^9$
6. approximately $8.771 \cdot 10^{42}$
9a. approximately $1.33x^4$
24. $\frac{10u^{12}v^3}{9}$
25. $\frac{2,187}{16,384}$
26. $\frac{3}{8v^3}$
27. $\frac{t^8}{4,096s^4}$
28. $\frac{m^9}{m^{11}}$
29. $\frac{9z^{14}}{y^{10}}$

30. 12
31. $8\sqrt{2}$
32. 5
33. $10\sqrt{21}$
34. $17m$
35. $\frac{2x}{y}$

Additional Answers

41. 0.368; $0.368^3 \approx 0.0498 \approx 0.05$

42. 2.154; $2.154^3 \approx 9.994 \approx 10$

43. It is not always true. Part c is a counterexample.

44e. Yes; By the Negative Exponent Property and the Power of a Product Property, for all nonzero real number values x and y and integer n, $(xy)^{-n} = \frac{1}{(xy)^n} = \frac{1}{x^n y^n}$.

45. Answers vary. Sample answer: $a = 1$

46. Answers vary. Sample answer: $x = 1$ and $y = 1$

47. Power of a Quotient Property

48. Product of Powers Property

49. Power of a Power Property or Zero Exponent Property

50. Negative Exponent Property

51. Product of Powers Property

52. Quotient of Powers Property

53. Answers vary. Sample answer: By first applying the Negative Exponent Property for Fractions and then the Power of a Quotient Property, $\left(\frac{12}{13}\right)^{-4} = \left(\frac{13}{12}\right)^4 = \frac{13^4}{12^4} = \frac{28,561}{20,736}$.

By applying the Power of a Quotient Property and then the Negative Exponent Property, $\left(\frac{12}{13}\right)^{-4} = \frac{12^{-4}}{13^{-4}} = \frac{13^4}{12^4} = \frac{28,561}{20,736}$.

In 41 and 42, estimate the number to the nearest thousandth and check your answer by an appropriate multiplication. 41–42. See margin.

41. $\sqrt[3]{0.05}$

42. $\sqrt[3]{10}$

PROPERTIES The principles behind the mathematics

OBJECTIVE F Test a special case to determine whether a pattern is true. (Lesson 8-9)

43. Tell whether the pattern $x^4 = x^3$ is true for the given value of x.

   a. $x = 1$ yes b. $x = 0$ yes c. $x = -1$ no

   d. Based on your answers to Parts a–c, do you have evidence that the pattern is true, or are you sure it is not always true? Explain your reasoning. See margin.

44. Consider the pattern $(xy)^{-2} = \frac{1}{x^2 y^2}$, where x and y are not zero. 44a–b. yes

   a. Is the pattern true when $x = 5$ and $y = 3$?

   b. Is the pattern true when $x = -4$ and $y = 0.5$?

   c. Do you have evidence that the pattern is true for all nonzero real number values of x and y? Explain your reasoning. See margin.

In 45 and 46, find a counterexample to the pattern.

45. $-4a = a^{-4}$ 46. $(x + y)^2 = x^2 + y^2$

45–46. See margin.

OBJECTIVE G Identify properties of powers that justify a simplification, from the following list: Zero Exponent Property (Chapter 7); Negative Exponent Property; Power of a Product Property; Power of a Quotient Property; Product of Powers Property; Quotient of Powers Property; Power of a Power Property. (Lessons 8-2, 8-3, 8-4, 8-5)

In 47–52, identify the property or properties that justify the simplification. Assume all variables represent positive numbers. 47–52. See margin.

47. $\left(\frac{1}{2}\right)^3 = \frac{1}{8}$ 48. $a^{10} = a^8 \cdot a^2$

49. $(b^4)^0 = 1$ 50. $2^{-n} = \frac{1}{2^n}$

51. $4^{-2} \cdot 4^3 = 4$ 52. $\frac{w^2 a^2}{w^2 h^{-1}} = aah$

53. Show and justify two different ways to simplify $\left(\frac{12}{13}\right)^{-4}$. See margin.

54. Show and justify two different ways to simplify $\frac{m^{-1}}{n^{-1}}$.

$\frac{m^{-1}}{n^{-1}} = \left(\frac{m}{n}\right)^{-1} = \frac{n}{m}$ and $\frac{m^{-1}}{n^{-1}} = \frac{n^1}{m^1} = \frac{n}{m}$

USES Applications of mathematics in real-world situations

OBJECTIVE H Use powers to count the number of sequences possible for repeated choices. (Lesson 8-1)

55. A test contains 5 questions where the choices are *always*, *sometimes but not always*, or *never*.

   a. How many different answer sheets are possible? 243 answer sheets

   b. If you guess, what is the probability that you will answer all 5 questions correctly? $\frac{1}{243}$

   c. If you guess, what is the probability that you will answer all 5 questions incorrectly? $\frac{32}{243}$

56. Excluding the five vowels A, E, I, O, and U in the English language, how many 4-letter acronyms are possible? 194,481 acronyms

57. A restaurant serves two different types of pizza (thin crust and deep dish), three sizes, and nine toppings. How many different pizzas with one topping are possible? 54 different pizzas

58. Imagine that a fair coin is tossed 12 times. The result of each toss is recorded as H or T.
    a. How many different sequences of H and T are possible? **4,096 sequences**
    b. What is the probability that all the tosses are heads? $\frac{1}{4,096}$
    c. What is the probability of getting the sequence HTHHTTTHTTTH? $\frac{1}{4,096}$

REPRESENTATIONS Pictures, graphs, or objects that illustrate concepts

OBJECTIVE I Represent squares, cubes, square roots, and cube roots geometrically. (Lesson 8-8)

59. The area of the tilted square below is 8 square units. What is the length of a side of the tilted square? $2\sqrt{2}$ **units**

60. A square has area 1,000 square units.
    a. Give the exact length of a side. $10\sqrt{10}$ **units**
    b. Estimate the length of a side to the nearest hundredth. **31.62 units**

61. If a square has side xy, what is its area? x^2y^2

62. If a cube has an edge of length 2.3 cm, what is its volume? **12.167 cm³**

63. A cube has a volume of 1 cubic meter. What is the length of an edge? **1 m**

64. A cube has a volume of 2 cubic meters. What is the length of an edge? $\sqrt[3]{2} \approx 1.26$ **m**

OBJECTIVE J Calculate distances on the *x-y* coordinate plane. (Lesson 8-8)

In 65 and 66, use the graph below.

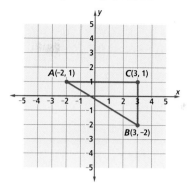

65. Find each length.
    a. AC 5   b. BC 3   c. AB $\sqrt{34}$

66. If O is the point $(0, 0)$, find OB and OC.
    $OB = \sqrt{13}$; $OC = \sqrt{10}$
    In 67–70, find the distance between the points.
    67–70. See margin.
    67. $(2, 11)$ and $(11, 2)$ 68. $(6, 5)$ and $(3, -5)$

69. (a, b) and $(-1, 4)$ 70. (x, y) and (h, k)

71. Stanton, Nebraska is about 8 miles east and 3 miles south of the center of Norfolk, Nebraska.
    a. On a straight line distance, is it true that Stanton is less than 9 miles from the center of Norfolk? **yes**
    b. Draw a picture to justify your answer to Part a. **See margin.**

Assessment

Evaluation The *Assessment Resources* provide four forms of the Chapter 8 Test. Forms A and B present parallel versions of a short-answer format. Form C consists of four to six short-response questions that cover the SPUR objectives from Chapter 8. Form D offers performance assessment that covers a subset (or even just one) of the SPUR objectives for the chapter.

Feedback After students have taken the test for Chapter 8 and you have scored the results, return the tests to students for discussion. Class discussion on the questions that caused trouble for most students can be very effective in identifying and clarifying misunderstandings. You might want to have them note the items they missed and work either in groups or at home to correct them. It is important for students to receive feedback on every chapter test, and we recommend that students see and correct their mistakes before proceeding too far into the next chapter.

Additional Answers

67. $9\sqrt{2}$
68. $\sqrt{109}$
69. $\sqrt{(a + 1)^2 + (b - 4)^2}$
70. $\sqrt{(x - h)^2 + (y - k)^2}$
71b.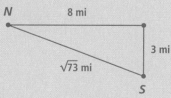

Quadratic Equations and Functions

Chapter Overview

	Local Standards	Pacing (in days)		
		Average	Advanced	Block
9-1 The Function with Equation $y = ax^2$ G Graph equations of the form $y = ax^2$ and interpret these graphs.		1	0.5	0.5
9-2 Solving $ax^2 = b$ A Solve quadratic equations of the form $ax^2 = b$. D Use quadratic equations to solve problems about paths of projectiles. E Solve geometric problems involving quadratic equations.		1	0.5	0.5
9-3 Graphing $y = ax^2 + bx + c$ H Graph equations of the form $y = ax^2 + bx + c$ and interpret these graphs.		1	1	0.75
QUIZ 1		0.5	0.5	0.25
9-4 Quadratics and Projectiles D Use quadratic equations to solve problems about paths of projectiles.		1	1	0.5
9-5 The Quadratic Formula B Solve quadratic equations using the Quadratic Formula.		1	1	0.5
9-6 Analyzing Solutions to Quadratic Equations B Solve quadratic equations using the Quadratic Formula. C Identify and use the properties of solutions to quadratic equations.		1	1	0.75
QUIZ 2		0.5	0.5	0.25
9-7 More Applications of Quadratics: Why Quadratics Are Important E Solve geometric problems involving quadratic equations. F Solve other real-world problems involving quadratic functions.		1	1	0.5
Self-Test		1	1	0.5
Chapter Review		2	2	1
Test		1	1	0.5
TOTAL		12	11	6.5

Technology Resources

Teacher's Assessment Assistant, Ch. 9
Electronic Teacher's Edition, Ch. 9

Differentiated Options Universal Access

	Accommodating the Learner	Vocabulary Development	Ongoing Assessment	Materials
9-1	pp. 527, 528	p. 529	written, p. 531	scientific or graphing calculator
9-2	pp. 534, 535	p. 533	group, p. 536	scientific or graphing calculator
9-3	pp. 539, 540		written, p. 543	scientific or graphing calculator
9-4	pp. 546, 547		oral, p. 551	scientific or graphing calculator
9-5	pp. 553, 554	p. 553	written, p. 557	scientific or graphing calculator
9-6	pp. 559, 560		group, p. 564	scientific or graphing calculator
9-7	pp. 567, 568		written, p. 570	scientific or graphing calculator

Objectives

	Lessons	Self-Test Questions	Chapter Review Questions
Ⓢkills			
A Solve quadratic equations of the form $ax^2 = b$.	9-2	1, 4	1–8
B Solve quadratic equations using the Quadratic Formula.	9-5, 9-6	2, 3, 5, 6	9–18
Ⓟroperties			
C Identify and use the properties of solutions to quadratic equations.	9-6	7, 21–24	19–27
Ⓤses			
D Use quadratic equations to solve problems about paths of projectiles.	9-2, 9-4	19, 20	28–31
E Solve geometric problems involving quadratic equations.	9-2, 9-7	15	32–34
F Solve other real-world problems involving quadratic functions.	9-7	11–14	35–37
Ⓡepresentations			
G Graph equations of the form $y = ax^2$ and interpret these graphs.	9-1	8, 9	38–42
H Graph equations of the form $y = ax^2 + bx + c$ and interpret these graphs.	9-3	10, 16–18	43–50

Resource Masters Chapter 9

Resource Master 1, Graph Paper (page 2), can be used as needed. **Resource Master 2, Four-Quadrant Graph Paper** (page 3), can be used with Lessons 9-1 through 9-4.

Resource Master 129 Lesson 9-1

Warm-Up

Suppose S is the surface area of a cube with edge e.

1. Give an equation for S in terms of e.
2. Graph the equation you found in Question 1.
3. Identify five points on the graph in Question 2.
4. When $S = 12$, what is the value of e and to what point on the graph does this question correspond?

Example 1

r	A
1	3.14
2	
3	
4	

Resource Master for Lesson 9-1

Resource Master 130 Lesson 9-1

Additional Examples

1. The period of a pendulum is the time it takes for the pendulum to swing back and forth. The period t (in seconds) of a pendulum of length L (in centimeters) is given by $L = 24.85t^2$. Sketch a graph of this equation.

   Step 1: Make a table of values for L when $t = 1, 2, 3,$ and 4. Estimate to the nearest hundredth.
   Step 2: Make a scale on each axis.
   Step 3: Graph the points (t, L) from the table.
   Step 4: Put an open dot at $(0, 0)$ since 0 is not in the domain of t. Connect $(0, 0)$ and the points with a parabola in Quadrant 1.

t	L (cm)
1	24.85
2	
3	
4	

2. The graph of $f(x) = -2x^2$ is shown. Estimate x if $f(x) = -8$.

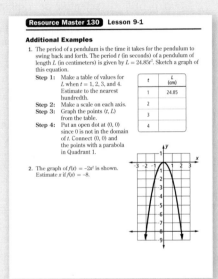

Resource Master for Lesson 9-1

Resource Master 131 Lesson 9-1

Activity

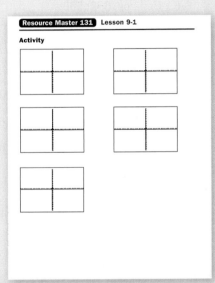

Resource Master for Lesson 9-1

Resource Master 133 Lesson 9-1
Resource Master 132 Lesson 9-1

Question 5

i.   ii.   iii.

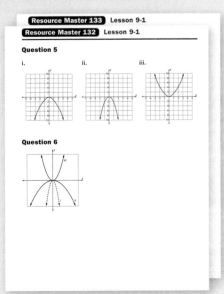

Question 6

Resource Masters for Lesson 9-1

Resource Master 134 Lesson 9-2

Warm-Up

Solve the quadratic equation.

1. $a^2 = 36$
2. $b^2 + 1 = 36$
3. $3c^2 = 36$
4. $3d^2 + 1 = 36$
5. $3(x - 8)^2 = 36$
6. $3(2y + 4)^2 = 36$
7. $\pi r^2 - 36 = 0$

Additional Examples

1. Solve $4x^2 = 100$.
2. A stone is dropped from the 555-foot Washington Monument, located on the National Mall in Washington, D.C. To determine how long the stone will be in the air, use Galileo's equation $d = 16t^2$. In the equation, t is the time in seconds that it takes a heavier-than-air object to fall d feet. Round your answer to the nearest tenth of a second.
3. Solve $6(4n - 3)^2 = 54$.

Resource Master for Lesson 9-2

Resource Master 135 Lesson 9-2

Question 1

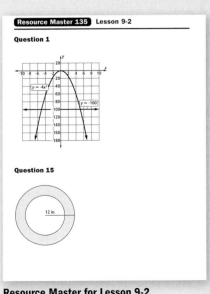

Question 15

12 in.

Resource Master for Lesson 9-2

Resource Master 136 Lesson 9-3

Warm-Up
1. Graph the equation $y = x^2 + 2bx$ when $b = 1, 2,$ and 3.
2. Find the vertex of each graph and generalize your answer in terms of b.
3. Predict what the graph will be when $b = -1$. Graph $y = x^2 - 2x$ to check your prediction.

Additional Examples
1. a. Graph f when $f(x) = 2x^2 + x - 15$. Use a window big enough to show the vertex of the parabola, the two x-intercepts, and the y-intercept.
   b. Estimate the vertex, x-intercepts, and y-intercept.
2. Find the exact location of the vertex of the parabola that is the graph of $f(x) = 2x^2 + x - 15$ from Additional Example 1.

Activity 2

Equation $y = ax^2 + bx + c$	b	Vertex of Parabola	y-intercept of Parabola	x-intercepts (if any)
$y = x^2 + 2x - 4$				
$y = x^2 + 4x - 4$				
$y = x^2 - 3x - 4$				

Resource Master for Lesson 9-3

Resource Master 138 Lesson 9-3
Resource Master 137 Lesson 9-3

Question 10   **Question 12**

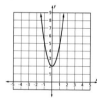

Question 13

A   B

Resource Masters for Lesson 9-3

Resource Master 139 Lesson 9-4

Warm-Up
Consider the situation of Example 1 on page 546. Use the equation describing the height h in feet of the ball after t seconds:
$h = -16t^2 + 32t + 6$.
1. How high will the ball be after half of a second?
2. How high will the ball be after 1.5 seconds?
3. What is the height of the ball when it hits the ground?

Additional Examples
1. A ball is thrown from an initial height of 10 feet with an initial velocity of 64 feet per second.
   a. Write an equation describing the height h in feet of the ball after t seconds.
   b. How high will the ball be after 3 seconds?
   c. What is the maximum height of the ball?
2. An object is dropped from an initial height of 40 meters.
   a. Write a formula describing the height of the object (in meters) after t seconds.
   b. After how many seconds does the object hit the ground?
   c. What is the maximum height of the object?
3. Suppose a ball is thrown upward with an initial upward velocity of 30 meters per second from an initial height of 10 meters.
   a. Write a formula for the height in meters of the object after t seconds.
   b. Estimate when the ball is 40 meters high.

Resource Master for Lesson 9-4

Resource Master 140 Lesson 9-4

Activity

x = horizontal distance ball has traveled							
y = height of the ball							

Questions 13–14

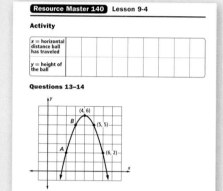

Resource Master for Lesson 9-4

Resource Master 141 Lesson 9-5

Warm-Up
From memory, write down the Quadratic Formula you learned on page 552. Memorize the formula. Be sure to state the formula with both the "if" and "then" parts.

Additional Examples
1. Solve $x^2 - 5x - 24 = 0$.
2. A first aid helicopter is dropping a package of medical supplies to the ground below. The function $h(t) = -16t^2 + 2t + 50$ gives the approximate height $h(t)$ in feet above the ground the package is at t seconds after the package is dropped. How many seconds elapse from the time the package leaves the helicopter until the package hits the ground?
3. Solve $x^2 - 7x = -2$.

Question 16

Resource Master for Lesson 9-5

Resource Master 142 Lesson 9-6

Warm-Up
An equation for a parabola is given.
   a. Find the value of the discriminant ($b^2 - 4ac$) of the equation.
   b. Find the x-intercepts of the parabola.
1. $y = 2x^2 - 7x + 10$
2. $y = 2x^2 - 7x + 6.125$
3. $y = 2x^2 - 7x + 6$

Additional Examples
1. A firefighter shoots a rescue flare from the top of a 5-story building. The path of the flare is modeled by the equation $y = -2.5x^2 + 20x + 60$. Graph and generate a table of the parabola with an equation to answer the following questions.
   a. Will the flare ever reach a height of 90 feet?
   b. Will the flare ever reach a height of 100 feet?
   c. Will the flare ever reach a height 110 feet?
2. Using the Quadratic Formula to find the solutions to the equation presented in Additional Example 1.
   a. Will the flare ever reach a height of 90 feet?
   b. Will the flare ever reach a height of 100 feet?
   c. Will the flare ever reach a height of 110 feet?
3. How many times does the graph of $y = 3x^2 - 12x + 12$ intersect the x-axis?

Resource Master for Lesson 9-6

Resource Master 143 Lesson 9-6

Quadratic Function	Value of $b^2 - 4ac$	Number of x-intercepts	Graph (all screens are shown in the standard viewing window)
$y = x^2 + x - 6$	$1^2 - 4(1)(-6) = 25$ positive	Two	
$y = x^2 - 6x + 9$	$(-6)^2 - 4(1)(9) = 0$ zero	One	
$y = x^2 + 2x + 7$	$2^2 - 4(1)(7) = -24$ negative	Zero	

Question 5

Resource Master for Lesson 9-6

Resource Master 144 Lesson 9-7

Warm-Up
1. Give the number of sides of the polygon, draw a convex example of this polygon, and tell how many diagonals the polygon has.
   a. hexagon   b. nonagon   c. triangle
   d. pentagon   e. heptagon   f. octagon
   g. quadrilateral   h. decagon
2. Use quadratic regression to find an equation of the parabola through these points.

Additional Example
1. Engineers are planning to build a suspension bridge similar to the one seen in the figure below.

Let the bridge be along the x-axis. Place the y-axis at one end of the roadway. The ends of the bridge are at (0, 0) and (800, 0). Because the parabola is symmetric to the line $x = 400$, the parabola passes through the points (0, 300), (400, 0), and (800, 300). You can use quadratic regression to find an equation for the parabola through these points. In standard form, the equation is given by $y = \frac{3}{1,600}x^2 - \frac{3}{2}x + 300$ where y is the length of each vertical cable at the distance x from the end of the roadway. Suppose two support cables of length 200 feet long are delivered to the construction site. How far from the left end of the bridge should the engineers place the cables?

Resource Master for Lesson 9-7

Resource Master 145 Lesson 9-7

Additional Examples
2. The formula $S = n^2$ can be used to find the sum of the first n odd natural numbers.
   a. What is the sum of the first 20 odd natural numbers?
   b. Can the sum of the first n odd natural numbers be 230? If so, how many odd numbers are being added? If not, explain why.

Question 7

Questions 18–19

Resource Master for Lesson 9-7

Pacing

The lessons in this chapter are meant to take about one day each. With a quiz, a day for the Self-Test, a day to review, and a day for the Chapter Test, this chapter should take between 11 and 13 days.

Using Pages 524–525

This opener leads directly into Lesson 9-1 with one of the classic examples of quadratics, namely the description of heights of projectiles over time. Galileo's equation is a special case of the more general equation $d = \frac{1}{2}gt^2 - vt + h$, where here the acceleration due to gravity is $g = 32 \frac{\text{feet}}{\text{second}}$ per second (because it is near the surface of the earth), the initial velocity $v = 0$ (because the object is dropped), and the initial height of the object $h = 0$ (because we are measuring from the point at which the object is dropped).

Students may not realize that the following are all examples of projectiles: an object that is dropped, a bullet that is fired in any direction, a baseball that is hit, a rocket found in fireworks, a missile that does not have a guidance system to change its trajectory. It is natural to start with the simplest situation: a dropped object.

You might ask students why it is unlikely that the formula $d = 16t^2$ would be found in Galileo's home country of Italy (d is in feet, and not meters). Because 16 feet ≈ 4.9 meters, the corresponding equation with d in meters is $d = 4.9t^2$. Galileo preceded the metric system by about 200 years so he would have had still another expression, but it was of the form $d - at^2$.

When an object is dropped from a high place, such as the roof of a building or an airplane, it does not fall at a constant speed. The longer it is in the air, the faster it falls. Furthermore, the distance d that a heavier-than-air object falls in a time t does not depend on its weight. In the early 1600s, the Italian scientist Galileo described the relationship between d and t mathematically. In our customary units of today, if d is measured in feet and t is in seconds, then $d = 16t^2$.

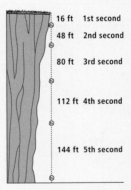

16 ft	1st second
48 ft	2nd second
80 ft	3rd second
112 ft	4th second
144 ft	5th second

A table of values and a graph of this equation are shown on the next page.

Chapter 9 Overview

The study of quadratic expressions and equations is a traditional topic for first-year algebra courses in the United States. The study concentrates on solving quadratic equations. Graphing is delayed until a later course. The technology of calculators and computers has reversed the order; now graphing is the easy thing to do, and graphs can be used to picture solutions to quadratic equations.

Lessons 9-1 and 9-2 discuss and graph the simple yet basic quadratic equation $ax^2 = b$ and the graphing of the related function with equation $y = ax^2$. Lessons 9-3 and 9-4 deal with the more general equation $y = ax^2 + bx + c$ and its application to projectile motion. The related equation $y = ax^2 + bx + c$ is solved using the Quadratic Formula in Lessons 9-5 and 9-6, and a variety of applications complete the chapter in Lesson 9-7.

(continued on next page)

Because d is a distance below the height at which the object is dropped, it is perhaps more instructive to graph $d = -16t^2$ than $d = 16t^2$ as in the student page. The graph of $d = -16t^2$ is more easily tied to the graph below.

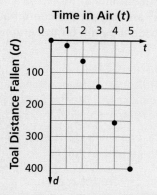

Time in Air (t)

t (sec)	d (ft)
0	0
1	16
2	64
3	144
4	256
5	400

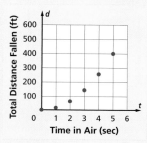

The expression $16t^2$ is a *quadratic expression,* the equation $d = 16t^2$ is an example of a *quadratic equation,* and the function whose independent variable is t and dependent variable is d is a *quadratic function.* The word "quadratic" comes from the Latin word *quadratum* for square. Think of the area x^2 of a square with side x.

From the time of the Ancient Greek mathematicians until about 1600, the only known physical applications of quadratic expressions were to the area of squares and other geometric figures. But, in the next hundred years, discoveries by Galileo, Kepler, Newton, Leibniz, and others found uses for quadratic expressions involving objects that were in motion. These discoveries explain everything from the path of a basketball shot to the orbits of planets around our sun. They enable us to talk to each other via cell phones and collect information about stars in distant space. They are important both for mathematics and for science. In this chapter you will learn about a wide variety of quadratic equations and functions, and their applications.

525

Chapter 9 Projects

At the end of each chapter, you will find projects related to the chapter. At this time, you might want to have students look over the Projects on pages 571 and 572. Have each student tentatively select a project on which to work. Then, as students read and progress through the chapter, they can finalize their project choices.

Notes

We present parabolas first because it is natural to examine the classic application of the path of a projectile. To determine when a projectile reaches a certain height (or when a graph has a certain value) requires solving a quadratic. Fewer than 5% of quadratics can be factored over the set of rational numbers. The Quadratic Formula always works and it is easy to learn.

Graphing calculators with scientific capability are a necessity for this chapter. They accurately show the shape of a

parabola and enable students to use numbers that arise from actual data. A CAS, with its ability to move from exact to approximate solutions to quadratics, is also helpful. A decimal estimate may have more meaning in the context of the original problem than an exact value written with radicals.

Lesson

9-1

The Function with Equation $y = ax^2$

GOAL

Graph equations of the form $y = ax^2$ and obtain the coordinates of individual points on the graphs.

SPUR Objective

(The SPUR Objectives for all of Chapter 9 are found in the Chapter Review on pages 576–579.)

G Graph equations of the form $y = ax^2$ and interpret these graphs.

Materials/Resources

· Lesson Master 9-1A or 9-1B
· Resource Masters 2 and 129–133
· Scientific or graphing calculator

HOMEWORK

Suggestions for Assignment

• Questions 1–23
• Question 24 (extra credit)
• Reading Lesson 9-2
• Covering the Ideas 9-2

Local Standards

1 Warp-Up

Suppose S is the surface area of a cube with edge e.

1. Give an equation for S in terms of e.
$S = 6e^2$

2. Graph the equation you found in Queston 1. **The graph is a parabola that opens up and contains the points (1, 6) and (−1, 6).**

3. Identify five points on the graph in Question 2. **Answers vary. Sample answer: (1, 6), (0, 0), (2, 24), (0.5, 1.5), (3, 54)**

4. When S = 12, what is the value of e and to what point on the graph does this question correspond?
$\sqrt{2}; (\sqrt{2}, 12)$

▶ **BIG IDEA** The graph of any quadratic function with equation $y = ax^2$, with $a \neq 0$, is a parabola with vertex at the origin.

Graphing $y = x^2$

The simplest quadratic function has equation $y = x^2$. A table of values for $y = x^2$ is given below. Notice the symmetry in the second row of the table. Each x value and its opposite have the same square. For example, 3^2 and $(-3)^2$ are both equal to 9. The bottom row of the table shows that the output of the function is positive for a pair of opposite positive and negative input values.

Mental Math

If (a, b) is in the 2nd quadrant, in which quadrant is:

a. $(-a, -b)$? IV

b. $(-a, b)$? I

c. $(a, -b)$? III

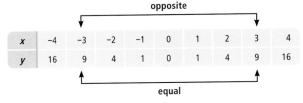

opposite

x	−4	−3	−2	−1	0	1	2	3	4
y	16	9	4	1	0	1	4	9	16

equal

This symmetry can be seen in the graph of the equation $y = x^2$ at the right, which is a **parabola.** Every positive number is the y-coordinate of two points on the graph with opposite x-coordinates. For example, 25 is the y-coordinate of the points (5, 25) and (−5, 25). For this reason, the parabola is its own *reflection image* over the y-axis. For this reason we say the parabola is **reflection-symmetric** to the y-axis. The y-axis is called the **axis of symmetry** of the parabola.

The intersection point of a parabola with its axis of symmetry is called the **vertex** of the parabola. The vertex of the graph of $y = x^2$ is (0, 0).

The function $y = x^2$ is of the form $y = ax^2$, with $a = 1$. You should be able to sketch the graph of any equation of this form.

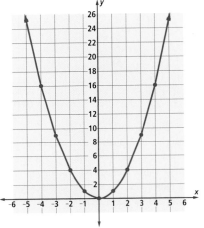

Background

Parabola is commonly defined two ways in mathematics: as the set of points of equal distance from a given point (the *focus*) and a given line (the *directrix*); and as the intersection of a cone and a plane parallel to an edge of the cone. At this point, we simply assert that a parabola is the graph of an equation $y = ax^2$, $a \neq 0$. Consequently, the parabolas for $y = ax^2$ and $y = bx^2$, with a and $b \neq 0$, are similar. The parabolas for $y = ax^2$ and $y = -ax^2$ are congruent because each is the reflection image of the other over the x-axis.

As the distance between the focus and the directrix increases, the parabola becomes larger but does not change shape. If we put it on a graph of fixed size, as the parabola gets larger we see less and less of it. We are usually looking at the parabola around its vertex, so we see the parabola looking as if it is getting flatter and wider.

Graphing $y = ax^2$

All equations of the form $y = ax^2$ have similar graphs.

Activity

Step 1 Use the window $-20 \leq x \leq 20$, and $-20 \leq y \leq 20$ to graph all three equations on your calculator. Sketch the graphs on a single grid on a separate sheet of paper.
  a. $f(x) = 3x^2$ **b.** $g(x) = -x^2$ **c.** $h(x) = -3x^2$

Step 2 Evaluate $f(2)$, $g(2)$, and $h(2)$. $f(2) = 12$, $g(2) = -4$, $h(2) = -12$

Step 3 Is $(-2, -12)$ a point on the graph of $h(x)$? Explain how you know.

Step 4 Use a graphing calculator to make a sketch of the following functions. Use the same window you used for Step 1.
  a. $j(x) = 0.2x^2$ **b.** $k(x) = -0.5x^2$

Step 5 Evaluate $j(3)$ and $k(3)$. $j(3) = 1.8$, $k(3) = -4.5$

Step 6 Is $(-3, 2.9)$ a point on the graph of $j(x)$? Explain how you know.
  See margin.

Step 7 If a parabola is opening up, what must be true about the value of a in $y = ax^2$? If a parabola is opening down, what must be true about a in $y = ax^2$? *a* is positive; *a* is negative.

Properties of the Graph of $y = ax^2$

The graph of $y = ax^2$, where $a \neq 0$, has the following properties:

1. It is a parabola symmetric to the y-axis.

2. Its vertex is $(0, 0)$.

3. If $a > 0$, the parabola opens up. If $a < 0$, the parabola opens down.

Finding Points on the Graph of $y = ax^2$

If you know the y-coordinate of a point on the graph of a parabola and the equation, you can find the x-coordinate or coordinates. We illustrate this with a different parabola.

GUIDED

Example 1

Consider the following situation: You know the area of a circle and want to find its radius.

(continued on next page)

Step 1a.

Step 1b.

Step 1c.

Step 3. Yes; we know $(2, -12)$ is on the graph of $h(x)$ and that the graph is symmetric with respect to the y-axis, so $h(2) = h(-2)$, and therefore $(-2, -12)$ is on $h(x)$.

Step 4a.

Step 4b.

---

2   Teaching

Notes on the Activity

Students can complete Steps 2, 3, 5, and 6 by evaluating each function by hand or by using their graphing calculators. Because each function is already entered in their graphing calculator, students can use CALC followed by value commands to evaluate each function for the given value of x. Students must know which curve they are evaluating when they use the value command.

Notes on the Lesson

Discuss an example in detail. Students should be able to identify as many points on the graph as desired. If the x-coordinate of a point is known, they can find the y-coordinate by substitution. If the y-coordinate of the point is known, they will need to solve an equation to find the x-coordinate. Students should be familiar with the vocabulary: parabola, reflection image, symmetric, axis of symmetry, vertex, minimum, maximum, "opens up," "opens down."

Additional Example

Example 1 The period of a pendulum is the time it takes for the pendulum to swing back and forth. The period t (in seconds) of a pendulum of length L (in centimeters) is given by $L = 24.85t^2$. Sketch a graph of this equation.

Solution

Step 1: Make a table of values for L when $t = 1, 2, 3,$ and 4. Estimate to the nearest hundredth.

t (sec)	L (cm)
1	24.85
2	99.40
3	223.65
4	397.60

(continued on next page)

Additional Answers

Activity Step 6. No; The graph of $j(x)$ is symmetric with respect to the y-axis, and $j(-3) = j(3)$ and $(3, 2.9)$ is not on the graph, so $(-3, 2.9)$ is not on the graph.

Activity. By graphing equations in the form $y = ax^2$, students see that all graphs of parabolas have the same shape. With a graphing calculator, the overall shape of the graph can easily be found. One also needs to be able to obtain the coordinates of key points on the graph. For the parabola, there is only one key point: its vertex. For parabolas with equations of the form $y = ax^2$, the vertex is always $(0, 0)$. The other key aspect of a parabola is whether it opens up or down.

Accommodating the Learner

Have students explore how the leading coefficient affects the apparent "width" of a parabola. Using an overhead graphing calculator, graph $f(x) = x^2$, $g(x) = \frac{1}{2}x^2$, and $h(x) = 2x^2$ on the same axes. Ask students to make a conjecture about how a affects the width, and have them test their conjecture by graphing other parabolas of the form $f(x) = ax^2$. Then ask students to compare the graphs of $u(x) = -x^2$, $v(x) = -3x^2$, and $w(x) = -\frac{1}{3}x^2$.

9-1

Example 1 continued

Step 2: Make a scale on each axis.

Step 3: Graph the points (t, L) from the table.

Step 4: Put an open dot at $(0, 0)$ since 0 is not in the domain of t. Connect $(0, 0)$ and the points with a parabola in Q1.

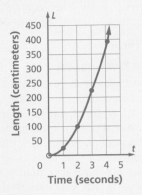

Example 2 The graph of $f(x) = -2x^2$ is shown below. Estimate x if $f(x) = -8$.

–2 and 2

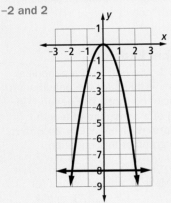

Solution Sketch a graph of the familiar formula $A = \pi r^2$, where A is the area of a circle with radius r.

Step 1 Make a scale on each axis. In doing this, ask yourself: What are the possible values of r? What are the possible values of A?

Step 2 Make a table of values for A when $r = 1, 2, 3,$ and 4. Estimate each to the nearest hundredth. The first value has been done for you.

Step 3 Graph the points (r, A) from the table. **Steps 3, 4. See margin.**

Step 4 Put an open circle at $(0, 0)$ because 0 is not in the domain of r. Connect $(0, 0)$ and the other points with a curve like a parabola.

Step 5 Use your graph to estimate the radius of a circle whose area is 12 square units. **about 2 units**

Step 1. A and r can only assume positive values; See margin for graph.

r	A	
1		3.14
2	?	12.57
3	?	28.27
4	?	50.27

Example 2

The graph of $f(x) = 1.5x^2$ is shown at the right. Estimate x if $f(x) = 10$.

Solution Draw the horizontal line $y = 10$. The graph intersects this line at two points. The x-coordinates of these points are approximately **2.5** and **–2.5**.

In the next lesson, you will see how to obtain the exact values of x with $f(x) = 10$.

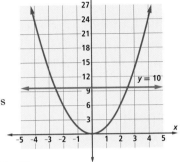

Questions

COVERING THE IDEAS

In 1 and 2, an equation of a function is given.
  a. Make a table of x and y for integer values of x from –4 to 4.
  b. Graph the equation.
  c. Tell whether the graph opens up or down. **1–2. See margin.**

1. $g(x) = \frac{1}{2}x^2$ 2. $f(x) = -\frac{1}{2}x^2$

3. Refer to the parabola at the right.
  a. Does the parabola open up or down? **down**
  b. The parabola is the graph of a function. Which does the function have, a maximum value or a minimum value? **maximum value**
  c. Give the coordinates of the vertex. **(0, 0)**
  d. Give an equation of the axis of symmetry of the parabola. $x = 0$

4. How are the graphs of $y = 7x^2$ and $y = -7x^2$ related to each other?

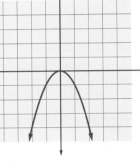

4. The graph of $y = -7x^2$ is the graph of $y = 7x^2$ reflected over the x-axis.

Guided Example 1

Step 1.

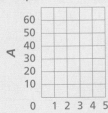

Steps 3, 4.

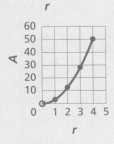

Accommodating the Learner

To reinforce the idea of symmetry in a parabola, have students graph the parabola $Y_1 = x^2$ on the following window: $-4 < x < 4, 0 < y < 20$. In the same window have them graph $Y_2 = 4, Y_3 = 9, Y_4 = 16$. Have them find the points of intersection with the parabola for each line and record their answers. Have them make a conjecture for the intersection of $y = n$ and the parabola. **–2, 2; –3, 3; –4, 4;** $x = \sqrt{n}$ and $-\sqrt{n}$ at the points where $y = n$ intersects the parabola

1a., 2a.

x	$g(x) = \frac{1}{2}x^2$	$f(x) = -\frac{1}{2}x^2$
–4	8	–8
–3	4.5	–4.5
–2	2	–2
–1	0.5	–0.5
0	0	0
1	0.5	–0.5
2	2	–2
3	4.5	–4.5
4	8	–8

5. Match each table with the graph it most accurately represents.

a.
iii

x	y
-2	4
0	0
2	4

b.
i

x	y
-2	-4
0	0
2	-4

c.
ii

x	y
-2	-10
0	0
2	-10

i. 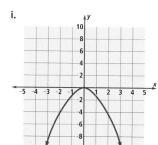 **ii.** 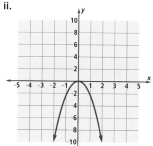 **iii.**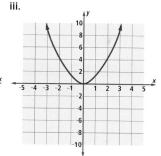

6. Match each graph at the right with one of the equations below.
   a. $y = x^2$ iii
   b. $y = -0.25x^2$ ii
   c. $y = -3x^2$ i

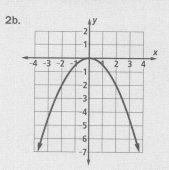

7. **Fill in the Blanks** Consider the graph of the function $f(x) = ax^2$.
   a. If a is positive, the graph is a parabola that opens
      ___?___. **up**
   b. If a is negative, the graph is a parabola that opens
      ___?___. **down**

8. Use the graph of $A = \pi r^2$ to estimate the radius of a circle whose area is 20 square units. **about 2.5 units**

9. Consider the graph of the function defined by $y = 5x^2$.
   a. Without plotting any points, sketch what you think the graph of this function looks like. **9a.–c. See margin on p. 530.**
   b. Make a table of values satisfying this function. Use $x = -2, -1.5, -1, -0.5, 0, 0.5, 1, 1.5,$ and 2.
   c. Draw a graph of this function from your table.
   d. From the graph, estimate the values of x for which $y = 14$.
      ≈ 1.7 and -1.7

The Function with Equation $y = ax^2$ **529**

---

3 Assignment

Recommended Assignment
- Questions 1–23
- Question 24 (extra credit)
- Reading Lesson 9-2
- Covering the Ideas 9-2

Note-Taking Tips

With each new vocabulary term, make sure students not only enter that term in their notebooks but that they also provide at least one example which illustrates the term's meaning. In many cases, this example should be a diagram of the figure with all important features labeled. For some students, terms such as *symmetric* or *reflection* represent completely new mathematical ideas, but the concepts become more accessible if connections are made to the everyday meanings of those terms.

Additional Answers

2b.

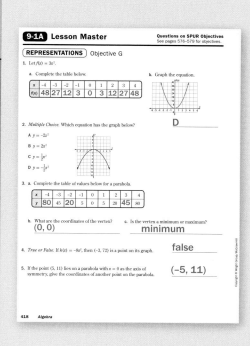

2c. down

Additional Answers

1b.

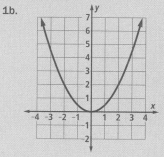

1c. up

9-1

Notes on the Questions

Questions 13 and 14 The point of these questions is to show that the sign of the expression depends not on whether x is positive or negative, but entirely on the coefficient of x^2.

Question 20 Part c may seem difficult. You can discuss it and check any answer by letting $x = 3$ or $x = 27$.

Question 24 This experiment relates to the definition of a parabola as a conic section. You might want to do it using a wall of the room without any graph paper. If the flashlight is such that all its light hits the wall, then the outline of the lit area will be an ellipse. If the flashlight is such that some of its light would never hit the wall even if the wall extended forever, then the outline of the lit area is one branch of a hyperbola. If the flashlight is such that the limit of the light is parallel to the wall, then the outline of the lit area on the wall will be a parabola.

Additional Answers

9a. Answers vary. Sample answer:

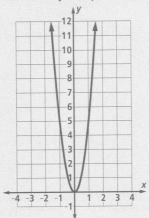

9b.

x	$y = 5x^2$
−2	20
−1.5	11.25
−1	5
−0.5	1.25
0	0
0.5	1.25
1	5
1.5	11.25
2	20

---

10. Consider the formula $A = s^2$ for the area A of a square with a side of length s. **See margin.**

    a. Graph all possible values of s and A on a coordinate plane.

    b. Explain how the graph in Part a is like and unlike the graph of $y = x^2$ at the start of this lesson.

11. The parabola at the right has equation $y = -5x^2$.

    a. Find y if $x = 0$. $y = 0$

    b. Find x if $y = -5$. $x = 1$ and $x = -1$

    c. Find x if $y = -20$. $x = 2$ and $x = -2$

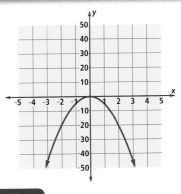

APPLYING THE MATHEMATICS

12. Refer to the parabola at the right. Points P and Q are reflection images of each other over the y-axis. What are the coordinates of Q? (3, 20)

In 13 and 14, fill in the blanks with _negative, zero,_ or _positive_.

13. **Fill in the Blanks** Consider the expression $-1x^2$.

    a. If x is negative, $-1x^2$ is ___?___. negative

    b. If x is zero, $-1x^2$ is ___?___. zero

    c. If x is positive, $-1x^2$ is ___?___. negative

    d. What do Parts a–c tell you about the graph of $y = -1x^2$?
       The graph has vertex (0, 0) and opens down.

14. **Fill in the Blanks** Consider the expression $4x^2$.

    a. If x is negative, $4x^2$ is ___?___. positive

    b. If x is zero, $4x^2$ is ___?___. zero

    c. If x is positive, $4x^2$ is ___?___. positive

    d. What do Parts a–c tell you about the graph of $y = 4x^2$?

15. What is the only real number whose square is not a positive number? 0

In 16 and 17, a graph of a function f with $f(x) = ax^2$ is shown. Find the value of a.

16. $a = \dfrac{10}{9}$

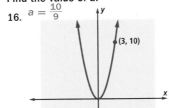

(3, 10)

17. $a = -1.5$

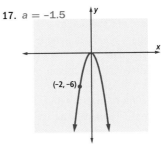

(−2, −6)

14d. The graph has vertex (0, 0) and opens up.

Additional Answers

9c.

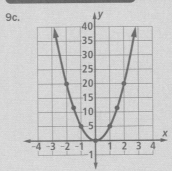

18. **Fill in the Blank** If $a = 0$, the graph of the function $y = ax^2$
   is ___?___. the x-axis

19. Consider the equation $d = 16t^2$, which gives the distance d in
   feet that an object dropped at time $t = 0$ will have fallen
   after t seconds.

   a. If an object falls 400 feet in t seconds, find t. $t = 5$

   b. Estimate how long it will take an object to fall 200 feet.
      about 3.5 sec

REVIEW

20. **Skill Sequence** Simplify each expression. (**Lesson 8-7**)

   a. $\sqrt{3} \cdot \sqrt{27}$ 9   **b.** $\sqrt{3x} \cdot \sqrt{27x}$ 9x   **c.** $\sqrt{3x} + \sqrt{27x}$ $4\sqrt{3x}$

21. Suppose a box has sides of length 6 inches,
   8 inches, and 12 inches. Find the length of
   the longest thin pole, like the one shown
   at the right, which can fit inside the box.
   (*Hint:* First find the diagonal of the base.)
   (**Lesson 8-6**) $\sqrt{244} \approx 15.6$ in.

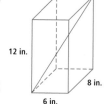

12 in.

8 in.

6 in.

22. Suppose that t years ago, Kendra deposited
   P dollars into a savings account with an
   annual yield of 3%. If she has not deposited
   or withdrawn any additional money and the account
   now contains \$500, write an equation involving t and P.
   (**Lesson 7-1**) $500 = P(1.03)^t$

23. Derek is a tennis instructor at his local gym. He gives lessons to
   3 people twice a week. If he charges \$25 per person for a lesson,
   and he works for 15 straight weeks, how much money will
   Derek earn? (**Lesson 5-4**) \$2,250

The United States Tennis
Association is the largest
tennis organization in
the world with more than
665,000 individual members
and 7,000 organizational
members.

Source: USTA

EXPLORATION

24. Draw a set of axes on graph
   paper. Aim a lit flashlight
   at the origin up the y-axis.
   What is the shape of the
   lit region? Keep the lit end
   of the flashlight over the
   origin but tilt the flashlight
   to raise its bottom. How
   does the shape of the lit
   region change? parabola;
   The parabola becomes
   wider as the flashlight is
   tipped up.

---

4 Wrap-Up

Ongoing Assessment

Ask a student to describe the two roles
that a plays when graphing parabolas
of the form $f(x) = ax^2$. Make sure that
the students understand that changing
a does not change the shape of the
parabola. The greater the value of $|a|$, the
less one sees of the parabola in a fixed
horizontal window.

Project Update

If you have not had students look over
the projects on pages 571 and 572,
you might want to do so now. Project 3,
The Focus of a Parabola, on page 571,
relates to the content of this lesson.

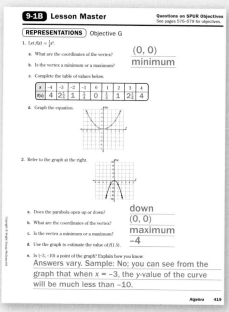

9-1B Lesson Master   Questions on SPUR Objectives
See pages 576–579 for objectives.

REPRESENTATIONS Objective G

1. Let $f(x) = \frac{1}{4}x^2$.

   a. What are the coordinates of the vertex?   (0, 0)

   b. Is the vertex a minimum or a maximum?   minimum

   c. Complete the table of values below.

   d. Graph the equation.

2. Refer to the graph at the right.

   a. Does the parabola open up or down?   down

   b. What are the coordinates of the vertex?   (0, 0)

   c. Is the vertex a minimum or a maximum?   maximum

   d. Use the graph to estimate the value of $f(1.5)$.   −4

   e. Is (−3, −10) a point of the graph? Explain how you know.
   Answers vary. Sample: No; you can see from the
   graph that when x = −3, the y-value of the curve
   will be much less than −10.

   Algebra **419**

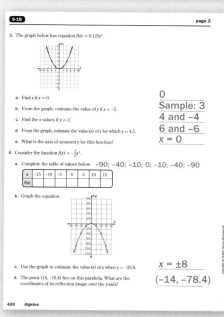

9-1B   page 2

3. The graph below has equation $f(x) = 0.125x^2$.

   a. Find y if x = 0.   0

   b. From the graph, estimate the value of y if x = −5.   Sample: 3

   c. Find the x values if y = 2.   4 and −4

   d. From the graph, estimate the value(s) of x for which y = 4.5.   6 and −6

   e. What is the axis of symmetry for this function?   x = 0

4. Consider the function $f(x) = -\frac{2}{5}x^2$.

   a. Complete the table of values below.   −90; −40; −10; 0; −10; −40; −90

   b. Graph the equation.

   c. Use the graph to estimate the value(s) of x when y = −25.6.   x = ±8

   d. The point (14, −78.4) lies on this parabola. What are the
   coordinates of its reflection image over the y-axis?   (−14, −78.4)

   420 *Algebra*

Additional Answers

10a.

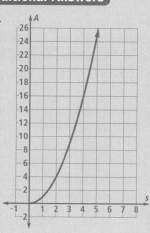

10b. The graph in Part a is like the graph of $y = x^2$
in that they are the same for values of x that
are greater than or equal to 0, but unlike the
graph of $y = x^2$ in that $A = s^2$ is undefined for
negative values, because negative values are
not meaningful when using measurements.

Lesson 9-2

Lesson 9-2

Solving $ax^2 = b$

GOAL

Solve equations equivalent to those of the form $ax^2 = b$, including situations where x is a linear expression.

SPUR Objectives

A Solve quadratic equations of the form $ax^2 = b$.

D Use quadratic equations to solve problems about paths of projectiles.

E Solve geometric problems involving quadratic equations.

Materials/Resources

· Lesson Master 9-2A or 9-2B
· Resource Masters 2, 134, and 135
· Scientific or graphing calculator

HOMEWORK

Suggestions for Assignment

• Questions 1–25
• Question 26 (extra credit)
• Reading Lesson 9-3
• Covering the Ideas 9-3

Local Standards

1 Warm-Up

In 1–7, solve the quadratic equation.

1. $a^2 = 36$ $a = \pm 6$

2. $b^2 + 1 = 36$ $b = \pm\sqrt{35}$

3. $3c^2 = 36$ $c = \pm 2\sqrt{3}$

4. $3d^2 + 1 = 36$ $d = \pm\sqrt{\frac{35}{3}}$

5. $3(x - 8)^2 = 36$ $x = \pm 2\sqrt{3} + 8$

6. $3(2y + 4)^2 = 36$ $y = \pm\sqrt{3} - 2$

7. $\pi r^2 - 36 = 0$ $r = \pm 6\sqrt{\frac{1}{\pi}}$

▶ **BIG IDEA**   When $\frac{b}{a}$ is not zero, the equation $ax^2 = b$ has two solutions, $x = \sqrt{\frac{b}{a}}$ and $x = -\sqrt{\frac{b}{a}}$.

Graphs and tables can be very helpful in seeing the behavior of equations of the form $ax^2 = b$.

Example 1

Solve $2x^2 = 32$.

Solution 1   Create and graph two functions from the equation. One is the parabola $y = 2x^2$. The other is the horizontal line $y = 32$. Notice that the graphs intersect at two points. This is because two different values of x make the equation true. Trace on the graph of the parabola to find the intersection points, $(-4, 32)$ and $(4, 32)$. Use the x-coordinates.

The solutions are $x = -4$ and $x = 4$.

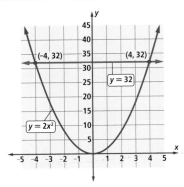

Solution 2   Create a table of values for the equation. Notice that there are two places where the expression $2x^2$ is equal to 32, when $x = -4$ and when $x = 4$. The solutions are $x = -4$ and $x = 4$.

Check

Does $2(4)^2 = 32$?   Does $2(-4)^2 = 32$?

$\quad 2(16) = 32$ $\quad 2(16) = 32$

$\quad\quad 32 = 32$ $\quad\quad 32 = 32$ Both -4 and 4 check.

x	$2x^2$
−5	50
−4	32
−3	18
−2	8
−1	2
0	0
1	2
2	8
3	18
4	32
5	50

Background

This lesson assumes student knowledge of the meaning of square roots and the Pythagorean Theorem (from Chapter 8 and from earlier courses). It introduces equations in order of increasing complexity: $x^2 = b$; $x^2 + a = b$; $ax^2 = b$; and $a(cx + d)^2 = b$. The biggest step in this order is from the next-to-last to the last of these equations.

Here we introduce the term *chunking* that comes from psychology and information processing: Chunking is the treatment of a group of symbols (the "chunk") as a single symbol. Chunking is usually used to remember telephone numbers. In fact, it is difficult to start in the middle of a telephone number because the brain stores chunks, not the individual digits or words. The significance of chunking in algebra is that if a property holds for all values of a variable, then it also holds for expressions that have those values. In this lesson, chunking is used to show students that they can solve an equation of the form $a(cx + d)^2 = b$ if they can solve $ax^2 = b$.

In Example 1, the graph and table helped to show that an equation like $2x^2 = 32$ has two solutions.

You can solve equations of the form $x^2 = b$ symbolically by recalling the meaning of *square root*. If $x^2 = b$, then $x = \sqrt{b}$ or $x = -\sqrt{b}$. Notice that it takes only one step to solve an equation of the form $x^2 = b$. With just one additional step, you can solve an equation of the form $ax^2 = b$.

Example 2

A quarter is dropped 60 feet from the roof of a school building. To determine how long the quarter will be in the air, use Galileo's equation $d = 16t^2$. In the equation, t is the time, in seconds, that it takes a heavier-than-air object to fall d feet.

Solution Here $d = 60$, so we need to solve $60 = 16t^2$.

$\frac{60}{16} = t^2$ Divide both sides by 16.

$t = \pm\sqrt{\frac{60}{16}}$ Take the square roots of both sides.

$t \approx \pm 1.936$ Approximate the square root.

$t \approx 1.936$ Only the positive solution makes sense in this situation.

The quarter will be in the air for approximately 1.9 seconds.

 QY

You can combine your knowledge of solving linear equations with what was done in Example 2 to solve some equations that look quite complicated. In the next example, you should think of $2n + 11$ as a single number. Psychologists call this idea *chunking*. Chunking is what you do when you read an entire word without thinking of the individual letters.

> **▶ QY**
>
> Find how long it will take an object to hit the ground if it falls from the top of Chicago's John Hancock Center, which is 1,127 feet tall.

Example 3

Solve $3(2n - 11)^2 = 75$.

Solution Think of $2n - 11$ as a single number, say x. Then this equation is $3x^2 = 75$. Some people like to write the x in place of $2n - 11$, but you do not have to do that.

$3(2n - 11)^2 = 75$

Divide both sides by 3.

$(2n - 11)^2 = 25$

(continued on next page)

Solving $ax^2 = b$ **533**

---

2 Teaching

Notes on the Lesson

Because this lesson proceeds in algorithmic order, we suggest going through it in that order. Example 1 provides the basic quadratic equation $ax^2 = b$, the type that is easy to solve and the type to which we want to convert any other quadratic. Emphasize the two solutions. You may wish to write them in the form of Example 4, in two columns, to prepare for that example.

Example 2 brings in Galileo's equation from the first page of the chapter. Again there is only one solution appropriate to the problem. Alert students that later in the chapter there will be applications in which both solutions are meaningful.

Additional Examples

Example 1 Solve $4x^2 = 100$. **−5 and 5**

Example 2 A stone is dropped from the 555-foot Washington Monument, located on the National Mall in Washington, D.C. To determine how long the stone will be in the air, use Galileo's equation $d = 16t^2$. In the equation, t is the time, in seconds, that it takes a heavier-than-air object to fall d feet. Round your answer to the nearest tenth of a second. **5.9 sec**

Example 3 Solve $6(4n - 3)^2 = 54$. **$n = 0$ and $n = 1.5$**

ENGLISH LEARNERS
Vocabulary Development

Students should understand an important distinction between the statements $x^2 = 100$ and $x = \sqrt{100}$. There are two values of x that satisfy $x^2 = 100$, namely 10 and –10. However, the symbol $\sqrt{100}$ refers to the principal square root of 100, which is nonnegative, so the only value that satisfies x in $x = \sqrt{100}$ is 10. Another way to express this relationship is that the solutions of $x^2 = 100$ are $\sqrt{100}$ and $-\sqrt{100}$, or 10 and –10, respectively.

9-2

3 Assignment

Recommended Assignment

- Questions 1–25
- Question 26 (extra credit)
- Reading Lesson 9-3
- Covering the Ideas 9-3

Take the square roots of both sides of the equation.

$$(2n - 11) = \pm\sqrt{25}$$
$$2n - 11 = \pm 5$$

Thus either $2n - 11 = 5$ or $2n - 11 = -5$.

Now there are two linear equations to be solved. It is good to separate the two processes.

$2n - 11 = 5$	or	$2n - 11 = -5$
$2n = 16$		$2n = 6$
$n = 8$		$n = 3$

So there are two solutions, $n = 8$ or $n = 3$.

Check Substitute 8 for n in the original equation.

Does $3(2 \cdot 8 - 11)^2 = 75$? Yes, because $3(5)^2 = 75$.

Substitute 3 for n in the original equation.

Does $3(2 \cdot 3 - 11)^2 = 75$? Yes, because $3 \cdot (-5)^2 = 75$.

Questions

COVERING THE IDEAS

1. Solve $-4x^2 = -100$ using the graph at the right. $x = \pm 5$

2. Solve $5x^2 + 7 = 7.8$ using the table below. $x = \pm 0.4$

x	−0.6	−0.4	−0.2	0	0.2	0.4	0.6
$5x^2 + 7$	8.8	7.8	7.2	7	7.2	7.8	8.8

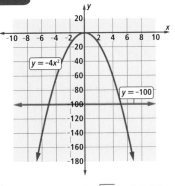

In 3–8, solve the equation.

3. $x^2 = 40$

4. $3{,}705 = y^2 + 436$

5. $12v^2 - 24 = 36$

6. $5w^2 = 400$

7. $3(a + 5)^2 = 12$

8. $(7v - 2)^2 = 81$

9. a. You drop a stone into a deep well and carefully time how long it takes until you hear the stone plop into the water. If it takes 2.4 seconds, about how far from the top is the water in the well? **about 92 ft**

   b. If the water was 64 feet from the top of the well, how long would it take until the stone hit the water? **2 sec**

10. A 30-foot ladder is placed against a wall so that its bottom is 9 feet away from the wall. How high up the wall is the top of the ladder? **about 28.6 ft**

3. $x = \pm\sqrt{40} \approx \pm 6.32$

4. $y = \pm\sqrt{3{,}269} \approx \pm 57.18$

5. $v = \pm\sqrt{5} \approx \pm 2.24$

6. $w = \pm\sqrt{80} \approx \pm 8.94$

7. $a = -3$ or $a = -7$

8. $v = \frac{11}{7}$ or $v = -1$

Accommodating the Learner

Tell students that the surface area of the cube shown below is 384 square inches. Ask them to find the length of each edge of the cube, then the length of the diagonal of one face of the cube, and then the interior diagonal of the cube. Have them round answers to the nearest tenth.

length = 8.0 in.;
diagonal of face = $8\sqrt{2}$ in. or 11.3 in.;
interior diagonal = 13.9 in.

APPLYING THE MATHEMATICS

11. If the area of a circle is 100 square units, then what is the radius of the circle, to the nearest hundredth of a unit? **5.64 units**

In **12** and **13**, solve the quadratic equation.

12. $\frac{1}{2}(2z + 3)^2 = 18$

13. $3v^2 + 10 = 7v^2 - 15$

14. Consider the figures drawn at the right. Suppose that the circle has the same area as the square. If the diameter of the circle is 4 feet, what is the length of the side of the square, to the nearest inch? (*Hint:* You will need to use the formulas for the area of a square and the area of a circle.) **43 in.**

12. $z = 1.5$ or $z = -4.5$

13. $v = \pm 2.5$

15. You wish to make a bull's-eye target so that the area of the inner circle equals the area of the outer ring between the two circles. If the radius of the outer circle is 12 inches, what should the radius of the inner circle be? **about 8.5 in.**

12 in.

REVIEW

16. **True or False** 0 is in the range of $y = ax^2$ for all values of a. (**Lesson 9-1**) **true**

In **17–19**, simplify the expression. (**Lessons 8-5, 8-3, 8-2**)

17. $n \cdot m^3 \cdot n^5 \cdot m^2$ 18. $\frac{12x^8}{8x^2}$ $\frac{3}{2}x^6$ 19. $\left(\frac{3}{5a}\right)^2$ $\frac{9}{25a^2}$
     m^5n^6

20. A company that manufactures combination locks wants each lock to have a unique 3-number combination. There are 36 numbers on each lock. (**Lesson 8-1**)

    a. How many locks can the company produce without having to use the same combination twice? **46,656 locks**

    b. Suppose a worker at the company forgets the combination of one of the locks, but he knows that it does not begin with 1. How many different combinations might he have to try to open the lock? **45,360 combinations**

21. Let $f(x) = 2x^2$. (**Lessons 7-6, 7-5**)

    a. What is the domain of f?   b. What is the range of f?

22. a. Determine a real situation that can be answered by solving $\frac{18}{24} = \frac{x}{32}$.

    b. Answer your question from Part a. (**Lesson 5-9**)
       24 pages

21a. the set of all real numbers

21b. the set of nonnegative real numbers

22a. Answers vary. Sample answer: If it takes 24 minutes to read 18 pages, how many pages can be read in 32 minutes?

Solving $ax^2 = b$ **535**

Notes on the Questions

We encourage going through the Questions 1–13 in order, not skipping any of them.

Question 15 You might ask students if the drawing in the book is accurate. That is, if one were to measure the radii and calculate areas, is the area of the inner circle equal to the area of the ring?

Question 24 This is a difficult problem. Students should calculate the time it took Jessica to travel from Cleveland to Chicago. This will enable them to calculate the time it took her to travel back. Then, knowing the time to travel back and the distance, they can find x.

Accommodating the Learner

Write the following equations and answers on the board:

(1) $3x^2 - 2 = 361$ (a) –4, 8

(2) $x^2 - 1.44 = 0$ (b) –11, 11

(3) $3(2 - x)^2 = 108$ (c) –1.2, 1.2

Ask students to use substitution to find the pair of numbers that satisfy each equation. After students match the equations and answers correctly, ask them to solve each of the equations using algebra. **1b; 2c; 3a**

Extension

A stone is dropped off a building that is 784 feet tall. Using Galileo's equation, $d = 16t^2$, determine how long the stone will be in the air. After students have solved the equation $784 = 16t^2$ for t, ask them to rewrite it by moving the $16t^2$ to the left side of the equation. Then set the left side of the equation equal to Y_1 in the Y= command of their graphing calculators. Have them choose an appropriate window and graph it. Ask students to make a conjecture about the meaning of the y-intercept and the positive x-intercept. **$t = 7$**

9-2

4 Wrap-Up

Ongoing Assessment

Group the students in pairs. On a piece of paper, each student should write an equation of the form $ax^2 = b$ where a and b are both greater than zero. Students should exchange papers, solve the equation, and have the equation writer verify that the solution(s) are correct.

23. Tickets for a school play cost $6 for adults and $4 for children. The organizers of the play have determined that they must sell at least $975 worth of tickets in order to cover their expenses. **(Lesson 6-9)**

   a. Write an inequality that represents this situation. $6x + 4y \geq 975$

   b. Graph the inequality. **See margin.**

   c. Suppose 86 adult tickets are sold. If exactly $1,000 were raised from ticket sales, how many children tickets must have been sold? **121 tickets**

24. Jessica is driving between Cleveland and Chicago, a distance of about 350 miles. From Cleveland to Chicago, she averages 65 miles per hour. On the return trip, she averages x miles per hour. If the round trip takes Jessica 12 hours, find her average speed x on the way back. **(Lessons 5-3, 3-4)** about 52.9 mi/hr

Since 1929, more than two million students have been honored for excellence in theater arts with invitations to join the International Thespian Society.

Source: Educational Theatre Association

25. **Multiple Choice** The graph below pictures solutions to which inequality? **(Lessons 3-7, 3-6)** B

   A $h - 3 \leq -8$ **B** $h + 7 > 2$ **C** $h - 5 \geq -10$ **D** $h + 5 < 0$

EXPLORATION

26. On a piece of graph paper, carefully draw a circle with center at (0, 0) and radius 10 units. This circle will contain the point (10, 0) and three other points on the axes.

   a. What are the coordinates of those other three points?

   b. The circle will contain 8 other points whose coordinates are both integers. Identify those 8 points.

   c. Find the coordinates of three other points in the 1st quadrant that are on the circle. (*Hint:* You may need to describe the coordinates with square roots.)

26a. (0, 10), (–10, 0), (0, –10)

26b. (8, 6), (6, 8), (–6, 8), (–8, 6), (–8, –6), (–6, –8), (6, –8), (8, –6)

26c. Answers vary. Sample answer: $(4, 2\sqrt{21})$, $(5, 5\sqrt{3})$, $(7, \sqrt{51})$

QY ANSWER

about 8.39 sec

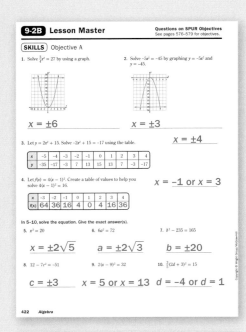

9-2B Lesson Master — Questions on SPUR Objectives. See pages 576–579 for objectives.

SKILLS Objective A

1. Solve $\frac{3}{4}x^2 = 27$ by using a graph. $x = \pm 6$

2. Solve $-5x^2 = -45$ by graphing $y = -5x^2$ and $y = -45$. $x = \pm 3$

3. Let $y = 2x^2 + 15$. Solve $-2x^2 + 15 = -17$ using the table. $x = \pm 4$

x	–5	–4	–3	–2	–1	0	1	2	3	4
y	–35	–17	–3	7	13	15	13	7	–3	–17

4. Let $f(x) = 4(x - 1)^2$. Create a table of values to help you solve $4(x - 1)^2 = 16$. $x = -1$ or $x = 3$

x	–3	–2	–1	0	1	2	3	4
f(x)	64	36	16	4	0	4	16	36

In 5–10, solve the equation. Give the exact answer(s).

5. $x^2 = 20$ $x = \pm 2\sqrt{5}$

6. $6a^2 = 72$ $a = \pm 2\sqrt{3}$

7. $b^2 - 235 = 165$ $b = \pm 20$

8. $12 - 7c^2 = -51$ $c = \pm 3$

9. $2(x - 9)^2 = 32$ $x = 5$ or $x = 13$

10. $\frac{2}{3}(2d + 3)^2 = 15$ $d = -4$ or $d = 1$

422   Algebra

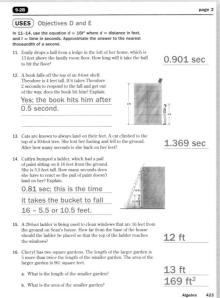

9-2B — page 2

USES Objectives D and E

In 11–14, use the equation $d = 16t^2$ where d = distance in feet, and t = time in seconds. Approximate the answer to the nearest thousandth of a second.

11. Emily drops a ball from a ledge in the loft of her home, which is 13 feet above the family room floor. How long will it take the ball to hit the floor? **0.901 sec**

12. A book falls off the top of an 8-foot shelf. Theodore is 4 feet tall. If it takes Theodore 2 seconds to respond to the fall and get out of the way, does the book hit him? Explain. **Yes; the book hits him after 0.5 second.**

13. Cats are known to always land on their feet. A cat climbed to the top of a 30-foot tree. She lost her footing and fell to the ground. After how many seconds is she back on her feet? **1.369 sec**

14. Caitlyn bumped a ladder, which had a pail of paint sitting on it 16 feet from the ground. She is 5.5 feet tall. How many seconds does she have to react so the pail of paint doesn't land on her? Explain. **0.81 sec; this is the time it takes the bucket to fall 16 – 5.5 or 10.5 feet.**

15. A 20-foot ladder is being used to clean windows that are 16 feet from the ground on Sean's house. How far from the base of the house should the ladder be placed so that the top of the ladder reaches the windows? **12 ft**

16. Cheryl has two square gardens. The length of the larger garden is 5 more than twice the length of the smaller garden. The area of the larger garden is 961 square feet.

   a. What is the length of the smaller garden? **13 ft**

   b. What is the area of the smaller garden? **169 ft²**

Algebra   423

Additional Answers

23b.

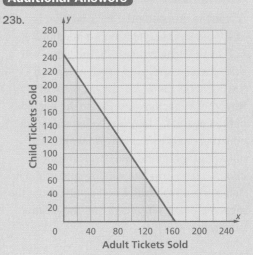

Lesson 9-3 Graphing $y = ax^2 + bx + c$

> ▶ **BIG IDEA** The graphs of any quadratic function with equation $y = ax^2 + bx + c, a \neq 0$, is a parabola whose vertex can be found from the values of a, b, and c.

If $a \neq 0$, the graph of $y = ax^2$ is a parabola with vertex $(0, 0)$. This lesson is about the graph of a more general function, $y = ax^2 + bx + c$. We begin with an important everyday use.

How Far Does a Car Travel after Brakes Are Applied?

When a driver decides to stop a car, it takes time to react and press the brake. Then it takes time for the car to slow down. The total distance traveled in this time is called the *stopping distance* of the car. The faster the car is traveling, the greater the distance it takes to stop the car. A formula that relates the speed x (in miles per hour) of a car and its stopping distance d (in feet) is $d = 0.05x^2 + x$.

This function is used by those who study automobile performance and safety. It is also important for determining the distance that should be maintained between a car and the car in front of it.

To find the distance needed to stop a car traveling 40 miles per hour, you can substitute 40 for x in the above equation.

$$d = 0.05(40)^2 + 40$$
$$= 0.05(1{,}600) + 40$$
$$= 80 + 40$$
$$= 120$$

Thus, a car traveling 40 mph takes about 120 feet to come to a complete stop after the driver decides to apply the brakes.

A table of values and a graph for the stopping distance formula is shown on the next page. The situation makes no sense for negative values of x or d, so the graph has points in the first quadrant only. The graph is part of a parabola.

Mental Math

Simplify.

a. $\sqrt{18}$ $3\sqrt{2}$

b. $\sqrt{200}$ $10\sqrt{2}$

c. $\dfrac{\sqrt{18}}{\sqrt{200}}$ $\dfrac{3}{10}$

Traffic lights were used before the advent of the motorcar. In 1868, a lantern with red and green signals was used at a London intersection to control the flow of horse buggies and pedestrians.

Source: www.ideafinder.com

Background

Properties of the graph of $y = ax^2 + bx + c$.
Students need to understand the graphical interpretation of a, b, and c. The parameter c has an easy interpretation, because when $x = 0$, $y = c$. Thus c is the y-intercept of the parabola. So, if a and b are kept constant but c changes, the graph of $y = ax^2 + bx + c$ will be translated up or down but not to the right or left.

When $a > 0$, the parabola opens up. When $a < 0$, the parabola opens down. Also, the larger that $|a|$ is, the less of the parabola

one sees in a fixed horizontal window, and the narrower the parabola looks.

If a and c are kept constant, then the value of b affects the location of the vertex of the parabola, but not in a simple way. The vertex of the parabola is $\left(-\dfrac{b}{2a}, \dfrac{4ac - b^2}{4a^2}\right)$. Therefore increasing b causes the parabola to be translated to the left and down.

(continued on next page)

GOAL

Identify key features of the graph of an equation of the form $y = ax^2 + bx + c$.

SPUR Objective

H Graph equations of the form $y = ax^2 + bx + c$ and interpret these graphs.

Materials/Resources

· Lesson Master 9-3A or 9-3B
· Resource Masters 2 and 136–138
· Scientific or graphing calculator
· Quiz 1

HOMEWORK

Suggestions for Assignment
· Questions 1–22
· Question 23 (extra credit)
· Reading Lesson 9-4
· Covering the Ideas 9-4

Local Standards

1 Warm-Up

1. Graph the equation $y = x^2 + 2bx$ when $b = 1$, 2, and 3.

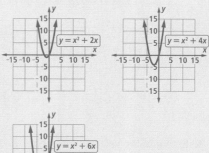

2. Find the vertex of each graph and generalize your answer in terms of b. $(-1, -1)$, $(-2, -4)$, $(-3, -9)$; The vertex is at $(-b, -b^2)$.

(continued on next page)

3. Predict what the graph will be when $b = -1$. Graph $y = x^2 - 2x$ to check your prediction. **Correct prediction is (1, −1).**

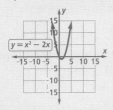

Speed x (mph)	Distance $d = 0.05x^2 + x$ (ft)
10	15
20	40
30	75
40	120
50	175
60	240
70	315

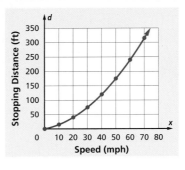

2 Teaching

Notes on the Lesson

There are two key ideas in this lesson. (1) From its equation, you can determine the *y*-intercept of a parabola and how it opens. (2) From the graph, you can determine the vertex in two ways: by tracing and zooming on the graph, or by noticing that two values of *x* give the same value of *y* and realizing that the average of these *x*-values is the *x*-coordinate of the vertex.

Properties of the Graph of $y = ax^2 + bx + c$

The equation $d = 0.05x^2 + x$ is of the form $y = ax^2 + bx + c$, with d taking the place of *y*, $a = 0.05$, $b = 1$, and $c = 0$. The graph of every equation of this form (provided $a \neq 0$) is a parabola. Moreover, every parabola with a vertical line of symmetry has an equation of this form. The values of *a, b,* and *c* determine where the parabola is positioned in the plane and whether it opens up or down. If $a > 0$ the parabola opens up, as in the situation above. If $a < 0$, the parabola opens down, as in Example 1.

Additional Example

Example 1

a. Graph *f* when $f(x) = 2x^2 + x - 15$. Use a window big enough to show the vertex of the parabola, the two *x*-intercepts, and the *y*-intercept. The window for the graph given below is $-10 \leq x \leq 10$ and $-16 \leq y \leq 8$.

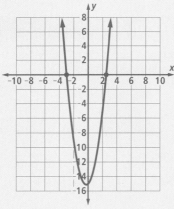

b. Estimate the vertex, *x*-intercepts, and *y*-intercept. **Answers vary. Sample answer: The vertex is near (0, −15). The *x*-intercepts are −3 and 2.5. The *y*-intercept is −15.**

Example 1

a. Graph $f(x) = -2x^2 - 3x + 8$. Use a window big enough to show the vertex of the parabola, the two *x*-intercepts, and the *y*-intercept.

b. Estimate its vertex, *x*-intercepts, and *y*-intercept.

Solutions

a. Here is a graph of $y = -2x^2 - 3x + 8$ on the window $-5 \leq x \leq 5; -10 \leq y \leq 10$.

b. From the window we have shown, we can only estimate the location of the vertex. **The vertex is near (−0.8, 9.1).** You do not have to estimate the *y*-intercept. It is *f*(0), the value of *y* when $x = 0$, and is easily calculated. **The graph has *y*-intercept 8.** On the other hand, you can only estimate its *x*-intercepts. They are the values of *x* when the graph intersects the *x*-axis. **The *x*-intercepts are near −2.9 and 1.4.**

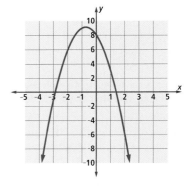

How far does a car travel after brakes are applied? The stopping distance is the sum of (1) the reaction distance and (2) the braking distance. The reaction distance is the distance the car travels before the driver steps on the brake. We assume a driver has the same reaction time regardless of the speed the vehicle is going, so if the speed is *x*, the reaction distance is *bx*. The braking distance is a result of the fact that the kinetic energy of a car is proportional to the square of the speed of the car. So if the speed is *x*, the braking distance is of the form ax^2.

(A detailed background can be found at www.physicsclassroom.com/mmedia/energy/cs.html.) Thus the stopping distance *d* can be found from an equation of the form $d = ax^2 + bx$. The values of *a* and *b* depend on the surface of the road, the mass of the car, and the tires on the car. So these values are different for every car (and they are greater for larger cars and trucks). The values that we use, 0.05 for *a* and 1 for *b*, are typical.

Using Tables to Determine the Vertex of a Parabola

We could only estimate the vertex in Example 1 from the graph. Even if you use the trace function on a calculator or computer, you might not happen to find the vertex exactly. But in some cases, the symmetry of a parabola can be used to determine its vertex.

Example 2

Find the exact location of the vertex of the parabola that is the graph of $f(x) = -2x^2 - 3x + 8$ from Example 1.

Solution Because we know that the vertex is near the point $(-0.8, 9.1)$, we find y for values of x between -1 and 0. Look in the table at the right for a pair of points which have the same y-coordinates. Notice that there are three pairs of points whose y-coordinates are the same. These pairs occur on either side of -0.75. This indicates that the vertex is the point for which $x = -0.75$. Because $f(-0.75) = 9.125$, the vertex is $(-0.75, 9.125)$.

x	y
−1.0	9
−0.9	9.08
−0.8	9.12
−0.7	9.12
−0.6	9.08
−0.5	9
−0.4	8.88
−0.3	8.72
−0.2	8.52
−0.1	8.28
0	8

From a graph, it is often not as easy to locate the x-intercepts of a parabola as it is the vertex. The next two activities explore how the intercepts of the parabolas change as the values of b and c change in the equation $y = ax^2 + bx + c$.

Activity 1

Step 1 Graph $y = 2x^2$ and $y = 2x^2 - 10$ on the same axes.

   a. What is the y-intercept of $y = 2x^2$? **0**

   b. What is the y-intercept of $y = 2x^2 - 10$? **−10**

   c. Describe how the two graphs are related to each other.

Step 1c. The graph of $y = 2x^2$ is the graph of $y = 2x^2 - 10$ shifted up by 10 units.

Step 2 Graph $y = -0.75x^2$ and $y = -0.75x^2 + 1$ on the same axes.

   a. What is the y-intercept of $y = -0.75x^2$? **0**

   b. What is the y-intercept of $y = -0.75x^2 + 1$? **1**

   c. Describe how the two graphs are related to each other.

Step 2c. The graph of $y = -0.75x^2$ is the graph of $y = -0.75x^2 + 1$ shifted down by 1 unit.

Step 3 Graph $y = 2x^2 + c$ for three different values of c, with at least one of these values negative.

   a. Give the equations that you graphed.

   b. What is the effect of c on the graphs? **The magnitude of c is the magnitude of the vertical shift the graph takes. $c < 0$ implies a downward shift; $c > 0$ implies an upward shift; and $c = 0$ implies no shift.**

Step 3a. Answers vary. Sample answer: $y = 2x^2 + 2$; $y = 2x^2 + 0$; and $y = 2x^2 - 3$

Additional Example

Example 2 Find the exact location of the vertex of the parabola that is the graph of $f(x) = 2x^2 + x - 15$ from Additional Example 1. **(−0.25, −15.125)**

Notes on the Activity

Activity 1 Students should quickly discover the effect on a graph of adding a constant to an equation of the form $y = ax^2$. Now see if students can write the equation of a graph if they know the parent function. For example, tell the students that the parent function is $y = 3x^2$. On the overhead graphing calculator graph the equation $y = 3x^2 + 5$ in a standard window and ask them to identify the equation of the graph. Repeat this for several different values of c.

Accommodating the Learner

Have students use the line of symmetry to find additional points on the graph of a parabola. Ask students to graph the parabola $y = x^2 + 4x - 12$ on their graphing calculators. Students should identify the parabola's vertex, x-intercepts, y-intercept, and line of symmetry. Tell students that the point $(1, -7)$ is on the graph and ask them to identify a second point on the parabola that is symmetric to it. Repeat this activity with several other points. vertex: $(-2, -16)$; x-intercepts: $2, -16$; y-intercept: -12; $(-5, -7)$

9-3

Notes on the Lesson

Activity 2 In Step 1, point out that all equations being graphed are of the form $y = ax^2 + bx + c$, with $a = 1$ and $c = -4$. Because $a = 1$, all these graphs are congruent to the graph of $y = x^2$.

Notes on the Activity

Activity 2 In Step 2, Part c, students may not readily see that the x-coordinate of the vertex is the average of the x-intercepts. Consider providing them with several equations of parabolas that have integral x-intercepts. Have students build a table. With enough simple examples, the students should discover the appropriate relationship.

Notes on the Questions

Questions 7–9 The vertex of a parabola can be found not only if you can find the x-intercepts, but also if you can find the x-coordinates of the points where the parabola intersects *any* horizontal line.

Additional Answers

7a.

x	y
−3	3
−2	−2
−1	−5
0	−6
1	−5
2	−2
3	3

7b.

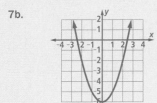

7c. y-intercept: -6; x-intercepts: $\pm\sqrt{6}$; vertex: $(0, -6)$

7d. $y \geq -6$

Activity 2

Step 1 To determine the effect of b on the graph of a quadratic function, consider the function $y = x^2 + bx - 4$.

a. Graph this function for the three different values of b given in the table below. Fill in the table.

Equation $y = ax^2 + bx + c$	b	Vertex of Parabola	y-intercept of Parabola	x-intercepts (if any)
$y = x^2 + 2x - 4$	?2	?(−1, −5)	?−4	?about −3.24, 1.24
$y = x^2 + 4x - 4$	?4	?(−2, −8)	?−4	?about −4.83, 0.83
$y = x^2 - 3x - 4$	?−3	?(1.5, −6.25)	?−4	?−1, 4

b. What features of the graph of $y = x^2 + bx - 4$ does the value of b affect?

c. What feature of the graph of $y = x^2 + bx - 4$ is not affected by the value of b? **y-intercept**

Step 2 Find a window that shows a graph of $y = \frac{1}{2}x^2 - 6x + 4$, including its vertex, its y-intercept and its x-intercept(s).

a. Describe your window.

b. Use the trace feature of the calculator to estimate or determine the vertex, the y-intercept, and the x-intercepts.

c. Tell how the x-coordinate of the vertex is related to the x-intercepts. The x-coordinate of the vertex is the mean of the two x-intercepts.

Questions

COVERING THE IDEAS

In 1–4, use the formula for automobile stopping distances given in this lesson, $d = 0.05x^2 + x$.

1. Define stopping distance.
the total distance traveled in the time it takes for a car to stop

2. Find the stopping distance for a car traveling 45 miles per hour.
146.25 ft

3. Find the stopping distance for a car traveling 55 miles per hour.
206.25 ft

4. **True or False** The stopping distance for a car traveling 50 mph is exactly double the stopping distance of a car traveling 25 mph. **false**

5. The equation $d = 0.05x^2 + x$ is of the form $f(x) = ax^2 + bx + c$. What are the values of a, b, and c? $a = 0.05$; $b = 1$; $c = 0$

6. Explain how you can tell by looking at an equation of the form $y = ax^2 + bx + c$ whether its graph will open up or down. If $a > 0$, the graph will open up. If $a < 0$, the graph will open down.

Step 1a.

Step 1b. It changes the vertex as well as the x-intercepts.

Step 2a. Answers vary. Sample answer: $-15 \leq y \leq 10$, $-10 \leq x \leq 15$

Step 2b. vertex: $(6, -14)$; y-intercept: 4; x-intercepts: about 0.71 and 11.29

Accommodating the Learner

Students need to recognize the effects of a and c on the graph of equations of the form $y = ax^2 + c$. On the board write the following three equations.

$$y = 3x^2 + 2 \qquad y = -4x^2 \qquad y = -2x^2 - 7$$

Ask students to identify which equation's graphs open up and which open down. Students should explain their reasoning. Ask students to write down the y-intercept of each of the equations. Again, students should explain their reasoning.

Extension

Have students explore the Intersect command in the Calc menu to approximate the x-intercepts of a parabola with irrational intercepts. Have students consider the equation $y = x^2 - 7$. It has irrational x-intercepts of $-\sqrt{7}$ and $\sqrt{7}$. First, have students graph the parabola and the equation for the y-intercept, $x = 0$. Next, have them use the Intersect command to approximate the x-intercept by pressing ENTER twice and then selecting a point near one of the points of intersection and pressing ENTER a third time. Repeat the process.

In 7–9, an equation for a function is given. **7–9. See margin.**

a. Make a table of x and y values when x equals –3, –2, –1, 0, 1, 2, and 3.

b. Graph the equation.

c. Identify the y-intercept, x-intercept(s), and vertex.

d. Describe the range of the function.

7. $y = x^2 - 6$ 8. $y = x^2 - 2x + 5$ 9. $y = 3x^2 + 4$

10. The parabola at the right contains (–3, 0) and (–1, 0) and its vertex has integer coordinates.

a. Find the coordinates of its vertex. **(–2, 1)**

b. Write an equation of its axis of symmetry. **$x = -2$**

11. Consider this table of values for a parabola.

x	-8	-7	-6	-5	-4	-3	-2	-1	0
y	-28	0	20	32	36	32	?	?	?

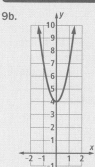

a. What are the coordinates of the vertex of the parabola? **(–4, 36)**

b. Use symmetry to find the coordinates of the points whose y values are missing in the table.
(–2, 20), (–1, 0), (0, –28)

APPLYING THE MATHEMATICS

12. The parabola at the right contains points with integer coordinates as shown by the dots.

a. Copy this graph on graph paper. Then use symmetry to graph more of the parabola. **See margin.**

b. Give the coordinates of the vertex. **(6, 9)**

c. Give an equation for the axis of symmetry. **$x = 6$**

d. At what points does the parabola intersect the x-axis?
(3, 0) and (9, 0)

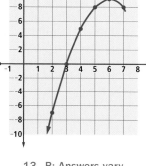

13. **Multiple Choice** Which of the two graphs is the graph of $y = x^2 - 6x + 8$? Justify your answer.

A
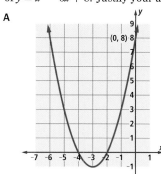

B
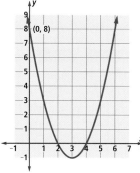

13. **B; Answers vary. Sample answer: When $x = 2$, $y = 0$. Only graph B intersects the x-axis at $x = 2$.**

Graphing $y = ax^2 + bx + c$ **541**

8a.

x	y
–3	20
–2	13
–1	8
0	5
1	4
2	5
3	8

8b.
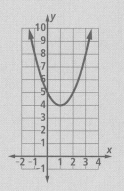

8c. y-intercept: 5; x-intercepts: none; vertex: (1, 4)

8d. $y \geq 4$

9a.

x	y
–3	31
–2	16
–1	7
0	4
1	7
2	16
3	31

---

3 Assignment

Recommended Assignment
- Questions 1–22
- Question 23 (extra credit)
- Reading Lesson 9-4
- Covering the Ideas 9-4

Additional Answers

9b.
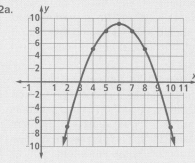

9c. y-intercept: 4; x-intercepts: none; vertex: (0, 4)

9d. $y \geq 4$

12a.
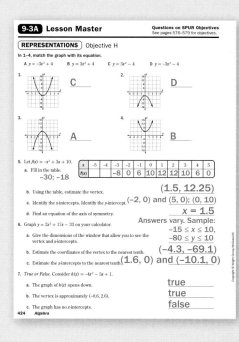

9-3

Notes on the Questions

Question 18 You might ask students why the graph represents the number of accidents per 50 million miles driven. Why not graph the number of accidents per age of driver? (Very young and very old drivers drive fewer miles than drivers of other ages, and there would be fewer accidents. This would disguise the fact that these drivers have more accidents for every mile they drive.) You also might ask students why they think that teenagers and older people have more accidents per mile. Finally, you might ask how the equation would change if y were the number of accidents per mile rather than per 50 million miles driven. (The equation would be $y = \dfrac{0.4x^2 - 36x + 1{,}000}{50{,}000{,}000}$, far more difficult to interpret, but still with a graph that is a parabola.)

Question 22 Because $d = rt$, $t = \dfrac{d}{r}$, so the problem is merely one of division. However, the units need to be consistent, and that is not easy. If students have only an answer in hours, you should ask them to change it to minutes by multiplying by conversion factors.

Question 23 This question asks students to take this question further by finding an equation of this parabola in the form $y = ax^2 + bx + c$. The hint to start with $y = -x^2$ comes from the fact that this parabola is congruent to the graph of $y = x^2$. Around the vertex, the points that are 1 unit to the right and left of the vertex are also 1 unit below it. This gives the value of a. The value of c can be found by determining the y-intercept, which can be found by noticing a nice pattern in the table of values for the parabola. And, finally, the value of b can be found by substituting one of the known pairs of values of x and y into the equation where everything else is known. The equation is $y = -x^2 + 12x - 27$.

Matching In 14–17, match the graph with its equation.

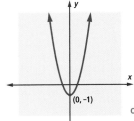

a. $y = 2x^2$ b. $y = 2x^2 + 1$

c. $y = 2x^2 - 1$ d. $y = -2x^2 - 1$

14.

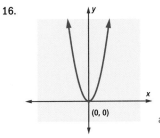

(0, -1) c

15.

(0, -1) d

16.

(0, 0) a

17.

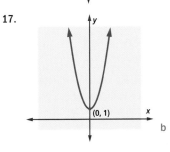

(0, 1) b

18. An insurance company reports that the equation $y = 0.4x^2 - 36x + 1{,}000$ relates the age of a driver x (in years) to the accident rate y (number of accidents per 50 million miles driven) when $16 \le x \le 74$.

   a. Graph this equation on your calculator. Give the window you used, the vertex, and the intercepts of the graph. **See margin.**

   b. Use the trace function of the graph to determine the age in which drivers have the fewest accidents per mile driven. About how many accidents do drivers of this age have per 50 million miles driven? **45 yr; 190 accidents**

   c. According to this model, an 18-year-old driver is how many times as likely to have an accident as a 45-year-old driver? **about 2.5 times as likely**

REVIEW

19. Consider Galileo's equation $d = 16t^2$. (**Lesson 9-2**)

   a. Find t when $d = 350$. $t = \sqrt{\dfrac{350}{16}} \approx 4.68$

   b. Write a question involving distance and time that can be answered using Part a. **Answers vary. Sample answer: If you drop a stone off of a 350-ft cliff, how long will it take for the stone to hit the ground?**

Additional Answers

18a.

window: $-200 \le y \le 700$ and $-20 \le x \le 80$; vertex: (45, 190); y-intercept: 1,000

20. Below are Charlotta's answers to questions about $y = \frac{x^2}{4}$. After she wrote this, she realized that she copied the equation incorrectly. It should be $y = -\frac{x^2}{4}$. What does Charlotta need to change to correct her work? (Lesson 9-1)

x	-4	-2	0	2	4
y	4	1	0	1	4

vertex = (0, 0)

axis of symmetry: $x = 0$

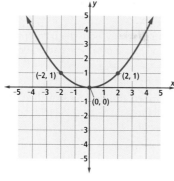

20. She should multiply all y-values in the table by −1 and reflect her graph over the x-axis.

21c. $4\sqrt{22}$ or about 18.76

22a. about 3.34 min, 3 min 21 sec, or 0.056 hr

21. **Skill Sequence** If $a = -6$, $b = 8$, and $c = 12$, find the value of each expression. (Lessons 8-6, 1-1)

a. $-4ac$ 288

b. $b^2 - 4ac$ 352

c. $\sqrt{b^2 - 4ac}$

22. A giant tortoise is walking at an average rate of $0.17 \frac{\text{mile}}{\text{hour}}$. Assume the tortoise continues walking at this rate.

a. How long will it take the tortoise to travel 50 feet?

b. How long will it take the tortoise to travel f feet?

(Lessons 5-4, 5-3) about $\frac{f}{897.6}$ hr or $\frac{f}{14.96}$ min

EXPLORATION

23. Begin with $y = -x^2$. With your calculator, experiment to find an equation for the parabola whose graph is used in Question 12.
$y = -x^2 + 12x - 27$

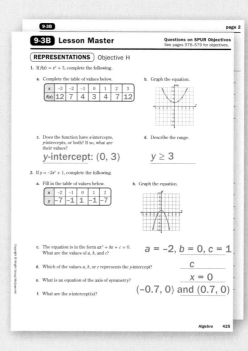

In the past, giant species of *Geochelone* (tortoise) were once found on all continents except Australasia, but today the giant forms are restricted to *G. elephantopus* in the Galapagos and *G. gigantea* on the island of Aldabara.

Source: Rochester Institute of Technology

4 Wrap-Up

Ongoing Assessment

Have students write an equation for a parabola that satisfies the following conditions.

(a) The parabola opens down and has a y-intercept of 5. Answers vary. Sample answer: $y = -x^2 + 5$

(b) The parabola opens up and has a y-intercept of −2. Answers vary. Sample answer: $y = x^2 - 2$

Then ask students to identify another point on a parabola that contains the point $(3, \sqrt{8})$ and a line of symmetry of $x = -2$. $(-7, \sqrt{8})$

Project Update

Project 4, Checking Whether Points Lie on a Parabola, on page 572, relates to the content of this lesson.

Lesson 9-4

Quadratics and Projectiles

force of gravity

initial upward velocity

initial height

GOAL

Use quadratics to determine the path of a projectile over time.

SPUR Objective

D Use quadratic equations to solve problems about paths of projectiles.

Materials/Resources

· Lesson Master 9-4A or 9-4B
· Resource Masters 2, 139, and 140
· Scientific or graphing calculator

HOMEWORK

Suggestions for Assignment

• Questions 1–16
• Question 17 (extra credit)
• Reading Lesson 9-5
• Covering the Ideas 9-5

Local Standards

1   Warm-Up

Consider the situation of Example 1 on page 546. Use the equation describing the height h in feet of the ball after t seconds: $h = -16t^2 + 32t + 6$.

1. How high will the ball be after half of a second? **18 ft**

2. How high will the ball be after 1.5 seconds? **18 ft**

3. What is the height of the ball when it hits the ground? **0 ft**

> **BIG IDEA**   Assuming constant gravity, both the path of a projectile and the height of a projectile over time can be described by an equation of the form $y = ax^2 + bx + c$, $a \neq 0$.

A *projectile* is an object that is thrown, dropped, or launched, and then proceeds with no additional force on its own. A ball thrown up into the air is considered a projectile.

Equations for the Paths of Projectiles

When there is a constant force of gravity, the path of a projectile is a parabola. The parabola shows the height of the projectile as a function of the *horizontal distance* from the launch.

Estimate to the nearest 10.

a. 24% of 82   20

b. 5% of 206   10

c. 61% of 92   60

Activity

Step 1 A classroom board should be partitioned into rectangles by drawing evenly spaced lines, as shown. Work in a group and assign two students the tasks of tossing and catching a ball. Position the tosser at the left end of the board and the catcher at the right end of the board. During the experiment, the tosser will toss the ball to the catcher so that it does not go higher than the top of the board. For each vertical division line on the board, assign a student to act as a spotter. The diagram at the right would require 7 spotters. When the ball is tossed, these spotters will observe the ball's height when it crosses their vertical line.

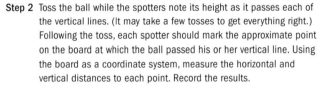

Step 2 Toss the ball while the spotters note its height as it passes each of the vertical lines. (It may take a few tosses to get everything right.) Following the toss, each spotter should mark the approximate point on the board at which the ball passed his or her vertical line. Using the board as a coordinate system, measure the horizontal and vertical distances to each point. Record the results.

Answers vary. Sample answers are given.

x = horizontal distance ball has traveled	? 0	? 1	? 2	? 3	? 4	? 5	? 6	? 7	? 8
y = height of the ball	? 0	? 1.6	? 2.75	? 3.6	? 4	? 3.6	? 2.75	? 1.6	? 0

Background

Two fundamental applications of quadratic equations to projectiles are presented in this lesson. The first is the relationship between the *height of a projectile* and its *horizontal distance along the ground*. This quadratic equation describes the *path* of the projectile. The problem in the Activity illustrates this use of quadratics.

Prior to the 16th century, the prevailing thought was that once a projectile reaches its peak, it then drops down rather quickly (Figure 1).

It took the work of the late 16th century scientists Tartaglia (1551) and Galileo (1600) to connect the physical motion

(continued on next page)

Figure 1

Step 3 Enter the data into lists L1 and L2 on your calculator. Perform *quadratic regression* on the data. Quadratic regression fits a parabola "of best fit" to three or more points in the plane. Here is how to apply quadratic regression on one calculator.

The calculator returns coefficients *a*, *b*, and *c* of the quadratic equation that most closely fit the data entered into lists L1 and L2.

Step 3:

Step 4:

Step 4 Next, set up a reasonable plot window to fit your data. Enter the equation obtained in Step 3 into your Y= menu. Plot the scatterplot and function on the same grid. How close is the scatterplot to the parabola of best fit?

Equations for the Heights of Projectiles over Time

The graph of Galileo's formula $d = -16t^2$ is also a parabola. That parabola describes the height of the projectile as a function of the *length of time* since the projectile was launched.

When a projectile is launched, several factors determine its height above the ground at various times:

1. The **force of gravity** pulls the projectile back to Earth. By Galileo's formula, gravity pulls the projectile towards Earth $16t^2$ feet in t seconds.

2. The **initial upward velocity** with which the projectile is thrown or shot contributes to its height at time t. We use v to stand for the initial velocity. In t seconds, the projectile would go vt feet if there were no gravity.

3. The **initial height** of the projectile. We call this height s (for starting height).

Quadratics and Projectiles **545**

of objects with the parabola and with quadratics (Figure 2). That these paths *must* be quadratics (in a situation where gravity is constant) was deduced by Isaac Newton from assumptions about the force of gravity.

Figure 2

The second application of quadratics studied in this lesson is the relationship between the *height of a projectile* and the *time* it has been in the air. Example 1 illustrates this use of quadratics. Students may need explicit instruction that this graph, while a parabola, is not a graph of the *path* of the projectile but rather it shows the relationship between distance and height.

9-4

Additional Example

Example 1 A ball is thrown from an initial height of 10 feet with an initial velocity of 64 feet per second.

a. Write an equation describing the height h in feet of the ball after t seconds. $h = -16t^2 + 64t + 10$

b. How high will the ball be after 3 seconds? **58 feet**

c. What is the maximum height of the ball? **74 feet**

Note-Taking Tips

Encourage students to apply ideas of symmetry when they analyze the graph of a parabola. After they label the vertex and axis of symmetry, they can label values symmetric to the y-intercept, to an x-intercept, or to other given values of the parabola.

Adding all these forces together yields a formula for the height of a projectile over time. Notice that the force of gravity is downward, so it has a negative effect on the height, while the launch velocity is considered to be upward and positive.

General Formula for the Height of a Projectile over Time

Let h be the height (in feet) of a projectile launched with an initial upward velocity v feet per second and an initial height of s feet. Then, after t seconds, $h = -16t^2 + vt + s$.

Since 16 feet ≈ 4.9 meters, if the units are in meters in the formula above, then $h = -4.9t^2 + vt + s$.

It is very easy to confuse the graph showing the height of a projectile as a function of time with a graph that represents the object's path, because they both are parabolas. However, even when a ball is tossed straight up and allowed to fall, its graph of height as a function of time is a parabola.

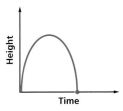

Ball's Path   **Ball's Height Graphed as a Function of Time**

Example 1

A ball is launched from an initial height of 6 feet with an initial upward velocity of 32 feet per second.

a. Write an equation describing the height h in feet of the ball after t seconds.

b. How high will the ball be 2 seconds after it is thrown?

c. What is the maximum height of the ball?

Solutions

a. Since units are provided in feet, use the general formula $h = -16t^2 + vt + s$. Substitute 6 for s and 32 for v.

$h = -16t^2 + 32t + 6$

Accommodating the Learner

This may be some students' introduction to how the force of gravity fits into a mathematics classroom. Initial upward/downward velocity might be confusing. Consider conducting a thought experiment to illustrate these ideas: Have them think of 3 people all throwing a ball at the same time. The first person throws a ball straight up, the second throws a ball straight out (horizontally), and the third throws a ball straight down. Then ask this series of questions: Will all the balls hit the ground? (yes) Why? (gravity) Which will hit the ground first, second, and third? (straight down; straight out; straight up) Why? (The vertical velocities are negative, zero, and positive, respectively.) Once students are comfortable with the concept of velocity, conduct a similar thought experiment varying the initial heights of the throwers.

b. Substitute 2 for t in $h = -16t^2 + 32t + 6$.

$$h = -16(2)^2 + 32(2) + 6$$
$$= -16(4) + 64 + 6$$
$$= -64 + 64 + 6$$
$$= 6$$

In 2 seconds, the ball will be 6 feet high.

c. Use a graphing calculator. Plot $y = -16x^2 + 32x + 6$. A graph of this function using the window $0 \le x \le 3$, and $0 \le y \le 25$ is shown at the right. The maximum height is the greatest value of h shown on the graph, the y-coordinate of the vertex. Trace along the graph, and read the y-coordinate as you go. When we did this using the window $0 \le x \le 3$, and $0 \le y \le 25$, our trace showed that (0.989, 21.998) and (1.021, 21.993) are on the graph. So try $t = 1$. This gives $h = 22$.

The maximum height reached is 22 feet.

Check You can verify the maximum height by using the MAXIMUM or VERTEX command on your calculator. The screen at the right shows the vertex as (1, 22).

GUIDED

Example 2

An object is dropped from an initial height of 90 meters.
a. Write a formula describing the height of the object (in meters) after t seconds.
b. After how many seconds does the object hit the ground?
c. What is the maximum height of the object?

Solutions

a. Because units are provided in meters, use the general formula
$h = -4.9t^2 + v \cdot t + s$.

Substitute 90 for s and 0 for v.

$$h = -4.9t^2 + \underline{\ ?\ } \cdot t + \underline{\ ?\ } \quad 0; 90$$
$$= -4.9t^2 + \underline{\ ?\ } \quad 90$$

b. The value(s) of t corresponding to $h = 0$ must be found when the object hits the ground.

$$0 = -4.9t^2 + \underline{\ ?\ } \quad 90$$
$$4.9t^2 = \underline{\ ?\ } \quad 90$$
$$t^2 \approx \underline{\ ?\ } \quad 18.37$$

Because t is positive (it measures time after launch), ignore the negative square root.

$$t \approx \underline{\ ?\ } \quad 4.3$$

(continued on next page)

Additional Example

Example 2 An object is dropped from an initial height of 40 meters.

a. Write a formula describing the height of the object (in meters) after t seconds.

b. After how many seconds does the object hit the ground?

c. What is the maximum height of the object?

Solution

a. Because units are provided in meters, use the general formula $h = -4.9t^2 + v \cdot t + s$. Substitute 40 for s and 0 for v.

$$h = -4.9t^2 + \underline{\ ?\ } \cdot t + \underline{\ ?\ } \quad 0; 40$$
$$= -4.9t^2 + \underline{\ ?\ } \quad 40$$

b. The value(s) of t corresponding to $h = 0$ must be found. So solve

$$0 = -4.9t^2 + \underline{\ ?\ } \quad 40$$
$$4.9t^2 \approx \underline{\ ?\ } \quad 40$$
$$t^2 \approx \underline{\ ?\ } \quad 8.2$$

Because t is positive (it measures time after launch), ignore the negative square root.

$$t \approx \underline{\ ?\ } \quad 2.9$$

c. A graph of $y = -4.9x^2 + 40$ is shown below. The graph shows that the object is farthest from the ground when it is launched. That is when $t = 0$ ($h = -4.9t^2 + 40 = -4.9(0)^2 + 40 = 40$). The maximum height is 40 meters. We know this because the object was dropped from that height, and the equation and graph confirm it.

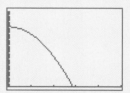

9-4

Additional Example

Example 3 Suppose a ball is thrown upward with an initial upward velocity of 30 meters per second from an initial height of 10 meters.

a. Write a formula for the height in meters of the object after t seconds.

b. Estimate when the ball is 40 meters high.

Solution

a. Since units are provided in meters, $h = -4.9t^2 + vt + s$.

$h =$? $h = -4.9t^2 + 30t + 10$

b. The values of t corresponding to $h = 40$ must be found. Graph the parabola and a horizontal line at $h = 40$ meters. Read the x-coordinate at the point of intersection. $x \approx$? and $x \approx$? 1.3 sec; 4.9 sec

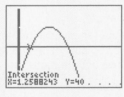

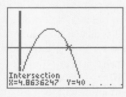

The ball is 40 meters off the ground at about ? seconds and ? seconds after being thrown. 1.3; 4.9

You should find that the object hits the ground in about 4.3 seconds.

c. A graph of $y = -4.9x^2 + 90$ is shown at the right. The graph shows that the object is farthest from the ground when it is launched. That is when $t = 0$. Then $h = -4.9t^2 + 90 = -4.9(0)^2 + 90 = 90$. The maximum height is 90 meters. We knew this because the object was dropped from this height, and the equation and graph confirm it.

If a projectile is thrown upward and comes back down to Earth, then it will reach some heights twice.

GUIDED

Example 3

Suppose a ball is thrown upward with an initial velocity of 22 meters per second from an initial height of 2 meters.

a. Write a formula for the height in meters of the ball after t seconds.

b. Estimate when the ball is 20 meters high.

Solutions

a. Because units are provided in meters, use $h = -4.9t^2 + vt + s$. Substitute 2 for s and 22 for v.

$h =$? $-4.9t^2 + 22t + 2$

b. The values of t corresponding to $h = 20$ must be found. Graph the equation you found in Part a on the window $0 \leq x \leq 6$, $10 \leq y \leq 30$. Draw a horizontal line $y = 20$ to indicate $h = 20$ feet. Use the **INTERSECT** command on your calculator to find both intersections. Our calculator shows that when $x \approx$? and $x \approx$?, $y \approx 20$. 1.1; 3.4

The ball is 20 meters off the ground at about ? seconds and ? seconds after being thrown. 1.1; 3.4

A method for finding exact answers without finding the intersections of two graphs is discussed in Lesson 9-5.

Questions

COVERING THE IDEAS

1. In your own words, define the term projectile. Give several real-life examples of projectiles.

2. Use quadratic regression on your calculator to find an equation for the parabola passing through the points (0, 6), (5, 30), and (10, 6). $y = -0.96x^2 + 9.6x + 6$

3. A ball is thrown from an initial height of 5 feet with an initial upward velocity of 30 feet per second. **a.** $h = -16t^2 + 30t + 5$
   a. Write a function describing the height of the ball after t seconds.
   b. How high will the ball be 2 seconds after it is thrown? **1 ft**
   c. What is the maximum height of the ball? **about 19.1 ft**

4. Suppose a ball is batted with an initial upward velocity of 26 meters per second from an initial height of 1 meter.
   a. Write a function describing the height in meters of the ball after t seconds. $h = -4.9t^2 + 26t + 1$
   b. Estimate when the ball is 5 meters high.
   about 0.2 sec and 5.2 sec

5. An object is dropped from an initial height of 40 feet.
   a. What is the object's initial velocity? What is its maximum height? **0 ft/sec; 40 ft**
   b. Write a formula for the height h in feet of the object after t seconds. $h = -16t^2 + 40$
   c. After how many seconds does the object hit the ground?
   about 1.6 sec

6. An object is dropped from an initial height of 150 meters.
   a. Write a formula for the height h in meters of the object after t seconds. $h = -4.9t^2 + 150$
   b. After how many seconds does the object hit the ground?
   c. What is the maximum height of the object? **150 m**

APPLYING THE MATHEMATICS

7. Use quadratic regression on your calculator to answer this question. A football kicker attempts to kick a 40-yard field goal. The kicker kicks the football from a height of 0 feet above the ground. The football is 26 feet above the ground at its peak (the vertex) at a distance of 22 yards from the kicker. The height of the crossbar (the bottom bar of the goal post) is 10 feet off the ground. Assuming the ball is kicked straight, will the kick clear the crossbar of the goal post? (*Hint:* Use the information given to determine a third point on the parabola and use quadratic regression.)

Los Angeles's Vladimir Guerrero hits a solo home run in the fourth inning of a baseball game in Oakland, California.
Source: Associated Press

1. Answers vary. Sample answer: A projectile is an object that is dropped or launched and travels through the air to get to a target. Cannonballs, baseballs, and tennis balls can all be considered projectiles.

6a. about 5.5 sec

7. No; at 40 yards from the kicker, the ball is only 8.6 ft high.

Quadratics and Projectiles   **549**

3 Assignment

Recommended Assignment
- Questions 1–16
- Question 17 (extra credit)
- Reading Lesson 9-5
- Covering the Ideas 9-5

Notes on the Questions

Question 2 This is an extension of the idea of using linear regression to obtain an equation for the line through two points, or to tell whether three or more points are collinear. You can also use a system of equations to find an equation for the parabola through three points. Because $y = ax^2 + bx + c$ for all pairs of points (x, y) on the parabola, substitute for (x, y) for each point:

> using (0, 6): $6 = a \cdot 0^2 + b \cdot 0 + c$
> using (5, 30): $30 = a \cdot 5^2 + b \cdot 5 + c$
> using (10, 6): $6 = a \cdot 10^2 + b \cdot 10 + c$

From this we have the system:

> $6 = c$
> $30 = 25a + 5b + c$
> $6 = 100a + 10b + c$

This system can be solved. First substitute 6 for c.

> $24 = 25a + 5b$
> $0 = 100a + 10b$

The second equation gives $b = -10a$. Substituting into the first equation, $24 = -25a$. So $a = -0.96$, from which $b = 9.6$. So $y = -0.96x^2 + 9.6x + 6$.

Questions 5c and 6b At this point, students are only expected to be able to answer these questions by solving an equation when an object is dropped, so that the initial velocity is zero.

9-4

Notes on the Questions

Question 9 This situation gives meaning to a negative height. The graph continues down past the point where $x = 6$. However, it does not make sense to include negative heights before time zero in this problem.

Question 13 Some students may feel that not enough information is given, but the fact that the second point is the vertex enables the symmetry of the parabola to be employed to find the coordinates of a third point.

Additional Answers

11a.

x	-3	-2	-1	0	1	2	3
y	2.25	1	0.25	0	0.25	1	2.25

11b.

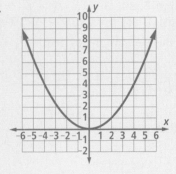

8. Refer to the graph at the right. It shows the height h in feet of a soccer ball t seconds after it is drop-kicked into the air.

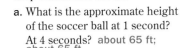

a. What is the approximate height of the soccer ball at 1 second? At 4 seconds? **about 65 ft; about 65 ft**

b. What is the greatest height the ball reaches? **102.5 ft**

c. At what times is the ball 38.5 feet high? **0.5 sec and 4.5 sec**

d. Approximately how long is the ball in the air? **about 5 sec**

e. For how many seconds is the ball more than 38.5 feet above the ground? **4 sec**

f. What does the h-intercept represent in this situation?

g. What does the t-intercept represent in this situation?

9. A small rocket is shot from the edge of a cliff. Suppose that after x seconds, the rocket is y meters above the cliff, where $y = 25x - 5x^2$.

a. Graph this equation using the window $0 \le x \le 8$, $-5 \le y \le 40$.

b. What is the greatest height the rocket reaches? **31.25 m**

c. How far above the edge of the cliff is the rocket after 4 seconds? **20 m**

d. Between which times is the rocket more than 20 feet above the cliff's edge? **between 1 and 4 sec after launch**

e. What is the height of the rocket after 6 seconds? **−30 m**

f. At approximately what time does the rocket fall below the height of the cliff's edge? **5 sec**

10. A ball is thrown from an initial height of 7 feet. After 5 seconds in the air, the ball reaches a maximum height of 18 feet above the ground.

a. What third point on the graph can be deduced from this information?

b. Use quadratic regression to find a formula for the height in feet of the ball after t seconds. $h = -0.44t^2 + 4.4t + 7$

c. Use the formula to find the initial velocity of the ball.

d. Use the graph to approximate how long the ball is in the air. **Answers vary. Sample answer: 11.25 sec**

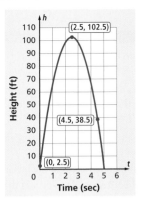

There were approximately 321,555 high school girl soccer players in the 2005–2006 school year.

Source: National Federation of High School Associations

8f. the initial height of the ball

8g. the time the ball hits the ground

9a.

10a. After 10 sec, the ball will again be at a height of 7 ft.

10c. 4.4 ft/sec

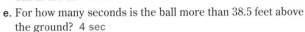

9-4A Lesson Master   Questions on SPUR Objectives
See pages 576–579 for objectives.

USES Objective D

1. Suppose the height h of a ball versus time t is given by the formula $h(t) = -16t^2 + 23t + 6$.

   a. Is the height of the ball being measured in feet or meters? **feet**

   b. At what height was the ball released? **6 ft**

   c. What was the initial upward velocity of the ball? **23 ft/sec**

2. Mourette is a member of her high school golf team. She hits a golf ball off the ground with an initial upward velocity of 60 meters per second.

   a. Write a formula describing the height h of the ball (in meters) after t seconds. $h(t) = -4.9t^2 + 60t$

   b. After how many seconds, to the nearest tenth, will the golf ball land on the ground? **12.2 sec**

   c. What is the maximum height the golf ball reaches? **183.7 m**

3. Suppose a soccer ball is kicked off of the ground with an initial upward velocity of 73 feet per second at the same time a baseball is released from a height of 5 feet 6 inches with an initial upward velocity of 24 feet per second.

   a. Which ball will stay in the air longer? Justify your answer. **Soccer ball; soccer ball hits the ground at 4.6 seconds and baseball hits the ground at 1.7 seconds.**

   b. Which ball will reach a higher point? Justify your answer. **Soccer ball; maximum height of the soccer ball is 83.3 feet and maximum height of the baseball is 14.5 feet.**

4. During Super Bowl XXXIII, Denver Bronco quarterback John Elway threw an 80-yard pass (longest of his career) to Rod Smith. Suppose Elway released the ball from a height of 6 feet 3 inches and that the maximum height the ball reached was 8 feet and this occurred 38 yards away from Elway.

   a. What is a third point that can be assumed on the path of the football from Elway to Smith? **76 yd from Elway and 6.25 ft high**

   b. Use the three points and quadratic regression to find a formula for the height of the football in feet based on the yards it is from Elway. $h(t) = -0.0001t^2 + 0.031t + 6.25$

   c. At about what height did Rod Smith catch the football? **5.86 ft**

Algebra 427

Extension

Consider having students work with one of several data collection devices that interface with students' graphing calculators. Students should repeat the activity of tossing the ball but this time have students use the data collection device and the software that comes with it. Have them compare the results from the activity with the results using the data collection device. Repeat the experiment using the data collection device changing the velocity with which the ball is tossed. Have them compare the results.

REVIEW

In 11 and 12, an equation is given. **11–12. See margin.**

 a. Make a table of values for integer values of x from -3 to 3.

 b. Graph the equation. (Lessons 9-3, 9-2)

11. $y = \frac{1}{4}x^2$

12. $y = 8x - 3x^2$

In 13 and 14, use the graph of the parabola at the right.
(Lessons 9-3, 9-1)

13. Use the symmetry of the parabola to find the coordinates of points A and B. $A = (2, 2)$, $B = (3, 5)$

14. Write an equation for the axis of symmetry. $x = 4$

15. **Multiple Choice** Which of the following is *not* equal to uv^2?
(Lessons 8-5, 8-2) **D**

 A $u \cdot v \cdot v$ **B** $(u)v^2$ **C** $u(v)^2$ **D** $(uv)^2$

(graph showing points labeled (4, 6), B, (5, 5), A, (6, 2))

16. The table below estimates the number of calories people of various weights burn per minute while participating in various activities. (Lessons 6-8, 6-5, 3-4)

Activity	Weight (lb)			
	105–115	127–137	160–170	180–200
Full-court Basketball	9.8	11.2	13.2	14.5
Jogging (5 mph)	8.6	9.2	11.5	12.7
Running (8 mph)	10.4	11.9	14.2	17.3
Volleyball	7.8	8.9	10.5	11.6
Bicycling (10 mph)	5.5	6.3	7.8	14.5

Source: www.coolnurse.com

 a. Suppose Vince, who weighs 168 pounds, works out by jogging and then playing basketball. Let $x =$ the number of minutes he jogs, and let $y =$ the number of minutes he plays basketball. If he burns a total of 445 calories, write an equation in standard form that describes x and y. $445 = 11.5x + 13.2y$

 b. Find the x- and y-intercepts of the line from Part a.

 c. If Vince plays basketball for 25 minutes, use your equation to calculate how long he must jog to burn 445 calories. **10 min**

EXPLORATION

17. Infinitely many parabolas have x-intercepts at 0 and 6. Find equations for three such parabolas. Answers vary. Sample answer: $y = x^2 - 6x$, $y = 2x^2 - 12x$, $y = -x^2 + 6x$

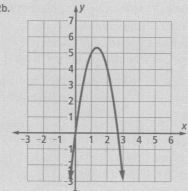

The state of California has produced the most high school All-American boy's basketball players (72) through the 2005–2006 season.

Source: mcdepk.com

16b. x-intercept:
 ≈ 38.7
 y-intercept:
 ≈ 33.7

Additional Answers

12a.

x	-3	-2	-1	0	1	2	3
y	-51	-28	-11	0	5	4	-3

12b.

(graph of a downward parabola)

---

4 Wrap-Up

Ongoing Assessment

Call upon a student to identify what each term in the equation $h = -16t^2 + 20t + 17$ represents. Ask the student to create a story problem with two questions that could be modeled by this equation. Have students exchange papers and solve the problem. Each student should then check and grade the work done on the original problem.

Project Update

Project 2, Verifying Projectile Motion, on page 571, relates to the content of this lesson.

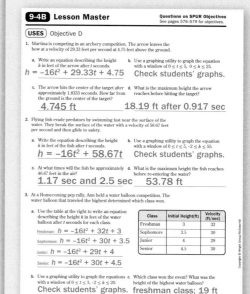

9-4B Lesson Master

Questions on SPUR Objectives
See pages 576–579 for objectives.

USES Objective D

1. Martina is competing in an archery competition. The arrow leaves the bow at a velocity of 29.33 feet per second at 4.75 feet above the ground.

 a. Write an equation describing the height h in feet of the arrow after t seconds.
 $h = -16t^2 + 29.33t + 4.75$

 b. Use a graphing utility to graph the equation with a window of $0 \le t \le 5$, $0 \le h \le 25$. Check students' graphs.

 c. The arrow hits the center of the target after approximately 1.8333 seconds. How far from the ground is the center of the target?
 4.745 ft

 d. What is the maximum height the arrow reaches before hitting the target?
 18.19 ft after 0.917 sec

2. Flying fish evade predators by swimming fast near the surface of the water. They break the surface of the water with a velocity of 58.67 feet per second and then glide to safety.

 a. Write the equation describing the height h in feet of the fish after t seconds.
 $h = -16t^2 + 58.67t$

 b. Use a graphing utility to graph the equation with a window of $0 \le t \le 5$, $-2 \le h \le 55$. Check students' graphs.

 c. At what times will the fish be approximately 46.67 feet in the air?
 1.17 sec and 2.5 sec

 d. What is the maximum height the fish reaches before re-entering the water?
 53.78 ft

3. At a Homecoming pep rally, Ann held a water balloon competition. The water balloon that traveled the highest determined which class won.

 a. Use the table at the right to write an equation describing the height h in feet of the water balloon after t seconds for each class.

 Freshman: $h = -16t^2 + 32t + 3$
 Sophomore: $h = -16t^2 + 30t + 3.5$
 Junior: $h = -16t^2 + 29t + 4$
 Senior: $h = -16t^2 + 30t + 4.5$

Class	Initial Height(ft)	Velocity (ft/sec)
Freshman	3	32
Sophomore	3.5	30
Junior	4	29
Senior	4.5	30

 b. Use a graphing utility to graph the equations with a window of $0 \le t \le 3$, $-2 \le h \le 20$. Check students' graphs.

 c. Which class won the event? What was the height of the highest water balloon?
 freshman class; 19 ft

428 Algebra

9-4B page 2

4. Lewis participates in the long-jump event on the track team. After his approach, he jumps in the air at a velocity of 8 meters per second.

 a. Write the equation describing the height h in meters of Lewis after t seconds.
 $h = -4.9t^2 + 8t$

 b. Use a graphing utility to graph the equation with a window of $0 \le t \le 5$, $-2 \le h \le 5$. Check students' graphs.

 c. What is the maximum height of his jump?
 ≈ 3.3 m

 d. At what time(s) is Lewis about 2 meters off the ground?
 ≈ 0.31 sec and ≈ 1.32 sec

 e. How long is Lewis in the air?
 ≈ 1.63 sec

5. Randy threw the shot put in a track competition at a velocity of 13.2 meters per second. The initial height of the shot put was 1.5 meters.

 a. Write the equation describing the height h in meters of the shot put after t seconds.
 $h = -4.9t^2 + 13.2t + 1.5$

 b. Use a graphing utility to graph the equation with a window of $0 \le t \le 5$, $-2 \le h \le 15$. Check students' graphs.

 c. Between what times was the shot put over 8 meters in the air?
 between 0.65 sec and 2.04 sec

 d. What does the h-intercept represent?
 the initial height of the shot put

6. Tayyika Haneef was part of the 2002 USA Women's World Volleyball Team. Suppose she serves the volleyball at a velocity of 25 meters per second. Her opponent returns the volleyball at a velocity of 13 meters per second at a height of 1.1 meters.

 a. Write the equation describing the height h in meters of the returned volleyball after t seconds.
 $h = -4.9t^2 + 13t + 1.1$

 b. Use a graphing utility to graph the equation with a window of $0 \le t \le 3$, $-2 \le h \le 10$. Check students' graphs.

 c. The height of the volleyball net for a women's court is 2.238 meters. Between which times was the height of the ball greater than the height of the net?
 between 0.091 sec and 2.562 sec

 d. What is the value of the t-intercept and what does the t-intercept represent?
 2.74 sec; the time the volleyball hits the ground

Algebra 429

Lesson
9-5

GOAL

Use the Quadratic Formula
$x = \dfrac{-b \pm \sqrt{b^2 - 4ac}}{2a}$ to solve
equations of the form
$ax^2 + bx + c = 0$.

SPUR Objective

B Solve quadratic equations using the Quadratic Formula.

Materials/Resources

· Lesson Master 9-5A or 9-5B
· Resource Master 141
· Scientific or graphing calculator

HOMEWORK

Suggestions for Assignment
• Questions 1–19
• Question 20 (extra credit)
• Reading Lesson 9-6
• Covering the Ideas 9-6

Local Standards

1 Warm-Up

Ask your students to write down the Quadratic Formula from memory as given on page 552. Students need to memorize the formula. Make sure that they state the formula with both the "if" and "then" parts.

Lesson
9-5 The Quadratic Formula

Vocabulary

quadratic equation
standard form of a quadratic equation

▶ **BIG IDEA** If an equation can be put into the form $ax^2 + bx + c$, it can be solved using the Quadratic Formula.

One of the most exciting events in amateur sports is 10-meter platform diving. Once a diver leaves a platform, the diver becomes a projectile. Consequently, during a dive, a diver's height above the water at any given time can be determined using a quadratic equation. This is important because for a diver to practice spins and somersaults, he or she must know how much time will pass before entering the water.

Suppose a diver jumps upward at an initial velocity of 4.3 meters per second. Then the diver's height $h(t)$ in meters t seconds into the dive; can be estimated using the equation $h(t) = -4.9t^2 + 4.3t + 10$ and graphed below. When the diver hits the water, $h(t)$ is zero. So solving the equation $0 = -4.9t^2 + 4.3t + 10$ gives the number of seconds from departing the platform to entering the water.

The equation $0 = -4.9t^2 + 4.3t + 10$ is an example of a *quadratic equation*. A **quadratic equation** is an equation that can be written in the form $ax^2 + bx + c = 0$ with $a \neq 0$. In this case, t is being used in place of x, $a = -4.9$, $b = 4.3$, and $c = 10$.

The Quadratic Formula

You can find the solutions to *any* quadratic equation by using the *Quadratic Formula*. This formula gives the value(s) of x in terms of a (the coefficient of x^2), b (the coefficient of x), and c (the constant term). The formula states that there are at most two solutions to a quadratic equation.

If $ax^2 + bx + c = 0$ and $a \neq 0$, then $x = \dfrac{-b + \sqrt{b^2 - 4ac}}{2a}$ or $x = \dfrac{-b - \sqrt{b^2 - 4ac}}{2a}$.

The calculations of the two solutions differ in only one way. $\sqrt{b^2 - 4ac}$ is added to $-b$ in the numerator of the first calculation, while $\sqrt{b^2 - 4ac}$ is subtracted from $-b$ in the second calculation.

Write as a power of 10.
a. $65 \div 0.65$ 10^2
b. $483 \div 48.3$ 10^1
c. $7.2 \div 7,200$ 10^{-3}

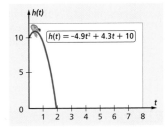

Background

The form of the Quadratic Formula found in the United States is not universal. In some countries, the standard form is $x^2 + 2bx + c = 0$, which yields the formula $x = -b \pm \sqrt{b^2 - c}$. The Quadratic Formula is not proved in this lesson; a proof is found in Chapter 13.

In the Quadratic Formula, the symbol $\pm$ represents one of two operations, addition or subtraction. It has a slightly different meaning in "if $x^2 = 4$, then $x = \pm 2$," where it means to keep the value or take its opposite.

We suggest that students memorize the Quadratic Formula as quickly as possible. Because students have calculators, we expect them to get decimal approximations of noninteger solutions for real situations. A solution of $\dfrac{2 + \sqrt{112}}{2}$ meters, such as that found in Example 3, conveys little meaning and is difficult to relate to the graph of $y = -x^2 + 2x + 27$ without a decimal approximation.

The work in calculating the two solutions is almost the same. So, the two expressions can be written as one expression using the symbol $\pm$, which means "plus or minus." This symbol means you do two calculations: one using the $+$ sign to add and one using the $-$ sign to subtract.

The Quadratic Formula

If $ax^2 + bx + c = 0$ and $a \neq 0$, then $x = \dfrac{-b \pm \sqrt{b^2 - 4ac}}{2a}$.

The quadratic equation $ax^2 + bx + c = 0$ and the Quadratic Formula $x = \dfrac{-b \pm \sqrt{b^2 - 4ac}}{2a}$ are equivalent equations. The quadratic equation was solved for x to generate the quadratic formula. In Chapter 13, you can see how this formula was found.

The quadratic formula is one of the most often used and most famous formulas in all mathematics. *You should memorize it today!*

Applying the Quadratic Formula

Example 1

Solve $x^2 + 8x + 7 = 0$.

Solution Recall that $x^2 = 1x^2$. So think of the given equation as $1x^2 + 8x + 7 = 0$ and apply the Quadratic Formula with $a = 1$, $b = 8$, and $c = 7$.

$$x = \frac{-b \pm \sqrt{b^2 - 4ac}}{2a}$$

$$= \frac{-8 \pm \sqrt{8^2 - 4 \cdot 1 \cdot 7}}{2 \cdot 1}$$

Follow the order of operations. Work under the radical sign (with its unwritten parentheses) first.

$$= \frac{-8 \pm \sqrt{64 - 28}}{2}$$

$$= \frac{-8 \pm \sqrt{36}}{2}$$

So, $x = \dfrac{-8 + 6}{2}$ or $x = \dfrac{-8 - 6}{2}$

$x = \dfrac{-2}{2} = -1$ or $x = \dfrac{-14}{2} = -7$

Check Do -1 and -7 make the equation $x^2 + 8x + 7 = 0$ true? Substitute -1 for x.

Does $(-1)^2 + 8(-1) + 7 = 0$?

$\qquad 1 + -8 + 7 = 0$ Yes, it checks.

(continued on next page)

> ▶ **READING MATH**
>
> On some calculators there is a key that is labeled $\pm$ or $+/-$. That key takes the opposite of a number. It does not perform the two operations $+$ and $-$ required in the Quadratic Formula.

---

2 Teaching

Notes on the Lesson

Example 1 is a simple application of the formula, when $a = 1$ and both b and c are positive.

Additional Example

Example 1 Solve $x^2 - 5x - 24 = 0$
-3 and 8

Accommodating the Learner ⬇

Students often have a difficult time using the Quadratic Formula. Sometimes they mix up the roles of a, b, and c. Write the following on the board:

$$x = \frac{-8 \pm \sqrt{(8)^2 - 4(2)(-3)}}{2(2)}.$$

Ask students to identify a, b, and c. Students should then write, in standard form, the equation which generated the expression on the board. Repeat this process with several other examples.

2, 8, and -3, respectively

ENGLISH LEARNERS
Vocabulary Development

This lesson can provide an opportunity to review the term *formula*. Students should be familiar with formulas for perimeter, area, and distance (e.g., $P = 2(\ell + w)$; $A = \ell \cdot w$, $A = \frac{1}{2}h(b_1 + b_2)$, $A = \pi r^2$; $d = r \cdot t$). They should also be able to describe a formula as an equation that expresses one quantity in terms of numbers, operations, and other quantities. In these terms, the *Quadratic Formula* expresses the value of the quantity x in terms of the coefficients a, b, and c in the equation $ax^2 + bx + c = 0$.

Notes on the Lesson

Example 2 involves decimals and an application, but otherwise poses no conceptual differences from Example 1. The decimals, however, stress the need for technology when dealing with quadratic equations.

Learning to use the Quadratic Formula requires practice, but practice without knowing whether answers are correct will often hide errors. Students need to learn ways of checking their answers. Students can check answers by substitution or by graphing. If students have a CAS, they can obtain both exact answers and decimal approximations.

Additional Example

Example 2 A first aid helicopter is dropping a package of medical supplies to the ground below. The function $h(t) = -16t^2 + 2t + 50$ gives the approximate height $h(t)$ in feet above the ground that the package is t seconds after the package is dropped. How many seconds elapse from the time the package leaves the helicopter until the package hits the ground?
approximately 1.8 sec; negative result is ignored because time must be positive

---

Substitute -7 for x.

Does $(-7)^2 + 8(-7) + 7 = 0$?

$49 + {-56} + 7 = 0$ Yes, it checks.

STOP QY

Sometimes you must decide whether or not a solution to a quadratic equation is reasonable, given the context of the problem. In Guided Example 2, we return to the diving situation described at the beginning of this lesson.

The x-axis represents a height of 0. The graph crosses the x-axis a little to the left of 2, which is close to 1.93. The INTERSECT feature on a graph is also helpful for finding a solution.

> **▶ QY**
>
> Solve
> $3y^2 - 10.5y + 9 = 0$.

GUIDED

Example 2

In 10-meter platform diving, the function $h(t) = -4.9t^2 + 4.3t + 10$ gives the approximate height $h(t)$ above the water in meters a diver is at t seconds after launching into the dive. How many seconds elapse from the time the diver leaves the 10-meter platform until the diver hits the water?

Solution The diver will hit the water when the diver's height above the water is zero, so solve the equation $0 = -4.9t^2 + 4.3t + 10$.

Apply the Quadratic Formula with $a = -4.9$, $b = 4.3$, and $c = 10$.

$$t = -4.3 \pm \frac{\sqrt{(\underline{\ ?\ })^2\ \underline{\ ?\ }\ 4(\underline{\ ?\ })(\underline{\ ?\ })}}{2(\underline{\ ?\ })\ {-4.9}}\qquad 4.3;\ -;\ {-4.9};\ 10$$

$$= \frac{-4.3 \pm \sqrt{\underline{\ ?\ }}}{-9.8}\qquad 214.49$$

So, $t = \dfrac{-4.3 + \sqrt{\underline{\ ?\ }}}{-9.8}$ or $t = \dfrac{-4.3 - \sqrt{\underline{\ ?\ }}}{-9.8}$.   214.49; 214.49

These are exact solutions to the quadratic equation. However, since the given information is not exact, it is more reasonable to want an approximation.

$$t \approx \frac{-4.3 + \underline{\ ?\ }}{-9.8}\quad \text{or}\quad t \approx \frac{-4.3 - \underline{\ ?\ }}{-9.8}\qquad 14.65;\ 14.65$$

$$t \approx -1.1\qquad \text{or}\quad t \approx 1.9$$

The diver cannot reach the water in negative time, so the solution -1.1 seconds does not make sense in this situation. We therefore eliminate this as an answer. The diver will hit the water about 1.9 seconds after leaving the diving platform.

Check Substituting 1.9 in for t in the equation $0 = -4.9t^2 + 4.3t + 10$ is one method you can use to check a solution. Other methods are looking at a table or a graph.

Juliana Veloso of Brazil competes in the women's 10-meter platform semifinals at the 2006 USA Grand Prix Diving Championships in Fort Lauderdale, Florida.

Accommodating the Learner ↑

Ask students to identify the mistake(s) made in using the Quadratic Formula in each of the examples.

a. $x^2 + 4x = 2$; $x = \dfrac{-4 \pm \sqrt{(4)^2 - 4(1)(2)}}{2(1)}$

b. $3 - 6x^2 - 2x = 0$;

$x = \dfrac{-(-6) \pm \sqrt{(-6)^2 - 4(3)(-2)}}{2(3)}$

c. $5x^2 + 9x - 2 = 0$; $x = -9 \pm \dfrac{\sqrt{(9)^2 - 4(5)(-2)}}{2(5)}$

Once students identify the mistake(s), ask them to use the Quadratic Formula to find the solution(s) to each equation.

a. The substitute for c is -2 not 2.
$x = -2 + \sqrt{6}$ or $x = -2 - \sqrt{6}$.

b. The substitute for a is 6. The substitute for b is 2, and the substitute for c is 3.
$x = \dfrac{-1 + \sqrt{19}}{6}$ or $x = \dfrac{-1 - \sqrt{19}}{6}$

c. The substitute b, -9, should be part of the numerator. $x = -2$, or $x = \dfrac{1}{5}$

In Example 3, the equation has to be put in $ax^2 + bx + c = 0$ form before the Quadratic Formula can be applied. This form is called the **standard form of a quadratic equation.** When the number under the radical sign in the Quadratic Formula is not a perfect square, approximations are often used in the last step of the process.

Example 3
Solve $x^2 - 3x = 37$.

Solution Put $x^2 - 3x = 37$ into standard form.

$x^2 - 3x - 37 = 37 - 37$ Subtract 37 from both sides.

$x^2 - 3x - 37 = 0$

Apply the Quadratic Formula, with $a = 1$, $b = -3$, and $c = -37$.

$$x = \frac{-(-3) \pm \sqrt{(-3)^2 - 4(1)(-37)}}{2(1)}$$

$$x = \frac{3 \pm \sqrt{9 + 148}}{2}$$

$$x = \frac{3 \pm \sqrt{157}}{2}$$

So $x = \frac{3 + \sqrt{157}}{2}$ or $x = \frac{3 - \sqrt{157}}{2}$.

These are exact solutions. You can approximate the solutions using a calculator.

Because $\sqrt{157} \approx 12.5$, $x \approx \frac{3 + 12.5}{2}$ or $x \approx \frac{3 - 12.5}{2}$. So $x \approx 7.75$ or $x \approx -4.75$.

Check Do the two values found work in the equation $x^2 - 3x = 37$?
Substitute 7.75 for x.
$(7.75)^2 - 3(7.75) = 36.8$. This is close to 37.
Substitute -4.75 for x.
$(-4.75)^2 - 3(-4.75) = 36.8$. This is close to 37.

In both cases the checks are not exact, but the solutions are approximations, so the check is close enough.

Questions

COVERING THE IDEAS

1. State the Quadratic Formula.

2. Is it true that the Quadratic Formula can be used to solve *any* quadratic equation?

3. Find the two values of $\frac{-3 \pm 9}{2}$. 3 and -6

1. If $ax^2 + bx + c = 0$ and $a \neq 0$, then $x = \frac{-b \pm \sqrt{b^2 - 4ac}}{2a}$.

2. Yes; as long as $b^2 - 4ac$ is nonnegative.

Additional Example
Example 3 Solve $x^2 - 7x = -2$.

Solution

Write $x^2 - 7x = -2$ in standard form.
$x^2 - 7x + \underline{?} = -2 + \underline{?}$ (Add 2 to both sides.) 2; 2
$x^2 - 7x + 2 = \underline{?}$ 0

Apply the quadratic formula.

$a = \underline{?}$, $b = \underline{?}$, $c = 2$ 1; -7

$$x = \frac{-(\underline{?}) \pm \sqrt{(\underline{?})^2 - 4(\underline{?})(\underline{?})}}{2(\underline{?})}$$ -7; -7; 1; 2

$$x = \frac{7 \pm \sqrt{(\underline{?}) - 8}}{2}$$ 49

$$x = \frac{7 \pm \sqrt{41}}{2}$$

So $x = \frac{7 + \sqrt{41}}{2}$ or $x = \underline{?}$. $\frac{7 - \sqrt{41}}{2}$

These are exact solutions. You can approximate the solutions using a calculator.

Since $\sqrt{41} \approx 6.4$, $x \approx \frac{7 + 6.4}{2}$ or $x \approx \frac{7 - 6.4}{2}$

So $x \approx 6.7$ or $x \approx \underline{?}$. 0.3

9-5

3 Assignment

Recommended Assignment

- Questions 1–19
- Question 20 (extra credit)
- Reading Lesson 9-6
- Covering the Ideas 9-6

Notes on the Questions

Question 13 Alan Shepard and Ed Mitchell spent 33.5 hours on the moon in early February 1971. Shepard was an avid golfer who had played at some of the best courses in the world. Under normal circumstances, bringing a golf club and ball on a space mission without telling the proper people would be cause for reprimand because weight is a very important and controlled commodity on these missions. Shepard's demonstration, despite thick gloves and a thick space suit that forced him to swing at the ball with only one hand, showed so dramatically the difference in gravity that not only was he forgiven but the golf shots have become the second most famous event on the moon (after the time in 1969 when Neil Armstrong made his first step onto the moon's surface).

In 4–7, use the Quadratic Formula to solve the equation. Give the exact solutions and check both solutions. 4–9. See margin for checks.

4. $x^2 + 15x + 54 = 0$
   x = −9 or x = −6

5. $t^2 + 4t + 4 = 0$ $t = -2$

6. $3m^2 + 2m = 4$

7. $3y^2 = 13y + 100$

In 8 and 9, use the Quadratic Formula to solve the equations. Round the solutions to the nearest hundredth and check both solutions.

8. $20n^2 - 6n - 2 = 0$

9. $3p^2 + 14 = -19p$

10. If a diver dives from a 20-foot platform with an initial upward velocity of 14 feet per second, then the diver's approximate height can be represented by the function $h(t) = -16t^2 + 14t + 20$, where $h(t)$ is the height and t is the time in seconds. (This formula is different from the one in this lesson because meters have been converted to feet.)

   a. Find $h(1)$. Write a sentence explaining what it means.

   b. Estimate to the nearest tenth of a second how much time the diver will be in the air before hitting the water. **about 1.6 sec**

APPLYING THE MATHEMATICS

11. The solutions to $ax^2 + bx + c = 0$ are the x-intercepts of the graph of $y = ax^2 + bx + c$.

    a. Use the Quadratic Formula to find the solutions to $3x^2 - 6x - 45 = 0$. x = −3 or x = 5

    b. Check your answers to Part a by graphing an appropriate function.

12. The graphs of $y = -0.5x^2 + 6$ and $y = 4$ intersect at two points.

    a. Find the x-coordinate of each of the intersecting points.

    b. Find both coordinates of the two points of intersection.

    c. Check your answers to Part b by graphing these equations.

13. In 1971, the astronaut Alan Shepard (who had been the first U.S. man in space 9 years earlier) snuck a collapsible golf club and a golf ball onto *Apollo 14*. Just before taking off from the moon to return to Earth, he hit two golf balls. In doing so, he vividly showed the difference between gravity on the moon and on Earth. On the moon the approximate height $h(t)$ of the ball (in feet) after t seconds is given by the function $h(t) = -0.8t^2 + 12t$.

    a. At what two times would the golf ball reach a height of 20 feet? (Round your answer to the nearest hundredth.)

    b. How long would it take for the ball to come back to the surface of the moon? **15 sec**

---

6. $m = \frac{-2 \pm \sqrt{52}}{6}$

   $= \frac{-1 \pm \sqrt{13}}{3}$

7. $y = -4$ or $y = \frac{25}{3}$

8. $n = -0.20$ or $n = 0.50$

9. $p = -5.48$ or $p = -0.85$

10a. $h(1) = 18$; $h(1)$ is the height of the diver after 1 sec.

11b.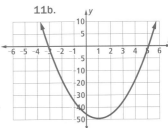

12a. $x = -2$ and $x = 2$

12b. (−2, 4) and (2, 4)

12c.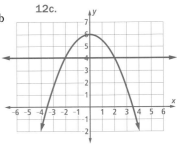

13a. $t = 1.91$ sec and $t = 13.09$ sec

Additional Answers

4. Does $(-9)^2 + 15(-9) + 54 = 0$?
   $81 + -135 + 54 = 0$ Yes, it checks;
   Does $(-6)^2 + 15(-6) + 54 = 0$?
   $36 + -90 + 54 = 0$ Yes, it checks.

5. Does $(-2)^2 + 4(-2) + 4 = 0$?
   $4 + -8 + 4 = 0$ Yes, it checks.

6. Does $3\left(\frac{-1 - \sqrt{13}}{3}\right)^2 + 2\left(\frac{-1 + \sqrt{13}}{3}\right) = 4$?
   $\frac{3 - 6\sqrt{13} + 39}{9} + \frac{-2 + 2\sqrt{13}}{3} = 4$?
   Yes, it checks.

   Does $3\left(\frac{-1 - \sqrt{13}}{3}\right)^2 + 2\left(\frac{-1 - \sqrt{13}}{3}\right) = 4$?
   $\frac{3 + 6\sqrt{13} + 39}{9} + \frac{-2 - 2\sqrt{13}}{3} = 4$
   Yes, it checks.

7. Does $3(-4)^2 = 13(-4) + 100$?
   $3(16) = -52 + 100$ Yes, it checks;
   Does $3\left(\frac{25}{3}\right)^2 = 13\left(\frac{25}{3}\right) + 100$?
   $3\left(\frac{625}{9}\right) = \frac{325}{3} + 100$ Yes, it checks.

14. The area of a rectangle is 240 cm². The length is 14 cm more than the width. What are the length and width of the rectangle?

14. The width is 10 cm and the length is 24 cm.

REVIEW

15. If the *x*-intercepts of a parabola are 8 and –4, what is the *x*-coordinate of its vertex? **(Lesson 9-3)** 2

16. Multiple Choice Which equation is graphed at the right? **(Lessons 9-3, 9-2)** C

A $y = 2x^2$ **B** $y = -2x^2$

C $y = 2x^2 + 2$ **D** $y = -2x^2 - 2$

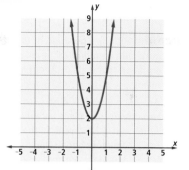

17. Find the radius of a circle if the center of the circle is at (–2, 6) and the point (1, 2) is on the circle. **(Lesson 8-8)** 5 units

18. Kristen is buying a new car. She can choose from 4 models, 2 transmission types, 9 exterior colors, and 6 interior colors. How many combinations of models, transmissions, exteriors, and interiors are possible? **(Lesson 8-1)** 432

19. Skill Sequence If $f(x) = \frac{5x - 6}{x}$, find each value. **(Lesson 7-6)**

   a. $f(2)$ 2   **b.** $f(3)$ 3   **c.** $f(x + 1)$ $\frac{5x - 1}{x + 1}$

EXPLORATION

20. a. Solve the equation $ax^2 + bx + c = 0$ for *x* using a CAS. In what form does the CAS put the two solutions?

   b. Add the two solutions using the CAS. What is the sum? $\frac{-b}{a}$

   c. Multiply the two solutions using the CAS. What is the product? $\frac{c}{a}$

   d. Use the results from Parts b and c to check the *exact* answers to Example 3 of this lesson. **The answers are correct:**

$$\frac{3 + \sqrt{157}}{2} + \frac{3 - \sqrt{157}}{2} = 3 \text{ and } \frac{-b}{a} = \frac{3}{1} = 3;$$

$$\left(\frac{3 + \sqrt{157}}{2}\right)\left(\frac{3 - \sqrt{157}}{2}\right) = -37 \text{ and } \frac{c}{a} = \frac{-37}{1} = -37.$$

20a. Answers vary. Sample answer: $x = \frac{-0.5b - \sqrt{0.25b^2 - ac}}{a}$

or $x = \frac{-0.5b + \sqrt{0.25b^2 - ac}}{a}$.

QY ANSWER

$y = 1.5$ or $y = 2$

---

4   Wrap-Up

Ongoing Assessment

Place the following equations on the overhead. Ask students to rewrite the equations in standard form. Students should identify *a*, *b*, and *c*. Instruct students to choose one of the equations and solve it using the Quadratic Formula.

a. $6x + 2x^2 = 56$ $x = -7$ or $x = 4$

b. $-32 = -2x^2$ $x = -4$ or $x = 4$

c. $-3x^2 = -21x + 30$ $x = 5$ or $x = 2$

Project Update

Project 1, Programming the Quadratic Formula, on page 571, relates to the content of this lesson.

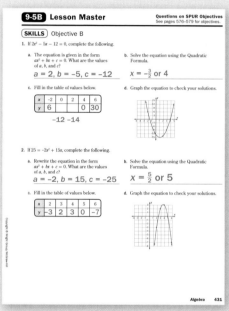

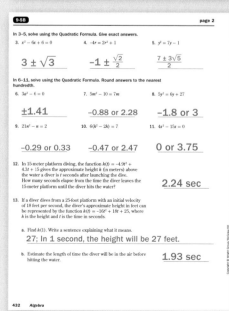

Lesson 9-6

GOAL

Analyze the discriminant $b^2 - 4ac$ to determine the number of solutions to the quadratic, and explore the relationship between the graphs of a quadratic equation and solutions to quadratic equations.

SPUR Objectives

B Solve quadratic equations using the Quadratic Formula.

C Identify and use the properties of solutions to quadratic equations.

Materials/Resources

· Lesson Master 9-6A or 9-6B
· Resource Masters 142 and 143
· Scientific or graphing calculator
· Quiz 2

HOMEWORK

Suggestions for Assignment
• Questions 1–24
• Question 25 (extra credit)
• Reading Lesson 9-7
• Covering the Ideas 9-7

Local Standards

1 Warm-Up

In 1–3, an equation for a parabola is given.
  a. Find the value of the discriminant $(b^2 - 4ac)$ of the equation.
  b. Find the x-intercepts of the parabola.

1. $y = 2x^2 - 7x + 10$ a. −31; b. There are no real x-intercepts.
2. $y = 2x^2 - 7x + 6.125$ a. 0; b. 1.75
3. $y = 2x^2 - 7x + 6$ a. 1; b. 2 and 1.5

Lesson 9-6 Analyzing Solutions to Quadratic Equations

Vocabulary

discriminant

> **BIG IDEA** The value of the discriminant $b^2 - 4ac$ of a quadratic equation $ax^2 + bx + c = 0$ can tell you whether the equation has 0, 1, or 2 real solutions.

In Acapulco, Mexico, cliff divers dive from a place called La Quebrada ("the break in the rocks") 27 meters above the water. As you have learned, a diver's path is part of a parabola that can be described using a quadratic equation. An equation that relates the distance x (in meters) away from the cliff and the distance y (in meters) above the water is $y = -x^2 + 2x + 27$. The graph at the right shows that when a diver pushes off the cliff, the diver arches upward and then descends.

Will the diver's height reach 27.75 meters? 28 meters? 30 meters? You can use the equation, the graph, or the table to determine whether or not a diver reaches a particular height.

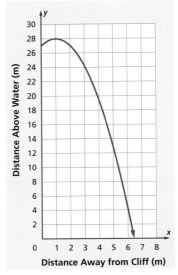

Using a Graph or Table to Determine Solutions to a Quadratic Equation

GUIDED

Example 1

Consider the situation of a La Quebrada diver. Graph and generate a table of the parabola with equation $y = -x^2 + 2x + 27$ to determine whether the diver will ever reach

a. 27.75 meters. b. 28 meters. c. 30 meters.

Mental Math

Solve the equation.

a. $a + 14 = 29$ $a = 15$

b. $b^2 + 14 = 39$ $b = \pm 5$

c. $(c - 6)^2 + 14 = 39$
  $c = 11$ or 1

Adele Laurent of Denver, Colorado, dives from the La Quebrada cliff during the International Cliff Diving Championships in 1996, the first year that women were allowed to participate in the championships.

Source: Associated Press

Background

In Lesson 9-5, students learned that a quadratic equation may have zero, one, or two solutions. Here they learn that the key to the number of solutions is found in the discriminant. This idea is related not just to the Quadratic Formula, but also to the graph of the equation and to the application of the cliff diver. The ties between these various representations are important.

It is at this point in a student's algebra experience that the idea of numbers other than real numbers appears. If the coefficients a, b, and c are real and the discriminant $b^2 - 4ac$ is negative, then there are two nonreal solutions. These can be written using the square roots of negative numbers that appear in the Quadratic Formula. Nonreal numbers have applications, but when they were first identified, no extra mathematical uses were known.

(continued on next page)

Solutions

a. A graph of $y = -x^2 + 2x + 27$ is shown on the right using the window $0 \leq x \leq 4$ and $25 \leq y \leq 30$. Also graphed is the line $y = 27.75$. This line crosses the parabola twice.

The diver reaches 27.75 meters twice, once on the way up and once on the way down.

A table of $y = -x^2 + 2x + 27$ is shown below. From the table it is evident that there are two distances x when $y = 27.75$ meters: once 0.5 meter from the cliff and again 1.5 meters away.

b. Suppose you draw the line $y = 28$ on the graph. How many times does the line appear to intersect the graph? __?__ **1**

Now look at the table. It appears the diver reaches the height of 28 meters __?__ time(s). The diver reaches the height of 28 meters __?__ meter(s) from the cliff. **1; 1**

c. Suppose you draw the line $y = 30$ on the graph. How many times does the line appear to intersect the graph? __?__ **0**

Now look at the table below. It appears the diver reaches the height of 30 meters __?__ time(s). **0**

Using the Quadratic Formula to Find the Number of Real Solutions

We can answer the same questions about the height of the diver using the Quadratic Formula.

Example 2

Will the diver ever reach a height of

a. 27.75 meters?   b. 28 meters?   c. 30 meters?

Solutions

a. Let $y = 27.75$ in the equation $y = -x^2 + 2x + 27$.

$$27.75 = -x^2 + 2x + 27$$

Add −27.75 to both sides to put the equation in standard form.

$$0 = -x^2 + 2x - 0.75$$

(continued on next page)

Analyzing Solutions to Quadratic Equations   **559**

This lesson may look long, but nearly three pages are devoted to a single example and nearly two pages are devoted to a summary of the important things to know about the discriminant. It is useful to go through the lesson in order.

Point out a limitation of the discriminant: it allows you to determine how many solutions a quadratic has, it does not tell whether the solutions make sense in a real-world situation.

Accommodating the Learner

Have students create quadratic equations of the form $y = ax^2 + bx + c$, each satisfying one of the following conditions:

(a) The graph of the quadratic intersects the x-axis in two different points.

(b) The graph of the quadratic intersects the x-axis in only one point.

(c) The graph of the quadratic does not intersect the x-axis.

Students should write reasons for choosing each equation. Have students graph each equation using their graphing calculators to verify that their equations are correct.

---

2 Teaching

Additional Example

Example 1 A firefighter shoots a rescue flare from the top of a 5-story building. The path of the flare is given in the equation $y = -2.5x^2 + 20x + 60$. Graph and generate a table of the parabola with equation to answer the following questions.

a. Will the flare ever reach a height of 90 feet?

b. Will the flare ever reach a height of 100 feet?

c. Will the flare ever reach a height 110 feet?

Solution

a. A graph of $y = -2.5x^2 + 20x + 60$ is shown below using the window $0 \leq x \leq 12$ and $0 \leq y \leq 110$. Also, graphed is the line $y = 90$. This line crosses the parabola twice.

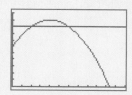

The flare reaches 90 feet twice, once on the way up at $x = 2$ and once on the way down at $x = 6$.

The table below confirms there are two values for x when $y = 90$ feet.

b. Draw the line $y = 100$ on the graph. The line appears to intersect the graph once. The table confirms that the flare reaches the height of 100 feet, 4 feet from the firefighter.

c. Draw the line $y = 110$ on the graph. The line does not intersect the graph.

The table confirms that the flare does not reach the height of 110 feet.

Additional Example

Example 2 Use the Quadratic Formula to find the solutions to the equation presented in Additional Example 1.

a. Will the flare ever reach a height of 90 feet? yes, twice; $20^2 - 4(-2.5) \cdot (-30) > 0$

b. Will the flare ever reach a height of 100 feet? yes, once; $20^2 - 4(-2.5) \cdot (-40) = 0$

c. Will the flare ever reach a height of 110 feet? no; $20^2 - 4(-2.5)(-50) < 0$

Note-Taking Tips

Students should keep their notes together on the quadratic formula and the discriminant property. For each of the three parts of the property, students should provide an example. Each example should include the algebraic calculation of the discriminant as well as a graph of the corresponding equation to reinforce what the algebra is telling them.

Let $a = -1$, $b = 2$, and $c = -0.75$ in the Quadratic Formula. Then

$$x = \frac{-2 \pm \sqrt{2^2 - 4(-1)(-0.75)}}{2(-1)}$$

$$x = \frac{-2 + \sqrt{1}}{-2} \quad \text{or} \quad x = \frac{-2 - \sqrt{1}}{-2}$$

$$x = 0.5 \quad \text{or} \quad x = 1.5$$

The diver reaches a height of 27.75 meters twice, first at 0.5 meter from the cliff and second at 1.5 meters from the cliff.

b. Let $y = 28$ in the equation $y = -x^2 + 2x + 27$.

$$28 = -x^2 + 2x + 27$$

Add -28 to both sides to place the equation in standard form.

$$0 = -x^2 + 2x - 1$$

Let $a = -1$, $b = 2$, and $c = -1$ in the Quadratic Formula.

$$x = \frac{-2 \pm \sqrt{2^2 - 4(-1)(-1)}}{2(-1)} = \frac{-2 \pm 0}{-2} = 1$$

So the diver reaches 28 meters just once, 1 meter up from the cliff. This agrees with the graph that shows the vertex to be (1, 28).

c. Let $y = 30$ in the equation $y = -x^2 + 2x + 27$.

$$30 = -x^2 + 2x + 27$$

Add -30 to both sides to place the equation in standard form

$$0 = -x^2 + 2x - 3$$

Let $a = -1$, $b = 2$, and $c = -3$ in the Quadratic Formula. Then

$$x = \frac{-2 \pm \sqrt{2^2 - 4(-1)(-3)}}{2(-1)} = \frac{-2 \pm \sqrt{-8}}{-2}$$

Because no real number multiplied by itself equals -8, there is no square root of -8 in the real number system. In fact, no negative number has a square root in the real number system. So $30 = -x^2 + 2x + 27$ does not have a real number solution. This means that the diver never reaches a height of 30 meters. This is consistent with the graph that shows there is no point on the parabola with a height of 30 meters.

The Discriminant of a Quadratic Equation

Look closely at the number under the square root in each of the solutions in Example 2. Notice that the number of solutions to a quadratic equation is related to this number, which is the number $b^2 - 4ac$ in the Quadratic Formula. In the solution to Part a, $b^2 - 4ac = 1$, which is positive. Adding $\sqrt{1}$ and subtracting $\sqrt{1}$ results in two solutions. In the solution to Part b, $b^2 - 4ac = 0$, and adding $\sqrt{0}$ and subtracting $\sqrt{0}$, yields the same result, 1. That quadratic equation has just one solution. There is no solution to the equation in Part c because $b^2 - 4ac = -8$, and -8 does not have a square root in the set of real numbers.

Accommodating the Learner ⬇

It will help some students if you reinforce the connection between the discriminant and what it is telling them with the graph of the corresponding equation. Have students calculate the value of the discriminant for each of the following equations and then have them graph the corresponding equation. Call upon students to explain the relationship between what they calculated and the graph.

(a) $x^2 - x - 6 = 0$; corresponding equation: $y = x^2 - x - 6$ discriminant $= 25$

(b) $2x^2 - 8x + 8 = 0$; corresponding equation: $y = 2x^2 - 8x + 8$ discriminant $= 0$

(c) $x^2 - x + 9 = 0$; corresponding equation: $y = x^2 - x + 9$
discriminant $= -35$

Because the value of $b^2 - 4ac$ *discriminates* among the various possible number of real number solutions to a specific quadratic equation, it is called the **discriminant** of the equation $ax^2 + bx + c = 0$. Stated below are the specific properties of the discriminant.

> **Discriminant Property**
>
> If $ax^2 + bx + c = 0$ and a, b, and c are real numbers ($a \neq 0$), then:
>
> When $b^2 - 4ac > 0$, the equation has exactly two real solutions.
>
> When $b^2 - 4ac = 0$, the equation has exactly one real solution.
>
> When $b^2 - 4ac < 0$, the equation has no real solutions.

An important use of the discriminant relates solutions of a quadratic equation to the x-intercepts of the related function. Specifically, the solutions to $ax^2 + bx + c = 0$ are the x-intercepts of $y = ax^2 + bx + c$. So the discriminant tells you how many times the function $f(x) = ax^2 + bx + c$ crosses the x-axis.

Quadratic Function	Value of $b^2 - 4ac$	Number of x-intercepts	Graph (All screens are shown in the standard viewing window.)
$y = x^2 + x - 6$	$1^2 - 4(1)(-6) = 25$ positive	two	
$y = x^2 - 6x + 9$	$(-6)^2 - 4(1)(9) = 0$ zero	one	
$y = x^2 + 2x + 7$	$2^2 - 4(1)(7) = -24$ negative	zero	

STOP QY

> ▶ **QY**
>
> Determine the number of real solutions to $6x^2 + 3x = -7$.

9-6

3 Assignment

Recommended Assignment
- Questions 1–24
- Question 25 (extra credit)
- Reading Lesson 9-7
- Covering the Ideas 9-7

Additional Example

Example 3 How many times does the graph of $y = 3x^2 - 12x + 12$ intersect the x-axis?

Solution

Find the value of the discriminant, $b^2 - 4ac$.

Here $a = \underline{\ ?\ }$ 3
$b = \underline{\ ?\ }$ −12
$c = \underline{\ ?\ }$ 12

So $b^2 - 4ac = \underline{\ ?\ }$. Therefore, the graph of $y = 3x^2 - 12x + 12$ intersects the x-axis $\underline{\ ?\ }$ time(s). 0; 1

GUIDED

Example 3

How many times does the graph of $y = 2x^2 + 16x + 32$ intersect the x-axis?

Solution Find the value of the discriminant $b^2 - 4ac$. Here $a = \underline{\ ?\ }$, $b = \underline{\ ?\ }$, and $c = \underline{\ ?\ }$. 2; 16; 32

So $b^2 - 4ac = \underline{\ ?\ }$. $(16)^2 - 4(2)(32)$

$\qquad = \underline{\ ?\ } = 0$ 256 − 256

Because the discriminant is $\underline{\ ?\ }$, the graph of $y = 2x^2 + 16x + 32$ intersects the x-axis $\underline{\ ?\ }$ time(s). zero; 1

Check You should check your answer by graphing the equation with a calculator.

Questions

COVERING THE IDEAS

In 1 and 2, refer to the La Quebrada cliff diver equation $y = -x^2 + 2x + 27$ from Example 1.

1. a. What equation can be solved to determine how far away (horizontally) from the cliff the diver will be when the diver is 27 meters above the water? $-x^2 + 2x = 0$

   b. Will the diver reach a height of 27 meters above the water? If so, how many times? yes, twice

2. How far from the cliff will the diver be at 10 meters above the water? 5.24 m

3. How many real solutions does a quadratic equation have when the discriminant is
   a. negative? 0
   b. zero? 1
   c. positive? 2

4. The discriminant of the equation $ax^2 + bx + c = 0$ is −1,200. What does this indicate about the graph of $y = ax^2 + bx + c$? It does not cross the x-axis.

5. The equation $y = \frac{1}{2}x^2 - x - \frac{3}{2}$ is graphed at the right. Use the graph to determine the number of real solutions to each equation.

   a. $\frac{1}{2}x^2 - x - \frac{3}{2} = -2$ 1
   b. $\frac{1}{2}x^2 - x - \frac{3}{2} = -3$ 0
   c. $\frac{1}{2}x^2 - x - \frac{3}{2} = 1$ 2
   d. $\frac{1}{2}x^2 - x - \frac{3}{2} = 5,000$ 2

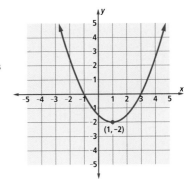

(1, −2)

In 6–9, a quadratic equation is given.
   a. Calculate the value of the discriminant.
   b. Give the number of real solutions.
   c. Find all the real solutions.

6. $2x^2 + x + 3 = 0$ 6a. -23

7. $-4n^2 + 56n - 196 = 0$ 7a. 0

8. $22q^2 = q + 3$ 8a. 265, 8b. 2

9. $x = \frac{x^2}{6} + \frac{1}{4}$ 9a. 120, 9b. 2

In 10 and 11, an equation of the form $y = ax^2 + bx + c$ is graphed. Tell whether the value of $b^2 - 4ac$ is *positive*, *negative*, or *zero*.

10.

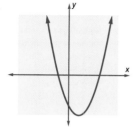

11.

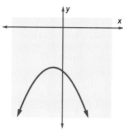

In 12 and 13, a quadratic function f is described.
   a. Calculate the value of the discriminant of the quadratic equation $f(x) = 0$.
   b. Give the number of x-intercepts of the graph of f.

12. $f(x) = 5x^2 + 20x + 20$
   12a. 0; 12b. 1

13. $f(x) = 2x^2 + x - 3$
   13a. 25; 13b. 2

APPLYING THE MATHEMATICS

14. For what value of h does $x^2 + 6x + h = 0$ have exactly one solution? 9

15. If the discriminant for the equation $2x^2 + 4x + c = 0$ is 8, what is the value of c? 1

16. In Lesson 9-5, a diver's height $h(t)$ above the water after t seconds was given by $h(t) = -4.9t^2 + 4.3t + 10$. Use the discriminant to find the time t when the diver reached the maximum height. about 0.44 sec

17. Can any parabolas with an equation of the form $y = ax^2 + bx + c$ *not* have a y-intercept? Why or why not?

18. By letting $x = m + 3$, solve $4(m + 3)^2 - 13(m + 3) - 35 = 0$ for m. $m = -4.75$ or $m = 2$

REVIEW

19. Solve $45x^2 - 100 = 0$. (**Lesson 9-5**) $x = \frac{-2\sqrt{5}}{3}$ or $x = \frac{2\sqrt{5}}{3}$

6b. There are no real solutions.

6c. There are no real solutions.

7b. There is one real solution.

7c. $n = 7$

8c. $x = \frac{1 - \sqrt{265}}{44}$ or $x = \frac{1 + \sqrt{265}}{44}$

9c. $x = \frac{6 - \sqrt{30}}{2}$ or $x = \frac{6 + \sqrt{30}}{2}$

10. positive

11. negative

17. No; All parabolas of the form $y = ax^2 + bx + c$ contain the point $(0, c)$.

Notes on the Questions

Question 14 This kind of question is often difficult for students the first time they see it. If they have difficulty, you might try various values of h similar to the three values found in the Warm-Up.

Question 24 The first four parts of this question increase in complexity. The structure of the items is the same and exemplifies chunking. Part d shows that the sum of the two solutions to the quadratic equation $ax^2 + bx + c = 0$ is $\frac{-b}{a}$ and provides a simple way to check solutions.

Question 25 You may wish to do this question as a whole-class activity.

9-6

4 Wrap-Up

Ongoing Assessment

Place students in pairs. On a piece of paper, each student should write an equation of the form $y = ax^2 + bx + c$. Have students exchange papers. Ask students to use the discriminant to determine how many x-intercepts the equation has. If the x-intercepts exist, they should use the Quadratic Formula to find them. Students should graph the equation to verify that their answers are correct.

In 20 and 21, use the following information. A softball pitcher tosses a ball to a catcher 50 feet away. The height h (in feet) of the ball when it is x feet from the pitcher is given by the equation $h = -0.016x^2 + 0.8x + 2$. (Lesson 9-4)

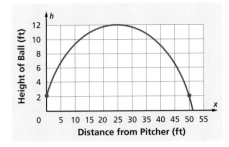

Height of Ball (ft) vs **Distance from Pitcher (ft)**

Softball was invented as an indoor sport by George Hamock of the Chicago Board of Trade in 1887.

Source: The History Channel

20. How high is the ball at its peak? **12 ft**

21. a. If the batter is 2 feet in front of the catcher, how far is the batter from the pitcher? **48 ft**

   b. How high is the ball when it reaches the batter? **about 3.5 ft**

In 22 and 23, state whether the parabola described by the equation opens up or down. (Lesson 9-3)

22. $y = -\frac{1}{3}x^2 - 6x + 1$ **down**   23. $y = 0.5x - 2x^2$ **down**

24. **Skill Sequence** In Parts a–d, simplify each statement. (Lesson 2-2)

   a. $\frac{-4+x}{2a} + \frac{-4-x}{2a}$

   b. $\frac{-b+y}{2a} + \frac{-b-y}{2a}$

   c. $\frac{-b+\sqrt{z}}{2a} + \frac{-b-\sqrt{z}}{2a}$

   d. $\frac{-b+\sqrt{b^2-4ac}}{2a} + \frac{-b-\sqrt{b^2-4ac}}{2a}$

   e. What does Part d tell you about the solutions to a quadratic equation? **The sum of the solutions is $\frac{-b}{a}$.**

24a. $\frac{-4}{a}$

24b. $\frac{-b}{a}$

24c. $\frac{-b}{a}$

24d. $\frac{-b}{a}$

EXPLORATION

25. Create a parabola in the following way. Take a plain sheet of notebook paper and draw a dark dot in the middle of the paper. Draw a line anywhere on the paper that is parallel to the bottom of the paper. Make sure the line stretches to both edges of the paper. Now fold the paper so that the dot falls on the line. Unfold the paper, and then fold the paper so that the dot falls on another place on the line. Repeat this 20 times so that the dot has fallen in different places on the line each time. The folds should outline a parabola that can be seen by unfolding the paper. Take another sheet and see what happens if the dot is farther from the line or closer to the line than the dot you used the first time.

25.

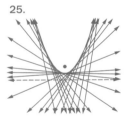

QY ANSWER

0

Lesson 9-7

More Applications of Quadratics: Why Quadratics Are Important

▶ **BIG IDEA** Quadratics have applications in engineering, geometry, and counting problems.

You may wonder why you are asked to memorize the Quadratic Formula or even why you need to know how to solve quadratic equations. There is a simple reason. Quadratic expressions, equations, and functions appear in a wide variety of situations. Furthermore, these situations are unlike those that lead to linear expressions. Many problems involving linear expressions can be solved by some people without algebra, using just intuition from arithmetic. Few people can solve problems that lead to quadratic expressions without using algebra.

You have seen applications of quadratic expressions in areas of squares and of circles, and to describe paths of projectiles. There are too many other applications to describe them all here. In this lesson, we give just a few.

Parabolas as Important Curves

In your future mathematics courses, you will study perhaps the most important property of a parabola: its reflective property. Because of its reflective property, a parabola is the shape of a cross-section of automobile headlights, satellite dishes, and radio telescopes.

Parabolas also appear on suspension bridges. When a chain is suspended between two fixed points, the curve it describes is a *catenary*. A catenary looks much like a parabola but is slightly deeper. But in a suspension bridge where the roadway is hung by support cables from the main cables, the shape of the main cable is a parabola.

Mental Math

Solve.

a. $E = mc^2$ for m. $m = \dfrac{E}{c^2}$

b. $A = \pi r^2$ for π. $\pi = \dfrac{A}{r^2}$

The total length of wires in the cables of the Brooklyn Bridge is approximately 3,600 miles.

Source: Endex Engineering, Inc.

Example 1

Suppose a team of engineers and construction workers are repairing a suspension bridge to strengthen it for use with increased traffic flow. The engineer uses scale models, such as the graph on the next page, to make decisions about repairs.

(continued on next page)

More Applications of Quadratics: Why Quadratics Are Important **565**

Background

There are still other applications of quadratics. In later courses, students will encounter applications of quadratics to the orbits of planets and comets and to statistics. Quadratics describe the conic sections in two dimensions and surfaces in three dimensions.

Before this chapter, students had seen quadratic expressions from geometry:

• area
• distance

In this chapter, attention has been given to applications that come from physics:

• paths of projectiles
• heights of projectiles over time

Students have also seen an example of quadratics as used in statistics:

• curve fitting (through quadratic regression)

(continued on next page)

Lesson 9-7

GOALS

Show even more applications of quadratics, thus cinching the importance of the idea and providing practice on many of the ideas of the chapter.

SPUR Objectives

E Solve geometric problems involving quadratic equations.

F Solve other real-world problems involving quadratic functions.

Materials/Resources

· Lesson Master 9-7A or 9-7B
· Resource Masters 144 and 145
· Scientific or graphing calculator

HOMEWORK
Suggestions for Assignment
• Questions 1–22
• Question 23 (extra credit)
• Reading Lesson 10-1
• Covering the Ideas 10-1

Local Standards

1   Warm-Up

1. Give the number of sides of the polygon, draw a convex example of this polgyon, and tell how many diagonals the polygon has.

a. hexagon	6 sides; 9 diag.
b. nonagon	9; 27
c. triangle	3; 0
d. pentagon	5; 5
e. heptagon	7; 14
f. octagon	8; 20
g. quadrilateral	4; 2
h. decagon	10; 35

2. Use quadratic regression to find an equation of the parabola through these points. $y = 0.5x^2 - 1.5x$

9-7

Notes on the Lesson

Example 1 illustrates the use of a quadratic function to describe a curve. Students should be able to find coordinates of points on such a curve. Given the first coordinate, they can substitute to find the second. Given the second coordinate (82.5 here), they need to solve a quadratic equation to find the one or two possible first coordinates.

If you work from the Warm-Up, you might have students graph the eight ordered pairs so that they see the parabola. Applying the Distributive Property to the formula in Example 2, $d = 0.5n^2 - 1.5n$. The application only allows integer values of n greater than 2, but all the eight ordered pairs lie on a parabola. In Part a, students substitute to find the second coordinate of the point on the parabola whose first coordinate is 15. In Part b, students see whether the intersection of this parabola with the line $y = 300$ has an integer coordinate for x.

Additional Example

Example 1 Engineers are planning to build a suspension bridge similar to the one seen in the figure below.

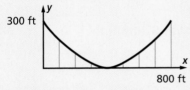

300 ft

800 ft

Let the bridge be along the x-axis. Place the y-axis at one end of the roadway. Then the ends of the bridge are at (0, 0) and (800, 0). Because the parabola is symmetric to the line $x = 400$, the parabola passes through the points (0, 300), (400, 0), and (800, 300). You can use quadratic regression to find an equation for the parabola through these points. In standard form, the equation is given by

$$y = \frac{3}{1,600}x^2 - \frac{3}{2}x + 300$$

where y is the length of each vertical cable at the distance x from the end of the roadway. Suppose two support cables of length 200 feet long are delivered to the construction site. How far from the left end of the bridge should the engineers place the cables?
73.4 feet, 726.6 feet

Let the roadway be along the x-axis. Place the y-axis at one end of the roadway. Then the ends of the bridge are at (0, 0) and (600, 0). The graph at the right shows that the parabola passes through points (0, 200), (300, 0), and (600, 200). By using quadratic regression, an equation for the parabola through these points can be found. In standard form, the equation is given by $y = \frac{1}{450}x^2 - \frac{4}{3}x + 200$, where y is the length of each vertical cable at the distance x from the end of the bridge. Suppose a support cable 82.5 feet long is delivered to the construction site. How far from the left end of the bridge should the cable be placed?

Length (ft)

Solution 1 Substitute 82.5 for y in the equation of the parabola. Then solve the equation for x.

$$82.5 = \frac{1}{450}x^2 - \frac{4}{3}x + 200$$

$$37,125 = x^2 - 600x + 90,000 \quad \text{Multiply both sides by 450.}$$

$$0 = x^2 - 600x + 52,875 \quad \text{Subtract 37,125 from both sides.}$$

Now the equation $x^2 - 600x + 52,875 = 0$ can be solved using the Quadratic Formula, with $a = 1$, $b = -600$, and $c = 52,875$.

$$x = \frac{-b \pm \sqrt{b^2 - 4ac}}{2a}$$

$$= \frac{-(-600) \pm \sqrt{(-600)^2 - 4(1)(52,875)}}{2(1)}$$

$$= \frac{600 \pm \sqrt{360,000 - 211,500}}{2}$$

$$= \frac{600 \pm \sqrt{148,500}}{2}$$

$$\approx \frac{600 \pm 385.4}{2}$$

$$x \approx 107.3 \text{ ft or } x \approx 492.7 \text{ ft}$$

The cable can be placed either 107.3 ft or 492.7 ft from the left end of the bridge.

Solution 2 Enter the equation of the parabola and the desired y value into a calculator, as shown at the right.

Graph each equation over the domain $0 \le x \le 600$. The solutions to the problem are intersection points of the two functions.

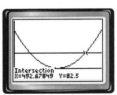

In this lesson, Example 1 shows a parabola in an application that derives from physics and geometry. Example 2 shows a quadratic equation from a counting situation. Questions 7 and 8 show applications of quadratic equations in geometric settings.

Example 1. The curve called a *catenary* is mentioned as the shape of a chain suspended between two points. Catenaries and parabolas look very much alike near their vertex. A comparison of graphs of the two can be found at mathforum.org/library/drmath/view/65729.html.

An equation for a catenary symmetric to the y-axis is $y = \frac{e^{ax} + e^{-ax}}{2a}$, where a is determined by the density and tension of the chain (see Question 23).

The x-coordinates of the intersections indicate that the cable is 82.5 feet long when x ≈ 107.3 ft and x ≈ 492.7 ft.

This makes sense because these distances are equally far from the center of the bridge at 300 ft.

A Geometry Problem Involving Counting

Many counting problems lead to quadratic equations. For example, the number d of diagonals of an n-sided convex polygon is given by the formula $d = \frac{n(n-3)}{2}$.

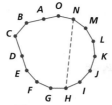

$\overline{NH}$ is one diagonal of this convex 15-sided polygon.

Example 2

a. How many diagonals does a convex polygon of 15 sides have?

b. Can a convex polygon have exactly 300 diagonals? If so, how many sides must that polygon have?

Solutions

a. When $n = 15$, $d = \frac{n(n-3)}{2} = \frac{15(15-3)}{2} = \frac{15 \cdot 12}{2} = 90$.
   A 15-sided polygon has 90 diagonals.

b. Substitute 300 for d in the formula.

$300 = \frac{n(n-3)}{2}$

$600 = n(n-3)$ Multiply both sides by 2.

$600 = n^2 - 3n$ Distributive Property

To solve, write the equation in standard form.

$0 = n^2 - 3n - 600$ Subtract 600 from both sides.

This equation is in standard form with $a = 1$, $b = -3$, and $c = -600$. Use the Quadratic Formula.

$n = \frac{-b \pm \sqrt{b^2 - 4ac}}{2a}$

$= \frac{-(-3) \pm \sqrt{(-3)^2 - 4 \cdot 1 \cdot (-600)}}{2 \cdot 1}$

$= \frac{3 \pm \sqrt{9 + 2{,}400}}{2}$

$= \frac{3 \pm \sqrt{2{,}409}}{2}$

Because the discriminant 2,409 is not a perfect square, the values of n that we get are not integers. But n has to be an integer because it is the number of sides of a polygon. So the discriminant signals that there is no polygon with exactly 300 diagonals.

Example 2 The formula $S = n^2$ can be used to find the sum of the first n odd natural numbers.

a. What is the sum of the first 20 odd natural numbers? **400**

b. Can the sum of the first n odd natural numbers be 230? If so, how many odd numbers are being added? If not, explain why.
no, $\sqrt{230}$ is not an integer.

Accommodating the Learner

Some students may appreciate this justification for one of the summation formulas. To add the first n natural numbers, instruct students to write the numbers 1 through 10 spread out on one line on a piece of paper. On the line below have students write the rest of the numbers in reverse order. Ask students to add each column and divide the sum by two. The process is modeled at the right.

1	2	3	4	5	6	7	8	9	10
+ 10	9	8	7	6	5	4	3	2	1
11	11	11	11	11	11	11	11	11	11

$= 10 \cdot 11 = 110$

Half of that is $\frac{110}{2} = 55$. In terms of n:

	1	2	3	...	n
+	n	$n-1$	$n-2$	...	1
	$(n+1)$	$(n+1)$	$(n+1)$	...	$(n+1)$

$= n \cdot (n+1)$

Half of that is $\frac{n(n+1)}{2}$.

3 Assignment

Recommended Assignment

- Questions 1–22
- Question 23 (extra credit)
- Reading Lesson 10-1
- Covering the Ideas 10-1

Notes on the Questions

Questions 1–4 These questions do not go beyond the Examples of the lesson.

Question 6 Students may wonder how the quadratic expression for the sum in this question was found. The sum of the integers from 1 to $n - 1$ is $0.5n(n - 1) = 0.5n^2 - 0.5n$. The sum of the integers from 1 to $2n$ is thus $0.5(2n + 1)(2n) = 2n^2 + n$. Subtracting the first expression from the second gives the expression found here for the sum of the integers from n to $2n$.

Question 7 This is an instance of the geometry theorem that the length of a tangent from an external point to the circle equals the product of the length of a secant and its external segment.

Question 8 $\triangle PSR$ is a right triangle. This question applies the theorem from geometry that the altitude to the hypotenuse of a right triangle is the mean proportional of the segments of the hypotenuse it forms.

Questions

COVERING THE IDEAS

1. A cable of length 100 feet is brought to the construction site in the situation of Example 1. How far from the left end of the bridge can that cable be placed?

2. Draw a convex decagon (10-sided polygon) and one of its diagonals. How many other diagonals does this polygon have?

3. Can a convex polygon have exactly 21 diagonals? If so, how many sides does that polygon have?

4. Can a convex polygon have exactly 2,015 diagonals? If so, how many sides does that polygon have?

5. The sum of the integers from 1 to n is $\frac{n(n + 1)}{2}$. If this sum is 7,260, what is n? **120**

6. The sum $5 + 6 + 7 + 8 + 9 + 10 = 45$ is an instance of the more general pattern that the sum of the integers from n to $2n$ is $1.5(n^2 + n)$.
   a. What is the sum of the integers from 100 to 200? **15,150**
   b. If the sum of the integers from n to $2n$ is 759, what is n? **22**

7. In the figure below, $\overline{PA}$ is *tangent* to the circle at point A. (It intersects the circle only at that point.) Another segment from P intersects the circle at points B and C. When you study geometry, you will learn that $PA^2 = PB \cdot PC$. Suppose $PA = 12$, $BC = 7$, and $PB = x$.

   a. Write an algebraic expression for PC. **$x + 7$**
   b. Substitute into $PA^2 = PB \cdot PC$ and solve the resulting quadratic equation to find PB. **9**

APPLYING THE MATHEMATICS

8. In any circle O with diameter $\overline{PR}$, $SQ^2 = PQ \cdot RQ$, as shown at the right.
   a. If $PR = 10$ and $PQ = x$, write an algebraic expression for QR. **$10 - x$**
   b. Substitute the values from Part a into the formula $SQ^2 = PQ \cdot RQ$ to find SQ when $PR = 10$ and $PQ = 3$. **$\sqrt{21}$**

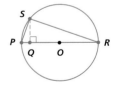

568 Quadratic Equations and Functions

Answers (right margin)

1. The cable can be placed either 87.87 ft away or 512.13 ft from the left end of the bridge.

2. It has 34 additional diagonals, so the total number is 35.

3. No, a polygon cannot have exactly 21 diagonals.

4. yes, 65

Accommodating the Learner ⬆

The George Washington Bridge, opened in 1931, connects New York and New Jersey over the Hudson River. It was and is an engineering marvel. As a suspension bridge, it models a catenary curve. The main span is 3,500 feet long and 212 feet above the water, and the top of each of the supporting towers is 604 feet above the water. Draw and label a diagram of the bridge. Using your graphing calculator, find a quadratic regression that models the path of the cable suspended between the two towers. From the left end of your drawing, where would support cables of length 300 feet be located on the bridge? (1.28×10^{-4}) $x^2 - 0.448x + 392 = 0$; about 219 ft and 3,281 ft

9. Suppose an architect is designing a building with arched windows in the shape of a parabola. The area under the arch will be divided into windowpanes as shown in the diagram below. The architect needs to know the lengths of the four horizontal bars at heights 2, 4, 6, and 8 units. If the parabola has equation $y = -0.5x^2 + 8x - 22$, find the length, to the nearest tenth of a unit, of the bar at the 6-unit height. **5.7 units**

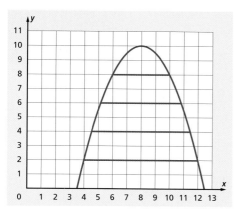

10. Secure telephone networks (ones in which each person is connected to every other person by a direct line) require $\frac{n(n-3)}{2} = \frac{1}{2}n^2 - \frac{1}{2}n$ cable lines for n employees. A company is interested in setting up a secure phone networking group. Each employee in the group is provided with a secure connection to all other employees in the group. Suppose enough money is allotted to provide cable for 500 such connections. How many employees can be enrolled in the group? **32 employees**

Radio and telecommunications equipment installers and repairers held about 222,000 jobs in 2004.

Source: U.S. Department of Labor

REVIEW

11. Suppose a quadratic equation has only one real solution. What can you conclude about its discriminant? **(Lesson 9-6)**
It is equal to 0.

In 12–15, determine whether the equation has 0, 1, or 2 real number solutions. (You do not need to find the solutions.) **(Lesson 9-6)**

12. $-a^2 + 3a - 5 = 0$ **0**

13. $b^2 + 4b + 4 = 0$ **1**

14. $2c(c - 5) = 11$ **2**

15. $3(d - 6) = 5(d^2 + 11)$ **0**

16. Find an equation for a parabola with vertex $(0, 0)$ that opens down. **(Lesson 9-1)** Answers vary. Sample answer: $y = -x^2$

17. **Skill Sequence** Solve the equation. **(Lessons 9-1, 8-6)**

   a. $\sqrt{a} = 6$ $a = 36$ **b.** $\sqrt{b + 8} = 6$ **c.** $\sqrt{4c - 5} = 6$

17b. $b = 28$

17c. $c = 10.25$

More Applications of Quadratics: Why Quadratics Are Important   **569**

4 Wrap-Up

Ongoing Assessment

Have students consider the formula $S = \frac{n(5n + 5)}{2}$. Ask them the following questions:

- For $S > 0$, will there ever be exactly one solution for n? Explain. No; for $S > 0$, the determinant will be positive so there will always be two solutions for n.
- If $S = 275$, find n. -11 or 10
- S is a formula to find the sum of multiples of 5 from 5 to $5n$. Show that 35 is not a sum of consecutive multiples of 5. Answers vary. Sample answer: Letting $S = 35$ leads to the equation $n^2 + n - 14 = 0$, which has an irrational solution.

Project Update

Project 5, Formulas for Sums of Consecutive Integers, and Project 6, Catenaries, Parabolas, and a Famous Landmark, on page 572, relate to the content of this lesson.

9-7B page 2

9-7B Lesson Master

Questions on SPUR Objectives
See pages 576–579 for objectives.

USES Objectives E and F

1. Consider the formula $d = \frac{n(n-3)}{2}$, where d is the number of diagonals of an n-sided polygon. Suppose a polygon has 20 diagonals. How many sides does this polygon have? 8
2. Can a polygon have 125 diagonals? Explain. No; the value of the discriminant for $\frac{n(n-3)}{2} = 125$ needs to be a perfect square, and 1,009 is not.
3. Draw a convex 9-sided polygon. How many diagonals does this polygon have? 27
4. The area of a triangle is 110 square inches. The height of the triangle is 8 less than 3 times its base. What are the height and base of the triangle? Round your answers to the nearest hundredth. base = 10 in., height = 22 in.
5. The area of a rectangle is 225 inches. The length is 5 more than twice its width. What are the length and width of the rectangle? Round your answers to the nearest hundredth. length = 23.86 in., width = 9.43 in.
6. The expression $1 + 3 + 5 + 7 + 9$ is the sum of the first five positive odd integers. A more general pattern can be stated as, "The sum of the first n positive odd integers is n^2."
   a. For the sum $1 + 3 + 5 + 7 + 9$, what is n? n^2? 5; 25
   b. Show two ways to find the sum of the first 10 positive odd integers. $1 + 3 + 5 + 7 + 9 + 11 + 13 + 15 + 17 + 19 = 100$, $10^2 = 100$
   c. If the sum of the first n positive odd integers is 625, what is n? 25
7. Joaquin wants to make a rectangular play area that is 75 square feet with the length equal to five more than twice the width.
   a. Write an equation to express the area in terms of the width. $75 = w(2w + 5)$
   b. Solve the resulting quadratic equation to find the length and width. length = 15 ft, width = 5 ft

Copyright © Wright Group/McGraw-Hill

438

Algebra 437

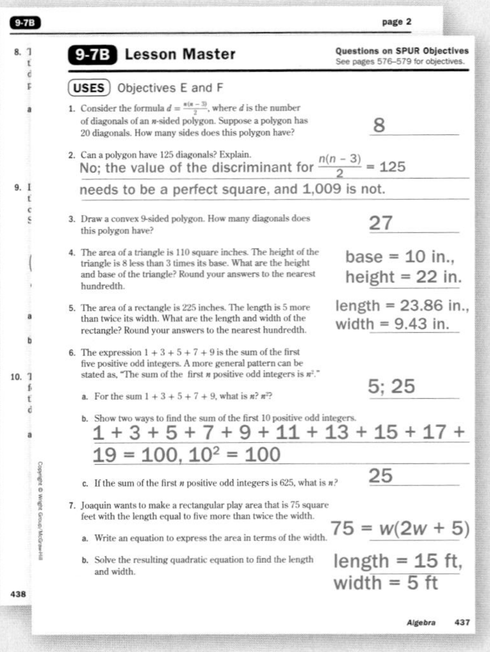

In 18 and 19, use the figure at the right, which represents the front view of a building plan for a cottage. The cottage is to be 24 feet wide. The edges $\overline{AC}$ and $\overline{BC}$ of the roof are to be equal in length and to meet at a right angle. (Lessons 8-8, 8-7)

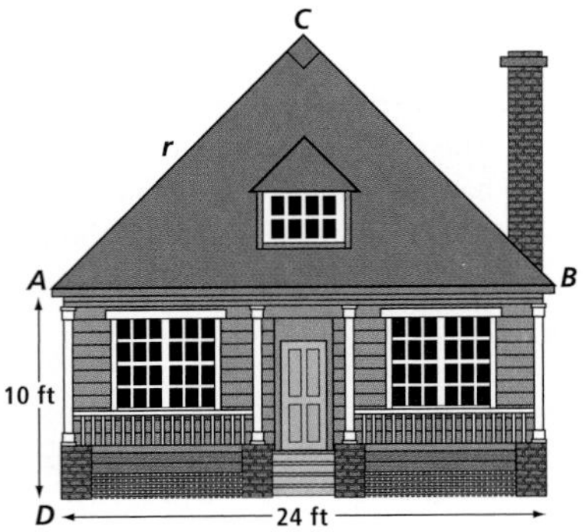

18. a. Find the length r of each edge as a simplified radical.
    b. Round the length of an edge to the nearest tenth of a foot.
19. Find BD. 26 ft
20. **True or False** If the growth factor of an exponential growth situation is 2, then an equation that represents this situation is $y = 2 \cdot b^x$. (Lesson 7-2) true
21. Consider the three points (2, 1), (–4, 31), and (7, –24). (Lessons 6-8, 6-3)
    a. Show that these points lie on the same line. See margin.
    b. Write an equation for the line in standard form. $5x + y = 11$
22. A school begins the year with 250 reams of paper. (A ream contains 500 sheets.) The teachers are using an average of 18 reams per week, and the school receives a shipment of 10 additional reams each week. (Lesson 2-2)
    a. How many reams will the school have after w weeks?
    b. Suppose the school year lasts 36 weeks. Assuming these rates continue, will the school run out of paper before the year ends? Yes, the school will run out of paper before the year ends.

18a. $r = 12\sqrt{2}$

18b. 17.0 ft

22a. $r = 250 - 8w$, where r is the number of reams left

EXPLORATION

23. Some telescopes use parabolic mirrors. Look on the Internet or in reference books to find out why it is useful to have mirrors shaped like parabolas and summarize your findings. Answers vary. Sample answer: A parabolic mirror allows the light rays to focus at the same point (the focus) so that the resulting image is sharp.

Additional Answers

21a. Answers vary. Sample answer:

$m = \frac{1 + 24}{2 - 7} = -5$

$y - 1 = -5(x - 2)$

$(31) - 1 = -5((-4) - 2)$

$30 = 30$

Since we can find the slope of the line between (2, 1) and (7, –24), we can find an equation for the line containing those two points. We then check to make sure that (–4, 31) is also on the line, which it is.

Chapter 9 Projects

1 Programming the Quadratic Formula

Use a computer or a graphing calculator to write a program that solves the equation $ax^2 + bx + c = 0$. The input of your program should be the numbers a, b, and c. Your program should state the number of real solutions and give them (if they exist). Your program should also work if $a = 0$.

2 Verifying Projectile Motion

For this project, you will need a device that can record video (such as a camcorder or a digital camera) and a television or computer on which to play the video you recorded. Have a friend throw a ball (or any other object), and use your recording device to film the path the ball takes. It is very important to keep the camera still the whole time, so be sure to stand far enough away from your friend. Tape a piece of tracing paper to a television. Play the video in slow motion and trace the path the ball takes. Does this path indeed seem to be a parabola? If possible, choose appropriate axes and find an equation for a parabola of best fit.

3 The Focus of a Parabola

Recall that a circle is the set of points at a fixed distance from a point called the center of the circle. Parabolas also have a definition involving distance from a special point called the *focus* of the parabola.

a. Look up this definition of a parabola, and write a paragraph that explains it.

b. Find out how the focus of a parabola is related to light reflecting from a mirror that is shaped like a parabola.

c. Parabolas are used in many manufactured items, such as satellite dishes and flashlights. Find three such uses that are related to the property you found in Part b, and explain why parabolas were used in these cases.

Project Rubric

Advanced	Student correctly provides all of the details asked for in the project as well as additional correct independent conclusions.
Proficient	Student correctly provides all of the details asked for in the project.
Partially proficient	Student correctly provides some of the details asked for in the project or provides all details with some inaccuracies.
Not proficient	Student correctly provides few of the details asked for in the project or provides all details with many inaccuracies.
No attempt	Student makes little or no attempt to complete the project.

Chapter 9

The projects relate to the content of the lessons of this chapter as follows:

Project	Lesson(s)
1	9-5
2	9-4
3	9-1
4	9-3
5	9-7
6	9-7

1 Programming the Quadratic Formula

Students may choose not to do this project because they have little programming experience. However, it gives a valuable opportunity for them to write a program involving if-then statements. If needed, provide support by suggesting that students first write a program in which all values of a, b, and c result in two real-number solutions.

2 Verifying Projectile Motion

This is an excellent project to do to get hands-on experience relating the path of a projectile with the quadratic equation modeling it. Students who are tactile and visual learners will find this project rewarding. They will have a better understanding of the relationships being presented in this chapter. Make sure that students choosing this project have access to the equipment needed to complete the project.

3 The Focus of a Parabola

If students want to link mathematics to the real world, this is the project to choose. Often the concepts being presented in a mathematics textbook are abstract to the students. They see no link to what is going on in their everyday life. This project can bridge the gap between the abstract and the practical. Consider having students share with their classmates the different ways parabolas are used.

4 Checking Whether or Not Points Lie on a Parabola

Organization will be key to successfully completing this project. Suggest ways students can organize their work so that they produce meaningful results. Most students have no experience with finite differences. It is even possible that they miss the point even though they process the data correctly. Consider expanding on the idea of differences once students complete the project. If possible, provide students with a connection to their practical applications.

5 Formulas for Sums of Consecutive Integers

This project foreshadows the ideas of sequences and series. Students may initially need some help with this project; for example, they may not readily see a way to establish that the sum of the first n integers is given by the formula $S = \frac{n(n+1)}{2}$. Share with them the story of Carl Gauss, who developed the formula when he was 10 years old to get around a classroom punishment of finding the sum of the numbers 1 though 100.

6 Catenaries, Parabolas, and a Famous Landmark

A common example of a catenary is the shape formed by a loose chain hanging from two supporting points. As a part of their project, students could prepare a poster with a large, upward-opening parabola. Then they could attach a length of flexible chain to two points on the parabola (on opposite sides of the vertex, but not necessarily symmetric points), and adjust the length of chain to give a concrete illustration comparing a parabola and a catenary.

4 Checking Whether Points Lie on a Parabola

a. Use a calculator or a spreadsheet to find the values of x^2, for $x = 1, 2, 3, \ldots, 100$. Then calculate the differences between the values for consecutive numbers, and plot them. For example, $2^2 - 1^2 = 3$, so you would plot the point $(2, 3)$, $3^2 - 2^2 = 5$, so your plot should include the point $(3, 5)$. There would be 99 points in all. What is an equation of a function that includes all 99 ordered pairs?

b. Choose three numbers: a, b, and c, and repeat Part a using $ax^2 + bx + c$ instead of x^2.

c. Repeat Part a using x^3 instead of x^2, and then using 2^x instead of x^2. Are the points on these plots still on a single line?

d. Parts a, b, and c suggest a method for checking if a collection of points are all on a parabola. Describe this method.

5 Formulas for Sums of Consecutive Integers

In this chapter, you saw the formula $S = \frac{n(n+1)}{2}$ for the sum of the integers from 1 to n.

a. Graph this formula for values of n, from 1 to 10.

b. Find and graph a formula for the sum of the even integers from 2 to $2n$.

c. Find and graph a formula for the sum of the multiples of 3 from 3 to $3n$.

d. Generalize Parts a, b, and c to find a formula for the sum of the multiples of k, from k to kn.

6 Catenaries, Parabolas, and a Famous Landmark

The Gateway Arch in St. Louis, Missouri is one of the most famous landmarks in the United States. At first view, the shape of the Arch appears to be a parabola.

a. In Lesson 9-7, a shape called a catenary was mentioned. This shape looks very much like a parabola. Find out if the shape of the Gateway Arch is a parabola or a catenary, and why one is a better choice than the other.

b. Use the Internet to find a picture of a catenary. Print a large copy of this image on a piece of paper. Next, create a graph of a parabola that looks similar to the catenary, and print it. Make sure both printouts have the same size. Using these printouts as guidelines, use clay (or any other sculpting medium) to create a parabolic and a catenary model of the Gateway Arch. Which seems to be more stable?

Notes

Chapter 9 Summary and Vocabulary

○ A **quadratic function** is a function f whose equation can be written in the form $f(x) = ax^2 + bx + c$ with $a \neq 0$. The simplest quadratic function is $f(x) = ax^2$. The **vertex** of the graph of $y = ax^2$ is at $(0, 0)$. The graph of $y = ax^2 + bx + c$ is a parabola symmetric to the vertical line through its vertex. If $a > 0$, the parabola opens up. If $a < 0$, the parabola opens down. To determine where this parabola crosses the horizontal line $y = k$, you can solve $ax^2 + bx + c = k$.

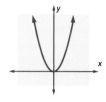
$y = ax^2$, if $a > 0$

$y = ax^2$, if $a < 0$

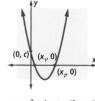
$y = ax^2 + bx + c$, if $a > 0$

○ Quadratic expressions, equations, and functions appear in a variety of situations. The word "squaring" comes from applications of quadratic expressions in such formulas as $A = s^2$ and $A = \pi r^2$. The **path of a projectile** can be described by a quadratic equation. The function whose input is the time t (in seconds) since launch and whose output is the height h (in feet) of the projectile has the formula $h = -16t^2 + vt + s$, where s is the height at launch and v is the upward launch velocity (in feet per second).

○ These situations, certain counting problems, and many geometric situations give rise to problems that can be solved by quadratic equations. The values of x that satisfy the equation $ax^2 + bx + c = 0$, where $a \neq 0$, can be found using the **Quadratic Formula**, $x = \frac{-b \pm \sqrt{b^2 - 4ac}}{2a}$.

○ The **discriminant** of the quadratic equation $ax^2 + bx + c = 0$ is $b^2 - 4ac$. If the discriminant is positive, there are two real solutions to the equation; if it is zero, there is one solution; and if it is negative, there are no real solutions.

Vocabulary

9-1
parabola
reflection-symmetric
axis of symmetry
vertex

9-4
force of gravity
initial upward velocity
initial height

9-5
quadratic equation
standard form of a
    quadratic equation

9-6
discriminant

Theorems and Properties

General Formula for the Height of a
    Projectile over Time (p. 546)

The Quadratic Formula (p. 553)
Discriminant Property (p. 561)

Summary and Vocabulary

The Summary gives an overview of the entire chapter and provides an opportunity for students to consider the material as a whole. Thus, the Summary can be used to help students relate and unify the concepts presented in the chapter.

Terms and symbols are listed by lesson to provide a checklist of concepts that students must know. Emphasize to students that they should read the vocabulary list carefully before starting the Self-Test on the next page. If students do not understand the meaning of a term, they should refer back to the indicated lesson.

Theorems and Properties covered in the chapter are listed below the Summary, with page references included to lead students back to the location in the chapter where the theorem or property is stated.

Chapter **9** **Self-Test**

Self-Test

For the development of mathematical competence, feedback and correction, along with the opportunity for practice, are necessary. The Self-Test provides the opportunity for feedback and correction; the Chapter Review provides additional opportunities for practice. We cannot overemphasize the importance of these end-of-chapter materials. It is at this point that the material "gels" for many students, allowing them to solidify skills and understanding. In general, student performance should improve after these pages.

Assign the Self-Test as a one-night assignment. Worked-out solutions for all questions are in the Selected Answers section of the student book. Encourage students to take the Self-Test honestly, grade themselves, and then be prepared to discuss the test in class.

Advise students to pay special attention to those Chapter Review questions (pages 576–579) that correspond to the questions they missed on the Self-Test.

Additional Answers

1. $x^2 = 81$; $\sqrt{x^2} = \sqrt{81}$; $x = 9, -9$

2. $n^2 - 8n - 10 = 0$; $n = \dfrac{-b \pm \sqrt{b^2 - 4ac}}{2a}$;

   $n = \dfrac{-(-8) \pm \sqrt{(-8)^2 - 4(1)(-10)}}{2(1)}$;

   $n = \dfrac{8 \pm \sqrt{64 + 40}}{2}$; $n = \dfrac{8 \pm \sqrt{104}}{2}$;

   $n = \dfrac{8 \pm 2\sqrt{26}}{2}$; $n = 4 + \sqrt{26}, 4 - \sqrt{26}$;

   $n \approx 9.10$, $n \approx -1.10$

3. $5y^2 - 11y - 1 = 0$; $y = \dfrac{-b \pm \sqrt{b^2 - 4ac}}{2a}$;

   $y = \dfrac{-(-11) \pm \sqrt{(-11)^2 - 4(5)(-1)}}{2(5)}$;

   $y = \dfrac{11 \pm \sqrt{121 + 20}}{10}$; $y = \dfrac{11 + \sqrt{141}}{10}$,

   $\dfrac{11 - \sqrt{141}}{10}$; $y \approx 2.29$, $y \approx -0.09$

4. $24 = \frac{1}{6}z^2$; $6 \cdot 24 = 6 \cdot \frac{1}{6}z^2$; $144 = z^2$;

   $z = 12, -12$

5. $v^2 - 16v + 64 = 0$; $v = \dfrac{-b \pm \sqrt{b^2 - 4ac}}{2a}$;

   $v = \dfrac{-(-16) \pm \sqrt{(-16)^2 - 4(1)(64)}}{2(1)}$;

   $v = \dfrac{16 \pm \sqrt{256 - 256}}{2}$; $v = \dfrac{16 \pm 0}{2}$; $v = 8$

6. $3p^2 - 9p + 7 = 0$; If there are any real solutions, then $b^2 - 4ac$ must be greater than or equal to 0.

   $b^2 - 4ac = (-9)^2 - 4(3)(7)$

   $= 81 - 84 = -3$;

   There are no real solutions.

Chapter 9

Chapter **9** **Self-Test**

Take this test as you would take a test in class. You will need a calculator. Then use the Selected Answers section in the back of the book to check your work.

In 1–6, find all real solutions. Round your answers to the nearest hundredth. If there are no real solutions, write that. **1–6. See margin.**

1. $2x^2 = 162$
2. $n^2 - 8n - 10 = 0$
3. $5y^2 - 1 = 11y$
4. $24 = \frac{1}{6}z^2$
5. $v^2 = 16v - 64$
6. $3p^2 - 9p + 7 = 0$

7. If the discriminant of a quadratic equation is 6, how many solutions does the equation have?
   2 because the discriminant is positive

8. **Multiple Choice** Which of these graphs is of the equation $y = 1.75x^2$? **A**

A

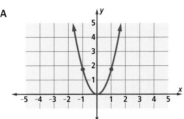

B

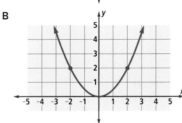

C

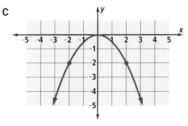

In 9 and 10, an equation is given.
   a. Make a table of values of x and y for integer values of x from $x = -3$ to $x = 3$.
   b. Graph the equation. **9–10. See margin.**

9. $y = 2x^2$
10. $y = -x^2 + 4x - 3$

In 11–13, consider the following. When a roller coaster goes down a hill, then $h = 0.049v^2$, where v is the velocity of the coaster (in meters per second) when it is h meters below the top of the hill.

11. Use the equation to determine at what distance below the top of the hill the roller coaster will reach a velocity of 20 meters per second. $h = 0.049(20)^2$; 19.6 m

12. Suppose the designer of the roller coaster builds the hill to be 44 meters high. At what velocity will the roller coaster be traveling when it reaches the bottom of the hill?
    $44 = 0.049v^2$; $897.96 = v^2$; 29.97 m/sec

13. Currently the fastest wooden roller coaster is Son of Beast located at Kings Island in Cincinnati, Ohio. The maximum speed of the roller coaster is 35 meters per second. What is the height of the top of the hill? $h = 0.049(35)^2$; 60 m

14. The product of two consecutive integers, n and $n + 1$, is 1,722. If the integers are both negative, what are the numbers?
    See margin.

15. A circle and a rectangle have equal areas. One side of the rectangle is 6 inches longer than the other side, and the perimeter of the rectangle is 24. Calculate the radius of the circle, to the nearest hundredth. **See margin.**

Additional Answers

9a.

x	$2x^2$
-3	18
-2	8
-1	2
0	0
1	2
2	8
3	18

9b.

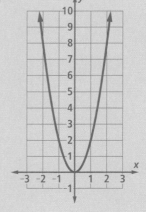

In 16–18, use the parabola with vertex V below.

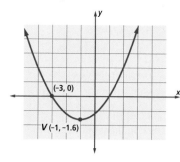

16. Find the minimum y value of the parabola. −1.6

17. Find the x-intercepts. −3, 1

18. Find an equation for the axis of symmetry of the parabola. $x = -1$

In 19 and 20, a tennis ball is thrown from the top of a building. The graph below shows $h = -16t^2 + 40t + 50$, giving the height h of the ball in feet after t seconds.

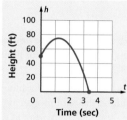

19–20. See margin.

19. To the nearest hundredth of a second, how long does it take the ball to reach the ground?

20. At what times is the ball 70 feet above the ground? Give your answer to the nearest hundredth of a second.

21. **True or False** The parabola $y = \frac{1}{2}x^2 - 7x - 35$ opens down. false

22. Suppose that the quadratic equation $ax^2 - 5x + 3 = 0$ has a discriminant of 1. Find the value of a. See margin.

In 23 and 24, use the discriminant to give the number of real solutions to the equation.

23. $-3x^2 + 12x - 7 = 0$

24. $x^2 - 4x = -4$

23–24. See margin.

Additional Answers

14. $n(n + 1) = 1{,}722$; $n^2 + n = 1{,}722$; $n^2 + n - 1{,}722 = 0$; $n = 41$ or $n = -42$; $n = -42$ or $n + 1 = -41$

15. $2(x) + 2(x + 6) = 24$; $4x = 12$; $x = 3$; $A = 3 \cdot 9 = 27$; πr^2; $8.59 \approx r^2$; $2.93 \approx r$

19. $0 = -16t^2 + 40t + 50$;
$t = \dfrac{-b \pm \sqrt{b^2 - 4ac}}{2a}$;
$t = \dfrac{-40 \pm \sqrt{(40)^2 - 4(-16)(50)}}{2(-16)}$;
$t = \dfrac{-40 \pm \sqrt{1{,}600 + 3{,}200}}{-32}$;
$t = \dfrac{-40 \pm \sqrt{4{,}800}}{-32}$; $t = \dfrac{-40 \pm 40\sqrt{3}}{-32}$;
$t \approx -0.92$, $t \approx 3.42$; 3.42 sec

20. $0 = -16t^2 + 40t - 20$;
$t = \dfrac{-b \pm \sqrt{b^2 - 4ac}}{2a}$;
$t = \dfrac{-40 \pm \sqrt{(40)^2 - 4(-16)(-20)}}{2(-16)}$;
$t = \dfrac{-40 \pm \sqrt{1{,}600 - 1{,}280}}{-32}$;
$t = \dfrac{-40 \pm \sqrt{320}}{-32}$; $t = \dfrac{-40 \pm 8\sqrt{5}}{-32}$;
$t \approx 0.69$, $t \approx 1.81$

22. $b^2 - 4ac = 1$; $(-5)^2 - 4(a)(3) = 1$; $25 - 12a = 1$; $12a = 24$; $a = 2$

23. $b^2 - 4ac = (12)^2 - 4(-3)(-7) = 144 - 84 = 60$; There are two real solutions because the discriminant has a value greater than 0.

24. $b^2 - 4ac = (-4)^2 - 4(1)(4) = 16 - 16 = 0$; There is one real solution because the discriminant has a value of 0.

Additional Answers

10a.

x	$-x^2 + 4x - 3$
−3	−24
−2	−15
−1	−8
0	−3
1	0
2	1
3	0

10b.

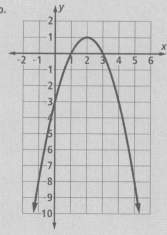

Chapter Review

The main objectives for the chapter are organized in the Chapter Review under the four types of understanding this book promotes—Skills, Properties, Uses, and Representations.

Whereas end-of-chapter material may be considered optional in some texts, in *UCSMP Algebra* we have selected these objectives and questions with the expectation that they will be covered. Students should be able to answer these questions with about 85% accuracy after studying the chapter.

You may assign these questions over a single night to help students prepare for a test the next day, or you may assign the questions over a two-day period. If you work the questions over two days, then we recommend assigning the *evens* for homework the first night so that students get feedback in class the next day, and then assigning the *odds* the night before the test because the answers are provided to the odd-numbered questions in the Selected Answers at the back of the book.

It is effective to ask students which questions they still do not understand and use the day as a total class discussion of the material that the class finds most difficult.

Resources

• Assessment Resources: Chapter 9 Test, Forms A–D; Chapter 9 Test, Cumulative Form; Comprehensive Test, Chapters 1–9

Technology Resources

Teacher's Assessment Assistant, Ch 9
Electronic Teacher's Edition, Ch. 9

SKILLS Procedures used to get answers

OBJECTIVE A Solve quadratic equations of the form $ax^2 = b$. (Lesson 9-2)
1–8. See margin.
In 1–8, solve without using the Quadratic Formula.

1. $4x^2 = 676$ 2. $9 = \frac{1}{4}h^2$

3. $k^2 + 15 = 100$ 4. $t^2 - 11 = 11$

5. $2(m + 3)^2 = 72$ 6. $69 = 5 + 2y^2$

7. $\frac{63}{16} = 7(4 - v)^2$ 8. $(6w - 1)^2 = \frac{25}{4}$

OBJECTIVE B Solve quadratic equations using the Quadratic Formula. (Lessons 9-5, 9-6)

In 9–18, solve the equation using the Quadratic Formula. Round your answers to the nearest hundredth. 9–16. See margin.

9. $m^2 + 7m + 12 = 0$ 10. $14x = x^2 + 49$

11. $y^2 - 6y = 3$ 12. $r^2 - \frac{11}{7} = \frac{4}{5}r$

13. $0 = p^2 + 10(p + 2.5)$ 14. $\frac{3}{4}x^2 - \frac{2}{3}x = 2$

15. $5n^2 + 9n = 2$ 16. $2a^2 - 8a = -8$

17. $b^2 + 5.4b - 19.75 = 0$ $b = 2.5$ or $b = -7.9$

18. $30 + 5(2z^2 - 10z) = 0$ $z = 0.70$ or $z = 4.30$

PROPERTIES The principles behind the mathematics

OBJECTIVE C Identify and use the properties of solutions to quadratic equations. (Lesson 9-6)

19. Give the values of x that satisfy the equation $ax^2 + bx + c = 0$. $x = \frac{-b \pm \sqrt{b^2 - 4ac}}{2a}$

20. **True or False** If a quadratic equation has two solutions, then it has two x-intercepts. true

---

In 21 and 22, calculate the discriminant.

21. $x^2 + 4x - 8 = 0$ 48

22. $7y^2 - y = 1$ 29

23. If the discriminant of the quadratic equation $x^2 + bx + 2 = 0$ is 8, find the possible value(s) of b. $b = 4$ or $b = -4$

In 24–27, find the number of real solutions to the equation by using the discriminant.

24. $g^2 - 3g - 8 = 0$ 2

25. $3v = 2v^2 + 4$ 0

26. $m^2 = 6m - 9$ 1

27. $w(w - 2) = -8$ 0

USES Applications of mathematics in real-world situations

OBJECTIVE D Use quadratic equations to solve problems about paths of projectiles. (Lessons 9-2, 9-4)

28. Regina is a track and field athlete competing in the shot put, an event that requires "putting" (throwing in a pushing motion) a heavy metal ball (the "shot") as far as possible. The height of the ball h when it is x feet from Regina can be described by the quadratic equation $h = -0.021x^2 + 0.6x + 6$.

   a. At what distances from Regina will the shot put be at a height of 8 feet? Round your answers to the nearest hundredth. 3.85 ft and 24.72 ft

   b. Will Regina's shot put travel 38 feet, the distance needed to win the event? Justify your answer. See margin.

Additional Answers

1. $x = 13, x = -13$

2. $h = 6, h = -6$

3. $k = \pm\sqrt{85}$

4. $t = \pm\sqrt{22}$

5. $m = 3, m = -9$

6. $y = \pm 4\sqrt{2}$

7. $v = 4.75, v = 3.25$

8. $w = \frac{7}{12}, w = -\frac{1}{4}$

9. $m = -3, m = -4$

10. $x = 7$

11. $y = -0.46, y = 6.46$

12. $r = -0.92, r = 1.72$

13. $p = -5$

14. $x = -1.25, x = 2.14$

15. $n = 0.2, n = -2$

16. $a = 2$

28b. No, when $x = 38$, $h = -1.5$ ft, so the shot put hits the ground before it can travel 38 ft.

In 29 and 30, when an object is dropped near the surface of a planet or moon, the distance d (in feet) it falls in t seconds is given by the formula $d = \frac{1}{2}gt^2$, where g is the acceleration due to gravity. Near Earth $g \approx 32$ ft/sec², and near Earth's moon $g \approx 5.3$ ft/sec².

29. A skydiver jumps from a plane at an altitude of 10,000 feet. She begins her descent in "free fall," that is, without opening the parachute. a. 3,600 ft

   a. How far will she fall in 15 seconds?

   b. The diver plans to open the parachute after she has fallen 6,000 feet. How many seconds after jumping will this take place? about 19 sec

30. An astronaut on the moon drops a hammer from a height of 6 feet.

   a. How long will it take the hammer to hit the ground? about 1.5 sec

   b. Suppose the astronaut is back on Earth and drops a hammer from a height of 6 feet. How long will it take the hammer to hit the ground? about 0.6 sec

31. Refer to the graph below of $h = -4.9t^2 + 20t$, which shows the height (in meters) of a ball t seconds after it is thrown from ground level at an initial upward velocity of 20 meters per second.

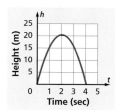

   a. Give the height of the ball after 1 second. 15.1 m

   b. Find when the ball will reach a height of 15 meters. about 1.0 sec and 3.1 sec

   c. Use the Quadratic Formula to calculate how long the ball will be in the air. about 4.1 sec

OBJECTIVE E Solve geometric problems involving quadratic equations.
(Lessons 9-2, 9-7)

32. Suppose a rectangle has length $2x$ inches and width $x + 3$ inches. Find the length and width given that the area of the rectangle is 5.625 square inches.
Length: 1.5 in.; width: 3.75 in.

33. Consider the rectangular region below. Luisa has 120 meters of fencing to build a fence around her yard.

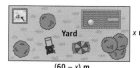

Yard x m

$(60 - x)$ m

33a. $A = 60x - x^2$

   a. Use the diagram to write an equation for the area A enclosed by the fencing.

   b. What value of x will result in the greatest possible area enclosed by the fencing?
   $x = 30$

34. Refer to the triangle below. If the area of the triangle is 18 square inches and the base of the triangle is 4 inches shorter than its height, find the length of the base of the triangle. Round your answer to the nearest hundredth of an inch. 4.32 in.

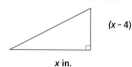

$(x - 4)$

x in.

OBJECTIVE F Solve other real-world problems involving quadratic functions. (Lesson 9-7)

35. The relationship between elevation above sea level in kilometers, e, and the boiling point of water in degrees Celsius, t, can be approximated by the equation $e = t^2 - 200.58t + 10,058$. Water boils at lower temperatures at higher elevations. Find the boiling point of water at the top of Mt. Ararat in Turkey, which is 5,166 meters high. about 98°C

Chapter 9 Review

Additional Answers

37a. Yes, the company's profits will have reached $124,000,000 by 2011.

38a.

x	$7x^2$
−2	28
−1	7
0	0
1	7
2	28

38b.

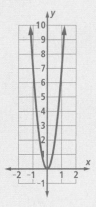

39a.

x	$\frac{3}{5}x^2$
−2	2.4
−1	0.6
0	0
1	0.6
2	2.4

39b.

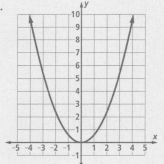

40a.

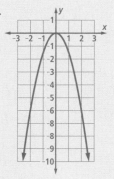

---

36. Consider the formula $d = \frac{n(n-3)}{2}$, where d is the number of diagonals of an n-sided convex polygon.

　a. How many diagonals does a dodecagon (12-sided polygon) have? **54**

　b. Is it possible for a polygon to have 27 diagonals? If so, how many sides does that polygon have? **yes; 9 sides**

37. A financial analyst working for an investment company projects the net profit P (in millions of dollars) of the company to be modeled by the equation $P = 4.23t^2 - 5.32t + 3.86$, where t is the number of years since 2005.

　a. Use the analyst's model to predict whether the net profit will reach 100 million dollars in 2011. **See margin.**

　b. Calculate, to the nearest tenth, when the company's net profit is projected to reach 75 million dollars.
　4.8 yr after 2005, or in late 2009

REPRESENTATIONS Pictures, graphs, or objects that illustrate concepts

OBJECTIVE G Graph equations of the form $y = ax^2$ and interpret these graphs. (Lesson 9-1)

In 38 and 39, an equation is given.
　a. Make a table of values.
　b. Graph the equation. **38–39. See margin.**

38. $y = 7x^2$ 　　　**39.** $y = \frac{3}{5}x^2$

40. Consider the quadratic equation $y = -1.5x^2$.

　a. Graph the equation. **See margin.**

　b. Determine the coordinates of the vertex. **(0, 0)**

　c. Tell whether the vertex is a maximum or a minimum. **maximum**

---

41. Multiple Choice Which equation is graphed below? **B**

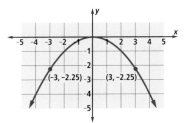

A $y = -4x^2$ 　　　**B** $y = -\frac{1}{4}x^2$

C $y = \frac{1}{4}x^2$ 　　　**D** $y = 4x^2$

42. True or False The axis of symmetry for the parabola with equation $y = 2x^2$ is the line $x = 0$. **true**

OBJECTIVE H Graph equations of the form $y = ax^2 + bx + c$ and interpret these graphs. (Lesson 9-3)

43. Use the parabola with vertex V below.

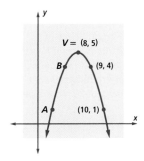

　a. What is the maximum value of the function? **5**

　b. What is an equation for its axis of symmetry? $x = 8$

　c. Find the coordinates of points A and B, the reflection images of the named points over the parabola's axis of symmetry. $A = (6, 1)$, $B = (7, 4)$

In 44 and 45, answer *true* or *false*.

44. Every parabola has a minimum value. **false**

45. The parabola $y = -4x^2 + 2x - 13$ opens down. **true**

46. What equation must you solve to find the x-intercepts of the parabola $y = ax^2 + bx + c$? **$ax^2 + bx + c = 0$**

47. The parabola $y = \frac{1}{8}x^2 - 6x + 22$ has x-intercepts 4 and 44. Find the coordinates of its vertex without graphing. **(24, −50)**

48. A table of values for a parabola is given below.

x	0	2	4	6	8	10	12
y	?	?	−6	−8	−6	0	10

10   0

a. Complete the table.

b. Write an equation for the parabola's axis of symmetry. **$x = 6$**

c. What are the coordinates of its vertex? **(6, −8)**

49. Consider the quadratic equation $y = -x^2 - 4x + 3$.

a. Make a table of x and y values for integer values of $-5 \leq x \leq 1$.

b. Graph the equation.

c. Determine whether the vertex is a minimum or a maximum. **maximum**

50. Which of these is the graph of $y = x^2 - 4x + 5$? **A**

A
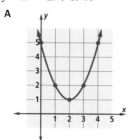

B
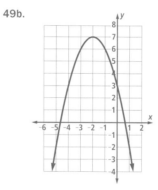

49a.

x	$-x^2 - 4x + 3$
−5	−2
−4	3
−3	6
−2	7
−1	6
0	3
1	−2

49b.
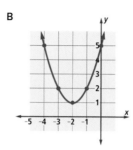

Assessment

Evaluation The *Assessment Resources* provide four forms of the Chapter 9 Test. Forms A and B present parallel versions of a short-answer format. Form C consists of four to six short-response questions that cover the SPUR objectives from Chapter 9. Form D offers performance assessment that covers a subset (or even just one) of the SPUR objectives for the chapter.

Feedback After students have taken the test for Chapter 9 and you have scored the results, return the tests to students for discussion. Class discussion on the questions that caused trouble for most students can be very effective in identifying and clarifying misunderstandings. You might want to have them note the items they missed and work either in groups or at home to correct them. It is important for students to receive feedback on every chapter test, and we recommend that students see and correct their mistakes before proceeding too far into the next chapter.

Chapter 10 — Linear Systems

Chapter Overview

	Local Standards	Pacing (in days)		
		Average	Advanced	Block
10-1 An Introduction to Systems I Find solutions to systems of equations by graphing.		1	1	0.5
10-2 Solving Systems Using Substitution A Solve systems using substitution. G Use systems of linear equations to solve real-world problems.		1	0.5	0.5
10-3 More Uses of Substitution A Solve systems using substitution. G Use systems of linear equations to solve real-world problems.		1	0.5	0.5
10-4 Solving Systems by Addition B Solve systems by addition and multiplication. G Use systems of linear equations to solve real-world problems.		1	0.5	0.5
QUIZ 1		0.5	0.5	0.25
10-5 Solving Systems by Multiplication B Solve systems by addition and multiplication. G Use systems of linear equations to solve real-world problems.		1	1	0.75
10-6 Systems and Parallel Lines F Determine whether a system has 0, 1, or infinitely many solutions. G Use systems of linear equations to solve real-world problems. I Find solutions to systems of equations by graphing.		1	0.5	0.5
10-7 Matrices and Matrix Multiplication C Multiply 2×2 matrices by 2×2 or 2×1 matrices.		1	1	0.5
10-8 Using Matrices to Solve Systems D Solve systems using matrices.		1	1	0.75
QUIZ 2		0.5	0.5	0.25
10-9 Systems of Inequalities H Use systems of linear inequalities to solve real-world problems. J Graphically represent solutions to systems of linear inequalities. K Write a system of inequalities given a graph.		1	0.5	0.5
10-10 Nonlinear Systems E Solve nonlinear systems. I Find solutions to systems of equations by graphing.		1	0.5	0.5
Self-Test		1	1	0.5
Chapter Review		2	2	1
Test		1	1	0.5
TOTAL		**15**	**12**	**8.0**

Technology Resources

Teacher's Assessment Assistant, Ch. 10

Electronic Teacher's Edition, Ch. 10

Differentiated Options Universal Access

	Accommodating the Learner	Vocabulary Development	Ongoing Assessment	Materials
10-1	pp. 583, 584		oral, p. 588	graphing calculator
10-2	pp. 590, 592	p. 591	written, p. 593	scientific or graphing calculator
10-3	pp. 595, 596		written, p. 600	graphing calculator, Computer Algebra System (CAS)
10-4	pp. 602, 603		oral, p. 607	scientific or graphing calculator
10-5	pp. 610, 611	p. 609	group, p. 615	scientific or graphing calculator
10-6	pp. 617, 618		oral, p. 621	graphing calculator
10-7	pp. 624, 625	p. 623	written, p. 628	graphing calculator
10-8	pp. 630, 631	p. 633	group, p. 634	graphing calculator
10-9	pp. 636, 637		oral, p. 639	graphing calculator
10-10	pp. 642, 643		written, p. 644	graphing calculator

Objectives

		Lessons	Self-Test Questions	Chapter Review Questions
Skills				
A	Solve systems using substitution.	10-2, 10-3	1	1–4
B	Solve systems by addition and multiplication.	10-4, 10-5	2, 3	5–10
C	Multiply 2×2 matrices by 2×2 or 2×1 matrices.	10-7	7, 8	11–14
D	Solve systems using matrices.	10-8	9	15–18
E	Solve nonlinear systems.	10-10	5	19, 20
Properties				
F	Determine whether a system has 0, 1, or infinitely many solutions.	10-6	6, 11	21–28
Uses				
G	Use systems of linear equations to solve real-world problems.	10-2, 10-3, 10-4, 10-5, 10-6	10, 17	29–34
H	Use systems of linear inequalities to solve real-world problems.	10-9	14	35–38
Representations				
I	Find solutions to systems of equations by graphing.	10-1, 10-6, 10-10	4, 13	39–43
J	Graphically represent solutions to systems of linear inequalities.	10-9	12, 15, 16	44–49
K	Write a system of inequalities given a graph.	10-9	18	50–52

Resource Masters Chapter 10

Resource Master 1, Graph Paper (page 2), can be used with Lessons 10-1 and 10-9. **Resource Master 2, Four-Quadrant Graph Paper** (page 3), can be used with Lessons 10-1, 10-3, 10-6, 10-9, and 10-10.

Resource Master 146 Lesson 10-1

Warm-Up

Graph each equation on the window $-5 \le x \le 5$, $-5 \le y \le 5$.

1. $x + y = 3$
2. $x - y = 1$
3. $y = 2x$
4. $x + y = -3$

Additional Examples

1. Consider the system: $\begin{cases} y = 4x - 11 \\ 5x + 2y = 4 \end{cases}$
   a. Verify that the ordered pair $(2, -3)$ is a solution of the system.
   b. Show that $(1, -7)$ is *not* a solution to the system.

2. A box of chocolates has 20 pieces of candy. There are 6 more chocolates with nuts than chocolates without nuts. Solve a system of equations to determine how many of the chocolates have nuts, and how many do not.

3. Find all solutions to the system $\begin{cases} y = \frac{1}{2}x - 3 \\ -x + 2y = -8 \end{cases}$.

4. A café has monthly fixed costs of $4,700, and a typical customer order costs the café $2. Therefore, the cost to serve x customers in a month is given by $y = 4,700 + 2x$. The typical order costs the customer $10. So the revenue equation is $y = 10x$. Find the break-even point for the café.

Resource Master for Lesson 10-1

Resource Master 147 Lesson 10-1

Question 13

Year	Men's Time	Women's Time	Year	Men's Time	Women's Time
1924	73.2	83.2	1972	56.58	65.78
1928	68.2	82.0	1976	55.49	61.83
1932	68.6	79.4	1980	56.33	60.86
1936	65.9	78.9	1984	55.79	62.55
1948	66.4	74.4	1988	55.05	60.89
1952	65.4	74.3	1992	53.98	60.68
1956	62.2	72.9	1996	54.10	61.19
1960	61.9	69.3	2000	53.72	61.21
1964	NA	67.7	2004	54.06	60.37
1968	58.7	66.2			

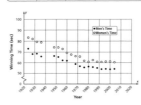

Resource Master for Lesson 10-1

Resource Master 148 Lesson 10-2

Warm-Up

Line m has slope 5 and y-intercept 3. Line n has slope -2 and y-intercept 4.

1. By hand, draw a picture of the two lines and estimate a point of intersection.
2. Give equations for the two lines and use the equations to find the x-coordinate of the point of intersection.
3. Substitute the x-value with one of the equations to find the y-coordinate of the point of intersection.

Additional Examples

1. Solve the system $\begin{cases} y = 2x + 8 \\ y = -5x - 27 \end{cases}$ using substitution.

2. The online catalog *Sockpuppet* will charge you $3.00 for shipping and handling, plus $0.50 per pair of socks you order. The *Footglove* catalog will charge you $3.90 for shipping and handling, plus $0.40 per pair. How many pairs of socks would you have to purchase to make the costs equal?

3. A tortoise challenges a hare to a 10-mile race. The tortoise moves at a steady speed of 0.2 mile per hour. The hare can move at a speed of 40 miles per hour. Since it knows the tortoise is so slow, the hare decides to wait until the tortoise is within 0.25 mile of the finish line before it even starts to race. Can the hare still win?

Resource Master for Lesson 10-2

Resource Master 149 Lesson 10-3

Warm-Up

1. Suppose $a = 2b + 3$, $b = 4c + 5$, $c = 6d + 7$, and $d = 8$. What is the value of a?

2. Suppose a, b, and c are the same as in Question 1 but no value of d is known. Give a formula for a in terms of d.

Additional Examples

1. A college vocal group needs to raise money for an upcoming trip, so the students decide to sell CDs and T-shirts at their next performance. The shirts sell for $8 each, and the CDs for $12 each. By the end of the night, they know that they've sold 35 items, and that they have raised $360. However, they forgot to keep track of how many of each item they sold. Use a system of equations to find out.

2. Find an equation of the line that passes through the points $(4, 1)$ and $(-6, 6)$.

3. Jotrenia wishes to stock up on coffee beans. She pays $5 per pound for decaffeinated and $6.50 per pound for regular. She ends up buying 5 pounds of coffee beans for $29.50. How much of each type of coffee did she buy?

4. Use a CAS to solve $\begin{cases} 5x - 2y = -41 \\ -4x + 3y = 37 \end{cases}$.

Resource Master for Lesson 10-3

Resource Master 150 Lesson 10-4

Warm-Up

You go to a place for breakfast. A sign says "1 egg with a slice of toast, $0.99; 2 eggs with a slice of toast, $1.69."

1. From this information, using just arithmetic, calculate what seems to be the price of 1 egg without toast and what seems to be the cost of a slice of toast.

2. Write and solve a system of equations to verify your answer to Question 1.

3. What should it cost for 3 eggs with 2 pieces of toast?

Additional Examples

1. For two days in a row, gas prices hovered around price p. On the first day, they were d dollars above price p, resulting in a price of $2.19 per gallon. On the second day, they were d dollars below price p, resulting in a price of $2.07. What price p are they hovering around? How much is the price fluctuating day by day?

2. Solve the system $\begin{cases} -3x + 2y = -11 \\ -3x + 5y = -14 \end{cases}$.

3. A sports clothing store is advertising two deals.

   Deal 1: 2 shirts and 2 caps for $32

   Deal 2: 2 shirts and 3 caps for $39

   At these rates, what is the price of one shirt and what is the price of one cap? (Assume there is no discount for 3 caps.)

Resource Master for Lesson 10-4

Resource Master 151 Lesson 10-4

Question 23

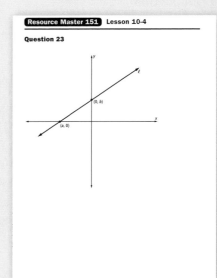

Resource Master for Lesson 10-4

Resource Master 152 Lesson 10-5

Warm-Up

State each form or property.
1. Standard form of an equation of a line
2. Slope-intercept form of an equation of a line
3. Point-slope form of an equation of a line
4. Distributive Property of Multiplication over Addition
5. Multiplication Property of Equality

Additional Examples

1. Solve the system $\begin{cases} 2x - 3y = -1 \\ 6x - 2y = -24 \end{cases}$.

2. Solve the system $\begin{cases} 6m + 5n = 38 \\ 4m - 7n = -16 \end{cases}$.

3. A homeowner wishes to put 6 new lamps around their home. They wish to use a total of 15 light bulbs. Lamp style A uses two bulbs, and lamp style B uses three bulbs. Can the homeowner use a certain number of each kind of lamp and use exactly 15 bulbs? If so, how many lamps of each style will she use?

Resource Master for Lesson 10-5

Resource Master 153 Lesson 10-6

Warm-Up

1. List all combinations of D dimes and Q quarters whose total value is $2.85.
2. Give an equation of a line that contains all the ordered pairs (D, Q) from Question 1.
3. Give an equation of a line that contains all the ordered pairs (D, Q) whose total value is $1.60.
4. Why must the lines from Questions 2 and 3 be parallel?

Additional Examples

1. Solve the system $\begin{cases} x + 5y = 7 \\ -10y = 2x - 14 \end{cases}$.

2. Find all solutions to $\begin{cases} 12x - 30y = 12 \\ -8x + 20y = -8 \end{cases}$.

Solution:

Step 1: Multiply both sides of the first equation by 2.

Step 2: Multiply both sides of the second equation by 3.

Step 3: Add the equations from steps 1 and 2.

Step 4: Interpret what you see in step 3. Does this system have 0 solutions, 1 solution, or infinitely many solutions?

Resource Master for Lesson 10-6

Resource Master 154 Lesson 10-6

Coincident Lines

Description of System	Graph	Number of Solutions to System	Slopes of Lines
Two intersecting lines	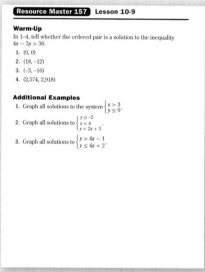	1 (the point of intersection)	Different
Two parallel and nonintersecting lines		0	Equal
One line (parallel and coincident lines)		Infinitely many	Equal

Resource Master for Lesson 10-6

Resource Master 155 Lesson 10-7

Warm-Up

Follow the pattern $[a\ b]\begin{bmatrix} x \\ y \end{bmatrix} = [ax + by]$. Give the product.

1. $[-2\ 6]\begin{bmatrix} x \\ y \end{bmatrix}$
2. $[-2\ 6]\begin{bmatrix} -4 \\ 35 \end{bmatrix}$
3. $[5\ 1]\begin{bmatrix} 3 \\ -4 \end{bmatrix}$
4. $\begin{bmatrix} 1 & 9 \\ 2 & 10 \end{bmatrix}\begin{bmatrix} -110 \\ 90 \end{bmatrix}$

Additional Examples

1. Write $\begin{cases} 3x - 4y = 5 \\ 4x + 8y = 2 \end{cases}$ in matrix form.

2. Perform the multiplication $\begin{bmatrix} 4 & -6 \\ -2 & -3 \end{bmatrix} \cdot \begin{bmatrix} 2 \\ -4 \end{bmatrix}$.

3. Find the product $\begin{bmatrix} -2 & -1 \\ 5 & 3 \end{bmatrix}\begin{bmatrix} 2 & 5 \\ 8 & 1 \end{bmatrix}$.

Resource Master for Lesson 10-7

Resource Master 156 Lesson 10-8

Warm-Up

1. Write the system $\begin{cases} 7x - 2y = 3 \\ -4x + 5y = 114 \end{cases}$ as a single matrix equation.

2. Multiply both sides of the equation in Question 1 by the matrix $\begin{bmatrix} \frac{5}{27} & \frac{2}{27} \\ \frac{4}{27} & \frac{7}{27} \end{bmatrix}$ to solve the system.

Additional Examples

Use matrices to solve the system $\begin{cases} 3x + 5y = -23 \\ -2x - 3y = 14 \end{cases}$.

Question 24

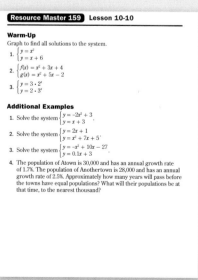

Resource Master for Lesson 10-8

Resource Master 157 Lesson 10-9

Warm-Up

In 1–4, tell whether the ordered pair is a solution to the inequality $4x - 3y > 36$.

1. (0, 0)
2. (18, -12)
3. (-3, -16)
4. (2,574, 2,918)

Additional Examples

1. Graph all solutions to the system $\begin{cases} x > 3 \\ y \le 0 \end{cases}$.

2. Graph all solutions to $\begin{cases} y \ge -2 \\ x < 4 \\ y < 2x + 3 \end{cases}$.

3. Graph all solutions to $\begin{cases} y > 4x - 1 \\ y \le 4x + 2 \end{cases}$.

Resource Master for Lesson 10-9

Resource Master 158 Lesson 10-9

Question 8

Question 9

Question 21

Resource Master for Lesson 10-9

Resource Master 159 Lesson 10-10

Warm-Up

Graph to find all solutions to the system.

1. $\begin{cases} y = x^2 \\ y = x + 6 \end{cases}$

2. $\begin{cases} f(x) = x^2 + 3x + 4 \\ g(x) = x^2 + 5x - 2 \end{cases}$

3. $\begin{cases} y = 3 \cdot 2^x \\ y = 2 \cdot 3^x \end{cases}$

Additional Examples

1. Solve the system $\begin{cases} y = -2x^2 + 3 \\ y = x + 3 \end{cases}$.

2. Solve the system $\begin{cases} y = 2x + 1 \\ y = x^2 + 7x + 5 \end{cases}$.

3. Solve the system $\begin{cases} y = -x^2 + 10x - 27 \\ y = 0.1x + 3 \end{cases}$.

4. The population of Atown is 30,000 and has an annual growth rate of 1.7%. The population of Anothertown is 28,000 and has an annual growth rate of 2.5%. Approximately how many years will pass before the towns have equal populations? What will their populations be at that time, to the nearest thousand?

Resource Master for Lesson 10-10

Pacing

Each lesson in this chapter is designed to be covered in one day. At the end of the chapter, you should plan to spend 1 day to review the Self-Test, 1 to 2 days for the Chapter Review, and 1 day for a test. You may wish to spend a day on projects and possibly a day is needed for quizzes. This chapter should therefore take 13 to 16 days. We strongly advise you to not spend more than 20 days on this chapter.

Using Pages 580–581

Why does one solve systems? One reason is found in this opener—to determine when two curves (in this case lines) meet. When the curves represent data, as they do here, their point of intersection has some meaning and the solution to the system gives us some information about the situation.

You can use the discussion about Olympic swimming times as an advance organizer to introduce important ideas of the chapter. Point out that the two lines in the graph represent the separate trends in winning times for men's and women's Olympic 100-meter freestyle swimming champions. An equation can be found for each of the lines using methods students saw in Chapter 7. The two equations together form a *system of equations*. The solution to this system is given by the point (2040, 41) on the graph where the two lines intersect. The coordinates of the point are the year, 2040, when the men's time and women's time would be the same, 41 seconds, if the trends continue.

Point out that even if the winning times never became nearly the same, it is still interesting to compare the two sets of data.

The table and graph below display the men's and women's winning times in the Olympic 100-meter freestyle swimming race for each Summer Olympic year from 1912 to 2004.

Year	Men's Time (sec)	Women's Time (sec)	Year	Men's Time (sec)	Women's Time (sec)
1912	63.4	82.2	1968	52.2	60.0
1920	60.4	73.6	1972	51.22	58.59
1924	59.0	72.4	1976	49.99	55.65
1928	58.6	71.0	1980	50.40	54.79
1932	58.2	66.8	1984	49.80	55.92
1936	57.6	65.9	1988	48.63	54.93
1948	57.3	66.3	1992	49.02	54.64
1952	57.4	66.8	1996	48.74	54.50
1956	55.4	62.0	2000	48.30	53.83
1960	55.2	61.2	2004	48.17	53.84
1964	53.4	59.5			

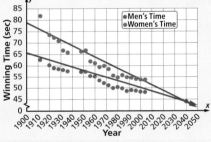

Source: *The World Almanac and Book of Facts*

Chapter 10 Overview

All four dimensions of the SPUR approach are quite evident in this chapter. The chapter begins with the well-known use of a graphical representation to solve systems (Lesson 10-1). Then algebraic methods—the traditional skills—are covered. The first method discussed is substitution (Lessons 10-2 and 10-3), then addition and multiplication (Lessons 10-4 and 10-5). The

chapter then moves to a property that helps to determine when a system has a solution, namely whether the lines are parallel (Lesson 10-6). Lessons 10-7 and 10-8 discuss a different and important method for solving systems: the use of matrices.

(continued on next page)

The graph shows two trends. First, both men's and women's Olympic winning times have been decreasing rather steadily since 1912. Second, the women's winning time has been decreasing faster than the men's winning times. Regression lines have been fitted to the data. These lines have the following equations:
$y = -0.1627x + 372.99$ (men) and
$y = -0.269x + 589.83$ (women), where x is the year and y is the winning time in seconds. The lines intersect near (2040, 41).

This means that if the winning times were to continue to decrease at the rates they have been decreasing, the women's winning time will be about equal to the men's in the Olympic year 2040. The winning times will then each be about 41 seconds.

Finding points of intersection of lines or other curves by working with their equations is called *solving a system*. In this chapter you will learn various ways of solving systems.

581

The chapter closes with a discussion of systems of linear inequalities (Lesson 10-9) and nonlinear systems (Lesson 10-10). Both of these help students understand linear systems better by providing contrast, but nonlinear systems can be optional if you are pressed for time. Throughout the chapter, realistic applications are used for motivation, for concept development, and for practice.

Chapter 10 Projects

At the end of each chapter, you will find projects related to the chapter. At this time you might want to have students look over the projects on pages 645 and 646. You might want to have students tentatively select a project on which to work. Then, as students read and progress through the chapter, they can finalize their project choices.

Sometimes students might work alone; at other times, you might let them collaborate with classmates for a presentation and discussion. We recommend that you allow for diversity and encourage students to use their imaginations when presenting their projects. As students work on projects throughout the year, they should see the many uses of mathematics in the real world.

Notes

Lesson

10-1

Lesson

10-1

An Introduction to Systems

GOAL

Understand what it means to solve a system numerically and graphically and find solutions to systems of equations by graphing.

SPUR Objective

(The SPUR Objectives for all of Chapter 10 are found in the Chapter Review on pages 650–653.)

I Find solutions to systems of equations by graphing.

Materials/Resources

· Lesson Master 10-1A or 10-1B
· Resource Masters 1, 2, 146, and 147
· Graphing calculator

HOMEWORK

Suggestions for Assignment

• Questions 1–21
• Question 22 (extra credit)
• Reading Lesson 10-2
• Covering the Ideas 10-2

Local Standards

1 Warm-Up

Graph each equation on the window $-5 \leq x \leq 5, -5 \leq y \leq 5$.

1. $x + y = 3$ 2. $x - y = 1$
3. $y = 2x$ 4. $x + y = -3$

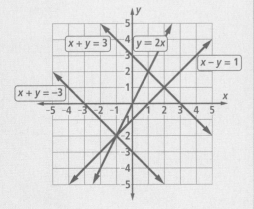

▶ **BIG IDEA**   Solving a system of equations means finding all the solutions that are common to the equations.

A **system** is a set of equations or inequalities joined by the word *and*, that together describe a single situation. The two equations at the beginning of this chapter describing the winning Olympic times of men and women in the 100-meter freestyle events are an example of a system of equations.

Systems are often signaled by using a single left-hand brace { in place of the word *and*. So we can write this system as $\begin{cases} y = -0.1627x + 372.99 \\ y = -0.269x + 589.83 \end{cases}$.

When you write a system in this way, it is helpful to align the equal signs under one another.

What Is a Solution to a System?

A **solution to a system** of equations with two variables is an ordered pair (x, y) that satisfies both equations in the system.

Example 1

Consider the system $\begin{cases} y = 3x - 7 \\ 2y - 2x = 10 \end{cases}$.

a. Verify that the ordered pair (6, 11) is a solution to the system.

b. Show that (1, −4) is *not* a solution to the system.

Solutions

a. In each equation, replace x with 6 and y with 11.

First equation: $y = 3x - 7$

Does $11 = 3 \cdot 6 - 7$?

     $11 = 18 - 7$ Yes.

Second equation: $2y - 2x = 10$

Does $2 \cdot 11 - 2 \cdot 6 = 10$?

         $22 - 12 = 10$ Yes.

(6, 11) is a solution because it satisfies both equations.

Swimmer Larsen Jensen of the United States celebrates his silver medal after finishing second in the 1500-meter freestyle during the 2004 Summer Olympic Games in Athens, Greece.

Background

Although this chapter emphasizes using symbolic algorithms to solve systems, students should be continually reminded that they can use the graphical interpretation to indicate numbers of solutions and to approximate the solutions. Advances in technology make solving systems with graphs easier than in the past. Also, most importantly, there are nonlinear systems that cannot be easily solved algebraically but can be easily solved graphically. Students saw such systems in their discussion of exponential functions and linear versus exponential growth in Chapter 7. In this lesson the examples are all systems of linear equations. In Lesson 10-10, students will see similar examples with nonlinear equations.

10-1

b. Substitute 1 for x and −4 for y in both equations. The pair (1, −4) is a solution to the first equation because −4 = 3 · 1 − 7. However, 2 · −4 − 2 · 1 = −10 ≠ 10. So (1, -4) is not a solution to the system.

STOP QY

▶ **QY**

Is the ordered pair (2, −1) a solution to the system in Example 1?

Solving Systems by Graphing

You can find the solutions to a system of equations with two variables by graphing each equation and finding the coordinates of the point(s) of intersection of the graphs.

Example 2

A second-grade class has 23 students. There are 5 more boys than girls. Solve a system of equations to determine how many boys and how many girls are in the class.

Solution Translate the conditions into a system of two equations. Let x be the number of boys and y be the number of girls. Because there are 23 students, x + y = 23. Because there are 5 more boys than girls, y + 5 = x. The situation is described by the system $\begin{cases} x + y = 23 \\ y + 5 = x \end{cases}$.

Graph the equations and identify the point of intersection.

There are 14 boys and 9 girls in the class. The solution is (14, 9), as graphed on the next page.

Check To check that (14, 9) is a solution, x = 14 and y = 9 must be checked in both equations.

Is (14, 9) a solution to x + y = 23? Does 14 + 9 = 23? Yes.

Is (14, 9) a solution to y + 5 = x? Does 9 + 5 = 14? Yes.

A total of 49.6 million children attended public and private schools in the United States in 2003.

Source: U.S. Census Bureau

The two conditions about the numbers of boys and girls can be seen by looking at tables of solutions for each equation.

x + y = 23

All these pairs add to 23, but only in this pair is the first number 5 greater than the second.

y + 5 = x

The first number in each pair is 5 greater than the second number, but only this pair has a sum of 23.

An Introduction to Systems **583**

---

2 Teaching

Notes on the Lesson

Use the Warm-Up. If desks can be put in rows and columns, you can introduce systems of equations this way. Assign each student in the class a point (x, y) with −4 ≤ x ≤ 4 and −4 ≤ y ≤ 4. This will be appropriate if a seat near the center of the room is (0, 0) and the other coordinates are based on their relationship to this seat. Use the equations from the Warm-Up. Ask students to stand if their seat is a solution to Question 1. Ask what type of geometric figure is formed by the students who stood. (a line) Then ask students to stand if their seat is a solution to Question 2. Who stood both times? How many people stood both times? (one) This illustrates that two distinct lines can intersect at most at one point. To solve the system, the ordered pair must be a solution of both equations. Repeat with other pairs of equations. Note that each pair of the Warm-Up equations intersects at a point with integer coordinates except 1 and 4, which do not intersect. This is like Example 3. But not all lines intersect at points with integer coordinates. This is the case in Example 4.

Throughout the chapter, stress the importance of the checking process. Because solving a system involves several steps, it is very easy to make a mistake. Also, each time they check a solution, students use the idea that it works in both equations. One way to emphasize the check is to ask not only for the solution to a system, but also for verification that the answer is correct.

Emphasize that solutions to a system must work in all sentences in the system. Example 1 stresses that point. In addition, when the intersection point does not have integer coordinates, you can estimate the coordinates from a graph, but it may be impossible to read the exact solution, as in Example 4.

10-1

Additional Examples

Example 1 Consider the system below.

$$\begin{cases} y = 4x - 11 \\ 5x + 2y = 4 \end{cases}$$

a. Verify that the ordered pair $(2, -3)$ is a solution of the system. **$(2, -3)$ is a solution because it satisfies both equations**

b. Show that $(1, -7)$ is *not* a solution to the system. **$(1, -7)$ is not a solution because it fails to satisfy $5x + 2y = 4$**

Example 2 A box of chocolates has 20 pieces of candy. There are 6 more chocolates with nuts than chocolates without nuts. Using a graphing calculator, solve a system of equations to determine how many chocolates have nuts and how many do not. **There are 7 chocolates without nuts and 13 chocolates with nuts.**

Example 3 Find all solutions to the system $\begin{cases} y = \frac{1}{2}x - 3 \\ -x + 2y = -8 \end{cases}$

Solution

Graph both equations using a graphing calculator.

1. How many times do the lines appear to intersect? _?_ **zero**

2. What is the slope of each line? _?_ **$\frac{1}{2}$**

3. If two lines do not intersect, they are called _?_ lines. **parallel**

Now look at the table of values on the graphing calculator.

4. Is there an ordered pair common to both lines? _?_ **no**

This is an example of a system of equation for which there is no solution. The solution set is Ø.

In general, there are four ways to indicate the solution to a system. They are shown below using the solution to the system in Example 2.

As an ordered pair	$(14, 9)$
As an ordered pair identifying the variables	$(x, y) = (14, 9)$
By naming the variables individually	$x = 14$ and $y = 9$
As a set of ordered pairs	$\{(14, 9)\}$

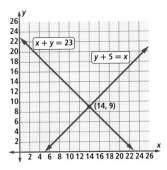

Systems with No Solutions

When the sentences in a system have no solutions in common, we say that there is no solution to the system. We cannot write the solution as an ordered pair or by listing the elements. The solution set is the set with no elements { }, written with the special symbol Ø. This set is called the **empty set** or **null set.**

GUIDED

Example 3
Find all solutions to the system $\begin{cases} y = -x + 4 \\ y = -x - 2 \end{cases}$.

Solution Graph both equations using a graphing calculator.

1. How many times do the lines appear to intersect? _?_ **zero**

2. What is the slope of each line? _?_ **-1**

3. If two lines in a plane do not intersect, they are called _?_ lines. **parallel**

Now look at the table of values on the graphing calculator.

4. Is there an ordered pair common to both lines? _?_ **no**

This is an example of a system of equations for which there is no solution. **The solution set is Ø.**

Cost and Revenue Equations

In manufacturing, a *cost equation* describes the cost y of making x products. *Fixed costs* are things like rent and employee salaries, which must be paid regardless of the number of products made. *Variable costs* include materials and shipping, which depend upon how many products are made. The total of fixed and variable costs is the amount of money the business pays out each month.

A *revenue equation* describes the amount y that a business earns by selling x products. The *break-even point* is the point at which the revenue and total costs are the same. This point tells the manufacturer how many items must be sold in order to make a profit.

584 Linear Systems

Accommodating the Learner ⬇

Students may benefit from examples that require them to describe the variables and write equations to represent the situation. Ask them to translate the situation into symbols. For Additional Example 2, ask them to describe the two kinds of candy in words, and then to label one as x and the other as y. Next, ask them to write what it means to have 20 pieces of candy in the box. This should look something like "The number of chocolates with nuts plus the number of chocolates without nuts will equal 20." Then ask them to write this using x and y. Repeat the procedure with the following statement: "There are 6 more chocolates with nuts than chocolates without nuts." Students may need practice with translating.

Example 4

A manufacturer of T-shirts has monthly fixed costs of $8,000, and the cost to produce each shirt is $3.40. Therefore, the cost y to produce x shirts is given by $y = 8,000 + 3.40x$. The business sells shirts to stores for $9 each. So the revenue equation is $y = 9x$. Find the break-even point for the shirt manufacturer.

Solution The break-even point can be found by solving the system $\begin{cases} y = 8,000 + 3.40x \\ y = 9x \end{cases}$.

Make a table to help you find reasonable x and y values to use in setting the window. The table below shows that the intersection point will be seen in the window $1,400 \leq x \leq 1,500, 12,600 \leq y \leq 13,500$.

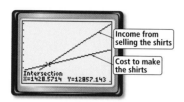

Children are shown silk-screening T-shirts. Silk-screening is a process in which color is forced into material like fabric or paper through a silk screen.

The INTERSECT command on a calculator shows that the point (1,429, 12,858) is an approximate solution. At the break-even point, 1,429 shirts are manufactured and sold. It costs about the same amount to make the shirts as the manufacturer earns from selling them. If more than 1,429 shirts are produced and sold, the business will earn a profit.

Check When $x = \$1,429$ in the cost equation, $y = \$8,000 + 3.40 \cdot \$1,429 = \$12,858.60$. When $x = 1,429$ in the revenue equation, $y = 9 \cdot \$1,429 = \$12,861$. These values are close enough to make 1,429 the first coordinate of the break-even point.

In Example 4, the solution is an approximation. When solutions do not have integer coordinates, it is likely that reading a graph will give you only an estimate. But graphs can be created quickly. In the next few lessons, you will learn algebraic techniques to find exact solutions to systems.

An Introduction to Systems **585**

Additional Example

Example 4 A café has monthly fixed costs of $4,700, and a typical customer order costs the café $2. Therefore, the cost to serve x customers in a month is given by $y = 4,700 + 2x$. The typical order costs the customer $10. So the revenue equation is $y = 10x$. Find the break-even point for the café using your graphing calculator. (587.5, 5,875) is the solution to the system, so if the café has 588 customers or more per month, it will earn a profit.

10-1

3 Assignment

Recommended Assignment
- Questions 1–21
- Question 22 (extra credit)
- Reading Lesson 10-2
- Covering the Ideas 10-2

Notes on the Question

Question 8 Some students will be able to find the answer using arithmetic. (Divide 518 in half and then go up and down 2 from that half.) Do not discourage this, but encourage those students to learn other methods.

Additional Answers

5c. $3(2) - 3 = 3$ and $2(2) + 3 = 7$

6a. $(4, 1)$

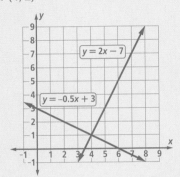

6b. $-2 + 3 = 1; 8 - 7 = 1$

10-1A Lesson Master

Questions on SPUR Objectives
See pages 650–653 for objectives.

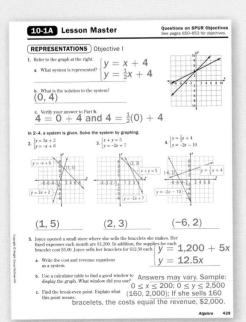

Questions

COVERING THE IDEAS

1. **True or False** When a system has two variables, each solution to the system is an ordered pair. **true**

2. What does the brace { represent in a system? **and**

3. a. Verify that $(8, -2)$ is a solution to the system $\begin{cases} -x = 4y \\ 2x + 3y = 10 \end{cases}$.
   b. Write this solution in two other ways.

4. Show that $(11, 8)$ is *not* a solution to $\begin{cases} y = x - 3 \\ x + 5y = 50 \end{cases}$.

5. Refer to the graph at the right.
   a. What system is represented? $\begin{cases} 3x - y = 3 \\ y = -2x + 7 \end{cases}$
   b. What is the solution to the system? **(2, 3)**
   c. Verify your answer to Part b. **See margin.**

In 6 and 7, a system is given.
   a. **Solve the system by graphing.**
   b. **Check your solution.** 6–7. See margin.

6. $\begin{cases} y = -\frac{1}{2}x + 3 \\ y = 2x - 7 \end{cases}$

7. $\begin{cases} y = x \\ 4x - 2y = 12 \end{cases}$

8. An elementary school has 518 students. There are 4 more girls than boys. 8a.–b. See margin.
   a. If g is the number of girls and b is the number of boys, translate the given information into two equations.
   b. Letting $x = g$ and $y = b$, graph the equations on a calculator.
   c. Using the graph from Part b, use the INTERSECT command to find the number of boys and girls in the school. **(261, 257)**

9. A small business makes wooden toy trains. The business has fixed expenses of $3,800 each month. In addition to this, the production of each train costs $4.25. The business sells the trains to stores for $12.50 each. 9a.–b. See margin.
   a. Write cost and revenue equations as a system.
   b. Use a calculator table to find a good window to display the graph. What window did you use?
   c. Find the break-even point. **about (461, 5,758)**
   d. Last month the business made and sold 518 trains. Did the business earn a profit? **yes**

10. Find all solutions to the system $\begin{cases} y = 3x - 5 \\ y = 3x - 1 \end{cases}$.
    There are no solutions.

3a. $-8 = 4(-2)$ and
$2(8) + 3(-2) =$
$16 + -6 = 10$

3b. Answers vary.
Sample answer:
$x = 8$ and $y = -2$;
$(x, y) = (8, -2)$

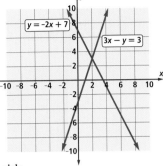

4. $11 + 5(8) =$
$11 + 40 = 51$,
$51 \neq 50$

Archaeologists have discovered jointed wooden dolls, carved horses, chariots, and even a crocodile with moveable jaws that date back to the year 1100 BCE.

Source: TDmonthly

Additional Answers

7a. $(6, 6)$

[graph with $y = x$ and $4x - 2y = 12$]

7b. $6 = 6; 24 - 12 = 12$

8a. $\begin{cases} g + b = 518 \\ g - b = 4 \end{cases}$

8b. [graph: Number of Boys vs Number of Girls]

9a. $\begin{cases} y = 3,800 + 4.25x \\ y = 12.5x \end{cases}$

9b. Answers vary. Sample answer: Xmin $= 400$; Xmax $= 800$; Ymin $= 3,800$; Ymax $= 8,000$

11. Consider the system $\begin{cases} y_1 = 2x + 5 \\ y_2 = 3x \end{cases}$.

The screen at the right shows solutions to $y_1 = 2x + 5$. Make a column for y_2 and use it to find the ordered pair that also satisfies $y_2 = 3x$, and therefore is a solution to the system. **See margin.**

APPLYING THE MATHEMATICS

12. The sum of two numbers is –19 and their difference is –5. Write a system of equations and solve it using a graph.

12. $\begin{cases} y + x = -19; \ (-7, -12) \\ y - x = -5 \end{cases}$

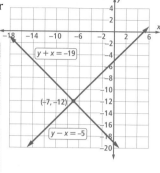

13. Below are a table and graph of the winning times in seconds for the Olympic men's and women's 100-meter backstroke events. **See margin.**

Year	Men's Time	Women's Time	Year	Men's Time	Women's Time
1924	73.2	83.2	1972	56.58	65.78
1928	68.2	82.0	1976	55.49	61.83
1932	68.6	79.4	1980	56.33	60.86
1936	65.9	78.9	1984	55.79	62.55
1948	66.4	74.4	1988	55.05	60.89
1952	65.4	74.3	1992	53.98	60.68
1956	62.2	72.9	1996	54.10	61.19
1960	61.9	69.3	2000	53.72	61.21
1964	NA	67.7	2004	54.06	60.37
1968	58.7	66.2			

Source: International Olympic Committee

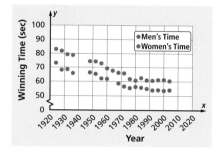

In Lesson 4-4, you were asked to estimate when the women's time might equal the men's time. Now repeat this question by finding equations for lines of best fit for the men's and women's times. Graph the two equations. According to these lines, will the women's winning time ever equal the men's winning time in the 100-meter backstroke? If yes, estimate the year when this will happen. If no, explain why not.

An Introduction to Systems **587**

Notes on the Questions

Question 12 This, too, can be solved without using algebra. But the algebra provides the avenue for a solution regardless of the numbers you start with.

Question 13 Note that Olympic times are missing for 1940 and 1944, so students must be careful when labeling the axes and plotting the points. Use your graphing utility or statistics package to fit lines to these data to compare the solutions students got by hand to the line of best fit by your software. You might also ask for other events in which men's and women's times over the years might be compared (for example, running, high jump, long jump).

Question 22 This question provides another way of looking at the swimming data. This helps point out that data sets can often be interpreted in many ways.

Additional Answers

11. (5, 15)

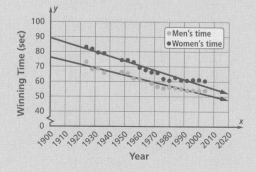

13. Answers vary. Sample answer: men:
$y = -0.1235x + 522.17$; women:
$y = -0.311x + 680.23$; Yes; both times will be equal in 2074. In 2076, the women's time will pass the men's time.

10-1

4) Wrap-Up

Ongoing Assessment

Ask students to consider the following systems.

System 1: $\begin{cases} y = 2x + 1 \\ y = 5 \end{cases}$

System 2: $\begin{cases} y = 5 \\ y = 3 \end{cases}$

Sketch a Venn diagram on the board. Label one circle "System 1" and the other "System 2." Label the overlapping part of the diagram "Similarities," and the nonoverlapping parts "Differences." Ask students to call out qualities to write in the different regions of the diagram. Qualities can include same or different slope, intersections, number of solutions, and shape of graphs.

Project Update

If you have not had students look over the projects on pages 645 and 646, you might want to do so now. Project 4, Adding and Subtracting Equations, on page 646, relates to the content of this lesson.

---

14. Buffy is hosting a meeting and plans to serve 4 dozen muffins. She wants to have twice as many blueberry muffins as plain muffins. The table at the right shows some of the possible ways to order 4 dozen muffins.

Number of Plain Muffins	Number of Blueberry Muffins
0	48
10	38
20	28
30	18
40	8
48	0

a. Using x for the number of plain muffins and y for the number of blueberry muffins, write a system of equations to describe this situation.

b. Graph your equations from Part a to find how many of each kind Buffy should order. **14a–b. See margin.**

REVIEW

15. **Skill Sequence** Solve each equation. (Lessons 9-5, 4-4, 3-4)

a. $5x + 6 = 3$ $-\frac{3}{5}$
b. $5x + 6 = 2x + 3$ -1
c. $5x + 6 = 2x^2 + 3$ $-\frac{1}{2}, 3$
d. $5x + 6 = 2x(x + 1)$

15d. –1.137, 2.637

In 16–18, simplify the expression. (Lessons 8-4, 8-3, 8-2)

16. $m^2 \cdot n^3 \cdot m \cdot n^4$ 17. $(-5x^7y^9)^4$ 18. $\dfrac{18r^2s^3}{6rs^4}$

16. m^3n^7

17. $625x^{28}y^{36}$

18. $\dfrac{3r}{s}$

19. Graph $\{(x, y): 4x - 8y < 2\}$. (Lesson 6-9) **See margin.**

20. Find the values of the variables so that the given point lies on the graph of $10x - 4y = 20$. (Lessons 6-8, 4-7)

a. $(5, p)$ 7.5
b. $(q, -2)$ 1.2
c. $(r, 0)$ 2

21. Two workers can dig a 20-foot well in 2 days. How long will it take 6 workers to dig a 90-foot well, assuming that each of these 6 workers dig at the same rate as each of the 2 workers? (Lessons 5-4, 5-3) **3 days**

EXPLORATION

22. Some experts believe that even though the women's swim times are decreasing faster than the men's, it is the ratio of the times that is the key to predictions. **22a–b. See margin.**

a. Compute the ratio of the men's time to the women's time for the 100-meter freestyle for each Olympic year in Question 13.

b. Graph your results.

c. What do you think the ratio will be in the year 2020? Does this agree with the prediction in Question 13?

Two men stand above a well that serves as an extractor of gold.

22c. Answers vary. Sample answer: 0.880. Yes, I predicted a fairly constant relationship.

588   Linear Systems

Additional Answers

14a. $\begin{cases} y + x = 48 \\ 2x = y \end{cases}$

14b. 16 plain, 32 blueberry

19.

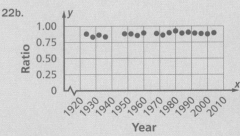

22a. 0.880, 0.832, 0.864, 0.835, 0.892, 0.880, 0.853, 0.893, N/A, 0.887, 0.860, 0.897, 0.926, 0.892, 0.904, 0.890, 0.884, 0.878, 0.895

22b.

Lesson 10-2

Solving Systems Using Substitution

▶ **BIG IDEA** Substituting an expression that equals a single variable is an effective first step for solving some systems.

When equations for lines in a system are in $y = mx + b$ form, a method of solving called *substitution* can be very efficient. Example 1 illustrates this method.

Example 1

Solve the system $\begin{cases} y = 7x + 25 \\ y = -5x - 11 \end{cases}$ using substitution.

Solution Because $7x + 25$ and $-5x - 11$ both equal y, they must equal each other. Substitute one of them for y in the other equation.

$7x + 25 = -5x - 11$	Substitution
$12x + 25 = -11$	Add $5x$ to both sides.
$12x = -36$	Subtract 25 from both sides.
$x = -3$	Divide both sides by 12.

Now you know $x = -3$. However, you must still solve for y. You can substitute -3 for x into either of the original equations. We choose the first equation.

$y = 7x + 25$

$y = 7(-3) + 25$

$y = -21 + 25$

$y = 4$

The solution is $x = -3$ and $y = 4$, or just $(-3, 4)$.

 QY

Check A graph shows that the lines with equations $y = 7x + 25$ and $y = -5x - 11$ intersect at $(-3, 4)$.

Suppose two quantities are increasing or decreasing at different constant rates. Then each quantity can be described by an equation of the form $y = mx + b$. To find out when the quantities are equal, you can solve a system using substitution. Example 2 illustrates this idea.

 Mental Math

Find the greatest common factor.

a. 15; 200 **5**

b. 1,500; 20,000 **500**

c. 14; 26; 53 **1**

d. 1,400; 2,600; 5,300 **100**

▶ **QY**

Check that $(-3, 4)$ is a solution to $y = -5x - 11$.

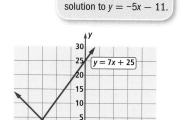

Solving Systems Using Substitution **589**

Background

In this lesson, the equations in the systems are in slope-intercept form, $y = ax + b$ and $y = cx + d$, and the justification for $ax + b = cx + d$ could be either substitution (substitute $cx + d$ for y in the first equation) or the Symmetric and Transitive Properties of Equality ($ax + b = y$ by the Symmetric Property; then $ax + b = cx + d$ by the Transitive Property). We call it substitution because the justification is more direct and

because it helps to set up the next lesson, in which one equation is in slope-intercept form and the other is not.

Point out the general form here: $A = B$ and $A = C$ is the given system, so we are able to say $B = C$. Notice the importance of chunking $ax + b$ as a single quantity.

Lesson 10-2

GOAL

Solve systems of two linear equations where both equations are of the form $y = mx + b$.

SPUR Objectives

A Solve systems using substitution.

G Use systems of linear equations to solve real-world problems.

Materials/Resources

· Lesson Master 10-2A or 10-2B
· Resource Master 148
· Scientific or graphing calculator

HOMEWORK

Suggestions for Assignment

• Questions 1–21
• Question 22 (extra credit)
• Reading Lesson 10-3
• Covering the Ideas 10-3

Local Standards

---

1 **Warm-Up**

Line m has slope 5 and y-intercept 3. Line n has slope -2 and y-intercept 4.

1. By hand, draw a picture of the two lines and estimate a point of intersection. **Answers vary. Sample answer: (0, 3.5)**

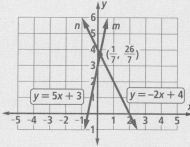

2. Give equations for the two lines and use them to find the x-coordinate of the intersection. $m: y = 5x + 3$; $n: y = -2x + 4$; $x = \frac{1}{7}$

3. Substitute the x-value with one of the equations to find the y-coordinate of the point of intersection. $\frac{26}{7}$

10-2

2 | Teaching

Notes on the Lesson

Example 1 Notice that because the scales on the axes in the graph are quite different, the value of y is not easily found from the graph.

Example 2 Taxi rates provide a nice setting for systems. Notice that the distance is in tenths of a mile. This makes it easier to find the equations in the system, but it means that the solution is a little more difficult to interpret.

Relate Example 2 to Question 8 and Questions 10–13. These are all constant-increase situations similar to those students have seen before. By the end of the chapter, students should be able to find the equations and solve the systems automatically.

Additional Examples

Example 1 Solve the system $\begin{cases} y = 2x + 8 \\ y = -5x - 27 \end{cases}$ using substitution. The solution is $x = -5$ and $y = -2$, or $(-5, -2)$.

Example 2 The online catalog *Sockpuppet* will charge you $3.00 for shipping and handling plus $0.50 per pair of socks you order. The *Footglove* catalog will charge you $3.90 for shipping and handling, plus $0.40 per pair. How many pairs of socks would you have to purchase to make the costs equal? **You would have to buy 9 pairs of socks**

Example 2

The Rapid Taxi Company charges $2.15 for a taxi ride plus 20¢ for each $\frac{1}{10}$ mile traveled. A competitor, Carl's Cabs, charges $1.50 for a taxi ride plus 25¢ for each $\frac{1}{10}$ mile traveled. For what distance do the rides cost the same?

Solution Let d = the distance of a cab ride in tenths of a mile.

Let C = the cost of a cab ride of distance d.
Rapid Taxi: $C = 2.15 + 0.20d$
Carl's Cabs: $C = 1.50 + 0.25d$

The rides cost the same when the values of C and d for Rapid Taxi equal the values for Carl's Cabs, so we need to solve the system formed by these two equations. Substitute $2.15 + 0.20d$ for C in the second equation.

$2.15 + 0.20d = 1.50 + 0.25d$
Now solve.

$$0.65 = 0.05d \qquad \text{Add } -1.50 \text{ and } -0.20d \text{ to both sides.}$$
$$d = 13 \qquad \text{Divide both sides by 0.05.}$$

The two companies charge the same amount for a ride that is 13 tenths of a mile long, or 1.3 miles long.

Check Check to see if the cost will be the same for a ride of 13 tenths of a mile.
The cost for Rapid Taxi is $2.15 + 0.20 \cdot 13 = 2.15 + 2.60 = 4.75$.
The cost for Carl's Cabs is $1.50 + 0.25 \cdot 13 = 1.50 + 3.25 = 4.75$.
The cost is $4.75 from each company, so the answer checks.

In Example 2, Carl's Cabs is cheaper at first, but as the number of miles increases, the prices become closer. Eventually the price for Carl's Cabs catches up with Rapid Taxi's price, and then Carl's is more expensive than Rapid. The next example also involves "catching up."

The average taxi fare in New York in 2006 was $9.65.

Source: MSNBC

GUIDED

Example 3

Bart was so confident that he could run faster than his little sister that he bragged, "I can beat you in a 50-meter race. I'm so sure that I'll give you a 10-meter head start!" Bart could run at a speed of 4 meters per second, while his sister could run 3 meters per second. Could Bart catch up to his sister before the end of the race?

Solution Let d be the distance that Bart and his sister have traveled after t seconds. Recall that distance = rate · time.

For Bart, $d = 4t$.

Accommodating the Learner ⬆

Ask students to consider systems such as

$\begin{cases} y = 2x - 1 \\ 2y + 4x = 6 \end{cases}$. Ask them to first

isolate the y in the second equation and solve. Encourage them to explore other ways to substitute. For example, they may see that another alternative is to substitute the first equation into the second as follows: $2(2x - 1) + 4x = 6$. $y = 2x - 1$ and $y = -2x + 3$, so $2x - 1 = -2x + 3$ and $4x = 4$. Thus $x = 1$ and $y = 2(1) - 1 = 1$. Solving $2(2x - 1) + 4x = 6$: $4x - 2 + 4x = 6$ and $8x = 8$. So $x = 1$ and $y = 1$.

Because Bart gives his sister a 10-meter head start, $d = 10 + 3t$. To know the time t when Bart will catch up to his sister, solve the system.

$$\begin{cases} d = \underline{}\ 4t \\ d = \underline{}\ 10 + 3t \end{cases}$$

Substitute $4t$ for d in the second equation.

$$\underline{} = \underline{} + \underline{} \quad 4t;\ 10;\ 3t$$

Solve this equation as you would any other.

$$t = \underline{}\quad 10$$

This means that after 10 seconds, Bart and his sister are at the same point. However, is the race finished at 10 seconds? Substitute 10 for t to find the distance. In 10 seconds Bart has run 40 meters. **Because the race is 50 meters long, the race is not over when Bart catches up to his sister. Therefore, Bart wins.**

Questions

COVERING THE IDEAS

In 1–5, a system is given.
a. Use substitution to find the solution.
b. Check your answer.

1. $\begin{cases} y = 3x - 4 \\ y = 5x - 10 \end{cases}$

2. $\begin{cases} b = 48 + a \\ b = 60 - a \end{cases}$

3. $\begin{cases} y = -\frac{1}{9}x + 6 \\ y = \frac{5}{3}x + 38 \end{cases}$

4. $\begin{cases} x = \frac{2}{3}y - 8 \\ x = -12.5y + 150 \end{cases}$

5. $\begin{cases} m = 8n + 33 \\ m = 3n - 78 \end{cases}$

6. Suppose that in Freeport, a taxi ride costs $2.50 plus 15¢ for each $\frac{1}{10}$ mile traveled. In Geneva, a taxi ride costs $1.70 plus 20¢ for each $\frac{1}{10}$ mile traveled. Write a system of equations and solve it to find the distance for which the costs are the same.

7. Recall from Example 3 that Bart ran 4 meters per second and his sister ran 3 meters per second. Bart's sister said to him, "You'll beat me if I have only a 10-meter head start. I'll race you if you give me a 15-meter head start." Solve a system of equations to find out if she would then beat him in a 50-meter race. $d = 15 + 3t,\ d = 4t$; The solution is (15, 60), so Bart's sister will win.

1a. (3, 5)

1b. $3(3) - 4 = 5$;
$5(3) - 10 = 5$

2a. (6, 54)

2b. $48 + 6 = 54$;
$60 - 6 = 54$

3a. (−18, 8)

3b. $-\frac{1}{9}(-18) + 6 = 8$;
$\frac{5}{3}(-18) + 38 = 8$

4a. (0, 12)

4b. $8 - 8 = 0$;
$-12.5(12) + 150 = 0$

5a. (−144.6, −22.2)

5b. $8(-22.2) + 33 = -144.6$;
$3(-22.2) - 78 = -144.6$

6. $\begin{cases} f = 1.5m + 2.50 \\ g = 2m + 1.70 \end{cases}$;
1.6 mi

Notes on the Lesson

Example 3 is extended in Question 7 and is similar to Question 9. To model the race, use 1 foot on a tile floor or a tape measure to represent 1 yard. Have one person represent Bart and another person represent his sister. Bart starts at the point marked 0 and his sister at 10. Move along the race course to show the positions after each second of the race until Bart catches up. Make a table to record the times and distances. Then show that the system of equations in Example 3 represents Bart and his sister's distance from the start as a function of time. Solve the system and verify that the result is the same as you found when you modeled the race.

Additional Example

Example 3 A tortoise challenges a hare to a 10-mile race. The tortoise moves at a steady speed of 0.2 mile per hour. The hare can move at a speed of 40 miles per hour. Because the tortoise is slow, the hare decides to wait until the tortoise is 0.25 mile from the finish line before it even starts to race. Can the hare still win?

Solution

Let d be the distance that the tortoise and the hare have traveled after t seconds. Recall that distance = rate · time. For the hare, $d = 40t$. For the tortoise, because the hare is giving it a 9.75 mile head start, $d = 9.75 + 0.2t$. To know the time t when the hare will catch up to the tortoise, substitute $40t$ for d in the second equation and solve the equation $\underline{} = \underline{}$. $40t;\ 9.75 + 0.2t$

Solve for t: $t = \underline{}$ 0.244975

This means that after the hare has been running for 0.244975 hour, the tortoise and the hare are at the same point. To find the distance, substitute 0.244975 for t. In 0.244975 hour the hare has run approximately 9.8 miles. The race is 10 miles long, so the hare wins.

Vocabulary Development

Discuss the term *substitution* and its meaning and uses in mathematics. Show students how we use the term *substitute* any time we replace a variable with a value, as in Examples a and b.

Some examples:

a. Evaluate $y = 2x - 1$ when $x = 2$.
b. Find x when $y = 2x + 3$ and $y = 3$.

Then use examples of substitution in solving systems.

3 Assignment

Recommended Assignment
- Questions 1–21
- Question 22 (extra credit)
- Reading Lesson 10-3
- Covering the Ideas 10-3

Notes on the Questions

Questions 10–13 Point out that in these constant-increase situations, if the starting amount and the amount of increase are given, the information is the same as if a point on the line and the slope of the line were given.

Questions 14 and 15 These linear-quadratic and quadratic-quadratic systems, usually not mentioned until a second course in algebra, show the power of the method of substitution in solving systems.

Question 22 We found taxi fares for many cities at www.schallerconsult.com/taxi/fares1.htm.

---

8. A tomato canning company has fixed monthly costs of $4,200. There are additional costs of $2.35 to produce each case of canned tomatoes. The company sells tomatoes to grocery stores for $5.85 per case.
   a. Write a system of equations to describe this situation.
   b. How many cases must the company sell to break even? **1,200 cases**
   c. Check your solution. **$5.85(1,200) = 7,020$;**
      $4,200 + 2.35(1,200) = 7,020$

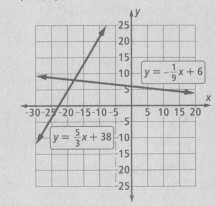

Approximately 124,900 acres of tomatoes were harvested in the United States in 2002.

Source: U.S. Department of Agriculture

APPLYING THE MATHEMATICS

9. A car leaves a gas station traveling at 60 mph. The driver has accidentally left his credit card at the gas station. Six minutes later, his friend leaves the station with the credit card, traveling at 65 mph to catch up to him.
   a. Write two equations to indicate the distance d that each car is from the gas station t hours after the first car leaves.
   b. Solve the system to determine when the second car will catch up to the first car. **(1.3, 78); after 1.3 hours**
   c. How far will they have traveled from the gas station when they meet? **78 mi**

10. Cameron has $450 and saves $12 a week. Sean has only $290, but is saving $20 a week.
    a. After how many weeks will they each have the same amount of money? **20 weeks**
    b. How much money will each person have then? **$690**

11. In 2000, the metropolitan area of Dallas had about 5,200,000 people and was growing at about 120,000 people a year. In 2000, the metropolitan area of Boston had about 4,400,000 people and was growing at about 25,000 people a year.
    a. If these trends had been this way for quite some time, in what year did Dallas and Boston have the same population? **about 8.42 yr before 2000 (1991)**
    b. What was this population? **about 4,189,474 people**

12. In July 2005, Philadelphia approved taxi fares with an initial charge of $2.30 and an additional charge of $0.30 for each $\frac{1}{7}$ mile. If $P(x)$ is the cost for taking a taxi x miles, then $P(x) = 2.30 + 0.30 \cdot 7x$. In October 2005, Atlanta established new taxi fares with an initial charge of $2.50 and an additional charge of $0.25 for each $\frac{1}{8}$ mile. If $A(x)$ is the cost of taking a taxi x miles in Atlanta, then $A(x) = 2.50 + 0.25 \cdot 8x$. Solve a system to approximate at what distance the fares for Philadelphia and Atlanta are the same. **2 mi**

8a. t = number of cases and c = cost in dollars

$$\begin{cases} c = 4{,}200 + 2.35t \\ c = 5.85t \end{cases}$$

9a. $\begin{cases} d = 60t \\ d = 65(t - \frac{1}{10}) \end{cases}$

Accommodating the Learner

Students may struggle with Example 3 because the solution to the system is not the final answer to the problem. Provide several examples in which students have to solve a system or an equation and use the solution to answer a related question. Remind students that if they cannot immediately see how to solve the entire problem, they should think about what they *can* find. Then, ask them to connect that with the original question.

Additional Answers

17. (−18, 8)

[graph showing $y = -\frac{1}{9}x + 6$ and $y = \frac{5}{3}x + 38$]

---

13. One plumbing company charges $55 for the first half hour of work and $25 for each additional half hour. Another company charges $35 for the first half hour and then $30 for each additional half hour. For how many hours of work will the cost of each company be the same?

In **14** and **15**, a system that involves a quadratic equation is given. Each system has two solutions.
   a. Solve the system by substitution.
   b. Check your answers.

14. $\begin{cases} y = \frac{1}{9}x^2 \\ y = 4x \end{cases}$

15. $\begin{cases} y = 2x^2 + 5x - 3 \\ y = x^2 - 2x + 5 \end{cases}$

REVIEW

16. Consider the system $\begin{cases} y = 20x + 8 \\ 24x - y = -6 \end{cases}$. Verify that $\left(\frac{1}{2}, 18\right)$ is a solution to the system, but that (1, 20) is not. (**Lesson 10-1**)

In **17** and **18**, solve the system of equations by graphing. (**Lesson 10-1**)

17. the system in Question 3   **17–18. See margin.**

18. the system in Question 4

19. a. Simplify $y(y - 9) + 4y + 1$. $y^2 - 5y + 1$
    b. Solve $y(y - 9) = 4y + 1$. (**Lesson 9-5**)

20. ***Skill Sequence*** Solve each equation. (**Lessons 9-1, 8-6**)
    a. $n^2 = 16$ **4, –4**   b. $\sqrt{n} = 16$ **256**   c. $\sqrt{n^2} = 16$ **16, –16**

21. What is the cost of x basketballs at $18 each and y footballs at $25 each? (**Lessons 5-3, 1-2**) $18x + 25y$ dollars

EXPLORATION

22. Find the taxi rates where you live or in a nearby community. Graph the rates to show how they compare to those in Question 12. **See margin.**

---

13. 2 hr

14a. (0, 0) and (36, 144)

14b. $\frac{1}{9}(0)^2 = 0$ and $4(0) = 0$; $\frac{1}{9}(36)^2 = 144$ and $4(36) = 144$

15a. (1, 4) and (–8, 85)

15b. $2(1^2) + 5(1) - 3 = 4$ and $1^2 - 2(1) + 5 = 4$; $2(-8)^2 + 5(-8) - 3 = 85$ and $(-8)^2 - 2(-8) + 5 = 85$

16. $20(0.5) + 8 = 18$; $24(0.5) + 6 = 18$; $20 + 8 = 28 \neq 20$

19b. $y = -0.076$ and $y = 13.076$

QY ANSWER

Does $4 = -5(-3) - 11$?
$4 = 15 - 11$
$4 = 4$ Yes, it checks.

10-2

4 Wrap-Up

Ongoing Assessment

Check students' understanding by asking them to use substitution to solve a system on a transparency and hand it in. Then select different solutions and analyze them as a class. Look for different correct methods and common errors.

Project Update

Project 5, Finding the Counterfeit, on page 646, relates to the content of this lesson.

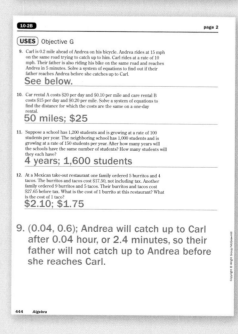

10-2B Lesson Master   Questions on SPUR Objectives
See pages 650–653 for objectives.

SKILLS Objective A

In 1–8, a system is given. Use substitution to find the solution.

1. $\begin{cases} y = 3x \\ y = -x + 4 \end{cases}$ (1, 3)

2. $\begin{cases} b = 2a + 5 \\ b = a + 3 \end{cases}$ (–2, 1)

3. $\begin{cases} y = 3x + 1 \\ y = 0.5x - 4 \end{cases}$ (–2, –5)

4. $\begin{cases} y = 2x - 5 \\ y = -2x + 7 \end{cases}$ (3, 1)

5. $\begin{cases} y = \frac{1}{2}x \\ y = 3x + 4 \end{cases}$ $\left(-\frac{8}{5}, -\frac{4}{5}\right)$

6. $\begin{cases} d = \frac{1}{3}c + 7 \\ d = \frac{2}{3}c + 8 \end{cases}$ (–3, 6)

7. $\begin{cases} y = \frac{1}{2}x + 5 \\ y = -4x - 4 \end{cases}$ (–2, 4)

8. $\begin{cases} y = 0.4 \\ y = 0.2x + 6 \end{cases}$ (–28, 0.4)

Algebra   443

10-2B   page 2

USES Objective G

9. Carl is 0.2 mile ahead of Andrea on his bicycle. Andrea rides at 15 mph on the same road trying to catch up to him. Carl rides at a rate of 10 mph. Their father is also riding his bike on the same road and reaches Andrea in 5 minutes. Solve a system of equations to find out if their father reaches Andrea before she catches up to Carl.
See below.

10. Car rental A costs $20 per day and $0.10 per mile and car rental B costs $15 per day and $0.20 per mile. Solve a system of equations to find the distance for which the costs are the same on a one-day rental.
50 miles; $25

11. Suppose a school has 1,200 students and is growing at a rate of 100 students per year. The neighboring school has 1,000 students and is growing at a rate of 150 students per year. After how many years will the schools have the same number of students? How many students will they each have?
4 years; 1,600 students

12. At a Mexican take-out restaurant one family ordered 5 burritos and 4 tacos. The burritos and tacos cost $17.50, not including tax. Another family ordered 9 burritos and 5 tacos. Their burritos and tacos cost $27.65 before tax. What is the cost of 1 burrito at this restaurant? What is the cost of 1 taco?
$2.10; $1.75

9. (0.04, 0.6); Andrea will catch up to Carl after 0.04 hour, or 2.4 minutes, so their father will not catch up to Andrea before she reaches Carl.

444   Algebra

Additional Answers

18. (0, 12)

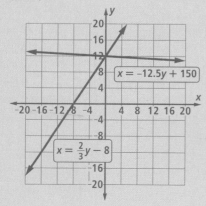

22. Answers vary. Sample answer: $B(x) = 1.75 + 0.30 \cdot 8x$ in Boston, MA.

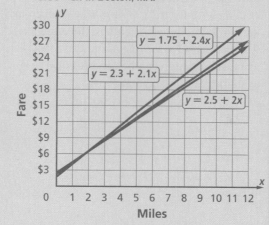

Lesson 10-3

GOAL

Solve systems in which one of the equations in the system is in slope-intercept form $y = mx + b$ or can be easily put into that form, but the other is not in that form.

SPUR Objectives

A Solve systems using substitution.

G Use systems of linear equations to solve real-world problems.

Materials/Resources

· Lesson Master 10-3A or 10-3B
· Resource Masters 2 and 149
· Graphing calculator
· Computer Algebra System (CAS)

HOMEWORK

Suggestions for Assignment
· Questions 1–22
· Question 23 (extra credit)
· Reading Lesson 10-4
· Covering the Ideas 10-4

Local Standards

9.0

1 · Warm-Up

1. Suppose $a = 2b + 3$, $b = 4c + 5$, $c = 6d + 7$, and $d = 8$. What is the value of a? **453**

2. Suppose a, b, and c are the same as in Question 1 but no value of d is known. Give a formula for a in terms of d. **$a = 48d + 69$**

Lesson 10-3 — More Uses of Substitution

▶ **BIG IDEA**   Substitution is a reasonable method to solve systems whenever you can easily solve for one variable in an equation.

In the previous lesson, you saw how to use substitution as a technique to solve systems of equations when the same variable was alone on one side of each equation. Substitution may also be used in other situations. Here is a typical situation that lends itself to substitution.

Mental Math

Estimate between two consecutive integers.

a. $\sqrt{26}$ 5 and 6
b. $\sqrt{171}$ 13 and 14
c. $-\sqrt{171}$ −13 and −14

Example 1

A grandfather likes to play guessing games with his grandchildren. One day he tells them, "I have only dimes and quarters in my pocket. They are worth $3.85. I have 14 fewer quarters than dimes. How many of each coin do I have?" Use a system of equations to answer his question.

Solution Translate each condition into an equation. Let D equal the number of dimes and Q equal the number of quarters. Dimes are worth $0.10 each, so D dimes are worth 0.10D. Quarters are worth $0.25 each, so Q quarters are worth 0.25Q. The total value of all the coins is $3.85. So $0.10D + 0.25Q = 3.85$.

There are 14 fewer quarters than dimes. That leads to a second equation $Q = D - 14$. Together the two equations form a system.

$$\begin{cases} 0.10D + 0.25Q = 3.85 \\ Q = D - 14 \end{cases}$$

Because $Q = D - 14$, substitute $D - 14$ for Q in the first equation.

$0.10D + 0.25(D - 14) = 3.85$	Substitution
$0.10D + 0.25D - 0.25(14) = 3.85$	Distributive Property
$0.10D + 0.25D - 3.5 = 3.85$	Arithmetic
$0.35D - 3.5 = 3.85$	Collect like terms.
$0.35D = 7.35$	Add 3.5 to both sides.
$D = 21$	Divide both sides by 0.35.

a grandfather posing with his three grandchildren

Background

In this lesson, the equations of one or both lines in the system begin in the linear combination form $Ax + By = C$. However, in each system, in one or both of the equations it is easy to solve for one of the variables. Then substitution can be used to solve the system, as in Lesson 10-2.

To find Q, substitute 21 for D in either equation. We use the second equation because it is solved for Q. When D = 21, Q = D − 14 = 21 − 14 = 7. So (D, Q) = (21, 7). The grandfather has 21 dimes and 7 quarters.

Check The 21 dimes are worth $2.10 and the 7 quarters are worth $1.75.
$2.10 + $1.75 = $3.85

In Chapter 6, you used the slope and y-intercept to find an equation of a line that passes through two given points. A different method for finding an equation through two points makes use of a system of equations.

Example 2

Find an equation of the line that passes through the points (3, 26) and (−2, 1).

Solution In slope-intercept form, the equation of the line is $y = mx + b$. If the values of m and b were known, each point on the line would make the equation true.

Substitute the coordinates of each given point for x and y to get two equations.

Using (3, 26), $26 = m \cdot 3 + b$.

Using (−2, 1), $1 = m \cdot -2 + b$.

This gives the system $\begin{cases} 26 = 3m + b \\ 1 = -2m + b \end{cases}$.

Either equation can be solved for b. From the second equation, $b = 2m + 1$. Now substitute $2m + 1$ for b in the first equation.

$26 = 3m + (2m + 1)$

$26 = 5m + 1$

$25 = 5m$

$5 = m$

This is the slope of the line. To find b, substitute 5 for m in either of the original equations. We use the second equation.

$1 = -2m + b$

$1 = -2 \cdot 5 + b$

$1 = -10 + b$

$11 = b$

This is the y-intercept. Thus, an equation of the line through (3, 26) and (−2, 1) is $y = 5x + 11$.

(continued on next page)

Accommodating the Learner

Ask students to explain why substitution is a good method to solve a system such as $\begin{cases} x = 2 \\ 3x + 5y = 2 \end{cases}$. Ask students to graph the lines and analyze what the substitution represents. They should see that they are evaluating the second equation for the value $x = 2$.

2 Teaching

Notes on the Lesson

Example 1 The sentence $0.10D + 0.25Q = 3.85$ in Example 1 arises from a classic linear combination situation. Each dime is worth 0.10 and each quarter 0.25, and each side of the equation represents the total value of the coins. A similar situation gives rise to the equation $20x + 30y = 2,450$ in Example 3.

You might ask students for variants of Example 1. What system would be solved to find out if the grandfather could have $3.85 with 14 quarters and nickels? ($0.05N + 0.25Q = 3.85; N + Q = 14$) Change the denominations, the total number of coins, or the total value. What if there were twice as many quarters as dimes—could he have $3.85? (No)

Example 2 This example shows how to use specific values of x and y to find the values of parameters. Students have seen this before when determining an equation of a line with a given slope and a given point on the line.

Additional Examples

Example 1 A college vocal group needs to raise money for an upcoming trip, so the students decide to sell CDs and T-shirts at their next performance. The shirts sell for $8 each, and the CDs for $12 each. By the end of the night, they know that they sold 35 items, and that they have raised $360. However, they forgot to keep track of how many of each item they sold. Use a system of equations to find out. **They sold 20 CDs and 15 T-shirts.**

Example 2 Find an equation of the line that passes through the points (4, 1) and (−6, 6). $y = -\frac{1}{2}x + 3$

10-3

Additional Example

Example 3 Jotrenia wishes to stock up on coffee beans. She pays $5 per pound for decaffeinated and $6.50 per pound for regular. She ends up buying 5 pounds of coffee beans for $29.50. How much of each type of coffee did she buy?

Solution

You want to find two amounts, so use two variables.

Let x = the number of pounds of decaffeinated beans, and let y = the number of pounds of regular beans.

There were a total of 5 pounds purchased, so $x + y = 5$.

The total cost is $29.50, so $5x + 6.5y = 29.50$.

Although neither equation is solved for a variable, the first equation is equivalent to $y = $ _?_ . **5 − x**

Now substitute _?_ for y in the second equation. **5 − x**

$5x + 6.5(\ ?\ ) = 29.50$ **5 − x**

$5x + \ ?\ − \ ?\ = 29.50$ Distributive
32.5; 6.5x Property

$32.5 + \ ?\ = 29.50$ Collect like
−1.5x terms.

$\ ?\ = -3$ Add −32.5 to
−1.5x both sides.

$x = \ ?\ $ Divide both
2 sides by −1.5.

To find y, substitute 2 for x in either of the two equations. We use the first equation because it is simpler.

$x + y = 5$

$\ ?\ + y = \ ?\ $ **2; 5**

$y = \ ?\ $ **3**

Jotrenia bought 2 pounds of decaffeinated coffee beans, and 3 pounds of regular coffee beans.

Check Does each ordered pair satisfy the equation of the line?

Does $26 = 5 \cdot 3 + 11$? Yes, $26 = 15 + 11$.
Does $(3, 26)$ satisfy $y = 5x + 11$? Yes, $(3, 26)$ is on the line.
Does $1 = 5 \cdot -2 + 11$? Yes, $1 = -10 + 11$.
Does $(-2, 1)$ satisfy $y = 5x + 11$? Yes, $(-2, 1)$ is on the line.

Some situations have been around for generations. Example 3 is taken from an 1881 algebra text; the prices are out of date, but the situation is not.

GUIDED

Example 3

A farmer purchased 100 acres of land for $2,450. He paid $20 per acre for part of it and $30 per acre for the rest. How many acres were there in each part?

Solution You want to find two amounts, so use two variables.

Let x = the number of acres at $20/acre, and y = the number of acres at $30/acre.

The farmer purchased a total of 100 acres, so $x + y = 100$.

The total cost is $2,450. So $20x + 30y = 2,450$.

Solve the system of these two equations.

$$\begin{cases} x + y = 100 \\ 20x + 30y = 2,450 \end{cases}$$

Although neither equation is solved for a variable, the first equation is equivalent to $y = $ ___?___ **100 − x**

$20x + 30(\underline{\ ?\ }) = 2,450$ Substitute ___?___ for y in the
$\quad\quad\quad\ 100 - x$ second equation. **100 − x**

$20x + \underline{\ ?\ } - \underline{\ ?\ } = 2,450$ Distributive Property **3,000; 30x**

$3,000 - \underline{\ ?\ } = 2,450$ Collect like terms. **10x**

$\underline{\ ?\ } = -550$ Add −3,000 to both sides. **−10x**

$x = 55$ Divide both sides by −10.

To find y, substitute 55 for x in either of the original equations. We use the first equation because it is simpler.

$$x + y = 100$$
$$55 + y = 100$$
$$y = 45$$

The farmer bought 55 acres at $20/acre, and 45 acres at $30/acre.

Accommodating the Learner ⬇

Many times, using substitution leads to working with equations such as $x = \dfrac{3y - 2}{3}$ and $x = \dfrac{3y - 3}{3}$. Take time to reinforce when students can and cannot cancel coefficients from the numerator and denominator.

Check Substitute 55 for x and 45 for y into the second equation.

Does $20x + 30y = 2{,}450$?
Yes, $20(55) + 30(45) = 1{,}100 + 1{,}350 = 2{,}450$.

A CAS can be used to solve systems of equations even when neither equation has an isolated variable.

Additional Example
Example 4 Use a CAS to solve.
$\begin{cases} 5x - 2y = -41 \\ -4x + 3y = 37 \end{cases}$ $(-7, 3)$

Example 4

Use a CAS to solve $\begin{cases} y = \frac{2}{3}x + \frac{10}{3} \\ 5x + 2y = 32 \end{cases}$.

Solution Since the first equation is already solved for y, simply substitute that expression for y into the second equation and solve the second equation for x. To do that quickly on a CAS, you can use the SOLVE command.

Step 1 Find the SOLVE command on your calculator and place it on the entry line. On some calculators you may find it in the Algebra menu.

Step 2 Enter the second equation with $\left(\frac{2}{3}x + \frac{10}{3}\right)$ in place of y as you would if you were solving the equation by hand. That is, enter
$5x + 2\left(\frac{2}{3}x + \frac{10}{3}\right) = 32$.

Step 3 The SOLVE command on many CAS requires you to specify the variable for which to solve. In this case it is x. You may need to enter a comma followed by x before you close the parentheses and hit ENTER. You should get $x = 4$.

Step 4 Now substitute this x value into the first equation to get $y = 6$.

So, the solution to the system is $(4, 6)$.

(continued on next page)

10-3

3 Assignment

Recommended Assignment

- Questions 1–22
- Question 23 (extra credit)
- Reading Lesson 10-4
- Covering the Ideas 10-4

Notes on the Questions

Questions 1 and 3 These questions exemplify what is sometimes called a *ratio situation*. In a ratio situation, a total is split into various parts, and the ratio of those parts is known. Questions 12 and 14 are also of this type.

Check Determining if a point is a solution to a system is easy to do on a CAS. Enter the two original equations and the specific values for each variable. The symbol " | " on one CAS means "with" or "such that" and indicates these values. The response "true" indicates that (4, 6) checks.

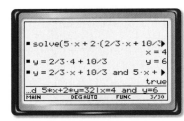

STOP QY

> **QY**
>
> Below is the solution to a system found by using a CAS.
> solve(4•x+3•(2−5•x) =17,x)
> $$x=-1$$
> y=2−5•-1
> $$y=7$$
> a. Find the system of equations.
> b. Check the solution by hand.

Questions

COVERING THE IDEAS

1. The owners of a carnival have found that twice as many children as adults come to the carnival. Solve a system to estimate the number of children and the number of adults at the carnival when 3,570 people attend.

2. A jar of coins has only nickels and quarters, which are worth a total of $9.40. There are 4 more quarters than nickels. How many nickels and quarters are in the jar? **28 nickels, 32 quarters**

3. The Drama Club and Service Club held a charity car wash. There were four times as many Service Club members as Drama Club members working, so the Service Club earned four times as much money. The car wash raised $280 in all. How much did each club earn for their charity?

In 4–7, a system is given. **4–7. See margin.**
a. Solve each system of equations by substitution.
b. Check your answer.

4. $\begin{cases} y = 2x \\ 3x + 2y = 21 \end{cases}$

5. $\begin{cases} n + 5w = 6 \\ n = -8w \end{cases}$

6. $\begin{cases} a - b = 2 \\ a + 5b = 20 \end{cases}$

7. $\begin{cases} y = x - 1 \\ 4x - y = 19 \end{cases}$

8. Here is another problem from the 1881 algebra textbook. A farmer bought 100 acres of land, part at $37 per acre and part at $45 per acre, at a total cost of $4,220. How much land was there in each part? **65 acres at $45, 35 acres at $37**

1. **1,190 adults, 2,380 children**

3. **$56 by the drama club, $224 by the service club**

Americans gave a total of $260.28 billion in contributions to charities in 2005.

Source: Giving USA Foundation

Additional Answers

4a. $x = 3, y = 6$

4b. $2(3) = 6$ and $3(3) + 2(6) = 21$

5a. $n = 16, w = -2$

5b. $16 + 5(-2) = 6$ and $-8(-2) = 16$

6a. $a = 5, b = 3$

6b. $5 - 3 = 2$ and $5 + 5(3) = 20$

7a. $x = 6, y = 5$

7b. $6 - 1 = 5$ and $4(6) - 5 = 19$

APPLYING THE MATHEMATICS

In 9 and 10,
  a. solve each system by substitution.
  b. check your answer by graphing the system. 9b–10b. See margin.

9. $\begin{cases} x + y = 8 \\ y = -3x \end{cases}$ 9a. (-4, 12)

10. $\begin{cases} x = 2y - 10 \\ 5x + 3 = 15 \end{cases}$ 10a. $\left(\frac{12}{5}, \frac{31}{5}\right)$

11. Solve the system $\begin{cases} b = -1.36a + 4.4 \\ 1.2a + 4.58b = -181 \end{cases}$ using a CAS. (40, -50)

12. Angles P and Q are complementary. If $m\angle P = 10x$ and $m\angle Q = 15x$, find x, $m\angle P$, and $m\angle Q$. $x = 3.6$, $m\angle P = 36°$, $m\angle Q = 54°$

13. A business made $120,000 more this year than it did last year. This was an increase of 16% over last year's earnings. If T and L are the earnings (in dollars) for this year and last year, respectively, then $\begin{cases} T = L + 120{,}000 \\ T = 1.16L \end{cases}$. Find the profits for this year and last year. $T = \$870{,}000$, $L = \$750{,}000$

14. Mrs. Rodriguez leaves money to her two favorite charities in her will. Charity A is to get 2.5 times as much money as Charity B. The total amount of money donated in the will is $28,000.
  a. Write a system of equations describing this situation.
  b. Solve to find the amount of money each charity will get.

14a. $\begin{cases} a = 2.5b \\ a + b = 28{,}000 \end{cases}$

14b. Charity A gets $20,000, Charity B gets $8,000

15. Anica received her results for mathematics and verbal achievement tests. Her mathematics score is 40 points higher than her verbal score. Her total score for the two parts is 1,230.
  a. Let v = Anica's verbal score, and m = her mathematics score. Write a system of equations for this situation.
  b. Find Anica's two scores. $m = 635$, $v = 595$

15a. $\begin{cases} m = v + 40 \\ m + v = 1{,}230 \end{cases}$

16. (3, –2); 3 – 5 = –2 and –4(3) + 10 = –2

REVIEW

In 16 and 17 solve the system and check. (Lessons 10-2, 10-1)

16. $\begin{cases} y = x - 5 \\ y = -4x + 10 \end{cases}$

17. $\begin{cases} y = 6x + 6 \\ y = 6x - 2 \end{cases}$ no solution

18. One hot-air balloon takes off from Albuquerque, New Mexico, and rises at a rate of 110 feet per minute. At the same time, another balloon takes off from Santa Fe, New Mexico, and rises at a rate of 80 feet per minute. The altitude of Albuquerque is 4,958 feet and the altitude of Santa Fe is 6,950 feet. (Lesson 10-2)
  a. When are the two balloons at the same altitude? after 66.4 min
  b. What is their altitude at that time? 12,262 ft

19. If $a^3b^{-4}c$ is equal to the reciprocal of $\dfrac{a^{-5}b^2c^3}{a^{-2}b^xc^4}$, find x. (Lessons 8-4, 8-3) $x = -2$

Hot-air balloons hold from 19,000 to 211,000 cubic feet of air and are from 50 to 90 feet tall.

Source: hotairballoons.com

More Uses of Substitution **599**

Additional Answers

9b.

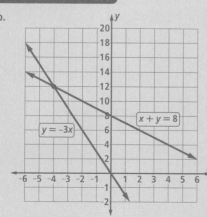

10b.

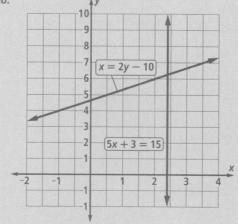

10-3

4 Wrap-Up

Ongoing Assessment

Ask students to write their own word problem using the students in the classroom. For example: *There are 24 students in the classroom, and there are 6 more students wearing jeans than students not wearing jeans.*

Then, ask students to write and solve a system of equations for their problem, and check to see if their solution is correct.

Project Update

Project 1, Cars and Computers, on page 645, relates to the content of this lesson.

In 20 and 21, graph the solution set
  a. on a number line.
  b. in the coordinate plane. (Lessons 6-9, 3-6)

20. $x < 6$
21. $-4y + 2 < 6$

22. In 2002, India ended its Police Pigeon Service. This is a system in which trained pigeons transport messages. The service was used when traditional communication broke down during natural disasters. Suppose a trained pigeon flies 41.3 mph in still air. (**Lesson 5-3**)

  a. How far can it fly in m minutes in still air? $0.688\overline{3}m$
  b. How fast can it fly *with* the wind if the wind speed is s mph?
  c. How fast can it fly *against* the wind if the wind speed is s mph?
  d. If the pigeon is flying down a highway that has a speed limit of 65 mph and there is a 21.9 mph tailwind, would you give it a speeding ticket?
     No, it is flying under the speed limit. Also, it's a bird.

EXPLORATION

23. Here is a nursery rhyme whose earliest traceable publication date is around 1730 in *Folklore,* now in the library of the British Museum. (St. Ives is a village in England.)

As I was going to St. Ives,
I met a man with seven wives.
Each wife had seven sacks,
Each sack had seven cats,
Each cat had seven kits:
Kits, cats, sacks, and wives,
How many were going to St. Ives?

  a. Let $W =$ the number of wives, $S =$ the number of sacks, $C =$ the number of cats, and $K =$ the number of kits. Write three equations that relate two of these variables to each other. $7W = S,\ 7S = C,\ 7C = K$
  b. Find the value of $K + C + S + W$. 2,800
  c. What is an answer to the riddle? Answers vary. Sample answer: 1

20a.

20b.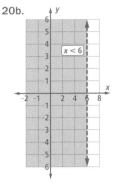
$x < 6$

21a.

21b.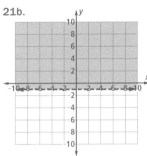

22b. $(41.3 + s)$ mph

22c. $(41.3 - s)$ mph

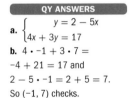

QY ANSWERS

a. $\begin{cases} y = 2 - 5x \\ 4x + 3y = 17 \end{cases}$

b. $4 \cdot {-1} + 3 \cdot 7 =$
$-4 + 21 = 17$ and
$2 - 5 \cdot {-1} = 2 + 5 = 7.$
So $(-1, 7)$ checks.

Lesson Master (10-3B)

10-3B Lesson Master
Questions on SPUR Objectives
See pages 650-653 for objectives.

SKILLS Objective A

In 1-10, a system is given. Solve each system by substitution.

1. $\begin{cases} x = 2y - 4 \\ 3x - 5y = -11 \end{cases}$ 2. $\begin{cases} g = 2h + 3 \\ 4g - 3h = -3 \end{cases}$

   $(-2, 1)$ $(-3, -3)$

3. $\begin{cases} n = 4m - 10 \\ 2n - 3m = 0 \end{cases}$ 4. $\begin{cases} y = 0.4z - 2.4 \\ 4y - 10z = -18 \end{cases}$

   $(4, 6)$ $(-2, 1)$

5. $\begin{cases} a + 7b = 49 \\ b = 7 + a \end{cases}$ 6. $\begin{cases} 4y - 2x = 2 \\ x = \frac{2}{3}y \end{cases}$

   $(0, 7)$ $\left(\frac{1}{2}, \frac{3}{4}\right)$

7. $\begin{cases} 0.2c - 0.4d = -0.4 \\ c = d - 2 \end{cases}$ 8. $\begin{cases} 3x - y = -2 \\ y = 2x + 12 \end{cases}$

   $(-2, 0)$ $(10, 32)$

9. $\begin{cases} x - y = 5 \\ 2x + y = 1 \end{cases}$ 10. $\begin{cases} b = -2a + 2 \\ a = b + 7 \end{cases}$

   $(2, -3)$ $(3, -4)$

446 Algebra

10-3B   page 2

SKILLS Objective A

11. To help Kyle study for a test, Cary asked him to solve the system $\begin{cases} 2x - 6y = 8 \\ 8x - 2y = 10 \end{cases}$ $2x - 6y = 8$
   $x = \frac{6y + 8}{2}$

   Kyle's solution was $(1, -1)$. Check his solution by filling in the missing portions at the right. Was Kyle's solution correct?
   Yes, his solution is correct.

   $x = \dfrac{3y + 4}{}$
   $8\left(\dfrac{3y + 4}{}\right) - 2y = 10$
   $\dfrac{24y + 32}{} - 2y = 10$
   $22y + 32 = 10$
   $22y = \dfrac{-22}{}$
   $y = \dfrac{-1}{}$ and
   $x = 1$

12a. $\begin{cases} 1.5b + 0.75c = 47.25 \\ b + c = 38 \end{cases}$

USES Objective G

12. Students having a brownie and cookie sale sold 38 items and earned a total of $47.25. They sold brownies for $1.50 each and cookies for $0.75 each.

   a. Let $b =$ the number of brownies they sold and $c =$ the number of cookies they sold. Write a system of equations for this situation.
   b. How many cookies did they sell? How many brownies did they sell?
   13 cookies; 25 brownies

13. A teacher is writing a test that is worth 100 points. Some of the questions are worth 4 points each and the rest of the questions are worth 5 points each. There is a total of 23 questions on the test.

   a. Describe the situation with a system of equations. $\begin{cases} x + y = 23 \\ 4x + 5y = 100 \end{cases}$
   b. How many of each kind of question is on the test?
   15 questions worth 4 points each; 8 questions worth 5 points each

Algebra 447

Lesson 10-4

Solving Systems by Addition

Vocabulary

addition method for solving a system

▶ **BIG IDEA** The sum of the left sides of two equations equals the sum of the right sides of those equations.

The numbers $\frac{1}{4}$ and 25% are equal even though they may not look equal; so are $\frac{17}{20}$ and 85%. If you add them, the sums are equal.

$$\frac{1}{4} = 25\% \qquad\qquad \frac{17}{20} = 85\%$$

So $\frac{1}{4} + \frac{17}{20} = 25\% + 85\%$.

Adding on each side, $\frac{22}{20} = 110\%$.

This is one example of the following generalization of the Addition Property of Equality.

Generalized Addition Property of Equality

For all numbers or expressions a, b, c, and d: If $a = b$ and $c = d$, then $a + c = b + d$.

The Generalized Addition Property of Equality can be used to solve some systems. Consider this situation: The sum of two numbers is 5,300. Their difference is 1,200. What are the numbers?

If x and y are the two numbers, with x the greater number, we can write the following system.

$$\begin{cases} x + y = 5{,}300 \\ x - y = 1{,}200 \end{cases}$$

Notice what happens when the left sides are added (combining like terms) and the right sides are added.

$$\begin{array}{r} x + y = 5{,}300 \\ + x - y = 1{,}200 \\ \hline 2x + 0 = 6{,}500 \end{array}$$

Because y and $-y$ sum to 0, the sum of the equations is an equation with only one variable. Solve $2x = 6{,}500$ as usual.

$$x = 3{,}250$$

Mental Math

Find the perimeter of

a. a square with sides of length 6.2x. **24.8x**

b. a regular octagon with sides of length 21ab. **168ab**

c. a regular pentagon with sides of length 4.5m + 1.5n. **22.5m + 7.5n**

Background

The systems in this lesson have one variable in which the coefficient in one of the equations is either the opposite of or is equal to the coefficient in the other equation. In the former case, "adding the equations," which is short for "adding the sides of one equation to the sides of the other equation," yields an equation in one variable and thus solves the system quite easily.

In the latter case, we multiply one of the equations by –1 and then add.

Some teachers prefer to avoid the multiplication step and subtract one equation from the other. Others feel that this leads to too many sign errors. Some teachers like to teach both methods.

Not only do some systems arise of each of these forms, as the examples indicate, but also in order to solve more general systems such as those to be encountered in Lesson 10-5. Students have to be able to solve these.

Lesson 10-4

GOAL

Solve systems in which either addition or subtraction of both sides leads to an equation in one variable.

SPUR Objectives

B Solve systems by addition and multiplication.

G Use systems of linear equations to solve real-world problems.

Materials/Resources

· Lesson Master 10-4A or 10-4B
· Resource Masters 150 and 151
· Scientific or graphing calculator
· Quiz 1

HOMEWORK

Suggestions for Assignment
• Questions 1–25
• Question 26 (extra credit)
• Reading Lesson 10-5
• Covering the Ideas 10-5

Local Standards

1 Warm-Up

You go to a place for breakfast. A sign says "1 egg with a slice of toast, $.99; 2 eggs with a slice of toast, $1.69."

1. From this information, using just arithmetic, calculate what seems to be the price of 1 egg without toast and what seems to be the cost of a slice of toast. **$0.70; $0.29**

2. Write and solve a system of equations to verify your answer to Question 1. $\begin{cases} e + t = 0.99 \\ 2e + t = 1.69 \end{cases}$ **$(e, t) = (0.7, 0.29)$**

3. What should it cost for 3 eggs with 2 pieces of toast? **$2.68**

10-4

2 Teaching

Notes on the Lesson

It is easy to follow the steps in the algorithm in this lesson because the equal signs are aligned and the variables are written in neat columns. Advise students that they are less likely to make errors if they do the same. To emphasize the benefit of having the variables and symbols properly organized, you might want to show a system slightly more complicated than those in the examples. For example, use the following system:

$$\begin{cases} 8x + 3y = 120 \\ -8x + 2y = 10x + 2 \end{cases}$$

It looks like addition is a good strategy, but the 10x on the right gets in the way.

None of the systems in the questions are as complicated as the one above. The questions are set up so that students should not have to perform extensive transformations on the equations. The only transformation needed is illustrated in Example 2—multiplication of both sides of the equation by −1.

The key to Example 1 is to know that tailwinds (with the wind) add speed to a plane and headwinds (against the wind) subtract speed. The addition is vector addition, so if the direction of the wind is not exactly the same as (or exactly the opposite of) the direction in which the plane is flying, the result is not the exact sum (or difference) of the speeds, but here we assume that the directions are the same or the opposite.

Additional Example

Example 1 For two days in a row, gas prices hovered around price *p*. On the first day, they were *d* dollars above price *p*, resulting in a price of $2.19 per gallon. On the second day, they were *d* dollars below price *p*, resulting in a price of $2.07. What price *p* are they hovering around? How much is the price fluctuating day by day? **They are hovering around the price $p = \$2.13$, and fluctuating by amount $d = 0.06$**

To find *y*, substitute 3,250 for *x* in one of the original equations. We choose $x + y = 5,300$.

$$\begin{aligned} x + y &= 5,300 \\ 3,250 + y &= 5,300 \\ y &= 2,050 \end{aligned}$$

The ordered pair (3,250, 2,050) checks in both equations:
$3,250 + 2,050 = 5,300$ and $3,250 - 2,050 = 1,200$.

So the solution to the system $\begin{cases} x + y = 5,300 \\ x - y = 1,200 \end{cases}$ is (3,250, 2,050).

Using the Generalized Addition Property of Equality to eliminate one variable from a system is sometimes called the **addition method for solving a system.** The addition method is an efficient way to solve systems when the coefficients of the same variable are opposites.

Example 1

A pilot flew a small plane 180 miles from North Platte, Nebraska, to Scottsbluff, Nebraska, in 1 hour against the wind. The pilot returned to North Platte in 48 minutes $\left(\frac{48}{60} = \frac{4}{5} \text{ hour}\right)$ with the wind at the plane's back. How fast was the plane flying (without wind)? What was the speed of the wind?

Solution Let A be the average speed of the airplane without wind and W be the speed of the wind, both in miles per hour. The total speed against the wind is then $A - W$, and the speed with the wind is $A + W$. There are two conditions given on these total speeds.

From North Platte to Scottsbluff the average speed of the plane was $\frac{180 \text{ miles}}{1 \text{ hour}} = 180 \frac{\text{miles}}{\text{hour}}$.
This was against the wind, so $A - W = 180$.

From Scottsbluff to North Platte the average speed of the plane was $\frac{180 \text{ miles}}{\frac{4}{5} \text{ hour}} = 225 \frac{\text{miles}}{\text{hour}}$.
This was with the wind, so $A + W = 225$.

We have the system $\begin{cases} A - W = 180 \\ A + W = 225 \end{cases}$.

Now solve the system. Since the coefficients of W are opposites (1 and −1), add the equations.

$$\begin{aligned} A - W &= 180 \\ \underline{A + W} &= \underline{225} \\ 2A &= 405 \qquad \text{Add.} \\ A &= 202.5 \qquad \text{Divide by 2.} \end{aligned}$$

There are more than 8,100 airports in the United States used only by small planes. They have runways shorter than 3,000 feet.

Source: Aircraft Owners and Pilots Association

Accommodating the Learner

The lesson includes many problems that again require students to translate situations into systems of equations. If students are still struggling with that skill, plan to spend extra time on these problems. Consider organizing students into pairs to work on translating a variety of problems.

Substitute 202.5 for A in either of the original equations. We choose the second equation.

$$202.5 + W = 225$$
$$W = 22.5$$

The average speed of the airplane was about 202.5 mph and the speed of the wind was 22.5 mph.

Check Refer to the original question. Against the wind, the plane flew at $202.5 - 22.5$ or 180 mph, so it flew 180 miles in 1 hour. With the wind, the plane flew at $202.5 + 22.5$ or 225 mph. At that rate, in 48 minutes the pilot flew $\frac{48}{60}$ hr $\cdot 225 \frac{mi}{hr} = 180$ miles, which checks with the given conditions.

Sometimes the coefficients of the same variable are equal. In this case, use the Multiplication Property of Equality to multiply both sides of one of the equations by –1. This changes all the numbers in that equation to their opposites. Then you can use the addition method to find solutions to the system.

Example 2

Solve $\begin{cases} 5x + 17y = 1 \\ 5x + 8y = -26 \end{cases}$.

Solution We rewrite the equations and number them to make it easy to refer to them later.

$\begin{cases} 5x + 17y = 1 & \text{Equation \#1} \\ 5x + 8y = -26 & \text{Equation \#2} \end{cases}$

Notice that the coefficients of x in the two equations are equal.

Multiply the second equation by -1. Call the resulting Equation #3.

$-5x - 8y = 26$ Equation #3

Now use the addition method with the first and third equations.

$$\begin{array}{ll} 5x + 17y = 1 & \text{Equation \#1} \\ + \; -5x \; - 8y = 26 & \text{Equation \#3} \\ \hline 9y = 27 & \text{Equation \#1 + Equation \#3} \\ y = 3 \end{array}$$

To find x, substitute 3 for y in one of the original equations.

$$5x + 17(3) = 1 \quad \text{We use Equation \#1.}$$
$$5x + 51 = 1$$
$$5x = -50$$
$$x = -10$$

So $(x, y) = (-10, 3)$.

(continued on next page)

Additional Example
Example 2 Solve the system.
$\begin{cases} -3x + 2y = -11 \\ -3x + 5y = -14 \end{cases}$ $(3, -1)$

Accommodating the Learner ⬆

Include additional word problems that require translation to utilize a variety of skills students have learned. For example, use different units for different values in the problem, thus requiring students to convert before they write the system. Alternately, include problems that will yield systems with fractions. Consider including a problem that will require students to sketch a diagram to solve.

10-4

Notes on the Lesson

Example 3 This example is a linear combination situation similar to those in the previous lesson.

Additional Example

Example 3 A sports clothing store is advertising two deals.

Deal 1: 2 shirts and 2 caps for $32

Deal 2: 2 shirts and 3 caps for $39

At these rates, what is the price of one shirt and what is the price of one cap? (Assume there is no discount for 3 caps.)

Solution

Let S = the price of one shirt.

Let C = the price of one cap.

Find each deal as an equation.

From Deal 1: $2S + 2C = 32$ #1

From Deal 2: _____?_____   #2
$2S + 3C = 39$

Notice the coefficients of S are the same, so multiply the Deal 2 equation by −1.

_____?_____   #3
$-2S - 3C = -39$

Add equations #1 and #3.

_____?_____ $-C = -7$

Does your last equation have only one variable? If so, solve this equation. If not, seek the help of your partner.

$C =$ _____?_____ 7

Substitute this value of C in either equation, and solve for S.
$(S, C) = ($ _?_ , _?_ $)$ 9, 7

How much is one shirt? _?_ $9

How much is one cap? _?_ $7

Check Substitute in both equations.

Equation #1 Does $5 \cdot -10 + 17 \cdot 3 = 1$? Yes.

Equation #2 Does $5 \cdot -10 + 8 \cdot 3 = -26$? Yes.

GUIDED

Example 3

A resort hotel offers two weekend specials.

Plan A: 3 nights with 6 meals for $564

Plan B: 3 nights with 2 meals for $488

At these rates, what is the cost of one night's lodging and what is the average cost per meal? (Assume there is no discount for 6 meals.)

Solution Let N = price of one night's lodging.

Let M = average price of one meal.

Write an equation to describe each weekend special.

From Plan A: $3N + 6M = 564$ Equation #1

From Plan B: _____?_____   Equation #2 $3N + 2M = 488$

Notice the coefficients of N are the same, so multiply Equation #2 by −1.

_____?_____   Equation #3 $-3N - 2M = -488$

_____?_____   Add Equations #1 and #3. $4M = 76$

Does your last equation have only one variable? If so, solve this equation. If not, ask someone for help.

$M =$ _____?_____ 19

Substitute this value of M in either equation, and solve for N.

$(N, M) = ($ _?_ , _?_ $)$ 150; 19

What is the price of one night's lodging? _____?_____ $150

What is the average cost of a meal? _____?_____ $19

The average hotel room rate in the United States in 2006 was $96.42 per night.

Source: Smith Travel Research

Questions

COVERING THE IDEAS

1. **a.** When is adding equations an appropriate method for solving systems? when the coefficients of the same variable are opposites

   b. What is the goal in adding equations to solve systems?
   to eliminate one variable from a system

2. Which property allows you to add to both sides of two equations to get a new equation? the Generalized Addition Property of Equality

---

Extension

Students often learn just as much from correcting errors as they do from seeing a problem worked correctly. Give students the opportunity to be the teacher. Create a worksheet that looks like a quiz a student has completed. When you write the solutions, make sure some answers are correct, and that others include some common mistakes students make with systems of equations. Give students worksheets and red pens and ask them to correct the paper. After they have worked individually for a short time, organize students into groups and allow them to compare results.

In 3 and 4, a system is given.

   a. Solve the system.

   b. Check your solution.

3. $\begin{cases} 3x + 9y = 75 \\ -3x - y = 15 \end{cases}$

4. $\begin{cases} a + b = -22 \\ a - b = 4 \end{cases}$

5. The sum of two numbers is 1,776 and their difference is 1,492. What are the numbers? **1,634 and 142**

6. Find two numbers whose sum is 20 and whose difference is 20. **20 and 0**

7. When is it useful to multiply an equation by –1 as a first step in solving a system?

8. Airlines schedule about 5.5 hours of flying time for an A320 Airbus to fly from Dulles International Airport near Washington, D.C., to Los Angeles International Airport. Airlines schedule about 4.5 hours of flying time for the reverse direction. The distance between these airports is about 2,300 miles. They allow about 0.4 hour for takeoff and landing.

   a. From this information, estimate (to the nearest 5 mph) the average wind speed the airlines assume in making their schedule. **45 mph**

   b. What average airplane speed (to the nearest 5 mph) do the airlines assume in making their schedule? **465 mph**

In 9 and 10, solve the system.

9. $\begin{cases} 14x - 5y = 9 \\ 17x - 5y = 27 \end{cases}$
$(x, y) = (6, 15)$

10. $\begin{cases} 17m + 7n = 8 \\ 17m + 5n = 13 \end{cases}$
$(m, n) = \left(\frac{3}{2}, -\frac{5}{2}\right)$

11. $(N, M) = (150, 19)$ is the solution to the system of equations
$\begin{cases} 3N + 6M = 564 \\ 3N + 2M = 488 \end{cases}$ in Example 3. Check this solution.
$3(150) + 6(19) = 564, 3(150) + 2(19) = 488$

12. A hotel offers the following specials. Plan A includes a two-night stay and one meal for $199. Plan B includes a 2-night stay and 4 meals for $247. What price is this per night and per meal?
$91.50 per night, $16 per meal

APPLYING THE MATHEMATICS

In 13 and 14, solve the system.

13. $\begin{cases} 2x - 6y = 34 \\ x = 2 - 6y \end{cases}$
$(x, y) = \left(12, -\frac{5}{3}\right)$

14. $\begin{cases} \frac{1}{4}z + \frac{3}{4}w = \frac{1}{2} \\ \frac{7}{4}w + \frac{1}{4}z = \frac{3}{8} \end{cases}$ $(w, z) = \left(-\frac{1}{8}, \frac{19}{8}\right)$

3a. $x = -\frac{35}{4}, y = \frac{45}{4}$

3b. $-3\left(-\frac{35}{4}\right) - \frac{45}{4} = 15$
$3\left(-\frac{35}{4}\right) + 9\left(\frac{45}{4}\right) = 75$

4a. $a = -9, b = -13$

4b. $-9 + -13 = -22$
$-9 - -13 = 4$

7. when one of the coefficients for a variable in one equation is the same as the variable's coefficient in another equation

---

3 Assignment

Recommended Assignment

- Questions 1–25
- Question 26 (extra credit)
- Reading Lesson 10-5
- Covering the Ideas 10-5

Notes on the Questions

Questions 13 and 14 Both systems have the variables in different orders in the equations. Students who commute the addition in one of the equations will probably solve the problems correctly. You should make sure that students who have not commuted in the first equations have not equated $2x - 6y$ with $6y - 2x$.

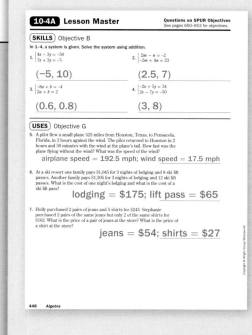

10-4

Notes on the Questions

Question 26 Students of previous UCSMP courses may have studied this idea in some detail. You might ask students to use this process to write $0.\overline{9}$ as a fraction. ($d = 0.\overline{9}$; $10d = 9.\overline{9}$; so $10d - d = 9.\overline{9} - 0.\overline{9} = 9$, so $9d = 9$ and $d = 1$) Many students will be surprised by the result. As further verification, they can add $0.\overline{3} + 0.\overline{6} = 0.\overline{9}$ by converting to fractions. But caution that $0.\overline{4} + 0.\overline{7} \neq 1.\overline{1}$.

15. As you know, $\frac{3}{5} = 60\%$ and $\frac{3}{8} = 37.5\%$.
    a. Is it true that $\frac{3}{5} - \frac{3}{8} = 60\% - 37.5\%$? Justify your answer.
    b. Is it true that $\frac{3}{5} \cdot \frac{3}{8} = 60\% \cdot 37.5\%$? Justify your answer.

16. In 2006, the tallest person playing professional basketball in the Women's National Basketball Association (WNBA) was Margo Dydek. The shortest person was Debbie Black. When they stood next to each other, Margo was 23 in. taller. If one stood on the other's head, they would have stood 12 ft 5 in. tall. How tall is each player? **Margo is 7'2", Debbie is 5'3"**

15a. yes; by the Generalized Addition Property of Equality

15b. Answers vary. Sample answer: Yes; because $\frac{3}{5} = 60\%$, they are simply different ways of writing the same value.

REVIEW

In 17 and 18, solve by using any method. (Lessons 10-3, 10-2, 10-1)

17. $\begin{cases} y = 2x - 3 \\ y = -8x + 6 \end{cases}$ $(x, y) = (0.9, -1.2)$

18. $\begin{cases} A = -5n \\ B = 6n \\ 4A + B = 39 \end{cases}$ $n = -\frac{39}{14}, A = \frac{195}{14}, B = -\frac{117}{7}$

19. a. Solve $x^2 + 3x - 28 = 0$. $x = -7, x = 4$
    b. Find the x-intercepts of the graph of $y = x^2 + 3x - 28$. (Lesson 9-5) $-7, 4$

20. The formula $d = 0.04s^2 + 1.5s$ gives the approximate distance d in feet needed to stop a particular car traveling on dry pavement at a speed of s miles per hour. How much farther will this car travel before stopping if it is traveling at 65 mph instead of 50 mph? (Lesson 9-3) **91.5 ft**

21. Let $f(x) = \sqrt{2x - 9}$. (Lessons 8-6, 7-6, 7-5)
    a. What is the domain of f? $\left\{x: x \geq \frac{9}{2}\right\}$
    b. What is the range of f? **All nonnegative numbers**

22. Simplify $x^{-1} + x - \frac{1}{x}$. (Lessons 8-4, 8-3) x

23. Find the slope of line ℓ pictured below. (Lesson 6-2) $-\frac{b}{a}$

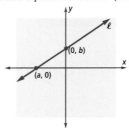

Margo Dydek

Debbie Black

24. In 2005, the total revenues of a cell phone company increased 5.5% from the previous year to $36.84 billion. What were the company's revenues in 2004? (**Lesson 4-1**)
approximately $34.92 billion

25. Solve $38(212 - x) = 0$ in your head. (**Lesson 3-4**) $x = 212$

EXPLORATION

26. Subtracting equations is part of a process that can be used to find simple fractions for repeating decimals. For example, to find a fraction for $0.\overline{72} = 0.7272727272...$, first let $d = 0.\overline{72}$. Then multiply both sides of the equation by an appropriate power of 10. Here we multiply by 10^2 because $0.\overline{72}$ has a two-digit block that repeats.

$$100d = 72.\overline{72} \qquad \text{Equation \#1}$$
$$d = 0.\overline{72} \qquad \text{Equation \#2}$$

Subtract the second equation from the first.

$$99d = 72 \qquad \text{Equation \#1} - \text{Equation \#2}$$

Solve for d and simplify the fraction.

$$d = \tfrac{72}{99} \text{ or } d = \tfrac{8}{11}$$

A calculator shows that $\tfrac{8}{11} = 0.7272727272....$

a. Use the above process to find a simple fraction equal to $0.\overline{15}$. $\tfrac{5}{33}$

b. Modify the process to find a simple fraction equal to $0.\overline{902}$. $\tfrac{902}{999}$

c. Find a simple fraction equal to $0.\overline{123456}$. $\tfrac{41,152}{333,333}$

Solving Systems by Addition **607**

10-4

4 Wrap-Up

Ongoing Assessment

Create a variety of transparencies containing either systems of equations or word problems that can be translated into systems of equations. Show them one at a time and ask students to tell which of the methods for solving equations would best fit with the problem. For the word problems, ask them to translate the problem into a system on their own papers before they tell the answer.

10-4B Lesson Master

Questions on SPUR Objectives
See pages 650–653 for objectives.

SKILLS Objective B

In 1–8, a system is given. Solve the system using addition.

1. $\begin{cases} 3x - 2y = -5 \\ 4x + 2y = -16 \end{cases}$ 2. $\begin{cases} 3r - 5s = -7 \\ -3r + 2s = 1 \end{cases}$

$(-3, -2)$ $(1, 2)$

3. $\begin{cases} 2m - n = 4 \\ 1.2m - 0.3n = 1.5 \end{cases}$ 4. $\begin{cases} x - y = -\frac{1}{5} \\ 10x + 5y = 7 \end{cases}$

$(\tfrac{1}{2}, -3)$ $(\tfrac{2}{5}, \tfrac{3}{5})$

5. $\begin{cases} 3a - 2b = -8 \\ -3a + 4b = 16 \end{cases}$ 6. $\begin{cases} \frac{1}{2}m - n = -30 \\ m + n = 15 \end{cases}$

$(0, 4)$ $(-10, 25)$

7. $\begin{cases} 2a + b = -80 \\ -3a + b = 120 \end{cases}$ 8. $\begin{cases} 4x - 2y = 0 \\ 4x + y = 0 \end{cases}$

$(-40, 0)$ $(0, 0)$

Algebra **449**

10-4B page 2

9. The ordered pair $(H, K) = (134, 256)$ is the solution to the system of equations $\begin{cases} 5H + 6K = 2,206 \\ -8H + 3K = -304 \end{cases}$ Check the solution in both equations.

$5(134) + 6(256) = 2,206$ and $-8(134) + 3(256) = -304$

10. Is $(x, y) = (-100, 3)$ a solution to the system of equations $\begin{cases} 4x - 2y = -406 \\ 3x + 5y = -315 \end{cases}$ Explain.

No, because $3(-100) + 5(3) \ne -315.$

USES Objective G

11. Two people paddle a canoe 8 miles upstream in two hours. Then they turn around and paddle 8 miles downstream in one hour. If they are paddling at the same rate both upstream and downstream, how fast are they paddling? How fast is the current?

paddling rate = 6 mph; current = 2 mph

12. A family has adopted a total of 13 cats and dogs from the local animal shelter. The number of cats they have is 2 less than twice the number of dogs. How many cats and dogs do they have?

8 cats, 5 dogs

13. At a furniture store, you can purchase 2 floor lamps and 3 table lamps for $360, or 3 floor lamps and 1 table lamp for $330. What is the cost of one floor lamp? What is the cost of one table lamp?

floor lamp = $90; table lamp = $60

14. On a lunch menu, a turkey sandwich with a cup of soup is $6.00 and a half of a turkey sandwich with a cup of soup is $3.75. Assuming the half sandwich costs exactly half as much as the whole sandwich, how much does the cup of soup cost?

$1.50

450 Algebra

Lesson
10-5
Solving Systems by Multiplication

GOAL

Solve linear systems by either addition or subtraction of both sides of the equations and learn to solve the general system of two linear equations and two variables.

SPUR Objectives

B Solve systems by addition and multiplication.

G Use systems of linear equations to solve real-world problems.

Materials/Resources

· Lesson Master 10-5A or 10-5B
· Resource Master 152
· Scientific or graphing calculator

HOMEWORK

Suggestions for Assignment

• Questions 1–23
• Question 24 (extra credit)
• Reading Lesson 10-6
• Covering the Ideas 10-6

Local Standards

1 Warm-Up

State each form or property.

1. Standard form of an equation of a line $Ax + By = C$
2. Slope-intercept form of an equation of a line $y = mx + b$
3. Point-slope form of an equation of a line $y - k = m(x - h)$
4. Distributive Property of Multiplication over Addition For all real numbers a, b, and c, $c(a + b) = ca + cb$.
5. Multiplication Property of Equality For all real numbers a, b, and c, if $a = b$, then $ca = cb$.

▶ **BIG IDEA** An effective first step in solving some systems is to multiply both sides of one of the equations by a carefully chosen number.

Recall that there are three common forms for equations of lines.

	Form	Example
Standard	$Ax + By = C$	$3x + 8y = 20$
Slope-Intercept	$y = mx + b$	$y = -2x + 1$
Point-Slope	$y - k = m(x - h)$	$y - 50 = \frac{3}{4}(x - 20)$

Mental Math

Classify the angle with the given measure as acute, right, or obtuse.

a. 134° obtuse

b. 84° acute

c. 0.23° acute

The substitution method described in Lessons 10-2 and 10-3 is convenient for solving systems in which one or both equations are in slope-intercept form. The addition method studied in Lesson 10-4 is convenient for solving systems in which both equations are in standard form and the coefficients of one variable are either equal or opposites. However, not all systems fall into one of these two categories.

Consider the following system.

$$\begin{cases} 3x - 4y = 7 \\ 6x - 5y = 20 \end{cases}$$

Adding or subtracting the two equations will not result in an equation with just one variable, because the x and the y terms are neither equal nor opposites. Substitution could be used, but it introduces fractions.

An easier method uses the Multiplication Property of Equality to create an *equivalent system* of equations. **Equivalent systems** are systems with exactly the same solutions. Notice that if you multiply both sides of the first equation by –2, the x terms of the resulting system have opposite coefficients.

Background

This lesson illustrates the following problem-solving strategy: If you cannot solve a problem, then transform it into a simpler one you can solve. In one step, any linear system of the form $ax + by = c$; $dx + ey = f$ can be transformed into a system in which the addition process of the previous lesson can be utilized.

The multiplication method is a very powerful way to solve systems that have integer coefficients. But even systems with

noninteger coefficients can be solved with the multiplication approach.

Consider $\begin{cases} 2x + y = 3 \\ x - \frac{1}{3}y = 4 \end{cases}$.

If the second equation is multiplied by 3, not only have you cleared the fractions, but also the result is the equivalent system $\begin{cases} 2x + y = 3 \\ 3x - y = 12 \end{cases}$, which is ready for the addition method.

Example 1

Solve the system $\begin{cases} 3x - 4y = 7 \\ 6x - 5y = 20 \end{cases}$.

Solution 1 Multiply both sides of the first equation by −2 and apply the Distributive Property.

$$\begin{cases} 3x - 4y = 7 \\ 6x - 5y = 20 \end{cases} \xrightarrow{\text{multiply by -2}} \begin{cases} -2(3x - 4y) = -2(7) \\ 6x - 5y = 20 \end{cases}$$

$$\begin{cases} -6x + 8y = -14 \\ 6x - 5y = 20 \end{cases}$$

$$3y = 6 \qquad \text{Add the equations.}$$

$$y = 2 \qquad \text{Solve for } y.$$

To find x, substitute 2 for y in one of the original equations.

$$3x - 4y = 7$$
$$3x - 4 \cdot 2 = 7$$
$$3x - 8 = 7$$
$$3x = 15$$
$$x = 5$$

So the solution is $(x, y) = (5, 2)$.

Solution 2 Multiply both sides of the second equation by $-\frac{1}{2}$. This also makes the coefficients of x opposites.

$$\begin{cases} 3x - 4y = 7 \\ 6x - 5y = 20 \end{cases} \xrightarrow{\text{multiply by } -\frac{1}{2}} \begin{cases} 3x - 4y = 7 \\ -\frac{1}{2}(6x - 5y) = -\frac{1}{2}(20) \end{cases}$$

$$\begin{cases} 3x - 4y = 7 \\ -3x + \frac{5}{2}y = -10 \end{cases}$$

$$-\frac{3}{2}y = -3 \qquad \text{Add.}$$

$$y = 2$$

Proceed as in Solution 1 to find x. Again $(x, y) = (5, 2)$.

Example 1 shows that the solution is the same no matter which equation is multiplied by a number. The goal is to obtain opposite coefficients for one of the variables in the two equations. Then the resulting equations can be added to eliminate that variable. This technique is sometimes called the **multiplication method for solving a system**.

 QY

▶ QY

$$\begin{cases} 7x + 3y = 22.5 \\ 2x - 12y = 45 \end{cases}$$
$$\downarrow$$
$$\begin{cases} 28x + 12y = 90 \\ 2x - 12y = 45 \end{cases}$$

a. Explain what operation occurred to go from the first system to the second system.

b. Finish solving the system.

2 Teaching

Notes on the Lesson

This is a good lesson in which to ask students to compare and contrast the structure of each example.

Example 1 This example requires that only one equation be multiplied by a number. The two solutions show students that either equation can be multiplied to eliminate the variable x. The answer is the same either way the problem is solved.

Additional Example

Example 1 Solve the following system.
$$\begin{cases} 2x - 3y = -1 \\ 6x - 2y = -24 \end{cases} (x, y) = (-5, -3)$$

Vocabulary Development

Review the terms *standard form* and *slope-intercept form* with students. Remind them that the term *form* in this context means that the same equation can be written multiple ways, depending on the way it is to be used.

10-5

Notes on the Lesson

Example 2 This example illustrates the strategy in which each equation is multiplied by a different number. You might wish to mention that both equations do not *have* to be multiplied by some number. If you multiplied the first equation by $\frac{4}{3}$, then the resulting equation would be $-4m + \frac{8}{3}n = 8$ and the two equations could be added. In the text we multiply both equations by numbers to avoid fractions. However, because computers are not bothered by complicated numbers, they are typically programmed to multiply only one equation.

Very frequently there is a best choice for multiplication—one that will keep the products small and minimize the arithmetic needed for the rest of the solution. Do not expect your students to make the ideal choice every time. Students need experience with the algorithm before they become skilled at selecting the most efficient multipliers.

Stress to students that a good strategy is to look for coefficients of the same variable that are multiples of each other. If such a pair of coefficients exists, then only one multiplication is needed.

Additional Example

Example 2 Solve the system.
$\begin{cases} 6m + 5n = 38 \\ 4m - 7n = -16 \end{cases}$ $(m, n) = (3, 4)$

Sometimes it is necessary to multiply *each* equation by a different number before adding.

Example 2
Solve the system $\begin{cases} -3m + 2n = 6 \\ 4m + 5n = -31 \end{cases}$.

Solution The idea is to multiply by a number so that one variable in the resulting system has a pair of opposite coefficients. To make the coefficients of m opposites, multiply the first equation by 4 and the second equation by 3.

$$\begin{cases} -3m + 2n = 6 \\ 4m + 5n = -31 \end{cases} \xrightarrow[\text{multiply by 3}]{\text{multiply by 4}} \begin{cases} -12m + 8n = 24 \\ 12m + 15n = -93 \end{cases}$$

Now add. $23n = -69$
$n = -3$

To find m, substitute -3 for n in either original equation. We use the first equation.

$-3m + 2 \cdot (-3) = 6$
$-3m - 6 = 6$
$-3m = 12$
$m = -4$

So $(m, n) = (-4, -3)$.

Check You should check your solution by substituting for m and n in each original equation.

Many situations naturally lead to linear equations in standard form. This results in a linear system that can be solved using the multiplication method.

Example 3
A marching band currently has 48 musicians and 18 people in the flag corps. The drum majors wish to form hexagons and squares like those diagrammed at the right. Are there enough members to create the formations with no people left over? If so, how many hexagons and how many squares can be made? If not, give a recommendation for the fewest people the drum majors would need to recruit and how many hexagons and how many squares could be made.

Hexagon
Flag bearer in center

Square
Two musicians in the center

Accommodating the Learner

Students should be able to quickly find the least common multiple of two numbers. If they have this skill, they will have less trouble recognizing that they can use multiplication to change $-3m$ and $4m$ into $-12m$. Similarly, they will be able to see that it will yield smaller numbers to change $6m$ and $4m$ into $12m$ than to change $5n$ and $7n$ into $35n$. The stronger their skills are with finding the least common multiple of two numbers, the less trouble they will have in this section. Consider reviewing how to find the least common multiple or providing students with a review worksheet to prepare for using the topic in class.

Solution Consider the entire formation to include h hexagons and s squares. There are two conditions in the system: one for musicians and one for the flag corps.

There are $6 \frac{\text{musicians}}{\text{hexagon}}$ and $2 \frac{\text{musicians}}{\text{square}}$.

So $6h + 2s = 48$ musicians.

There are $1 \frac{\text{flag bearer}}{\text{hexagon}}$ and $4 \frac{\text{flag bearers}}{\text{square}}$.

So $h + 4s = 18$ flag bearers.

To find h, multiply the first equation by -2, and add the result to the second equation.

$$\begin{array}{r} -12h + -4s = -96 \\ h + 4s = 18 \\ \hline -11h = -78 \\ h = 7.\overline{09} \end{array}$$

Because h is not a positive integer in this solution, these formations will not work with 48 musicians and 18 flag bearers.

-78 is not divisible by -11, but -77 is. By recruiting one additional member to the flag corps we get a number divisible by -11. This would create the following system.

$$\begin{array}{r} -12h + -4s = -96 \\ h + 4s = 19 \\ \hline -11h = -77 \\ h = 7 \end{array}$$

Now $h = 7$. Substituting for h in the second equation of this new system, you find that $s = 3$.

All 48 musicians and 19 flag bearers could be arranged into 7 hexagons and 3 squares, so the drum major needs to recruit 1 more flag bearer.

Check Making 7 hexagons would use 42 musicians and 7 flag bearers. Making 3 squares would use 6 musicians and 12 flag bearers. This setup uses exactly 48 musicians and 19 flag bearers.

When the equations in a system are not given in either standard or slope-intercept form, it is wise to rewrite the equations in one of these forms before proceeding. For example, to solve the system below, you could use one of three methods.

$$\begin{cases} n - 3 = \frac{3}{2}m \\ 4m + 5n = -31 \end{cases}$$

Marching bands perform in competitions, at sporting events, and in parades.

Solving Systems by Multiplication **611**

Notes on the Lesson

Example 3 In this example, emphasize that the multiplication method will always find a solution to the *system* if one exists, but the *situation* requires that the solution be an integer. This Example is related to Questions 5 and 24.

Additional Example

Example 3 A homeowner wishes to put 6 new lamps around her home. She wishes to use a total of 15 light bulbs. Lamp style *A* uses two bulbs, and lamp style *B* uses three bulbs. Can the homeowner use a certain number of each kind of lamp and use exactly 15 bulbs? If so, how many lamps of each style will she use? The homeowner will use 3 of each type of lamp.

Accommodating the Learner

Once students have mastered the new method, provide them with extra practice in deciding which method is easiest to use in solving a system. Provide students with a variety of systems to solve. For each method of solving systems, include at least one system that is best solved using that method. Encourage students to find the simplest and shortest method to solve each system, and describe when each method is easiest to use.

10-5

Method 1 Multiply the first equation by 2 to eliminate fractions.

$$\begin{cases} 2n - 6 = 3m \\ 4m + 5n = -31 \end{cases}$$

Add $-3m$ and 6 to both sides of the first equation. The result is the system of Example 2, which is in standard form.

Method 2 Add 3 to both sides of the first equation.

$$\begin{cases} n = \frac{3}{2}m + 3 \\ 4m + 5n = -31 \end{cases}$$

To finish solving this system you could use substitution by substituting n into the second equation.

Method 3 Use substitution on a CAS to solve the system.

Step 1 Use the SOLVE command to solve one of the equations for one of the variables. We choose the first equation and solve for n.

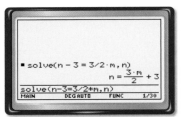

Step 2 Substitute this value for n into the second equation and solve for m. Most CAS will allow you to copy and paste so that you do not have to type expressions multiple times. The display shows $m = -4$.

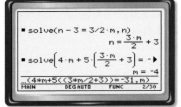

Step 3 Then substitute -4 for m into the first equation to get $n = -3$.

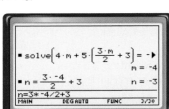

Questions

COVERING THE IDEAS

1. Consider the system $\begin{cases} 5x + 3d = 9 \\ 2x + d = 26 \end{cases}$.

   a. **Fill in the Blanks** If the ___?___ equation is multiplied by ___?___, then adding the equations will eliminate ___?___.

   b. Solve the system. $(x, d) = (69, -112)$

1a. Answers vary.
Sample answer:
second; -3; d

2. A problem on a test was to solve the system $\begin{cases} -8n + m = -19 \\ 4n - 3m = -8 \end{cases}$.

Three students used three different methods to solve the system. Their first steps are shown.

Annisha's Method	Maxandra's Method	Victor's Method
$\begin{cases} -8n + m = -19 \\ 8n - 6m = -16 \end{cases}$	$\begin{cases} m = -19 + 8n \\ 4n - 3m = -8 \end{cases}$	$\begin{cases} -24n + 3m = -57 \\ 4n - 3m = -8 \end{cases}$

a. Which student(s) used substitution to solve the system?

b. Which variable will Annisha's method eliminate? Explain what she did to make an equivalent system.

c. Which variable will Victor's method eliminate? Explain what he did to make an equivalent system.

d. Pick one of the methods and finish solving the system.

3. Consider the system $\begin{cases} 7r - 3s = 9 \\ 2r + 5s = 26 \end{cases}$.

a. By what two numbers can you multiply the equations so that, if you add the results, you will eliminate r?

b. By what two numbers can you multiply the equations so that, if you add the results, you will eliminate s?

c. Use one of these methods to solve the system. $(r, s) = (3, 4)$

4. Consider the system $\begin{cases} 10t + u = 85 \\ 2t + 3u = 31 \end{cases}$.

a. Write an equivalent system that would eliminate t first.

b. Write an equivalent system that would eliminate u first.

c. Use one of the methods to solve the system. $(t, u) = (8, 5)$

5. A marching band has 60 musicians and 30 flag bearers. They wish to form pentagons and squares like those diagrammed at the right.

a. If the formation has 3 pentagons and 4 squares, how many musicians and flag bearers will be involved? **31 musicians and 26 flag bearers**

b. Is it possible to change the numbers of pentagons and squares so that every person will have a spot? If so, how many of each formation will be needed? **No, it is not possible.**

6. Solve the system $\begin{cases} n + 7 = \frac{1}{3}m \\ 7m - 3n = 57 \end{cases}$. $(m, n) = (6, -5)$

2a. Maxandra

2b. n; she multiplied the second equation by 2.

2c. m; he multiplied the first equation by 3.

2d. $(m, n) = (7, 3.25)$

3a. Answers vary. Sample answer: The first equation can be multiplied by 2 and the second equation can be multiplied by −7.

3b. The first equation can be multiplied by 5 and the second equation can be multiplied by 3.

4a. $\begin{cases} 10t + u = 85 \\ -10t - 15u = -155 \end{cases}$

4b. $\begin{cases} -30t - 3u = -255 \\ 2t + 3u = 31 \end{cases}$

Solving Systems by Multiplication **613**

Extension

Use this lesson as an opportunity to review fractions. By using systems for which students will have to solve by multiplying to clear denominators, they can see that fractional systems all have related systems with integer numbers. For example, ask students to solve the following system:

$\begin{cases} \frac{1}{2}x + \frac{2}{3}y = 3 \\ \frac{3}{5}x + \frac{1}{2}y = \frac{27}{10} \end{cases}$.

They will find that they can multiply the equations by 6 and 10, respectively, to obtain the following system:

$\begin{cases} 3x + 4y = 18 \\ 6x + 5y = 27 \end{cases}$.

Include a variety of fractional systems on a worksheet for students to do individually or in pairs.

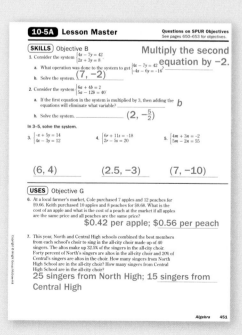

Notes on the Questions

Question 11 There are a number of places in this question where students can get confused. It should be discussed.

Question 15 Many students may find it easier to answer this question without algebra. You might ask them to apply their method to Questions 13 and 14.

Question 18 This question applies the Putting-Together Model for Addition.

In 7–10, solve the system.

7. $\begin{cases} 24x + 15y = 20 \\ 4x + 3y = 5 \end{cases}$ $(x, y) = (-\frac{5}{4}, \frac{10}{3})$

8. $\begin{cases} 7a - 8b = 1 \\ 6a - 7b = 1 \end{cases}$ $(a, b) = (-1, -1)$

9. $\begin{cases} 9y + x = -8 \\ 2 = y - x \end{cases}$ $(x, y) = (-\frac{13}{5}, -\frac{3}{5})$

10. $\begin{cases} 113.2 = 4x - 2y \\ 331.4 = 6x + 5y \end{cases}$ $(x, y) = (38.4, 20.2)$

APPLYING THE MATHEMATICS

11. Solve the system by first rewriting each equation in standard

    form. $\begin{cases} 0.2x + 0.3(x + 4) = 0.16y \\ 0.04y - 0.07 = 0.08x \end{cases}$ $(x, y) = (-5.\overline{1}, -8.47\overline{2})$

12. Milo feels that the probability that he will be elected to the student council is $\frac{1}{10}$ of the probability that he will not be elected. What does Milo think is the probability that he will be elected? (Remember that the sum of the probabilities that he will be elected and not be elected is 1.) $\frac{1}{11}$

13. A test has m multiple-choice (MC) questions and e extended-response (ER) questions. If the MC questions are worth 2 points each and the ER questions are worth 7 points each, the test will be worth a total of 95 points. If the MC questions are worth 3 points each and the ER questions are worth 8 points each, the test will be worth a total of 130 points. How many MC questions and how many ER questions are on the test?
    5 ER, 30 MC

Three students are participating in student council elections.

14. A security guard counted 82 vehicles in a parking lot. The only vehicles in the lot were cars and motorcycles. To double-check his count, the security guard counted 300 wheels. How many motorcycles and how many cars are in the parking lot?
    14 motorcycles, 68 cars

15. Delise and Triston's class went on a field trip to a local farm. The farm raised cows and chickens. Delise counted 27 heads and Triston counted 76 legs. How many cows and how many chickens are on the farm?

    a. Answer this question by solving a system. **11 cows, 16 chickens**

    b. Write a few sentences explaining how to answer the question without using algebra.

15b. Answers vary. Sample answer: By assuming there will be 14 chickens and 13 cows, a person would count 80 legs. For every cow replaced by a chicken, we lose 2 legs. Therefore, someone could conclude that there were 16 chickens and 11 cows.

REVIEW

In 16 and 17, solve the system using any method.
(Lessons 10-4, 10-3, 10-2, 10-1)

16. $\begin{cases} 6x + 2y = 26 \\ 4x + 2y = 8 \end{cases}$ $(x, y) = (9, -14)$

17. $\begin{cases} y = \frac{2}{3}x - 4 \\ y = \frac{1}{4}x + 1 \end{cases}$ $(x, y) = (12, 4)$

18. The two diagrams below illustrate a system of equations.
(Lessons 10-4, 10-2)

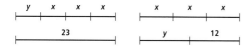

      y   x   x   x   x   x   x

         23   y   12

a. Write an equation for the diagram at the left. $y + 3x = 23$

b. Write an equation for the diagram at the right. $3x = y + 12$

c. Solve the system for x and y. $(x, y) = \left(\frac{35}{6}, \frac{11}{2}\right)$

d. Check your work.

18d. $\frac{11}{2} + 3\left(\frac{35}{6}\right) = 23$

$3\left(\frac{35}{6}\right) = \frac{11}{2} + 2$

19. Ashlyn has $600 and saves $30 each week. Janet has $1,500 and spends $30 each week. (Lesson 10-2)

a. How many weeks from now will they each have the same amount of money? 15 wk

b. What will this amount be? $1,050

20. A 16-foot ladder leans against a house. If the base of the ladder is 6 feet from the base of the house, at what height does the top of the ladder touch the house? (Lessons 9-1, 8-6) 14.83 ft

In 21 and 22, consider a garage with a roof pitch of $\frac{3}{12}$ at the right. The garage is to be 20 feet wide.
(Lessons 6-3, 5-9)

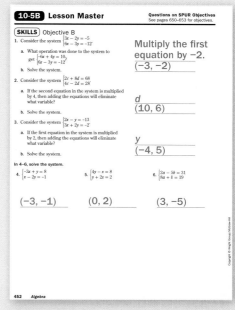

21. What is the slope of $\overline{AB}$? $-\frac{1}{4}$

22. a. What is the height h of the roof? 2.5 ft

b. Find the length r of one rafter.
approximately 10.3 ft

23. True or False (Lesson 5-6)

a. Probabilities are numbers from 0 to 1. true

b. A probability of 1 means that an event must occur. true

c. A relative frequency of –1 cannot occur. true

EXPLORATION

24. Create formations of a college band consisting of 110 musicians and a flag corps of 36 with no members left over.
Answers vary. Sample answer:

2 of these   24 of these   2 of these

QY ANSWERS

a. The first equation was multiplied by 4.

b. $(x, y) = (4.5, -3)$

10-5

4 Wrap-Up

Ongoing Assessment

Organize students into pairs, and provide them with the following system:
$$\begin{cases} 2k - 5m = -9 \\ 3k + m = -5 \end{cases}$$

Ask students to solve the system by using multiplication and adding the equations. Ask one student in the pair to eliminate k, and the other to eliminate m. Then, ask students to compare answers and methods. Ask them to decide if one method was easier than the other, and why.

Project Update

Project 3, Systems with More Variables, on page 645, relates to the content of this lesson.

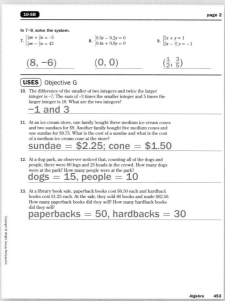

Lesson 10-6

Lesson 10-6

Systems and Parallel Lines

GOAL

Use the slope-intercept form of the equation to show when lines are or are not parallel.

SPUR Objectives

F Determine whether a system has 0, 1, or infinitely many solutions.

G Use systems of linear equations to solve real-world problems.

I Find solutions to systems of equations by graphing.

Materials/Resources

· Lesson Master 10-6A or 10-6B
· Resource Masters 2, 153, and 154
· Graphing calculator

HOMEWORK

Suggestions for Assignment

• Questions 1–21
• Question 22 (extra credit)
• Reading Lesson 10-7
• Covering the Ideas 10-7

Local Standards

---

1 Warm-Up

1. List all combinations of D dimes and Q quarters whose total value is $2.85. **1, 11; 6, 9; 11, 7; 16, 5; 21, 3; 26, 1**

2. Give an equation of a line that contains all the ordered pairs (D, Q) from Question 1. **$10D + 25Q = 285$**

3. Give an equation of a line that contains all the ordered pairs (D, Q) whose total value is $1.60. **$10D + 25Q = 160$**

4. Why must the lines from Questions 2 and 3 be parallel? **Any selection of dimes and quarters whose total value is $1.60 cannot at the same time have a total value of $2.85, so no point can satisfy both equations.**

▶ **BIG IDEA** Systems having 0, 1, or infinitely many solutions correspond to lines having 0 or 1 point of intersection, or being coincident.

The idea behind parallel lines is that they "go in the same direction." So we call two lines parallel if and only if they are in the same plane and either are the same line or do not intersect. All vertical lines are parallel to each other. So are all horizontal lines. But not all oblique lines are parallel. For oblique lines to be parallel, they must have the same slope.

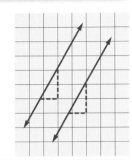

Slopes and Parallel Lines Property

If two lines have the same slope, then they are parallel.

Nonintersecting Parallel Lines

You have learned that when two lines intersect in exactly one point, the coordinates of the point of intersection can be found by solving a system. But what happens when the lines are parallel? Consider this linear system.

$$\begin{cases} 5x - 2y = 11 \\ 15x - 6y = -25 \end{cases}$$

You can solve the system by multiplying the first equation by –3, and adding the result to the second equation.

$$\begin{array}{r} -15x + 6y = -33 \\ + \ 15x - 6y = -25 \end{array}$$

Notice that when you add you get $0 = -58$.

This is impossible! When an equation with no solution (such as $0 = -58$) results from correct applications of the addition and multiplication methods on a system of linear equations, the original conditions must also be impossible. There are no pairs of numbers that work in *both* equations.

Background

Our use of the term *parallel* includes defining identical lines as parallel. This is very common in higher mathematics; for example, equivalent vectors are those with the same length lying on parallel lines, and under a translation, lines are parallel to their images.

Our definition allows us to say simply, "If two lines have the same slope, then they are parallel." We can also say, "Two nonvertical lines have the same slope if and only if they are parallel." The algebra is simplified as

well. Lines in a plane either intersect in one point or are parallel.

Some people like to use the words *consistent* and *inconsistent* to describe systems in which there is at least one solution (consistent) or no solution (inconsistent). We do not use these because we feel there is already enough vocabulary associated with these ideas.

Thus, the system has no solutions. The lines do not intersect. The graph of the system is two parallel nonintersecting lines, as shown at the right. As another check, rewrite the equations for the lines in slope-intercept form.

line ℓ: $5x - 2y = 11$
$$-2y = -5x + 11$$
$$y = 2.5x - 5.5$$

line m: $15x - 6y = -25$
$$-6y = -15x - 25$$
$$y = 2.5x + 4.1\overline{6}$$

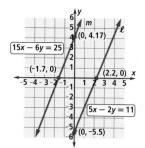

Both lines ℓ and m have the same slope of 2.5, but different y-intercepts. Thus, they are parallel.

 QY1

Coincident Lines

Some systems have infinitely many solutions. They can be solved using any of the techniques you have studied in this chapter.

> ▶ **QY1**
>
> Show that the system
> $$\begin{cases} -4x + 2y = -16 \\ 6x - 3y = 18 \end{cases}$$
> has no solution.

Example 1

Solve the system $\begin{cases} 4x + 2y = 6 \\ y = -2x + 3 \end{cases}$.

Solution 1 Rewrite the first equation in slope-intercept form.

$4x + 2y = 6$
$\quad 2y = -4x + 6$ Add $-4x$ to each side.
$\quad\ y = -2x + 3$ Divide each side by 2.

Notice that this equation is identical to the second equation in the system. So, any ordered pair that is a solution to one equation is also a solution to the other equation. The graphs of the two equations are the same line.

Solution 2 Use substitution. Substitute $-2x + 3$ for y in the first equation.

$4x + 2(-2x + 3) = 6$
$\quad 4x - 4x + 6 = 6$
$\qquad\qquad\ \ 6 = 6$

The sentence $6 = 6$ is *always* true. So, any ordered pair that is a solution to one equation is also a solution to the other equation in the system. The graphs of the two equations are the same line.

The solution set consists of all ordered pairs on the line with equation $y = -2x + 3$, as shown at the right.

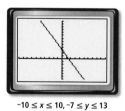

$-10 \le x \le 10, -7 \le y \le 13$

(continued on next page)

Systems and Parallel Lines   **617**

Accommodating the Learner

Remind students that when they add two equations and reach a solution such as $x = 0$, this is a system with intersecting lines that intersect at the value $x = 0$. Obtaining 0 does not automatically mean that the system has no solutions or infinitely many solutions. Once students obtain $x = 0$, remind them to substitute 0 for x to find y, and then to check their final solution with both equations.

Additional Example

Example 2 Find all solutions.

$$\begin{cases} 12x - 30y = 12 \\ -8x + 20y = -8 \end{cases}$$

1. Multiply both sides of the first equation by 2. _?_ $24x - 60y = 24$

2. Multiply both sides of the second equation by 3. _?_ $-24x + 60y = -24$

3. Add the equations from Steps 1 and 2. _?_ $0 = 0$

4. Interpret what you see in Step 3. Does this system have 0 solutions, 1 solution, or infinitely many solutions? **infinitely many solutions**

Note-Taking Tips

The Slopes and Parallel Lines Property and the table before Guided Example 2 are useful summaries of this section. Encourage students to copy these into their notes for future reference.

Check As a partial check, find an ordered pair that satisfies one of the equations of the original system. We use $y = -2x + 3$ to find the ordered pair (0, 3). Check that this ordered pair also satisfies the other equation. Does $4 \cdot 0 + 2 \cdot 3 = 6$? Yes, $6 = 6$.

STOP QY2

Whenever a sentence that is always true (such as $0 = 0$ or $6 = 6$) occurs from correct work with a system of linear equations, the system has infinitely many solutions. We say that the lines *coincide* and that the graph of the system is two **coincident lines.**

You have now studied all the ways that two lines in the plane can be related, and all the types of solutions a system of two linear equations might have. The table below summarizes these relationships.

Description of System	Graph	Number of Solutions to System	Slopes of Lines
Two intersecting lines		1 (the point of intersection)	Different
Two parallel and nonintersecting lines		0	Equal
One line (parallel and coincident lines)		Infinitely many	Equal

> **▶ QY2**
>
> Find a second ordered pair that satisfies one of the equations in Example 1 and show that it satisfies the other equation.

GUIDED

Example 2

Find all solutions to $\begin{cases} 12x - 10y = 2 \\ -18x + 15y = -3 \end{cases}$.

Solution

Step 1 Multiply both sides of the first equation by 3. _?_ $36x - 30y = 6$

Step 2 Multiply both sides of the second equation by 2. _?_ $-36x + 30y = -6$

Step 3 Add the equations from Steps 1 and 2. _?_ $0 = 0$

618 Linear Systems

Accommodating the Learner ⬆

Ask students to describe a real-world situation that might yield a system of equations with no solution. For example, consider two companies starting out at different levels of profit whose profits are growing at the same rate. Next, ask students to describe a real-world situation that might yield a system of equations with infinitely many solutions, such as two different drugs that have the same effect on blood sugar over the same amount of time.

The solution set consists of all ordered pairs on the line with equation $12x - 10y = 2$.

Questions

COVERING THE IDEAS

1. What is true about the slopes of parallel lines? They are equal.

2. Which two lines among Parts a–d are parallel? a and c
   a. $y = 8x + 500$ b. $y = 2x + 500$
   c. $y = 8x + 600$ d. $x = 2y + 500$

3. a. Graph the line with equation $y = \frac{1}{3}x + 5$.
   b. Draw the line parallel to it through the origin.
   c. What is an equation of the line you drew in Part b? $y = \frac{1}{3}x$

4. Give an example of a system with two nonintersecting lines.

5. Give an example of a system with two coincident lines.

In 6 and 7, a system is given.
   a. Determine whether the system includes *nonintersecting* or *coincident* lines.
   b. Check your answer to Part a by graphing.

6. $\begin{cases} 12a = 6b - 3 \\ 4a - 2b = -3 \end{cases}$ 7. $\begin{cases} y - x = 5 \\ 3y - 3x = 15 \end{cases}$

8. **Matching** Match the description of the graph with the number of solutions to the system.
   a. lines intersect in one point   iii   i. no solution
   b. lines do not intersect   i   ii. infinitely many solutions
   c. lines coincide   ii   iii. one solution

APPLYING THE MATHEMATICS

9. a. How many pairs of numbers M and N satisfy both conditions i and ii below? none
   i. The sum of the numbers is –2.
   ii. The average of the numbers is 1.
   b. Explain your answer to Part a. See margin.

10. Could the situation described here have happened? Justify your answer by using a system of equations. A pizza parlor sold 36 pizzas and 21 gallons of soda for $456. The next day, at the same prices, they sold 48 pizzas and 28 gallons of soda for $608. See margin.

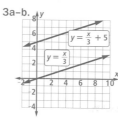

3a–b.

4. Answers vary.
   Sample answer:
   $\begin{cases} y = 5x \\ y = 5x - 12 \end{cases}$

5. Answers vary.
   Sample answer:
   $\begin{cases} y = 2x + 3 \\ 2y = 4x + 6 \end{cases}$

6a. nonintersecting

6b.
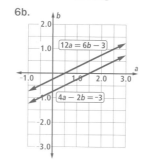

7a. coincident

7b.
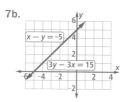

3 Assignment

Recommended Assignment

- Questions 1–21
- Question 22 (extra credit)
- Reading Lesson 10-7
- Covering the Ideas 10-7

Notes on the Questions

Question 10 Students should write a system of equations. They do not have to solve the system; they can just look at the graphs or at the slopes and intercepts. You might wish to go over the problems and show how, by dividing the given numbers in the first equation by 3 and in the second by 4, they could answer the question without solving a system.

Additional Answers

9b. Answers vary. Sample answer: The system
$\begin{cases} x + y = -2 \\ \dfrac{x + y}{2} = 1 \end{cases}$ has no solution.

10. Yes, the two lines are coincident lines.
$\begin{cases} 36p + 21s = 456 \\ 48p + 28s = 608 \end{cases}$

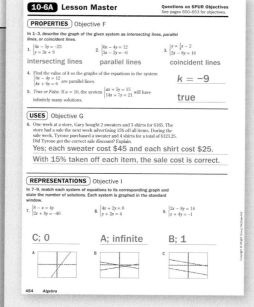

Notes on the Questions

Question 15 One way to answer this question is by solving the system of equations determined by what Melissa's friends paid, and then seeing if Melissa's costs fit that solution.

In 11–14, describe the graph of the system as two intersecting lines, two parallel nonintersecting lines, or coincident lines.

11. $\begin{cases} a = b \\ b - a = 0 \end{cases}$

12. $\begin{cases} y = 5 - 3x \\ 6x + 2y - 10 = 0 \end{cases}$

13. $\begin{cases} 10x + 20y = 30 \\ y + 2x = 3 \end{cases}$

14. $\begin{cases} \frac{4}{5}c - \frac{3}{5}d = 3.6 \\ 8c = 6d + 72 \end{cases}$

11–12. coincident lines

13. two intersecting lines

14. two parallel nonintersecting lines

15. Melissa is the costume manager for a theater company and is supposed to receive a 15% professional discount from a fabric store. Last week, she bought 40 yards of a red material and 35 yards of a black fabric and paid $435.63. Two friends of hers went to the same store the following week. One bought 20 yards of red material and 10 yards of black fabric for $185, and the other bought 15 yards of red material and 40 yards of black fabric for $447.50. Did Melissa receive a discount? If so, was it the correct percentage? **Yes, she got her 15% discount.**

A dancer is performing in a stage production.

REVIEW

16. A band has 59 musicians (M) with an additional 24 flag bearers (F). They plan to form pentagons and squares with one person in the middle, as shown below.

Let p be the number of pentagons formed and s be the number of squares formed. Can all musicians and flag bearers be accommodated into these formations? Why or why not?
(**Lesson 10-5**)

16. No. Answers vary. Sample answer: The system implied by the question does not have an integer solution.

17. Each diagram at the right represents an equation involving lengths t and u.
(**Lesson 10-4**) a. $t + u = 16$, $t + 3u = 28$

a. Write a pair of equations describing these relationships.

b. Use either your equations or the diagrams to find the lengths of t and u. Explain your reasoning. $t = 10$, $u = 6$

c. Check your work. $6 + 10 = 16$, $10 + 18 = 28$

18. Find the *x*-intercepts of the graph of $y = x^2 + 9x - 5$ using each method. (**Lessons 9-5, 9-3**) 18a. approximately 0.525, and −9.525
    a. Let $y = 0$ and use the Quadratic Formula.
    b. Use a graphing calculator and zoom in on the intercepts.

19. a. Simplify $\sqrt{d^8 + 3d^8}$. $2d^4$
    b. Check your answer from Part a by testing the special case where $d = 2$. (**Lesson 8-9**)

20. In December of 1986, Dick Rutan and Jeana Yeager flew the *Voyager* airplane nonstop around Earth without refueling, the first flight of its kind. The average rate for the 24,987-mile trip was 116 mph. How many days long was this flight?
    (**Lesson 5-3**) 8 days 23 hr

A chase plane follows the *Voyager* as it flies over Southern California.

21. a. Identify an equation of the vertical line through the point (−6, 18). $x = -6$
    b. Identify an equation of the horizontal line through the point (−6, 18). (**Lesson 4-2**) $y = 18$

EXPLORATION

22. Consider the general system $\begin{cases} ax + by = e \\ cx + dy = f \end{cases}$ of two linear equations in two variables, *x* and *y*.

    a. Find *y* by multiplying the first equation by *c* and the second equation by -*a* and then adding. $y = \dfrac{ec - fa}{cb - da}$

    b. Find *x* by multiplying the first equation by *d* and the second equation by -*b* and then adding. $x = \dfrac{ed - fb}{ad - bc}$

    c. Your answers to Parts a and b should be fractions. Write them with the denominator $ad - bc$ if they are not already in that form. $y = -\dfrac{ec - fa}{ad - bc}$

    d. Use a CAS to solve this system and compare the CAS solution with what you found by hand. The solutions should be identical.

18b.

19b. $\sqrt{2^8 + 3(2)^8} = 32 = 2(2)^4$

QY ANSWERS

1. Multiply the top equation by 3 and the bottom equation by 2, then add the equations. You should get $0 = -48 + 36 = -12$. This is never true, so the system has no solution.

2. Answers vary. Sample answer: (1, 1) satisfies $4x + 2y = 6$. Since $-2(1) + 3 = 1$, (1, 1) also satisfies $y = -2x + 3$.

Systems and Parallel Lines **621**

4 Wrap-Up

Ongoing Assessment

Write the equation $y = 2x + 1$ on the board, and write the following three headings: Parallel Lines, Coincident Lines, and Intersecting Lines. Ask students for equations of lines that are parallel to that line. Write systems under the appropriate heading. Next, ask students for equations of lines that coincide with the line. Finally, ask students for equations of lines that will intersect with the line. Help students notice that to create these lines, they must change the slope of the line.

Project Update

Project 2, When Do Systems Have Integer Solutions?, on page 645, relates to the content of this lesson.

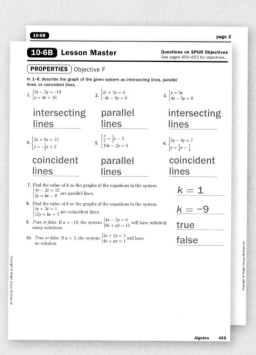

GOAL

Multiply 2 × 2 matrices by 2 × 1 or 2 × 2 matrices and represent a system in matrix form.

SPUR Objective

C Multiply 2 × 2 matrices by 2 × 2 or 2 × 1 matrices.

Materials/Resources

· Lesson Master 10-7A or 10-7B
· Resource Master 155
· Graphing calculator

HOMEWORK

Suggestions for Assignment

• Questions 1–21
• Question 22 (extra credit)
• Reading Lesson 10-8
• Covering the Ideas 10-8

Local Standards

1 Warm-Up

Follow the pattern $[a\ b]\begin{bmatrix} x \\ y \end{bmatrix} = [ax + by]$.
Give the product.

1. $[-2\ 6]\begin{bmatrix} x \\ y \end{bmatrix}$ $[-2x + 6y]$

2. $[-2\ 6]\begin{bmatrix} -4 \\ 35 \end{bmatrix}$ $[218]$

3. $[5\ 1]\begin{bmatrix} 3 \\ -4 \end{bmatrix}$ $[11]$

4. $\begin{bmatrix} \frac{1}{2} & \frac{9}{10} \end{bmatrix}\begin{bmatrix} -110 \\ 90 \end{bmatrix}$ $[26]$

Lesson
10-7   Matrices and Matrix Multiplication

Vocabulary

matrix (matrices)
elements
dimensions
matrix form
2 × 2 identity matrix

▶ **BIG IDEA**   Rectangular arrays called matrices can sometimes be multiplied and represent systems of linear equations.

When you use a method like multiplication or addition to solve systems of linear equations, you do the same steps over and over. Once a linear system to be solved for x and y is in the form

$\begin{cases} ax + by = e \\ cx + dy = f \end{cases}$, the processes for solving it are the same. The different

solutions are caused by the numbers a, b, c, and d that are the coefficients and the numbers e and f that are the constants.

A mathematical tool called a *matrix* allows you to separate those numbers from the overall structure of the problem. A **matrix** (the

plural is **matrices**) is a rectangular array, such as $\begin{bmatrix} 3 & -4 \\ 15 & 0 \end{bmatrix}$.

The brackets [ ] identify the numbers that are in the matrix. The objects in the array are the **elements** of the matrix. The elements of

the matrix $\begin{bmatrix} 3 & -4 \\ 15 & 0 \end{bmatrix}$ are 3, –4, 15, and 0. They are identified by the

row and the column of the matrix they are in. The rows are counted from the top; the columns from the left. So –4 is the element in the 1st row and 2nd column.

The number of rows and the number of columns of a matrix are its

dimensions. Because it has 2 rows and 2 columns, the matrix $\begin{bmatrix} 3 & -4 \\ 15 & 0 \end{bmatrix}$

is a 2 × 2 (read "2 by 2") matrix, while the matrix $\begin{bmatrix} x \\ y \end{bmatrix}$ is a 2 × 1
matrix because it has 2 rows and 1 column.

The linear system $\begin{cases} 2x + 6y = 2 \\ x + 4y = -5 \end{cases}$ is described by three matrices:

the 2 × 2 *coefficient matrix* $\begin{bmatrix} 2 & 6 \\ 1 & 4 \end{bmatrix}$, the 2 × 1 *variable matrix* $\begin{bmatrix} x \\ y \end{bmatrix}$,

and the 2 × 1 *constant matrix* $\begin{bmatrix} 2 \\ -5 \end{bmatrix}$.

What is the probability that

a. a randomly-chosen one-digit number is odd? $\frac{1}{2}$

b. a randomly-selected day in the year 2015 is in June? $\frac{6}{73}$

c. a fair, 6-sided die shows a 3 or 5? $\frac{1}{3}$

Background

In mathematics a *matrix* is a rectangular array of objects. The plural is *matrices*. The term "matrix" was introduced by the British mathematician James J. Sylvester in 1848.

This lesson gives the minimal amount of information needed in order to solve a 2 × 2 system with matrices. The matrix method of solution will be given in Lesson 10-8.

Matrix multiplication was invented by Arthur Cayley in 1855 as a way of keeping track of coefficients in the composition of linear transformations. Today there are

four common elementary applications of matrix multiplication: applications to systems as discussed in Lesson 10-8, to geometric transformations, to business, and to networks, which students will see in later UCSMP courses.

You might think that matrix multiplication is difficult for students to learn. It is not difficult if you follow the approaches that are given in the lesson and recommended in these notes.

In *matrix form,* the system on the previous page is

$\begin{bmatrix} 2 & 6 \\ 1 & 4 \end{bmatrix} \cdot \begin{bmatrix} x \\ y \end{bmatrix} = \begin{bmatrix} 2 \\ -5 \end{bmatrix}$. In general, the **matrix form** of the system

$\begin{cases} ax + by = e \\ cx + dy = f \end{cases}$ is $\begin{bmatrix} a & b \\ c & d \end{bmatrix} \cdot \begin{bmatrix} x \\ y \end{bmatrix} = \begin{bmatrix} e \\ f \end{bmatrix}$.

Example 1

Write $\begin{cases} 4x = 5y + 10 \\ 2x - 3y = 20 \end{cases}$ in matrix form.

Solution The first step is to rewrite the system with each equation in

standard form: $\begin{cases} 4x - 5y = 10 \\ 2x - 3y = 20 \end{cases}$. Then form three matrices to describe the

coefficients, variables, and constants in the standard-form system.

$\begin{bmatrix} 4 & -5 \\ 2 & -3 \end{bmatrix} \cdot \begin{bmatrix} x \\ y \end{bmatrix} = \begin{bmatrix} 10 \\ 20 \end{bmatrix}$

coefficient matrix · variable matrix = constant matrix

Matrix Multiplication

Above, we have put a dot between the coefficient and variable matrices. This is because these matrices are multiplied. Matrices can be added, subtracted, and multiplied; but in this lesson you will learn only about matrix multiplication.

The matrix form of the system in Example 1 shows that the matrix $\begin{bmatrix} 4 & -5 \\ 2 & -3 \end{bmatrix}$ is multiplied by $\begin{bmatrix} x \\ y \end{bmatrix}$. What does it mean to multiply these matrices? To multiply these matrices, we combine each row of the 2×2 matrix $\begin{bmatrix} 4 & -5 \\ 2 & -3 \end{bmatrix}$ with the 2×1 matrix $\begin{bmatrix} x \\ y \end{bmatrix}$ to form a product 2×1 matrix. Each element in the product matrix is the product of the first entries plus the product of the second entries. Multiplying the top row of $\begin{bmatrix} 4 & -5 \\ 2 & -3 \end{bmatrix}$ by $\begin{bmatrix} x \\ y \end{bmatrix}$ gives $4x + -5y$. Multiplying the bottom row of $\begin{bmatrix} 4 & -5 \\ 2 & -3 \end{bmatrix}$ by $\begin{bmatrix} x \\ y \end{bmatrix}$ gives $2x + -3y$.

Matrices and Matrix Multiplication **623**

Vocabulary Development

Help students understand the new matrix terminology by showing several examples to illustrate the terms. For the term *dimensions,* encourage students to compare the matrix to a rectangle. If they think of each row and column as one unit, they can see that the matrices in this section compare to a rectangle of dimensions 2 units by 2 units and 2 units by 1 unit. Reinforce the concept of dimensions by showing students examples of 2 by 3, 3 by 3, and 4 by 6 matrices. Take time to

explain that *matrix form* is simply a representation of a system. Compare this to slope-intercept and standard form for a line to reinforce the idea that different forms can be used to represent the same mathematical object.

10-7

2 Teaching

Notes on the Lesson
The first thing to discuss with students is how to read a matrix. The matrix $\begin{bmatrix} a & b \\ c & d \end{bmatrix}$ is read "a, b, c, d", that is, from left to right starting at the top, just as in normal reading.

Matrix multiplication. You may wish to go from the Warm-Up to Example 2 and hold off on representing the system in matrix form until students have done matrix arithmetic. We recommend the following approach when teaching matrix multiplication:

1. Explain the concept of multiplying a row (on the left) by a column (on the right).
2. Point out that, because a row is multiplied by a column, matrices can be multiplied only when the number of columns in the left matrix equals the number of rows in the right matrix.
3. Find each element of the product matrix as the product of the row and the column that the element is in. For example, the element in the 1st row, 2nd column of the product matrix is the product of the 1st row of the left matrix and the 2nd column of the right matrix.
4. You may wish to discuss Question 22 and the multiplication of larger matrices. The product matrix will have the same number of rows as the left matrix and the same number of columns as the right matrix.

Emphasize the pairing of the elements in a row with the elements in a column. In $[a \ b] \begin{bmatrix} x \\ y \end{bmatrix}$, a is paired with (multiplied by) x and b is paired with (multiplied by) y. Then go back and look at Example 1, which shows how a system is going to be represented by a single matrix multiplication, or you can do Example 3 first, in which students multiply matrices where there is more than one column on the right.

Additional Example
Example 1 Write $\begin{cases} 3x - 4y = 5 \\ 4x + 8y = 2 \end{cases}$ in matrix form. $\begin{bmatrix} 3 & -4 \\ 4 & 8 \end{bmatrix} \cdot \begin{bmatrix} x \\ y \end{bmatrix} = \begin{bmatrix} 5 \\ 2 \end{bmatrix}$

10-7

Additional Examples

Example 2 Perform the multiplication.

$$\begin{bmatrix} 4 & -6 \\ -2 & -3 \end{bmatrix} \cdot \begin{bmatrix} 2 \\ -4 \end{bmatrix} \quad \begin{bmatrix} 32 \\ 8 \end{bmatrix}$$

Example 3 Find the product.

$$\begin{bmatrix} -2 & -1 \\ 5 & 3 \end{bmatrix} \begin{bmatrix} 2 & 5 \\ 8 & 1 \end{bmatrix} \quad \begin{bmatrix} -12 & -11 \\ 34 & 28 \end{bmatrix}$$

Notes on the Lesson

Calculators handle matrices as objects. Students should learn how to locate a matrix in their calculators. They will have to specify the dimensions of the matrix and then put in its elements. They may be surprised that a single letter is used to name a matrix, and that the same key used for multiplication of numbers is used for multiplication of matrices.

So $\begin{bmatrix} 4 & -5 \\ 2 & -3 \end{bmatrix} \cdot \begin{bmatrix} x \\ y \end{bmatrix} = \begin{bmatrix} 4x - 5y \\ 2x - 3y \end{bmatrix}$. This is why we say that the system

$\begin{cases} 4x - 5y = 10 \\ 2x - 3y = 20 \end{cases}$ is equivalent to the matrix equation

$\begin{bmatrix} 4 & -5 \\ 2 & -3 \end{bmatrix} \cdot \begin{bmatrix} x \\ y \end{bmatrix} = \begin{bmatrix} 10 \\ 20 \end{bmatrix}$. In the same way, two matrices can be

multiplied when both matrices contain numbers.

Example 2

Perform the multiplication $\begin{bmatrix} 10 & 3 \\ -2 & 5 \end{bmatrix} \cdot \begin{bmatrix} 4 \\ 11 \end{bmatrix}$.

Solution The result will be a 2 × 1 matrix. So write down places for the elements of this matrix.

$$\begin{bmatrix} 10 & 3 \\ -2 & 5 \end{bmatrix} \cdot \begin{bmatrix} 4 \\ 11 \end{bmatrix} = \begin{bmatrix} \underline{?} \\ \underline{?} \end{bmatrix}$$

Multiply the top row by the column to obtain the top element:

$10 \cdot 4 + 3 \cdot 11 = 73$. Multiply the bottom row by the column to obtain the bottom element: $-2 \cdot 4 + 5 \cdot 11 = 47$.

$$\begin{bmatrix} 10 & 3 \\ -2 & 5 \end{bmatrix} \cdot \begin{bmatrix} 4 \\ 11 \end{bmatrix} = \begin{bmatrix} 10 \cdot 4 + 3 \cdot 11 \\ -2 \cdot 4 + 5 \cdot 11 \end{bmatrix} = \begin{bmatrix} 73 \\ 47 \end{bmatrix}$$

Multiplying 2 × 2 Matrices

Not all matrices can be multiplied. For a product AB of two matrices A and B to exist, each row of A must have the same number of elements as each column of B. This is so that row-by-column multiplication can be performed. The element in row i and column j of the product is the result of multiplying row i of A and the column j of B.

Example 3

Find the product $\begin{bmatrix} 1 & 2 \\ 5 & 3 \end{bmatrix} \cdot \begin{bmatrix} -4 & 6 \\ 30 & 5 \end{bmatrix}$.

Solution The product will be a 2 × 2 matrix. First write down the spaces for the elements of the product. The product will have the same number of rows as the first matrix and the same number of columns as the second matrix.

$$\begin{bmatrix} 1 & 2 \\ 5 & 3 \end{bmatrix} \cdot \begin{bmatrix} -4 & 6 \\ 30 & 5 \end{bmatrix} = \begin{bmatrix} \underline{?} & \underline{?} \\ \underline{?} & \underline{?} \end{bmatrix}$$

624 Linear Systems

Accommodating the Learner

Remind students that to write a system in matrix form, it is easiest to work with a system that has equations in standard form. For example, to write the system

$\begin{cases} y = \frac{1}{2}x - 1 \\ 4x = 2y - 3 \end{cases}$ in matrix form, ask

students to first change the linear equations to standard form. They should obtain the

system $\begin{cases} -x + 2y = -2 \\ 4x - 2y = -3 \end{cases}$. This will be easier to

write in matrix form. Provide opportunities for students to practice this skill.

Pick an element of the product matrix.

For the element in the 1st row, 1st column of the product, multiply the 1st row of the left matrix by the 1st column of the right matrix.

$1 \cdot {-4} + 2 \cdot 30 = 56$

$$\begin{bmatrix} 1 & 2 \\ 5 & 3 \end{bmatrix} \cdot \begin{bmatrix} -4 & 6 \\ 30 & 5 \end{bmatrix} = \begin{bmatrix} 56 & ? \\ ? & ? \end{bmatrix}$$

For the element in the 1st row, 2nd column of the product, multiply the 1st row of the left matrix by the 2nd column of the right matrix.

$1 \cdot 6 + 2 \cdot 5 = 16$

$$\begin{bmatrix} 1 & 2 \\ 5 & 3 \end{bmatrix} \cdot \begin{bmatrix} -4 & 6 \\ 30 & 5 \end{bmatrix} = \begin{bmatrix} 56 & 16 \\ ? & ? \end{bmatrix}$$

The other two elements are found in a similar manner.

$5 \cdot {-4} + 3 \cdot 30 = 70$ and $5 \cdot 6 + 3 \cdot 5 = 45$

$$\begin{bmatrix} 1 & 2 \\ 5 & 3 \end{bmatrix} \cdot \begin{bmatrix} -4 & 6 \\ 30 & 5 \end{bmatrix} = \begin{bmatrix} 56 & 16 \\ 70 & 45 \end{bmatrix}$$

In matrix multiplication, the left and right matrices play different roles. So you should not expect that reversing the order of the matrices will give the same product. For the matrices of Example 3, $\begin{bmatrix} -4 & 6 \\ 30 & 5 \end{bmatrix} \cdot \begin{bmatrix} 1 & 2 \\ 5 & 3 \end{bmatrix} = \begin{bmatrix} 26 & 10 \\ 55 & 75 \end{bmatrix}$. Matrix multiplication is not commutative.

Questions

COVERING THE IDEAS

1. Consider the matrix $\begin{bmatrix} a & b & c \\ d & e & f \end{bmatrix}$.

   a. What are the dimensions of this matrix? 2×3

   b. Name the elements in the first row. *a, b, c*

   c. Which element is in the 2nd row, 3rd column? *f*

2. The matrix equation $\begin{bmatrix} -4 & 6 \\ 3 & -7 \end{bmatrix} \cdot \begin{bmatrix} d \\ g \end{bmatrix} = \begin{bmatrix} 18 \\ 54 \end{bmatrix}$ describes a system

   of equations. Write the system. $\begin{cases} -4d + 6g = 18 \\ 3d - 7g = 54 \end{cases}$

In 3 and 4, a system is given.

   a. Write the coefficient matrix.

   b. Write the constant matrix.

3. $\begin{cases} 5a - 2b = -4 \\ 3a + 4b = 34 \end{cases}$

4. $\begin{cases} 5x + 3(y + 1) = 85 \\ 2x = 7y \end{cases}$

3a. $\begin{bmatrix} 5 & -2 \\ 3 & 4 \end{bmatrix}$

3b. $\begin{bmatrix} -4 \\ 34 \end{bmatrix}$

4a. $\begin{bmatrix} 5 & 3 \\ 2 & -7 \end{bmatrix}$

4b. $\begin{bmatrix} 82 \\ 0 \end{bmatrix}$

Matrices and Matrix Multiplication   **625**

Accommodating the Learner

Take time to discuss the ideas of the identity and zero matrices with students. Discuss how they compare to the numbers 1 and 0 in the real number system. In addition, help students explore which matrices can and cannot be multiplied together. Guide them to recognize that to multiply two matrices together, they must have dimensions $a \times b$ and $b \times c$, in that order. In other words, the "middle" dimension must match.

10-7

3 Assignment

Recommended Assignment

- Questions 1–21
- Question 22 (extra credit)
- Reading Lesson 10-8
- Covering the Ideas 10-8

Notes on the Questions

We recommend going through Questions 1–7 in order to cover the basic ideas of the lesson.

Questions 1, 3, and 4 These are important questions for the vocabulary of the lesson.

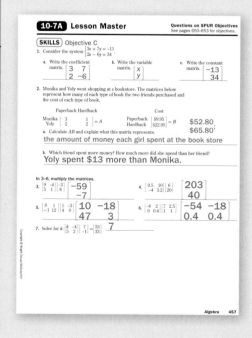

10-7

Notes on the Questions

Question 9 The discussion of noncommutativity is just before the Questions section and may not have been thought to be important by students. Use student examples to show that matrix multiplication is typically not commutative.

Question 10 The identity matrix is found in the reading of the next lesson; this is preparation.

Question 12 You may have to point out that the matrix on the right of the equation is a 2 × 1 matrix even though it may look like it is 2 × 2.

Question 13 It is important that students see matrices as individual objects. This will come automatically as they use single letters to name matrices and when they find inverses of matrices using technology.

Question 14 The matrix M in this question is a matrix for a rotation of 90° counterclockwise about the origin, because $M \cdot \begin{bmatrix} x \\ y \end{bmatrix} = \begin{bmatrix} -y \\ x \end{bmatrix}$. Four rotations of 90° bring one back to the original point, which is why M^4 is the identity matrix.

5. What is the result when the row [−4 6] is combined with the column $\begin{bmatrix} 0.25 \\ -0.50 \end{bmatrix}$ in a matrix multiplication? −4

In 6–8, multiply the two matrices.

6. $\begin{bmatrix} 3 & 5 \\ -2 & 4 \end{bmatrix} \cdot \begin{bmatrix} 6 \\ 1 \end{bmatrix}$

7. $\begin{bmatrix} 5 & -8 \\ 4 & 11 \end{bmatrix} \cdot \begin{bmatrix} 0.5 & 0 \\ -2 & 4 \end{bmatrix}$

8. $\begin{bmatrix} 0 & -1 \\ 1 & 2 \end{bmatrix} \cdot \begin{bmatrix} 3 & 4 \\ 5 & -6 \end{bmatrix}$

9. Give an example different from the one provided in this lesson to show that multiplication of 2 × 2 matrices is not commutative.

6. $\begin{bmatrix} 23 \\ -8 \end{bmatrix}$

7. $\begin{bmatrix} 18.5 & -32 \\ -20 & 44 \end{bmatrix}$

8. $\begin{bmatrix} -5 & 6 \\ 13 & -8 \end{bmatrix}$

9. Answers vary.
   Sample answer:
   $\begin{bmatrix} 2 & -1 \\ 1 & 2 \end{bmatrix} \cdot \begin{bmatrix} 3 & -1 \\ -3 & 2 \end{bmatrix} =$
   $\begin{bmatrix} 9 & -4 \\ -3 & 3 \end{bmatrix}, \begin{bmatrix} 3 & -1 \\ -3 & 2 \end{bmatrix} \cdot$
   $\begin{bmatrix} 2 & -1 \\ 1 & 2 \end{bmatrix} = \begin{bmatrix} 5 & -5 \\ -4 & 7 \end{bmatrix}$

APPLYING THE MATHEMATICS

10. The matrix $\begin{bmatrix} 1 & 0 \\ 0 & 1 \end{bmatrix}$ is called the **2 × 2 identity matrix** for multiplication. To see why, calculate the products in Parts a and b.

    a. $\begin{bmatrix} 1 & 0 \\ 0 & 1 \end{bmatrix} \cdot \begin{bmatrix} a & b \\ c & d \end{bmatrix}$ $\begin{bmatrix} a & b \\ c & d \end{bmatrix}$

    b. $\begin{bmatrix} a & b \\ c & d \end{bmatrix} \cdot \begin{bmatrix} 1 & 0 \\ 0 & 1 \end{bmatrix}$ $\begin{bmatrix} a & b \\ c & d \end{bmatrix}$

    c. **True or False** Matrix multiplication of a 2 × 2 matrix with the 2 × 2 identity matrix is commutative. true

11. Solve $\begin{bmatrix} -9 & 2 \\ 0 & 15 \end{bmatrix} \cdot \begin{bmatrix} x \\ 5 \end{bmatrix} = \begin{bmatrix} 100 \\ 75 \end{bmatrix}$ for x. −10

12. Solve $\begin{bmatrix} a & b \\ c & d \end{bmatrix} \cdot \begin{bmatrix} x \\ y \end{bmatrix} = \begin{bmatrix} 3x - 4y \\ 2x + y \end{bmatrix}$ for $a, b, c,$ and d. $a = 3, b = -4, c = 2, d = 1$

13. Create three different 2 × 2 matrices $M, N,$ and P. 13a–d. See margin.
    a. Calculate MN.
    b. Calculate $(MN)P$.
    c. Calculate NP.
    d. Calculate $M(NP)$.
    e. Do your answers to Parts b and d tell you that matrix multiplication is definitely not associative, or do they tell you that matrix multiplication might be associative? It might be associative.

14. When a matrix M is multiplied by itself, the product $M \cdot M$ is called M^2 for short. $M^2 \cdot M = M^3, M^3 \cdot M = M^4$, and so on. Let $M = \begin{bmatrix} 0 & -1 \\ 1 & 0 \end{bmatrix}$. Show that M^4 is the identity matrix of Question 10.

    $M^2 \times M^2 = \begin{bmatrix} -1 & 0 \\ 0 & -1 \end{bmatrix} \cdot \begin{bmatrix} -1 & 0 \\ 0 & -1 \end{bmatrix} = \begin{bmatrix} 1 & 0 \\ 0 & 1 \end{bmatrix}$

626 Linear Systems

Extension

Ask students to generalize the skill of writing systems of equations in matrix form. Provide students with examples of systems with different numbers of equations and unknowns. Consider the following examples.

a. $\begin{cases} 3x - 4y + 5z = 3 \\ 3x - 2y + 6z = 4 \\ 4x - 5y + 2z = 10 \end{cases}$ $\begin{bmatrix} 3 & -4 & 5 \\ 3 & -2 & 6 \\ 4 & -5 & 2 \end{bmatrix} \begin{bmatrix} x \\ y \\ z \end{bmatrix} = \begin{bmatrix} 3 \\ 4 \\ 10 \end{bmatrix}$

b. $\begin{cases} 2x - 5y + 3z = 2 \\ 5x - 4z = 10 \end{cases}$ $\begin{bmatrix} 2 & -5 & 3 \\ 5 & 0 & -4 \end{bmatrix} \begin{bmatrix} x \\ y \\ z \end{bmatrix} = \begin{bmatrix} 2 \\ 10 \end{bmatrix}$

c. $5x - 4 = 13$ $[5 \; -4] \begin{bmatrix} x \\ 1 \end{bmatrix} = [13]$

Additional Answers

13a. Answers vary. Sample answer:
$M = \begin{bmatrix} 1 & 1 \\ 1 & 1 \end{bmatrix}, N = \begin{bmatrix} 2 & 1 \\ 1 & 2 \end{bmatrix}, P = \begin{bmatrix} 0 & -1 \\ 3 & 1 \end{bmatrix},$
$MN = \begin{bmatrix} 3 & 3 \\ 3 & 3 \end{bmatrix}$

13b. $MN(P) = \begin{bmatrix} 9 & 0 \\ 9 & 0 \end{bmatrix}$

13c. $NP = \begin{bmatrix} 3 & -1 \\ 6 & 1 \end{bmatrix}$

13d. $M(NP) = \begin{bmatrix} 9 & 0 \\ 9 & 0 \end{bmatrix}$

REVIEW

15. Without drawing any graphs, explain how you can tell whether the graphs of $17x + 20y = 84$ and $16x + 20y = 85$ are two intersecting lines, one line, or two nonintersecting parallel lines. (**Lesson 10-6**)

15. two intersecting lines, by comparing the slopes and y-intercepts

In 16 and 17, solve by using any method. (**Lessons 10-6, 10-5, 10-4, 10-2, 10-1**)

16. $\begin{cases} 3x + 2y = 40 \\ 9x + 6y = 120 \end{cases}$

16. all ordered pairs on the line $3x + 2y = 40$

17. $\begin{cases} y = 10 - 4x \\ y = 4x - 10 \end{cases}$ (2.5, 0)

18. A hardware store placed two orders with a manufacturer. The first order was for 18 hammers and 14 wrenches, and totaled $582. The second order was for 12 hammers and 10 wrenches, and totaled $396. What is the cost of one hammer and of one wrench? (**Lesson 10-5**) $23 per hammer, $12 per wrench

19. Consider the equations $2x + y = 4$, $x = 5$, and $y = 3$. The graph of these equations forms a triangle. (**Lessons 10-1, 8-8, 8-6**)
    a. Find the vertices of the triangle. (0.5, 3), (5, 3), (5, –6)
    b. Find the length of each side of the triangle. 4.5, 9, and approximately 10.06
    c. Find the area of the triangle. 20.25 units²

20. **Skill Sequence** Find an equivalent expression without a fraction. (**Lessons 8-4, 8-3**)
    a. $\frac{x^5}{x}$ x^4 b. $\frac{x^5}{x^3}$ x^2 c. $\frac{x^5}{y^3}$ $x^5 y^{-3}$

21. An Aztec calendar is being placed on a rectangular mat that is 1.25 times as high and 2.25 times as wide as the calendar. What percent of the mat is taken up by the calendar? (**Lesson 5-7**) approximately 27.9%

2.25d

1.25d

Matrices and Matrix Multiplication   **627**

10-7

4 Wrap-Up

Ongoing Assessment

Ask students to use matrix multiplication to write a justification in their own words of why the system $\begin{bmatrix} a & b \\ c & d \end{bmatrix} \cdot \begin{bmatrix} x \\ y \end{bmatrix} = \begin{bmatrix} e \\ f \end{bmatrix}$ is an equivalent form of the system $\begin{cases} ax + by = e \\ cx + dy = f \end{cases}$. Go over the descriptions to check students' understanding of the concept.

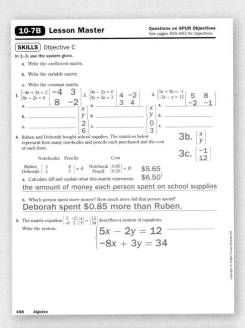

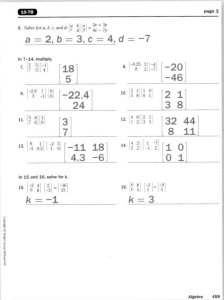

EXPLORATION

22. Rows and columns with 3 elements are multiplied as follows.

$$[a \quad b \quad c] \cdot \begin{bmatrix} d \\ e \\ f \end{bmatrix} = [ad + be + cf]$$

3×3 matrices can be multiplied using the same row-by-column idea as is used with 2×2 matrices. The product MN of two 3×3 matrices M and N is a 3×3 matrix. The element in row i and column j of MN is the result of multiplying row i of M and the column j of N.

a. Use this idea to find MN when $M = \begin{bmatrix} 2 & 1 & 0 \\ -1 & 5 & 2 \\ 0 & 3 & 10 \end{bmatrix}$ and

$$N = \begin{bmatrix} 0 & 3 & -3 \\ 4 & 6 & 1 \\ -0.5 & 0 & 12 \end{bmatrix}. \quad \begin{bmatrix} 4 & 12 & -5 \\ 19 & 27 & 32 \\ 7 & 18 & 123 \end{bmatrix}$$

b. Show that $\begin{bmatrix} 1 & 0 & 0 \\ 0 & 1 & 0 \\ 0 & 0 & 1 \end{bmatrix}$ is the identity matrix for 3×3 matrix

multiplication. (*Hint:* Calculate products as in Question 10.)
Answers vary. Sample answer:

For any 3×3 matrix, $\begin{bmatrix} a & b & c \\ d & e & f \\ g & h & i \end{bmatrix}$,

$$\begin{bmatrix} a & b & c \\ d & e & f \\ g & h & i \end{bmatrix} \cdot \begin{bmatrix} 1 & 0 & 0 \\ 0 & 1 & 0 \\ 0 & 0 & 1 \end{bmatrix} = \begin{bmatrix} a & b & c \\ d & e & f \\ g & h & i \end{bmatrix} \text{ and}$$

$$\begin{bmatrix} 1 & 0 & 0 \\ 0 & 1 & 0 \\ 0 & 0 & 1 \end{bmatrix} \cdot \begin{bmatrix} a & b & c \\ d & e & f \\ g & h & i \end{bmatrix} = \begin{bmatrix} a & b & c \\ d & e & f \\ g & h & i \end{bmatrix}.$$

Lesson

10-8

Using Matrices to Solve Systems

▶ **BIG IDEA** By finding the inverse of a matrix, you can solve systems of linear equations.

The matrix method for solving systems follows a pattern like the one used to solve the equation $\frac{2}{7}x = 28$.

To solve this equation, you would multiply both sides of the equation by the number that makes the coefficient of x equal to 1. This is the multiplicative inverse of $\frac{2}{7}$, or $\frac{7}{2}$.

$$\frac{7}{2} \cdot \frac{2}{7}x = \frac{7}{2} \cdot 28$$
$$1 \cdot x = 98$$

When the coefficient is 1, the equation simplifies to become a statement of the solution, $x = 98$.

The 2 × 2 Identity Matrix

Refer to the solution to the above equation. Working backwards, the key to the solution $x = 98$ is to have obtained $1 \cdot x = 98$ in the previous step. For a system of two linear equations, if (e, f) is the solution, then the solution can be written $\begin{cases} x = e \\ y = f \end{cases}$. What is the previous step?

Working backwards, this is the same as $\begin{cases} 1x + 0y = e \\ 0x + 1y = f \end{cases}$. The coefficient matrix of this system is $\begin{bmatrix} 1 & 0 \\ 0 & 1 \end{bmatrix}$. Recall from Question 10 in Lesson 10-7 that the matrix $\begin{bmatrix} 1 & 0 \\ 0 & 1 \end{bmatrix}$ is called the 2 × 2 identity matrix because when it multiplies a 2 × 2 or 2 × 1 matrix, it does not change that matrix.

$$\begin{bmatrix} 1 & 0 \\ 0 & 1 \end{bmatrix} \cdot \begin{bmatrix} h \\ k \end{bmatrix} = \begin{bmatrix} h \\ k \end{bmatrix}$$

Thus, you can solve a system with matrices if you can convert it into an equivalent system in which the coefficient matrix is the identity matrix. This is done by multiplying both sides of the original matrix equation by a new matrix, called the **inverse** of the coefficient matrix. You can use technology to help you find the inverse matrix.

Vocabulary

inverse (of a matrix)

Mental Math

If $g(t) = -4t^2$, calculate
a. $g(10)$. -400
b. $g(5)$. -100
c. $\frac{g(10)}{g(5)}$. 4
d. $g(2)$. -16

Using Matrices to Solve Systems **629**

GOAL

Solve a 2 × 2 linear system using matrices.

SPUR Objective

D Solve systems using matrices.

Materials/Resources

· Lesson Master 10-8A or 10-8B
· Resource Master 156
· Graphing calculator
· Quiz 2

HOMEWORK

Suggestions for Assignment
• Questions 1–24
• Question 25 (extra credit)
• Reading Lesson 10-9
• Covering the Ideas 10-9

Local Standards

1 Warm-Up

1. Write the system $\begin{cases} 7x - 2y = 3 \\ -4x + 5y = 114 \end{cases}$ as a single matrix equation.
$$\begin{bmatrix} 7 & -2 \\ -4 & 5 \end{bmatrix} \begin{bmatrix} x \\ y \end{bmatrix} = \begin{bmatrix} 3 \\ 114 \end{bmatrix}$$

2. Multiply both sides of the equation in Question 1 by the matrix $\begin{bmatrix} \frac{5}{27} & \frac{2}{27} \\ \frac{4}{27} & \frac{7}{27} \end{bmatrix}$ to solve the system.
$(x, y) = (9, 30)$

Background

The use of matrices to solve systems follows a pattern that students have seen twice before. In solving $a + x = b$ for x, they have added $-a$ to both sides, giving $x = -a + b$. In solving $ax = b$ for x, they have multiplied both sides by $\frac{1}{a}$, giving $x = \frac{1}{a} \cdot b$. Note that we can write the solution to $ax = b$ as $a^{-1} \cdot b$. Similarly, with the equation $A \cdot X = B$ when A, X, and B are matrices, we multiply both sides by A^{-1}, the multiplicative inverse of A, and we obtain the matrix solution $X = A^{-1} \cdot B$.

Here are three reasons why students are learning another way to solve systems: matrix methods generalize the solving of systems with many equations and many variables, something that is done in real-world applications used by businesses; matrix methods are the ones used by computers; and matrix methods tell exactly when a system has a solution, providing an arithmetic way of determining whether there is or is not exactly one solution.

2 Teaching

Notes on the Lesson

Because this lesson is likely to be completely new to your students, you may wish to read through it with them. This will give students practice in reading matrices orally, something they likely have never done. When you get to the Example, bring out technology that will automatically compute the inverse of the matrix. Before calculators, mathematics classes spent a good amount of time developing a method for calculating the inverse of a matrix. Today, people may memorize the formula for the inverse of a 2 × 2 matrix, but very few people calculate the inverses of larger matrices by hand.

Additional Example

Example Use matrices to solve the

system. $\begin{cases} 3x + 5y = -23 \\ -2x - 3y = 14 \end{cases}$ The solution

is $(x, y) = (-1, -4)$

Example

Use matrices to solve the system $\begin{cases} 2x - 5y = 4 \\ -4x + 11y = -6 \end{cases}$.

Solution First, write the system in matrix form.

$$\begin{bmatrix} 2 & -5 \\ -4 & 11 \end{bmatrix} \cdot \begin{bmatrix} x \\ y \end{bmatrix} = \begin{bmatrix} 4 \\ -6 \end{bmatrix}$$

Use technology to find the inverse of the coefficient matrix as shown on one particular calculator below.

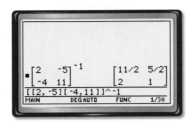

So the inverse of $\begin{bmatrix} 2 & -5 \\ -4 & 11 \end{bmatrix}$ is $\begin{bmatrix} 5.5 & 2.5 \\ 2 & 1 \end{bmatrix}$. Multiply each side of the matrix

equation by $\begin{bmatrix} 5.5 & 2.5 \\ 2 & 1 \end{bmatrix}$ on the left.

$$\underbrace{\begin{bmatrix} 5.5 & 2.5 \\ 2 & 1 \end{bmatrix} \cdot \begin{bmatrix} 2 & -5 \\ -4 & 11 \end{bmatrix}} \cdot \begin{bmatrix} x \\ y \end{bmatrix} = \underbrace{\begin{bmatrix} 5.5 & 2.5 \\ 2 & 1 \end{bmatrix} \cdot \begin{bmatrix} 4 \\ -6 \end{bmatrix}}$$

This produces the identity matrix. Multiply these matrices.

$$\begin{bmatrix} 1 & 0 \\ 0 & 1 \end{bmatrix} \cdot \begin{bmatrix} x \\ y \end{bmatrix} = \begin{bmatrix} 5.5 \cdot 4 + 2.5 \cdot -6 \\ 2 \cdot 4 + 1 \cdot -6 \end{bmatrix}$$

$$\begin{bmatrix} x \\ y \end{bmatrix} = \begin{bmatrix} 7 \\ 2 \end{bmatrix}.$$

The solution is $(x, y) = (7, 2)$.

Check Substitute $x = 7$ and $y = 2$ into each of the original equations.

Does $2 \cdot 7 - 5 \cdot 2 = 4$? Yes, $14 - 10 = 4$.

Does $-4 \cdot 7 + 11 \cdot 2 = -6$? Yes, $-28 + 22 = -6$.

Accommodating the Learner

Ask students to take time to justify why

the system $\begin{cases} 1x + 0y = e \\ 0x + 1y = f \end{cases}$ is the same as

$\begin{cases} x = e \\ y = f \end{cases}$. Further, ask students to translate

$\begin{cases} 1x + 0y = e \\ 0x + 1y = f \end{cases}$ into matrix form. They may

need to repeat the procedure several times. Encourage them to try other matrices that they might confuse with the identity matrix,

such as $\begin{bmatrix} 1 & 1 \\ 1 & 1 \end{bmatrix}$ or $\begin{bmatrix} 0 & 1 \\ 1 & 0 \end{bmatrix}$.

Inverse 2 × 2 Matrices

In the previous example, we asserted that the inverse of $\begin{bmatrix} 2 & -5 \\ -4 & 11 \end{bmatrix}$

is $\begin{bmatrix} 5.5 & 2.5 \\ 2 & 1 \end{bmatrix}$. While a calculator or computer may automatically

give you the inverse, you still need to be able to check that what you are given is correct. This is done by doing the row-by-column multiplication,

$$\begin{bmatrix} 2 & -5 \\ -4 & 11 \end{bmatrix} \cdot \begin{bmatrix} 5.5 & 2.5 \\ 2 & 1 \end{bmatrix} = \begin{bmatrix} 2 \cdot 5.5 + -5 \cdot 2 & 2 \cdot 2.5 + -5 \cdot 1 \\ -4 \cdot 5.5 + 11 \cdot 2 & -4 \cdot 2.5 + 11 \cdot 1 \end{bmatrix} = \begin{bmatrix} 1 & 0 \\ 0 & 1 \end{bmatrix}.$$

When two matrices are inverses, you can multiply them in either order and you will still get the identity matrix.

 QY

The inverse of the matrix A is denoted by the symbol A^{-1}. We write

$\begin{bmatrix} 2 & -5 \\ -4 & 11 \end{bmatrix}^{-1} = \begin{bmatrix} 5.5 & 2.5 \\ 2 & 1 \end{bmatrix}$. With powers of real numbers, $x \cdot x^{-1} = 1$,

the multiplicative identity for real numbers. With matrices,

$A \cdot A^{-1} = \begin{bmatrix} 1 & 0 \\ 0 & 1 \end{bmatrix}$, the multiplicative identity for 2×2 matrices.

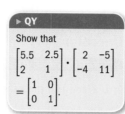

▶ QY

Show that

$$\begin{bmatrix} 5.5 & 2.5 \\ 2 & 1 \end{bmatrix} \cdot \begin{bmatrix} 2 & -5 \\ -4 & 11 \end{bmatrix}$$

$$= \begin{bmatrix} 1 & 0 \\ 0 & 1 \end{bmatrix}.$$

Summary of the Matrix Method

The matrix method of solving a system of linear equations is useful because it can be applied to systems with more than two variables in exactly the same way as it is applied to systems with two variables. You will work with these larger systems in later courses. The process is always the same.

$A \cdot \begin{bmatrix} x \\ y \end{bmatrix} = B$ 　　Write the system as the product of three matrices: coefficients · variables = constants.

$A^{-1} \cdot A \cdot \begin{bmatrix} x \\ y \end{bmatrix} = A^{-1} \cdot B$ 　　Multiply (on the left) each side by the inverse of the coefficient matrix.

$\begin{bmatrix} 1 & 0 \\ 0 & 1 \end{bmatrix} \cdot \begin{bmatrix} x \\ y \end{bmatrix} = A^{-1} \cdot B$ 　　Because A and A^{-1} are inverses, their product is the identity matrix.

$\begin{bmatrix} x \\ y \end{bmatrix} = A^{-1} \cdot B$

Using Matrices to Solve Systems 　　**631**

Notes on the Lesson

Students may wonder why the inverse of a 2 × 2 matrix A is not written as $\frac{1}{A}$ or perhaps as $\frac{I}{A}$, where I is the identity matrix. One reason is that, because matrix multiplication is not commutative, $B \cdot A^{-1}$ is not necessarily the same matrix as $A^{-1} \cdot B$. So if we wrote $\frac{B}{A}$, it could not equal both $B \cdot \frac{I}{A}$ and $\frac{I}{A} \cdot B$ and thus it would be ambiguous. Therefore, there is no division of matrices.

Students may wonder how the inverses of the 2 × 2 matrices in this lesson were found. Question 25 shows this.

Note-Taking Tips

Suggest that students set aside a section of their notes to review calculator skills. They should write a description of how to compute the multiplicative inverse of a matrix with a calculator.

Accommodating the Learner ⬆

Ask students to write several systems that have no solutions and several systems that have infinitely many solutions. Then, ask the students to write each system in matrix form and try to use their calculators to find the inverse. Discuss the result.

10-8

3 Assignment

Recommended Assignment

- Questions 1–24
- Question 25 (extra credit)
- Reading Lesson 10-9
- Covering the Ideas 10-9

Notes on the Questions

Question 5 Multiply the two matrices in both orders to show that when a matrix is multiplied by its inverse in either order, the result is the identity.

Questions 7–9 If you do not have technology for this lesson, we recommend having a formula for the inverse of a 2 × 2 matrix visible in the room so that it is easily available to students.

The left side gives the variables. The right side gives the solutions. *Caution:* Just as 0 has no multiplicative inverse, not all 2 × 2 matrices have multiplicative inverses. When a coefficient matrix does not have an inverse, then there is not a unique solution to the system. There may be infinitely many solutions, or there may be no solution.

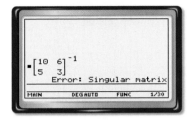

Questions

COVERING THE IDEAS

In 1–3, consider the system $\begin{cases} 1x + 0y = 7 \\ 0x + 1y = -3 \end{cases}$.

1. Solve this system. $(7, -3)$

2. Write the coefficient matrix for the system.

3. Write the matrix form for the system.

4. Write the 2 × 2 identity matrix for multiplication.

5. Show that the inverse of $\begin{bmatrix} 1 & -2 \\ 5 & 4 \end{bmatrix}$ is $\begin{bmatrix} \frac{2}{7} & \frac{1}{7} \\ -\frac{5}{14} & \frac{1}{14} \end{bmatrix}$.

6. **Multiple Choice** Which of these matrices is the inverse of $\begin{bmatrix} 3 & 4 \\ 5 & 7 \end{bmatrix}$?
   C

   A $\begin{bmatrix} -3 & -4 \\ -5 & -7 \end{bmatrix}$ B $\begin{bmatrix} -2 & -4 \\ -5 & -6 \end{bmatrix}$ C $\begin{bmatrix} 7 & -4 \\ -5 & 3 \end{bmatrix}$ D $\begin{bmatrix} \frac{1}{3} & 0 \\ 0 & \frac{1}{17} \end{bmatrix}$

In 7–9, use the given system. 7ab–9ab. See margin.
   a. Write the system in matrix form.
   b. Use technology to find the inverse of the coefficient matrix.
   c. Solve the system.

7. $\begin{cases} 3x + 5y = 27 \\ 2x + 3y = 17 \end{cases}$ 8. $\begin{cases} 2x + 3y = 18 \\ 3x + 4y = 21 \end{cases}$ 9. $\begin{cases} 2m - 6t = -6 \\ 7.5m - 15t = -37.5 \end{cases}$

APPLYING THE MATHEMATICS

10. a. Show that $\begin{bmatrix} 1 & 0 \\ 0 & -1 \end{bmatrix}$ equals its multiplicative inverse.

    b. What real numbers equal their multiplicative inverses?

    1 and −1

2. $\begin{bmatrix} 1 & 0 \\ 0 & 1 \end{bmatrix}$

3. $\begin{bmatrix} 1 & 0 \\ 0 & 1 \end{bmatrix}\begin{bmatrix} x \\ y \end{bmatrix} = \begin{bmatrix} 7 \\ -3 \end{bmatrix}$

4. $\begin{bmatrix} 1 & 0 \\ 0 & 1 \end{bmatrix}$

5.

$\begin{bmatrix} 1 & -2 \\ 5 & 4 \end{bmatrix} \cdot \begin{bmatrix} \frac{2}{7} & \frac{1}{7} \\ -\frac{5}{14} & \frac{1}{14} \end{bmatrix} = $

$\begin{bmatrix} \frac{2}{7} & \frac{1}{7} \\ -\frac{5}{14} & \frac{1}{14} \end{bmatrix} \cdot \begin{bmatrix} 1 & -2 \\ 5 & 4 \end{bmatrix} = $

$\begin{bmatrix} 1 & 0 \\ 0 & 1 \end{bmatrix}$

7c. $(x, y) = (4, 3)$

8c. $(x, y) = (-9, 12)$

9c. $(m, t) = (-9, -2)$

10a. $\begin{bmatrix} 1 & 0 \\ 0 & -1 \end{bmatrix} \cdot \begin{bmatrix} 1 & 0 \\ 0 & -1 \end{bmatrix}$

$= \begin{bmatrix} 1 & 0 \\ 0 & 1 \end{bmatrix}$

10-8A Lesson Master

Questions on SPUR Objectives
See pages 650–653 for objectives.

SKILLS Objective D

In 1–3, match each system of equations to its system in matrix form.

1. $\begin{cases} x + 2y = 5 \\ 3x - 4y = 25 \end{cases}$ **A**   2. $\begin{cases} x + 3y = 5 \\ 2x - 4y = 25 \end{cases}$ **C**   3. $\begin{cases} x + 2y = 5 \\ 3x + 4y = 25 \end{cases}$ **B**

A $\begin{bmatrix} 1 & 2 \\ 3 & -4 \end{bmatrix}\begin{bmatrix} x \\ y \end{bmatrix} = \begin{bmatrix} 5 \\ 25 \end{bmatrix}$ B $\begin{bmatrix} 1 & 2 \\ 3 & 4 \end{bmatrix}\begin{bmatrix} x \\ y \end{bmatrix} = \begin{bmatrix} 5 \\ 25 \end{bmatrix}$ C $\begin{bmatrix} 1 & 3 \\ 2 & -4 \end{bmatrix}\begin{bmatrix} x \\ y \end{bmatrix} = \begin{bmatrix} 5 \\ 25 \end{bmatrix}$

4. Consider the system $\begin{cases} 7x - 3y = 23 \\ 4x + y = 43 \end{cases}$

   a. Write the matrix form of the system. $\begin{bmatrix} 7 & -3 \\ 4 & 1 \end{bmatrix}\begin{bmatrix} x \\ y \end{bmatrix} = \begin{bmatrix} 23 \\ 43 \end{bmatrix}$

   b. Use technology to find the inverse of the coefficient matrix. $\approx \begin{bmatrix} 0.053 & 0.158 \\ -0.211 & 0.368 \end{bmatrix}$

   c. Solve the system. $\begin{bmatrix} 8 \\ 11 \end{bmatrix}$

In 5 and 6, use matrices to solve the system.

5. $\begin{cases} 8x - 4y = 80 \\ x - 6.5y = 10 \end{cases}$ 6. $\begin{cases} 3m + 6n = -18 \\ -m + 3n = -19 \end{cases}$

   $(10, 0)$ $(4, -5)$

7. On a math test, there were multiple choice and show-your-work problems. Nanette got 7 multiple choice problems correct and 6 show-your-work problems correct. She received 62 points on the test. Zach got 9 multiple choice problems correct and 5 show-your-work problems correct. He received 58 points on the test.

   $\begin{cases} 7m + 6s = 62 \\ 9m + 5s = 58 \end{cases}$

   a. Write a system of equations to represent the problem.

   b. Write the system in matrix form. $\begin{bmatrix} 7 & 6 \\ 9 & 5 \end{bmatrix}\begin{bmatrix} m \\ s \end{bmatrix} = \begin{bmatrix} 62 \\ 58 \end{bmatrix}$

   c. Solve the system. Explain what the solution means.

   d. If the test had 10 multiple choice problems and 6 show-your-work problems, how many total points was the test worth? **68 points**

7c. $\begin{bmatrix} 2 \\ 8 \end{bmatrix}$; the multiple choice questions were worth 2 points each and the show-your-work problems were worth 8 points each.

Additional Answers

7a. $\begin{bmatrix} 3 & 5 \\ 2 & 3 \end{bmatrix}\begin{bmatrix} x \\ y \end{bmatrix} = \begin{bmatrix} 27 \\ 17 \end{bmatrix}$

7b. $\begin{bmatrix} -3 & 5 \\ 2 & -3 \end{bmatrix}$

8a. $\begin{bmatrix} 2 & 3 \\ 3 & 4 \end{bmatrix}\begin{bmatrix} x \\ y \end{bmatrix} = \begin{bmatrix} 18 \\ 21 \end{bmatrix}$

8b. $\begin{bmatrix} -4 & 3 \\ 3 & -2 \end{bmatrix}$

9a. $\begin{bmatrix} 2 & -6 \\ 7.5 & -15 \end{bmatrix}\begin{bmatrix} m \\ t \end{bmatrix} = \begin{bmatrix} -6 \\ -37.5 \end{bmatrix}$

9b. $\begin{bmatrix} -1 & 4 \\ -.5 & .13 \end{bmatrix}$

In 11 and 12, a system is given. **11a, c–12a, c. See margin.**
  a. Using inverse matrices, write the product of two matrices that
     will find the solution.
  b. Give the solution.
  c. Check the solution.

11. $\begin{cases} 2.3x + y = -5.5 \\ 3.1x + 2.4y = -1.1 \end{cases}$ 12. $\begin{cases} 0.5m + 1.5t = 10 \\ t + 14 = 0.5m \end{cases}$

11b. $(x, y) = (-5, 6)$

12b. $(m, t) = (24.8, -1.6)$

13. Consider the three systems below.

  i. $\begin{cases} x - 8y = -35 \\ 5x + 8y = 65 \end{cases}$ ii. $\begin{cases} y = x - 3 \\ 2x + 3y = 16 \end{cases}$ iii. $\begin{cases} 4x - 5y = 8 \\ 12x - 15y = 3 \end{cases}$

13a. iii; $\begin{bmatrix} 4 & -5 \\ 12 & -15 \end{bmatrix}$

  a. Choose the system which describes two parallel lines, and
     write its coefficient matrix.
  b. What is your calculator's response when you try to find the
     inverse of the coefficient matrix of the system you chose in
     Part a? Answers vary. Sample answer: Error: Singular matrix.

14. Show that the matrix $\begin{bmatrix} 3 & 5 \\ 9 & 15 \end{bmatrix}$ has no multiplicative inverse by
    writing the matrix equation $\begin{bmatrix} 3 & 5 \\ 9 & 15 \end{bmatrix} \cdot \begin{bmatrix} a & b \\ c & d \end{bmatrix} = \begin{bmatrix} 1 & 0 \\ 0 & 1 \end{bmatrix}$ as two
    systems of equations and showing that those systems have
    no solution.

14. $\begin{cases} 3a + 5c = 1 \\ 9a + 15c = 0 \end{cases}$,
    $\begin{cases} 3b + 5d = 0 \\ 9b + 15d = 1 \end{cases}$
    No solutions, the lines
    are parallel.

REVIEW

In 15 and 16, multiply the given matrices. (Lesson 10-7) See margin.

15. $\begin{bmatrix} 5 & 6 \\ 2 & -3 \end{bmatrix} \cdot \begin{bmatrix} -4 & 1 \\ 0 & 2 \end{bmatrix}$ 16. $\begin{bmatrix} 1 & 2 \\ 4 & 3 \end{bmatrix} \cdot \begin{bmatrix} 8 \\ -2 \end{bmatrix}$

17. Solve $\begin{bmatrix} -4 & 1 \\ 3 & 6 \end{bmatrix} \cdot \begin{bmatrix} 5 \\ a \end{bmatrix} = \begin{bmatrix} -12 \\ 63 \end{bmatrix}$ for a. (Lesson 10-7) $a = 8$

In 18 and 19, determine whether the lines are parallel and
nonintersecting, coincident, or intersecting in only one point.
(Lesson 10-6)

18. $\begin{cases} y = 4x - 6 \\ 28x - 7y = -10 \end{cases}$ 19. $\begin{cases} 8x + 6y = 10 \\ 4x - 3y = -5 \end{cases}$

20. A jar of change contains 64 coins consisting only of quarters
    and dimes. The total value of the coins in the jar is $13.60. Let
    q = the number of quarters, and d = the number of dimes.
    (Lesson 10-4) 20a. $q + d = 64$, $0.25q + 0.10d = 13.60$
  a. Write two equations that describe the information given above.
  b. How many of each type of coin is in the jar? **48 quarters and
     16 dimes**

Each dime has 118 reeds and
each quarter has 119 reeds
along its outer edge.

Source: U.S. Mint

Questions 13 and 14 These questions
show the relationship between systems
that have no solution or infinitely many
solutions and the inverses of matrices.
It is a beautiful relationship and one
that may surprise many students
because of its simplicity.

Additional Answers

11a. $\begin{bmatrix} 0.992 & -0.413 \\ -1.281 & 0.950 \end{bmatrix} \begin{bmatrix} -5.5 \\ -1.1 \end{bmatrix}$

11c. Substitute
     $2.3(-5) + 6 = -5.5$
     $3.1(-5) + 2.4(6) = -1.1$

12a. $\begin{bmatrix} 0.8 & -1.2 \\ 0.4 & 0.4 \end{bmatrix} \begin{bmatrix} 10 \\ -14 \end{bmatrix}$

12c. Substitute
     $0.5(24.8) + 1.5(-1.6) = 10$
     $-0.5(24.8) + 1(-1.6) = -14$

15. $\begin{bmatrix} -20 & 17 \\ -8 & -4 \end{bmatrix}$

16. $\begin{bmatrix} 4 \\ 26 \end{bmatrix}$

18. parallel and
    nonintersecting

19. intersecting at
    only one point

10-8

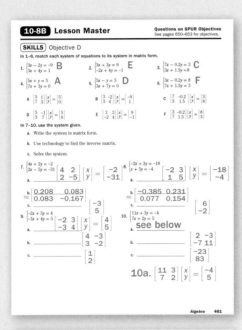

21. **Skill Sequence** Solve each equation. (Lessons 9-5, 9-2, 8-6)

 a. $x^2 = 144$ $x = 12, x = -12$

 b. $x^2 + 44 = 144$ $x = 10, x = -10$

 c. $4x^2 + 44 = 144$ $x = 5, x = -5$

 d. $4x^2 + 44x + 265 = 144$ $x = -5.5$

22. Simplify the expression $\sqrt{x} \cdot \sqrt{x} \cdot \sqrt{x^3}$. (Lessons 8-7, 8-6) $x^2\sqrt{x}$

23. Suppose a bank offers a 4.60% annual yield on a 4-year CD. What would be the amount paid at the end of the 4 years to an investor who invests $1,800 in this CD? (Lesson 7-1) $2,154.76

24. Ms. Brodeur wants to lease about 2,000 square meters of floor space for a business. She noticed an advertisement in the newspaper regarding a set of 3 vacant stores. Their widths are given in the floor plan at the right. How deep must these stores be to meet Ms. Brodeur's required area? (Lesson 2-1)
 31.25 m deep

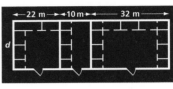

EXPLORATION

25. A formula for the inverse of a 2×2 matrix $\begin{bmatrix} a & b \\ c & d \end{bmatrix}$ can be found by following these steps.

 Step 1 Write $\begin{bmatrix} a & b \\ c & d \end{bmatrix} \cdot \begin{bmatrix} x & u \\ y & v \end{bmatrix} = \begin{bmatrix} 1 & 0 \\ 0 & 1 \end{bmatrix}$ as two systems of equations. Keep a, b, c, and d as the coefficients. One system will have the variables x and y and the other will have u and v.

 Step 2 Solve for x, y, u, and v in terms of a, b, c, and d. Find a formula in this way and check it with at least two different matrices. You may want to use a CAS to find the formula.

 Answers vary. Sample answer: $x = \dfrac{d}{ad - bc}$, $y = \dfrac{-c}{ad - bc}$,

 $u = \dfrac{-b}{ad - bc}$, $v = \dfrac{a}{ad - bc}$; $\begin{bmatrix} a & b \\ c & d \end{bmatrix}^{-1} = \dfrac{1}{ad - bc}\begin{bmatrix} d & -b \\ -c & a \end{bmatrix}$

25. Step 1

$\begin{cases} ax + by = 1 \\ cx + dy = 0 \end{cases}$

$\begin{cases} au + bv = 0 \\ cu + dv = 1 \end{cases}$

QY ANSWER

$\begin{bmatrix} 5.5 & 2.5 \\ 2 & 1 \end{bmatrix} \cdot \begin{bmatrix} 2 & -5 \\ -4 & 11 \end{bmatrix} =$

$\begin{bmatrix} 5.5 \cdot 2 + 2.5 \cdot -4 & 5.5 \cdot -5 + 2.5 \cdot 11 \\ 2 \cdot 2 + 1 \cdot -4 & 2 \cdot -5 + 1 \cdot 11 \end{bmatrix}$

$= \begin{bmatrix} 1 & 0 \\ 0 & 1 \end{bmatrix}$

Lesson 10-9 — Systems of Inequalities

> **BIG IDEA** The graph of the solutions to a system of linear inequalities is a region bounded by lines.

In Lesson 6-9, you graphed linear inequalities like $y < 11$ and $y \geq 4x + 3$ on a coordinate plane. These inequalities describe half-planes. In this lesson, you will see how to graph regions described by a system of two or more inequalities. Solving a system of inequalities involves finding the common solutions of two or more inequalities.

Example 1

Graph all solutions to the system $\begin{cases} x \geq 0 \\ y \geq 0 \end{cases}$.

Solution First graph the solution to $x \geq 0$. It is shown at the left below. Then graph the solution $y \geq 0$, shown at the right below.

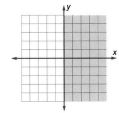 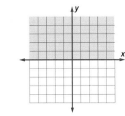

The solution to the system is the set of points common to both of the sets above. At the right we show the solutions to the two inequalities superimposed. At the far right is the solution to the system. The solution is the intersection of the two solution sets above shown in green. It consists of the first quadrant and the nonnegative parts of the x- and y-axes.

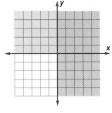 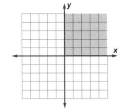

Recall that in general, the graph of $Ax + By < C$ is a half-plane, and that it lies on one side of the boundary line $Ax + By = C$.

Mental Math

Refer to the figure. Find c if

a. $a = 75°$ and $b = 40°$
65°
b. $a = 75°$ and $b = 39°$
66°
c. $a = b$ $180° - 2a$ or $180 - 2b$

GOAL

Graphically solve systems of linear inequalities in two variables.

SPUR Objectives

H Use systems of linear inequalities to solve real-world problems.

J Graphically represent solutions to systems of linear inequalities.

K Write a system of inequalities given a graph.

Materials/Resources

- Lesson Master 10-9A or 10-9B
- Resource Masters 1, 2, 157, and 158
- Graphing calculator

HOMEWORK

Suggestions for Assignment
- Questions 1–20
- Question 21 (extra credit)
- Reading Lesson 10-10
- Covering the Ideas 10-10

Local Standards

1 Warm-Up

In 1–4, tell whether the ordered pair is a solution to the inequality $4x - 3y > 36$.

1. (0, 0) no
2. (18, −12) yes
3. (−3, −16) no (It is on the border.)
4. (2,574, 2,918) yes (more easily determined by estimating than by exact calculation)

Background

Graphing systems of inequalities gives another visual image for the idea that solutions of systems must satisfy all the conditions. Systems of inequalities are the basis of linear programming, a topic studied in some detail in *UCSMP Advanced Algebra*.

Example 1. This example shows that the first quadrant can be described as the solution to the system of linear inequalities $x > 0$ and $y > 0$. The systems in Questions 1 and 2 give the fourth and second quadrants, respectively.

Example 2. This example shows how the solutions to a system of linear inequalities can describe the interior of a polygon.

10-9

2 Teaching

Notes on the Lesson

Example 1 Because Example 1 describes the first quadrant with a system, and Questions 1 and 2 deal with the fourth and second quadrants, you might wish to begin by asking students for a system that describes the third quadrant.

Graphing systems of inequalities is not easy for many students. Use a calculator projection device to show the overlap. Shade the graphs of two inequalities differently. Show them separately to make sure that students understand which half-plane should be shaded for each inequality. Then place them on the same grid so that students can see that the region where the individual graphs overlap is the solution region.

Additional Examples

Example 1 Graph all solutions to the system. $\begin{cases} x > 3 \\ y \le 0 \end{cases}$

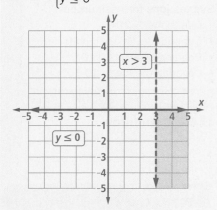

Example 2 Graph all solutions.
$\begin{cases} y \ge -2 \\ x < 4 \\ y < 2x + 3 \end{cases}$

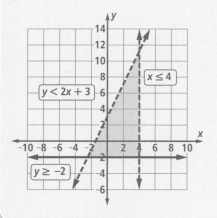

Example 2

Graph all solutions to the system $\begin{cases} y \le 3 \\ x > -2 \\ y > x - 1 \end{cases}$.

Solution The graph of the system is the set of points in common to all three half-planes. So graph all three inequalities.

Inequality 1 Graph $y \le 3$. First graph the boundary line $y = 3$. Graphically, $y \le 3$ consists of all points below (less than) or on (equal to) the solid boundary line. This is shaded in blue at the right.

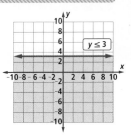

Inequality 2 Graph $x > -2$. Graph the boundary line $x = -2$. This line is dashed since we want only values greater than -2. $x > -2$ tells us to shade to the right of the line in red where values are greater than -2.

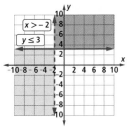

Inequality 3 Graph $y > x - 1$. Graph the dashed boundary line $y = x - 1$ and shade above the line as shown in yellow below.

The solution is the region shown below and includes one of the sides of the triangle. The graph at the far right shows what your final graph should look like.

Check A partial check is to choose a point in the intersection region. We choose $(1, 2)$. Substitute the point into all the inequalities.

Is $2 \le 3$? Yes.

Is $1 > -2$? Yes.

Is $2 > 1 - 1$? Yes.

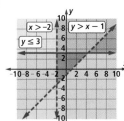 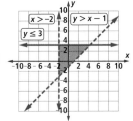

When an intersection point cannot be found easily from a graph, you need to solve a system of equations to find it.

GUIDED

Example 3

Graph all solutions to the system $\begin{cases} y < 2x + 3 \\ y > 2x - 2 \end{cases}$.

Solution

1. The boundary lines $y = 2x + 3$ and $y = 2x - 2$ have the same slope. So they are _____?_____ lines. **parallel**

2. Graph the lines.

2.

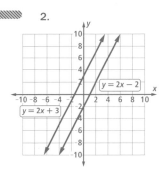

Accommodating the Learner ⬇

Consider assigning a review worksheet to remind students how to graph linear inequalities. Check to make sure most students are proficient with this topic before beginning Lesson 10-9.

3. The solutions to $y < 2x + 3$ comprise the half-plane ___?___ the boundary line. The solutions to $y > 2x - 2$ make up the
(above/below)
half-plane ___?___ the line.
(above/below)
You saw in Lesson 10-6 that a system whose graph is made up of nonintersecting and parallel lines has no solutions. Is this necessarily true for a system of inequalities whose boundary lines are nonintersecting and parallel? Explain. ___?___

4. Graph the intersection of the two half-planes in Step 3.

Questions

COVERING THE IDEAS

1. The graph of all solutions to $\begin{cases} x > 0 \\ y < 0 \end{cases}$ consists of all points in which quadrant? **IV**

2. Graph the solutions to the system $\begin{cases} x < 0 \\ y > 0 \end{cases}$.

3. Consider the system $\begin{cases} y \le 4x + 1 \\ y > 2x + 1 \end{cases}$.

   a. How is the graph of all solutions to the system related to the graphs of $y \le 4x + 1$ and $y > 2x + 1$?

   b. **Fill in the Blank** The graph of $y > 2x + 1$ is a ___?___ half-plane.

   c. Why does the graph of $y \le 4x + 1$ include its boundary line?

   d. Is $(2, 5)$ a solution to this system? How can you tell?
   No, it is not because it is on the boundary line $y = 2x + 1$.

In 4 and 5, graph the solution to the system. 4–5. See margin.

4. $\begin{cases} x > 0 \\ y > 0 \\ 3x + y < 10 \end{cases}$ 5. $\begin{cases} x \ge -3 \\ y \le 4 \\ y \ge 2x + 1 \end{cases}$

6. Consider the system $\begin{cases} x > 0 \\ y > 0 \\ x + y < 30 \\ x + y > 20 \end{cases}$.

   a. The graph of all solutions to this system is the interior of a quadrilateral with what vertices?

   b. Name two points that are solutions to the system.

   c. Is $(9, 10)$ a solution to the system? Why or why not?

Example 3

3. below; above; No, because the half-planes can intersect even if the lines do not.

4.
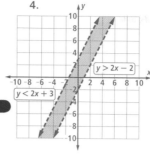

Question 2.

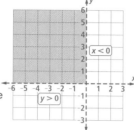

3a. It is the intersection of the half-planes below or on the line $y = 4x + 1$ and above $y = 2x + 1$.

3c. Because $\le$ means less than or equal to, not just less than.

6a. $(0, 20)$, $(0, 30)$, $(20, 0)$, $(30, 0)$

6b. Answers vary. Sample answer: $(2, 20)$, $(8, 15)$

6c. No, because $9 + 10 < 20$, and all solutions (a, b) must be such that $a + b > 20$.

Systems of Inequalities   **637**

Additional Example

Example 3 Graph all solutions.
$\begin{cases} y > 4x - 1 \\ y \le 4x + 2 \end{cases}$

Solution

1. The boundary lines $y = 4x - 1$ and $y = 4x + 2$ have the same slope. So they are ___?___ lines. **parallel**

2. Graph the lines.

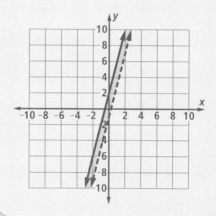

Accommodating the Learner ⬆

Ask students to consider Additional Example 3, but with the inequality symbols reversed. In other words, ask them to consider the system $\begin{cases} y < 4x - 1 \\ y \ge 4x + 2 \end{cases}$.

They should realize that, in this case, the two regions fail to overlap. Thus, there are no solutions to the system. Remind students that the graph of the solution will be a blank coordinate plane, not even including the line $y = 4x + 2$.

Additional Answers

4.
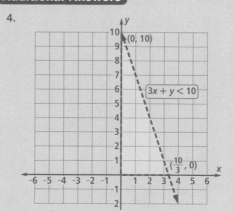

5. See answer on page 638.

Notes on the Questions

You will want to cover Questions 1–7 in order to get at the basic ideas of this lesson.

Question 10 Ask students to give a system of inequalities for the interior of a parallelogram that is not a rectangle and has no vertical or horizontal sides.

Questions 11–13 In each of these situations, the solutions are identified by points with integer coordinates.

Question 21 You might point out to students that the figures drawn in computer games are often described by giving inequalities. This is how the computer knows to shade regions rather than just draw stick figures.

Additional Answers

5.

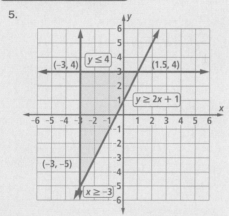

11a. $\begin{cases} 10L + 8P \leq 60 \\ P \geq 0 \\ L \geq 0 \end{cases}$

11b.

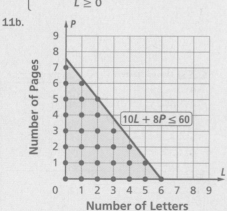

7. The solution to a system of equations that involves different parallel lines is Ø (empty set). You saw in Example 3 this is not necessarily true of a system of inequalities that involves parallel lines. Is it possible to have a system of inequalities whose solution is Ø? Why or why not? **Yes it is possible. If there are no solutions satisfying both conditions, then the solution is Ø.**

APPLYING THE MATHEMATICS

In 8 and 9, describe the shaded region with a system of inequalities.

8.

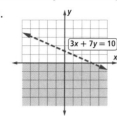

9.

8. $\begin{cases} x \geq 0 \\ y \leq 0 \\ 2x - y \leq 10 \end{cases}$

9. $\begin{cases} y \leq 0 \\ 3x + 7y < 10 \end{cases}$

10. $\begin{cases} y < 10 \\ y > -1 \\ x < 5 \\ x > -3 \end{cases}$

10. Write the system of inequalities whose solution is the interior of the rectangle with vertices (–3, 10), (5, 10), (5, –1), and (–3, –1).

11. It takes Tippie about 10 minutes to type a letter of moderate length and about 8 minutes to type a normal double-spaced page.
    a. Write a system of inequalities that describes the total number of letters *L* and pages *P* Tippie can type in an hour or less. Assume the number of letters typed is greater than or equal to zero, as is the number of pages. **11a-b. See margin.**
    b. Accurately graph the set of points that satisfies the system.

12. An actress is paid $300 per day to understudy a part and $750 per day to perform the role before an audience. During one run, an actress earned between $4,000 and $7,000. **12a. 9 times**
    a. At most, how many times might she have performed the role?
    b. What is the maximum number of times she might have been an understudy? **23 times**
    c. Graph all possible ways she might have earned her salary. **See margin.**

13. A hockey team is scheduled to play 14 games during a season. Its coach estimates that it needs at least 20 points to make the playoffs. A win is worth 2 points and a tie is worth 1 point.
    a. Make a graph of all the combinations of wins *w* and ties *t* that will get the team into the playoffs. **See margin.**
    b. How many ways are there for the team to make the playoffs? **25**

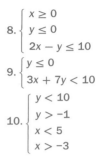

Actors' Equity Association, founded in 1913, is the labor union that represents more than 45,000 actors and stage managers in the United States.

Source: Actors' Equity Association

638   Linear Systems

Additional Answers

12c. integer values within this range

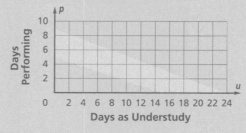

13a.

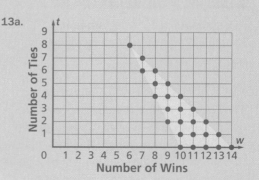

REVIEW

In 14 and 15, a system of equations is given.
  a. Write the system in matrix form.
  b. Use technology to find the inverse of the coefficient matrix.
  c. Solve the system. (Lesson 10-8)

14. $\begin{cases} y = 3x - 8 \\ 4x + 4y = 12 \end{cases}$

15. $\begin{cases} 6x + 4y = 14 \\ -2x - 3y = -18 \end{cases}$

16. Let ℓ be the line with equation $y = -4x + 9$. Write an equation of a line that (Lesson 10-6) Answers vary. Sample answers are given.
  a. coincides with ℓ.
    $2y = -8x + 18$
  b. does not intersect ℓ.
    $y = -4x + 2$

17. Solve the system $\begin{cases} 2.5x + y = 6 \\ 9x + 4y = 17.5 \end{cases}$ using any method.
  (Lessons 10-5, 10-4, 10-2, 10-1) $(6.5, -10.25)$

In 18–20, use the formula $h = -16t^2 + 94t + 2$ for the height h in feet of a model rocket t seconds after being fired straight up from a stand 2 feet off the ground. (Lessons 9-5, 9-4, 9-3)

18. a. Graph the equation. See margin.
  b. Use the graph to find the maximum height of the rocket. 140.063 ft

19. a. Find the height of the rocket after 6 seconds. -10 ft
  b. Interpret your answer to Part a.
    The rocket has already landed.
20. Use the Quadratic Formula to calculate at what time(s) the rocket is at a height of 100 feet. about 1.36 and 4.52 sec

EXPLORATION

21. Find a system of linear inequalities whose solution on a coordinate plane is a region like the one shown at the right.

14a. $\begin{bmatrix} -3 & 1 \\ 4 & 4 \end{bmatrix} \cdot \begin{bmatrix} x \\ y \end{bmatrix} = \begin{bmatrix} 8 \\ 12 \end{bmatrix}$

14b. $\begin{bmatrix} -0.25 & 0.0625 \\ 0.25 & 0.1875 \end{bmatrix}$

14c. $(2.75, 0.25)$

15a. $\begin{bmatrix} 6 & 4 \\ -2 & -3 \end{bmatrix} \cdot \begin{bmatrix} x \\ y \end{bmatrix} = \begin{bmatrix} 14 \\ -18 \end{bmatrix}$

15b. $\begin{bmatrix} \frac{3}{10} & \frac{2}{5} \\ -\frac{1}{5} & -\frac{3}{5} \end{bmatrix}$

15c. $(-3, 8)$

21. Answers vary.
  Sample answer:
  $\begin{cases} y \geq 0 \\ x \geq 0 \\ y \leq x + 4 \\ y \leq -x + 10 \\ y \leq 5 \\ x \leq 4 \end{cases}$

Additional Answers

18a.

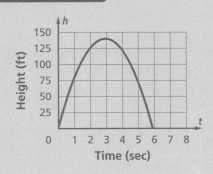

4) Wrap-Up

Ongoing Assessment

Write a system of inequalities on the board, and ask students to individually graph the solution to the system. Then ask for volunteers who can teach the class how to do the problem by explaining his or her method to a student at the board. Make sure the student at the board does only and exactly what the student instructs, and allow classmates to correct if the "instructor" makes a mistake.

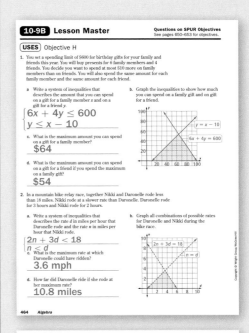

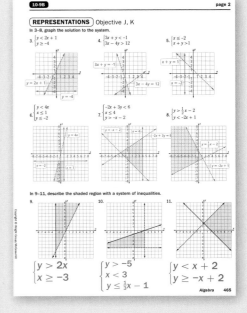

Lesson 10-10

GOAL

Apply the techniques of the chapter to the solution of systems in which at least one equation is not linear.

SPUR Objectives

E Solve nonlinear systems.

I Find solutions to systems of equations by graphing.

Materials/Resources

· Lesson Master 10-10A or 10-10B
· Resource Masters 2 and 159
· Graphing calculator

HOMEWORK

Suggestions for Assignment
• Questions 1–18
• Question 19 (extra credit)
• Reading Lesson 11-1
• Covering the Ideas 11-1

Local Standards

1 Warm-Up

In 1–3, graph to find all solutions to the system.

1. $\begin{cases} y = x^2 \\ y = x + 6 \end{cases}$ (3, 9) and (−2, 4)

2. $\begin{cases} f(x) = x^2 + 3x + 4 \\ g(x) = x^2 + 5x - 2 \end{cases}$ (3, 22)

3. $\begin{cases} y = 3 \cdot 2^x \\ y = 2 \cdot 3^x \end{cases}$ (1, 6)

Lesson 10-10 Nonlinear Systems

Vocabulary

nonlinear system

Mental Math

Refer to the rectangle.

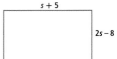

a. What is the area of the rectangle? $2s^2 + 2s - 40$

b. What is the perimeter of the rectangle? $6s - 6$

▶ **BIG IDEA** The ideas used to solve systems of linear equations can be applied to solve some systems of nonlinear equations.

Previously in this chapter you have worked with systems of linear equations. In these systems, every graph involved is a line. In this lesson, we consider systems that involve curves. A **nonlinear system** is a system of equations or inequalities in which at least one of the equations or inequalities is nonlinear.

GUIDED

Example 1

Solve the system $\begin{cases} y = x^2 + 3 \\ y = x + 9 \end{cases}$.

Solution Look at the graphs at the right. The solutions occur at the points of intersection. These graphs intersect at (−2, _?_) and (3, _?_); therefore, the system has two solutions. **7; 12**

The solutions are (_?_) and (_?_). **−2, 7; 3, 12**

🛑 **QY**

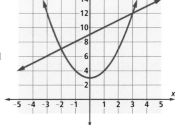

Solving algebraically using substitution is also an option. You may need to use the Quadratic Formula.

▶ **QY**

Check your answer to Guided Example 1 by substituting the coordinates of each point into both equations to verify that they are solutions to the system.

Example 2

Solve the system $\begin{cases} y = -2x + 8 \\ y = -x^2 + 4x - 1 \end{cases}$.

Solution Because both expressions in x are equal to y, they are equal to each other at the point of intersection.

$$-2x + 8 = -x^2 + 4x - 1 \qquad \text{Substitution}$$
$$8 = -x^2 + 6x - 1 \qquad \text{Add } 2x \text{ to both sides.}$$
$$0 = -x^2 + 6x - 9 \qquad \text{Subtract 8 from both sides.}$$
$$x = \frac{-6 \pm \sqrt{6^2 - 4(-1)(-9)}}{2(-1)} \qquad \text{Quadratic Formula}$$
$$x = \frac{-6 \pm \sqrt{36 - 36}}{-2} = \frac{-6 \pm 0}{-2} \text{ or } 3$$

640 Linear Systems

Background

This lesson serves two purposes. First, it helps students understand the special nature of linear systems by showing them systems that are not linear. Otherwise students might think that the only systems that exist are linear. Second, it shows students the power that they have acquired by learning the methods of the previous lessons of the chapter, for they can now apply these methods (substitution, addition and subtraction, multiplication) to nonlinear systems.

Example 1. This example shows that there may be more than one solution to a nonlinear system. It gets students to realize that for each x-coordinate of a point of intersection, there is a corresponding y-coordinate and thus a solution.

Example 2. The system in this example, like Example 1, involves a linear equation and a quadratic equation. But here there is exactly one solution. So the line intersects the parabola in exactly one point.

(continued on next page)

Now find the y-coordinate of the point of intersection.

$y = -2x + 8$

$y = -2(3) + 8 = -6 + 8 = 2$

The solution is (3, 2).

Check The graph reinforces that there is only one solution and that it is at (3, 2), as shown on the screen at the right.

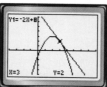

Some nonlinear systems have no solutions.

Example 3

Solve the system $\begin{cases} y = x^2 + 6x + 11 \\ y = -x^2 + 6x - 9 \end{cases}$.

Solution 1 Use substitution.

$x^2 + 6x + 11 = -x^2 + 6x - 9$

$2x^2 + 6x + 11 = 6x - 9$	Add x^2.
$2x^2 + 11 = -9$	Subtract $6x$.
$2x^2 = -20$	Subtract 11.
$x^2 = -10$	Divide by 2.
$x = \pm\sqrt{-10}$	Take the square root.

The solutions $\sqrt{-10}$ and $-\sqrt{-10}$ are not real numbers, so there is no solution for this system in the set of real numbers.

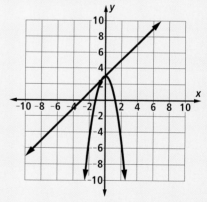

Solution 2 Graph the equations.

The parabolas never intersect, so there is no solution to this system.

When you don't know how to solve a system of equations algebraically, you can use a graphing approach to make very good approximations.

Example 4

Jonas is working on a science fair project. He wants to study the result of combining equal populations (in weight) of two types of bacteria. The first bacteria (in grams) grow according to the function $f(x) = 15(0.8)^x$ where $x =$ the time from now (in hours). The other bacteria growth (in grams) is modeled by $g(x) = 4(1.5)^x$, where $x =$ the time from now (in hours). If Jonas wants to combine them when the two populations are equal, how long will he have to wait? How many grams of each type of bacteria will there be at that time?

(continued on next page)

Example 3. Two different parabolas can intersect in as many as 4 points. Consider $y = x^2 - 5$ and $x = (y + 1)^2 + 5$. These parabolas do not intersect at all. Algebraically, the signal is that the solutions to the system are not real numbers.

Example 4. Two exponential curves of this type intersect in at most one point.

---

2 Teaching

Notes on the Lesson

This lesson is designed to give students a taste of the more complicated systems they might encounter in later mathematics courses. Do not expect mastery here.

Point out to students that when they solved an equation such as $9 = x^2 - 5x + 13$ by graphing Y1 = 9 and Y2 = $x^2 - 5x + 13$, they were turning a single equation into a system of equations. So they have solved systems involving quadratic equations well before this lesson.

Each example in this lesson is graphed. Advise students to do the same with each system that they solve in the Questions even when they are not asked to graph.

Additional Examples

Example 1 Solve the system.

$\begin{cases} y = -2x^2 + 3 \\ y = x + 3 \end{cases}$

Solution

Look at the graphs.

Just as with two linear equations, the solutions occur at the points of intersection. These graphs intersect at (0, _?_); therefore, the system has one solution. 3

The solution is (0, _?_). 3

Example 2 Solve the system.

$\begin{cases} y = 2x + 1 \\ y = x^2 + 7x + 5 \end{cases}$ (−1, −1)

Example 3 Solve the system.

$\begin{cases} y = -x^2 + 10x - 27 \\ y = 0.1x + 3 \end{cases}$ There is no solution to this system.

10-10

Additional Example

Example 4 The population of Atown is 30,000 and has an annual growth rate of 1.7%. The population of Anothertown is 28,000 and has an annual growth rate of 2.5%. Approximately how many years will pass before the towns have equal populations? What will their populations be at that time, to the nearest thousand? *It will be 8 years, and their populations will be approximately 34,000.*

Solution This situation can be represented by the following system.

$$\begin{cases} f(x) = 15(0.8)^x \\ g(x) = 4(1.5)^x \end{cases}$$

Graph the two functions on your calculator. Be sure to include any intersections in the viewing window. Use the INTERSECT command to find an accurate approximation for the solution.

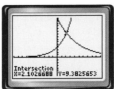

Intersection X=2.1026688 Y=9.3825653

Jonas should combine the bacteria in approximately 2.10 hours (or 2 hours and 6 minutes). There will be about 9.4 grams of bacteria in each population at that time.

Questions

COVERING THE IDEAS

In 1 and 2, solve the system using substitution.

1. $\begin{cases} y = 2x^2 + 12x + 17 \\ y = -x^2 - 6x - 10 \end{cases}$ (−3, −1) 2. $\begin{cases} y = x^2 + 4x + 3 \\ y = 3x + 1 \end{cases}$ no solution

3. Solve the system $\begin{cases} y = 3x^2 \\ y = -4x^2 \end{cases}$ by picturing the graph in your head. (0, 0)

In 4–6, solve the system.

4. $\begin{cases} y = x^2 - 6x + 1 \\ y = -x^2 + 4x + 1 \end{cases}$ (0, 1), (5, −4)

5. $\begin{cases} p = 9q + 25 \\ p = 2q^2 + 7q + 1 \end{cases}$ (4, 61), (−3, −2)

6. $\begin{cases} y = x^2 + 3 \\ y = -x + 1 \end{cases}$ no solution

In 7 and 8, solve the system by graphing. Round solutions to the nearest hundredth.

7. $\begin{cases} y = 5x^2 + 5 \\ y = 0.5x^2 \end{cases}$ 8. $\begin{cases} y = 2.718^x \\ y = 3.14(0.25)^x \end{cases}$ (0.48, 1.62)

APPLYING THE MATHEMATICS

In 9 and 10, solve the system by graphing.

9. $\begin{cases} y = |x - 3| \\ y = -2x^2 + 12x - 18 \end{cases}$ 10. $\begin{cases} y = x^2 \\ y = 2^x \end{cases}$ See margin.

7. no solution

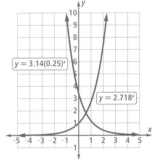

$y = 5x^2 + 5$
$y = 0.5x^2$

8.

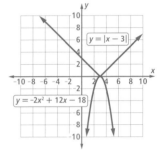

$y = 3.14(0.25)^x$
$y = 2.718^x$

9. (3, 0)

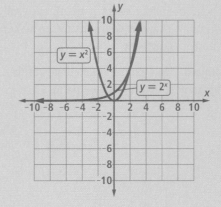

$y = |x - 3|$
$y = -2x^2 + 12x - 18$

Accommodating the Learner

Review the use of the quadratic formula with students. Remind them that the only time the quadratic formula yields a nonreal solution is when the discriminant, or $b^2 - 4ac$, is negative. For instance, in Additional Example 2, the discriminant is 9, so the answer is real.

Additional Answers

10. (−0.77, 0.59), (2, 4)

$y = x^2$
$y = 2^x$

11. Solve the system of Example 3 by addition. See margin.

12. A quarterback passes a football to a receiver downfield. The path of the ball is described by the equation $h = -0.025x^2 + x + 6$, where $x =$ the horizontal distance (in yards) of the ball from the quarterback and h is the height of the ball (in feet) above the ground. The receiver catches the ball 40 yards downfield. A bird flies over the quarterback in the same direction as the ball. Its flight is described by the equation $y = \frac{7}{60}x + 10$, where $x =$ the distance from the quarterback (in yards) and y is the bird's height (in feet).

   a. When the quarterback first threw the ball, how high was it off the ground? 6 ft

   b. How high was the bird when it was right over the quarterback? 10 ft

   c. How many times did the path of the bird and the football cross? twice

   d. Give these points of intersection. $(5.\overline{3}, 10.6\overline{2})$, and $(30, 13.5)$

   e. Notice that the time when the bird or the football is moving is not given. Explain why this means the bird and ball might not have hit each other. See margin.

13. During a spring training game in 2001, baseball pitching great Randy Johnson threw a fastball. A bird flew in the ball's path and was accidentally struck by the ball. This is the only time in Major League Baseball that a bird has been struck by a pitch. A possible equation for the height of Randy Johnson's pitch is $h = -5.56t^2 - 1.39t + 4.25$, where t is the time in seconds since he threw the ball and h is the ball's height in feet above the ground. A possible equation for the bird's height is $h = -24.42t^2 + 3.94t + 5.14$, where t is the time in seconds since Randy's pitch and h is the bird's height above the ground in feet.

   a. For the ball and the bird to collide, what must be true of the system $\begin{cases} h = -5.56t^2 - 1.39t + 4.25 \\ h = -24.42t^2 + 3.94t + 5.14 \end{cases}$?

   b. Find how long after the pitch was thrown that it struck the bird. 0.41 sec

   c. What was the height of the bird when it got struck by the ball? about 2.76 ft

   d. Does the graph of the parabola $h = -5.56t^2 - 1.39t + 4.25$ represent the flight of the ball? Explain.

Philadelphia Eagles quarterback Donovan McNabb throws a pass against the Tampa Bay Buccaneers in the first quarter of the NFC championship game at Veterans Stadium in Philadelphia, January 19, 2003.

Source: Associated Press

13a. The system must have exactly one solution.

13d. Answers vary. Sample answer: No, the graph represents the height with respect to time; if the graph were of height with respect to distance traveled, then the graph would be of the ball's flight.

Nonlinear Systems   **643**

10-10

4 Wrap-Up

Ongoing Assessment

Ask students to draw pairs of functions they have worked with so far in the course that do not intersect. Use this as an opportunity to discuss the difference between not intersecting on a small domain, such as a small calculator window, and never intersecting over all real numbers.

---

14. Company One's stock values during the month of January can be represented by $V = 40(0.9)^x$, where x is time in days since the beginning of the month. Company Two's stock values can be represented by $V = |2x - 9|$ for the same time period.

    a. Approximate when Companies One and Two had the same stock value and give that value. **on the 10th day; 12.73**

    b. Describe how well each company's stock values changed over the month (from $x = 0$ to $x = 31$).

    c. When would have been the best time to buy Company Two's stock? Explain your answer.

REVIEW

15. Solve $\begin{bmatrix} 1 & -2 \\ 3 & 1.5 \end{bmatrix} \cdot \begin{bmatrix} -3 \\ 2 \\ n \end{bmatrix} = \begin{bmatrix} -11.5 \\ 3 \end{bmatrix}$ for n. **(Lesson 10-8)** $n = 5$

16. Solve $\begin{cases} x - 1.5y = 11 \\ 5x + 9y = 11 \end{cases}$ by any method. **(Lessons 10-5, 10-4, 10-3)**

17. Suppose Rodney bought a car 32 years ago for $8,000. It lost 6% of its value each year for the first 15 years. Then its value stayed the same for 3 years. When it was 18 years old, the car became a collector's item and its value increased 21% each year. Find the value of the car now. **(Lessons 7-3, 7-2)** $45,604

18. Graph the solutions to the inequality $-4.5y - 18x + 3 < 12$ on a coordinate grid. **(Lesson 6-9)** See margin.

EXPLORATION

19. An equation for a circle with radius 2 centered at the origin is $x^2 + y^2 = 4$. Use your calculator to find a pair of values of m and b so that the number of solutions to the system
$$\begin{cases} x^2 + y^2 = 4 \\ y = mx + b \end{cases} \text{ is}$$

    a. 2. **b.** 1. **c.** 0.

14b. Answers vary. Sample answer: Company One began with a good stock value, but by the end of the month, it was approaching 0; whereas Company Two began low, bottomed out, but then began a dramatic and continual increase.

14c. On the fourth day because that was when the value of its stock was lowest and before it started to rise

16. $\left(7, -\dfrac{8}{3}\right)$

19a–c. Answers vary. Sample answers are given.

19a. $m = 1, b = 0$

19b. $m = 0, b = 2$

19c. $m = 0, b = 12$

QY ANSWER

For (−2, 7):
Does $7 = (-2)^2 + 3$? Yes.
Does $7 = -2 + 9$? Yes.

For (3, 12):
Does $12 = 3^2 + 3$? Yes.
Does $12 = 3 + 9$? Yes.
Both solutions check.

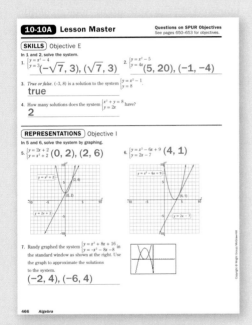

Additional Answers

18.

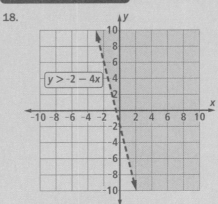

Chapter 10 Projects

1 Cars and Computers

For the years 1985, 1990, 1995, 2000, and 2005, find the number of cars in the United States and the number of personal computers.

a. Find lines of best fit for these two sets of data.

b. Find the year in which these two lines meet.

c. Do you think your calculation in Part b is a good prediction of when the number of computers in the United States will be the same as the number of cars? Explain your answer.

2 When Do Systems Have Integer Solutions?

Suppose you have a system of the form
$$\begin{cases} ax + by = e \\ cx + dy = f \end{cases}$$
where $a, b, c, d, e,$ and f are all integers.

a. Create three systems of this form that have a single solution whose coordinates are integers. In each case calculate $ad - bc$.

b. Create three systems of this form that have a single solution whose coordinates are not two integers. In each case calculate $ad - bc$.

c. When do you think that a system as described above has a solution with integer coordinates?

3 Systems with More Variables

In mathematics and in many of its applications, sometimes you need to solve systems with more than just two variables. Just as a system with two variables had two equations, a system with n variables has n equations. The methods for solving these systems are basically the same as the methods you studied in this chapter.

a. Explain how you could solve the system
$$\begin{cases} x + y + z = 3 \\ x + 2y = 5 \\ 3x - 2y = -1 \end{cases}$$
. (*Hint:* You might want to solve a certain system with two variables in the process.)

b. Using methods similar to the methods in this chapter, what could you do to the system
$$\begin{cases} 3x - 2y - 2z = 0 \\ x + y + z = 0 \\ 7x + 10y + z = 9 \end{cases}$$
to make it look more like the system in Part a, in which only one equation had the variable z in it? Do this, then solve the system.

c. Write a short explanation on how to solve systems with three variables for someone who knows how to solve systems with only two variables.

Project Rubric

Advanced	Student correctly provides all of the details asked for in the project as well as additional correct independent conclusions.
Proficient	Student correctly provides all of the details asked for in the project.
Partially proficient	Student correctly provides some of the details asked for in the project or provides all details with some inaccuracies.
Not proficient	Student correctly provides few of the details asked for in the project or provides all details with many inaccuracies.
No attempt	Student makes little or no attempt to complete the project.

The projects relate to the content of the lessons of this chapter as follows:

Project	Lesson(s)
1	10-3
2	10-6
3	10-5
4	10-1
5	10-2

1 Cars and Computers

Students may notice that the graph has a distinct curve, and does not appear to be linear. In this case, ask students to address the issue in Part c of their project. If they choose, students can guess at a curve that models the function. Then, they can make two different predictions based on the two different curves.

2 When Do Systems Have Integer Solutions?

Suggest that students look up Cramer's Rule for solving a system of two equations in two variables using determinants. The value $ad - bc$ is the denominator of both x and y. Therefore, x and y will be integers when they are divided by 1 or −1. Encourage students to explain how Cramer's Rule relates to this project.

3 Systems with More Variables

There are many hints in this problem that encourage the student to solve the system using elimination. However, some students will notice that some problems are solvable using the inverse on a graphing calculator. Encourage students to pursue any method they wish to solve the problem, either by hand or on a calculator.

Chapter **10** Projects

4 Adding and Subtracting Equations

When students create the linear equations, they can use their graphing calculators to find the intersection. A nice alternative is to create the solution to the system first, and then write two equations that have that solution. For Part e, consider giving students some hints about which feature to look at. These might include slope, *y*- or *x*-intercept, and intersection points.

5 Finding the Counterfeit

Suggest that students make a list of the possible weights of the twelve coins. Remind them that the weights must be exact values.

4 Adding and Subtracting Equations

Write two linear equations and do the following.

a. Graph the two linear equations and find their intersection.

b. Graph the equation found by adding the two selected equations.

c. Graph the equation found by subtracting them.

d. Multiply each equation by a number, and add them again.

e. Do the graphs have any common features? If so, describe them.

f. Verify your calculations starting with a different pair of equations.

5 Finding the Counterfeit

A math-savvy pirate finds 12 gold coins, and he fears that several might be counterfeit. (Counterfeit coins are lighter.) He measures all 12 coins on a scale and finds that together they weigh 1.3 kilograms. He removes one coin, and finds that together they weigh 1.15 kilograms. He removes yet another coin, and finds that together they weigh 1 kilogram. At this point, his scale broke. Find out how many counterfeit coins (if any) the pirate found. Explain how systems of equations can be used to find the solution.

Notes

Chapter 10 — Summary and Vocabulary

○ A **system** is a set of sentences that together describe a single situation. Situations that lead to linear equations can lead to a **linear system.** All that is needed is that more than one condition must be satisfied. This chapter discusses ways of solving systems in which the sentences are equations or inequalities in two variables.

○ The **solution set to a system** is the set of all solutions common to all of the sentences in the system. A solution to a system of two linear equations is an ordered pair (x, y) that satisfies each equation. Systems of two linear equations may have zero, one, or infinitely many solutions. Other systems may have other numbers of solutions.

○ One way to solve a system is by graphing. There are as many solutions as intersection points. Graphing is also a way to describe solutions of systems that have infinitely many solutions, for example, systems of **coincident lines** and **systems of linear inequalities,** with overlapping half-planes.

○ However, graphing does not always yield exact solutions. In this chapter, four strategies are presented for finding exact solutions to systems of linear equations. 1. Substitution is a good method to use if at least one equation is given in $y = mx + b$ form. 2. Addition is appropriate if the same term has opposite signs in the two equations in the system. 3. Multiplication is a good method when both equations are in $Ax + By = C$ form. Each of these methods changes the system into an equivalent system whose solutions are the same as those of the original system. 4. With **matrices,** the system $\begin{cases} ax + by = e \\ cx + dy = f \end{cases}$ becomes $\begin{bmatrix} a & b \\ c & d \end{bmatrix} \cdot \begin{bmatrix} x \\ y \end{bmatrix} = \begin{bmatrix} e \\ f \end{bmatrix}$. This matrix equation is of the form $AX = B$, where A is the coefficient matrix $\begin{bmatrix} a & b \\ c & d \end{bmatrix}$, X is the variable matrix $\begin{bmatrix} x \\ y \end{bmatrix}$, and B is the constant matrix $\begin{bmatrix} e \\ f \end{bmatrix}$. Multiplying both sides of $AX = B$ by the **multiplicative inverse** A^{-1} of the matrix A results in $X = A^{-1}B$.

Theorems and Properties

Generalized Addition Property of Equality (p. 601)
Slopes and Parallel Lines Property (p. 616)

Vocabulary

10-1
system
solution to a system
empty set, null set

10-4
addition method for solving a system

10-5
equivalent systems
multiplication method for solving a system

10-6
coincident lines

10-7
matrix (matrices)
elements
dimensions
matrix form
2 × 2 identity matrix

10-8
inverse (of a matrix)

10-10
nonlinear system

Summary and Vocabulary

The Summary gives an overview of the entire chapter and provides an opportunity for students to consider the material as a whole. Thus, the Summary can be used to help students relate and unify the concepts presented in the chapter.

Terms and symbols are listed by lesson to provide a checklist of concepts that students must know. Emphasize to students that they should read the vocabulary list carefully before starting the Self-Test on the next page. If students do not understand the meaning of a term, they should refer back to the indicated lesson.

Theorems and Properties covered in the chapter are listed below the Summary, with page references included to lead students back to the location in the chapter where the theorem or property is stated.

Self-Test

For the development of mathematical competence, feedback and correction, along with the opportunity for practice, are necessary. The Self-Test provides the opportunity for feedback and correction; the Chapter Review provides additional opportunities for practice. We cannot overemphasize the importance of these end-of-chapter materials. It is at this point that the material "gels" for many students, allowing them to solidify skills and understanding. In general, student performance should improve after these pages.

Assign the Self-Test as a one-night assignment. Worked-out solutions for all questions are in the Selected Answers section of the student book. Encourage students to take the Self-Test honestly, grade themselves, and then be prepared to discuss the test in class.

Advise students to pay special attention to those Chapter Review questions (pages 650–653) that correspond to the questions they missed on the Self-Test.

Additional Answers

1. $(x, y) = (-18, 25)$

   $x - 7 = 1.5x + 2$

   $-0.5x = 9$

   $x = -18$

   $y = -25$

2. $(d, f) = (6, 3)$

   $4f = 12$

   $f = 3$

   $d = 6$

3. $(g, h) = \left(\frac{-6}{13}, \frac{10}{13}\right)$

   $\begin{cases} 7h + 3g = 4 \\ 6h - 3g = 6 \end{cases}$

   $13h = 10$

   $h = \frac{10}{13}$

   $g = -\frac{6}{13}$

Take this test as you would take a test in class. You will need a calculator. Then use the Selected Answers section in the back of the book to check your work.

In 1–4, solve the system by the indicated method.

1–5. See margin.

1. $\begin{cases} y = x - 7 \\ y = 1.5x + 2 \end{cases}$ substitution

2. $\begin{cases} -4d + 9f = 3 \\ 4d - 5f = 9 \end{cases}$ addition

3. $\begin{cases} 7h + 3g = 4 \\ 2h - g = 2 \end{cases}$ multiplication

4. $\begin{cases} 3a - b = 6 \\ \frac{3}{5}b = 37 - 4a \end{cases}$ graphing

5. Solve $\begin{cases} y = x^2 + 3x - 5 \\ y = 6x - 7 \end{cases}$ by using any method.

6. Determine whether the system $\begin{cases} 3s = 2t - 5 \\ \frac{2}{3}t - \frac{1}{3}s = -5 \end{cases}$ has 0, 1, or infinitely many solutions. See margin.

In 7 and 8, multiply. 7–8. See margin.

7. $\begin{bmatrix} 2 & 7 \\ 1 & 0 \end{bmatrix} \cdot \begin{bmatrix} 3 \\ 4 \end{bmatrix}$

8. $\begin{bmatrix} 3 & 5 \\ 4 & 6 \end{bmatrix} \cdot \begin{bmatrix} 2 & 8 \\ 1 & 7 \end{bmatrix}$

9. Solve the system $\begin{cases} 3p + 5q = 5 \\ p - q = 7 \end{cases}$ using matrices. Use a calculator to find the inverse of the matrix. See margin.

10. An electronics store receives two large orders. The first order is for 6 high-definition televisions and 3 DVD players, and totals $6,795. The second order is for 4 high-definition televisions and 4 DVD players, and totals $4,860. What is the cost of one high-definition television and what is the cost of one DVD player? See margin.

11. Give values for m, n, c, and d so that the system $\begin{cases} y = mx + c \\ y = nx + d \end{cases}$ has infinitely many solutions. See margin.

12. Rosie is buying posies and roses. She wants to spend no more than $40. Roses are $5 each, and posies are $2 each. Accurately graph all combinations of flowers that she can buy. See margin.

13. Solve the system $\begin{cases} y = 3x + 50 \\ y = -2x + 70 \end{cases}$ by graphing. See margin.

14. A passenger airplane took 2 hours to fly from St. Louis, Missouri, to Orlando, Florida, in the direction of the jet stream. On the return trip against the jet stream, the airplane took 2 hours and 30 minutes. If the distance between the two cities is about 1,000 miles, find the airplane's speed in still air and the speed of the jet stream. See margin.

15. Akando bought 80 feet of chicken wire to make a coop on his farm. He needs the coop to be at least 10 feet wide and 15 feet long.

    a. Draw a graph to show all possible dimensions (to the nearest foot) of the coop. See margin.

    b. At most, how wide can the coop be? 25 ft

16. Graph all solutions to the system $\begin{cases} y \leq x + 3 \\ y \geq -2x + 4 \end{cases}$. See page 649.

---

4. $(a, b) = (7, 15)$

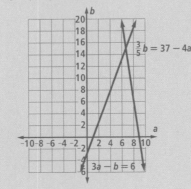

$\frac{3}{5}b = 37 - 4a$

$3a - b = 6$

5. $(1, -1)$ and $(2, 5)$. Answers vary. Sample answer: $6x - 7 = x^2 + 3x - 5$; $x^2 - 3x + 2 = 0$; $x = 1$ or $x = 2$. When $x = 1$, $y = -1$. When $x = 2$, $y = 5$.

6. This is a linear system of 2 lines with different slopes. Thus there is one solution.

7. $\begin{bmatrix} 2 \cdot 3 + 7 \cdot 4 \\ 1 \cdot 3 + 0 \cdot 4 \end{bmatrix} = \begin{bmatrix} 34 \\ 3 \end{bmatrix}$

8. $\begin{bmatrix} 3 \cdot 2 + 5 \cdot 1 & 3 \cdot 8 + 5 \cdot 7 \\ 4 \cdot 2 + 6 \cdot 1 & 4 \cdot 8 + 6 \cdot 7 \end{bmatrix} = \begin{bmatrix} 11 & 59 \\ 14 & 74 \end{bmatrix}$

17. Kele paid for his lunch with 15 coins. He used only quarters and dimes. If his lunch cost $2.40, how many of each coin did he use?

18. Write a system of inequalities to describe the shaded region below.

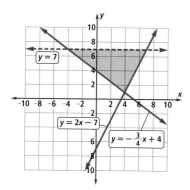

$$18. \begin{cases} y < 7 \\ y \geq 2x - 7 \\ y \geq -\frac{3}{4}x + 4 \end{cases}$$

16.

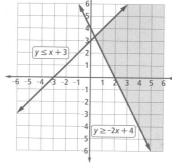

17. $\begin{cases} q + d = 15 \\ 0.25q + 0.10d = 2.40; q = 15 - d, \end{cases}$
$0.25(15 - d) + 0.10d = 2.40,$
$3.75 - 0.25d + 0.10d = 2.40,$
$-0.15d = -1.35, d = 9, q = 6;$
9 dimes and 6 quarters

Additional Answers

12.

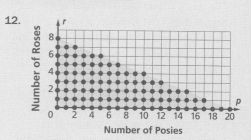

13. (4, 62)

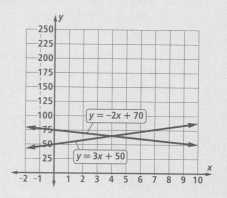

14. $\begin{cases} 2j + 2w = 1,000 \\ 2.5j - 2.5w = 1,000 \end{cases}$
$j = 500 - w;$
$2.5(500 - w) - 2.5w = 1,000;$
$1,250 - 2.5w - 2.5w = 1,000; 5w = 250; w = 50; j = 450$
airplane's speed: 450 mph; speed of jet stream: 50 mph

15a.

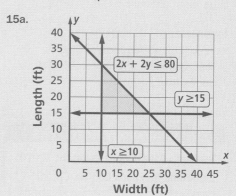

9. $\begin{bmatrix} 3 & 5 \\ 1 & -1 \end{bmatrix}\begin{bmatrix} p \\ q \end{bmatrix} = \begin{bmatrix} 5 \\ 7 \end{bmatrix}$
$\begin{bmatrix} \frac{1}{8} & \frac{5}{8} \\ \frac{1}{8} & -\frac{3}{8} \end{bmatrix}\begin{bmatrix} 3 & 5 \\ 1 & -1 \end{bmatrix}\begin{bmatrix} p \\ q \end{bmatrix} = \begin{bmatrix} \frac{1}{8} & \frac{5}{8} \\ \frac{1}{8} & -\frac{3}{8} \end{bmatrix}\begin{bmatrix} 5 \\ 7 \end{bmatrix}$
$\begin{bmatrix} p \\ q \end{bmatrix} = \begin{bmatrix} 5 \\ -2 \end{bmatrix}$

10. $\begin{cases} 3d + 6t = 6,795 \\ 4d + 4t = 4,860 \end{cases}$
$\begin{cases} -6d - 12t = -13,590 \\ 12d - 12t = 14,580 \end{cases}$
$6d = 990; d = 165; t = 1,050;$ DVD players cost $165 each; high-definition televisions cost $1,050 each

11. Answers vary. Sample answer:
$m = n = 5, c = d = 4$

Chapter Review

The main objectives for the chapter are organized in the Chapter Review under the four types of understanding this book promotes—Skills, Properties, Uses, and Representations.

Whereas end-of-chapter material may be considered optional in some texts, in *UCSMP Algebra* we have selected these objectives and questions with the expectation that they will be covered. Students should be able to answer these questions with about 85% accuracy after studying the chapter.

You may assign these questions over a single night to help students prepare for a test the next day, or you may assign the questions over a two-day period. If you work the questions over two days, then we recommend assigning the *evens* for homework the first night so that students get feedback in class the next day, and then assigning the *odds* the night before the test because the answers are provided to the odd-numbered questions in the Selected Answers at the back of the book.

It is effective to ask students which questions they still do not understand and use the day as a total class discussion of the material that the class finds most difficult.

Resources

• Assessment Resources: Chapter 10 Test, Forms A–D; Chapter 10 Test, Cumulative Form

Technology Resources

Teacher's Assessment Assistant, Ch 10

Electronic Teacher's Edition, Ch. 10

SKILLS
PROPERTIES
USES
REPRESENTATIONS

SKILLS Procedures used to get answers

OBJECTIVE A Solve systems using substitution. (Lessons 10-2, 10-3)

In 1 and 2, solve the system by using substitution.

1. $\begin{cases} m = n \\ 3m - 4 = n \end{cases}$ $m = 2, n = 2$

2. $\begin{cases} 2p = q + 5 \\ 2q = 4(p + 2) \end{cases}$ no solution

In 3 and 4, two lines have the given equations. Find the point of intersection, if any.

3. Line ℓ: $y = 2x + 5$;

   Line m: $y = -3x + 4$ $(-0.2, 4.6)$

4. Line p: $y = \frac{2}{3}x + \frac{1}{9}$;

   Line q: $y = \frac{1}{5}x - 4$ $\left(-\frac{185}{21}, -\frac{121}{21}\right)$

OBJECTIVE B Solve systems by addition and multiplication. (Lessons 10-4, 10-5)

In 5 and 6, solve the system by addition.

5. $\begin{cases} 3b + 4 = a \\ -3b - 5 = 2a \end{cases}$ $(a, b) = \left(-\frac{1}{3}, -\frac{13}{9}\right)$

6. $\begin{cases} 0.4x + 0.75y = 2.7 \\ 0.4x - 2y = 2.5 \end{cases}$ $(x, y) = \left(\frac{291}{44}, \frac{4}{55}\right)$

In 7–10, solve the system by multiplication.

7. $\begin{cases} 3f + g = 41 \\ f - 2g = 20 \end{cases}$ $(f, g) = \left(\frac{102}{7}, -\frac{19}{7}\right)$

8. $\begin{cases} 3t - u = 5 \\ 6t + 3u = 7 \end{cases}$ $(t, u) = \left(\frac{22}{15}, -\frac{3}{5}\right)$

9. $\begin{cases} 5w + 2v = 6 \\ 7 + 5v = w \end{cases}$ $(v, w) = \left(-\frac{29}{27}, \frac{44}{27}\right)$

10. $\begin{cases} 3x - 5 = y \\ 2x - 7y = 9 \end{cases}$ $(x, y) = \left(\frac{26}{19}, -\frac{17}{19}\right)$

OBJECTIVE C Multiply 2×2 matrices by 2×2 or 2×1 matrices. (Lesson 10-7)

In 11–14, multiply.

11. $\begin{bmatrix} 2 & -4 \\ 3 & 5 \end{bmatrix} \cdot \begin{bmatrix} 7 \\ 4 \end{bmatrix}$ $\begin{bmatrix} -2 \\ 41 \end{bmatrix}$

12. $\begin{bmatrix} 6 & -0.5 \\ 0.5 & 2 \end{bmatrix} \cdot \begin{bmatrix} 6 \\ 12 \end{bmatrix}$ $\begin{bmatrix} 30 \\ 27 \end{bmatrix}$

13. $\begin{bmatrix} -6 & 8 \\ -9 & 7 \end{bmatrix} \cdot \begin{bmatrix} 1 & 3 \\ 4 & 2 \end{bmatrix}$ $\begin{bmatrix} 26 & -2 \\ 19 & -13 \end{bmatrix}$

14. $\begin{bmatrix} 2 & 11 \\ 0 & 7 \end{bmatrix} \cdot \begin{bmatrix} 0 & -4 \\ 5 & 9 \end{bmatrix}$ $\begin{bmatrix} 55 & 91 \\ 35 & 63 \end{bmatrix}$

OBJECTIVE D Solve systems using matrices. (Lesson 10-8)

In 15–18, a system is given. 15–18. See margin.

a. Write the system in matrix form.

b. Use technology to find the inverse.

c. Solve the system.

15. $\begin{cases} 3x + 2y = 7 \\ 5x + 7y = 9 \end{cases}$

16. $\begin{cases} 6m + 4d = 7 \\ 4m + 3d = 13 \end{cases}$

17. $\begin{cases} 5p - 7q = 20 \\ 4p - 8q = 14 \end{cases}$

18. $\begin{cases} w + 3z = 5 \\ 4z - 5w = 9 \end{cases}$

Additional Answers

15a. $\begin{bmatrix} 3 & 2 \\ 5 & 7 \end{bmatrix} \begin{bmatrix} x \\ y \end{bmatrix} = \begin{bmatrix} 7 \\ 9 \end{bmatrix}$

15b. $\begin{bmatrix} \frac{7}{11} & -\frac{2}{11} \\ -\frac{5}{11} & \frac{3}{11} \end{bmatrix}$

15c. $\begin{bmatrix} x \\ y \end{bmatrix} = \begin{bmatrix} \frac{31}{11} \\ -\frac{8}{11} \end{bmatrix}$

16a. $\begin{bmatrix} 6 & 4 \\ 4 & 3 \end{bmatrix} \begin{bmatrix} m \\ d \end{bmatrix} = \begin{bmatrix} 7 \\ 13 \end{bmatrix}$

16b. $\begin{bmatrix} \frac{3}{2} & -2 \\ -2 & 3 \end{bmatrix}$

16c. $\begin{bmatrix} m \\ d \end{bmatrix} = \begin{bmatrix} -15.5 \\ 25 \end{bmatrix}$

17a. $\begin{bmatrix} 5 & -7 \\ 4 & -8 \end{bmatrix} = \begin{bmatrix} p \\ q \end{bmatrix} = \begin{bmatrix} 20 \\ 14 \end{bmatrix}$

17b. $\begin{bmatrix} \frac{2}{3} & -\frac{7}{12} \\ \frac{1}{3} & -\frac{5}{12} \end{bmatrix}$

17c. $\begin{bmatrix} p \\ q \end{bmatrix} = \begin{bmatrix} \frac{31}{6} \\ \frac{5}{6} \end{bmatrix}$

18a. $\begin{bmatrix} 1 & 3 \\ -5 & 4 \end{bmatrix} \begin{bmatrix} w \\ z \end{bmatrix} = \begin{bmatrix} 5 \\ 9 \end{bmatrix}$

18b. $\begin{bmatrix} \frac{4}{19} & -\frac{3}{19} \\ \frac{5}{19} & \frac{1}{19} \end{bmatrix}$

18c. $\begin{bmatrix} w \\ z \end{bmatrix} = \begin{bmatrix} -\frac{7}{19} \\ \frac{34}{19} \end{bmatrix}$

OBJECTIVE E Solve nonlinear systems. (Lesson 10-10)

In 19 and 20, solve by substitution.

19. $\begin{cases} y = -2x^2 \\ y + x^2 = -1 \end{cases}$ $(-1, -2), (1, -2)$

20. $\begin{cases} 2x^3 - 2y = x^2 - 5 \\ y = x^3 - 2x \end{cases}$ $(-1, 1), (5, 115)$

PROPERTIES Principles behind the mathematics

OBJECTIVE F Determine whether a system has 0, 1, or infinitely many solutions. (Lesson 10-6)

In 21–24, determine whether the given system has 0, 1, or infinitely many solutions.

21. $\begin{cases} 2y + 3x = 5 \\ 2y = 4 - 3x \end{cases}$ 0 solutions

22. $\begin{cases} y + 3x = 7 \\ y = 3x + 7 \end{cases}$ 1 solution

23. $\begin{cases} 3p = 7q + 2 \\ 6p = 10q + 5 \end{cases}$ 1 solution

24. $\begin{cases} 4p + 5q = 7 \\ 2p = 3\frac{1}{2} - \frac{5}{2}q \end{cases}$ infinitely many solutions

25. When will the system $\begin{cases} y = mx + a \\ y = mx + b \end{cases}$ have no solution? Explain your answer. See margin.

26. Can the given set of points be the intersection of two lines?

a. exactly one point yes

b. exactly two points no

c. infinitely many points yes

d. no points yes

27. **Fill in the Blank** Two lines are parallel only if they have the same ___?___. slope

28. **True or False** Two lines can intersect in more than one point if they have different y-intercepts. false

USES Applications of mathematics in real-world situations

OBJECTIVE G Use systems of linear equations to solve real-world problems. (Lessons 10-2, 10-3, 10-4, 10-5, 10-6)

Austin: 280 mi, Antonio: 70 mi
29. Austin drove four times as far as Antonio. Together, they drove 350 miles. How far did they each drive?

30. Car A costs $2,800 down and $100 per month. Car B costs $3,100 down and $50 per month. After how many months is the amount paid for the cars equal?
after 6 mo

31. Good Job offers $30,000 per year, plus a $1,000 raise each year. Nice Job offers $32,000 per year, plus a $500 raise each year. When will you make more money per year with Good Job?
after the fourth year

32. Tickets to see an orchestra cost $30 for adults and $15 for students. One night, the total number of tickets sold was 633. If they sold $15,945 worth of tickets, how many adults and how many students attended? 430 adults, 203 students

33. A chemist wishes to mix a 15% acid solution with 30% acid solution to make a 25% acid solution. If the chemist wants to make 8 pints of the solution, how many pints of each solution should the chemist use? $\frac{8}{3}$ pints of the 15% solution and $\frac{16}{3}$ pints of the 30% solution

34. From 1990 to 2000, the population of Seattle, Washington, grew at a rate of about 4,700 people per year, to a population of about 565,000. Baltimore, Maryland, decreased at a rate of about 8,400 people per year, to a population of about 650,000. If these rates continue, in about how many years will Seattle and Baltimore have the same population? about $6\frac{1}{2}$ yr

Additional Answers

25. when $a \neq b$, because equating y and subtracting mx from both sides yields $a = b$

Chapter Review **651**

Additional Answers

35.

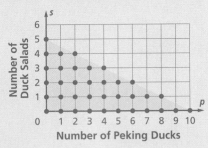

36. integer values within this region

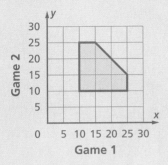

37a.

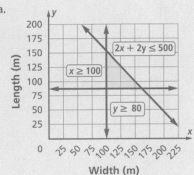

38a.

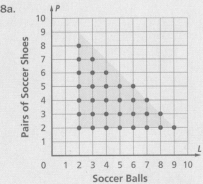

OBJECTIVE H Use systems of linear inequalities to solve real-world problems. (Lesson 10-9)

35. A chef has 10 ducks and wants to make Peking duck and duck salad. It takes 1 duck to make Peking duck, and 2 ducks to make duck salad. Make a graph to show all the combinations of duck dishes that the chef can make. 35-36. See margin.

36. Suppose 40 students want to play 2 games. If each game must have at least 10 students and at most 25 students, make a graph of the number of ways the students could divide up to play the games.

37. Jackie is running around a rectangular track with a perimeter of at most 500 feet. The track is at least 80 feet wide and 100 feet long.

  a. Draw a graph to show all possible dimensions (to the nearest foot) of the track. **See margin.**

  b. What is the maximum length of the track? **650 ft**

  c. What is the maximum width of the track? **670 ft**

38. Nihad won $300 in a soccer all-stars contest. She wants to buy soccer balls for $25 and pairs of soccer shoes for $30. She wants to buy at least two balls and at least two pairs of shoes.

  a. Graph all the combinations she could buy. **See margin.**

  b. What is the maximum number of pairs of shoes she can buy? **8**

  c. What is the maximum number of balls she can buy? **9**

REPRESENTATIONS Pictures, graphs, or objects that illustrate concepts

OBJECTIVE I Find solutions to systems of equations by graphing. (Lessons 10-1, 10-6, 10-10)

In 39-43, solve the system by graphing. Round your answers to the nearest tenth.

39. $\begin{cases} 5x + 4y = 7 \\ 3x + 2y = 6 \end{cases}$ $(5, -4.5)$

40. $\begin{cases} 16x - 16y = 16 \\ \frac{1}{2}x + \frac{1}{2}y = -2 \end{cases}$ $(-1.5, -2.5)$

41. $\begin{cases} 0.5x - 0.4y = 0.8 \\ x - 1.6 = 0.8y \end{cases}$ infinitely many solutions

42. $\begin{cases} y = 2^x \\ y = 1.32x + 2.67 \end{cases}$ $(-1.8, 0.3), (2.6, 6.1)$

43. $\begin{cases} 2y - 3x = 7 \\ x^2 + y = 15 \end{cases}$ $(-4.2, -2.8), (2.7, 7.6)$

OBJECTIVE J Graphically represent solutions to systems of linear inequalities. (Lesson 10-9)

In 44-47, graph all solutions to the system.

44. $\begin{cases} y \leq 3x \\ y \geq 2x + 1 \end{cases}$ 44-47. See margin.

45. $\begin{cases} x + 4 > 7 + 2y \\ x - 4 < y + 2 \end{cases}$

46. $\begin{cases} y > -2 \\ x + y < 0 \\ x - y \geq 1 \end{cases}$

47. $\begin{cases} x \geq 0 \\ y \geq 0 \\ x + y < 9 \end{cases}$

Additional Answers

44.

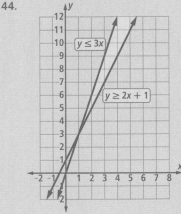

45.

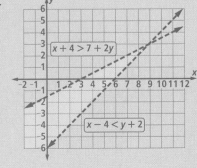

In 48 and 49, accurately graph the set of points that satisfies the situation.

48. An elephant can eat 70 pounds of food in a meal. If the elephant eats P sacks of peanuts averaging 7 pounds each and L bunches of leaves weighing 5 pounds each, how many sacks and bunches can the elephant eat? **See margin.**

49. Conan wants to watch t television shows and m movies. Each show lasts 30 minutes, and each movie lasts 90 minutes. If he has 5 hours of viewing time available, how many full shows and movies can he watch? **See margin.**

OBJECTIVE K Write a system of inequalities given a graph. (Lesson 10-9)

In 50–52, write a system of inequalities to describe the shaded region.

50.

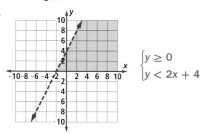

$$\begin{cases} y \geq 0 \\ y < 2x + 4 \end{cases}$$

51.

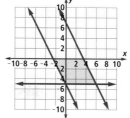

$$\begin{cases} y \leq 0 \\ y \geq -5 \\ y \leq -2x + 7 \\ y \geq -2x - 5 \end{cases}$$

52.

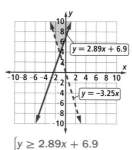

$$\begin{cases} y \geq 2.89x + 6.9 \\ y > -3.25x \end{cases}$$

Assessment

Evaluation The *Assessment Resources* provide four forms of the Chapter 10 Test. Forms A and B present parallel versions of a short-answer format. Form C consists of four to six short-response questions that cover the SPUR objectives from Chapter 10. Form D offers performance assessment that covers a subset (or even just one) of the SPUR objectives for the chapter.

Feedback After students have taken the test for Chapter 10 and you have scored the results, return the tests to students for discussion. Class discussion on the questions that caused trouble for most students can be very effective in identifying and clarifying misunderstandings. You might want to have them note the items they missed and work either in groups or at home to correct them. It is important for students to receive feedback on every chapter test, and we recommend that students see and correct their mistakes before proceeding too far into the next chapter.

Additional Answers

48.

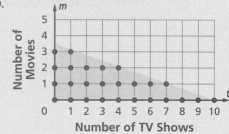

49.

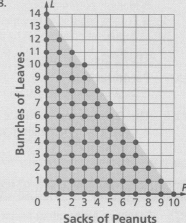

Additional Answers

46.

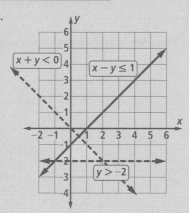

47.

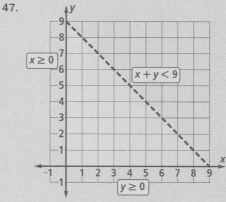

Chapter

11 Polynomials

Chapter Overview

	Local Standards	Pacing (in days)		
		Average	Advanced	Block
11-1 Investments and Polynomials A Add and subtract polynomials. F Translate investment situations into polynomials.		1	1	0.5
11-2 Classifying Polynomials A Add and subtract polynomials. E Classify polynomials by their degree or number of terms.		1	0.5	0.5
11-3 Multiplying a Polynomial by a Monomial B Multiply polynomials. I Represent polynomials by areas.		1	1	0.75
QUIZ 1		0.5	0.5	0.25
11-4 Common Monomial Factoring C Find common monomial factors of polynomials.		1	0.5	0.5
11-5 Multiplying Polynomials B Multiply polynomials. I Represent polynomials by areas.		1	0.5	0.5
11-6 Special Binomial Products B Multiply polynomials. D Expand squares of binomials. I Represent polynomials by areas.		1	0.5	0.75
QUIZ 2		0.5	0.5	0.25
11-7 Permutations G Determine numbers of permutations.		1	1	0.5
11-8 The Chi-Square Statistic H Use a chi-square statistic to determine whether or not statistics support a conclusion.		1	1	0.5
Self-Test		1	1	0.5
Chapter Review		2	2	1
Test		1	1	0.5
TOTAL		**13**	**11**	**7.0**

Technology Resources

Teacher's Assessment Assistant, Ch. 11

Electronic Teacher's Edition, Ch. 11

Differentiated Options Universal Access

	Accommodating the Learner	Vocabulary Development	Ongoing Assessment	Materials
11-1	pp. 657, 658	p. 657	oral, p. 662	scientific calculator
11-2	pp. 665, 666	p. 665	oral, p. 668	
11-3	pp. 670, 671	p. 670	written, p. 674	algebra tiles, Computer Algebra System (CAS)
11-4	pp. 676, 677		oral, p. 679	Computer Algebra System (CAS)
11-5	pp. 681, 682		written, p. 684	Computer Algebra System (CAS)
11-6	pp. 686, 687		written, p. 690	Computer Algebra System (CAS)
11-7	p. 693		oral, p. 696	scientific calculator
11-8	pp. 698, 699		written, p. 702	scientific calculator

Objectives

	Lessons	Self-Test Questions	Chapter Review Questions
Skills			
A Add and subtract polynomials.	11-1, 11-2	10	1–4
B Multiply polynomials.	11-3, 11-5, 11-6	1, 3, 4, 6, 11	5–17
C Find common monomial factors of polynomials.	11-4	9, 13	18–22
D Expand squares of binomials.	11-6	2, 5	23–27
Properties			
E Classify polynomials by their degree or number of terms.	11-2	7, 8, 12	28–33
Uses			
F Translate investment situations into polynominals.	11-1	17, 18	34, 35
G Determine numbers of permutations.	11-7	15, 16	36–43
H Use a chi-square statistic to determine whether or not statistics support a conclusion.	11-8	21	44–46
Representations			
I Represent polynomials by areas.	11-3, 11-5, 11-6	14, 19, 20, 22	47–52

Resource Masters Chapter 11

Resource Master 5, Spreadsheet (page 6), can be used with Lesson 11-1.
Resource Master 2, Four-Quadrant Graph Paper (page 3), can be used with
Lesson 11-5.

Resource Master 160 Lesson 11-1

Warm-Up
A relative gives you $5,000 to put away for college.

1. You put the money in an account that pays an annual yield of 4% the first year. How much will you have at the end of the year?

2. The account pays an annual yield of 4% during the second year. How much will you have after the second year?

3. The interest rate changes to an annual yield of 4.25% during the third year. How much will there be in the account at the end of three years?

Additional Examples

1. Every year after they are married, a couple deposits $2,000 into an account that pays an annual yield of 6.5%. The couple starts by depositing $2,000 when they are married in 2003. How much money will they have saved by their 10th wedding anniversary in 2013?

2. Suppose the couple in Question 1 decided to deposit $2,000 the first year and then increase their deposit by $100 every year. If the yearly scale factor is x, how much money will they have saved by their wedding anniversary in 2013?

3. Tina decides to start saving for her child's college expenses right after the baby is born. For 10 years, she saves $1,000 each year. Then she stops making deposits. Her sister, Karin, has a baby at the same time, but decides to wait eight years before she starts to save. She then saves $1,300 each year for ten years. They will each deposit their savings into a special account earning 5.5% interest compounded annually. How much will each have after eighteen years?

Resource Master for Lesson 11-1

Resource Master 161 Lesson 11-1

Questions 8–11

	Clara	Mona	Odella
In 2003	$200	$250	$100
In 2004	$300	$250	$500
In 2005	$250	$250	nothing

Question 27

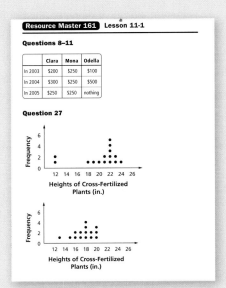

Heights of Cross-Fertilized Plants (in.)

Resource Master for Lesson 11-1

Resource Master 162 Lesson 11-2

Warm-Up

1. a. Write 123,456,789 as a polynomial in base 10.
   b. What is the greatest power of 10?
   c. What is the coefficient of the 10^5 term?

2. Consider the expression $x^5 + 5x^5 - 2^7$.
   a. What is the greatest power of x?
   b. Is this a monomial, binomial, trinomial, or other type of polynomial?
   c. What is the coefficient of the squared term?

Additional Example
Collect like terms and determine the degree of the resulting polynomial.

1. $(5x^2 - 8) - (2 + x^2) = $ ___?___
   degree 2   degree 2   degree 2

2. $(a^2 + 2ab) - (a^2 - 3ab) = 5ab$
   degree 2   degree 2   degree ___?___

3. $(2x^3 - 2x) + (x^2 + 3x) = $ ___?___
   degree 3   degree 2   degree ___?___

4. $(x^3 - 2x + 5) + (-2x^2 + 3x^2) = $ ___?___
   degree 3   degree 3   degree ___?___

Resource Master for Lesson 11-2

Resource Master 163 Lesson 11-2

Question 11

Question 12

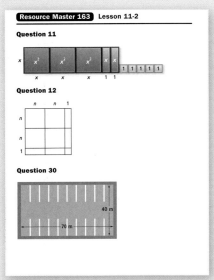

Question 30

Resource Master for Lesson 11-2

Resource Master 165 Lesson 11-3
Resource Master 164 Lesson 11-3

Warm-Up

1. Multiply $6 \cdot 10^3 + 2 \cdot 10^2 + 7$ by 10^4 in two ways:
   a. by rewriting each number in base 10.
   b. by using the Distributive Property without rewriting.

2. Are the answers you got in Question 1 equal?

3. Replace 10 by x in Question 1 and repeat the multiplication.

4. If x is replaced by 5 in Question 3, does the product of the values of the two polynomials being multiplied equal the value of the product?

Additional Examples

1. Give two equivalent expressions for the total area of the rectangle pictured below.

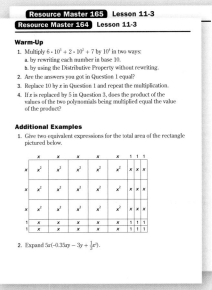

2. Expand $5x(-0.35xy - 3y + \frac{1}{3}x^2)$.

Resource Masters for Lesson 11-3

Resource Master 167 Lesson 11-3
Resource Master 166 Lesson 11-3

Question 5

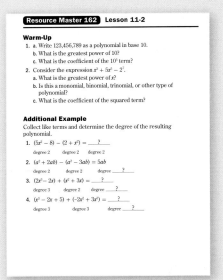

Question 6

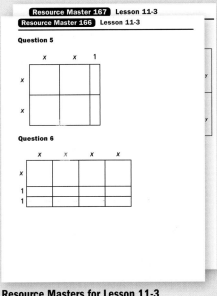

Resource Masters for Lesson 11-3

Resource Master 168 — Lesson 11-4

Warm-Up

1. What are the factors of 392?
2. Give the prime factorization of 108.
3. Find the greatest common factor of 108 and 54.
4. What are the factors of $25n^3$?
5. What is the greatest common factor of x^{10} and x^{12}?

Additional Examples

1. What are the factors of $6xy$?
2. Find the greatest common factor of $12x^3y$ and $16x^2$.
3. Factor $36d^2fg^3 - 9d^2fg + 3d^3g$ completely.
4. Simplify $\frac{4x^2y - 8xy^2}{2xy}$. ($x \neq 0$ and $y \neq 0$)

Question 25

Resource Master for Lesson 11-4

Resource Master 169 — Lesson 11-5

Warm-Up

Multiply 357 by 246 by writing the product as $(300 + 50 + 7)(200 + 40 + 6)$ and using the Expanded Distributive Property. Verify that your answer is the same as the one you would get calculating some other way.

Additional Examples

1. Suppose Cassandra used the EXPAND feature on a CAS to multiply the polynomials $x^3 - 3x + 2$ and $4x^2 - 3x - 1$. Her result is shown below.

The CAS does not display steps that most people would show in order to find the answer. Using the Extended Distributive Property, show the steps that the CAS does not display to expand $(x^3 - 3x + 2)(4x^2 - 3x - 1)$.

Resource Master for Lesson 11-5

Resource Master 170 — Lesson 11-5

Additional Examples

2. Expand $(5x - 2)(3x + 1)$.
3. Expand $y^2(2y - 1)(3y + 2)$.

Question 16

Resource Master for Lesson 11-5

Resource Master 171 — Lesson 11-6

Warm-Up

Ask students to try to do these in their heads using the special binomial products of this lesson.

1. Multiply 87 by 93 as binomials by thinking of them as $(90 - 3)$ and $(90 + 3)$.
2. Multiply 18 by 22 in the same way as Question 1.
3. Calculate 105^2 by thinking of it as the square of a binomial $(100 + 5)^2$.

Additional Examples

1. Calculate 32^2.
2. The area of a square with side $4d - 3$ is $(4d - 3)^2$. Expand this binomial.
3. Compute $23 \cdot 27$ in your head.
4. Expand $(3x^3 - 2)(3x^3 + 2)$.

Resource Master for Lesson 11-6

Resource Master 172 — Lesson 11-6

Activity 1

$(a + b)^2$	$a^2 + 2ab + b^2$	$(a - b)^2$	$a^2 - 2ab + b^2$
$(x + 1)^2$		$(x - 1)^2$	
$(x + 2)^2$		$(x - 2)^2$	
$(x + 3)^2$		$(x - 3)^2$	
$(x + 4)^2$		$(x - 4)^2$	
$(x + 15)^2$		$(x - 15)^2$	
$(x + n)^2$		$(x - n)^2$	

Activity 2

$(a + b)(a - b)$	$a^2 - b^2$
$(x + 1)(x - 1)$	
$(x + 2)(x - 2)$	
$(x + 3)(x - 3)$	
$(x + 4)(x - 4)$	
$(x + 15)(x - 15)$	
$(x + n)(x - n)$	

Resource Master for Lesson 11-6

Resource Master 173 — Lesson 11-7

Warm-Up

1. How many 1-digit numbers are odd?
2. How many 2-digit numbers consist of two odd digits?
3. How many 2-digit numbers consist of two different odd digits?
4. Which numbers are counted in Question 2 and not in Question 3?
5. How many 3-digit numbers consist of three different odd digits?

Additional Examples

1. After a student asks a classmate for his phone number, they notice that the last four digits of the number contain only numbers from 1 to 4. They wondered if this was unusual.
   a. How many 4-digit numbers are there with digits from 1 to 4?
   b. The student looks more closely, and notices that the numbers are all different. How many possible 4-digit numbers fit the criteria?
2. A concert will feature five different bands. In how many different orders can the concert producer organize the bands?
3. There are 10 people in a race. Assuming none of them tie, in how many ways can they arrive at the finish line?

Resource Master for Lesson 11-7

Resource Master 174 — Lesson 11-7

Question 22

(figure: shaded rectangle $6w + 2$ by $10w$ with inner rotated rectangle $2w + 1$ by $4w$)

Question 24

◇	A	B	C
1	Years From Now	Exponential Growth	Constant Increase
2	0	1200	1200
3	1	1260	1275
4	2	1323	1350
5	3		
6	4		
7	5		
8	6		
9	7		

Resource Master for Lesson 11-7

Resource Master 175 — Lesson 11-8

Warm-Up

Suppose a spinner is divided into four congruent regions labeled A, B, C, and D, and region D is twice the size of each of the other three regions.

1. If you spin the spinner 100 times, how many times would you expect the spinner to land in region B?
2. Suppose the spinner landed on A seventeen times, on B twenty-five times, on C twenty-four times, and on D thirty-four times. For each region calculate $\frac{(a - e)^2}{e}$ for each frequency, where a is the actual frequency and e is the expected frequency.
3. Add the four numbers you obtained in Question 2 to find the chi-square statistic.
4. Use row 3 of the table on page 699 to determine whether the frequencies differ significantly from what would be expected just by typical variations.

Additional Example

The table below shows the weather forecast based on a new method and actual temperatures for a week in November. Is there evidence that the new method is unreliable?

Temperature	Su	M	T	W	Th	F	Sa
Actual high	66	55	57	58	56	50	42
Predicted high	46	50	52	55	61	52	56

Resource Master for Lesson 11-8

Resource Master 177 — Lesson 11-8
Resource Master 176 — Lesson 11-8

Critical Chi-square Values

$n - 1$	0.10	0.05	0.01	0.001
1	2.71	3.84	6.63	10.8
2	4.61	5.99	9.21	13.8
3	6.25	7.81	11.34	16.3
4	7.78	9.49	13.28	18.5
5	9.24	11.07	15.09	20.5
6	10.6	12.6	16.8	22.5
7	12.0	14.1	18.5	24.3
8	13.4	15.5	20.1	26.1
9	14.7	16.9	21.7	27.9
10	16.0	18.3	23.2	29.6
15	22.3	25.0	30.6	37.7
20	28.4	31.4	37.6	45.3
25	34.4	37.7	44.3	52.6
30	40.3	43.8	50.9	59.7
50	63.2	67.5	76.2	86.7

Resource Masters for Lesson 11-8

Pacing

Each lesson in this chapter is designed to be covered in one day. At the end of the chapter, you should plan to spend 1 day to review the Self-Test, 1 to 2 days for the Chapter Review, and 1 day for a test. You may wish to spend a day on projects and possibly a day is needed for quizzes. This chapter should therefore take 11 to 14 days. We strongly advise you to not spend more than 15 days on this chapter; there is ample opportunity to review ideas in later chapters.

Projects

At the end of each chapter, you will find projects related to the chapter. At this time you might want to have students look over the projects on pages 703 and 704. You might want to have students tentatively select a project on which to work. Then, as students read and progress through the chapter, they can finalize their project choices.

Sometimes students might work alone; at other times, you might let them collaborate with classmates for a presentation and discussion. We recommend that you allow for diversity and encourage students to use their imaginations when presenting their projects. As students work on projects throughout the year, they should see the many uses of mathematics in the real world.

Chapter

11 **Polynomials**

Expressions such as those below are *polynomials*.

$1 \cdot 10^3 + 4 \cdot 10^2 + 9 \cdot 10^1 + 2$

s^3

$2\ell w + 2wh + 2\ell h$

$1,000x^4 + 500x^3 + 100x^2 + 200x$

Polynomials form the basic structure of our base 10 arithmetic. The expanded form of a number like 1,492, or $1 \cdot 10^3 + 4 \cdot 10^2 + 9 \cdot 10^1 + 2 \cdot 10^0$, is a polynomial in x with the base 10 substituted for x.

654

Chapter 11 Overview

Two applications (investments and permutations) and one application/representation (area) are the recurring contexts for this chapter. Lesson 11-1 reinforces the addition and subtraction of polynomials in the context of investments with periodic interest. Lesson 11-2 provides the vocabulary of polynomials. Lessons 11-3 through 11-6 use areas of rectangles to practice the multiplication of polynomials. Lesson 11-7 introduces permutations without replacement to provide another context for

this multiplication. The last lesson in the chapter, Lesson 11-8, presents a statistic that involves the squares of binomials.

The Distributive Property plays a major role in the new algorithms of this chapter. This skill is reviewed in enough detail in this chapter to be repeated as an objective. In the earlier lessons, it is used in adding like terms in polynomials:

$$ax^n + bx^n = (a + b)x^n$$

(continued on next page)

Polynomials are also found in geometry. For example, the monomial s^3 represents the volume of a cube with edge s, as shown below. The trinomial $2\ell w + 2wh + 2\ell h$ represents the surface area of a box of dimensions ℓ by w by h, as shown below.

Algebra is filled with polynomials. The linear expression $ax + b$ is a polynomial, as is the quadratic expression $ax^2 + bx + c$. In Chapter 7, you calculated compound interest for a single deposit. When several deposits are made, the total amount of money accumulated can be expressed as

a polynomial. For example, the polynomial $1{,}000x^4 + 800x^3 + 600x^2 + 250x$ represents the amount of money you would have if you had invested \$1,000 four years ago, added \$800 to it three years ago, added \$600 to it two years ago, and added \$250 to it one year ago, all earning at the same rate $x - 1$.

In this chapter you will study these and other situations that give rise to polynomials and how to add, subtract, multiply, and factor them.

655

and in multiplying a monomial by a polynomial:

$$a(x + y + z) = ax + ay + az$$

In Lesson 11-5, the Distributive Property is extended to multiply two polynomials.

$$(a + b + c)(x + y + z) = ax + ay + az + bx + by + bz + cx + cy + cz$$

A special case of the Extended Distributive Property is the multiplication of two

binomials, discussed in Lesson 11-6 and in more detail in Chapter 12:

$$(a + b)(c + d) = ac + ad + bc + bd$$

Also presented are the special cases:

$$(a + b)^2 = a^2 + 2ab + b^2 \text{ and}$$
$$(a + b)(a - b) = a^2 - b^2$$

The chapter leads naturally into Chapter 12, where the multiplication of binomials is discussed in connection with factoring.

Lesson 11-1

Lesson 11-1

Investments and Polynomials

GOAL

See how situations in which money is periodically invested in a savings account can lead to polynomials, and do the requisite calculations.

SPUR Objectives

(The SPUR Objectives for all of Chapter 11 are found in the Chapter Review on pages 708–711.)

A Add and subtract polynomials.

F Translate investment situations into polynomials.

Materials/Resources

· Lesson Masters 11-1A and 11-1B
· Resource Masters 5, 160, and 161
· Scientific calculator

HOMEWORK

Suggestions for Assignment
• Questions 1–27
• Question 28 (extra credit)
• Reading Lesson 11-2
• Covering the Ideas 11-2

Local Standards

1 Warm-Up

A relative gives you $5,000 to put away for college.

1. You put the money in an account that pays an annual yield of 4% the first year. How much will you have at the end of the year? **$5,200**

2. The account pays an annual yield of 4% during the second year. How much will you have after the second year? **$5,408**

3. The interest rate changes to an annual yield of 4.25% during the third year. How much will there be in the account at the end of three years? **$5,637.84**

▶ **BIG IDEA** When amounts are invested periodically and earn interest from the time of investment, the total value can be represented by a polynomial.

Among the most important money matters adults commonly deal with are salary or wages, savings, payments on loans for cars or trips or other items, and home mortgages or rent.

Each of these items involves paying or receiving money each month, every few months, or every year. But what is the total amount paid or received? The answer is not easy to calculate because interest starts at different times. Here is an example of this kind of situation.

Mental Math

Find the distance between

a. (x, y) and $(0, 0)$.

b. $(a, 5)$ and $(a, -11)$. **16**

c. $(m, m - n)$ and (m, m). $|n|$

a. $\sqrt{x^2 + y^2}$

Example 1

Each birthday from age 12 on, Jessica has received $500 from her grandparents. She saves the money in an account that pays an annual yield of 6%. How much money will she have by the time she is 18?

Solution Write down how much Jessica has on each birthday. On her 12th birthday she has $500. She then receives interest on that $500. She receives an additional $500 on her 13th birthday. So on her 13th birthday she has $500(1.06) + 500 = \$1,030.00$.

Each year interest is paid on all the money previously saved and each year another $500 gift is added. The totals for her 12th through 15th birthdays are given below.

Birthday	Expression	Total
12th	500	= $500
13th	500(1.06) + 500	= $1,030.00
14th	$500(1.06)^2 + 500(1.06) + 500$	= $1,591.80
15th	$500(1.06)^3 + 500(1.06)^2 + 500(1.06) + 500$	= $2,187.31

from 12th birthday   from 13th birthday   from 14th birthday   from 15th birthday

Background

The work on compound interest and exponential growth in Chapter 7 is applied in this lesson. This application involves *annuities* (investments involving periodic deposits or withdrawals). In an annuity, the principal amounts can be different (have different coefficients in the compound-interest formula) and grow for different lengths of time (have different exponents in the compound-interest formula). That is, if $x = 1 + r$, where r represents the annual yield, the polynomial $ax^2 + bx + c$ can stand

for the total when an amount a has been invested (or received) for 2 time periods, an amount b has been in the annuity for 1 time period, and the amount c has just been invested. If the annual yield were to change for the second investment to be s and $y = 1 + s$, then the total amount would be $ay^2 + by + c$. If the annual yield were to change for both investments in the second year to be s, then the total amount would be $axy + by + c$.

You can see the pattern. By her 18th birthday, Jessica will have three more gifts of $500 and earn interest on this money for three more years. The total will be $500(1.06)^6 + 500(1.06)^5 + 500(1.06)^4 + 500(1.06)^3 + 500(1.06)^2 + 500(1.06) + 500 = \$4{,}196.91$.

This total of $4,196.91 that she has by her 18th birthday is $696.91 more than the total $3,500 she received as gifts because of the interest earned.

Letting $x = 1.06$, the amount of money Jessica has (in dollars) after her 18th birthday is given by the polynomial
$500x^6 + 500x^5 + 500x^4 + 500x^3 + 500x^2 + 500x + 500$.

This expression is called a *polynomial in x*. A **polynomial in x** is a sum of multiples of powers of x. In this situation the polynomial is useful because if the interest rate is different, you only have to substitute a different value for x. We call x in this situation a *scale factor*. For example, had Jessica invested her money at an annual yield of 4%, the scale factor would be 104% = 1.04. At the end of 6 years, Jessica's investment (in dollars) would be $500(1.04)^6 + 500(1.04)^5 + 500(1.04)^4 + 500(1.04)^3 + 500(1.04)^2 + 500(1.04) + 500$.

You should verify with a calculator that this sum equals $3,949.14.

GUIDED

Example 2

Suppose Rajib's parents gave him $100 on his 12th birthday, $120 on his 13th, $140 on his 14th, and $160 on his 15th. If he invests all the money in an account with a yearly scale factor x, how much money will he have on his 15th birthday?

Solution By his 15th birthday, the __?__ from Rajib's 12th birthday will earn 3 years' worth of interest. It will have grown to __?__ $\cdot x^?$. **$100; 100; 3**

The __?__ from his 13th birthday will have grown to __?__. **$120; 120x^2**

The __?__ from his 14th birthday will have grown to __?__. **$140; 140x^1**

On his 15th birthday he receives __?__. **$160**

Through his 15th birthday, the total dollar amount Rajib will have from his birthday gifts is $100x^3 + 120x^2 + 140x + 160$.

Rajib's aunt gave him $50 on each of these 4 birthdays. If he puts this money into the same account, the amount available from the aunt's gifts would be $50x^3 + 50x^2 + 50x + 50$.

Investments and Polynomials **657**

Vocabulary Development

Discuss the definition of a *polynomial* in greater detail and ask students to determine whether certain expressions are polynomials. Make sure to include monomial, binomial, and constant expressions. Also include expressions with negative and fractional exponents and with negative, fractional, and decimal coefficients.

Accommodating the Learner

Ask students to refer back to Lesson 7-1 on compound interest and the formula $P(1+r)^t$. Ask them to compare the polynomial pattern with this formula. Ask students to describe how the ideas are different.

2 Teaching

Notes on the Lesson

Spend time reading Example 1 with students to ensure that they understand it. This example illustrates how polynomials arise, and it also demonstrates the value of writing *uncalculated* arithmetic expressions to describe situations. If students were to find the value of the expression at every birthday, they would not see the polynomial pattern. However, students should check the values of the Total column with their calculators.

Example 2 differs from Example 1 because the coefficients vary. This is because the amounts given each year are different. The paragraph below Example 2 shows how natural polynomial addition becomes in this context.

Additional Examples

Example 1 Every year after they are married, a couple deposits $2,000 into an account that pays an annual yield of 6.5%. The couple starts by depositing $2,000 when they are married in 2003. How much money will they have saved by their 10th wedding anniversary in 2013? $2{,}000(1.065)^{10} + 2{,}000(1.065)^9 + 2{,}000(1.065)^8 + 2{,}000(1.065)^7 + 2{,}000(1.065)^6 + 2{,}000(1.065)^5 + 2{,}000(1.065)^4 + 2{,}000(1.065)^3 + 2{,}000(1.065)^2 + 2{,}000(1.065) + 2{,}000 = \$30{,}743.12$

Example 2 Suppose the couple in Example 1 decided to deposit $2,000 the first year and then increase their deposit by $100 every year. If the yearly scale factor is x, how much money will they have saved by their wedding anniversary in 2013?

Solution

By 2013, the __?__ from the couple's first deposit in 2003 will earn 10 years' worth of interest. It will have grown to __?__ $\cdot x^?$. **$2,000; $2,000; 10**

On their 10th wedding anniversary, the total dollar amount they will have saved is $2{,}000x^{10} + 2{,}100x^9 + 2{,}200x^8 + 2{,}300x^7 + 2{,}400x^6 + 2{,}500x^5 + 2{,}600x^4 + 2{,}700x^3 + 2{,}800x^2 + 2{,}900x + 3{,}000$.

11-1

Notes on the Lesson

You can use Example 3 to point out an advantage to investing over a longer period of time. As a project, you could have students develop a plan for saving for a long-term goal such as college tuition, a new car, or a vacation. First, students will have to decide on the amount of money and the time that will be needed to achieve the goal. Have them decide on a reasonable estimate of a rate of return on an investment and develop a plan that enables them to reach the goal.

Additional Example

Example 3 Tina decides to start saving for her child's college expenses right after the baby is born. For 10 years, she saves $1,000 each year. Then she stops making deposits. Her sister, Karin, has a baby at the same time, but decides to wait eight years before she starts to save. She then saves $1,300 each year for ten years. They will each deposit their savings into a special account earning 5.5% interest compounded annually. How much will each have after eighteen years?

	A	B	C	D	E
1	Year	Tina's Deposit ($)	Tina's End-of-Year balance ($)	Karin's Deposit ($)	Karin's End-of-Year balance ($)
2	1	1,000	1,055	0	0
3	2	1,000	2,168.03	0	0
4	3	1,000	3,342.27	0	0
5	4	1,000	4,581.09	0	0
6	5	1,000	5,888.05	0	0
7	6	1,000	7,266.89	0	0
8	7	1,000	8,721.57	0	0
9	8	1,000	10,256.26	0	0
10	9	1,000	11,875.35	1,300	1,371.50
11	10	1,000	13,583.50	1,300	2,818.43
12	11	0	14,330.59	1,300	4,344.95
13	12	0	15,118.78	1,300	5,955.42
14	13	0	15,950.31	1,300	7,654.47
15	14	0	16,827.57	1,300	9,446.96
16	15	0	17,753.09	1,300	11,338.04
17	16	0	18,729.51	1,300	13,333.14
18	17	0	19,759.63	1,300	15,437.96
19	18	0	20,846.41	1,300	17,658.55

Eighteen years from now, Tina will have about $21,000 and Karin will have about $18,000.

The total amount he would have from all these gifts is found by adding these two polynomials.

$$(100x^3 + 120x^2 + 140x + 160) + (50x^3 + 50x^2 + 50x + 50)$$

Recall that this sum can be simplified. First, use the Associative and Commutative Properties of Addition to rearrange the polynomials so that like terms are together.

$$= (100x^3 + 50x^3) + (120x^2 + 50x^2) + (140x + 50x) + (160 + 50)$$

Then use the Distributive Property to add like terms.

$$= (100 + 50)x^3 + (120 + 50)x^2 + (140 + 50)x + (160 + 50)$$
$$= 150x^3 + 170x^2 + 190x + 210$$

Notice what the answer means in relation to Rajib's birthday presents. The first year he got $150 ($100 from his parents, $50 from his aunt). The $150 has 3 years to earn interest. The $170 from his next birthday earns interest for 2 years. And so on. Also notice that in these examples we have written the polynomials in the form of decreasing powers of x. This is called **standard form for a polynomial.** Polynomials are often written in standard form.

When comparing investments, it is often useful to make a table or construct a spreadsheet.

Example 3

Kelsey and Chip plan to save money for a round-the-world trip when they retire 10 years from now. Kelsey plans to save $2,000 per year for the first 5 years, and then will stop making deposits. Chip plans to wait 5 years to begin saving, but then hopes to save $2,500 per year for 5 years. They will each deposit their savings at the beginning of the year into a special account earning 6% interest compounded annually. How much will each have after 10 years?

Miami was the top cruise ship departure port of the United States in 2004 with 641 departures.

Source: Bureau of Transportation Statistics

Solution Make a spreadsheet showing the amount of money each person will have at the end of each year. At the end of the first year Kelsey will have $1.06(2,000) = 2,120$. At the end of the second year, she will have 106% of the sum of the previous balance and the new deposit of $2,000. In all, she will have $1.06(2,120 + 2,000) = \$4,367.20$. This pattern continues. But after 5 years, she deposits no more money. So her money only accumulates interest. Kelsey's end-of-year balance in the spreadsheet on the next page was computed by entering the formula =1.06*B2 into cell C2 and the formula =1.06*(C2+B3) into cell C3. The formula in cell C3 was then replicated down column C to C11. A similar set of formulas generated Chip's end-of-year balance.

Accommodating the Learner

In problems involving polynomials, students must be careful to only combine like terms. Review the topic of like terms with students and ask them to add and subtract polynomials to practice.

◇	A	B	C	D	E
1	Year	Kelsey's Deposits ($)	Kelsey's End-of-Year Balance ($)	Chip's Deposits ($)	Chip's End-of-Year Balance ($)
2	1	2,000	2,120.00	0	0
3	2	2,000	4,367.20	0	0
4	3	2,000	6,749.23	0	0
5	4	2,000	9,274.19	0	0
6	5	2,000	11,950.64	0	0
7	6	0	12,667.68	2,500	2,650.00
8	7	0	13,427.74	2,500	5,459.00
9	8	0	14,233.40	2,500	8,436.54
10	9	0	15,087.40	2,500	11,592.73
11	10	0	15,992.65	2,500	14,938.30

Ten years from now Kelsey will have about $16,000 and Chip will have about $15,000.

In Example 3, notice that even though Kelsey deposits $10,000 and Chip deposits $12,500 at the same rate of interest, compounding interest over a longer period of time gives Kelsey about $1,055 more than Chip. Here is what has happened. After 10 years:

Kelsey has $2{,}000x^{10} + 2{,}000x^9 + 2{,}000x^8 + 2{,}000x^7 + 2{,}000x^6$.

Chip has $2{,}500x^5 + 2{,}500x^4 + 2{,}500x^3 + 2{,}500x^2 + 2{,}500x$.

When $x = 1.06$, Kelsey has more than Chip.

Questions

COVERING THE IDEAS

1. Refer to Example 1. Suppose Jessica is able to get an annual yield of 5% on her investment.
   a. How much money will she have in her account by her 18th birthday? **$4,071**
   b. How much less is this than what she would have earned with a 6% annual yield? **$125.90**

2. Mary's grandfather will receive a $3,000 bonus from his employer on each of his birthdays from age 61 to age 65 if he indicates he will retire at 65. **2a. $17,080.92**
   a. If he saves the money in an account paying an annual yield of 6.5%, how much will he have by the time he retires at age 65?
   b. How much will he have accumulated by the time he retires at age 65 if his investment grows by a scale factor of x each year?
   2b. $3{,}000x^4 + 3{,}000x^3 + 3{,}000x^2 + 3{,}000x + 3{,}000$

Investments and Polynomials **659**

3 Assignment

Recommended Assignment
- Questions 1–27
- Question 28 (extra credit)
- Reading Lesson 11-2
- Covering the Ideas 11-2

Notes on the Questions

Questions 1–7 These questions parallel the lesson and might be discussed along with the examples.

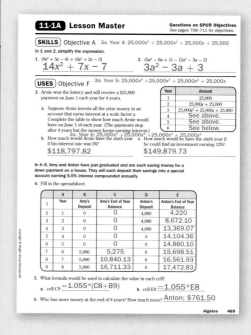

Notes on the Questions

Question 3 This question is important to discuss because it uses the addition of polynomials.

Question 7 This should be review for students. If it is not review, discuss the idea carefully because problems involving base 10 are used throughout the chapter.

3. Refer to Example 2. Suppose Rajib also gets $75, $85, $95, and $105 from cousin Lilly on his four birthdays. He puts this money into his account also.

   a. By his 15th birthday, how much money will Rajib have from just his cousin? $75x^3 + 85x^2 + 95x + 105$

   b. What is the total Rajib will have saved by his 15th birthday from all of his birthday presents?
   $225x^3 + 255x^2 + 285x + 315$

In 4–6, refer to Example 3.

4. Explain why Chip had less money saved than Kelsey at the end of the 10-year period even though he put more money into his account than Kelsey.

5. Chip said to Kelsey, "I might have less money now, but I am catching up to you, and even if we put no more money into our accounts, the amount in my account will be greater after a few more years." Kelsey said, "You have less now and you will always have less." Who is right? **Kelsey is correct.**

6. Suppose Kelsey and Chip were able to earn 3% on their investments. Recalculate the balances in the spreadsheet and describe the end result. **See margin.**

7. Refer to page 654. Write the number 84,267 as a polynomial in base 10.
   $84{,}267 = 8 \cdot 10^4 + 4 \cdot 10^3 + 2 \cdot 10^2 + 6 \cdot 10^1 + 7 \cdot 10^0$

4. Kelsey begins saving first, so her interest compounds for a longer period of time. Since the interest that Kelsey receives each time is greater than the sum of Chip's interest and the difference between Chip and Kelsey's deposits, Kelsey has more money saved at the end.

APPLYING THE MATHEMATICS

In 8–11, Clara, Mona, and Odella are friends who have the same birthday. They received the following cash presents on their birthdays. Each put all her money into a bank account that paid a 6% annual yield.

	Clara	Mona	Odella
In 2003	$200	$250	$100
In 2004	$300	$250	$500
In 2005	$250	$250	nothing

8. How much money did Clara have on her birthday in 2003? **$200**

9. How much did Mona have on her birthday in 2004? **$515**

10. How much did Odella have on her birthday in 2005? **$642.36**

11. In 2006, Clara received $300 on her birthday. If all the money from 2003 to 2006 had been and remains in an account with scale factor *x*, how much would she have had by her birthday in each of the following years? **11a–d. See margin.**

    a. 2005

    b. 2006

    c. 2007

    d. 2008

Out of a class of 24 students, the probability of any 3 that share a birthday is about 16.6%.

Additional Answers

6. At the end of 10 years, Chip would have $13,671.02, while Kelsey would have $12,678.77. So at an interest rate of 3% over 10 years, Chip would have more money than Kelsey.

	A Year	B Kelsey's Deposit ($)	C Kelsey's End-of-Year balance ($)	D Chip's Deposit ($)	E Chip's End-of-Year balance ($)
2	1	2,000	2,060.00	0	0
3	2	2,000	4,181.80	0	0
4	3	2,000	6,367.25	0	0
5	4	2,000	8,618.27	0	0
6	5	2,000	10,936.82	0	0
7	6	0	11,264.92	2,500	2,575.00
8	7	0	11,602.87	2,500	5,227.25
9	8	0	11,950.96	2,500	7,959.07
10	9	0	12,309.49	2,500	10,772.84
11	10	0	12,678.77	2,500	13,671.02

12. Suppose in 1999 Tanya received $100 on her birthday. From 2000 to 2003 she received $150 on her birthday. She put the money in a shoe box. The money is still there.

   a. How much money did Tanya have after her 2003 birthday? $700

   b. How much more would she have had if she had invested her money at an annual yield of 4% each year? $170.94

13. **Multiple Choice** Which is the sum of $x^4 + x^3 + x^2$? D

   A x^9 B $3x^9$

   C x^{24} D None of these

In 14–17, simplify the expression.

14. $(2y^2 + 13y - 14) + (4y^2 - 3y - 24)$ $6y^2 + 10y - 38$

15. $6(11n + 8n^2 - 2) + (6n^2 - n - 9)$ $54n^2 + 65n - 21$

16. $(7w^2 - 2w + 16) - 4(7w^2 + 15)$ $-21w^2 - 2w - 44$

17. $(x^3 + 2x^2 + 8) - (2x - 5x^3 + 6)$ $6x^3 + 2x^2 - 2x + 2$

18. Solve the equation $(3x^2 + 2x + 4) + (3x^2 + 11x + 2) = 0$. $x = -\frac{2}{3}$ or $x = -\frac{3}{2}$

19. Solve the equation $(3x^2 + 2x + 4) - (3x^2 + 11x + 2) = 0$. $x = \frac{2}{9}$

In 20 and 21, find the missing polynomial.

20. $(91x^2 + 4x - 15) + (\underline{\ ?\ }) = 110x^2 + 62$ $19x^2 - 4x + 77$

21. $(3y^2 - 2y - 1) - (\underline{\ ?\ }) = -4y^2 - 6y + 21$ $7x^2 + 4y - 22$

22. A *cord* of wood is an amount of wood equal to about 128 cubic feet. A wood harvester has planted trees in a forest each spring for four years, as shown in the table at the right.

   Suppose each tree contains 0.01 cord of wood when planted, and the cordage grows with a scale factor x each year. How many cords of wood are in the forest after planting the fourth spring?
   $100x^3 + 150x^2 + 200x + 180$

Year	Number of Trees Planted
1	10,000
2	15,000
3	20,000
4	18,000

Forests cover 747 million acres in the United States.

Source: U.S. Department of Agriculture

REVIEW

23. If 8 pencils and 5 erasers cost $4.69 and 3 pencils and 4 erasers cost $2.80, find the cost of 2 pencils. (Lesson 10-2) $0.56

24. Write an equation for the line which passes through the points $(4, -8)$ and $(-10, 6)$. (Lesson 6-6) $y = -x - 4$

Investments and Polynomials **661**

Notes on the Questions

Question 12 Part *b* is essentially asking how much interest Tanya would have received.

Question 13 The choices are common errors.

Questions 17, 19, and 21 Be careful that students distribute the opposite over all the terms of the subtrahend.

Questions 18 and 19 Students may be surprised that one equation leads to a quadratic and one leads to a linear equation.

Questions 20 and 21 In anticipation of Question 26 in the next lesson, you could put these expressions into a fact triangle.

Additional Answers

11a. $200x^2 + 300x + 250$

11b. $200x^3 + 300x^2 + 250x + 300$

11c. $200x^4 + 300x^3 + 250x^2 + 300x$

11d. $200x^5 + 300x^4 + 250x^3 + 300x^2$

11-1

Notes on the Questions

Question 25b Some students will factor the numerator of the fraction. Others will multiply both sides by $6(2h - 1)$. You might compare methods and note how each method is special when $h = \dfrac{-1}{n(n+1)}$.

4 Wrap-Up

Ongoing Assessment

Write the polynomial $100x^4 + 120x^3 + 140x^2 + 160x + 180$ on the board and ask students to give an example of a real-life situation that the polynomial models.

---

25. Consider the equation $\dfrac{30(4h - 2)}{6(2h - 1)} = 10$. **(Lesson 5-5)**

a. For what value of h is $\dfrac{30(4h - 2)}{6(2h - 1)}$ undefined? $h = \dfrac{1}{2}$

b. Solve for h. h can be any real number but $\dfrac{1}{2}$.

26. In one of his studies, discussed in the book *The Effects of Cross- and Self-Fertilization in the Vegetable Kingdom,* Charles Darwin compared the heights of two groups of plants. One group was cross-pollinated, meaning they were fertilized by pollen from other plants. The other group was self-fertilized. For the cross-fertilized plants, the mean height was 20.2, and for the self-fertilized plants the mean height was 17.6. Darwin's data are shown below. (*Note:* The values were rounded before plotting in Question 27.) **(Lessons 1-7, 1-6)**

Cross-Fertilized (in.)	23.5	12.0	21.0	22.0	19.1	21.5	22.1	20.4	18.3	21.6	23.3	21.0	22.1	23.0	12.0
Self-Fertilized (in.)	17.4	20.4	20.0	20.0	18.4	18.6	18.6	15.3	16.5	18.0	16.3	18.0	12.8	15.5	18.0

a. Find the range of the data for each type of plant.

b. Find the mean for each type of plant.

c. Find the mean absolute deviation for each type of plant.

27. Use the two dot plots below. **(Lesson 1-7)**

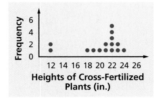

Heights of Cross-Fertilized Plants (in.)

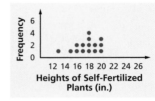

Heights of Self-Fertilized Plants (in.)

a. Classify each dot plot as skewed right, skewed left, symmetric, or uniform.

b. Based on Darwin's data, what advice would you give to a farmer who wants to grow tall plants?

EXPLORATION

28. Refer to Kelsey and Chip in Example 3 and Questions 4–6.

a. For what interest rates does Kelsey end up with more money after 10 years than Chip?

b. For what interest rates does Chip end up with more money than Kelsey? **Chip ends up with more than Kelsey at interest rates less than 4.56% after 10 years.**

26a. cross-fertilized: 11.5 in.; self-fertilized: 7.6 in.

26b. cross-fertilized: 20.2 in.; self-fertilized: 17.6 in.

26c. cross-fertilized: 2.58 in.; self-fertilized: 1.56 in.

27a. cross-fertilized: skewed left; self-fertilized: symmetric

27b. Cross-fertilize the plants because the mean is greater than that of self-fertilized plants.

28a. Kelsey ends up with more than Chip at interest rates greater than 4.56% after 10 years.

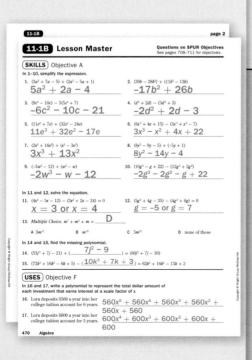

Lesson 11-2
Classifying Polynomials

> ▸ **BIG IDEA** Polynomials are classified by their number of terms and by their degree.

Classifying Polynomials by Numbers of Terms

Recall that a *term* can be a single number, variable, or product of numbers and variables. In an expression, addition (or subtraction, which is "adding the opposite") separates terms.

Polynomials are identified by their number of terms. A **monomial** is a single term in which the exponent for every variable is a positive integer. A **polynomial** is an expression that is either a monomial or sum of monomials. Polynomials with two or three terms are used so often they have special names. A **binomial** is a polynomial that has two terms. A **trinomial** is a polynomial that has three terms. Here are some examples.

Monomials	Not Monomials	
$6x$	$6x + y$	(a binomial)
$-16t^2$	$-16t^{-2}$	(negative exponent on a variable)
x^2y^4	$\frac{x^2}{y^4}$	(variables divided)

Binomials	Not Binomials	
$x + 26\sqrt{2}$	$26x\sqrt{2}$	(monomial)
$\frac{x}{3} - y^3$	$-\frac{xy^3}{3}$	(monomial)
$0.44 - 2^{-10}pq^4$	$0.44 - 2^{-10}p + q^4$	(trinomial)

Trinomials	Not Trinomials	
$18x^2 + 5x + 9$	$(15x^2)(5x)(9)$	(monomial)
$a^2 + 2ab - b^{20}$	$a^{-2} + 2ab - b^{-20}$	(negative exponent on variables)
$pq + qr + rp$	$\frac{1}{pq + qr + rp}$	(variables divided)

There are no special names for polynomials with more than three terms.

Background

Polynomials can be classifed in many ways. We often classify by degree: *linear, quadratic, cubic, quartic,* and *quintic* are the names we give to polynomials of degrees 1, 2, 3, 4, and 5, respectively. In this lesson, we classify by number of terms: *monomial, binomial, trinomial* are the names we give to polynomials with 1, 2, and 3 terms. We sometimes sort by the type of coefficients and speak of polynomials *over the integers, rationals, reals,* or *complex numbers.*

The definition of the *degree* of a polynomial comes from the fact that all polynomials are *polynomials in a variable or variables.* The polynomial $3x$ is a polynomial in x. Unless we are told otherwise, the polynomial x^2y^4 is a polynomial in x and y, and we add the degrees of x and y to determine that it is of degree 6. In certain circumstances, we might think of the polynomial x^2y^4 as a polynomial in y; then its degree is 4.

(continued on next page)

GOAL

Understand the basic terminology of polynomials and the classification of polynomials by the number of terms or by their degree.

SPUR Objectives

A Add and subtract polynomials.

E Classify polynomials by their degree or number of terms.

Materials/Resources

· Lesson Masters 11-2A or 11-2B
· Resource Masters 162 and 163

HOMEWORK

Suggestions for Assignment

• Questions 1–34
• Question 35 (extra credit)
• Reading Lesson 11-3
• Covering the Ideas 11-3

Local Standards

---

1   Warm-Up

1. a. Write 123,456,789 as a polynomial in base 10. $1 \cdot 10^8 + 2 \cdot 10^7 + 3 \cdot 10^6 + 4 \cdot 10^5 + 5 \cdot 10^4 + 6 \cdot 10^3 + 7 \cdot 10^2 + 8 \cdot 10 + 9$

   b. What is the greatest power of 10? **8**

   c. What is the coefficient of the 10^5 term? **4**

2. Consider the expression $x^3 + 5x^5 - 2^7$.

   a. What is the greatest power of x? **5**

   b. Is this a monomial, binomial, trinomial, or other type of polynomial? **trinomial**

   c. What is the coefficient of the squared term? **0**

Vocabulary

monomial
polynomial
binomial
trinomial
degree of a monomial
degree of a polynomial
linear polynomial
quadratic polynomial

Mental Math

Refer to the graph of a function.

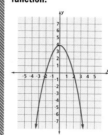

a. State the domain of the function.

b. State the range of the function.

c. State the x-intercepts.

d. State the y-intercept. **4**

a. the set of all real numbers

b. the set of all real numbers such that $y \le 4$.

c. –2 and 2

2 | Teaching

Notes on the Lesson

In a polynomial, every exponent for a variable must be a nonnegative integer. For example, $\frac{3}{x}$ is not a polynomial because it is equivalent to $3x^{-1}$. The term $16\sqrt{t}$ is not a polynomial because it involves taking a square root of a variable and is equal to $16t^{0.5}$.

When a polynomial has only one variable, it is easy to determine the degree of the polynomial. It is the greatest exponent of the variable. However, if any term of the polynomial involves more than one variable, then the degrees of the individual variables in each term must be added.

Polynomials may be classified by degree or by the number of terms. The following table may help.

degree	name of polynomial
1	linear
2	quadratic
3	cubic
4	quartic (in older books, biquadratic)
5	quintic
6 +	no special name

number of terms	name of polynomial
1	monomial
2	binomial
3	trinomial
4 +	no special name

Students are familiar with the prefixes bi- and tri- and perhaps mono-.

- bicycle (2 wheels), tricycle (3 wheels), monocycle (1 wheel)
- biped (animal that stands on two feet, like man or a bird), tripod (camera support resting on three legs)

Classifying Polynomials by Degree

Every nonconstant term of a polynomial has one or more exponents. For example, $3x^2$ has 2 as its exponent. $10t$ has an unwritten exponent of 1, since $t^1 = t$. $15a^2b^3c^4$ has 2, 3, and 4 as its exponents.

The **degree of a monomial** is the sum of the exponents of the variables in the expression.

> $3x^2$ has degree 2.
>
> $10t$ has degree 1.
>
> $15a^2b^3c^4$ has degree $2 + 3 + 4$, or 9.

The degree of a single number, such as 15, is considered to be 0 because $15 = 15x^0$. However, the number 0 is said not to have any degree, because $0 = 0 \cdot x^n$, where n could be any number. The **degree of a polynomial** is the highest degree of any of its monomial terms after the polynomial has been simplified. For example, $6x - 17x^4 + 8 + x^2$ has degree 4. $p + q^2 + pq^2 + p^2q^3$ has degree 5 (because $2 + 3 = 5$).

STOP QY1

When a polynomial has only one variable, writing it in standard form makes it easy to determine its degree. When the polynomial in x above is written in standard form, the degree is the exponent of the leftmost term.

> $-17x^4 + x^2 + 6x + 8$ has degree 4.

Function notation can be used to represent a polynomial in a variable. For example, let $p(x) = -17x^4 + x^2 + 6x + 8$. Then values of the polynomial are easily described. For example, $p(2) = -17 \cdot 2^4 + 2^2 + 6 \cdot 2 + 8 = -248$.

STOP QY2

The polynomial $p + q^2 + pq^2 + p^2q^3$ is a polynomial in p and q. There is no standard form for writing polynomials that have more than one variable, like this one. However, sometimes one variable is picked and the polynomial is written in decreasing powers of that variable. For example, written in decreasing powers of q, this polynomial is $p^2q^3 + pq^2 + q^2 + p$, or, to emphasize the powers of q, $p^2q^3 + (p + 1)q^2 + p$.

A polynomial of degree 1, such as $13t - 6$, is called a **linear polynomial.** A polynomial of degree 2, such as $2x^2 + 3x + 1$ or ℓw, is called a **quadratic polynomial.** Linear and quadratic polynomials whose coefficients are positive integers can be represented by tiles.

▶ **QY1**

Classify each polynomial by the number of its terms and its degree.

a. $x^6 + x^7 + x^5$
b. $8y^3z^2 - 40yz^6$
c. $\frac{4}{3}\pi r^3$

▶ **QY2**

If $p(x) = -x + 3 + 4x^4$, what is $p(-2)$?

If x^2y^4 is considered as a polynomial in x, then its degree is 2.

In solving the equation $ax^2 + bx + c = 0$ for x, the equation is of degree 2. But if we were solving that equation for b, then the equation is of degree 1.

Polynomials are *in* a variable or variables, but they are also *over* the set from which their coefficients are chosen. This idea will be important in Chapter 12, which discusses factoring and analyzing solutions

to quadratic equations. In this lesson, you might note that the polynomial forms that represent whole numbers in base 10 are over the set {0, 1, 2, 3, 4, 5, 6, 7, 8, 9}, the set of digits.

Although our definition of a polynomial is as a "sum of monomials," we identify $x^2 - xy$ as a polynomial even though it is a difference. Subtraction is "adding the opposite." If we solve $3x^2 - 8x + 5 = 0$ using that formula, we think of the coefficient of x as being –8.

The tiles below represent the polynomial $2x^2 + 3x + 1$ because this polynomial is the area of the figure.

Using the Degree of a Polynomial to Check Operations with Polynomials

The simplest polynomials in one variable are the monomials x, x^2, x^3, x^4, and so on. You know how to add, subtract, multiply, and divide these monomials. For example, $x^2 \cdot x^3 = x^5$, so in this case a polynomial of degree 2 multiplied by a polynomial of degree 3 gives a polynomial of degree 5. In general, the degree of an answer to a polynomial computation is as easy to determine with complicated polynomials as it is with the simplest ones. Consider these examples of polynomial addition and subtraction.

GUIDED

Example

Collect like terms and determine the degree of the resulting polynomial.

1. $(17w + 14) - (6 - 5w) = \underline{\quad?\quad}$ $22w + 8$
   degree 1   degree 1   degree 1

2. $(6ab - 22) + (2a + 8b) = 6ab + 2a + 8b - 22$
   degree 2   degree 1   degree $\underline{\quad?\quad}$ 2

3. $(4x + x^3 - 7) - (x^2 + 4x + 5) = \underline{\quad?\quad}$ $x^3 - x^2 - 12$
   degree 3   degree 2   degree $\underline{\quad?\quad}$ 3

4. $(x^7 + 4x - 5) + (3 - 2x - x^7) = \underline{\quad?\quad}$ $2x - 2$
   degree 7   degree 7   degree $\underline{\quad?\quad}$ 1

Notice that the degree of the sum or difference of two polynomials is never greater than the highest degree of the polynomial addends. Can you see why this is so?

Questions

COVERING THE IDEAS

1. Explain why $3x^2 + 4$ is a polynomial but $\frac{3}{x^2} + 4$ is not.

2. **Fill in the Blank** A binomial is a polynomial with $\underline{\quad?\quad}$ term(s).
   two

---

1. $3x^2 + 4$ is a sum of monomials, while $\frac{3}{x^2} + 4$ includes a quotient of monomials.

Accommodating the Learner

Take extra time to work with students on the distinction between the number of terms in an expression and the degree. For example, Question 7 asks students if xyz is a trinomial. Discuss the distinction between xyz and $x + y + z$. Continue comparing the ideas by discussing expressions such as $x + x + x$, which simplifies to a monomial of degree 1.

ENGLISH LEARNERS

Vocabulary Development

Help students make a connection between the meaning of the mathematical terms and the prefixes mono-, bi-, tri-, and poly-. Emphasize that the term polynomial includes all monomials, binomials, and trinomials, as well as expressions with four or more terms. Students often mistakenly think that it applies only to expressions with many terms.

11-2

3 Assignment

Recommended Assignment

- Questions 1–34
- Question 35 (extra credit)
- Reading Lesson 11-3
- Covering the Ideas 11-3

Notes on the Questions

Question 8 This question is designed to help students distinguish the difference between classifying polynomials by the number of terms and classifying them by degree. You might ask for an example of a binomial of degree 1, a binomial of degree 4, a trinomial of degree 4, and so on.

Question 10 When we write polynomials in one variable in standard form, the variable is written at the right of each term.

Question 11 Tiles not only present a concrete example but also illustrate the role of area in explaining polynomials.

In 3–6, an expression is given.

   a. Tell whether the expression is a monomial.

   b. If it is a monomial, state its degree.

3. $17x^{11}$ a. monomial b. 11

4. $2w^{-4}$ a. not a monomial b. not a monomial

5. $\frac{1}{2}bh$ a. monomial b. 2

6. $2a^4b^5$ a. monomial b. 9

7. Is xyz a trinomial? Explain your reasoning.

8. Classify each polynomial by its degree and number of terms.

   a. $x^2 + 10$ 2; binomial
   b. $x^2 + 10x + 21$ 2; trinomial
   c. $x^2 + 10xy + y^2$ 2; trinomial
   d. $x^3 + 10x^2 + 21x$ 3; trinomial

9. Write the polynomial $12 - 4x - 3x^5 + 8x^2$ in standard form.

10. a. Write the polynomial $a^3 - 3ab^2 - b^3 - 3a^2b$ in standard form as a polynomial in a. $a^3 - 3a^2b - 3ab^2 - b^3$

   b. Write the polynomial $a^3 - 3ab^2 - b^3 - 3a^2b$ in standard form as a polynomial in b. $-b^3 - 3ab^2 - 3a^2b + a^3$

In 11 and 12, what polynomial is represented by the tiles?

11.

$3x^2 + 2x + 5$

12.

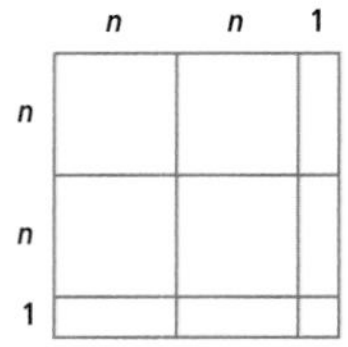

$4n^2 + 4n + 1$

13. Fill in the blank with *always*, *sometimes but not always*, or *never*. Explain your answer. The degree of the sum of two polynomials is ___?___ greater than the degree of either polynomial addend.

APPLYING THE MATHEMATICS

In 14–18, an expression is given.

   a. Show that the expression can be simplified into a monomial.

   b. Give the degree of the monomial.

14. $10x - 14x$ a. $-4x$ b. 1

15. $10x(-14x)$ a. $-140x^2$ b. 2

16. $(5n^3)(6n)^2$ a. $180n^5$ b. 5

17. $xy + yx$ a. $2xy$ b. 2

18. $12x^4 - (3x^4 + 2x^4 + x^4)$
   a. $6x^4$ b. 4

Answers (right margin):

7. xyz is not a trinomial, it is a monomial because there is only one term.

9. $-3x^5 + 8x^2 - 4x + 12$

13. never; Polynomials with the same degree are like terms; to find their sum you add the coefficients. Thus, the degrees of the sum may be less than or equal to, but will never be greater than the degree of either addend.

11-2A Lesson Master

Questions on SPUR Objectives
See pages 708–711 for objectives.

SKILLS Objective A

In 1 and 2, simplify the expression.

1. $(7m^3 - 9m^2 + 8m - 1) + (m^2 + 3m + 13)$ $7m^3 - 8m^2 + 11m + 12$

2. $(5n^2 + 6n + 2) - (5n^3 + 10n - 8)$ $-5n^3 + 5n^2 - 4n + 10$

PROPERTIES Objective E

3. *Multiple Choice.* Which expression is a binomial? **C**

  A $\frac{x}{y} + \frac{3x}{y^2}$ B $2(y^2 + 9)^2$ C $n + 3$ D $5x^2$

In 4 and 5, an expression is given. If the expression is a monomial, state its degree.

4. $6x^4$ **4**

5. x^2y^5 **7**

6. a. Write a monomial in x whose degree is 6. Sample answer: $-4x^6$

   b. Write a monomial in x and y whose degree is 6. Sample answer: $3xy^5$

7. a. What is the degree of the monomial 12? **0**

   b. Give an example of another monomial with the same degree as 12. Sample answer: 13

In 8–10, give the degree of the polynomial.

8. $x^3 - 2x^7$ **7**

9. $5x^2 + 7x - 3$ **2**

10. $2x^3 + 5x^4 - 3x^6$ **6**

11. a. Write a trinomial in x whose degree is 6. Sample answer: $x^6 + x + 1$

   b. Write a trinomial in x and y whose degree is 6. Sample answer: $xy^5 + x + 1$

12. Give an example of a trinomial of degree 5. Sample answer: $x^5 + xy - 4$

13. Give an example of a binomial of degree 3. Sample answer: $x^3 - 4$

Accommodating the Learner

Ask students to discuss the strengths and weaknesses of the tile visualization of a polynomial. Some questions to consider include: What if x is zero or negative? What happens to the visualization as we consider polynomials of degree 3 or higher?

19. Let $p(x) = 50x^3 + 50x^2 + 50x + 50$ and $q(x) = 100x^3 + 120x^2 + 140x + 160$. Give the degree of each polynomial.
   a. $p(x)$ 3
   b. $q(x)$ 3
   c. $p(x) + q(x)$ 3
   d. $p(x) - q(x)$ 3

20. Repeat Question 19 if $p(x) = x^{200} - x^{100} + 1$ and $q(x) = x^{100} - x^{200} + 1$. a. 200 b. 200 c. 0 d. 200

In 21–24, give the degree of these polynomials used to find length, area, and volume of geometric figures.

21. perimeter of a triangle $= a + b + c$ 1

22. volume of a circular cone $= \frac{1}{3}\pi r^2 h$ 3

23. area of a trapezoid $= \frac{1}{2}hb_1 + \frac{1}{2}hb_2$ 2

24. surface area of a cylinder $= 2\pi r^2 + 2\pi rh$ 2

25. a. Write a monomial with one variable whose degree is 70.
   b. Write a monomial with two variables whose degree is 70.

26. Complete the fact triangle below and write the related polynomial addition and subtraction facts.

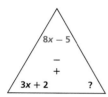

27. a. Give an example of two trinomials in x of degree 5 whose sum is of degree 5.
   b. Give an example of two trinomials in x of degree 5 whose sum is not of degree 5.

28. a. Write 318 and 4,670 as polynomials with 10 substituted for the variable. 31.8x, 467x, where $x = 10$
   b. Add your polynomials from Part a. Is your sum equal to the sum of 318 and 4,670?

REVIEW

29. a. If you received $1,000 as a present on the day you were born, and the money was put into an account at an annual scale factor of x, how much would be in your account on your 18th birthday? $1,000x^{18}$
   b. Evaluate the amount in Part a if $x = 1.05$. **(Lesson 11-1)**
   $2,406.61

25a. Answers vary.
   Sample answer:
   x^{70}
25b. Answers vary.
   Sample answer:
   $x^{35}y^{35}$
26. $5x - 7$; $(8x - 5) - (3x + 2) = 5x - 7$, $(8x - 5) - (5x - 7) = 3x + 2$, $(3x + 2) + (5x - 7) = 8x - 5$; $(5x - 7) + (3x + 2) = 8x - 5$
27a. Answers vary.
   Sample answer:
   $x^5 + x + 1$,
   $x^5 + x + 6$
27b. Answers vary.
   Sample answer:
   $x^5 + 6x + 8$,
   $-x^5 + 4x + 2$
28b. $31.8x + 467x = 498.8x = 4,988$.
   Yes, the sum is equal.

Notes on the Questions

Questions 21–24 Point out that the one-dimensional measure (perimeter) is described by a polynomial of degree 1; the two-dimensional measures (area and surface area) are described by polynomials of degree 2; and the three-dimensional measure (volume) is described by a polynomial of degree 3. This is not a coincidence. We multiply dimensions to get these measures, and each multiplication adds a degree to the product.

Question 26 The use of the fact triangle emphasizes that polynomial addition still involves the adding of numbers and has the same properties, which are familiar to students.

Question 31 This question is meant to be solved by letting the width of the sidewalk be w, finding an expression for the area in w (a linear expression), and then setting it equal to the difference in areas of the outer and inner rectangles. However, it could also be solved purely arithmetically by factoring 3,256 as $2^3 \cdot 11 \cdot 37 = 44 \cdot 74$. This indicates that the outer dimensions are 4 more than the inner dimensions, so the width of the walk is 2 meters. Do not dismiss the arithmetic solution because it shows a use for factoring in solving problems of this type.

Extension

Provide several basic examples where students multiply monomials and binomials. Ask students to use the degree of the polynomials to check their operations. Then ask students to predict the degree of the product of more complicated polynomials (monomial times trinomial, binomial times binomial, etc.). Show students the simplified products and discuss the pattern.

11-2

4 Wrap-Up

Ongoing Assessment

Write different polynomials on the board and ask the students to tell the classification, first by number of terms, then by degree. Finally, ask students to say *yes* or *no* depending on whether or not it is in standard form.

Project Update

If you have not had students look over the projects on pages 703 and 704, you might want to do so now. Project 3, Representing Positive Integers Using Powers, on pages 703 and 704, relates to the content of this lesson.

11-2B Lesson Master

Questions on SPUR Objectives
See pages 708–711 for objectives.

SKILLS Objective A

In 1–10, simplify the expression.

1. $(3x^2 + 18x - 12) + (3x + 18)$
$3x^2 + 21x + 6$

2. $(9y^3 + 2y^2 + 8y) - (2y^3 - 8y^2 - 13)$
$7y^3 + 10y^2 + 8y + 13$

3. $(12m^2 + 7m - 6) + (28m^2 + 77m)$
$40m^2 + 84m - 6$

4. $(50p^3 + 130p^2 + 80p - 90) - (11p^3 + 5)$
$39p^3 + 130p^2 + 80p - 95$

5. $(63r + 119) + (85r^2 + 153)$
$85r^2 + 63r + 272$

6. $(65x^2 - 169x + 91) - (24x^2 - 36x - 8)$
$41x^2 - 133x + 99$

7. $(3b^3 + 8b^2 - 15b + 1) + (4b^2 - 1)$
$3b^3 + 12b^2 - 15b$

8. $(t^3 - 7t^2 + 16) - (10t^3 + 6t^2 - 8)$
$-9t^3 - 13t^2 + 24$

9. $(9x^4 - 16x^3 + 15) + (7x^4 - 7x^2 + 5)$
$16x^4 - 16x^3 - 7x^2 + 20$

10. $(78z^5 + 72z^4) - (33z^3 + 66z^2 + 22z)$
$78z^5 + 72z^4 - 33z^3 - 66z^2 - 22z$

11. Write the perimeter of the rectangle as a polynomial in standard form.
$72x^3 + 4x^2 + 274x + 18$

[box: $36x^3 + 85x$] [$2x^2 + 52x + 9$]

PROPERTIES Objective E

12. Classify each polynomial by its degree and number of terms.

a. $x^2y^{14} + 19$
21; binomial

b. $8z^7 + 17a^{10} - 12$
10; trinomial

c. $2w + 17$
1; binomial

d. $18x^4 - 8x^3 + 7$
4; trinomial

Algebra 473

11-2B page 2

13. Let $p(v) = 4v^3 + 13v^2 + 7$ and $q(v) = v^3 - 17v^2 + 14v + 5$. Give the degree of each polynomial.

a. $p(v) + q(v)$
3

b. $p(v) - q(v)$
3

14. Let $f(x) = 8x^2 - 15x + 4$ and $g(x) = 11x + 6$. Give the degree of each polynomial.

a. $g(x) + f(x)$
2

b. $g(x) - f(x)$
2

In 15–18, an expression is given.
a. Tell whether the expression is a monomial.
b. If it is a monomial, state its degree.

15. $6x^{17}$
a. yes
b. 17

16. $4ac^{-9}$
a. no
b. not a monomial

17. $7x^2y^{-5}$
a. no
b. not a monomial

18. $11a^4b^{12}$
a. yes
b. 16

19. a. Write a monomial in w whose degree is 3.
Sample answer: $7w^3$
b. Write a monomial in w and z whose degree is 3.
Sample answer: $7w^2z$

20. Give an example of a binomial of degree 9.
Sample answer: $4x^9 + 1$

21. Give an example of a trinomial of degree 6.
Sample answer: $8x^6 + 9x^2 + 3$

474 *Algebra*

---

30. Consider the system $\begin{cases} a - 2b = 50 \\ b = -4c \end{cases}$. To solve this system, one student substituted $-4c$ for b in the first equation. The student then wrote $a - 8c = 50$. (**Lessons 10-3, 10-2**)

   a. Is the student's work correct? no

   b. If it is correct, finish solving the system. If not, describe the error the student made.

31. A parking lot with length 70 meters and width 40 meters is to have a pedestrian sidewalk surrounding it, increasing its total area to 3,256 square meters. What will be the width of the sidewalk? (**Lesson 9-7**) 2 m

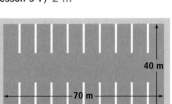

In 32–34, use the Distributive Property to expand the expression. (**Lesson 2-1**)

32. $4x(x - 9)$
$4x^2 - 36x$

33. $n(n + 52)$
$n^2 + 52n$

34. $(3m + 19.2)80$
$240m + 1,536$

EXPLORATION

35. Suppose three polynomials of the same degree n are added.

   a. What is the highest possible degree of their sum? Explain your answer.

   b. What is the lowest possible degree of their sum? 0

30b. If $-4c$ is substituted for b, the resulting equation is $a - 2(-4c) = 50$, or $a + 8c = 50$.

35a. The highest possible degree of their sum is n. The sum of two terms whose sum of powers is n, such as x^n or $a^{n-3}b^{n+3}$, is either one term whose sum of powers is n, two terms whose sum of powers is n, or they cancel out.

QY ANSWERS

1a. trinomial, degree 7

b. binomial, degree 7

c. monomial, degree 3

2. 69

Lesson 11-3

Multiplying a Polynomial by a Monomial

> **BIG IDEA** To multiply a polynomial by a monomial, multiply each term of the polynomial by the monomial and add the products.

In earlier chapters, you saw several kinds of problems involving multiplication by a monomial. To multiply a monomial by a monomial, you can use properties of powers.

$$(9a^4b^5)(8a^3b) = 9 \cdot 8 \cdot a^{4+3}b^{5+1}$$
$$= 72a^7b^6$$

To multiply a monomial by a binomial, you can use the Distributive Property $a(b + c) = ab + ac$.

$$2x(5x + 3) = 2x \cdot 5x + 2x \cdot 3$$
$$= 10x^2 + 6x$$

Some products of monomials and binomials can be pictured using the Area Model for Multiplication. For example, the product $2x(5x + 3)$ is the area of a rectangle with dimensions $2x$ and $5x + 3$. Such a rectangle is shown below at the left.

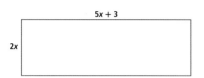

This rectangle can be split into tiles as shown above at the right. The total area of the rectangle is $10x^2 + 6x$, which agrees with the result obtained using the Distributive Property.

Example 1

Find two equivalent expressions for the total area of the rectangle pictured at the right.

(continued on next page)

Mental Math

Find the multiplicative inverse of each number.

a. $-5x$ $\quad -\frac{1}{5x}$

b. $\frac{4q}{-9}$ $\quad \frac{-9}{4q}$

c. 0 does not exist

d. $a + b$ $\quad \frac{1}{a+b}$

Lesson 11-3

GOAL

Apply the Distributive Property to multiply a polynomial by a monomial, using area models to picture the products.

SPUR Objectives

B Multiply polynomials.

I Represent polynomials by areas.

Materials/Resources

· Lesson Masters 11-3A or 11-3B
· Resource Masters 164–167
· Algebra tiles
· Computer Algebra System (CAS)
· Quiz 1

HOMEWORK

Suggestions for Assignment

• Questions 1–31
• Question 32 (extra credit)
• Reading Lesson 11-4
• Covering the Ideas 11-4

Local Standards

1 Warm-Up

1. Multiply $6 \cdot 10^3 + 2 \cdot 10^2 + 7$ by 10^4 in two ways:
   a. by rewriting each number in base 10. $6{,}207 \cdot 10{,}000 = 62{,}070{,}000$
   b. by using the Distributive Property without rewriting. $6 \cdot 10^7 + 2 \cdot 10^6 + 7 \cdot 10^4$

2. Are the answers you got in Question 1 equal? yes

3. Replace 10 by x in Question 1 and repeat the multiplication. $(6x^3 + 2x^2 + 7) \cdot x^4 = 6x^7 + 2x^6 + 7x^4$

4. If x is replaced by 5 in Question 3, does the product of the values of the two polynomials being multiplied equal the value of the product? yes

---

Background

This lesson extends properties from earlier chapters. If a monomial is multiplied by a monomial, then only the Product of Powers Property ($x^m \cdot x^n = x^{m+n}$) and the Commutative and Associative Properties of Multiplication are needed. However, if a monomial is multiplied by a polynomial other than a monomial, then, because either addition or subtraction is involved, the Distributive Property must also be used.

The representation of area by rectangles (and perhaps concretely by algebra tiles, if you have them) is accurate only when polynomials being multiplied are of degree 0 or 1.

11-3

2 Teaching

Notes on the Lesson

As suggested in the background for this lesson, you may wish to use algebra tiles or some other concrete materials to show the Distributive Property. It is critical that students understand the diagrams on page 669 and the storefront display on page 670. First show the storefront display as a single rectangle with area $h(L_1 + L_2 + L_3 + L_4)$, and then as the sum of the areas of smaller rectangles $hL_1 + hL_2 + hL_3 + hL_4$.

Note-Taking Tips

The tile activities in this section are intended to help students visualize the Distributive Property. Ask students to explain how the visualizations work. In addition, ask them to explain in detail the connection between the Distributive Property and the visualizations. Taking the time to do this in their notes may help them retain the understanding for when they learn binomial multiplication patterns.

Additional Examples

Example 1 Give two equivalent expressions for the total area of the rectangle pictured below.

	x	x	x	x	x	1	1	1
x	x^2	x^2	x^2	x^2	x^2	x	x	x
x	x^2	x^2	x^2	x^2	x^2	x	x	x
x	x^2	x^2	x^2	x^2	x^2	x	x	x
1	x	x	x	x	x	1	1	1
1	x	x	x	x	x	1	1	1

$(5x + 3)(3x + 2) = 15x^2 + 19x + 6$

Example 2 Expand $5x(-0.35xy - 3y + \frac{1}{3}x^2)$. $-1.75x^2y - 15xy + \frac{5}{3}x^3$

Solution The total area is the same as the sum of the areas of the individual tiles, or $3x^2 + 6x$. Also, the total area is length times width, or $3x(x + 2)$.

So this drawing shows $3x(x + 2) = 3x^2 + 6x$.

The area representation of a polynomial shows how to multiply a monomial by any other polynomial. The picture shows a view of some storefronts at a shopping mall.

The displays in the windows are used to attract shoppers, so store owners and mall managers are interested in the areas of storefronts. Note that the height h of each storefront is a monomial, and the sum of the lengths of the storefronts $(L_1 + L_2 + L_3 + L_4)$ is a polynomial.

The total area of the four windows can be computed in two ways. One way is to consider all the windows together. They form one big rectangle with length $(L_1 + L_2 + L_3 + L_4)$ and height h. Thus, the total area equals $h \cdot (L_1 + L_2 + L_3 + L_4)$.

A second way is to compute the area of each storefront and add the results. Thus, the total area also equals $hL_1 + hL_2 + hL_3 + hL_4$.

These areas are equal, so
$h \cdot (L_1 + L_2 + L_3 + L_4) = hL_1 + hL_2 + hL_3 + hL_4$.

In general, to multiply a monomial by a polynomial, extend the Distributive Property: multiply the monomial by each term in the polynomial and add the results.

Example 2
Expand $6r(x^2 - \sqrt{3}x + 7rx)$.

Solution Multiply each term in the trinomial by the monomial $6r$.

$$6r(x^2 - \sqrt{3}x + 7rx) = 6r \cdot x^2 - 6r \cdot \sqrt{3}x + 6r \cdot 7rx$$
$$= 6rx^2 - 6\sqrt{3}rx + 42r^2x$$

Accommodating the Learner ⬆

Ask students to write a product of a binomial and a trinomial. Then ask them to sketch a representation of the product using tiles. Finally, students should write an expression for the expanded product and look for a pattern. Help students write their answers in a manner that will enable them to see the repeated use of the Distributive Property. They can check their work using a CAS.

ENGLISH LEARNERS
Vocabulary Development

Reinforce the relationship between the terms *factoring* and *expanding*. Carefully redefine the terms and illustrate the relationship and difference between them using several examples.

Check 1 Test a special case by substituting for both r and x. We let $r = 5$ and $x = 3$.

Does
$6 \cdot 5(3^2 - \sqrt{3} \cdot 3 + 7 \cdot 5 \cdot 3) = 6 \cdot 5 \cdot 3^2 - 6\sqrt{3} \cdot 5 \cdot 3 + 42 \cdot 5^2 \cdot 3?$
Remember to follow order of operations on each side.

Does $30(114 - 3\sqrt{3}) = 270 - 90\sqrt{3} + 3{,}150?$

A calculator shows that each side has the value $3{,}264.115\ldots$.

Check 2 Use a CAS. Enter
`EXPAND(6*r*(x^2-[√](3)*x+7*r*x)).`
You should get an expression equivalent to the answer.

As always, you must be careful with the signs in polynomials.

Activity

A student was given the original expressions below and asked to expand them. The student's answers are shown below.

Original Expressions	Student's Expanded Expressions
1. $2x(3x^2y^3z^7)$	1. $6x^3 + 2xy^3 + 2xz^7$
2. $-3a^2(4a^2b + 7ab - 5a^3b^2)$	2. $-12a^4b - 21a^3b + 15a^5b^2$
3. $7m^3n(4mn^4)$	3. $28m^4n^5$
4. $7xy(2x^3y - 5xy^5 + x^2y)$	4. $14x^4y^2 - 5xy^5 + x^2y$
5. $\frac{1}{4}a^5b(8ab^2 + 2a^2 - 20a^3b)$	5. $2a^6b^3 + \frac{1}{2}a^7b - 5a^8b^2$

Step 1 Identify the expressions you believe the student expanded correctly.

Step 2 Expand the original expressions. Did you accurately find the expanded expressions with mistakes? Answers vary.

Step 3 For each expression the student did not expand correctly, write a sentence explaining what the student did incorrectly.

Explaining a Rule from Arithmetic

Recall the rule for multiplying a decimal by a power of 10: To multiply by 10^n, move the decimal point n places to the right. Multiplication of a monomial by a polynomial can show why this rule works. For example, suppose $81{,}026$ is multiplied by $1{,}000$. Write $81{,}026$ as a polynomial in base 10, and $1{,}000$ as the monomial 10^3.

$$1{,}000 \cdot 81{,}026 = 10^3 \cdot (8 \cdot 10^4 + 1 \cdot 10^3 + 2 \cdot 10 + 6)$$

Step 1. Expressions 2, 3, and 5 are expanded correctly.

Step 3. 1. The student expanded the multiplication in $3x^2y^3z^7$ as if it were addition instead of multiplication. 4. The student used the Distributive Property incorrectly. Each of the three terms in the parentheses should be multiplied by $7xy$, but the student only multiplied the first term.

Multiplying a Polynomial by a Monomial　**671**

Notes on the Lesson
Explaining a rule from arithmetic.
We strongly urge you to discuss the explanation of the rule for multiplying by a power of 10. It provides a nice example of the power of algebra to explain. It is related to the Exploration Question 32.

Notes on the Activity
Encourage students to take their time on Step 1. They may need to expand the expressions themselves before they check the work in the problem. This will make them less likely to make the mistake. For problems where they thought the student expanded correctly, but the CAS revealed an error, encourage students to circle the problem and make a special note of the mistake. This may keep them from making that mistake later.

Accommodating the Learner
Expand the explanation of the rule for multiplying a decimal by a power of 10. Help students recognize the reason for the pattern by writing several polynomials in base 10 and multiplying by a power of 10.

11-3

3 Assignment

Recommended Assignment

- Questions 1–31
- Question 32 (extra credit)
- Reading Lesson 11-4
- Covering the Ideas 11-4

Notes on the Questions

Questions 8–11 There is more practice on this type of question. The practice is distributed throughout the rest of this set and in later lessons of the chapter rather than concentrated here.

Now use the Distributive Property.

$$= 10^3 \cdot 8 \cdot 10^4 + 10^3 \cdot 1 \cdot 10^3 + 10^3 \cdot 2 \cdot 10 + 10^3 \cdot 6$$

The products can be simplified using the Product of Powers Property and the Commutative and Associative Properties of Multiplication.

$$= 8 \cdot 10^7 + 1 \cdot 10^6 + 2 \cdot 10^4 + 6 \cdot 10^3$$

Now simplify the polynomial.

$$= 81{,}026{,}000$$

This same procedure can be repeated to explain the product of any decimal and any integer power of 10.

Questions

COVERING THE IDEAS

In 1 and 2, find the product.

1. $(5x)(11x)$ $55x^2$

2. $(200xy^3)(3x^2y)$ $600x^3y^4$

In 3 and 4,
  a. find the product, and
  b. draw a rectangle to represent the product.

3. $3h(h + 5)$ a. $3h^2 + 15h$

4. $4n(n + 3)$ a. $4n^2 + 12n$

In 5 and 6, a large rectangle is shown.
  a. Express its area as the sum of areas of smaller rectangles.
  b. Express its area as length times width.
  c. Write an equality from Parts a and b.

5.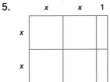
  a. $4x^2 + 2x$

6.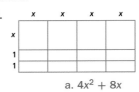
  a. $4x^2 + 8x$

7. **Fill in the Blank** Using the Distributive Property, $a(b - c + d) = \underline{\quad?\quad}$. $ab - ac + ad$

In 8–11, expand the expression.   8. $3x^4 + 6x^3 - 24x^2$

8. $3x^2(x^2 + 2x - 8)$

9. $5x(-5x^2 - x + 6.2)$

10. $p(2 + p^2 + p^3 + 5p^4)$

11. $-0.5ab(4b - 2a + 10)$

12. Use multiplication of a monomial by a polynomial to explain why the product of 7,531 and 100,000 is 753,100,000.
$7{,}531 \cdot 100{,}000 = (7 \cdot 10^3 + 5 \cdot 10^2 + 3 \cdot 10^1 + 1) \cdot 10^5 =$
$7 \cdot 10^3 \cdot 10^5 + 5 \cdot 10^2 \cdot 10^5 + 3 \cdot 10^1 \cdot 10^5 + 1 \cdot 10^5 =$
$7 \cdot 10^8 + 5 \cdot 10^7 + 3 \cdot 10^6 + 1 \cdot 10^5 = 753{,}100{,}000$

3b.

4b.

5b. $2x(2x + 1)$

5c. $4x^2 + 2x = 2x(2x + 1)$

6b. $(x + 2)4x$

6c. $4x^2 + 8x = (x + 2)4x$

9. $-25x^3 - 5x^2 + 31x$

10. $2p + p^3 + p^4 + 5p^5$

11. $-2ab^2 + a^2b - 5ab$

APPLYING THE MATHEMATICS

13. Suppose the building below had to increase its height by 2 feet.

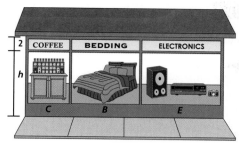

$(2 + h)C + (2 + h)B + (2 + h)E$

a. Express the entire building's new storefront area as the sum of the three individual stores' storefront areas.

b. Express the entire building's new storefront area as new height times length. $(2 + h)(C + B + E)$

c. Express the new storefront area as the sum of its old area and the additional area. $h(C + B + E) + 2(C + B + E)$

14. The arrangement of rectangles at the right is used by children in many countries for playing hopscotch. What is the total area? $4x^2 + 4xy$

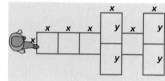

In 15–17, write the expression as a polynomial in standard form.

15. $(6x)(3x) - (5x)(2x) - (4x)(x)$ $4x^2$

16. $2(x^2 + 3x) + 3x^2$ $5x^2 + 6x$

17. $m^3(m^2 - 3m + 2) - m^2(m^3 - 5m^2 - 6)$ $2m^4 + 2m^3 + 6m^2$

In 18 and 19, simplify the expression.

18. $a(2b - c) + b(2c - a) + c(2a - b)$ $ab + ac + bc$

19. $(x^2 + 2xy + y^2) - (x^2 - 2xy + y^2)$ $4xy$

20. At the right is a circle in a square.

20c. $9r^2 - \pi r^2$
20d. $27r^2 - 3\pi r^2$

a. What is the area of the square? $9r^2$

b. What is the area of the circle? πr^2

c. What is the area of the shaded region?

d. If a person had 3 copies of the shaded region, how much area would be shaded?

e. If a person had c copies of the shaded region, how much area would be shaded? $9cr^2 - \pi cr^2$

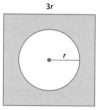

Notes on the Questions

Question 18 This expression is an example of a symmetric polynomial. Specifically, a, b, and c can be distributed in the expression and an equivalent expression occurs. Consequently, when the expression is simplified, a, b, and c can also be factored.

Question 21 This question previews common monomial factoring in Lesson 11-4 and should be discussed.

Multiplying a Polynomial by a Monomial **673**

11-3

4 Wrap-Up

Ongoing Assessment

Ask each student to write a product of a monomial and a polynomial. Suggest that they use polynomials with three or fewer terms. Then, on a separate sheet of paper, ask students to sketch tiles to describe the product. Pair students and ask them to exchange the sketches and write two equivalent expressions for the area pictured. Finally, ask them to check each other's answers, and discuss any differences.

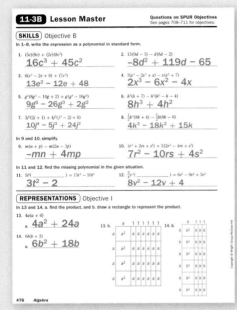

21. Fill in the Blank Find the missing polynomial in the given equation.

$$3n^2 \cdot (\underline{}) = 60n^4 + 27n^3 - 30n^2 \; 20n^2 + 9n - 10$$

22. a. What is the rule for dividing a decimal by 1,000?

b. Make up an example like the one on pages 671–672 to explain why the rule works.

REVIEW

In 23 and 24, an expression is given.

a. Tell whether the expression is a polynomial.

b. If it is a polynomial, give its degree. If it is not a polynomial, explain why not. (Lesson 11-2)

23. $4a^4 + 2a^{-2}$
   a. not a polynomial

24. $n^3m^5 + n^2m^4 + nm^3$
   a. polynomial b. 8

25. Write a trinomial with degree 4. (Lesson 11-2)

26. After five years of birthdays, T.J. has received and saved $50x^4 + 70x^3 + 45x^2 + 100x + 80$ dollars. He put the money in a savings account at a yearly scale factor x. (Lessons 11-1, 7-1)

a. How much did T.J. get on his last birthday? **$80**

b. How much did T.J. get on the first of these birthdays? **$50**

c. If $x = 1$, how much has T.J. saved? **$345**

d. What does a value of 1 for x mean?

27. For what value(s) of c does the quadratic equation $3x^2 - 4x + c = 0$ have no solutions? (Lesson 9-6) $c > \frac{4}{3}$

In 28 and 29, simplify the expression. (Lessons 8-4, 5-2)

28. $\dfrac{18xy^3}{6xy}$ $3y^2$

29. $\dfrac{4m}{9} \div \dfrac{6m^3}{15m}$ $\dfrac{10}{9m}$

In 30 and 31, write an equation for the line with the given characteristics.

30. contains the points $(8, -2)$ and $(3, 13)$ (Lesson 6-6) $y = -3x + 22$

31. slope $\frac{1}{2}$, x-intercept 1 (Lesson 6-4) $y = \frac{1}{2}(x - 1)$

EXPLORATION

32. a. Suppose a monomial of degree 3 is multiplied by a monomial of degree 4. What must be true about the degree of the product? Support your answer with an example.

b. Suppose a monomial of degree m is multiplied by a monomial of degree n. What must be true about the degree of the product? Support your answer with an example. **The degree of the product is $m + n$. For example, $x^m \cdot y^n = x^m y^n$.**

22a. Move the decimal point three places to the left.

22b. Answers vary. Sample answer: Divide 1,987,720 by 1,000.
$1,987,720 \div 1,000 = (1 \cdot 10^6 + 9 \cdot 10^5 + 8 \cdot 10^4 + 7 \cdot 10^3 + 7 \cdot 10^2 + 2 \cdot 10) \div 10^3 = (1 \cdot 10^3 + 9 \cdot 10^2 + 8 \cdot 10 + 7 \cdot 10^0 + 7 \cdot 10^{-1} + 2 \cdot 10^{-2}) = 1,987.72$

23b. The term $2a^{-2}$ is not a monomial and polynomials are all monomials or sums of monomials.

25. Answers vary. Sample answer: $x^4 + x + 1$

26d. T.J. received no interest on his savings.

32a. The degree of the product is 7. For example, $x^3 \cdot x^4 = x^7$.

Lesson 11-4

Common Monomial Factoring

Vocabulary

factoring

trivial factors

greatest common factor

factorization

prime polynomials

complete factorization

> ▶ **BIG IDEA** Common monomial factoring is the process of writing a polynomial as a product of two polynomials, one of which is a monomial that factors each term of the polynomial.

When two or more numbers are multiplied, the result is a single number. *Factoring* is the reverse process. In **factoring,** we begin with a single number and express it as the product of two or more numbers. For example, the product of 7 and 4 is 28. So, factoring 28, we get $28 = 7 \cdot 4$. In Lesson 11-3, you multiplied monomials by polynomials to obtain polynomials. In this lesson you will learn how to reverse the process.

If factors are not integers, then every number has infinitely many factors. For example, 8 is not only $4 \cdot 2$ and $8 \cdot 1$, but also $24 \cdot \frac{1}{3}$ and $2.5 \cdot 3.2$. For this reason, in this book all factoring is *over the set of integers*.

Factoring Monomials

Every expression has itself and the number 1 as a factor. These are called the **trivial factors.** If a monomial is the product of two or more variables or numbers, then it will have factors other than itself and 1.

Example 1

What are the factors of $49x^3$?

Solution The factors of 49 are 1, 7, and 49. The monomial factors of x^3 are 1, x, x^2, and x^3. The factors of $49x^3$ are the 12 products of a factor of 49 with a factor of x:

   $1, 7, 49, x, 7x, 49x, x^2, 7x^2, 49x^2, x^3, 7x^3, 49x^3$

 QY

The **greatest common factor** (GCF) of two or more monomials is the product of the greatest common factor of the coefficients and the greatest common factors of the variables.

> ▶ **QY**
>
> Which of the factors of $49x^3$ are trivial factors?

Common Monomial Factoring   **675**

Background

Factoring is the reverse process of multiplication. Specifically, in the Distributive Property $a(b + c + d) = ab + ac + ad$, the process from left to right is multiplication, and the process from right to left is factoring. Fact triangles can be quite useful in picturing this idea.

Because the factoring of integers into prime numbers over the set of integers is unique, we would like the factorization of polynomials over the integers also to be unique. However, integers present a

problem. Consider that $(x - y)^2 = (y - x)^2$. Which, then, should be viewed as the factorization of $x^2 + y^2 - 2xy$? The solution is to realize that $x - y = -1 \cdot (y - x)$. So we obtain unique factorization when we consider integer multiples of factors to be alike. This is why the Unique Factorization Theorem allows us to disregard integer multiples of its factors.

Prime polynomials are often called *irreducible polynomials*.

Lesson 11-4

GOAL

Understand factoring as the reverse process of multiplication, concentrating on common monomial factors and their application to the division of a polynomial by a monomial.

SPUR Objective

C Find common monomial factors of polynomials.

Materials/Resources

· Lesson Masters 11-4A and 11-4B
· Resource Master 168
· Computer Algebra System (CAS)
· Algebra tiles

HOMEWORK

Suggestions for Assignment
• Questions 1–27
• Question 28 (extra credit)
• Reading Lesson 11-5
• Covering the Ideas 11-5

Local Standards

1 Warm-Up

1. What are the factors of 392? **1, 2, 4, 7, 8, 14, 28, 49, 56, 98, 196, 392**
2. Give the prime factorization of 108. **$2^2 \cdot 3^3$**
3. Find the greatest common factor of 108 and 54. **54**
4. What are the factors of $25n^3$? **1, 5, 25, n, $5n$, $25n$, n^2, $5n^2$, $25n^2$, n^3, $5n^3$, $25n^3$**
5. What is the greatest common factor of x^{10} and x^{12}? **x^{10}**

11-4

2 Teaching

Notes on the Lesson

Examples 1 and 2 If you do the Warm-Up, point out the similarity between Examples 1 and 2 and Questions 1 and 2 in the Warm-Up. Substitute 2 for x in Example 1 and Question 1 results; substituting 2 for x and 3 for y in Example 2 results in Question 2. In this way, the Questions can be thought of as a check of the answers given in the Examples.

Activity This activity is important for showing students that there are many ways to factor some polynomials, just as there are many ways to factor some integers, but when we continue the process, the result is a unique factorization except for the order of terms and (for polynomials) integer multiples.

Notes on the Activity

If students are struggling with Step 1, ask them to think about other ways they can arrange each category of rectangles. For example, what other rectangles can they make with the 6 blocks of x^2? Remind them that the sides should line up appropriately. They can line up a rectangle that is 1 by x only one way with an x^2 tile.

Additional Examples

Example 1 What are the factors of $6xy$? 1, 2, 3, 6, x, $2x$, $3x$, $6x$, y, $2y$, $3y$, $6y$, xy, $2xy$, $3xy$, $6xy$

Example 2 Find the greatest common factor of $12x^3y$ and $16x^2$. $4x^2$

Additional Answers

Step 1.   Answers vary. Sample answers:

Example 2

Find the greatest common factor of $6xy^2$ and $18y$.

Solution The GCF of 6 and 18 is 6. The GCF of xy^2 and y is y. Because the factor x does not appear in all terms, it does not appear in the GCF.

So the GCF of $6xy^2$ and $18y$ is $6 \cdot y$, which is $6y$.

Notice that the GCF of the monomials includes the GCF of the coefficients of the monomials. It also includes any common variables raised to the *least* exponent of that variable found in the terms.

As with integers, the result of factoring a polynomial is called a **factorization.** Here is a factorization of $6x^2 + 12x$.

$$6x^2 + 12x = 2x(3x + 6)$$

Again, as with integers, a factorization with two factors means that a rectangle can be formed with the factors as its dimensions. Here is a picture of the factorization.

Activity   Step 1. See margin.

Step 1 Build or draw two other rectangles with an area of $6x^2 + 12x$.

Step 2 Write the factorization that is shown by each rectangle.

Step 3 Do any of the rectangles have the greatest common factor of $6x^2$ and $12x$ as a side length? If so, which rectangle?

The Activity points out that there is more than one way to factor $6x^2 + 12x$. When factoring a polynomial, the goal is that the GCF of all the terms is one factor. In $6x^2 + 12x$, $6x$ is the greatest common factor, so $6x^2 + 12x = 6x(x + 2)$.

Monomials such as $6x$, and polynomials such as $x + 2$ that cannot be factored into polynomials of a lower degree, are called **prime polynomials.** To factor a polynomial completely means to factor it into prime polynomials. When there are no common numerical factors in the terms of any of the prime polynomials, the result is called a **complete factorization.** The complete factorization of $6x + 12$ is $6(x + 2)$.

Step 2. Answers vary.
Sample answer:
$(x + 2)6x$, $3x(2x + 4)$
Step 3. yes; the rectangle with side lengths $x + 6$ and $6x$

Accommodating the Learner ⬆

Take class time to discuss the details of the Unique Factorization Theorem for Polynomials. For example, discuss why the theorem specifies "disregarding order and integer multiples." Compare this to the factorization of integers.

There are many techniques for factoring polynomials, and you will study several in this and the next chapter. No matter which technique you use, you will obtain the same answer. As with integers, the prime factorization of a polynomial is unique except for order.

Unique Factorization Theorem for Polynomials

Every polynomial can be represented as a product of prime polynomials in exactly one way, disregarding order and integer multiples.

GUIDED

Example 3

Factor $20a^3b + 8a - 12a^5b^2$ completely.

Solution The greatest common factor of 20, 8, and −12 is __?__. The greatest common factor of a^3, a, and a^5 is __?__. Because the variable b does not appear in all terms, b does not appear in the greatest common factor. **4; a**

The greatest common factor of $20a^3b$, $8a$, and $-12a^5b^2$ is __?__. **4a**

Divide each term by the GCF to find the terms in parentheses. With practice you'll be able to do these steps in your head.

$$\frac{20a^3b}{4a} = \underline{\ ?\ } \quad \frac{8a}{4a} = \underline{\ ?\ } \quad \frac{-12a^5b^2}{4a} = \underline{\ ?\ } \quad 5a^2b; \ 2; \ -3a^4b^2$$

So $20a^3b + 8a - 12a^5b^2 = 4a(\underline{\ ?\ } + \underline{\ ?\ } - \underline{\ ?\ })$. **$5a^2b$; 2; $3a^4b^2$**

Factoring provides a way of simplifying some fractions.

Example 4

Simplify $\frac{22m + 4m^2}{m}$. ($m \neq 0$)

Solution 1 Factor the numerator, simplify the fraction, and multiply.

$$\frac{22m + 4m^2}{m} = \frac{2m(11 + 2m)}{m} = 2(11 + 2m) = 22 + 4m$$

Solution 2 Separate the given expression into the sum of two fractions and then simplify each fraction.

$$\frac{22m + 4m^2}{m} = \frac{22m}{m} + \frac{4m^2}{m} = 22 + 4m$$

Check The solutions give the same answer, so they check.

Common Monomial Factoring **677**

Notes on the Lesson

Example 3 In the example, we use the greatest common factor $4a$. But you could start by factoring out a, and then 2, and then 2 again.

Example 4 You could show how factoring and division are related using a fact triangle.

Additional Examples

Example 3 Factor $36d^2fg^3 - 9d^2fg + 3d^3g$ completely.

Solution

The greatest common factor of 36, −9, and 3 is __?__. The greatest common factor of d^2fg^3, d^2fg, and d^3g is __?__. Because the variable f does not appear in all terms, f does not appear in the greatest common factor. **3; d^2g**

The greatest common factor of $36d^2fg^3$, $-9d^2fg$, and $3d^3g$ is __?__. **$3d^2g$**

Thus $36d^2fg^3 - 9d^2fg + 3d^3g = 3d^2g(\underline{\ ?\ } + \underline{\ ?\ } + \underline{\ ?\ })$. **$12fg^2$; $-3f$; d**

Example 4 Simplify $\frac{4x^2y - 8xy^2}{2xy}$. ($x \neq 0$ and $y \neq 0$) **$2x - 4y = 2(x - 2y)$**

Accommodating the Learner ⬇

Help students transition as they factor polynomial expressions by including the following intermediate step. To factor $36d^2fg^3 - 9d^2fg + 3d^3g$, ask students to use the GCF to first rewrite the terms as $12fg^2 \cdot 3d^2g - 3f \cdot 3d^2g + d \cdot 3d^2g$. This can help them when they get to more complicated factoring problems involving fractional and negative exponents.

3 Assignment

Recommended Assignment

- Questions 1–27
- Question 28 (extra credit)
- Reading Lesson 11-5
- Covering the Ideas 11-5

Notes on the Questions

Question 8 In this question, we show blanks for each factor. This gives students the form of the factor. In Questions 11–14, no blanks are shown and students need to use this form.

Questions 11–14 Encourage students to check using a CAS or by substituting a number for each variable.

Questions 18 and 19 Although π is not a variable, it factors like one. Ask students if they can see how the two expressions are related. (The surface area in Question 19 is πr^2 more than the surface area in Question 18. This is the area of the top of the can.)

Question 28 On the surface, some students may think this question is difficult. However, if students proceed systematically, writing out the integers and their factors in order, a simple pattern and its explanation can become clear. To see the pattern, students might need to write the prime factorization of every number from 1 to 20 or 1 to 25.

Questions

COVERING THE IDEAS

1. List all the factors of $33x^4$. 1, 3, 11, 33, x, x^2, x^3, x^4, 3x, 3x^2, 3x^3, 3x^4, 11x, 11x^2, 11x^3, 11x^4, 33x, 33x^2, 33x^3, 33x^4

In 2 and 3, find the GCF.

2. $25y^5$ and $40y^2$ 5y^2

3. $17a^2b^2$ and $24ba^2$ a^2b

4. Represent the factorization $12x^2 + 8x = 4x(3x + 2)$ with rectangles.

5. a. Factor $15c^2 + 5c$ by finding the greatest common factor of the terms.
   b. Illustrate the factorization by drawing a rectangle whose sides are the factors.

6. Showing tiles, draw two different rectangles each with area equal to $16x^2 + 4x$. **See margin.**

7. Explain why $x^2 + xy$ is not a prime polynomial.

8. In Parts a–c, complete the products.
   a. $36x^3 + 18x^2 = 6(\underline{\ ?\ } + \underline{\ ?\ })$ $6x^3$; $3x^2$
   b. $36x^3 + 18x^2 = 18(\underline{\ ?\ } + \underline{\ ?\ })$ $2x^3$; x^2
   c. $36x^3 + 18x^2 = 18x^2(\underline{\ ?\ } + \underline{\ ?\ })$ $2x$; 1
   d. Which of the products in Parts a–c is a complete factorization of $36x^3 + 10x^2$? Explain your answer.

9. Simplify $\frac{24n^6 + 20n^4}{4n^2}$. $6n^4 + 5n^2$

10. Find the greatest common factor of $28x^5y^2$, $-14x^4y^3$, and $49x^3y^4$. $7x^3y^2$

In 11–14, factor the polynomial completely.

11. $33a - 33b + 33ab$
    $33(a - b + ab)$

12. $x^{2,100} - x^{2,049}$ $x^{2,049}(x^{51} - 1)$

13. $12v^9 + 16v^{10}$ $4v^9(3 + 4v)$

14. $46cd^3 - 69cd^2 + 18c^2d^2$

APPLYING THE MATHEMATICS

15. The area of a rectangle is $14r^2h$. One dimension is $2r$. What is the other dimension? $7rh$

16. The top vertex in the fact triangle at the right has the expression $27abc - 45a^2b^2c^2$. What expression belongs in the position of the question mark? $3b - 5ab^2c$

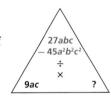

678 Polynomials

4.

	x	x	x	1	1
x	x^2	x^2	x^2	x	x
x	x^2	x^2	x^2	x	x
x	x^2	x^2	x^2	x	x
x	x^2	x^2	x^2	x	x

5a. The greatest common factor of $15c^2 + 5c$ is $5c$. So $15c^2 + 5c = 5c(3c + 1)$.

5b.

	c	c	c	1
c	c^2	c^2	c^2	c
c	c^2	c^2	c^2	c
c	c^2	c^2	c^2	c
c	c^2	c^2	c^2	c
c	c^2	c^2	c^2	c

7. The factor of both x^2 and xy is x and thus, it is factorable.

8d. The product in Part c is a complete factorization of $36x^3 + 18x^2$ because there are no common numerical factors in the terms in any of the prime polynomials.

14. $cd^2(46d - 69 + 18c)$

Extension

Help students visualize prime polynomials. First, give them a list of several polynomial expressions and ask them to try to factor them. Then, ask them to draw as many sketches as they can of rectangles with the area of the expression. They should notice that the only way to draw prime polynomials is to have the entire expression on one side, and 1 on the other side. Help them recognize that this has nothing to do with whether or not the numbers in the expression are prime numbers.

Additional Answers

6.

	x	x	x	x	1
x	x^2	x^2	x^2	x^2	x
x	x^2	x^2	x^2	x^2	x
x	x^2	x^2	x^2	x^2	x
x	x^2	x^2	x^2	x^2	x

	x	x	x	x	x	x	x	x	1	1
x	x^2	x^2	x^2	x^2	x^2	x^2	x^2	x^2	x	x
x	x^2	x^2	x^2	x^2	x^2	x^2	x^2	x^2	x	x

17. a. Graph $y = 2x^2 - 8x$. **17a–b. See margin.**

b. Graph $y = 2x(x - 4)$.

c. What do you notice about the graphs of the equations? Explain why this occurs.

In 18 and 19, a circular cylinder with height h and radius r is pictured at the right. Factor the expression giving its surface area.

18. $\pi r^2 + 2\pi rh$, the surface area with an open top $\pi r(r + 2h)$

19. $2\pi r^2 + 2\pi rh$, the surface area with a closed top $2\pi r(r + h)$

In 20 and 21, simplify the expression.

20. $\dfrac{9x^2y + 54xy - 9xy^2}{9xy}$

$x + 6 - y$ for $xy \neq 0$

21. $\dfrac{-100n^{100} - 80n^{80} + 60n^{60}}{2n^2}$

$-50n^{98} - 40n^{78} + 30n^{58}$ for $n \neq 0$

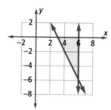

17c. The two graphs are the same because $2x(x - 4)$ is a factored form of $2x^2 - 8x$, so the two equations describe the same graph.

REVIEW

In 22 and 23, simplify the expression. **(Lesson 11-3)**

22. $-4x^3(3 - 5x^2 + 7x^4)$ **23.** $k(k + 2k^2 + n) - 2n(k - 2n) - k^2$

24. Which investment plan is worth more at the end of 10 years if the annual yield is 6%? Justify your answer. **(Lesson 11-1)**

Plan A: Deposit $50 each year on January 2, beginning in 2008.

Plan B: Deposit $100 every other year on January 2, beginning in 2008. **See margin.**

22. $-28x^7 + 20x^5 - 12x^3$

23. $2k^3 - kn + 4n^2$

25. Multiple Choice Which system of inequalities describes the shaded region in the graph at the right? **(Lesson 10-9)** **B**

A $\begin{cases} y - x < 6 \\ x \leq 0 \\ y \leq 6 \end{cases}$ B $\begin{cases} y + 2x \geq 6 \\ x \leq 6 \\ y \leq 0 \end{cases}$ C $\begin{cases} y + 2x \leq 6 \\ x \leq 0 \\ y \leq 0 \end{cases}$ D $\begin{cases} y \leq 6 + 4x \\ x \geq 3 \\ y \geq 1 \end{cases}$

26. Simplify $\sqrt{50x^3y^4}$. **(Lesson 8-6)** $5xy^2\sqrt{2x}$

27. There are 4 boys, 7 girls, 6 men, and 5 women on a community youth board. How many different leadership teams consisting of one adult and one child could be formed from these people? **(Lesson 8-1)** **121**

EXPLORATION

28. The number 6 has four factors: 1, 2, 3, and 6. The number 30 has eight factors: 1, 2, 3, 5, 6, 10, 15, and 30.

a. Find five numbers that each have an odd number of factors.

b. Give an algebraic expression that describes all numbers with an odd number of factors. Explain why you think these numbers have an odd number of factors. **See margin.**

28a. Answers vary. Sample answer: 1, 4, 9, 16, 25

QY ANSWER

1 and $49x^3$

Additional Answers

17a–b.

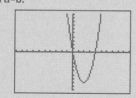

28b. Answers vary. Sample answer: n^2 where n is an integer. Their roots are counted as only one factor as opposed to two factors, so they end up with an odd number of factors.

24. Plan B is worth more at the end of 10 years. At the end of 10 years, Plan A yields

$50(1.06^{10} + 1.06^9 + 1.06^8 + 1.06^7 + 1.06^6 + 1.06^5 + 1.06^4 + 1.06^3 + 1.06^2 + 1.06^1) = \$698.58$; In comparison, Plan B yields $100(1.06^{10} + 1.06^8 + 1.06^6 + 1.06^4 + 1.06^2) = \$718.92$.

11-4

4 **Wrap-Up**

Ongoing Assessment

Write a polynomial on the board, and then ask students to tell what the greatest common factor is for the polynomial. For example, write $32x^3y - 8xyz + 4x$ on the board. When you point to the number 32, students should call out "4." When you point to the x^3, students should call out "x." When you point to the y, students should call out either "nothing" or "1." Finally, write the GCF and factor the expression. You can do this together as a class or with individual students.

Project Update

Project 1, Dividing Polynomials, on page 703 relates to the content of this lesson.

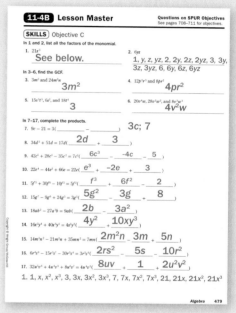

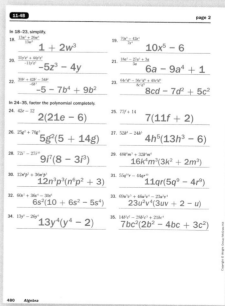

Lesson
11-5

Lesson
11-5

Multiplying Polynomials

GOAL

Multiply polynomials having two or more terms.

SPUR Objectives

B Multiply polynomials.

I Represent polynomials by areas.

Materials/Resources

· Lesson Masters 11-5A and 11-5B
· Resource Masters 2, 169, and 170
· Computer Algebra System (CAS)

HOMEWORK

Suggestions for Assignment

• Questions 1–20
• Questions 21–22 (extra credit)
• Reading Lesson 11-6
• Covering the Ideas 11-6

Local Standards

---

1 | Warm-Up

Multiply 357 by 246 by writing the product as $(300 + 50 + 7)(200 + 40 + 6)$ and using the Expanded Distributive Property. Verify that your answer is the same as the one you would get from calculating some other way. $60,000 + 12,000 + 1,800 + 10,000 + 2,000 + 300 + 1,400 + 280 + 42 = 87,822$

> ▶ **BIG IDEA**   To multiply a polynomial by a polynomial, multiply each term of one polynomial by each term of the other polynomial and add the products.

Picturing the Multiplication of Polynomials with Area

The Area Model for Multiplication shows how to multiply two polynomials with many terms. For example, to multiply $a + b + c + d$ by $x + y + z$, draw a rectangle with length $a + b + c + d$ and width $x + y + z$.

	a	b	c	d
x	ax	bx	cx	dx
y	ay	by	cy	dy
z	az	bz	cz	dz

The area of the largest rectangle equals the sum of the areas of the twelve smaller rectangles.

   total area $= ax + ay + az + bx + by + bz + cx + cy + cz + dx + dy + dz$

But the area of the biggest rectangle also equals the product of its length and width.

   total area $= (a + b + c + d) \cdot (x + y + z)$

The Distributive Property can be used to justify why the two expressions must be equal. Distribute $(x + y + z)$ over $(a + b + c + d)$ to get $(a + b + c + d) \cdot (x + y + z) = a(x + y + z) + b(x + y + z) + c(x + y + z) + d(x + y + z) = ax + ay + az + bx + by + bz + cx + cy + cz + dx + dy + dz$.

Because of the multiple use of the Distributive Property, we call this general property the *Extended Distributive Property*.

Extended Distributive Property

To multiply two sums, multiply each term in the first sum by each term in the second sum and then add the products.

Mental Math

Evaluate.

a. $27^{\frac{1}{3}}$ 3

b. $27^{\frac{2}{3}}$ 9

c. $27^{-\frac{2}{3}}$ $\frac{1}{9}$

Background

The Area Model for Multiplication is applied here to represent the multiplication of a polynomial by a polynomial. In Example 2, before multiplying, a note is made of the number of terms that will be in the result. This application of the Multiplication Counting Principle can help students to organize and check their work.

Notice that we discuss the more general pattern in this lesson—the Extended Distributive Property—before the special cases that occur in Lesson 11-7. You always

have to decide whether it is more effective to give special cases and then generalize or to give a general case and then specialize. We put the general case first because the algorithm for the multiplication of polynomials is in some sense easier than its special case. For the multiplication of binomials, every term is next to a right or left parenthesis. When polynomials with many terms are multiplied, the parentheses cause less distraction.

If one polynomial has *m* terms and the second has *n* terms, there will be *mn* terms in their product. This is due to the Multiplication Counting Principle. If some of these are like terms, you can simplify the product by combining like terms.

GUIDED

Example 1

Cassandra used the EXPAND feature on a CAS to multiply the polynomials $x^2 - 4x + 8$ and $5x - 3$. Her result is shown at the right.

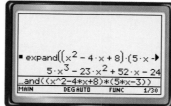

The CAS does not display steps that most people would show in order to find the answer. Using the Extended Distributive Property, show the steps that the CAS does not display to expand $(x^2 - 4x + 8)(5x - 3)$.

Solution $(x^2 - 4x + 8)(5x - 3)$

$= x^2 \cdot \underline{} + x^2 \cdot \underline{} + (-4x) \cdot \underline{} + (-4x) \cdot \underline{} +$
$8 \cdot \underline{} + 8 \cdot \underline{}$ $5x$; (-3); $5x$; (-3); $5x$; (-3)

$= \underline{} + \underline{} + \underline{} + \underline{} + \underline{} + \underline{}$ $5x^3$; $(-3x^2)$; $(-20x^2)$; $12x$; $40x$; (-24)

Now combine like terms.

$= \underline{} - \underline{} + \underline{} - \underline{}$ $5x^3$; $-23x^2$; $52x$; 24

Example 2

Expand $(4x + 3)(x - 6)$.

Solution Think of $x - 6$ as $x + -6$. Multiply each term in the first polynomial by each in the second. There will be four terms in the product.

$(4x + 3)(x - 6) = 4x \cdot x + 4x \cdot (-6) + 3 \cdot x + 3 \cdot (-6)$
$= 4x^2 + (-24)x + 3x + (-18)$

Now simplify by adding or subtracting like terms.

$= 4x^2 - 21x - 18$

Check 1 Let $x = 10$. (Ten is a nice value to use in checks because powers of 10 are so easily calculated.) Then $(4x + 3)(x - 6) =$
$(4 \cdot 10 + 3)(10 - 6) = 43 \cdot 4 = 172$.
When $x = 10$, $4x^2 - 21x - 18 = 4 \cdot 10^2 - 21 \cdot 10 - 18 =$
$400 - 210 - 18 = 172$; so it checks.

(continued on next page)

Multiplying Polynomials **681**

Accommodating the Learner ⬇

Help students recognize the Distributive Property pattern by demonstrating as follows. Suppose we have $U(a + b + c + d)$ $= (a + b + c + d)U = aU + bU + cU + dU$.

Now, suppose instead of U, we use $(x + y + z)$. Then the above equation becomes:

$(x + y + z)(a + b + c + d)$
$= (a + b + c + d)(x + y + z)$
$= a(x + y + z) + b(x + y + z) + c(x + y + z)$
$\quad + d(x + y + z)$
$= ax + ay + az + bx + by + bz + cx + cy +$
$\quad cz + dx + dy + dz$.

---

2 Teaching

Notes on the Lesson

A key to understanding the rectangle that opens the lesson is to realize that its dimensions are $a + b + c + d$ and $x + y + z$. Then the area of the rectangle can be found as the product of its dimensions, or as the sum of the areas of the 12 smaller rectangles.

You could also work backward by factoring:

$ax + bx + cx + dx + ay + by + cy + dy + az + bz + cz + dz$
$= (a + b + c + d)\mathbf{x} + (a + b + c + d)\mathbf{y}$
$\quad + (a + b + c + d)\mathbf{z}$
$= (a + b + c + d)(\mathbf{x} + \mathbf{y} + \mathbf{z})$.

As the number of multiplications increases, it is easy to lose track of the products. In our examples, we always distribute a term from the first polynomial over all terms of the second polynomial. Not all students are as well organized. It helps to have a consistent pattern.

Example 1 Ask students how they would check this multiplication if they did not have a CAS. Substitute a value for x and evaluate. A second way might be to write the product in the reverse order and do the multiplication.

Additional Example

Example 1 Suppose Cassandra used the EXPAND feature on a CAS to multiply the polynomials $x^3 - 3x + 2$ and $4x^2 - 3x - 1$. Her result is shown below.

The CAS does not display steps that most people would show in order to find the answer. Using the Extended Distributive Property, show the steps that the CAS does not display to expand $(x^3 - 3x + 2)(4x^2 - 3x - 1)$.
$x^3 \cdot 4x^2 + x^3 \cdot -3x + x^3 \cdot -1 + (-3x) \cdot 4x^2 + (-3x) \cdot -3x + (3x) \cdot -1 + 2 \cdot 4x^2 + 2 \cdot -3x + 2 \cdot -1 = 4x^5 - 3x^4 - 3x^3 - 12x^3 + 9x^2 + 3x + 8x^2 - 6x - 2 = 4x^5 - 3x^4 - 15x^3 + 17x^2 - 3x - 2$

Notes on the Lesson

Example 2 For products of binomials, as in Example 2, many teachers like to use the acronym FOIL (First terms, Outside terms, Inside terms, Last terms). Here the first terms are $4x$ and x, the outside terms are $4x$ and -6, the inside terms are 3 and x, and the last terms are 3 and -6. Some people think that use of this acronym hurts understanding, but we have no evidence of that.

Example 3 This product can occur as a result of permutations with replacement, a topic introduced in Lesson 11-7. Because there are three factors, one might wonder if the product is affected by the order in which the factors are multiplied. Because multiplication is associative, it makes no difference. In this example, a good check is to substitute 2, 1, and 0 for n. Each substitution should yield a value of 0 in the product. This is good practice for solving equations using factoring.

Note-Taking Tips

Encourage students to describe the process of the Extended Distributive Property including a fully worked example in their notes. They should also include common errors, such as $(x + 2)(x + 6) = x^2 + 12$, and a description of why this answer is incorrect.

Additional Examples

Example 2 Expand $(5x - 2)(3x + 1)$.
$15x^2 - x - 2$

Example 3 Expand $y^2(2y - 1)(3y + 2)$.
$6y^4 + y^3 - 2y^2$

Check 2 It is possible that when $x = 10$, the expression $(4x + 3)(x - 6)$ just happened to have the same value as $4x^2 - 21x - 18$? A better check is to set each expression equal to y and graph the resulting equation.

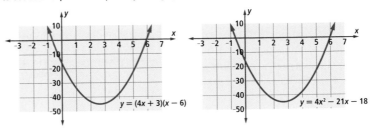

The two graphs are identical, so it checks.

STOP **QY**

Because multiplication is associative and commutative, to multiply three polynomials you can start by multiplying any two of them, and then multiply their product by the third polynomial.

Example 3

Expand $n(n - 1)(n - 2)$.

Solution 1 Multiply n by $n - 1$ first.

$n(n - 1)(n - 2) = n(n - 1) \cdot (n - 2)$

$\qquad\qquad\qquad = (n^2 - n)(n - 2)$

$\qquad\qquad\qquad = n^2 \cdot n + n^2(-2) - n \cdot n - n(-2)$

$\qquad\qquad\qquad = n^3 - 2n^2 - n^2 + 2n$

$\qquad\qquad\qquad = n^3 - 3n^2 + 2n$

Solution 2 Multiply $n - 1$ by $n - 2$ first.

$n(n - 1)(n - 2) = n \cdot (n - 1)(n - 2)$

$\qquad\qquad\qquad = n \cdot (n \cdot n + n \cdot (-2) - 1 \cdot n - 1 \cdot (-2))$

$\qquad\qquad\qquad = n \cdot (n^2 - 2n - n + 2)$

$\qquad\qquad\qquad = n \cdot (n^2 - 3n + 2)$

$\qquad\qquad\qquad = n^3 - 3n^2 + 2n$

> ▶ **QY**
>
> Austin used a CAS to multiply $a^2 + 5n - 14$ by $4n + 1$. The screen shows $4a^2n + a^2 + 20n^2 - 51n - 14$.
>
> a. How many terms did the CAS combine to get the product shown?
>
> b. Which like terms produced a^2?
>
> c. Which like terms produced $20n^2$?
>
> d. Which like terms produced $-51n$?

Accommodating the Learner ⬆

Discuss other applications of factoring and multiplying polynomials. For example, to solve a quadratic equation using the Quadratic Formula, the polynomial must be in standard form. In addition, if students ever need to add or subtract polynomials, they will probably need to expand products first. On the other hand, discuss some times that students may prefer to use factored form, such as when cancellation is possible or when they are looking for zeros of a function. Emphasize that students need to decide which form is best suited to their purposes before they factor or expand.

Questions

COVERING THE IDEAS

1. a. What multiplication is shown at the right? $(y + 12) \cdot (y^2 + 5y + 7)$

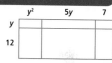

	y^2	$5y$	7
y			
12			

   b. Do the multiplication.
   $y^3 + 17y^2 + 67y + 84$

2. Simone used a CAS to multiply $2n - 5$ by $n^2 + 3n + 6$. The screen at the right shows her result. Explain which multiplications were done and combined to get each term in the product.

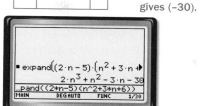

3. a. Multiply $2x - 5$ by $6x + 4$.

   b. Check your answer by letting $x = 10$.

   c. Check your answer by graphing $y = (2x - 5)(6x + 4)$ and graphing your answer. 3a–c. See margin.

In 4–7, expand and simplify the expression.

4. $(3x^2 + 7x + 4)(x + 6)$
   $3x^3 + 25x^2 + 46x + 24$

5. $(n + 1)(2n^2 + 3n - 1)$
   $2n^3 + 5n^2 + 2n - 1$

6. $(m^2 - 10m - 3)(2m^2 - 5m - 4)$

7. $4(x^2 + 2x + 2)(x^2 - 2x + 2)$

8. Find the area of the rectangle at the right, and simplify the result.
   $a^2 + b^2 + 2ab + 14a + 14b + 40$

	a	b	10
a			
b			
4			

9. Expand $(5c - 4d + 1)(c - 7d)$.
   $5c^2 + 28d^2 - 39cd + c - 7d$

10. a. Expand $(n - 3)(n + 4)(2n + 5)$ by first multiplying $n - 3$ by $n + 4$, then multiplying that product by $2n + 5$.

    b. Do the same expansion starting with a different multiplication.
    $(n - 3) \cdot [(n + 4)(2n + 5)] = 2n^3 + 7n^2 - 19n - 60$

APPLYING THE MATHEMATICS

11. a. Expand $(3x + 5)(4x + 2)$. $12x^2 + 26x + 10$

    b. Expand $(3x - 5)(4x - 2)$. $12x^2 - 26x + 10$

    c. Make a generalization from the pattern of answers in Parts a and b.

12. a. Expand $(4p - 1)(2p + 3)$. $8p^2 + 10p - 3$

    b. Expand $(4p + 1)(2p - 3)$. $8p^2 - 10p - 3$

    c. Make a generalization from the pattern of answers in Parts a and b.

13. Expand $\left(\frac{1}{5}x - 2.7\right)^2$ by writing the power as $\left(\frac{1}{5}x - 2.7\right)\left(\frac{1}{5}x - 2.7\right)$.

2. $2n \cdot n^2$ gives $2n^3$, $2n \cdot 3n$ combined with $(-5) \cdot n^2$ gives n^2, $2n \cdot 6$ combined with $(-5) \cdot 3n$ gives $(-3n)$, and $(-5) \cdot 6$ gives (-30).

6. $2m^4 - 25m^3 + 40m^2 + 55m + 12$

7. $4x^4 + 16$

10a. $2n^3 + 7n^2 - 19n - 60$

11c. The expansion of $(a - b)(c - d)$ is the same as the expansion of $(a + b)(c + d)$, except the second term has the opposite sign.

12c. The expansion of $(a - b)(c + d)$ is the same as the expansion of $(a + b)(c - d)$, except the second term has the opposite sign.

13. $\frac{1}{25}x^2 - 1.08x + 7.29$

---

3 Assignment

Recommended Assignment

- Questions 1–20
- Questions 21–22 (extra credit)
- Reading Lesson 11-6
- Covering the Ideas 11-6

Notes on the Questions

Questions 11 and 12 The patterns in these questions are helpful for quick factoring of quadratic expressions.

Question 14 Substitute 4 for n to check the answer. The volume of a cube with edge length 5 is almost twice the volume of a cube with edge length 4.

Question 15 Watch out for the error of forgetting about the 57 on the right side of the equation and applying the Quadratic Formula to the expression on the left side.

Question 21 A CAS can be very helpful in doing this problem.

Extension

Ask students to consider the multiplication $(x + 2)(x + 2)$. Write the expression $x^2 + 4$ on the board. Ask students if the two expressions are equal. Then, ask them to verify that they are not equal using three different methods. First, they can represent the product using tiles. Second, ask them to use the Extended Distributive Property to multiply. Finally, ask them to expand the expression using a CAS. If time permits, repeat the procedure with a variety of binomial products they will be studying in Lesson 11-6.

Additional Answers

3a. $12x^2 - 22x - 20$

3b. $(2(10) - 5) \cdot (6(10) + 4) = 960$;
   $12(10)^2 - 22(10) - 20 = 960$

3c.

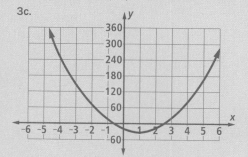

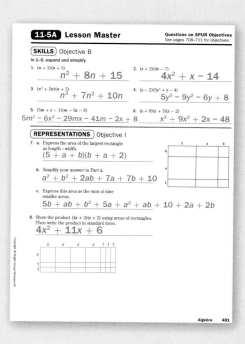

11-5

4 Wrap-Up

Ongoing Assessment

Write a product of polynomials on the board. Ask students to sketch the product using area of tiles and use the drawing to write an equivalent expression. Next to the sketch, ask them to write a paragraph describing why the area of the tiles represents the product.

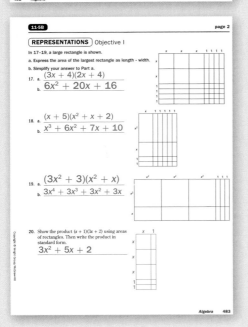

14. How much larger is the volume of a cube with edges of length $n + 1$ than the volume of a cube with edges of length n?

15. Solve the equation $(2n - 7)(n + 14) = 57$ by multiplying the binomials and then using the Quadratic Formula. $n = 5$ or $n = -\frac{31}{2}$

REVIEW

16. The sector at the right is one-third of a circle with radius r. Write a formula for the perimeter p of this sector in factored form. (Lesson 11-4) $p = 2r\left(\frac{\pi}{3} + 1\right)$

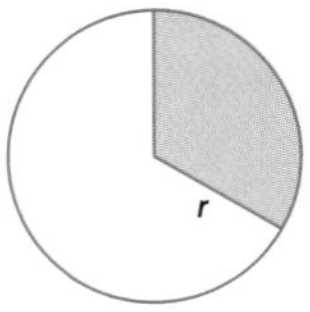

17. If $p(x) = 2x^2 + 5$ and $q(x) = 3x^2 + 6$, simplify $2 \cdot p(x) - 3 \cdot q(x)$. (Lesson 11-3) $-5x^2 - 8$

18. Twice the larger of two numbers is six more than four times the smaller. If the sum of eight times the smaller and three times the larger is 93, what are the two numbers? (Lessons 10-5, 10-4, 10-2)

19. Given $f(x) = 4^{-x} + 2$, find each value. (Lessons 8-4, 7-6)
    a. $f(2)$ $\frac{33}{16}$
    b. $f(-1)$ 6
    c. $f(0) + f(-3)$ 69

20. Find two algebraic fractions whose product is $\frac{14m}{39p}$. (Lesson 5-1)
    Answers vary. Sample answer: $\frac{14m}{8n} \cdot \frac{8n}{39p}$

EXPLORATION

21. Multiply each of the polynomials in Parts a–d by $x + 1$.
    a. $x - 1$ $x^2 - 1$
    b. $x^2 - x + 1$ $x^3 + 1$
    c. $x^3 - x^2 + x - 1$ $x^4 - 1$
    d. $x^4 - x^3 + x^2 - x + 1$ $x^5 + 1$
    e. Look for a pattern and use it to multiply
       $(x + 1)(x^8 - x^7 + x^6 - x^5 + x^4 - x^3 + x^2 - x + 1)$. $x^9 + 1$
    f. Predict what you think the product of $(x + 1)$ and
       $(x^{100} - x^{99} + x^{98} - x^{97} + \dots + x^2 - x + 1)$ is when simplified. Can you explain why your answer is correct?

22. A multidigit number in base 10 is shorthand for a polynomial in x. When $x = 10$, $436 = 4x^2 + 3x + 6$, and $2{,}187 = 2x^3 + 1x^2 + 8x + 7$.

    When you multiply 2,187 by 436, you are essentially multiplying two polynomials.

    $$(4x^2 + 3x + 6)(2x^3 + 1x^2 + 8x + 7)$$

    Multiply these polynomials and show how their product equals the product of 436 and 2,187 when $x = 10$.

Sidebar (right margin):

14. The cube with edge length $n + 1$ has $(3n^2 + 3n + 1)$ cubic units more volume than the cube with edge length n.

18. The larger number is 15, the smaller number is 6.

21f. $x^{101} + 1$; the product of x and x^{100} is x^{101} and the product of 1 and 1 is 1, and the other terms will all add to zero.

22. $(4x^2 + 3x + 6)(2x^3 + 1x^2 + 8x + 7) = 8x^5 + 10x^4 + 47x^3 + 58x^2 + 69x + 42 = 8(10)^5 + 10(10)^4 + 47(10)^3 + 58(10)^2 + 69(10) + 42 = 953{,}532$; $436 \cdot 2{,}187 = 953{,}532$

QY ANSWERS

a. two like terms were combined
b. a^2 times 1
c. $5n$ times $4n$
d. $5n$ times 1 and -14 times $4n$

Lesson Master (left sidebar):

11-5B Lesson Master
Questions on SPUR Objectives
See pages 708–711 for objectives.

SKILLS Objective B

In 1–16, expand and simplify.
1. $(2x - 1)(3x + 2)$ $6x^2 + x - 2$
2. $(7a - 6)(3a + 5)$ $21a^2 + 17a - 30$
3. $(4c - 7)(2c - 2)$ $8c^2 - 22c + 14$
4. $(6d + 7)(d + 8)$ $6d^2 + 55d + 56$
5. $(5e^2 - 4)(3e^2 + 6)$ $15e^4 + 18e^2 - 24$
6. $(4f^2 + 8)(f - 1)$ $4f^3 - 4f^2 + 8f - 8$
7. $(x + 2y)(3x - 4y)$ $3x^2 + 2xy - 8y^2$
8. $(5g - h)(2g + 3h)$ $10g^2 + 13gh - 3h^2$
9. $\left(w - \frac{7}{4}\right)(8w^2 - 16w + 1)$ $8w^3 - 22w^2 + 13w - \frac{3}{4}$
10. $\frac{1}{2}k(8k - 6)(k^2 - 2k + 10)$ $4k^4 - 10k^3 + 44k^2 - 20k$
11. $r(s + 2r)(s - 3r)$ $rs^2 - r^2s - 6r^3$
12. $(7j - 1)(j^2 + 3j - 6)$ $7j^3 + 20j^2 - 45j + 6$
13. $m(m^2 + 2)(m - 1)$ $m^4 - m^3 + 2m^2 - 2m$
14. $2n(n - 6)(8n - 3)$ $16n^3 - 102n^2 + 36n$
15. $(3q - 1)(q + 7)(5q + 9)$ $15q^3 + 127q^2 + 145q - 63$
16. $(p + 1)(p - 7)(2p + 3)$ $2p^3 - 9p^2 - 32p - 21$

482 Algebra

11-5B page 2

REPRESENTATIONS Objective I

In 17–19, a large rectangle is shown.
a. Express the area of the largest rectangle as length · width.
b. Simplify your answer to Part a.

17. a. $(3x + 4)(2x + 4)$
    b. $6x^2 + 20x + 16$

18. a. $(x + 5)(x^2 + x + 2)$
    b. $x^3 + 6x^2 + 7x + 10$

19. a. $(3x^2 + 3)(x^2 + x)$
    b. $3x^4 + 3x^3 + 3x^2 + 3x$

20. Show the product $(x + 1)(3x + 2)$ using areas of rectangles. Then write the product in standard form.
    $3x^2 + 5x + 2$

Algebra **483**

Lesson 11-6

Special Binomial Products

Vocabulary

perfect square trinomials

difference of squares

▶ **BIG IDEA** The square of a binomial $a + b$ is the expression $(a + b)^2$ and can be found by multiplying $a + b$ by $a + b$ as you would multiply any polynomials.

Can you compute $46 \cdot 54$ in your head? How about 103^2? Studying products of special binomials can help you find the answers quickly without a calculator. Two such products are used so frequently that they are given their own names: Perfect Squares and the Difference of Two Squares.

Perfect Squares: The Square of a Sum

Just as numbers and variables can be squared, so can algebraic expressions. Given any two numbers a and b, you can expand $(a + b)^2$ or $(a - b)^2$. These are read "a plus b, quantity squared" and "a minus b, quantity squared."

How can you expand $(a + b)^2$? One way is to write the power as repeated multiplication.

$$(a + b)^2 = (a + b)(a + b)$$

Next, use the Distributive Property.

$$= a(a + b) + b(a + b)$$

Then apply the Distributive Property again to the first and second products.

$$= (a^2 + ab) + (ba + b^2)$$

And finally combine like terms (because $ab = ba$).

$$= a^2 + 2ab + b^2$$

The square of a sum of two terms is the sum of the squares of the terms plus twice their product.

Geometrically, $(a + b)^2$ can be thought of as the area of a square with sides of length $a + b$. As the figure shows, its area is $a^2 + 2ab + b^2$.

 QY

▶ **QY**

Expand $(x + 8)^2$.

Mental Math

A circle has diameter 10 centimeters. Estimate

a. its circumference.

b. its area.

Answers vary. Sample answers are provided.

a. 31 cm

b. 75 cm

Background

The perfect square pattern $(a + b)^2 = a^2 + 2ab + b^2$ has a variety of applications, including arithmetic shortcuts, proofs in geometry, completing the square, and generalizations to powers of binomials leading to Pascal's Triangle. The first of these is found in this lesson. The second is found in the next chapter. The third is found in Chapter 13. And the last is found in later UCSMP courses.

The difference of squares pattern is also very important because it has all of the applications mentioned above except Pascal's Triangle.

Perfect squares of binomials. We show the expansion of both $(a + b)^2$ and $(a - b)^2$. Some teachers prefer to give only the square of a sum because $(a - b)^2$ can be viewed as $(a + -b)^2$. We think it helps if students are given both patterns, so they can see one more time that the square of a binomial is a trinomial.

Lesson 11-6

GOAL

Apply two patterns of binomial multiplication, the square of a binomial and the difference of squares, to do arithmetic multiplication mentally and to illustrate how a knowledge of algebra can contribute to increased arithmetic proficiency.

SPUR Objectives

B Multiply polynomials.

D Expand squares of polynomials.

I Represent polynomials by areas.

Materials/Resources

· Lesson Masters 11-6A and 11-6B
· Resource Masters 171 and 172
· Computer Algebra System (CAS)
· Quiz 2

HOMEWORK

Suggestions for Assignment
• Questions 1–36
• Question 37 (extra credit)
• Reading Lesson 11-7
• Covering the Ideas 11-7

Local Standards

---

1 Warm-Up

In 1–3, ask students to try to do these in their heads using the special binomial products of this lesson.

1. Multiply 87 by 93 as binomials by thinking of them as $(90 - 3)$ and $(90 + 3)$. $90 \cdot 90 + 90 \cdot 3 - 3 \cdot 90 - 3 \cdot 3 = 8{,}091$

2. Multiply 18 by 22 in the same way as Question 1. $(20 - 2)(20 + 2) = 20 \cdot 20 + 20 \cdot 2 + -2 \cdot 20 + -2 \cdot 2 = 396$

3. Calculate 105^2 by thinking of it as the square of a binomial $(100 + 5)^2$. $100^2 + 2 \cdot 100 \cdot 5 + 5^2 = 10{,}000 + 1{,}000 + 25 = 11{,}025$

11-6

2 Teaching

Additional Examples

Example 1 Calculate 32^2.
$32^2 = (30 + 2)^2 = 30^2 + 2 \cdot 30 \cdot 2 + 2^2 = 900 + 120 + 4 = 1{,}024$

Example 2 The area of a square with side $4d - 3$ is $(4d - 3)^2$. Expand this binomial.

Solutions

1. Use the rule for the square of a binomial.

$(4d + 3)^2 = (4d)^2 + \underline{?} + \underline{?} = \underline{?}\ d^2$
$\qquad + \underline{?} + \underline{?}.$ 2(4d)(3); $(3)^2$; 16; 24d; 9

2. Rewrite the square as a multiplication and expand using the Distributive Property.

$(4d + 3)^2 = (4d + 3)(4d + 3)$
$\qquad = \underline{?}\ (4d + 3) + \underline{?}\ (4d + 3)$
$\qquad\quad 4d; 3$
$\qquad = 4d \cdot 4d + 4d \cdot (3) +$
$\qquad\quad (3) \cdot 4d + (-3) \cdot (3)$
$\qquad = \underline{?}\ d^2 + \underline{?}\ d + \underline{?}.$
$\qquad\quad 16; 24; 9$

3. Draw a square with side $4d + 3$. Subdivide it into smaller rectangles and find the sum of their areas.

$(4d + 3)^2 = 16d^2 + 24d + 9$

	4d	3
4d	$16d^2$	12d
3	12d	9

Example 1
Calculate 103^2.

Solution 1 Write 103 as the sum of two numbers whose squares you can calculate in your head. $103 = 100 + 3$, so $103^2 = (100 + 3)^2$. Then use the special binomial product rule for the square of a sum.
$(100 + 3)^2 = 100^2 + 2 \cdot 3 \cdot 100 + 3^2 = 10{,}000 + 600 + 9$
$\qquad = 10{,}609$

Solution 2 Write the square as a multiplication and expand.

$103^2 = (100 + 3)(100 + 3)$
$\qquad = 100 \cdot 100 + 100 \cdot 3 + 3 \cdot 100 + 3 \cdot 3$
$\qquad = 10{,}000 + 300 + 300 + 9 = 10{,}609$

With practice, either of the solutions to Example 1 can be done in your head.

GUIDED

Example 2
The area of a square with side $7c + 5$ is $(7c + 5)^2$. Expand this binomial.

Solution 1 Use the rule for the square of a binomial.

$(7c + 5)^2 = (7c)^2 + \underline{?} + \underline{?}$ $2 \cdot 7c \cdot 5; 5^2$
$\qquad = \underline{?}\ c^2 + \underline{?}\ c + \underline{?}$ 49; 70; 25

Solution 2 Rewrite the square as a multiplication and expand using the Distributive Property.

$(7c + 5)^2 = (7c + 5)(7c + 5)$
$\qquad = \underline{?}\ (7c + 5) + \underline{?}\ (7c + 5)$ 7c; 5
$\qquad = \underline{?} \cdot 7c + \underline{?} \cdot 5 + \underline{?} \cdot 7c + \underline{?} \cdot 5$ 7c; 7c; 5; 5
$\qquad = \underline{?}\ c^2 + \underline{?}\ c + \underline{?}$ 49; 70; 25

Solution 3 Draw a square with side $7c + 5$. Subdivide it into smaller rectangles and find the sum of their areas. $49c^2 + 70c + 25$

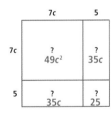

	7c	5
7c	? $49c^2$	? $35c$
5	? $35c$	? 25

Check Test a special case. Let $c = 3$. Then $7c + 5 = \underline{?}$ and $(7c + 5)^2 = \underline{?}$. 26; 676

Also $\underline{?}\ c^2 + \underline{?}\ c + \underline{?} = \underline{?} \cdot 9 + \underline{?} \cdot 3 + \underline{?} = \underline{?}$. It checks. 49; 70; 25; 49; 70; 25; 676

Accommodating the Learner

Some students will have to be especially diligent about using parentheses to expand correctly. For example, some students expand $(3x + 2)^2$ to $3x^2 + 2(3x)(2) + 2^2 = 3x^2 + 12x + 4$ instead of $3x(3x) + 2(3x)(2) + 2(2) = 9x^2 + 12x + 4$. Help students avoid this mistake by teaching them to write the pattern $a^2 + 2ab + b^2$ as $(a)^2 + 2(a)(b) + (b)^2$. This will remind them to square the entire a or b term.

Perfect Squares: The Square of a Difference

To square the difference $(a - b)$, think of $a - b$ as $a + -b$. Then apply the rule for the perfect square of a sum.

$$(a - b)^2 = (a + -b)^2$$
$$= a^2 + 2a(-b) + (-b)^2$$
$$= a^2 - 2ab + b^2$$

The square of a difference of two terms is the sum of the squares of the terms minus twice their product.

Squaring a binomial always results in a trinomial. Trinomials of the form $a^2 + 2ab + b^2$ or $a^2 - 2ab + b^2$ are called **perfect square trinomials** because each is the result of squaring a binomial.

> ### Perfect Squares of Binomials
>
> For all real numbers a and b, $(a + b)^2 = a^2 + 2ab + b^2$ and $(a - b)^2 = a^2 - 2ab + b^2$.

Activity 1

Complete the table.

$(a + b)^2$	$a^2 + 2ab + b^2$	$(a - b)^2$	$a^2 - 2ab + b^2$	
$(x + 1)^2$	?	$(x - 1)^2$	?	$x^2 + 2x + 1;\ x^2 - 2x + 1$
$(x + 2)^2$	?	$(x - 2)^2$	?	$x^2 + 4x + 4;\ x^2 - 4x + 4$
$(x + 3)^2$	?	$(x - 3)^2$	?	$x^2 + 6x + 9;\ x^2 - 6x + 9$
$(x + 4)^2$	?	$(x - 4)^2$	?	$x^2 + 8x + 16;\ x^2 - 8x + 16$
$(x + 15)^2$	?	$(x - 15)^2$	?	$x^2 + 30x + 225;\ x^2 - 30x + 225$
$(x + n)^2$	?	$(x - n)^2$	?	$x^2 + 2nx + n^2;\ x^2 - 2nx + n^2$

The Difference of Two Squares

Another special binomial product is the sum of two numbers times their difference. Let x and y be any two numbers. What is $(x + y)(x - y)$?

$$(x + y)(x - y) = x(x - y) + y(x - y) \quad \text{Distributive Property}$$
$$= x^2 - xy + yx - y^2 \quad \text{$-xy$ and yx are opposites.}$$
$$= x^2 - y^2$$

The product of the sum and difference of two numbers is the **difference of squares** of the two numbers.

Notes on the Lesson

A common error is to distribute the power over the binomial and obtain the incorrect $(a - b)^2 = a^2 - b^2$ and $(a + b)^2 = a^2 + b^2$. If this error occurs, be sure to substitute numbers for a and b to show students the error. Then substitute numbers in the correct expansions.

Here is an area model for the square of a difference.

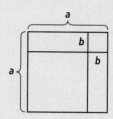

$(a - b)^2 =$ area of larger square
  $-$ area of two rectangles
  $+$ area of smaller square
$= a^2 - ab - ab + b^2$,
$= a^2 - 2ab + b^2$.

Notes on the Activity

Ask students to pay special attention to the sign of the middle term. Consider creating a similar table as a handout to help students complete the Activity. If you make a handout, you may wish to include the Extension on page 688.

11-6

Notes on the Lesson

We use the direction "Expand" in Example 4, as is found in many CAS utilities. Some people might think to use "Multiply," but there is a sense in which the product is already written. Expanding the power of a polynomial means to rewrite that power in the standard form for a polynomial. An everyday meaning of the word "expand" is quite a bit like its mathematical meaning: express in full or write out in greater detail.

Notes on the Activity

Some steps of the Activity may be confusing for students. Single variables may even be difficult. In the context of algebra, students do not always think of a variable as a number.

Additional Examples

Example 3 Compute $23 \cdot 27$ in your head. $(25 - 2)(25 + 2) = 625 - 4 = 621$

Example 4 Expand $(3x^3 - 2)(3x^3 + 2)$. $9x^6 - 4$

> **Difference of Two Squares**
>
> For all real numbers x and y, $(x + y)(x - y) = x^2 - y^2$.

Activity 2

Complete the table at the right.

The difference of two squares can be used to multiply two numbers that are equidistant from a number whose square you know.

$(a + b)(a - b)$	$a^2 - b^2$
$(x + 1)(x - 1)$	? $x^2 - 1$
$(x + 2)(x - 2)$	? $x^2 - 4$
$(x + 3)(x - 3)$	? $x^2 - 9$
$(x + 4)(x - 4)$	? $x^2 - 16$
$(x + 15)(x - 15)$	? $x^2 - 225$
$(x + n)(x - n)$	? $x^2 - n^2$

Example 3

Compute $46 \cdot 54$ in your head.

Solution 46 and 54 are the same distance from 50. So think of $46 \cdot 54$ as $(50 - 4)(50 + 4)$. This is the product of the sum and difference of the same numbers, so the product is the difference of the squares of the numbers.

$$(x - y)(x + y) = x^2 - y^2$$
$$(50 - 4)(50 + 4) = 50^2 - 4^2 = 2{,}500 - 16 = 2{,}484$$

Example 4

Expand $(8x^5 + 3)(8x^5 - 3)$.

Solution This is the sum of and difference of the same numbers, so the product is the difference of squares of the numbers.

$$(8x^5 + 3)(8x^5 - 3) = (8x^5)^2 - 3^2 = 64x^{10} - 9$$

Check Let $x = 2$.

$$(8x^5 + 3)(8x^5 - 3) = (8 \cdot 2^5 + 3)(8 \cdot 2^5 - 3)$$
$$= (8 \cdot 32 + 3)(8 \cdot 32 - 3)$$
$$= 259 \cdot 253 = 65{,}527$$

$64x^{10} - 9 = 64 \cdot 2^{10} - 9 = 64 \cdot 1{,}024 - 9 = 65{,}527$, so it checks.

Questions

COVERING THE IDEAS

In 1–3, expand and simplify the expression.

1. $(g + h)^2$
   $g^2 + 2gh + h^2$

2. $(g - h)^2$
   $g^2 - 2gh + h^2$

3. $(g + h)(g - h)$
   $g^2 - h^2$

688 Polynomials

Extension

After students complete the activities, and the patterns are fresh in their minds, add several rows to the bottom of the tables on pages 687 and 688 and fill in the $a^2 + 2ab + b^2$, $a^2 - 2ab + b^2$, and $a^2 - b^2$ columns. Ask students to fill in the remaining columns using the pattern backward. This will help them recognize the use of the patterns for factoring.

4. What is a *perfect square trinomial*? the square of a binomial

5. Give an example of a perfect square trinomial.
Answers vary. Sample answer: $x^2 + 2x + 1$

In 6 and 7, a square is described.

   a. Draw a picture to describe the situation.

   b. Write the area of the square as the square of a binomial.

   c. Write the area as a perfect square trinomial.

6. A square with sides of length $2n + 1$. 6c. $4n^2 + 4n + 1$

7. A square with sides of length $5p + 11$. 7b. $(5p + 11)^2$
   7c. $25p^2 + 110p + 121$

8. Verify that $(a - b)^2 = a^2 - 2ab + b^2$ by substituting numbers for a and b.

In 9–16, expand and simplify the expression. 10. $9 - n^2$

9. $(x - 5)^2$ 10. $(3 + n)(3 - n)$ 11. $(n^2 + 4)(n^2 - 4)$ $n^4 - 16$

12. $(13s + 11)^2$ 13. $(9 - 2x)^2$ 14. $\left(10 + \frac{1}{2}t\right)^2$

15. $(3x + yz)(3x - yz)$ $9x^2 - y^2z^2$ 16. $(2a + 5b)(-5b + 2a)$
                                                     $4a^2 - 25b^2$

17. Compute in your head. Then write down how you did each computation. See margin.

   a. 30^2 b. $29 \cdot 31$ c. $28 \cdot 32$ d. $27 \cdot 33$

In 18–20, compute in your head. Then write down how you did each computation.

18. $16 \cdot 24$ 19. 201^2 20. $75 \cdot 65$

APPLYING THE MATHEMATICS

In 21–25, tell whether the expression is a perfect square trinomial, difference of squares, or neither of these.

21. $u^2 - 2uj + j^2$

22. $9 - v^2$ difference of squares

23. $2sd + s^2 + d^2$

24. $xy - 16$ neither

25. $-i^2 + p^2$ difference of squares

26. Solve $\frac{x - 4}{7} = \frac{6}{x + 4}$. $\pm\sqrt{58}$

27. The numbers being multiplied in each part of Question 17 add to 60. Use the pattern found there to explain why, of all the pairs of numbers that add to 100, the largest product occurs when both numbers are 50.

In 28 and 29, expand and simplify the expression.

28. $\left(\sqrt{11} + \sqrt{13}\right)\left(\sqrt{11} - \sqrt{13}\right)$ -2

29. $(3x + y)^2 + (3x - y)^2$ $18x^2 + 2y^2$

27. If the sum is 100, the two numbers can be written as $(50 + x)$ and $(50 - x)$ and the product is $2{,}500 - x^2$. That value is greatest when $x^2 = 0$, or $x = 0$, so the numbers are 50 and 50.

Special Binomial Products   **689**

6a.

	2n	1
2n		
1		

6b. $(2n + 1)^2$

7a.

	5p	11
5p		
11		

8. Answers vary.
Sample answer:
$a = 3, b = 2;$
$(3 - 2)^2 =$
$9 - 12 + 4 = 1$

9. $x^2 - 10x + 25$

12. $169s^2 + 286s + 121$

13. $81 - 36x + 4x^2$

14. $100 + 10t + 0.25t^2$

18. 384; Answers vary.
Sample answer:
$16 \cdot 24 =$
$(20 - 4)(20 + 4) =$
$20^2 - 4^2 = 384$

19. 40,401; Answers
vary. Sample
answer: $201^2 =$
$(200 + 1)(200 + 1)$
$= 200^2 + 2 \cdot 200 \cdot$
$1 + 1^2 = 40{,}401$

20. 4,875; Answers
vary. Sample
answer: $75 \cdot 65 =$
$(70 + 5)(70 - 5) =$
$70^2 - 5^2 = 4{,}875$

21. perfect square
trinomial

23. perfect square
trinomial

---

3 Assignment

Recommended Assignment

- Questions 1–36
- Question 37 (extra credit)
- Reading Lesson 11-7
- Covering the Ideas 11-7

Notes on the Questions

Question 17 The general pattern of these products is $(30 - x)(30 + x)$ $= 900 - x^2$. You might ask students what Part e would look like if there was one, and what the product would be. $(26 \cdot 34) = 900 - 4^2 = 884$. Either graphing $y = 900 - x^2$ or realizing that x^2 is never negative lets one know that the maximum value is 900 and the greater x is, the less y is.

Question 28 Students should check this with their calculators by using decimal approximations for the square roots. They may be quite surprised that the result is as simple as it is.

Question 37 The pattern is simple and may be surprising.

Additional Answers

17a. 900; Answers vary. Sample answer:
   $30^2 = (3 \cdot 10)^2 = 3^2 \cdot 10^2 = 900$

17b. 899; Answers vary. Sample answer:
   $29 \cdot 31 = (30 - 1)(30 + 1) = 30^2 - 1^2 = 899$

17c. 896; Answers vary. Sample answer:
   $28 \cdot 32 = (30 - 2)(30 + 2) = 30^2 - 2^2 = 896$

17d. 891; Answers vary. Sample answer:
   $27 \cdot 33 = (30 - 3)(30 + 3) = 30^2 - 3^2 = 891$

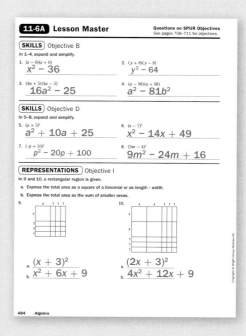

11-6

4 Wrap-Up

Ongoing Assessment

Ask students to write a short description of the different binomial products in the section. They should use the Expanded Distributive Property to demonstrate where each pattern comes from. Then, ask them to list several examples for each pattern. Finally, ask students to describe common errors in expanding, such as forgetting the "2ab" in $a^2 + 2ab + b^2$.

Project Update

Project 4, Differences of Higher Powers, on page 704, relates to the content of this lesson.

REVIEW

30. **a.** Expand $(x - 12)(x + 10)$. $x^2 - 2x - 120$
    b. Solve $(x - 12)(x + 10) = 85$. (**Lessons 11-6, 9-5**)

31. After 7 years of putting money into a retirement account at a scale factor x, Lenny has saved $800x^6 + 1{,}000x^5 + 1{,}500x^4 + 1{,}200x^3 + 1{,}400x^2 + 1{,}800x + 2{,}000$ dollars. (**Lesson 11-1**)
    a. How much did Lenny put in during the most recent year? $2,000
    b. How much did Lenny put in during the first year? $800
    c. Give an example of a reasonable value for x, and evaluate the polynomial for that value of x.

32. Richard wants to construct a rectangular prism with height and width of x inches and length of 5 inches. He wants his prism to have the same volume as surface area. Construct a system with equations for the volume and surface area. Then solve for x. (**Lesson 10-10**) $V = 5x^2$, $S = 2x^2 + 4(5x)$, $x = \frac{20}{3}$ in.

In 33–35, describe a situation that might yield the given polynomial. (**Lesson 8-2**)

33. e^3 34. $6x^2$ 35. $\pi r^2 - \pi s^2$

36. In 1965, Gordon Moore stated that computing speed in computers doubles every 24 months (Moore's Law). Computing speed is measured by transistors per circuit. (**Lesson 7-2**)
    a. In 1971, engineers could fit 4,004 transistors per circuit. Use Moore's Law to write an expression for the number of transistors per circuit that were possible in 1979.
    b. Many experts believe that Moore's Law will hold until 2020. Estimate the number of transistors per circuit possible in 2020, given that processors developed in 2000 had about 100 million transistors per circuit. $100(20)^{10} = 102.4$ billion

EXPLORATION

37. A CAS will be helpful in this question. After collecting terms, the expansion of $(a + b)^2$ has 3 unlike terms. Expand $(a + b + c)^2$. You should find that the expansion of $(a + b + c)^2$ has 6 unlike terms. How many unlike terms does the expansion of $(a + b + c + d)^2$ have? Try to generalize the result.

30b. $1 - \sqrt{206}$, $1 + \sqrt{206}$

31c. Answers vary. Sample answer: $x = 1.03$; $10,453.31

33. Answers vary. Sample answer: the volume of a cube with side e
34. Answers vary. Sample answer: the volume of a rectangular prism with width and height x and length 6
35. Answers vary. Sample answer: the area of the region between a circle with radius s that is inside a circle with radius r
36a. $4,004(2)^4$
37. $a^2 + b^2 + c^2 + 2ab + 2ac + 2bc$; $(a + b + c + d)^2$ has 10 unlike terms. If n is the number of terms, the number of unlike terms in the square will be: $\frac{n(n + 1)}{2}$.

QY ANSWER

$x^2 + 16x + 64$

Lesson 11-7 Permutations

Lesson 11-7

Vocabulary

permutation

n!, n factorial

circular permutation

▶ **BIG IDEA** From a set of n symbols, the number of permutations of length r without replacement is given by the product of the polynomials $\underbrace{n(n-1)(n-2)...}_{r \text{ factors}}$.

In Lesson 8-1, you saw the following problem: How many 3-letter acronyms (like JFK, IBM, BMI, or TNT) are there in English? The answer is 26^3 because the first letter can be any one of the 26 letters of the alphabet, and so can the second letter, and so can the third letter. Think of the spaces to be filled and use the Multiplication Counting Principle: $\underline{26} \cdot \underline{26} \cdot \underline{26} = 17{,}576$.

Now suppose that the letters in the acronym have to be different. Then TNT and other acronyms with duplicate letters are not allowed. The first letter can still be any one of the 26 letters of the alphabet, but the second letter can only be one of the 25 letters remaining, and the third letter can only be one of the 24 letters remaining. So the total number of 3-letter acronyms in English with different letters is $\underline{26} \cdot \underline{25} \cdot \underline{24} = 15{,}600$.

The first situation is called an *arrangement with replacement* because a letter can be used more than once. The second situation, where a letter cannot be used more than once, is called a **permutation.** So, a permutation is an arrangement without replacement. The above situation shows that, with 26 letters, there are 17,576 arrangements with replacement of length 3, and 15,600 permutations of length 3.

Suppose there were only three letters, A, B, and C. Notice the difference between the two types of arrangements.

Length 2 with replacement	AA, AB, AC, BA, BB, BC, CA, CB, CC
Length 2 without replacement	AB, AC, BA, BC, CA, CB
Length 3 with replacement	AAA, AAB, AAC, ABA, ABB, ABC, ACA, ACB, ACC, 9 starting with B, and 9 more starting with C, a total of 3^3 or 27 arrangements
Length 3 without replacement	ABC, ACB, BAC, BCA, CAB, CBA
Length 4 with replacement	AAAA, AAAB, AAAC, …, AABA, AABB, AABC, …. and so on, a total of 3^4 or 81 arrangements
Length 4 without replacement	None! (Do you see why?)

Mental Math

Suppose n is an integer. Determine if the following statements are *always, sometimes but not always,* or *never* true.

a. If $x > 0$, $x^n > 0$.

b. If $x < 0$, $x^n > 0$.

c. If $x < 0$, $2x^n < 0$.

a. always true

b. sometimes but not always true

c. sometimes but not always true

Permutations **691**

Background

In Lesson 8-1, we dealt with arrangements with replacement. Sometimes people do not call those problems permutation problems because objects can be repeated. This lesson deals with a classic problem, the number of permutations of n things r at a time, often abbreviated nPr or $_nP_r$ or sometimes $P(n, r)$. Calculators tend to use the abbreviation nPr.

A connection with polynomials.

$_nP_2 = n(n-1)$, $_nP_3 = n(n-1)(n-2)$, and in general, $nPr = n(n-1)(n-2)... (n-(r-1))$. This is a difficult formula to comprehend and we do not give it here, but you may wish to present it for better students. Notice that nPr can be written as a polynomial in n of degree r.

The factorial symbol. Students may be familiar with the factorial symbol from previous courses.

Lesson 11-7

GOAL

Find the number of permutations of objects without replacement. Introduce factorial notation.

SPUR Objective

G Determine numbers of permutations.

Materials/Resources

· Lesson Masters 11-7A and 11-7B
· Resource Masters 173 and 174
· Scientific calculator

HOMEWORK

Suggestions for Assignment

• Questions 1–24
• Question 25 (extra credit)
• Reading Lesson 11-8
• Covering the Ideas 11-8

Local Standards

1 Warm-Up

1. How many 1-digit numbers are odd? 5
2. How many 2-digit numbers consist of two odd digits? $5 \cdot 5 = 25$
3. How many 2-digit numbers consist of two different odd digits? $5 \cdot 4 = 20$
4. Which numbers are counted in Question 2 and not in Question 3? 11, 33, 55, 77, 99
5. How many 3-digit numbers consist of three different odd digits? $5 \cdot 4 \cdot 3 = 60$

11-7

2 Teaching

Notes on the Lesson

There is no substitute for writing out the permutations to show how many there are. In Example 1b, you might begin by noting that there are five possibilities for the first digit, and asking students for the digit they want. (Suppose they say 7.) Then how many possibilities are there for the 2nd digit? (4) What digit would they want? (Suppose they say 3.) Continue through the 5th digit. Then write out all the permutations that start with 7. There are only 24 of these, so they can be written. Then students should realize that there would be 24 permutations starting with any other number. Thus the total is $5 \cdot 24$, or 120.

Additional Examples

Example 1 After a student asks a classmate for his phone number, they notice that the last four digits of the number contain only numbers from 1 to 4. They wondered if this was unusual.

a. How many 4-digit numbers are there with digits from 1 to 4? **256**

b. The student looks more closely, and notices that the numbers are all different. How many possible 4-digit numbers fit the criteria? **24**

Example 2 A concert will feature five different bands. In how many different orders can the concert producer organize the bands?

Solution

This is a permutation ___?___ **without** replacement situation. with/without

Any of _?_ bands could play first. **5**

After that band, any of _?_ bands could play second. **4**

Next, any of _?_ bands could play third. **3**

Then, any of _?_ bands could play fourth. **2**

Finally, _?_ band(s) is/are remaining to play last. **1**

So, there are _?_ · _?_ · _?_ · _?_ · _?_, or _?_ possible orders. **5; 4; 3; 2; 1; 120**

Example 1

Dori saw a license plate with the numbers 15973. She noticed that all the digits were different odd digits. She wondered if this was unusual.

a. How many 5-digit numbers are there with only odd digits?

b. How many 5-digit numbers are there with only odd digits, all of them different?

Solution

a. This is a situation of arrangements with replacement. Each digit could be any of 5 numbers. Think of spaces to be filled.

$$\underline{5} \cdot \underline{5} \cdot \underline{5} \cdot \underline{5} \cdot \underline{5} = 3{,}125$$

b. This is a situation of permutations. The first digit can be any one of the 5 odd numbers. But then the second digit must be different, so it can only be one of the 4 odd numbers that remain. The third digit can only be one of the 3 odd numbers that remain after the first two have been chosen. The 4th digit can only be one of the 2 that remain. The fifth digit can only be the remaining digit. Filling spaces, you can picture this as

$$\underline{5} \cdot \underline{4} \cdot \underline{3} \cdot \underline{2} \cdot \underline{1} = 120.$$

There is quite a difference between the two kinds of arrangements! So it is not so unusual that Dori saw a license plate with all odd digits, but rather unusual that all the digits would be different.

GUIDED

Example 2

Three of the 11 members of a jazz band will each perform a solo at a concert. In how many orders can three people be picked from the band to perform a solo?

Solution This is an arrangment ___?___ replacement situation.
without
(with/without)

Any of _?_ people could perform the first solo. **11**

After that soloist, any of _?_ people could perform the second solo. **10**

Then any of _?_ people could perform the third solo. **9**

So there are _?_ · _?_ · _?_ or _?_ possible orders. **11; 10; 9; 990**

Jazz music developed in the last part of the 19th century in New Orleans.

Source: *Columbia Encyclopedia*

A Connection with Polynomials

Suppose you begin with n letters. *Without* replacement, there are $n \cdot (n - 1)$ acronyms of length 2. Using the Distributive Property, you can see that $n(n - 1) = n^2 - n$, which is a polynomial of degree 2. There are $n \cdot (n - 1) \cdot (n - 2)$ acronyms of length 3.

Extension

Show students how to use trees to visualize the total set of possibilities. Begin with a basic example, such as the set of all addresses in an apartment complex if the first character is a number between 1 and 3 and the second character is a letter from A to D. Create the tree as shown on the right.

Then, help students visualize the difference between Part a and Part b of Example 1 by creating outlines of the related trees.

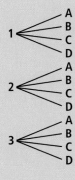

Using the Extended Distributive Property, this product equals $n^3 - 3n^2 + 2n$, a polynomial of degree 3. Example 1b asked for permutations of length 5. Since $n = 5$ in Example 1b, the multiplication was $\underline{5} \cdot \underline{(5-1)} \cdot \underline{(5-2)} \cdot \underline{(5-3)} \cdot \underline{(5-4)}$. In general, there are $\underline{n} \cdot \underline{(n-1)} \cdot \underline{(n-2)} \cdot \underline{(n-3)} \cdot \underline{(n-4)}$ such permutations.

This product equals $n^5 - 10n^4 + 35n^3 - 50n^2 + 24n$, a 5th degree polynomial. In general, the number of permutations of length n can be calculated by evaluating a polynomial of degree n.

Permutations Using All the Items

With five different items, there cannot be permutations of length 6 because there are only 5 different items. However, the situation of permutations using all the items is quite common, as Example 3 shows.

Example 3

You have 13 books to put on a shelf. In how many ways can they be arranged?

Solution This is a permutation problem. Any one of the 13 books can be farthest left. Once it has been chosen, there are 12 choices for the book to its right. Then there are 11 choices for the book to the right of the first two; and so on. The total number of permutations of the books is $\underline{13} \cdot \underline{12} \cdot \underline{11} \cdot \underline{10} \cdot \underline{9} \cdot \underline{8} \cdot \underline{7} \cdot \underline{6} \cdot \underline{5} \cdot \underline{4} \cdot \underline{3} \cdot \underline{2} \cdot \underline{1}$, or 6,227,020,800.

The answers to Examples 1b and 3 each are the product of the integers from 1 to n. This product is denoted as $n!$ and called **n factorial**. Using factorial notation, the answer to Example 1b is 5! and the answer to Example 3 is 13!

$$n! = n(n-1)(n-2) \cdot \ldots \cdot 3 \cdot 2 \cdot 1$$

Specifically, $1! = 1$.

$2! = 2 \cdot 1 = 2$
$3! = 3 \cdot 2 \cdot 1 = 6$
$4! = 4 \cdot 3 \cdot 2 \cdot 1 = 24$
$5! = 5 \cdot 4 \cdot 3 \cdot 2 \cdot 1 = 120$
$6! = 6 \cdot 5 \cdot 4 \cdot 3 \cdot 2 \cdot 1 = 720$, and so on.

Notice how $n!$ gets large quite quickly as n grows.

 QY

> ▶ QY
>
> a. A baseball manager is setting the batting order for the 9 starting players. How many different batting orders are possible?
>
> b. What is 8!?

11-7

Notes on the Lesson

The factorial symbol. Students generally find this symbol interesting and easy to calculate. But problems like those in Questions 9–12 are not easy for many students. Point out to students that their calculators can compute factorials and show them where to find the command (perhaps in a probability menu).

Additional Example

Example 3 There are 10 people in a race. Assuming none of them tie, in how many ways can they arrive at the finish line? $10 \cdot 9 \cdot 8 \cdot 7 \cdot 6 \cdot 5 \cdot 4 \cdot 3 \cdot 2 \cdot 1 = 10! = 3{,}628{,}800$

Accommodating the Learner ⬇

Consider using physical objects in the classroom to picture permutations or arrangements without replacement. For example, use different colored pieces of chalk or paper clips to demonstrate the number of choices remaining when the object is not replaced.

Accommodating the Learner ⬆

Continue the discussion of the connection between polynomials and permutations. Ask the students to write a polynomial that describes the number of acronyms of length 20. Then, ask them to find the first and last term of the polynomial. The first term will be n^{20} and the last term will be $-(19!)n$

Recommended Assignment

- Questions 1–24
- Question 25 (extra credit)
- Reading Lesson 11-8
- Covering the Ideas 11-8

Notes on the Questions

Questions 9–12 You may wish to extend these questions to their algebraic counterparts. Write the following with polynomials in the numerator or denominator: for Question 9, $\frac{(n+2)!}{(n)!}$; for Question 10, $\frac{n!}{(n-1)!}$; for Question 11, $\frac{(n-1)!}{(n+1)!}$; for Question 12, $\frac{n!}{(n+4)!}$. $(n+2)(n+1)$; n; $\frac{1}{n(n+1)}$; $\frac{1}{(n+4)(n+3)(n+2)(n+1)}$

Factorial notation is very convenient for describing numbers of permutations. You saw at the beginning of this lesson the product of three numbers 26 · 25 · 24. This product can be written as the quotient of two factorials.

$$26 \cdot 25 \cdot 24 = 26 \cdot 25 \cdot 24 \cdot \frac{23 \cdot 22 \cdot 21 \cdot \ldots \cdot 3 \cdot 2 \cdot 1}{23 \cdot 22 \cdot 21 \cdot \ldots \cdot 3 \cdot 2 \cdot 1}$$

$$= \frac{26 \cdot 25 \cdot 24 \cdot 23 \cdot 22 \cdot 21 \cdot \ldots \cdot 3 \cdot 2 \cdot 1}{23 \cdot 22 \cdot 21 \cdot \ldots \cdot 3 \cdot 2 \cdot 1}$$

$$= \frac{26!}{23!}$$

So, with a factorial key on a calculator, you can calculate any number of permutations just by dividing two factorials.

Questions

COVERING THE IDEAS

1. **a.** Identify two of the permutations of length 4 from the six letters A, B, C, D, E, and F.
   b. How many permutations are there of length 4 from the six letters A, B, C, D, E, and F?

2. You have 8 of your favorite pictures that you would like to hang on a wall, but there is room for only 3 of the pictures. How many different permutations of 3 pictures are possible from your 8 favorites, assuming you arrange the pictures in a straight line so that their order matters? **336 permutations**

3. How many different permutations of length 2 are there from n objects when $n \geq 2$? $n(n-1)$

4. How many different permutations of length 7 are there from n objects when $n \geq 7$?

5. **a.** Identify two of the permutations of length 5 from the five letters V, W, X, Y, and Z.
   b. How many permutations of length 5 are there from these five letters? **120 permutations**

6. A volleyball coach is deciding the serving order for the six starting players. How many different starting orders are possible? **720**

7. In how many different orders can n objects be arranged on a shelf? $n!$

8. Give the values of 7!, 8!, 9!, and 10!.

In 9–12, write as a single number in base 10 or as a simple fraction in lowest terms.

9. $\frac{8!}{6!}$ 56
10. $\frac{100!}{99!}$ 100
11. $\frac{15!}{17!}$ $\frac{1}{272}$
12. $\frac{2!}{6!}$ $\frac{1}{360}$

1a. Answers vary. Sample answer: ABCD, ABCE

1b. 360 permutations

4. $n(n-1)(n-2) \cdot (n-3)(n-4) \cdot (n-5)(n-6)$, or $\frac{n!}{(n-7)!}$

5a. Answers vary. Sample answer: VWXYZ, ZYXWV

8. 7! = 5,040, 8! = 40,320, 9! = 362,880, 10! = 3,628,800

The forearm pass, or "dig" is a type of shot used when receiving a serve or playing a hard, low hit ball.

APPLYING THE MATHEMATICS

13. Consider the following pattern.

    $2! = 2 \cdot 1!$ $3! = 3 \cdot 2!$ $4! = 4 \cdot 3!$

    Are all three instances above true? If so, describe the general pattern using one variable. If not, correct any instances that are false. **Yes; $n! = n \cdot (n-1)!$, for $n \geq 1$**

14. Three hundred people enter a raffle. The first prize is a computer and the second prize is a cell phone.

    a. How many different ordered pairs of people are eligible to win these prizes? **89,700**

    b. Suppose you and your best friend are among the 300. If the winning tickets are chosen at random, what is the probability that you will win the computer and your best friend will win the cell phone? $\frac{1}{89,700}$

15. a. How many license plate numbers with 4 digits have all different odd digits, with the first digit being 3? **24**

    b. Write down all these license plate numbers.

16. How many license plate numbers with 6 digits have all different odd digits? **0**

17. A **circular permutation** is an ordering of objects around a circle. Some permutations that are different along a line are considered the same around a circle. For example, the two arrangements of A, B, C, and D pictured here are considered to be the same.

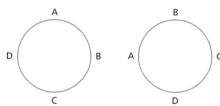

Write all the circular permutations of 4 objects around a circle.
ABCD, ABDC, ACBD, ACDB, ADBC, ADCB

A raffle is used in many organizations looking to raise funds.

15b. 3157, 3159,
3175, 3179,
3195, 3197,
3517, 3519,
3571, 3579,
3591, 3597,
3715, 3719,
3751, 3759,
3791, 3795,
3915, 3917,
3951, 3957,
3971, 3975

REVIEW

18. Expand and simplify $(-a + 6b)(-a - 6b)$. (**Lesson 11-6**) $a^2 - 36b^2$

19. How much smaller is the area of a circle with radius $(r - 4)$ than that of a circle with radius r (assume $r > 4$)? (**Lesson 11-5**)

19. The smaller circle has $8\pi(r - 2)$ square units less area.

In 20 and 21, simplify the expression. (**Lessons 11-4, 8-3**)

20. $\frac{25n^2 - 21n}{n}$ $25n - 21, n \neq 0$ 21. $\frac{8x^3 + 16x^2 + 24x^6}{4x^2}$

21. $6x^4 + 2x + 4$, $x \neq 0$

Notes on the Questions

Question 13 The relation $n! = n \cdot (n-1)!$, along with $1! = 1$, can be used to define $n!$ for integers recursively. This is a natural definition, because the usual method of calculating factorials is to use each factorial to calculate the next (5! to calculate 6!, 6! to calculate 7!, etc.).

Question 15 We have avoided problems with even digits because of the question of whether a leftmost digit can be 0. If this problem were to ask for all the plates with 4 different even digits, the answer would be $4 \cdot 4 \cdot 3 \cdot 2$, or 96.

Question 17 If n objects are on a line, there are $n!$ permutations of them. Here they are in a circle and each permutation is one of n permutations that are viewed as the same, so the number of circular permutations is $\frac{n!}{n}$, or $(n-1)!$.

11-7

4 Wrap-Up

Ongoing Assessment

Write the expression $5 \cdot 5 \cdot 5 \cdot 5$ on the board and ask students to call out different situations that this expression might represent for permutations. Repeat the procedure with $5 \cdot 4 \cdot 3 \cdot 2 \cdot 1$. Give students a chance to explain the difference between the expressions in their own words.

Project Update

Project 2, The Right Order, on page 703, and Project 5, Switches and Sorting, on page 704, relate to the content of this lesson.

---

22. A rectangle with dimensions $4w$ and $2w + 1$ is contained in a rectangle with dimensions $10w$ and $6w + 2$, as shown in the diagram at the right. (Lesson 11-3)

    a. Write an expression for the area of the larger rectangle. $10w(6w + 2)$

    b. Write an expression for the area of the smaller rectangle.

    c. Write a polynomial in standard form for the area of the shaded region. $52w^2 + 16w$

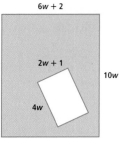

23. Consider the polynomial $3x^3 - 4x^2 + x + 6$. Give an example of a polynomial of degree 3 that when added to this will give a polynomial of degree 1. (Lesson 11-2)

24. The spreadsheet below shows an investment of \$1,200 increasing in two different ways. (Lesson 7-7)

◇	A	B	C
1	Years From Now	Exponential Growth	Constant Increase
2	0	1200	1200
3	1	1260	1275
4	2	1323	1350
5	3		
6	4		
7	5		
8	6		
9	7		

a. What formula should be entered in cell B5? C5?

b. Describe the difference in investments after 7 years.

c. Which investment will be worth more in 10 years? Justify your answer.

EXPLORATION

25. Here are polynomial expressions for the number of permutations of n symbols with various lengths: See margin.

    Length 2: $n(n - 1) = n^2 - n$

    Length 3: $n(n - 1)(n - 2) = n^3 - 3n^2 + 2n$

    Length 4: $n(n - 1)(n - 2)(n - 3) = n^4 - 6n^3 + 11n^2 - 6n$

    Length 5: $n(n - 1)(n - 2)(n - 3)(n - 4) = n^5 - 10n^4 + 35n^3 - 50n^2 + 24n$

    a. Use a CAS to find a polynomial expression for the number of permutations of n symbols with length 6.

    b. Identify some patterns in these polynomials that enable you to predict some features of the polynomial for the number of permutations of n symbols with length 7.

22b. $4w(2w + 1)$

23. Answers vary.
    Sample answer:
    $-3x^3 + 4x^2 + 7$

24a. $1{,}200 \cdot (1.05)\^A5$
     or $= B4 \cdot 1.05$;
     $1{,}200 + 75 \cdot A5$
     or $= C4 + 75$

24b. exponential growth: \$1,688.52; constant increase; \$1,725. The difference is \$36.48.

24c. exponential growth, since $1{,}200 \cdot (1.05)^{10} = 1{,}954.67$ and constant increase $= 1{,}200 + 75 \cdot (10) = 1{,}950$.

QY ANSWERS

1. 362,880

2. 40,320

Additional Answers

25a. $n^6 - 15n^5 + 85n^4 - 225n^3 + 274n^2 - 120n$

25b. Answers vary. Sample answer: The coefficient of the term with degree 1 of an mth-degree polynomial is $(m - 1)!$, and it alternates in sign. So the last term of the Length 7 polynomial will be $120n$.

Lesson 11-8
The Chi-Square Statistic

Vocabulary

expected number

deviation

chi-square statistic

▶ **BIG IDEA** The chi-square statistic is found by adding squares of binomials and provides evidence for whether data found in certain tables represent events that are occurring randomly.

The *chi-square* statistic is different from any statistic you have yet seen. This statistic compares actual frequencies with the frequencies that would be expected by calculating probabilities, as shown below.

The following table shows the average daily numbers of live births in California between 1995 and 1997. Are birthdays randomly distributed among the days of the week?

Day of the Week	Mon.	Tues.	Wed.	Thurs.	Fri.	Sat.	Sun.
Actual Numbers of Births	1,473	1,629	1,602	1,588	1,593	1,272	1,159

Source: *Journal of the American Medical Association*

The **expected number** of births is the mean number of births for a given day that is predicted by a probability. If the births occurred randomly, then the expected number for each day would be the same. There were 10,316 births each week on average. So the expected number of births for each day is $\frac{10,316}{7}$ which, rounded to the nearest integer, is 1,474.

Day of the Week	Mon.	Tues.	Wed.	Thurs.	Fri.	Sat.	Sun.
Expected Numbers of Births	1,474	1,474	1,474	1,474	1,474	1,474	1,474

As you know, even if events occur randomly, it is not common for all events to occur with the same frequency. When you toss a coin ten times, you would not usually get 5 heads even if the coin were fair. Similarly, if there were 1,460 births on 4 days and 1,425 on the other three days, that would not seem to be much of a difference from the expected numbers. So the question is: Do the actual numbers deviate enough from the expected numbers that we should think that the births happen more often on certain days of the week?

If we let an expected number be e and an actual observed number be a, then $|e - a|$. The absolute value of the difference between these numbers is called the **deviation** of a from e. For example, the deviation on Saturday is $|1,474 - 1,272|$, or 202.

Mental Math

Solve.

a. $|n| = 14$ 14 or –14

b. $|n| = -14$

c. $|-n| = 14$

d. $-|n| = 14$

b. no solution

c. 14 or –14

d. no solution

Background

The statistics that students have seen (mean, range, median, etc.) are *descriptive statistics*—they describe data. The chi-square statistic is an *inferential statistic*, one that is used to help in decision making. The chi-square statistic is perhaps the easiest inferential statistic to calculate; it can often be done without a calculator. It can be used on data that are accessible to students, and its calculation involves only simple probability and elementary algebra.

The idea behind the chi-square statistic is the set of chi-square distributions. Each distribution in the set displays the probability of obtaining a chi-square value that is greater than a particular number for a specified number of degrees of freedom. (The table of critical chi-square values is on page 699.) In the examples in these materials, the chi-square statistic is being used to compare a set of n observed values with a corresponding set of n expected values. The number of degrees of freedom is $n - 1$.

GOAL

Use the chi-square statistic to determine whether a set of discrete data differs significantly from values that would be expected when certain probabilities are given.

SPUR Objective

H Use the chi-square statistic to determine whether or not statistics support a conclusion.

Materials/Resources

· Lesson Masters 11-8A and 11-8B
· Resource Masters 175–177
· Scientific calculator

HOMEWORK

Suggestions for Assignment

• Questions 1–17
• Question 18 (extra credit)
• Reading Lesson 12-1
• Covering the Ideas 12-1

Local Standards

1 Warm-Up

Suppose a spinner is divided into four congruent regions labeled A, B, C, and D, and region D is twice the size of each of the other three regions.

1. If you spin the spinner 100 times, how many times would you expect the spinner to land in region B? **20**

2. Suppose the spinner landed on A 17 times, on B 25 times, on C 24 times, and on D 34 times. For each region calculate $\frac{(a - e)^2}{e}$ where a is the actual frequency and e is the expected frequency. $A = \frac{9}{20}$, $B = \frac{25}{20}$, $C = \frac{16}{20}$, and $D = \frac{36}{40}$

(continued on next page)

Have students complete Questions 3 and 4 after teaching the lesson.

3. Add the four numbers you obtained in Question 2 to find the chi-square statistic. 3.4

4. Use row 3 of the table on page 699 to determine whether the frequencies differ significantly from what would be expected just by typical variations. Because $3.4 < 6.25$, these frequencies are not at all unusual.

2 Teaching

Notes on the Lesson

This is a lesson you might want to read with your students. Return to Questions 3 and 4 in the Warm-Up after completing work on calculating the chi-square statistic and how to read a chi-square table. Emphasize that the table on page 699 should be read one row at a time. In the example of live births in Caliornia given in the lesson, because $n = 7$, we examine row 6 of the table. If births occurred randomly, one would expect a chi-square value as high as 10.6 only 10% of the time, a chi-square value as high as 12.6 about 5% of the time, a value as large as 16.8 about 1% of the time, and a value as large as 22.5 about 0.1% of the time. The value of 279.8 that is calculated would be quite unusual, and so we conclude that it is very likely that births are not equally distributed among the days of the week. The value for Sunday contributes so much to the chi-square statistic (over 196 by itself) that we can conclude that there is a significantly greater frequency of births on Sunday than might be expected.

Point out that data such as the births in California are collected every year. So it would not be unusual for *one* year in 100 to have a chi-square statistic greater than 16.8, maybe even two or three years with such high statistics. Even rare events can become expected if there are enough repetitions of an experiment. The chi-square statistic can never indicate that a distribution of frequencies is unlikely, but it does help to give evidence one way or the other.

Students may wonder how the values in the chi-square table were calculated. That process is well beyond the scope of this course. The theory requires calculus and college-level statistics and is often not studied until graduate school.

In 1900, the English statistician Karl Pearson introduced the **chi-square statistic** as a way of determining whether the difference in two frequency distributions is greater than that expected by chance. ("Chi" is pronounced *ky* as in *sky*.) The algorithm for calculating this statistic uses the squares of deviations, which is why we study it in this lesson.

Calculating the Chi-Square Statistic

Step 1 Count the number of events. Call this number n. In the above situation, there are 7 events, one each for Mon., Tues., Wed., Thurs., Fri., Sat., and Sun.

Step 2 Let $a_1, a_2, a_3, a_4, a_5, a_6$, and a_7 be the actual frequencies.

In this example, $a_1 = 1{,}473$, $a_2 = 1{,}629$, $a_3 = 1{,}602$, $a_4 = 1{,}588$, $a_5 = 1{,}593$, $a_6 = 1{,}272$, and $a_7 = 1{,}159$.

Step 3 Let $e_1, e_2, e_3, e_4, e_5, e_6$, and e_7 be the expected frequencies.

In this example, $e_1 = e_2 = e_3 = e_4 = e_5 = e_6 = e_7 = 1{,}474$.

Step 4 Calculate $\frac{(a_1 - e_1)^2}{e_1}, \frac{(a_2 - e_2)^2}{e_2}, ..., \frac{(a_n - e_n)^2}{e_n}$. Each number is the square of the deviation, divided by the expected frequency.

$$\frac{(a_1 - e_1)^2}{e_1} = \frac{1}{1{,}474}, \frac{(a_2 - e_2)^2}{e_2} = \frac{24{,}025}{1{,}474}, \frac{(a_3 - e_3)^2}{e_3} = \frac{16{,}384}{1{,}474}, \frac{(a_4 - e_4)^2}{e_4} =$$
$$\frac{12{,}996}{1{,}474}, \frac{(a_5 - e_5)^2}{e_5} = \frac{14{,}161}{1{,}474}, \frac{(a_6 - e_6)^2}{e_6} = \frac{40{,}804}{1{,}474}, \frac{(a_7 - e_7)^2}{e_7} = \frac{99{,}225}{1{,}474}$$

Step 5 Add the n numbers found in Step 4. This sum is the chi-square statistic.

$$\frac{1}{1{,}474} + \frac{24{,}025}{1{,}474} + \frac{16{,}384}{1{,}474} + \frac{12{,}996}{1{,}474} + \frac{14{,}161}{1{,}474} + \frac{40{,}804}{1{,}474} + \frac{99{,}225}{1{,}474} =$$
$$\frac{207{,}596}{1{,}474} \approx 140.8$$

The chi-square statistic measures how different a set of actual observed numbers is from a set of expected numbers. The larger the chi-square statistic is, the greater the difference. But is 140.8 unusually large? You can find that out by looking in chi-square tables. These tables give the values for certain values of n and certain probabilities. On the next page is such a table. In this table, n is the number of events. The other columns of the table correspond to probabilities of 0.10 (an event expected to happen $\frac{1}{10}$ of the time), 0.05 (or $\frac{1}{20}$ of the time), 0.01 (or $\frac{1}{100}$ of the time), and 0.001 (or $\frac{1}{1{,}000}$ of the time). You are not expected to know how the values in the table were calculated. The mathematics needed to calculate them is normally studied in college.

Accommodating the Learner

Take time to discuss Step 4 in calculating the chi-square statistic in greater detail. Make sure students understand why the value of the sum corresponds to the deviation in each case from the mean. You may want to illustrate this using several examples, including some with deviation that is not significant.

Critical Chi-Square Values				
$n - 1$	0.10	0.05	0.01	0.001
1	2.71	3.84	6.63	10.8
2	4.61	5.99	9.21	13.8
3	6.25	7.81	11.34	16.3
4	7.78	9.49	13.28	18.5
5	9.24	11.07	15.09	20.5
6	10.6	12.6	16.8	22.5
7	12.0	14.1	18.5	24.3
8	13.4	15.5	20.1	26.1
9	14.7	16.9	21.7	27.9
10	16.0	18.3	23.2	29.6
15	22.3	25.0	30.6	37.7
20	28.4	31.4	37.6	45.3
25	34.4	37.7	44.3	52.6
30	40.3	43.8	50.9	59.7
50	63.2	67.5	76.2	86.7

How to Read a Chi-Square Table

Examine the number 14.1, which appears in column 0.05, row 7. This means that, with 8 events, a chi-square value greater than 14.1 occurs with probability 0.05 or less.

On page 698, we obtained a chi-square value of 140.8 with $n = 7$ events. So we look in row $n - 1$, which is row 6. A value as large as 140.8 would occur with probability less than 0.001, that is, less than 1 in 1,000 times. So we have evidence that the births in California are not evenly distributed among the days of the week. The data should be examined to determine why Saturdays and Sundays have fewer births.

Suppose the frequencies of the births had led to a chi-square value of 10.9. Then, looking across row 6, we would see that this value is between the listed values 10.6 and 12.6. So 10.9 has a probability between 0.10 and 0.05. That means that a chi-square value as high as 10.9 would occur between $\frac{1}{10}$ and $\frac{1}{20}$ of the time just by chance. Statisticians normally do not consider this probability to be low enough to think there is reason to question the expected values.

When a chi-square value is found that occurs with probability less than 0.05, statisticians question whether the assumptions that led to the expected values are correct. With this criterion, the above distribution of births is highly unusual. So we would question whether the births are occurring randomly.

 QY

▶ QY

a. Why do you think there are fewer births on Saturday than on Monday through Friday?

b. Why do you think there are even fewer births on Sunday?

Note-Taking Tips

In this lesson, complete understanding of terminology is critical to grasping the concept. Students may find it helpful to practice identifying the observed scores, expected values, and deviation for a variety of examples. They can include these examples in their notes. Ask them to carefully read and discuss the written explanation. They should include in their notes a description of when the chi-square statistic is used.

Accommodating the Learner ⬆

Take time to discuss why as the chi-square value increases, the probability that the difference is a matter of chance decreases. Take extra time to discuss the meaning of the probability associated with a chi-square value and n.

11-8

Additional Example

Example The table below shows the weather forecast based on a new method and actual temperatures for a week in November. Is there evidence that the new method is unreliable?

Temperature	Su	M	T	W	Th	F	Sa
Actual high	66	55	57	58	56	50	42
Predicted high	46	50	52	55	61	52	56

The chi-square statistic is 13.8 and $n - 1$ is 6, so the probability is between 0.05 and 0.01, but closer to 0.05. This is enough evidence of unreliability that further testing should be done.

Notes on the Questions

Questions 4 and 5 These are real data from the two years. Together they give strong support to the view that traffic deaths do not occur randomly on days of the week. Ask students why they think there are more traffic accidents on weekends.

Question 8 As a challenge question, you might ask how many times a coin would need to land on heads in 1,000 tosses in order to feel with 99% confidence that the coin was not fair. Solve $\frac{(n - 500)^2}{500} + \frac{(n - 500)^2}{500} \geq 6.63$ to obtain $n \leq 459$ or $n \geq 541$.

Question 9 Looking at the data, we would be surprised if the chi-square value was not significant. In fact, people do speak of the "tornado season." In the northern plains states and upper Midwest, the peak season is June or July. In the southern plains states, it is during May or early June. And in the Gulf states, it is earlier in the spring. Graphics with probabilities of occurrences within 25 miles of any point in the U.S. can be found at www.nssl.noaa.gov/hazard.

Example

Suppose 90 students were asked to name the United States President in 1950 from the names listed below. Suppose: 24 picked Dwight Eisenhower, 31 picked John Kennedy, and 35 picked Harry Truman (the correct answer). Is there evidence to believe the people were just guessing?

Solution Calculate the chi-square statistic following the steps given above.

Step 1 Find the number of events. $n = 3$.

Step 2 Identify the actual observed values. $a_1 = 24$; $a_2 = 31$; $a_3 = 35$.

Step 3 Calculate the expected values. If people were just guessing, we would expect each of the three names to be picked by the same number of people. Since there were 90 people in all, each name would be picked by 30. So, $e_1 = 30$; $e_2 = 30$; $e_3 = 30$.

Step 4 Calculate $\frac{(a_1 - e_1)^2}{e_1}$, $\frac{(a_2 - e_2)^2}{e_2}$, and $\frac{(a_3 - e_3)^2}{e_3}$.

$\frac{(a_1 - e_1)^2}{e_1} = \frac{(24 - 30)^2}{30} = \frac{36}{30}$; $\frac{(a_2 - e_2)^2}{e_2} = \frac{(31 - 30)^2}{30} = \frac{1}{30}$;

$\frac{(a_3 - e_3)^2}{e_3} = \frac{(35 - 30)^2}{30} = \frac{25}{30}$

Step 5 The sum of the numbers in Step 4 is $\frac{36 + 1 + 25}{30} = \frac{62}{30} \approx 2.07$.

Now examine the table. When $n = 3$, $n - 1 = 2$. So, look at the second row. The number 2.07 is less than the value 4.61 that would occur with probability 0.10. The numbers 24, 31, and 35 are like those that could randomly appear more than 10% of the time. It is quite possible that the people were guessing.

The chi-square statistic can be used whenever there are actual frequencies and you have some way of calculating expected frequencies. However, the chi-square value is not a good measure of the deviation from the expected frequencies when there is an expected frequency that is less than 5.

Harry S. Truman was the 33rd President of the United States.

Questions

COVERING THE IDEAS

1. What does the chi-square statistic measure?

2. When was the chi-square statistic developed, and by whom?

3. For what expected frequencies should the chi-square statistic not be used? **for expected frequencies less than 5**

1. how different a set of actually observed scores is from a set of expected scores

2. in 1900 by Karl Pearson

In 4 and 5, average number of traffic deaths per day of the week in the United States are given for a particular year.

a. Calculate the chi-square statistic assuming that traffic deaths occur randomly on days of the week. 4a. 34.4, 5a. 23.7

b. Is there evidence to believe that the deaths are not occurring randomly on the days of the week?

		Mon.	Tues.	Wed.	Thurs.	Fri.	Sat.	Sun.
4.	Year 1985	100	105	105	110	145	170	140
5.	Year 1995	100	100	100	105	140	150	130

6. Suppose in the Example of this lesson that 40 students had picked Harry Truman, 30 had picked Dwight Eisenhower, and 20 had picked John Kennedy. Would there still be evidence that students were guessing randomly?

APPLYING THE MATHEMATICS

7. You build a spinner as shown at the right and spin it 50 times with the following outcomes. Use the chi-square statistic to determine whether or not the spinner seems to be fair.
The spinner seems to be fair.

Outcome	1	2	3	4	5
Frequency	13	13	9	8	7

8. A coin is tossed 1,000 times and lands heads up 537 times. Compare the numbers of heads and tails with what would be expected if the coin were fair. Use the chi-square statistic to test whether the coin is fair. See margin.

9. *The World Almanac and Book of Facts 2006* lists 64 notable tornadoes in the United States since 1925. The table at the right shows their frequencies by season of the year. Use the chi-square statistic to determine whether these figures support a view that more tornadoes occur at certain times of the year than at other times of the year. See margin.

Season	Number of Tornadoes
Autumn	8
Winter	15
Spring	38
Summer	3

10. Here are the total points scored in each quarter from the 16 National Football League games played December 17–19, 2005.

Quarter	1	2	3	4	Total
Points	122	196	133	150	601

Source: National Football League

Use the chi-square statistic to answer this question. Do football teams tend to score more points in one quarter than in any other?

4b. Yes, the chi-square value of 34.4 for 7 events occurs with probability less than 0.001.

5b. Yes, the chi-square value of 23.7 for 7 events occurs with probability less than 0.001.

6. There are 3 events and the chi-square value is 6.67. This occurs with a probability between 0.05 and 0.01, so there is evidence the answers were not random.

10. Yes, football teams tend to score more points in the second quarter than in any other.

The Chi-Square Statistic **701**

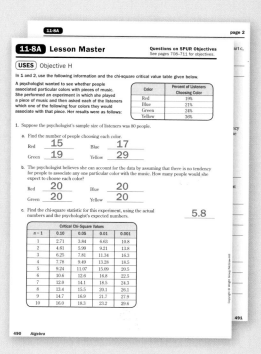

Additional Answers

8. heads: 537; tails: 463; fair: 500; The chi-square value of 5.48 for 2 events occurs with probability between 0.05 and 0.01, so there is some evidence that the coin might not be fair.

9. The chi-square value of 44.9 for 4 events occurs with probability less than 0.001, so there is evidence for the view that more tornadoes occur during certain times of the year (spring) than during others.

11-8

3 Assignment

Recommended Assignment

- Questions 1–17
- Question 18 (extra credit)
- Reading Lesson 12-1
- Covering the Ideas 12-1

Notes on the Questions

Question 10 We were surprised by these data. You might want to check with other data your students collect. We did expect that there might be more points scored in the 2nd and 4th quarters because coaches often use timeouts during the last 2 minutes of a half to stop the clock. More data would be needed before one could conclude that the 2nd quarter is likely to produce more points than any other.

Question 18 This question poses a real-world situation in which the chi-square statistic might be quite important to use. The data here, however, are made up.

11-8

4 Wrap-Up

Ongoing Assessment

Provide students with several examples including the related chi-square statistics. Ask them to use the table to decide if the difference between the actual and expected values is statistically significant.

Project Update

Project 6, Testing Astrology, on page 704, relates to the content of this lesson.

REVIEW

11. **a.** How many different permutations can be made using the letters of HORSE? **120**

 b. How many different permutations can be made using the letters of MONKEY? (**Lesson 11-7**) **720**

12. **a.** Which holds more, a cube with edges of length 6, or a rectangular box with dimensions 5 by 6 by 7?
 (**Lessons 11-6, 11-5**) **b. See margin.**

 b. Which holds more, a cube with edges of length x, or a box with dimensions $x - 1$ by x by $x + 1$?; Justify your answer.

In 13–15, expand and simplify the expression. (**Lessons 11-6, 11-5**)

13. **a.** $(2x + y)^2$ **b.** $(2x - y)^2$ **c.** $(2x - y)(2x + y)$ $4x^2 - y^2$

14. $(8 - a)(a - 8)$ 15. $(3k^2 - 6km + 3m^2)^2$

16. Draw a picture of the following multiplication using rectangles.
 $4x(x + 6) = 4x^2 + 24x$ (**Lesson 11-3**) **See margin.**

17. On the fifth day after planting, a Moso bamboo tree was 38.5 cm. On the 14th day, the tree was 70.9 cm. (**Lessons 6-1, 5-4**)

 a. What was the average rate of change in height per day between the 5th and 14th days? **3.6 cm/day**

 b. Express the rate in Part a in cm/week. **25.2 cm/wk**

EXPLORATION

18. A new high school for mathematics and science was opened in Cityville. Four hundred girls and 600 boys applied for 150 slots. A committee considered the applications and accepted 65 girls and 85 boys. Some people complained that there was discrimination.

 a. One complaint was that too few girls were accepted. This person's opinion was that there should have been equal numbers of boys and girls accepted and that the numbers accepted deviated too much from equality. Use the chi-square statistic to test whether this deviation could have occurred easily by chance. **18a–c. See margin.**

 b. A second complaint was that too many girls were accepted. This person's position was that the numbers of boys and girls accepted should have been proportional to the number of applicants who were boys and girls. Use the chi-square statistic to test whether this deviation could have occurred easily by chance.

 c. If you were on the school board, would you agree with either complaint? Explain your answer.

12a. The cube with edges of length 6 holds more.

13a. $4x^2 + 4xy + y^2$
13b. $4x^2 - 4xy + y^2$
14. $-a^2 + 16a - 64$
15. $9k^4 - 36k^3m + 54k^2m^2 - 36m^3k + 9m^4$

Moso bamboo was introduced into the United States in about 1890.

Source: BAMBOO The Magazine of The American Bamboo Society

QY ANSWERS

a. Answers vary. Sample answer: With the ability to schedule deliveries, many physicians opt to schedule them during the week.

b. Answers vary. Sample answer: Many physicians choose Sunday as their day off and do not schedule deliveries for that day.

Additional Answers

12b. The cube with edges of length x holds more. The volume of the cube with edges of length x is x^3, and the volume of the cube with dimensions $x - 1$, x, $x + 2$ is $(x - 1)(x)(x + 1)$ $= x^3 - x$, and $x^3 > x^3 - x$ for all positive x.

16.

	x	6
x	x^2	$6x$
x	x^2	$6x$
x	x^2	$6x$
x	x^2	$6x$

18a. The chi-square value of 2.667 for 2 events occurs with probability greater than 0.10, so this deviation could have occurred by chance.

18b. The chi-square value of 0.6944 for 2 events occurs with probability greater than 0.10 so this deviation could have occurred by chance.

18c. Answers vary. See students' work.

11-8B Lesson Master

Questions on SPUR Objectives
See pages 708–711 for objectives.

USES Objective H

In 1–3, use the chi-square critical value table given below.

1. The president of the junior class surveyed all 549 members of the junior class to see whether more members of the class attended a particular homecoming event. Her results were as follows:

Event	Number of People Attending
Pep rally	36%
Dance	23%
Football game	41%

a. Find the number of people attending each event.
Pep rally **198** Dance **126** Game **225**

b. The class president believes she can account for the data by assuming each event was attended equally. How many would she expect to attend each event?
Pep rally **183** Dance **183** Game **183**

c. Find the chi-square statistic for this experiment, using the actual numbers and the president's expected numbers. **≈ 28.62**

Critical Chi-Square Values

$n - 1$	.10	.05	.01	.001
1	2.71	3.84	6.63	10.8
2	4.61	5.99	9.21	13.8
3	6.25	7.81	11.34	16.3
4	7.78	9.49	13.28	18.5
5	9.24	11.07	15.09	20.5
6	10.6	12.6	16.8	22.5
7	12.0	14.1	18.5	24.3
8	13.4	15.5	20.1	26.1
9	14.7	16.9	21.7	27.9
10	16.0	18.3	23.2	29.6

d. Refer to the Critical Chi-square Values table above. Using your answer to Part c, what can you conclude about the president's assumption?

Sample answer: The president's assumption is invalid since there is less than 0.1% chance the results would occur in the equally likely cases.

492 **Algebra**

11-8B page 2

2. In 2005, the U.S. Department of Labor reported the following results for three categories of their Consumer Expenditures Survey that asked Americans how they spend their income.

Category	Percent of Income Spent
Food at home	7%
Food away from home	6%
Entertainment	5%

a. Based on the Department of Labor survey, how much did the average family in the United States spend on each item in 2005 if the average annual expenditure was $46,409?
Food at home **$3,248.63** Food away from home **$2,784.54** Entertainment **$2,320.45**

b. Amy assumed that the average family spent the same amount on each of these three items. How much does she assume they spend on each item?
Food at home **$2,784.54** Food away from home **$2,784.54** Entertainment **$2,784.54**

c. Find the chi-square statistic for this experiment, using the Department of Labor numbers and Amy's expected numbers. **≈ 154.70**

d. Using your answer to Part c, what can you conclude about Amy's assumption?

Sample answer: Amy's assumption is invalid since there is less than 0.01% chance that Americans spend the same amount on food at home, food away from home, and entertainment.

3. Jason believes that the music club at his school consists of 10% freshmen, 20% sophomores, 30% juniors, and 40% seniors. This year there were 10 freshmen, 21 sophomores, 40 juniors, and 32 seniors in the club. Use the chi-square statistic to determine if Justin's assumption is correct.

Sample answer: The chi-square statistic is about 4.59. This shows that Jason's assumption is valid since there is greater than a 10% chance the results would occur for the distribution assumed by Jason.

Algebra 493

Chapter 11 Projects

1 Dividing Polynomials

If you wanted to check if 23 is a factor of 10,373, you could divide 10,373 by 23, and check if there is a remainder in the division. One way to do this would be to use long division. There is an algorithm for long division with polynomials, which is similar to an algorithm for long division with numbers. Here are two examples: one in which $x^3 - 4x^2 + 7x - 4$ is divided by $(x - 1)$, and the other in which $x^2 - 9$ is divided by $(x + 2)$.

$$
\begin{array}{r}
x^2 - 3x + 4 \\
x - 1{\overline{\smash{\big)}\,x^3 - 4x^2 + 7x - 4}} \\
\underline{-(x^3 - x^2)} \\
0x^3 - 3x^2 + 7x - 4 \\
\underline{-(-3x^2 + 3x)} \\
0x^2 + 4x - 4 \\
\underline{-(4x - 4)} \\
0
\end{array}
$$

$$
\begin{array}{r}
x - 2 \\
x + 2{\overline{\smash{\big)}\,x^2 - 9}} \\
\underline{-(x^2 + 2x)} \\
0x^2 - 2x - 9 \\
\underline{-(-2x - 4)} \\
-5
\end{array}
$$

In the first example, the result is $x^2 - 3x + 4$ with no remainder. In the second example the result is $(x - 2)$ with remainder –5.

a. Is $(x - 1)$ a factor of $x^3 - 4x^2 + 7x - 4$? Is $(x - 2)$ a factor of $x^2 - 9$?

b. Divide $x^3 + 3x^2 + 9x + 27$ by $(x + 3)$.

c. Write a description of the long division algorithm and explain it to a friend.

2 The Right Order

When performing complex actions, the order in which you do them is often important. For example, when dressing yourself in the winter, you might choose to put on pants, then a shirt, then a sweater, then socks, then shoes, and finally a jacket. The order in which you perform these actions is important.

a. How many different permutations of these actions are there?

b. Give four permutations of this order that would result in you not being dressed properly. Describe what happens in each case.

c. Give four permutations of this order that would result in you being dressed properly.

d. Give another sequence of events in which order matters. Answer Parts a, b, and c for this sequence.

3 Representing Positive Integers Using Powers

a. Every positive integer can be written as a sum of different powers of 2, where each power is added at most once. For example, $50 = 2^5 + 2^4 + 2^1$. You may be surprised to learn that for each number there is only one way to write it as a sum of powers of 2. Find the powers of 2 representation for the integers from 1 to 16. Explain why there is only one such representation and how this relates to writing numbers in base 10.

(continued on next page)

Project Rubric

Advanced	Student correctly provides all of the details asked for in the project as well as additional correct independent conclusions.
Proficient	Student correctly provides all of the details asked for in the project.
Partially proficient	Student correctly provides some of the details asked for in the project or provides all details with some inaccuracies.
Not proficient	Student correctly provides few of the details asked for in the project or provides all details with many inaccuracies.
No attempt	Student makes little or no attempt to complete the project.

Chapter 11

The projects relate to the content of the lessons of this chapter as follows:

Project	Lesson
1	11-4
2	11-7
3	11-2
4	11-6
5	11-7
6	11-8

1 Dividing Polynomials

Remind students that they can show extra work off to the side. For example, when dividing $x^3 - 4x^2 + 7x - 4$ by $x - 1$, they may want to work out products such as $x^2(x - 1) = x^3 - x^2$ on paper. Emphasize that they are only trying to match up the first term of each expression. To extend the project, include some examples with zero coefficients, such as determining if $(x - 2)$ is a factor of $x^3 - x - 6$.

2 The Right Order

Suggest students abbreviate the different clothes items, such as *p* for pants and *sh* for shirts. Clarify that you are assuming that each person is going to wear exactly one of each item. For instance, everyone is going to wear a sweater. The only flexibility is deciding in what order he or she will put them on.

3 Representing Positive Integers Using Powers

Encourage students to write several different numbers as powers of 2. They should notice that here the coefficients are all 1. This is because as they write out a term such as $2^3 + 2^3$ twice, the sum is double, or $2(2^3) = 2^4$. Discuss why, in Part b, they specify that each power is added at most twice. What would happen if this restriction were removed?

(continued on next page)

Consider if a term is written out three times, as in the case $3^n + 3^n + 3^n = 3(3^n)$. Then the expression is more effectively written as 3^{n+1}. Similarly, help students realize that for writing numbers in base 10, each power can be added at most 9 times. If they master this idea, it can help them understand why every number can be written as powers of 2 with coefficients of 1. However, to write numbers using powers of 10, we need to use coefficients between 1 and 9.

4 Differences of Higher Powers

Help students generalize the pattern in part a by using the formula for $x^3 - (-y)^3$. They will thus find the formula for $x^3 + y^3$. For Part c, suggest that they work with students doing Project 1. Once they find the pattern $\frac{x^n - 1}{x - 1} = x^{n-1} + x^{n-2} + \dots + x^2 + x + 1$, they can test it out using polynomial long division for $n = 3, 4, 5$, and 6. Remind students that for Part d, they must use the formula from Part c to compute. They cannot simply compute the sum.

5 Switches and Sorting

Notice that the project is not asking for the minimum number of switches. Students may also be confused by the instructions "describe an algorithm." Consider showing several examples of algorithms that may help them understand the usage and definition of the term. To expand the project, ask students to compare the number of switches they have to use to put the letters in alphabetical order for DCBA, DCAB, DABC, and ABDC. They may notice that all of these took fewer than 9 switches. This fits with the pattern $(n - 1)^2$, which is used to bound the number of switches of n letters.

6 Testing Astrology

Remind students to think about how many of the 100 famous people would have each sign if the signs were evenly distributed. Suggest that students set up a table to compare actual with expected frequencies. Suggest that students limit their search to a particular field that is likely to be well publicized, such as presidents or actors.

b. Every positive integer can be represented as a sum of powers of 3, where each power is added at most twice. For example, $50 = 3^3 + 3^2 + 3^2 + 3^1 + 3^0 + 3^0$. Find the powers of 3 representation for all the integers from 1 to 16. Explain why there is only one such representation for each number.

4 Differences of Higher Powers

In this chapter you saw why $x^2 - y^2 = (x - y)(x + y)$. This is only one instance of a general pattern.

a. Use the Extended Distributive Property to show that $x^3 - y^3 = (x - y)(x^2 + xy + y^2)$ and that $x^4 - y^4 = (x - y)(x^3 + x^2y + yx^2 + y^3)$.

b. Find similar factors for $x^5 - y^5$ and then generalize them to find similar factors for $x^n - y^n$.

c. Suppose $y = 1$. What does your answer from Part b say that $\frac{x^n - 1}{x - 1}$ is equal to?

d. Use the formula from Part c to calculate $1 + 2 + 2^2 + 2^3 + \dots + 2^{10}$. (You can use the fact that $2^{10} = 1,024$.)

5 Switches and Sorting

One special type of permutation, in which the positions of two elements are changed, is called a *switch*. For example, a switch could change the acronym BADC into the acronym ABDC. Another switch could change ABDC to ABCD. Suppose you are given an acronym and you want to put it into alphabetical order. (This sort of problem comes up very often in computer programming.)

a. Find and describe an algorithm to put an acronym into alphabetical order using a sequence of switches.

b. Use your algorithm to sort the acronym UNESCO. How many switches were required to do this?

6 Testing Astrology

From a book (like *Who's Who*) or online source, find at least 100 famous people in a field and note their birthdays. Identify the astrological sign of each person. Then tabulate the number of people with each sign. Do these data lead you to believe that certain birth signs are more likely to produce famous people? Use a chi-square statistic assuming a random distribution of the birthdays among the 12 astrological signs is expected. Although $n - 1 = 11$ here, refer to row 10 from the chi-square table on page 699.

Notes

_____
_____
_____
_____
_____
_____
_____
_____
_____
_____

Chapter 11 Summary and Vocabulary

○ A **monomial** is a product of terms. The **degree of a monomial** is the sum of the exponents of its variables. A **polynomial** is an expression that is either a monomial or a sum of monomials. The **degree of a polynomial** is taken to be the largest degree of its monomial terms. **Linear polynomials** are polynomials of degree 1. **Quadratic polynomials** are polynomials of degree 2.

○ Polynomials emerge from a variety of situations. Our customary way of writing whole numbers in base 10 can be considered as a polynomial with 10 substituted for the variable. If different amounts of money are invested each year at a **scale factor** x, the total amount after several years is a **polynomial in x.** The number of permutations of n objects can be represented by a polynomial in n.

○ Addition and subtraction of polynomials are based on adding like terms, one of the forms of the Distributive Property that you studied earlier in this book. Multiplication of polynomials is also justified by the Distributive Property. To multiply one polynomial by a second, multiply each term in the first polynomial by each term in the second polynomial, then add the products. For example:

monomial by a polynomial: $a(x + y + z) = ax + ay + az$

two polynomials: $(a + b + c)(x + y + z) =$
$$ax + ay + az + bx + by + bz + cx + cy + cz$$

two binomials: $(a + b)(c + d) = ac + ad + bc + bd$

perfect square: $(a + b)^2 = (a + b)(a + b) = a^2 + 2ab + b^2$

difference of two squares: $(a + b)(a - b) = a^2 - b^2$

○ If each of the terms of a polynomial has a common factor, then so does their sum. It can be factored out using the Distributive Property.

○ The square of the difference of actual and expected values in an experiment, $(a - e)^2$, appears in the calculation of the **chi-square statistic.** This statistic can help you decide whether the assumptions that led to the expected values are correct.

Vocabulary

11-1
polynomial in x
standard form for a polynomial

11-2
monomial
polynomial
binomial
trinomial
degree of a monomial
degree of a polynomial
linear polynomial
quadratic polynomial

11-4
factoring
trivial factors
greatest common factor
factorization
prime polynomials
complete factorization

11-6
perfect square trinomials
difference of squares

11-7
permutation
$n!$, n factorial
circular permutation

11-8
expected number
deviation
chi-square statistic

Summary and Vocabulary

The Summary gives an overview of the entire chapter and provides an opportunity for students to consider the material as a whole. Thus, the Summary can be used to help students relate and unify the concepts presented in the chapter.

Terms and symbols are listed by lesson to provide a checklist of concepts that students must know. Emphasize to students that they should read the vocabulary list carefully before starting the Self-Test on the next page. If students do not understand the meaning of a term, they should refer back to the indicated lesson.

Theorems and Properties covered in the chapter are listed below the Summary, with page references included to lead students back to the location in the chapter where the theorem or property is stated.

Theorems and Properties

Unique Factorization Theorem for Polynomials (p. 677)	Extended Distributive Property (p. 680) Perfect Squares of Binomials (p. 687)	Difference of Two Squares (p. 688)

Self-Test

For the development of mathematical competence, feedback and correction, along with the opportunity for practice, are necessary. The Self-Test provides the opportunity for feedback and correction; the Chapter Review provides additional opportunities for practice. We cannot overemphasize the importance of these end-of-chapter materials. It is at this point that the material "gels" for many students, allowing them to solidify skills and understanding. In general, student performance should improve after these pages.

Assign the Self-Test as a one-night assignment. Worked-out solutions for all questions are in the Selected Answers section of the student book. Encourage students to take the Self-Test honestly, grade themselves, and then be prepared to discuss the test in class.

Advise students to pay special attention to those Chapter Review questions (pages 708–711) which correspond to the questions they missed on the Self-Test.

Additional Answers

1. $3x(10 - 4x + x^3)$
   $= 30x - 12x^2 + 3x^4$
   $= 3x^4 - 12x^2 + 30x$
2. $(2b - 5)^2$
   $= (2b - 5)(2b - 5)$
   $= (2b)^2 - 2(2b)(5) + 5^2$
   $= 4b^2 - 20b + 25$
3. $(8z + 3)(8z - 3)$
   $= (8z)^2 - 3^2$
   $= 64z^2 - 9$
4. $6a(2a^2 + 9a - 1)$
   $= 12a^3 + 54a^2 - 6a$
5. $(5a^2 - a)(5a^2 - a)$
   $= (5a^2)^2 - 2(5a^2)(a) + a^2$
   $= 25a^4 - 10a^3 + a^2$
6. $(2 - 6c)(4 + 3c)$
   $= 2(4 + 3c) - 6c(4 + 3c)$
   $= 8 + 6c - 24c - 18c^2$
   $= -18c^2 - 18c + 8$
8. In standard form the polynomial is
   $19x^3 - 9x^2 + 2x - 5$ and has four
   terms, so it is not a monomial, a
   binomial, nor a trinomial.

Take this test as you would take a test in class. You will need a calculator. Then use the Selected Answers section in the back of the book to check your work.

1–6. See margin.
In 1–6, expand and simplify the expression.

1. $3x(10 - 4x + x^3)$

2. $(2b - 5)^2$

3. $(8z + 3)(8z - 3)$

4. $6a(2a^2 + 9a - 1)$

5. $(5a^2 - a)(5a^2 - a)$

6. $(2 - 6c)(4 + 3c)$

In 7 and 8, consider the polynomial
$8x^3 - 5 + 2x + 11x^3 - 9x^2$.

7. What is the degree of this polynomial? 3

8. Is the polynomial a *monomial, binomial, trinomial,* or *none of these*? See margin.

9. Factor completely: $6x^2y^2(2x - 4y + 5y^2)$
   $12x^3y^2 - 24x^2y^3 + 30x^2y^4$.
10–11. See margin.
In 10 and 11, write as a single polynomial.

10. $(20n^2 - 8n - 12) + (16n^3 - 7n^2 + 5)$

11. $9p^4 + p^2 - 5 - p(3p^3 + p - 2)$

12. **True or False** The expression
    $3v^2 + 3v - 1$ is a trinomial of degree 3.
    See margin.
13. Simplify the fraction $\frac{28w^3 - 18w}{2w}$, assuming
    that $w \neq 0$. See margin.

14. Write the area of the shaded portion of the rectangular region as a polynomial in standard form. See margin.

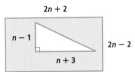

15. A swim team has 7 swimmers available to race a 4-person relay. How many different orders of swimmers are possible? 840; See margin for explanation.
16. Twenty-five art students entered a competition in which 1st, 2nd, and 3rd place prizes were to be awarded. How many permutations of students could receive these prizes? 13,800; See margin for explanation.
In 17 and 18, consider the following. On Ashley's 16th birthday, she received $200. She received $150 on her 17th birthday, and $300 on each of her 18th and 19th birthdays. 17–18. See margin.

17. If she invested all of this money each year in a savings account with a yearly scale factor x, how much money would she have on her 21st birthday?

18. Evaluate your answer to Question 17 if the savings account had an interest rate of 3%.

19. **a.** What is the area of the largest rectangle below? $9x^2 + 18x$

   b. What factorization of the rectangle's area is shown? $3x(3x + 6)$

   c. Is this a complete factorization? Explain your answer. No, 3 can be factored out of the parentheses, and it can be factored completely to get $9x(x + 2)$.

Additional Answers

10. $(20n^2 - 8n - 12) + (16n^3 - 7n^2 + 5)$
    $= 16n^3 + (20n^2 - 7n^2) - 8n + (5 - 12)$
    $= 16n^3 + 13n^2 - 8n - 7$
11. $9p^4 + p^2 - 5 - p(3p^3 + p - 2)$
    $= 9p^4 + p^2 - 5 - 3p^4 - p^2 + 2p$
    $= 6p^4 + 2p - 5$
12. False; The expression has three terms so it is a trinomial, but the highest power of a variable term is 2 so it has degree 2.
13. $\frac{28w^3 - 18w}{2w} = \frac{28w^3}{2w} - \frac{18w}{2w} = 14w^2 - 9$

14. area of rectangle: $(2n + 2)(2n - 2)$;
    area of triangle: $\frac{1}{2}(n + 3)(n - 1)$;
    area of shaded region:
    $4n^2 - 4 - \frac{1}{2}n^2 - n + \frac{3}{2} = \frac{7}{2}n^2 - n - \frac{5}{2}$
15. There are 7 swimmers to choose from to swim first, then 6 left to choose the second swimmer, 5 left to choose the third swimmer, and 4 swimmers left to pick the final racer. Thus, there are $7 \cdot 6 \cdot 5 \cdot 4 = 840$ possible orders.

20. Represent the product $(x + 2y)(5 + z)$
    using areas of rectangles. See margin.

21. Jerry believes a die is weighted to favor
    certain numbers. The table below shows
    the outcome of 198 random tosses of
    the die.

Number	Outcomes
1	24
2	44
3	31
4	30
5	43
6	26

The probability
of the chi-square
value of 11.03 for
6 events is between
0.10 and 0.05, so
the results aren't
very far from a
random distribution;
the die is probably
not weighted.

Use the chi-square statistic to provide
evidence as to whether Jerry's view is
correct. Justify your answer.

22. Represent the product $(x + 4)^2$ using
    areas of rectangles. Write your answer
    in standard form. $x^2 + 8x + 16$;
    See students' work.

Chapter **11** Self-Test

Additional Answers

16. There are 25 students who could get 1st
    place, then 24 remaining who could get
    2nd place, and 23 remaining to get 3rd
    place. $25 \cdot 24 \cdot 23 = 13,800$ different
    permutations.

17. For each year that she has had a certain
    amount of money she receives interest
    on that amount at the rate of x, thus
    M dollars received n years ago will
    be worth Mx^n dollars. So on her 21st
    birthday she will have $200x^5 + 150x^4 +$
    $300x^3 + 300x^2$ dollars.

18. $200(1.03)^5 + 150(1.03)^4 + 300(1.03)^3$
    $+ 300(1.03)^2 = 1,046.76$; she would
    have $1,046.76 on her 21st birthday.

Additional Answers

20.

$5x + xz + 10y + 2yz$

Chapter 11 Review

Chapter Review

The main objectives for the chapter are organized in the Chapter Review under the four types of understanding this book promotes—Skills, Properties, Uses, and Representations.

Whereas end-of-chapter material may be considered optional in some texts, in *UCSMP Algebra* we have selected these objectives and questions with the expectation that they will be covered. Students should be able to answer these questions with about 85% accuracy after studying the chapter.

You may assign these questions over a single night to help students prepare for a test the next day, or you may assign the questions over a two-day period. If you work the questions over two days, then we recommend assigning the *evens* for homework the first night so that students get feedback in class the next day, and then assigning the *odds* the night before the test because the answers are provided to the odd-numbered questions in the Selected Answers at the back of the book.

It is effective to ask students which questions they still do not understand and use the day as a total class discussion of the material that the class finds most difficult.

Resources

- Assessment Resources: Chapter 11 Test, Forms A–D; Chapter 11 Test, Cumulative Form

Technology Resources

Teacher's Assessment Assistant, Ch 11
Electronic Teacher's Edition, Ch. 11

Chapter 11 Chapter Review

SKILLS
PROPERTIES
USES
REPRESENTATIONS

SKILLS Procedures used to get answers

OBJECTIVE A Add and subtract polynomials. (Lessons 11-1, 11-2)

In 1–4, simplify the expression and write the answer in standard form. 1–4. See margin.

1. $(-k^3 + 2k^2 - 17k + 8) + (5k^3 - 2k^2 - 8)$

2. $\frac{4}{3}h^3 + 4 - \frac{2}{3}h^3 + \frac{1}{7}h^2 - 5$

3. $(5.4s^4 + 9.8s^2 - 8) - (-3.7s^3 - 4 + 5.2s)$

4. $(12w^3 - 3w^2 + -8w - 9) - (80w + 8)$

OBJECTIVE B Multiply polynomials. (Lessons 11-3, 11-5, 11-6)

5. **Fill in the Blank** $(-6x + 9) \cdot \left(\frac{5}{3}x + 6\right) = -10x^2 - \underline{\ ?\ }x + 54$ –21

In 6–16, write as a single polynomial in standard form. 7. $9p^4 + 9p^3 - 54p^2 + 45p$

6. $m(7m^2 - 13m + 12)$ $7m^3 - 13m^2 + 12m$

7. $9p(p^3 + p^2 - 6p + 5)$

8. $-3x^2\left(12x^2 + \frac{2}{3}x\right)$ $-36x^4 - 2x^3$

9. $-\frac{1}{7}q^8(-q^3 + 14q^2 - 112q + 5)$

10. $2(g + 3g^2 + 19g^3 - g^6) + g(-3g^5 + 2g + 6g^3)$ 9–10. See margin.

11. $(b - 3)(b + 3)$ $b^2 - 9$

12. $(8x - 2)(2x - 1)$ $16x^2 - 12x + 2$

13. $2(1 + 6w)(1 - 6w)$ $-72w^2 + 2$

14. $3(a^2 + a - 1)(a + 1)$ $3a^3 + 6a^2 - 3$

15. $(n - 2)(n - 3)(n - 4)$ $n^3 - 9n^2 + 26n - 24$

16. $(c^2 + 10c - 4)(2c^2 - 8c + 1)$
$2c^4 + 12c^3 - 87c^2 + 42c - 4$

---

17. $\frac{51}{2}x^2 - \frac{11}{2}x - 1$

17. The length of one leg of a right triangle is $(3x - 1)$, and the length of the other leg is $(17x + 2)$. Express the area of the triangle as a polynomial in standard form.

OBJECTIVE C Find common monomial factors of polynomials. (Lesson 11-4)
18–21. See margin.
In 18–21, factor the polynomial completely.

18. $9k^3 + 6k^2$ 19. $u^2v - uv^2$

20. $-84y^3 - 18y^2 + 93y$

21. $45a^9b^5 + 60a^6b^4 - 15a^5b^3 + 420a^3b^2$

22. **Multiple Choice** Which is a complete factorization of $24y^7 + 18y^5 - 90y^3$? D

A $y^3(24y^4 + 18y^2 - 90)$

B $3y^3(8y^7 + 6y^5 - 30y^3)$

C $6y^7(4 + 3y^{-2} + 15y^{-4})$

D $6y^3(4y^4 + 3y^2 - 15)$

OBJECTIVE D Expand squares of binomials. (Lesson 11-6)
25. $2,025z^2 - 990z + 121$
In 23–26, expand and simplify the expression.

23. $(p + 6)^2$ 24. $(-u - 5)^2$
$p^2 + 12p + 36$ $u^2 + 10u + 25$
25. $(11 - 45z)^2$ 26. $(-w + 2)^2$
                            $w^2 - 4w + 4$

27. **Multiple Choice** The square of which binomial below is $64c^4 + -80c^3 + 25c^2$? B

A $8c - 5$ B $8c^2 - 5c$

C $8c^2 + 5c$ D $8c^3 + 5c$

PROPERTIES The principles behind the mathematics

OBJECTIVE E Classify polynomials by their degrees or number of terms. (Lesson 11-2)

Additional Answers

1. $4k^3 - 17k$

2. $\frac{2}{3}h^3 + \frac{1}{7}h^2 - 1$

3. $5.4s^4 + 3.7s^3 + 9.8s^2 - 5.2s - 4$

4. $12w^3 - 3w^2 - 88w - 17$

9. $\frac{1}{7}q^{11} - 2q^{10} + 16q^9 - \frac{5}{7}q^8$

10. $-5g^6 + 6g^4 + 38g^3 + 8g^2 + 2g$

18. $3k^2(3k + 2)$

19. $uv(u - v)$

20. $-3y(28y^2 + 6y - 31)$

21. $15a^3b^2(3a^6b^3 + 4a^3b^2 - a^2b + 28)$

28–29. See margin.

28. Give an example of a monomial of degree 5.

29. Give an example of a trinomial of degree 5.

In 30–33, consider the polynomials below.

    a. $n^2 - 5$ b. $2m^2 + 4m - 7$

    c. $12a^4 - 16a^2 + 3$ d. $8w^2y + 9wy$

30. Which are binomials? a and d

31. Which are trinomials? b and c

32. Which have degree 2? a and b

33. Which have degree 4? c

USES Applications of mathematics in real-world situations

34a. $5{,}000y^8 + 3{,}000y^7 + 2{,}000y^6$

OBJECTIVE F Translate investment situations into polynomials. (Lesson 11-1)

34. Flora decides to open a retirement account with an annual interest rate y. In the first year, Flora invests $5,000. The second year, she invests $3,000, and then in the third year she invests $2,000. She keeps the money in the account at the same scale factor for five years after her last deposit.

    a. Write a polynomial that describes how much money she has in this account at the end of that time.

    b. If $y = 1.07$, how much money does Flora have in her retirement account after the five years? $16,409.73

35. Jeffrey is saving money during his high school years to go on a trip to Egypt after he graduates. The trip costs $3,000. At the end of his freshman year, he deposits $1,200 in a savings account with an annual scale factor of x. At the end of his sophomore year, he deposits $700 in the same account. At the end of his junior year, he deposits $500. It is now the end of his senior year. 35a. $1{,}200x^3 + 700x^2 + 500x$

    a. Write an expression that shows how much money Jeffrey has in his account.

    b. If the savings account pays 4% annual interest, how much more money does he need to afford the trip? $373.05

OBJECTIVE G Determine numbers of permutations. (Lesson 11-7) 36–38. See margin.

In 36–38, Beth has 7 different blouses in her closet.

36. How many different ways can she select a blouse for each of the 7 days of the week?

37. How many different ways can she select a blouse for each of the 5 school days of the week?

38. Suppose Beth wants to wear her favorite blouse on Monday. How many different ways can she select a blouse for each of the remaining 4 school days of the week?

In 39–41, Kyle has recently opened a bank account and is asked to set the 4-digit PIN (Personal Identification Number) for his ATM card, in which each digit can be any number from 0 to 9.

39. How many different ways can Kyle select a PIN? 10,000 different ways

40. If the digits of the PIN must all be different, how many ways can Kyle select the PIN? 5,040 different ways

41. If the first digit of the PIN is *not* allowed to be zero, how many different ways can Kyle a select PIN, assuming the digits cannot be repeated? 4,536 different ways

42. Six guests arrive for a dinner party and are to be seated around a large circular table. How many different ways can the host of the party seat the guests around the table? 720 different ways

43. During a track meet, 9 runners are racing in the 100-yard dash, but only the top 3 runners receive an award. How many different ways are there for the top 3 runners to place? 504 different ways

Additional Answers

28. Answers vary. Sample answer: x^5

29. Answers vary. Sample answer:
    $xy^3z + 3y + 9$

36. 5,040 different ways

37. 2,520 different ways

38. 360 different ways

44a. chocolate A: 30 people, chocolate B: 30 people

OBJECTIVE H Use a chi-square statistic to determine whether or not statistics support a conclusion. (Lesson 11-8)

44. Sixty people were surveyed in a taste test of two types of chocolate. 26 people preferred chocolate A and 34 people preferred chocolate B.

a. If the chocolates were equally tasty, what would be the expected numbers of preference for each chocolate?

b. Calculate the chi-square statistic for this situation using the actual numbers and the expected numbers from Part a. **1.0667**

c. Use the chi-square table on page 699. Does the evidence support the fact that chocolate B is preferred to chocolate A? Explain why or why not. **See margin.**

45. A company was open only Monday through Friday. Because it was not open Saturday or Sunday, it expected that it would get about the same amount of mail each day Tuesday through Friday, but three times this amount on Monday. However, some people thought there was too much mail coming on Monday. When the numbers of pieces of mail for each day for a few weeks were totaled, here were the numbers on each day.

Day	Mon.	Tues.	Wed.	Thurs.	Fri.
Pieces of Mail	122	30	41	35	27

a. How many pieces of mail did the company expect each day? **See margin.**

b. Calculate the chi-square statistic for this situation using the actual numbers and the expected numbers from Part a. **5.523**

c. Use the chi-square table on page 699. Does the evidence support the company's expectations on how much mail to expect? Justify your answer.

See margin.

46. A large factory believes that its floor manager is becoming careless towards the end of his shift each day. Below is a table that shows the hour of his shift and the number of accidents that occurred during that hour.

Hour	1	2	3	4	5	6	7	8
Accidents	5	4	4	7	9	8	11	10

a. If the factory were to have an equal number of accidents each hour, find the expected number. **7.25 accidents per hour**

b. Calculate the chi-square statistic for this situation using the actual numbers and the expected number from Part a. **7.1**

c. Use the chi-square table on page 699. Does the evidence support the factory's belief about the floor manager? Justify your answer.

No, the evidence suggests that the increase of accidents is within the realm of random chance.

REPRESENTATIONS Pictures, graphs, or objects that illustrate concepts

OBJECTIVE I Represent polynomials by areas. (Lessons 11-3, 11-5, 11-6)

47. a. Write the area of the largest rectangle below as the sum of 4 terms.
$ab + 2a + 6b + 12$

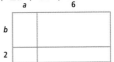

b. Write the area of the largest rectangle as the product of 2 binomials.
$(a + 6)(b + 2)$

c. Are the answers to Parts a and b equal? **Yes, the answers are equal.**

48. Represent $(n + m)(p + q)$ using areas of rectangles. **See margin.**

Additional Answers

44c. The evidence does not support that chocolate B is preferred to chocolate A, because a chi-square value of 1.0667 for 2 events has a probability of greater than 0.1, meaning it is likely the deviation from the expected numbers of preference is due to random chance.

45a. The company expected 36 pieces of mail each day Tuesday through Friday and 109 pieces on Monday.

45c. There is no evidence for the belief that there was too much mail coming on Monday. The probability of a chi-square value of 5.523 for 5 events is greater than 0.1, so it is likely the deviation from the expected amount of mail was due to random chance.

49. a. What polynomial multiplication is represented by the area of the largest rectangle below? $3x(2x + 1)$

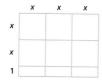

x x x

x

x

1

b. What is the product in standard form? $6x^2 + 3x$

50. Show the product $(3x + 1)^2$ using areas of rectangles. Write your answer in standard form. $9x^2 + 6x + 1$; See students' work.

51. Show a factorization of $3x^2 + 9x$ by rearranging these tiles into a different rectangle. **See margin.**

x x^2 x^2 x^2 x x x x x x x x x

x   x   x   1 1 1 1 1 1 1 1 1

52. Show $4x^2 + 4x + 1 = (2x + 1)^2$ by rearranging these tiles into a square with sides $2x + 1$.

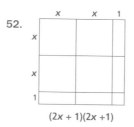

x x^2 x^2 x^2 x^2 x x x x

x   x   x   x   1 1 1 1

1

52.

x   x   1

x

x

1

$(2x + 1)(2x + 1)$

Assessment

Evaluation The *Assessment Resources* provide five forms of the Chapter 11 Test. Forms A and B present parallel versions of a short-answer format. Form C consists of four to six short-response questions that cover the SPUR objectives from Chapter 11. Form D offers performance assessment that covers a subset (or even just one) of the SPUR objectives for the chapter. The fifth type of test is a Chapter 11 Test, Cumulative Form. About 50% of this test covers Chapter 11, and the remaining 50% covers the previous 10 chapters evenly.

Feedback After students have taken the test for Chapter 11 and you have scored the results, return the tests to students for discussion. Class discussion on the questions that caused trouble for most students can be very effective in identifying and clarifying misunderstandings. You might want to have them note the items they missed and work either in groups or at home to correct them. It is important for students to receive feedback on every chapter test, and we recommend that students see and correct their mistakes before proceeding too far into the next chapter.

Additional Answers

48.

n   m

p

q

51. $3x(x + 3)$

x   x   x

x

1

1

1

More Work with Quadratics

Chapter Overview

	Local Standards	Pacing (in days)		
		Average	Advanced	Block
12-1 Graphing $y - k = a(x - h)^2$ G Solve problems involving areas and perimeters of rectangles that lead to quadratic functions or equations. H Graph quadratic functions whose equations are given in vertex form.		1	1	0.5
12-2 Completing the Square A Complete the square on a quadratic expression. I Find the vertex of a parabola whose equation is given in standard form.		1	0.5	0.5
12-3 The Factored Form of a Quadratic Function J Graph quadratic functions whose equations are given in factored form.		1	1	0.75
QUIZ 1		0.5	0.5	0.25
12-4 Factoring $x^2 + bx + c$ B Factor quadratic expressions of the form $x^2 + bx + c$ and $ax^2 + bx + c$. E Determine whether a quadratic polynomial can be factored over the integers.		1	1	0.5
12-5 Factoring $ax^2 + bx + c$ B Factor quadratic expressions of the form $x^2 + bx + c$ and $ax^2 + bx + c$. E Determine whether a quadratic polynomial can be factored over the integers.		1	0.5	0.5
12-6 Which Quadratic Expressions Are Factorable? E Determine whether a quadratic polynomial can be factored over the integers.		1	1	0.75
QUIZ 2		0.5	0.5	0.25
12-7 Graphs of Polynomial Functions of Higher Degree C Find the product of three or more binomials. F Apply the Factor Theorem.		1	1	0.5
12-8 Factoring and Rational Expressions D Use factoring to write rational expressions in lowest terms.		1	1	0.5
Self-Test		1	1	0.5
Chapter Review		2	2	1
Test		1	1	0.5
TOTAL		13	12	7.0

Technology Resources

Teacher's Assessment Assistant, Ch. 12

Electronic Teacher's Edition, Ch. 12

Differentiated Options Universal Access

	Accommodating the Learner	Vocabulary Development	Ongoing Assessment	Materials
12-1	pp. 715, 716		oral, p. 722	graphing calculator, computer with graphing software
12-2	p. 724		written, p. 728	graphing calculator, Computer Algebra System (CAS)
12-3	pp. 731, 733	p. 732	group, p. 735	graphing calculator, Computer Algebra System (CAS)
12-4	p. 738	p. 739	written, p. 741	graphing calculator, Computer Algebra System (CAS)
12-5	pp. 743, 744		written, p. 747	graphing calculator
12-6	pp. 749, 750		written, p. 753	scientific or graphing calculator, Computer Algebra System (CAS)
12-7	pp. 756, 757		oral, p. 760	graphing calculator, Computer Algebra System (CAS)
12-8	pp. 762, 763	p. 763	group, p. 767	graphing calculator, Computer Algebra System (CAS)

Objectives

Ⓢkills	Lessons	Self-Test Questions	Chapter Review Questions
A Complete the square on a quadratic expression.	12-2	5	1–4
B Factor quadratic expressions of the form $x^2 + bx + c$ and $ax^2 + bx + c$.	12-4, 12-5	1–3	5–12
C Find the product of three or more binomials.	12-7	14	13–16
D Use factoring to write rational expressions in lowest terms.	12-8	6	17–21

Ⓟroperties			
E Determine whether a quadratic polynomial can be factored over the integers.	12-4, 12-5, 12-6	4, 16	22–27
F Apply the Factor Theorem.	12-7	8, 17	28–32

Ⓤses			
G Solve problems involving areas and perimeters of rectangles that lead to quadratic functions or equations.	12-1	9, 15	33–38

Ⓡepresentations			
H Graph quadratic functions whose equations are given in vertex form.	12-1	12, 18	39–42
I Find the vertex of a parabola whose equation is given in standard form.	12-2	10, 11	43–50
J Graph quadratic functions whose equations are given in factored form.	12-3	7, 13	51–54

Resource Masters Chapter 12

Resource Master 1, Graph Paper (page 2), can be used as needed. **Resource Master 2, Four-Quadrant Graph Paper** (page 3) can be used with Lessons 12-1, 12-3 through 12-5, 12-7, and 12-8.

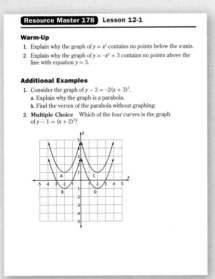

Resource Master 178 Lesson 12-1

Warm-Up

1. Explain why the graph of $y = x^2$ contains no points below the x-axis.
2. Explain why the graph of $y = -x^2 + 3$ contains no points above the line with equation $y = 3$.

Additional Examples

1. Consider the graph of $y - 3 = -2(x + 3)^2$.
   a. Explain why the graph is a parabola.
   b. Find the vertex of the parabola without graphing.
2. **Multiple Choice** Which of the four curves is the graph of $y - 1 = (x + 2)^2$?

Resource Master for Lesson 12-1

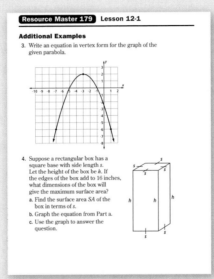

Resource Master 179 Lesson 12-1

Additional Examples

3. Write an equation in vertex form for the graph of the given parabola.

4. Suppose a rectangular box has a square base with side length s. Let the height of the box be h. If the edges of the box add to 16 inches, what dimensions of the box will give the maximum surface area?
   a. Find the surface area SA of the box in terms of s.
   b. Graph the equation from Part a.
   c. Use the graph to answer the question.

Resource Master for Lesson 12-1

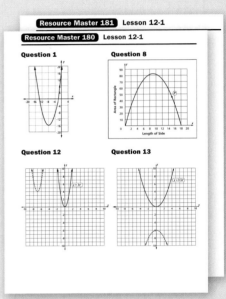

Resource Master 181 Lesson 12-1

Resource Master 180 Lesson 12-1

Question 1

Question 8

Question 12

Question 13

Resource Masters for Lesson 12-1

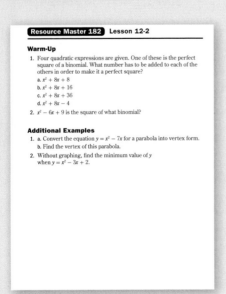

Resource Master 182 Lesson 12-2

Warm-Up

1. Four quadratic expressions are given. One of these is the perfect square of a binomial. What number has to be added to each of the others in order to make it a perfect square?
   a. $x^2 + 8x + 8$
   b. $x^2 + 8x + 16$
   c. $x^2 + 8x + 36$
   d. $x^2 + 8x - 4$
2. $x^2 - 6x + 9$ is the square of what binomial?

Additional Examples

1. a. Convert the equation $y = x^2 - 7x$ for a parabola into vertex form.
   b. Find the vertex of this parabola.
2. Without graphing, find the minimum value of y when $y = x^2 - 3x + 2$.

Resource Master for Lesson 12-2

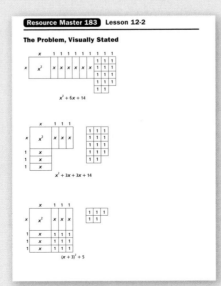

Resource Master 183 Lesson 12-2

The Problem, Visually Stated

$x^2 + 6x + 14$

$x^2 + 3x + 3x + 14$

$(x + 3)^2 + 5$

Resource Master for Lesson 12-2

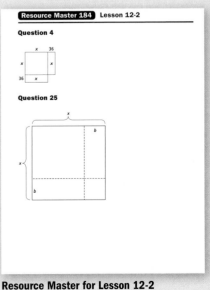

Resource Master 184 Lesson 12-2

Question 4

Question 25

Resource Master for Lesson 12-2

Resource Master 185 — Lesson 12-3

Warm-Up

In 1–4, graph these quadratic functions. Use the window $-10 \le x \le 10$, $-40 \le y \le 40$.

1. $y = (x + 6)(3 - x)$
2. $y = (2x - 6)(x + 6)$
3. $y = (3x + 18)(x - 3)$
4. $y = (x + 6)(x - 6)$
5. Three of the four have the same x-intercepts. How could you tell before even graphing?

Additional Examples

1. Consider the equation $y = (x - 3)(x + 2)$.
   a. Find the x-intercepts of its graph.
   b. Graph the equation.
2. a. Find the x-intercepts of the graph of $y = (2x + 3)(4x - 1)$.
   b. Find the vertex of the parabola.

Resource Master for Lesson 12-3

Resource Master 186 — Lesson 12-3

Activity 1

r_1	r_2	$f(x) = (x - r_1)(x - r_2)$	Points of intersection of graph and x-axis
5	2	$f(x) = (x - 5)(x - 2)$	(? , 0) and (? , 0)
−4	−3		
0	−1		
3	3		
		$f(x) = (x + 2)(x - 4)$	
		$f(x) = (x + 5)(x + 5)$	

Activity 2

a	r_1	r_2	$f(x) = a(x - r_1)(x - r_2)$	Does the parabola open up or down?
2	2	−3	$f(x) = 2(x - 2)(x + 3)$	
−1	−4.1	5		
5	−6	−6		up
−3	−5	0		

Resource Master for Lesson 12-3

Resource Master 187 — Lesson 12-4

Warm-Up

In 1–4, find two integers whose sum is b and whose product is c.

1. $b = 18$, $c = 45$
2. $b = 36$, $c = 203$
3. $b = -2$, $c = -3$
4. $b = 1$, $c = -72$
5. Find two numbers whose sum is 0 and whose product is 10.

Additional Examples

1. Factor $x^2 + 7x + 12$.
2. Factor $x^2 - 17x + 42$.
3. Factor $x^2 - 4x - 12$.
4. Factor $p^2 + 6p - 7$.

Resource Master for Lesson 12-4

Resource Master 188 — Lesson 12-4

Example 2

Product is −30	Sum of Factors
−1, 30	29
−2, ?	
−3, ?	
−5, ?	
−6, ?	
−10, ?	
? , ?	
? , ?	

Question 12

x^2 | x

x | 1

x | 1

x | 1

$x + 3$

$x + 1$

Resource Master for Lesson 12-4

Resource Master 189 — Lesson 12-5

Warm-Up

1. Suppose that $8x^2 - 27x - 20 = (dx + e)(fx + g)$ for all values of x. How are d, e, f, and g related to the coefficients 8, −27, and −20?
2. Use the information in Question 1 to determine the values of d, e, f, and g.

Additional Examples

1. Factor $35x^4 + 35x^3 - 420x^2$.
2. Factor $7x^2 - 33x - 10$.
3. Factor $6z^2 + 13z - 5$.
4. Solve $6z^2 + 13z - 5 = 0$.

Question 23

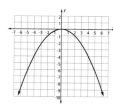

Resource Master for Lesson 12-5

Resource Master 190 — Lesson 12-6

Warm-Up

A quadratic expression of the form $ax^2 + bx + c$ is given. Determine the value of $\sqrt{b^2 - 4ac}$ and tell whether that value is rational, irrational, or not real. If the value is rational, factor the quadratic.

1. $3x^2 + 4x + 5$
2. $17 - 2n^2 + 15n$
3. $9y^2 + 12y + 4$
4. $25z^2 - 25z - 25$

Additional Examples

1. Is $10x^2 - x - 24$ factorable into polynomials with integer coefficients?
2. Is the polynomial $5x^2 - 1 - 3x$ factorable?
3. What can be learned by applying the Discriminant Theorem to the quadratic equation $x^2 - 8 = 0$?
4. Solve $p^2 - 4p + 7 = 0$ by any method.

Activity

Trial	a	b	c	$ax^2 + bx + c$	Factorable?
1	2	−3	7	$2x^2 - 3x + 7$	Prime
2					
3					

Resource Master for Lesson 12-6

Resource Master 191 — Lesson 12-7
Resource Master 192 — Lesson 12-7

Warm-Up

The quadratic equation $8x^2 - 14x - 15 = 0$ has rational solutions.

1. Find the solutions.
2. Use the solutions to indicate, without graphing, where the graph of $y = 8x^2 - 14x - 15$ intersects the x-axis.
3. Check your answer to Question 2 by graphing.

Additional Examples

1. A polynomial function P has x-intercepts at −2, 4, 3, 21 and −30. What is a possible equation for the function?
2. Rewrite the polynomial $r(x) = (x - 3)(3x + 2)(x + 2)^2$ in standard form.

Activity 2

Polynomial	Far Right: Up or Down?	Far Left: Up or Down?	Polynomial	Far Right: Up or Down?	Far Left: Up or Down?
$f(x) = x(x - 3)(x + 7)$			$-f(x)$		
$g(x) = x(x - 3)(x + 7)^2$			$-g(x)$		
$h(x) = x(x - 3)^2(x + 7)^2$			$-h(x)$		
$j(x) = x^2(x - 3)^2(x + 7)^3$			$-j(x)$		

Resource Masters for Lesson 12-7

Resource Master 193 — Lesson 12-7
Resource Master 194 — Lesson 12-7

Question 8

i.

ii.

iii.

iv.

Question 9

Resource Masters for Lesson 12-7

Resource Master 195 — Lesson 12-8

Warm-Up

Write the fraction in lowest terms. Assume variables do not have values that would make the denominator 0.

1. $\frac{23 \cdot 19}{19 \cdot 24}$
2. $\frac{mp}{pq}$
3. $\frac{(2x - 7)(x + 4)}{(x + 4)(3x - 1)}$
4. $\frac{ab^2}{bcd}$
5. $\frac{3x - 6}{2x^2 - 3x - 2}$

Additional Examples

1. Write $\frac{6x^2 - x - 2}{3x^2 + x - 2}$ in lowest terms.
2. Simplify the expression $\frac{2x^4 - 6x^3 - 20x^2 + 48x}{4x^4 - 4x^3 - 88x^2 + 160x}$.
3. Write $\frac{2}{x} - \frac{3}{y}$ as a single rational expression.
4. Write $\frac{3}{x^2 + x} + \frac{4 + x}{x^2 - 1}$ as a single rational expression.

Question 21

0.3x	?
x	

x | 0.3x

Resource Master for Lesson 12-8

Pacing

Each lesson in this chapter is designed to be covered in one day. At the end of the chapter, you should plan to spend 1 day to review the Self-Test, 1 to 2 days for the Chapter Review, and 1 day for a test. You may wish to spend a day on projects, and possibly a day is needed for quizzes. This chapter should therefore take 11 to 14 days. We strongly advise you to not spend more than 18 days on this chapter.

Using Pages 712–713

In Chapter 9, students graphed quadratic functions whose equations were given in the standard form $y = ax^2 + bx + c$. In this chapter, students will deal with two new forms: the vertex form $y - k = a(x - h)^2$ and the factored form $y = a(x - r_1)(x - r_2)$. Each form has its advantages. Consider the intercepts and vertex of the graph of an equation in each form:

form	intercepts	vertex of parabola
standard form $y = ax^2 + bx + c$	$\dfrac{-b \pm \sqrt{b^2 - 4ac}}{2a}$	$\left(-\dfrac{b}{2a}, \dfrac{4ac - b^2}{4a}\right)$
vertex form $y - k = a(x - h)^2$	$\pm\sqrt{\dfrac{-k}{a}} + h$	(h, k)
factored form $y = a(x - r_1)(x - r_2)$	r_1, r_2	$\left(\dfrac{r_1 + r_2}{2}, a\left(\dfrac{r_1 + r_2}{2}\right)^2 + b\left(\dfrac{r_1 + r_2}{2}\right) + c\right)$

Comparison of these forms shows that if a quadratic equation can be factored, the factored form is the easiest form from which to see the intercepts (and thus the solutions). From the vertex form, as its name suggests, the vertex of the graph is easily found.

▶ Contents

In writing it is important to know and use synonyms for the same idea. A picture may be beautiful or pretty, or it may be dazzling or brilliant, or it may be dull or drab or gray. Synonyms help convey ideas more clearly and one word may fit a situation just a little better than another.

Equivalent expressions in mathematics are like synonyms in writing. Equivalent expressions are often classified by their form.

Here are four ways to write the same number:

2,048	base 10
$2 \cdot 10^3 + 4 \cdot 10^1 + 8 \cdot 1$	expanded form
2^{11}	exponential form
$2.048 \cdot 10^3$	scientific notation

There are occasions when each of these forms is most appropriate or most helpful to understanding a situation. Base 10 is our normal compact way of writing numbers. Expanded form shows the meaning of base 10. Exponential form arises in many counting situations and situations of growth. Scientific notation is useful when comparing numbers that differ greatly in size.

Chapter 12 Overview

This chapter deals with a traditional algebra skill: using completing the square and factoring to solve quadratic equations. The approach utilizes graphing and CAS technology to provide insights that in the past would be difficult to grasp.

This chapter has two main themes: graphing and factoring. Continuing the work of Chapter 9 on quadratic functions,

Lesson 12-1 uses graphing technology to deal with the square form $y - k = a(x - h)^2$ of a parabola. This form provides the foundation for completing the square, the skill discussed in Lesson 12-2.

(continued on next page)

Equivalent equations are also like synonyms. Consider the line that contains the two points (2, 9) and (8, 11). Three equivalent equations for this line are in forms that you saw in Chapter 6.

$y = \frac{1}{3}x + \frac{25}{3}$ slope-intercept form

$x - 3y = -25$ standard form

$y - 9 = \frac{1}{3}(x - 2)$ point-slope form

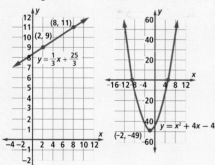

In this chapter, we return to quadratic equations and parabolas. Here are three equivalent equations for the parabola that is graphed at the left.

$y = x^2 + 4x - 45$ standard form

$y + 49 = (x + 2)^2$ vertex form

$y = (x - 5)(x + 9)$ factored form

In Chapter 9, you saw that standard form enables you to use the Quadratic Formula to find the x-intercepts of the graph. Standard form also is very useful for solving equations. The vertex form, which opens the chapter, lets you quickly find the vertex of the parabola. This is useful for graphing and for obtaining the minimum (or maximum) value of y. The factored form, which you will study later in this chapter, shows the x-intercepts of the graph.

713

Lessons 12-3 through 12-6 deal with factoring quadratics. Activities in these lessons show students patterns in factoring that enable them to easily determine when a quadratic polynomial can be factored. Lesson 12-7 provides a glimpse into the graphs of polynomial functions of higher degree and connects their behavior with factoring. Lesson 12-8 provides reasons for factoring other than the solving of polynomial equations. If time is an issue, Lesson 12-7 can be omitted.

Lesson 12-1 · Graphing $y - k = a(x - h)^2$

Vocabulary

vertex form of an equation for a parabola

GOAL

Understand that the graph of a function with equation $y - k = a(x - h)^2$ is a parabola with vertex (h, k).

SPUR Objectives

G Solve problems involving areas and perimeters of rectangles that lead to quadratic functions or equations.

H Graph quadratic functions whose equations are given in vertex form.

Materials/Resources

· Lesson Master 12-1A or 12-1B
· Resource Masters 2 and 178–181
· Graphing calculator
· Computer with graphing software

HOMEWORK

Suggestions for Assignment

- Questions 1–25
- Question 26 (extra credit)
- Reading Lesson 12-2
- Covering the Ideas 12-2

Local Standards

1 Warm-Up

1. Explain why the graph of $y = x^2$ contains no points below the x-axis.

   Points below the x-axis have negative coordinates. The value of x^2 must be either positive or 0, so y cannot be negative.

2. Explain why the graph of $y = -x^2 + 3$ contains no points above the line with equation $y = 3$.

   The value of $-x^2$ must be negative or 0, so its maximum value is 0. Add 3 to that, and the maximum value is 3.

▶ **BIG IDEA** The graph of the equation $y - k = a(x - h)^2$ is a parabola whose vertex can be easily found.

In Chapter 9, you graphed many parabolas with equations in the *standard form* $y = ax^2 + bx + c$. When an equation is in this form, the vertex of the parabola is not obvious. In Activity 1, you are asked to examine some parabolas with equations in the form $y - k = a(x - h)^2$. When an equation is in this form, its graph is a parabola whose vertex can be found rather easily.

Activity 1

In 1–6, set a graphing calculator for the window $-15 \le x \le 15$, $-10 \le y \le 10$.

a. Graph the equation on your calculator. (You will have to solve the equation for y if it is not already solved for y.) Copy the graph by hand onto your paper. **1–6. See Additional Answers on page T88.**

b. Label the vertex with its coordinates.

c. Draw the axis of symmetry as a dotted line. Label the axis of symmetry with its equation.

  1. $y - 4 = (x - 3)^2$ **2.** $y + 3 = (x - 5)^2$
  3. $y - 1 = (x + 4)^2$ **4.** $y + 8 = -(x + 6)^2$
  5. $y - 12 = -(x - 4)^2$ **6.** $y = (x - 0.35)^2$

7. Look back at your graphs for Questions 1–6 and the equations that produced them. Explain how to look at an equation like $y - k = (x - h)^2$ to help determine the vertex of its graph.

   7. The vertex is (h, k).

In 8 and 9, each graph is of an equation of the form $y - k = (x - h)^2$. The vertex and axis of symmetry of the parabola are given. Use what you learned in Questions 1–7.

a. Write an equation for the graph.

b. Check your equation by graphing it on your calculator. Do you get the graph you expected?

Mental Math

Suppose $b(x) = 2|x| - 4$. Evaluate

a. $b(5)$. **6**

b. $b(-5)$. **6**

c. $b(5) - b(-5)$. **0**

d. $\dfrac{b(5)}{b(-5)}$. **1**

Background

A *parabola* can be defined geometrically as the set of points that are equidistant from a given point F (*the focus*) and a given line d (*the directrix*). (Another geometric definition is the intersection of a cone and a plane parallel to the edge of the cone.) We can derive an equation for one specific parabola, but the argument is similar for any parabola with a horizontal directrix.

If the point F is $(0, 1)$ and the directrix is $y = -1$, then the distance of (x, y) from $(0, 1)$ equals the distance of (x, y) from the line $y = -1$. The distance of (x, y) from the line $y = -1$ is the same as the distance from (x, y) to $(x, -1)$. So, by the Pythagorean Distance formula,

$$\sqrt{(x - 0)^2 + (y - 1)^2} = \sqrt{(x - x)^2 + (y + 1)^2}.$$

Squaring both sides,

$$(x - 0)^2 + (y - 1)^2 = (y + 1)^2.$$
$$x^2 + y^2 - 2y + 1 = y^2 + 2y + 1$$
$$x^2 = 4y$$

or, equivalently, $\quad y = \tfrac{1}{4}x^2$.

(continued on next page)

8.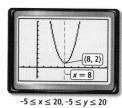

$-5 \le x \le 20, -5 \le y \le 20$

9.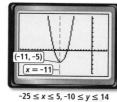

$-25 \le x \le 5, -10 \le y \le 14$

8a. $y - 2 = (x - 8)^2$
8b. Graphs should match.
9a. $y + 5 = (x + 11)^2$
9b. Graphs should match.

Example 1

Consider the graph of $y - 7 = 6(x - 15)^2$.

a. Explain why the graph is a parabola.

b. Find the vertex of this parabola without graphing.

Solution

a. If the equation can be written in the form $y = ax^2 + bx + c$, its graph is a parabola. Work with the given equation to get it into that form.

$y - 7 = 6(x - 15)^2$

$y - 7 = 6(x^2 - 30x + 225)$ Square of a Binomial

$y - 7 = 6x^2 - 180x + 1,350$ Distributive Property

$y = 6x^2 - 180x + 1,357$ Add 7 to both sides.

This equation is of the form $y = ax^2 + bx + c$, with $a = 6$, $b = -180$, and $c = 1,357$, so its graph is a parabola.

b. To find its vertex, examine the original equation $y - 7 = 6(x - 15)^2$. Add 7 to both sides.

$$y = 6(x - 15)^2 + 7$$

Since $(x - 15)^2$ is the square of a real number, $(x - 15)^2$ cannot be negative. The least value $(x - 15)^2$ can have is 0, and that occurs when $x = 15$. Thus the least value that $6(x - 15)^2$ can have is 0, and the least value that $6(x - 15)^2 + 7$ can have is 7. All of these least values occur when $x = 15$. As a consequence, the vertex of the parabola is at the point on the parabola with x-coordinate 15. When $x = 15$, substitution shows that $y = 7$. **So the vertex is (15, 7).** Since 7 is the least value of y, the parabola must open up.

Check You should graph the equation $y - 7 = 6(x - 15)^2$ with a graphing calculator, making sure that the window contains the point (15, 7). (You will likely have to solve the equation for y before graphing.)

The argument in Example 1 can be repeated in general. It demonstrates the theorem on the next page.

If the focus is $\left(0, \frac{1}{4a}\right)$ and the directrix $y = -\frac{1}{4a}$, then an equation of the parabola is $y = ax^2$.

The move from $y = ax^2$ to $y - k = a(x - h)^2$ replaces x with $x - h$ and replaces y with $y - k$. This translates the parabola h units to the right and k units up. Thus the parabola with equation $y - k = a(x - h)^2$ has vertex (h, k), focus $\left(h, k + \frac{1}{4a}\right)$ and directrix with equation $y = k - \frac{1}{4a}$.

Accommodating the Learner ⬇

Some students will struggle with the transition from $y + 2 = y - (-2) = (y - k)$, so $k = -2$. Take extra time to practice this step with students.

2 Teaching

Notes on the Lesson

Activity 1 This activity deals with equations of the form $y - k = a(x - h)^2$ where $a = 1$. The graph of every equation of this type is a parabola with vertex (h, k). The value of a determines the size of the parabola; a is the amount the parabola goes up (if a is positive) or down (if a is negative) from the vertex as x goes 1 unit to the right or left from the vertex.

You may wish to do Question 1 of the Activity with your class, and then Question 2 with the class (to deal with $y + 3$), before letting students do Questions 3–7. Make sure that students understand Questions 1–7 before they go on to Questions 8 and 9. Students will probably need to add k to both sides of the equation before graphing.

Example 1 The key idea in this lesson is that the graph of $y - k = a(x - h)^2$ is a parabola with vertex (h, k). While this fact can be memorized, it is far better if students have some justification for it. Example 1 indicates why the y values of ordered pairs satisfying this equation cannot be less than $-k$ when a is positive. Generally, if a is positive, then the minimum value of $a(x - h)^2$ is 0 when $x = h$. Because $y = a(x - h)^2 + k$, the minimum value of y is k, again occurring when $x = h$.

Notes on the Activity

Activity 1 Decide if you wish students to estimate the vertex or to use the MIN or MAX function on their calculators to find the vertex. Before they begin, ask students to pay careful attention to positive and negative signs. By the end of the activity, they should be able to recognize the pattern for finding the coordinates of the vertex and the direction the parabola opens.

Additional Example

Example 1 Consider the graph of $y - 3 = -2(x + 3)^2$.

a. Explain why the graph is a parabola. The equation is of the form $y = ax^2 + bx + c$ with $a = -2$, $b = -12$, and $c = -16$, so its graph is a parabola.

b. Find the vertex of the parabola without graphing. $(-3, 3)$

Notes on the Lesson

Example 2 Students often have difficulty dealing with forms that involve subtraction. You might ask what the value of $y - k$ is when $k = -3$. $(y + 3)$ Check that by substituting 20 for y. So what is the value of $y - k$ when $k = -3$ and $y = 20$: Is it $y + 3$? Is it 23? The answer to all of these is yes.

Activity 2 The purpose of this activity is to show the effects of a, h, and k on the graph of $y - k = a(x - h)^2$. These parameters have an effect on the size and location of the parabola. The parameter a affects the size of the parabola—that is, how much you can see in a calculator window of a particular size. (Many people think it affects the shape of the parabola, but that is just an illusion; all parabolas have the same shape.) The parameters h and k give the location of the vertex.

Additional Example

Example 2 Multiple choice Which of the four curves is the graph of $y - 1 = (x + 2)^2$?

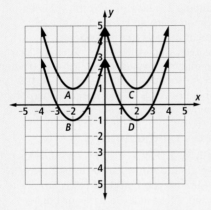

The vertex is $(-2, 1)$, so the parabola is choice A.

Notes on the Activity

Activity 2 To help students retain and understand the patterns that they recognize, organize students into pairs. Then, before they do Steps 4, 5, and 6, ask them to predict what the corresponding values for a will do to the function. They should write their prediction for each step, compare it with their partner's prediction, and then perform the step to check their answer. Then they should write a mathematical justification for each step.

Parabola Vertex Theorem

The graph of all ordered pairs (x, y) satisfying an equation of the form $y - k = a(x - h)^2$ is a parabola with vertex (h, k).

▶ **QY**

Give the vertex of the parabola with equation $y - 8 = 3(x + 15)^2$.

STOP QY

The form $y - k = a(x - h)^2$ is called the **vertex form of an equation for a parabola** because you can easily find the vertex from the equation.

Example 2

Multiple Choice Which of the four curves at the right is the graph of $y + 3 = (x - 4)^2$?

Solution Rewrite $y + 3 = (x - 4)^2$ so it corresponds to the general equation $y - k = a(x - h)^2$.

$$y - -3 = (x - 4)^2$$

The vertex is given by (h, k). So the vertex of the graph is $(4, -3)$. The parabola with this vertex is choice D.

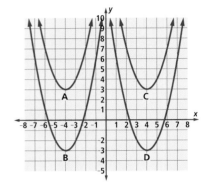

Activity 2

Use a dynamic graphing system to do the following.

Step 1 Create three sliders that include positive and negative numbers.
Name one slider a. (Or create a parameter a that is based on the slider.)
Name one slider h. (Or create a parameter h that is based on the slider.)
Name one slider k. (Or create a parameter k that is based on the slider.)

Step 2 Move the sliders so $a = 1$, $h = 0$, and $k = 0$.

Step 3 Create the equation $y - k = a(x - h)^2$, using the parameters for a, h, and k. Plot the equation. The graph should show $y - 0 = 1(x - 0)^2$ or $y = x^2$.

  a. Make a table of values for $-3 \leq x \leq 3$.

  b. Find the differences between the y-coordinates as the x-coordinates increase by 1. Does this pattern look familiar?

Step 3a.

x	y
-3	9
-2	4
-1	1
0	0
1	1
2	4
3	9

3b. -5, -3, -1, 1, 3, 5; these are consecutive odd numbers.

Accommodating the Learner ⬆

Ask students to demonstrate that $y - k = a(x - h)^2$ is a parabola by rewriting it in standard form $y = ax^2 + bx + c$. Then have them apply the Quadratic Formula to determine the x-intercept of the graph of the equation. $y = ax^2 - 2ahx + ah^2 + k$; $x = h \pm \sqrt{-k}$

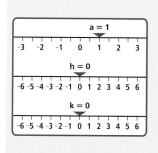

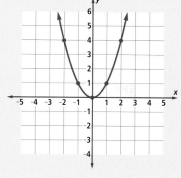

$$y - k = a(x - h)^2$$
$$y - 0 = 1(x - 0)^2$$

Step 4 Slowly move the *a* slider from 1 to 0.   **4–5. See margin.**

  a. What happens to the graph for $0 < a < 1$?

  b. Move the *a* slider to 0.5. Make a table of values for $-3 < x < 3$. How do the *y*-coordinates compare to those in the table in Step 3?

  c. Find the differences between the *y*-coordinates as the *x*-coordinates increase by 1. How do the differences compare to those in Step 3?

Step 5 Now move the *a* slider to the right of 1.

  a. What happens to the graph when $a > 1$?

  b. Move the *a* slider to 2. Make a table of values for $-3 < x < 3$. How do the *y*-coordinates compare to those in the table in Step 3?

  c. Find the differences between the *y*-coordinates as the *x*-coordinates increase by 1. How do the differences compare to those in Step 3?

Step 6 Is the effect *a* has on the differences in the *y*-coordinates of $y = ax^2 + bx + c$ the same as or different from the effect *a* has on the differences in the *y*-coordinates of $y - k = a(x - h)^2$? Explain.

Step 7 Write a prediction of what you think happens to the graph when *a* is between –1 and 0.

Write a prediction of what you think happens to the graph when *a* is less than –1.

Step 8 Move the *a* slider to test your predictions. Were you correct? Explain how your predictions in Step 7 are similar to and different from what occurred in Steps 4 and 5.

Step 9 Sketch what you think the graph of each function will look like.

$$y - 5 = 2(x - 1)^2 \quad y + 3 = 0.25(x - 2)^2 \quad y = -3(x + 4)^2$$

(continued on next page)
                    See margin.

Step 6. Both changes shift the graph in similar ways; however, the difference is not necessarily the same. The value of *a* affects more than just one term in the second equation.

Step 7. Answers vary. Sample answer: The parabola will be reflected over the *x*-axis. When *a* is between –1 and 0, the parabola will open down and be wide. When $a < -1$, the parabola will open down and be narrow.

Step 8. This is simply flipping the graph over the *x*-axis, where the absolute value of *a* determines the level of magnification.

Graphing $y - k = a(x - h)^2$ **717**

Note-Taking Tips

Ask students to write a summary of the results of each Activity in their notes for future reference. This will help them synthesize what they have learned.

Additional Answers

Step 5b. These are twice as large.

x	y
−3	18
−2	8
−1	2
0	0
1	2
2	8
3	18

Step 5c. −10, −6, −2, 2, 6, 10; these are twice as large.

Step 9. $y - 5 = 2(x - 1)^2$

$y + 3 = 0.25(x - 2)^2$

$y = -3(x + 4)^2$

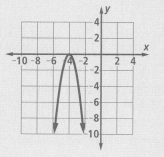

Additional Answers

Activity 2

Step 4a. The parabola gets wider as *a* approaches 0.

Step 4b. They are half as large.

x	y
−3	4.5
−2	2
−1	0.5
0	0
1	0.5
2	2
3	4.5

Step 4c. −2.5, −1.5, −0.5, 0.5, 1.5, 2.5; they are half as large.

Step 5a. The parabola gets narrower as *a* increases.

12 1

Notes on the Lesson

Example 3 A way of dealing with the form $(x - h)^2$ is to pick a value of h, like 100, and ask for the values of $(x - h)^2$ when $x = 97, 98, 99, 100, 101, 102,$ and 103. Then students should see that the values are symmetric—a value of x a certain amount below 100 gives the same value of $(x - h)^2$ as a value that amount above 100. This shows why a graph of $y = (x - 100)^2$ would be symmetric about $x = 100$.

Example 4 Part c is important to discuss. Draw rectangles with sides of length x and $12 - x$. The area of the rectangle is $x(12 - x)$, or $12x - x^2$. Show by substitution that the rectangle with maximum area occurs when $x = 6$ and that values of x on either side of 6 give the same area.

Additional Examples

Example 3 Write an equation in vertex form for the graph of the given parabola.

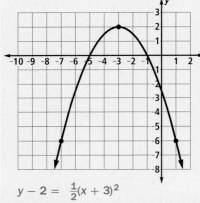

$y - 2 = \frac{1}{2}(x + 3)^2$

Example 4 Suppose a rectangular box has a square base with side length s. Let the height of the box be h. If the edges of the box add to 16 inches, what dimensions of the box will give the maximum surface area?

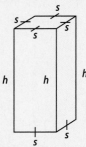

a. Find the surface area SA of the box in terms of s.

b. Graph the equation from Part a.

c. Use the graph to answer the question.

(continued on next page)

Step 10 Check your predictions from Step 9 by moving sliders a, h, and k to match the values in the function.

Step 11 Write a possible equation in vertex form for the graph of the parabola at the right.
Step 11. Answers vary. Sample answer: $y - 4 = -0.8(x + 2)^2$

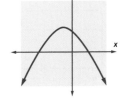

Example 3

Write an equation in vertex form for the graph of the parabola at the right.

Solution 1 First locate the vertex and substitute it into the vertex form of an equation for a parabola, $y - k = a(x - h)^2$.

The vertex is at $(4, -1)$, so $y - -1 = a(x - 4)^2$.

Next find the value of a. Compare the pattern in the change of the y-coordinates as the x-coordinates change by 1 in the graph to that of $y = x^2$.

Pattern change in y-coordinates for $y = x^2$: 1, 3, 5, ...

Pattern change in y-coordinates for graph: 2, 6, 10, ...

The pattern change for the graph is double the pattern change of $y = x^2$, so $a = 2$.

The equation for the parabola is $y + 1 = 2(x - 4)^2$.

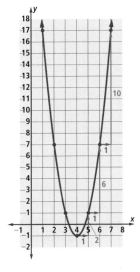

Solution 2 As in Solution 1, first locate the vertex and substitute it into the vertex form of an equation for a parabola, $y - k = a(x - h)^2$.

The vertex is at $(4, -1)$, so $y - -1 = a(x - 4)^2$.

Next find the value of a. Pick a point on the graph that is not the vertex and substitute it into the equation. Then solve for a. We pick point $(6, 7)$.

$$7 + 1 = a(6 - 4)^2$$
$$8 = a(2)^2$$
$$8 = 4a$$
$$2 = a$$

Substitute a and the vertex into the equation.

The equation for the parabola is $y + 1 = 2(x - 4)^2$.

Check Pick a point on the graph and substitute it into the equation. We'll use the point $(3, 1)$.

$$1 + 1 = 2(3 - 4)^2$$
$$2 = 2(-1)^2$$
$$2 = 2 \cdot 1$$
$$2 = 2 \text{ So it checks.}$$

Problems involving area can lead to parabolas. Consider the following problem.

Example 4

There are many possible rectangles with a perimeter of 24 units. Suppose the length of one side of such a rectangle is L.

a. Find the area A of the rectangle in terms of L.

b. Graph the equation from Part a.

c. Use the graph to determine the maximum area of a rectangle with perimeter of 24 units.

Solutions

a. You know that the perimeter P of a rectangle is given by the formula $P = 2L + 2W$. So in this case, $24 = 2L + 2W$.

Now solve this equation for W.

___?___ = 2W   24 − 2L

Divide both sides by 2.

___?___ = W   12 − L

Since the area $A = LW$, substituting ___?___ for W gives the following formula for A.   12 − L

$A = L$ ___?___ $(12 − L)$

b. Letting $x = L$ and $y = A$, a graph of $y = x(12 − x)$ is shown here. The graph is a parabola because $y = 12x − x^2$ is of the form $y = ax^2 + bx + c$. The only part of the parabola that makes sense in this problem is for values of x between 0 and 12, so we use that window.

c. Each value of y in $y = x(12 − x)$ is the area of a particular rectangle. If $x = L = 2$, then $W = 12 − 2 = 10$ units. The area is $y = 2 \cdot 10 = 20$ units^2. That is, the point $(2, 20)$ on the parabola means that when one side of the rectangle is 2 units, the area of the rectangle is 20 units^2.

If $x = L = 3$, then $W =$ ___?___. The area $y =$ ___?___ = ___?___.
9 units; 3 • 9; 27 units^2
If $x = L = 10$, then $W =$ ___?___. The area $y =$ ___?___ = ___?___.
2 units; 10 • 2; 20 units^2
The maximum value of y is at the vertex of the parabola. From the graph the vertex is $(6, 36)$. So the maximum area of the rectangle is ___?___, occurring when $L =$ ___?___ and $W =$ ___?___, that is, when the rectangle is a square.   36 units^2; 6 units; 6 units

The equation graphed in Example 4 is not in vertex form. That makes it difficult to know the vertex. In Lesson 12-2, you will see how to convert an equation into vertex form.

Graphing $y − k = a(x − h)^2$ **719**

a. You know that the edges must add to 16. Using this, we can obtain the equation _?_ $h +$ _?_ $s = 16$. 4; 8

Now, solve this equation for h.
_?_ $h = 16 − 8s$; $h =$ _?_. 4; 4 − 2s

Because the surface area $SA = 4sh + 2s^2$, substituting _?_ for h gives the following formula for SA.
$SA = 4s($ _?_ $) + 2s^2$ 4 − 2s; 4 − 2s;
$SA =$ _____?_____ $16s − 6s^2$

b. Letting $x = s$ and $y = SA$, a graph of $y = 16x − 6x^2$ is shown here. The graph is a parabola because $y = 16x − 6x^2$ is of the form $y = ax^2 + bx + c$. Because $SA = 6s\left(\frac{8}{3} − s\right)$, the only part of the parabola that makes sense for this problem is for values of x between 0 and $\frac{8}{3}$, so we use that window.

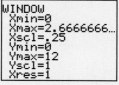

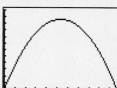

c. Each value of y in $y = 16x − 6x^2$ is the surface area of a particular box.

If $x = s = 1$, then $h = 4 − 2(1) = 2$. The surface area is $y = 4(1)(2) + 2(1)^2 = 10$. That is, the point $(1, 10)$ on the parabola means that when the side length of the base is 1 inch, the surface area of the box is 10 square inches.

If $x = s = 0.5$, then $h =$ _?_. 3
The surface area $y =$ _?_ = _?_
$4(0.5)(3) + 2(0.5)^2$; 6.5

If $x = s = 2$, then $h =$ _?_. 0
The surface area $y =$ _?_ = _?_
$4(2)(0) + 2(2)^2$; 8

The maximum value of y is at the vertex of the parabola. From the graph, the vertex is $\left(1\frac{1}{3}, 10\frac{2}{3}\right)$. So the maximum surface area of the box is _?_, occurring when $s = 1\frac{1}{3}$ in. and $h = 1\frac{1}{3}$ in., that is, when the box is a cube. $10\frac{2}{3}$ in^2

3 Assignment

Recommended Assignment

- Questions 1–25
- Question 26 (extra credit)
- Reading Lesson 12-2
- Covering the Ideas 12-2

Notes on the Questions

Question 2 Make certain that students understand how each part relates to the next.

Question 8 This question mirrors Example 4.

Question 10 This is a hard problem for many students but one that should be discussed, as it shows a skill students will encounter and need in later mathematics courses.

Additional Answers

10b.

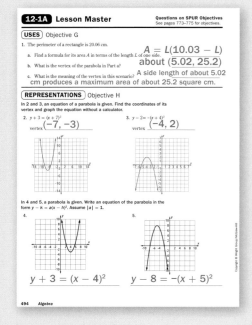

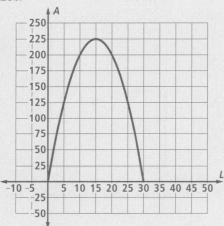

Questions

COVERING THE IDEAS

1. The graph at the right shows a parabola.

   a. What are the coordinates of its vertex? $(-8, -16)$

   b. Give an equation for its axis of symmetry. $x = -8$

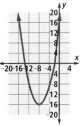

2. Give the minimum value of each expression.

   a. x^2 0   b. $(x + 6)^2$ 0   c. $3(x + 6)^2$ 0   d. $3(x + 6)^2 - 8$ -8

3. Explain why 7 is the maximum value of the expression $-4(x - 5)^2 + 7$.

In 4–7, an equation of a parabola is given.

   a. Find the coordinates of its vertex.

   b. Write an equation for its axis of symmetry.

   c. Tell whether the parabola opens up or down.

4. $y + 8 = -5(x - 9)^2$

5. $y - 21 = 0.2(x - 15)^2$

6. $y - 43 = 8x^2$ a. $(0, 43)$ b. $x = 0$ c. up

7. $y + \frac{1}{2} = -(x + 6)^2$ a. $(-6, -0.5)$ b. $x = -6$ c. down

8. The equation $y = x(18 - x)$ gives the area of a rectangle with perimeter of 36 where x is the length of one of its sides. This equation is graphed at the right.

   a. Give the areas of the three rectangles for which $x = 4$, 5, and 11. 56 units², 65 units², 77 units²

   b. Point P on the graph represents a rectangle. Give the rectangle's side lengths and area. 15 by 3; 45 units²

   c. What is the maximum area of a rectangle with perimeter 36? 81 units²

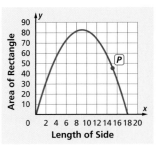

9. Explain the similarities and differences in the graphs of the functions.

   a. $y + 8 = (x - 4)^2$

   b. $y + 8 = 1.25(x - 4)^2$

   c. $y + 8 = 0.75(x - 4)^2$

APPLYING THE MATHEMATICS

10. A rectangle has perimeter 60.

    a. Find a formula for its area A in terms of the length L of one side. $A = L\left(\dfrac{60 - 2L}{2}\right)$

    b. Graph the formula you found in Part a. See margin.

    c. What is the maximum area of this rectangle? 225 units²

11. A parabola has vertex $(-12, 9)$ and contains the point $(-10, 5)$. Give an equation for the parabola. $y - 9 = -(x + 12)^2$

720   More Work with Quadratics

3. Because $(x - 5)^2$ is never negative, $-4(x - 5)^2$ is never positive, and the greatest nonpositive number is 0, and so the greatest value of $-4(x - 5)^2 + 7$ is 7.

4a. $(9, -8)$
4b. $x = 9$
4c. down
5a. $(15, 21)$
5b. $x = 15$
5c. up
9. All 3 graphs have $(4, -8)$ as their vertex, c opens up wider than a, and a opens up wider than b.

Extension

Expand Step 6 of Activity 2 by asking students to create a slider for a in $y = ax^2 + bx + c$. They can then redo Step 4 and Step 5 using this new slider. Then, ask students if there is any relationship between a, b, and c. By rewriting the equation $y - k = a(x - h)^2$ in standard form, they will obtain $y = ax^2 - 2ahx + ah^2 + k$. This will help them recognize that the a in each equation is the same thing, both representing the coefficient of x^2. In addition, they should be able to conclude that $b = -2ah$ and $c = ah^2 + k$. This will help them understand why the x value of the vertex is $h = \dfrac{-b}{2a}$.

In 12 and 13, an equation of the form $y = ax^2$ and its graph are given. A translation image of the parabola is graphed with a dashed curve. Write an equation for the image.

12.

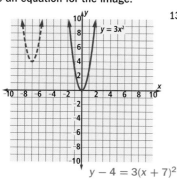

$y = 3x^2$

$y - 4 = 3(x + 7)^2$

13.

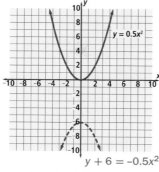

$y = 0.5x^2$

$y + 6 = -0.5x^2$

14. Write an equation for the graph of the parabola at the right.

In 15 and 16, find equations for two different parabolas that fit the description.

15. The vertex is $(5, -18)$ and the parabola opens down.

16. The axis of symmetry is $x = 2$ and the parabola opens up.

In 17 and 18, a graph of a parabola and a point on it are given. Find the coordinates of a second point on the parabola that has the same y-coordinate as the given point.

17.

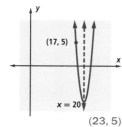

$(17, 5)$

$x = 20$

$(23, 5)$

18.

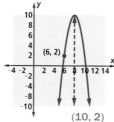

$(6, 2)$

$(10, 2)$

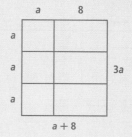

14. $y - 6 = -\frac{1}{2}(x + 2)^2$

15. Answers vary.
Sample answer:
$y + 18 = -(x - 5)^2$
and
$y + 18 = -2(x - 5)^2$

16. Answers vary.
Sample answer:
$y - 5 = (x - 2)^2$
and
$y - 4 = 3(x - 2)^2$

REVIEW

19. Draw rectangles picturing $3a(a + 8) = 3a^2 + 24a$. (**Lesson 11-3**) See margin.

20. The sum of the legs of a right triangle is 34 cm. If the hypotenuse is 26 cm, calculate the length of each of the legs. (**Lessons 10-2, 8-6**) 10 and 24

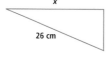

26 cm

x

y

Notes on the Questions

Questions 12 and 13 Students are expected to find the vertex of the parabola from the graph.

Question 14 Students need to use the symmetry of the parabola.

Question 26 Notice that the units of the height of the ball and the distance it travels are different. Students are expected to do this question by finding the vertex of the parabola and substituting the origin into the square form to find the coefficient of x^2. The answer can be checked by graphing or by quadratic regression.

Additional Answers

19. Answers vary. Sample answer:

	a	8
a		
a		
a		

$a + 8$

$3a$

12-1

4 Wrap-Up

Ongoing Assessment

Create several graphs of parabolas to show the class. As you show students each graph, ask them to call out the vertex. Similarly, give students a vertex, and ask them to write the equation of a parabola that has that vertex. Remember that there are many possible equations for a given vertex.

21. Find all values of m that satisfy
$(m^2)^2 - 15m^2 + 36 = 0$. **(Lesson 9-5)**
$m = \pm\sqrt{3}$ or $m = \pm 2\sqrt{3}$

22. Suppose a basketball team wins 9 of its first 11 games during a season. At this rate, how many games would you expect the team to win in a 28-game season? **(Lesson 5-9)**
about 23 games

23. A climber is ascending Mount Kilimanjaro, the highest mountain in Africa. At 9 A.M. the climber is at an elevation of 15,416 feet and at 10:15 A.M. the climber is at an elevation of 16,004 feet. At this rate, when would the climber reach the 19,336-foot summit? **(Lesson 5-5)**
5:20 P.M.

24. Simplify $5\pi \div \frac{4\pi}{3}$. **(Lesson 5-2)** $\frac{15}{4}$

25. Solve the equation or inequality. **(Lessons 4-5, 4-4)**

a. $2x = 3x$ $x = 0$
b. $2x > 3x$ $x < 0$

EXPLORATION

26. Tiger Woods drives golf balls 300 yards before they hit the ground. Suppose one of his drives is 80 feet high at its peak, and that the path of the ball is a parabola.

a. With a suitable placement of coordinates, find an equation for this parabola.

b. How far from the tee (where the drive begins) is the ball 50 feet up in the air? Answers vary. Sample answer: 58.1 ft and 241.9 ft

Mount Kilimanjaro is not only the highest peak on the African continent; it is also the tallest freestanding mountain in the world at 19,336 feet.

Source: Mount Kilimanjaro National Park

26a. Answers vary.
Sample answer:
$y - 80 = -\frac{4}{1,125}(x - 150)^2$

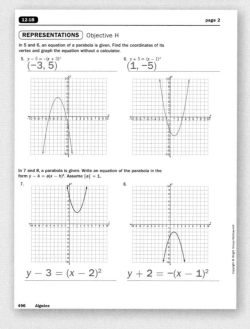

QY ANSWER

$(-15, 8)$

Lesson 12-2 Completing the Square

▶ **BIG IDEA** Completing the square is a process that converts an equation for a parabola from standard form into vertex form.

You have now seen two forms of equations whose graphs are parabolas.

Standard form $y = ax^2 + bx + c$

Vertex form $y - k = a(x - h)^2$

From the vertex form you can read the vertex of the parabola and also the maximum or minimum possible value of y. For example, from this form, you could tell the highest point that a baseball or a rocket reaches if you have an equation for its path.

But equations for paths are usually found in standard form $y = ax^2 + bx + c$. So the goal of this lesson is for you to learn how to convert an equation in standard form to one in vertex form.

The Problem, Visually Stated

Consider the equation $y = x^2 + 6x + 14$. Visually, you can picture this quadratic expression as 1 square, 6 lengths, and 14 units as shown at the right.

We want to convert it into vertex form. The idea is to move half of the lengths to try to create a bigger square as shown at the right.

It will take 9 of the units to fill in the bottom right corner to complete the square. The new bigger square, pictured below, has an area $x^2 + 3x + 3x + 9$. But its length and width are each $x + 3$. So it has area $(x + 3)^2$.

And because 5 units are left over, we have shown that $x^2 + 6x + 14 = (x + 3)^2 + 5$.

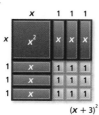

Now, if $y = x^2 + 6x + 14$, then $y = (x + 3)^2 + 5$, which means that $y - 5 = (x + 3)^2$.

$x^2 + 6x + 14$

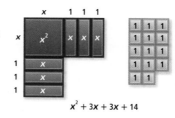

$x^2 + 3x + 3x + 14$

$(x + 3)^2 + 5$

Completing the Square **723**

Background

Completing the square is a method used to find the vertex of a parabola, derive the Quadratic Formula, and find the centers of circles, ellipses, and hyperbolas whose equations are given in standard form.

The examples in this lesson involve expressions of the form $x^2 + bx + c$ where b is an even (positive or negative) integer. The process, however, is the same regardless of the value of b. In general:

$$x^2 + bx + c = \left(x + \frac{b}{2}\right)^2 + c - \left(\frac{b}{2}\right)^2$$

Even more generally, $ax^2 + bx + c =$

$$a\left(\left(x + \frac{b}{2a}\right)^2 + \frac{c}{a} - \left(\frac{b}{2a}\right)^2\right) =$$

$$a\left(\left(x + \frac{b}{2a}\right)^2 + \frac{4ac - b^2}{4a^2}\right)$$

The problem, visually stated. In only certain cases are the squares, lengths, and units such that they can be rearranged to form one large square. In those cases, the quadratic expression is the square of a binomial. In other cases, one must add units to make the square. This amount that is added is what is meant by "completing the square."

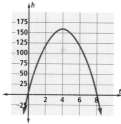

12-2

2 Teaching

Notes on the Lesson

Activity Students must realize that the expression $x^2 + bx + c$ is represented by 1 square (signifying $1x^2$), b lengths, and c units. Representing the expression as one large square is usually not possible without adding some units. To determine the number of units, the b lengths are placed at the right and below the single square. So there are $\frac{b}{2}$ lengths on the side, and $\frac{b}{2}$ lengths below. This means that $\left(\frac{b}{2}\right)^2$ units will "complete the square." If you do not have algebra tiles, students can use slips of paper of the appropriate sizes, or they can simply make drawings.

Remind students that in completing the square they are not solving an equation but rewriting an expression.

Notes on the Activity

Activity If you are short on time for the activity, consider replacing the numbers 18, 30, and 52 with smaller numbers. This will help students draw faster, but should not compromise the activity. If you have extra time, help students recognize which numbers contribute to the perfect square they are forming by asking them to do several examples where a and b are the same, and c changes. They will recognize that the perfect square is the same for all of these. Then ask them to use the blocks to explain why.

Additional Example

Example 1
a. Convert the equation $y = x^2 - 7x$ for a parabola into vertex form. $y + \frac{49}{4} = \left(x - \frac{7}{2}\right)^2$
b. Find the vertex of this parabola. $\left(\frac{7}{2}, -\frac{49}{4}\right)$

Additional Answers

Activity

1a.

2a.
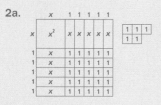

Activity

In 1–4, an equation for a parabola is given.
  a. Using algebra tiles, build the given quadratic expression with a square, lengths, and units.
  b. Rearrange the square, lengths, and units to convert the equation to vertex form. 1a., 2a., 3–4. See margin.

1. $y = x^2 + 4x + 18$ 2. $y = x^2 + 10x + 30$
3. $y = x^2 + 10x + 25$ 4. $y = x^2 + 14x + 52$

1b. $y - 14 = (x + 2)^2$

The General Process

In the expression $x^2 + 6x + 14$ on the previous page, we separated $6x$ into $3x + 3x$ and added 9 units to get the square. In general, the goal is to add a number to $x^2 + bx$ so that the right side of the equation contains a perfect square. We know, from the square of a binomial, that $(x + h)^2 = x^2 + 2hx + h^2$. Our goal is to find a number h^2 so that $x^2 + bx + h^2$ is a perfect square.

Comparing $x^2 + 2hx + h^2$ with $x^2 + bx$, we see that $b = 2h$. So $h = \frac{1}{2}b$. This means that $h^2 = \left(\frac{1}{2}b\right)^2$. And so $\left(x + \frac{1}{2}b\right)^2 = x^2 + bx + \left(\frac{1}{2}b\right)^2$.

Thus, to **complete the square** on $x^2 + bx$, add $\left(\frac{1}{2}b\right)^2$.

2b. $y - 5 = (x + 5)^2$

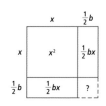

For example, in $x^2 + 6x$, $b = 6$ and $h = 3$. Then $h^2 = 9$.

Converting from Standard Form to Vertex Form

By completing the square, you can convert an equation in standard form to one in vertex form.

Example 1
a. Convert the equation $y = x^2 + 9x$ for a parabola into vertex form.
b. Find the vertex of this parabola.

Solutions

a. Think of $x^2 + 9x$ as $x^2 + bx$. Then $b = 9$. So $\left(\frac{1}{2}b\right)^2 = (4.5)^2$. Thus, using the above argument, if you add 4.5^2 to $x^2 + 9x$, you will have the square of a binomial. But in an equation, you cannot add something to one side without adding it to the other.

Accommodating the Learner ⬇

At this point, some students often begin making mistakes. For example, they add $\frac{b}{2}$ to both sides without squaring it. Another common mistake is writing $(x - b)^2$ instead of $\left(x - \frac{b}{2}\right)^2$. Help students avoid these mistakes by asking them to continue to sketch the visual. Consider including a worksheet with some common errors and ask them to use the visual statement of the problem or another mathematical justification to explain why the problem is incorrect.

Accommodating the Learner ⬆

Ask students to complete the square on $y = ax^2 + bx + c$. This will be best used in conjunction with the Extension on page 726. They will need to show all work and check every step carefully. The answer is the Quadratic Formula.

$$y = x^2 + 9x$$
$$y + 4.5^2 = x^2 + 9x + 4.5^2 \quad \text{Add } (4.5)^2 \text{ to both sides.}$$
$$y + 4.5^2 = (x + 4.5)^2 \qquad \text{Square of a binomial}$$

b. From Part a, we see that the vertex is (-4.5, -4.5²), that is, (-4.5, -20.25).

Check Graph the two parabolas with equations $y = x^2 + 9x$ and $y + 4.5^2 = (x + 4.5)^2$ on the same grid. The graphs are identical to the one shown at the right, and the vertex is (-4.5, -20.25).

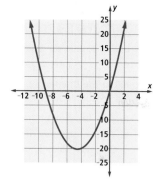

Completing the Square on $y = x^2 - bx$

Recall from Lesson 11-6 that $(x - h)^2 = x^2 - 2hx + h^2$.

Consequently, to complete the square on $x^2 - 2hx$ you add h^2. That is, to complete the square on $x^2 - bx$ you add the same amount as you do to complete the square on $x^2 + bx$.

Example 2

Without graphing, find the minimum value for y when $y = x^2 - 6x - 13$.

Solution You can find the minimum value of y if you know the vertex of the parabola that is the graph of $y = x^2 - 6x - 13$. First add 13 to both sides to isolate $x^2 - 6x$ on the right side.

$$y = x^2 - 6x - 13$$
$$y + 13 = x^2 - 6x$$

Now complete the square on $x^2 - 6x$. Here $b = -6$, so add $\left(\frac{-6}{2}\right)^2$, or 9, to both sides.

$$y + 13 + 9 = x^2 - 6x + 9$$
$$y + 22 = (x - 3)^2$$

So the vertex is (3, -22).

Consequently, the minimum value of y is -22.

Check 1 Try values of x near the vertex and see what values of y result.

When $x = 4$, $y = 4^2 - 6 \cdot 4 - 13 = -21$.

When $x = 2$, $y = 2^2 - 6 \cdot 2 - 13 = -21$ also.

The symmetry confirms that -22 is a minimum value for y when $x = 3$, because it is less than -21.

Check 2 Graph the equation $y = x^2 - 6x - 13$. We leave that to you.

2 Teaching

Notes on the Lesson

Example 2 Point out that here we are neither solving an equation nor finding an equivalent expression. We are adding something to the expression. This means that if we want to keep the expression with the same value, we must subtract the amount we added. So, in this case, we have to add 9 to complete the square on $x^2 - 6x$ on the right side of the equation. As a result, we must add 9 to the left side of the equation.

Additional Example

Example 2 Without graphing, find the minimum value of y when $y = x^2 - 3x + 2$. $\left(\frac{3}{2}, -\frac{1}{4}\right)$

Additional Answers

Activity

3a.

3b. $y = (x + 5)^2$

4a.

4b. $y - 3 = (x + 7)^2$

3 Assignment

Recommended Assignment

- Questions 1–24
- Question 25 (extra credit)
- Reading Lesson 12-3
- Covering the Ideas 12-3

Notes on the Questions

Question 7 This question is likely to give trouble because it is the first question with an odd coefficient of the linear term. Go to Example 1 for guidance.

Question 11 This question also involves an odd coefficient of the linear term and combines the ideas of Examples 1 and 2.

Questions

COVERING THE IDEAS

In 1 and 2, square the binomial.

1. $x + 7$ $x^2 + 14x + 49$
2. $n - 6.5$ $n^2 - 13n + 42.25$

3. **Fill in the Blanks** To complete the square for $x^2 + 20x$, add __?__. The result is the square of the binomial __?__.   100; $x + 10$

4. a. Give the sum of the areas of the three rectangles below. $x^2 + 72x$
   b. What is the area of the undrawn rectangle needed to complete the large square? **1,296**
   c. What algebraic expression will the completed large square below picture? $(x + 36)^2$

In 5–9, a quadratic expression is given.
   a. **What number must be added to the expression to complete the square?**
   b. **After adding that number, the expression is the square of what binomial?**

5. $x^2 + 2x$ a. **1**   b. $x + 1$
6. $t^2 + 30t$ a. **225**   b. $t + 15$
7. $r^2 - 7r$ a. **12.25**   b. $r - 3.5$
8. $v^2 + bv$ a. $\frac{1}{4}b^2$ b. $v + \frac{1}{2}b$
9. $w^2 - bw$ a. $\frac{1}{4}b^2$ b. $w - \frac{1}{2}b$

10. a. Convert the equation $y = x^2 + 14x$ into vertex form. $y + 49 = (x + 7)^2$
    b. Find the vertex of this parabola. $(-7, -49)$

11. a. Convert the equation $y = x^2 - 3x + 1$ into vertex form. $y + 1.25 = (x - 1.5)^2$
    b. Find the minimum value of y. -1.25

APPLYING THE MATHEMATICS

12. In this lesson, all the parabolas are graphs of equations of the form $y = x^2 + bx + c$. To deal with an equation of the form $y = -x^2 + bx + c$, first multiply both sides of the equation by -1, then complete the square, and finally multiply by -1 again so that y will be on the left side. Try this method to find the vertex of the parabola with equation $y = -x^2 + 5x + 2$. $(2.5, 8.25)$

Extension

With a short additional step, students can learn how to complete the square when $a \neq 1$. Showing students this additional step can be particularly helpful if you plan to use completing the square to demonstrate the derivation of the Quadratic Formula. Change Example 2 to $y = -2x^2 - 8x - 13$. They will begin solving the same way, and obtain $y + 13 = -2x^2 - 8x$.

Next, ask students to obtain a coefficient of 1 for x^2 by dividing both sides by -2:

$$\frac{y + 13}{-2} = x^2 + 4x.$$

Then, ask students to complete the square as usual. Here, $b = 4$, so add 2^2, or 4, to both sides.

$$\frac{y + 13}{-2} + 4 = x^2 + 4x + 4$$

$$\frac{y + 13}{-2} + 4 = (x + 2)^2$$

They can complete the transition to vertex form by multiplying both sides by -2.

$$y + 13 - 8 = -2(x + 2)^2$$

$$y + 5 = -2(x + 2)^2$$

13. In Lesson 9-4, the equation $h = -16t^2 + 32t + 6$ described the height h of a ball t seconds after being thrown from a height of 6 feet with an initial upward velocity of 32 feet per second. Put this equation into vertex form using the following steps.

Step 1 Substitute y for h and x for t.

Step 2 Divide both sides of the equation by –16 so that the coefficient of x^2 is 1.

Step 3 Complete the square on the right side of the equation and add the appropriate amount to the left side.

Step 4 Multiply both sides of the equation by –16 so that the coefficient of y on the left side of the equation is 1.

a. What is the vertex of the parabola? (1, 22)

b. Is this a minimum or a maximum? maximum

14. The equation $h = -0.12x^2 + 2x + 6$ describes the path of a basketball free throw, where h is the height of the ball in feet when the ball is x feet forward of the free-throw line.

a. Use the steps in Question 13 to put this equation into vertex form. $y - \frac{43}{3} = -0.12\left(x - \frac{25}{3}\right)^2$

b. What is the greatest height the ball reaches? $\frac{43}{3}$ ft or 14 ft 4 in.

15. If $y = x^2 - x + 1$, can y ever be negative? Explain your answer.

15. No, because the minimum value of y is 0.75 since the vertex is (0.5, 0.75).

16. The process of completing the square can be used to solve quadratic equations. Consider the equation $y^2 - 10y + 24 = 0$.

a. Add –24 to both sides. $y^2 - 10y = -24$

b. Complete the square on $y^2 - 10y$ and add the constant term to both sides. $y^2 - 10y + 25 = -24 + 25$

c. You now have an equation of the form $(y - 5)^2 = k$. What is k? 1

d. Solve the equation in Part c by taking the square roots of both sides. $y = 4$ or $y = 6$

17. Use the process described in Question 16 to solve $x^2 + 24x + 7 = 0$. $x = \sqrt{137} - 12$ or $x = -\sqrt{137} - 12$

REVIEW

18. Consider the parabola with quadratic equation $y + 8 = 3(x + 2)^2$. (**Lesson 12-1**)

a. Find the vertex of the parabola. (–2, –8)

b. Graph the parabola.

Kevin Garnett shoots a free throw for the Minnesota Timberwolves of the National Basketball Association.

Source: Associated Press

18b.

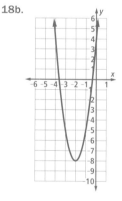

Completing the Square **727**

Notes on the Questions

Questions 12 and 13 The idea here is to isolate a quadratic expression of the form $x^2 + bx + c$ on the right side of the equation by first dividing both sides by the original coefficient of x^2. (Dividing by −1 yields the same results as multiplying by −1.) Then the process of completing the square is applied to that expression, and then both sides are again multiplied by the original coefficient of x^2 in order to isolate y on the left side.

Question 14 The arithmetic in this problem is best done with a calculator. Some students may remember that one way to find the greatest height is to determine the roots of the equation $0 = -0.12x^2 + 2x + 6$. This takes advantage of the symmetry of the parabola. Let m be the midpoint of the two roots. The value of $f(m) = -0.12m^2 + 2m + 6$ is the maximum height. You can use this idea to check the answer that students might obtain by completing the square.

12-2

4 Wrap-Up

Ongoing Assessment

Ask students to write a short explanation of what completing the square does to an equation and some common mistakes to avoid. If there is time, ask them to describe why some quadratic expressions, when considered visually, have units left over and others do not.

Notes on the Questions

Question 25 This question should be discussed as it opens the eyes of students to the notion that subtraction can also be pictured by algebra tiles.

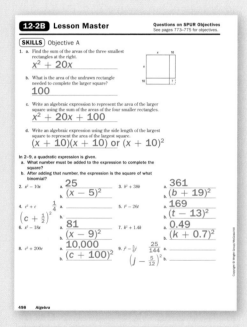

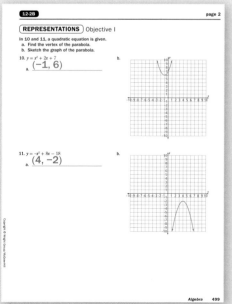

19. Two parents of blood type AB will produce children of three different blood types: A, B, and AB. One inheritance hypothesis argues that when parents of blood type AB produce children, 25% will have blood type A, 25% will have blood type B, and 50% will have blood type AB. Consider the table below that gives the blood types of 248 children born of 100 couples with both parents of blood type AB. Use a chi-square test to determine whether the data support the hypothesis. Justify your reasoning. **(Lesson 11-8)** See margin.

Blood Type	Number of Children
A	58
B	51
AB	139

20. a. How many solutions does the system $\begin{cases} y = |x| \\ y = 2 \end{cases}$ have? 2

  b. Find the solutions. **(Lesson 10-1)** $(-2, 2), (2, 2)$

In **21** and **22**, solve. **(Lessons 9-2, 5-2)**

21. $\frac{4}{x} = \frac{8}{15}$ 7.5

22. $\frac{m}{7} = \frac{20}{m}$ $\pm 2\sqrt{35}$

23. A watch company increases the price of its watches by 8%. If their watch now sells for $130.50, what did it sell for before the increase? **(Lesson 4-1)** $120.83

24. Solve $6(3x^2 - 3x) - 9(2x^2 + 1) = 12$. **(Lessons 3-4, 2-1)** $-\frac{7}{6}$

EXPLORATION

25. Explain how the drawing below can be used to show $(x - b)^2 = x^2 - 2bx + b^2$. See margin.

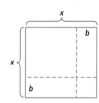

Additional Answers

19. The data do support the hypothesis. The chi-square statistic yielded a value of approximately 4. For $n = 3$, this occurs with a probability greater than 0.10. So there is no reason to question the expected values of the hypothesis.

25. Answers may vary. Sample answer: The length of the sides of the square in the upper left part of the largest square is $x - b$. Thus the area of that smaller square is $(x - b)^2$. That area can also be expressed as the area of the largest square minus the area of the bottom rectangle, right rectangle, and the square in the bottom right. Thus $(x - b)^2 = x^2 - b(x - b) - b(x - b) - b^2 = x^2 - 2bx + b^2$.

Lesson 12-3

The Factored Form of a Quadratic Function

Vocabulary

factored form (of a quadratic function)

▶ **BIG IDEA** The graph of the equation $y = a(x - r_1)(x - r_2)$ is a parabola that intersects the x-axis at $(r_1, 0)$ and $(r_2, 0)$.

You have seen two forms of equations for a quadratic function: standard form and vertex form. In this lesson, you will see some advantages of a third form called *factored form*. Below are graphs of three equations: $y + 4 = (x - 3)^2$, $y = (x - 1)(x - 5)$, and $y = x^2 - 6x + 5$.

Mental Math

Using one fair, 6-sided die, what is the probability of rolling

a. a 3? $\frac{1}{6}$

b. an even number? $\frac{1}{2}$

c. a number less than 3? $\frac{1}{3}$

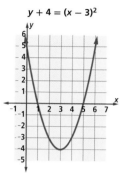

$y + 4 = (x - 3)^2$

Vertex form

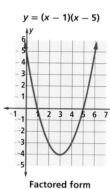

$y = (x - 1)(x - 5)$

Factored form

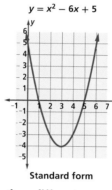

$y = x^2 - 6x + 5$

Standard form

They are in fact the same parabola described in three different ways. You can check this by converting the first two equations into standard form.

$$y + 4 = (x - 3)^2$$
$$y + 4 = (x - 3)(x - 3)$$
$$y + 4 = x^2 - 6x + 9$$
$$y = x^2 - 6x + 5$$

$$y = (x - 1)(x - 5)$$
$$y = x^2 - 1x - 5x + 5$$
$$y = x^2 - 6x + 5$$

Different key aspects of the graph are revealed by each form. From the vertex form, you can easily determine the vertex, $(3, -4)$. From the factored form, you can easily determine the x-intercepts, 1 and 5. In standard form, the y-intercept is clearly 5.

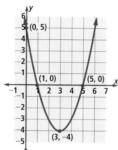

The Factored Form of a Quadratic Function **729**

Background

The vertex form of a parabola can tell how high a projectile goes, or the maximum area of a rectangle with a given perimeter, or other maxima or minima. It is useful in graphing because the vertex is an important point on the parabola. But in solving an equation, we want to know where the parabola intersects a particular horizontal line. If the points of intersection are rational numbers, then we can obtain their values by factoring.

The key idea of the lesson is that the x-intercepts of the graph of

$y = a(x - r_1)(x - r_2)$ are r_1 and r_2. This statement is an outgrowth of the Zero Product Property and the definition of x-intercept. Here is a formal proof: Consider the graph of $y = a(x - r_1)(x - r_2)$. An x-intercept is a value of x for which $y = 0$. So an x-intercept is a solution to $0 = a(x - r_1)(x - r_2)$. The right side of the equation is a product of three numbers, and it can equal 0 if and only if one of the factors is 0.

(continued on next page)

GOAL

Learn the advantages of the factored form of a quadratic expression in interpreting the graph of a quadratic function.

SPUR Objective

J Graph quadratic functions whose equations are given in factored form.

Materials/Resources

- Lesson Master 12-3A or 12-3B
- Resource Masters 2, 185, and 186
- Graphing calculator
- Computer Algebra System (CAS)
- Quiz 1

HOMEWORK

Suggestions for Assignment

- Questions 1–20
- Question 21 (extra credit)
- Reading Lesson 12-4
- Covering the Ideas 12-4

Local Standards

1 **Warm-Up**

In 1–4, graph these quadratic functions. Use the window $-10 \le x \le 10$, $-40 \le y \le 40$.

1. $y = (x + 6)(3 - x)$

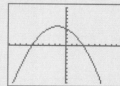

2. $y = (2x - 6)(x + 6)$

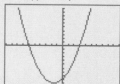

(continued on next page)

12-3

3. $y = (3x + 18)(x - 3)$

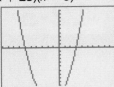

4. $y = (x + 6)(x - 6)$

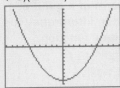

5. Three of the four have the same x-intercepts. How could you tell before even graphing?

The first three have the same x-intercepts, 3 and −6. You could tell by setting $y = 0$ and solving each equation for x.

Notes on the Activity

Activity 1 Help students remember the patterns they recognize during the activity by asking them to write a full description for Step 6. At the end of the lesson, ask them to justify the results mathematically using the Zero Product Property.

Additional Answers

Activity 1

Step 7:

a. 3 and −1

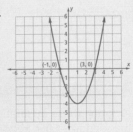

b. 0 and −6

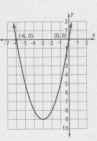

c. 2

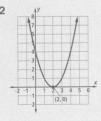

Activity 1

Use a dynamic graphing system.

Step 1 Create two sliders with values between −6 and 6. Label one r_1 and the other r_2.

Step 2 Slide bars so $r_1 = 1$ and $r_2 = 4$.

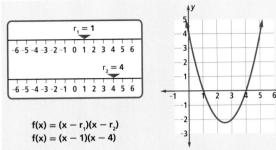

$f(x) = (x - r_1)(x - r_2)$
$f(x) = (x - 1)(x - 4)$

Step 3.

Step 3 Graph the function $f(x) = (x - r_1)(x - r_2)$.

Step 4 Give the points of intersection of the graph of f and the x-axis.

Step 4. (1, 0), (4, 0)

Step 5 Move the sliders to complete the table below.

r_1	r_2	$f(x) = (x - r_1)(x - r_2)$	Points of intersection of graph and x-axis
5	2	$f(x) = (x - 5)(x - 2)$	(?, 0) and (?, 0) 5; 2
−4	−3	? $f(x) = (x + 4)(x + 3)$	? (−4, 0) and (−3, 0)
0	−1	? $f(x) = x(x + 1)$	? (−1, 0) and (0, 0)
3	3	? $f(x) = (x - 3)(x - 3)$	? (3, 0)
−2?	4?	$f(x) = (x + 2)(x - 4)$	? (−2, 0) and (4, 0)
−5?	−5?	$f(x) = (x + 5)(x + 5)$	? (−5, 0) and (−5, 0)

Step 6 Explain how the factored form of a quadratic in the third column reveals the x-intercepts of the graph of that quadratic.

Step 6: If
$f(x) = (x - a)(x - b)$,
then the x-intercepts
are a and b.

Step 7 Give the x-intercepts of the following functions using their graphs.

a. $f(x) = (x - 3)(x + 1)$ **b.** $g(x) = x(x + 6)$ **c.** $h(x) = (x - 2)(x - 2)$

Step 7. See margin.

How the Factored Form Displays the x-Intercepts

The equation $y = ax^2 + bx + c$ is in **factored form** when it is written as $y = a(x - r_1)(x - r_2)$.

For the function with equation $y = (x - 1)(x - 4)$ graphed in Activity 1, $a = 1$, $r_1 = 1$, and $r_2 = 4$.

The x-intercepts of the function are the values of x for which $y = 0$. So they are the values of x that satisfy the equation $0 = (x - 1)(x - 4)$.

730 More Work With Quadratics

Because the expression is quadratic, $a \neq 0$. So either $x - r_1 = 0$ or $x - r_2 = 0$. Thus either $x = r_1$ or $x = r_2$. All quadratics of the form $y = a(x - r_1)(x - r_2)$ have the same x-intercepts regardless of the value of a.

Recall the Zero Product Property from Lesson 2-8: When the product of two numbers is zero, at least one of the numbers must be 0. In symbols, if $ab = 0$, then $a = 0$ or $b = 0$. Consequently, $y = 0$ when either $x - 1 = 0$ or $x - 4 = 0$. So $y = 0$ when either $x = 1$ or $x = 4$.

In general, the x-intercepts of a parabola can be determined from factored form in the same way that the vertex can be determined from vertex form.

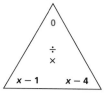

Factor Theorem for Quadratic Functions

The x-intercepts of the graph of $y = a(x - r_1)(x - r_2)$ are r_1 and r_2.

Example 1

Consider the equation $y = (x + 4)(x - 2)$.

a. Find the x-intercepts of its graph.

b. Graph the equation.

Solutions

a. The x-intercepts occur when $y = 0$. So solve $(x + 4)(x - 2) = 0$. By the Zero Product Property, either $x + 4 = 0$ or $x - 2 = 0$, so either $x = -4$ or $x = 2$. So the x-intercepts are –4 and 2.

b. Recall that the x-coordinate of the vertex is the mean of the x-intercepts –4 and 2. So the vertex has x-coordinate –1. When $x = -1$, $y = (-1 + 4)(-1 - 2) = -9$. So the vertex is $(-1, -9)$. With this information, you can sketch a graph.

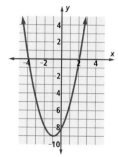

In the equation $y = (x + 4)(x - 2)$, the value of a, the coefficient of x^2, is 1. If the factors $x + 4$ and $x - 2$ remain the same but the value of a is changed, notice the similarities and changes in the graphs.

$y = (x + 4)(x - 2)$	$y = 2(x + 4)(x - 2)$	$y = -(x + 4)(x - 2)$	$y = -3(x + 4)(x - 2)$
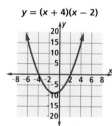	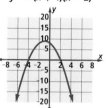		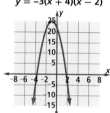
x-intercepts: –4 and 2 vertex: $(-1, -9)$	x-intercepts: –4 and 2 vertex: $(-1, -18)$	x-intercepts: –4 and 2 vertex: $(-1, 9)$	x-intercepts: –4 and 2 vertex: $(-1, 27)$

Accommodating the Learner

Continuing the use of the fact triangle may help students picture the Zero Product Property more easily. Ask students to write the equation $4b = 0$ using a fact triangle. Then, ask them to write the related facts. They will obtain the equations $\frac{0}{4} = b$ and $\frac{0}{b} = 4$. Discuss the related equations. Help students recognize that only one of the factors needs to be zero in order to get a product of zero. Take more time with fact triangles to help students understand.

2 Teaching

Notes on the Lesson

You may wish to use this lesson as a model of how students might read a mathematics lesson that has a great deal of symbolism. Have students use CAS technology with the lesson. There are seven parts to the lesson.

1. For the three graphs at the beginning of the lesson, have students use a CAS to verify that the vertex and factored forms are equivalent.
2. Do Activity 1. This shows how the parabola "moves" along the x-axis as its equation changes.
3. Have students read the material up to Example 1.
4. Have students read Example 1 aloud, checking the graph with their technology.
5. Have students check the graphs between Example 1 and Activity 2.
6. Have students do Activity 2 on their own. It mimics Activity 1, this time showing that the coefficient of x^2 in factored form has no effect on the x-intercepts of the parabola.
7. Have students read Example 2 and check the solution with a CAS. Then discuss Question 4, which is similar.

Additional Example

Example 1 Consider the equation $y = (x - 3)(x + 2)$.

a. Find the x-intercepts of its graph.
   The x-intercepts are –2 and 3.

b. Graph the equation.

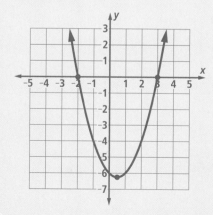

12-3

Notes on the Activity

Activity 2 Ask students to compare the effect of a in $y = a(x - r_1)(x - r_2)$ to a in $y - k = a(x - h)^2$. Students should write a brief summary in their notes describing a's impact on the graph of each equation.

To see them better, all four equations can be placed on the same set of axes.

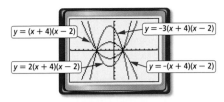

$y = (x + 4)(x - 2)$ $y = -3(x + 4)(x - 2)$

$y = 2(x + 4)(x - 2)$ $y = -(x + 4)(x - 2)$

All four graphs have the same pair of x-intercepts, -4 and 2, so each goes through the points $(-4, 0)$ and $(2, 0)$.

Activity 2

Use a dynamic graphing system. You can use the previous Activity's set-up for this Activity.

Step 1 Create two sliders with values between -6 and 6. Label one r_1 and the other r_2.

Step 2 Create a third slider with values between -6 and 6 and label it a.

Step 3 Slide bars so $r_1 = 1$, $r_2 = 4$, and $a = 1$.

Step 4 Plot the function $f(x) = a \cdot (x - r_1)(x - r_2)$.

Step 5 Slide a. Do the x-intercepts change? **no**

Step 6 Make $r_1 = -3$ and $r_2 = -3$. Slide a. Do the x-intercepts change? **no**

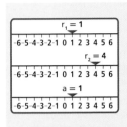
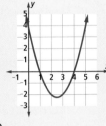

$f(x) = a \cdot (x - r_1)(x - r_2)$
$f(x) = 1 \cdot (x - 1)(x - 4)$

Step 7 Move r_1 and r_2 to other values and then slide a. Explain your observations about the relationship between the value of a and the x-intercepts.

Step 8 Slide a into the positive values. What is true about the shape of the parabola when a is positive? **The parabola opens up.**

Step 9 Slide a into the negative values. What is true about the shape of the parabola when a is negative? **The parabola opens down.**

Step 10 Slide a to zero. Describe what happens to the graph.

Step 7: The x-intercepts do not depend on a. Although the steepness of the parabola changes, the points where it crosses the x-axis do not.
Step 10: The graph becomes the line $y = 0$.

Step 11 Complete the table. Verify your results by graphing.

a	r_1	r_2	$f(x) = a(x - r_1)(x - r_2)$	Does the parabola open up or down?
2	2	-3	$f(x) = 2(x - 2)(x + 3)$	? **up**
-1	-4.1	5	? $f(x) = -(x + 4.1)(x - 5)$	? **down**
5	-6	-6	? $f(x) = 5(x + 6)^2$	**up**
-3	-5	0	? $f(x) = -3x(x + 5)$	? **down**

ENGLISH LEARNERS
Vocabulary Development

This lesson reinforces the meaning of the term *form*. Remind students that different forms of equations always represent the same mathematical equation. Therefore, they will always have the same graph. As demonstrated in the text, students can verify that equations are the same by putting them in the same form. Remind students that each form is useful for different purposes. For example, vertex form allows for easily finding the vertex.

When a quadratic expression is in factored form and equal to 0, you can solve equations and find x-intercepts quite easily. You can also determine vertices and maximum and minimum values of the expression.

Example 2

a. Find the x-intercepts of the graph of $y = (3x - 5)(2x + 1)$.

b. Find the vertex of the parabola.

Solutions

a. Solve $0 = (3x - 5)(2x + 1)$. Use the Zero Product Property.

Either $3x - 5 = 0$ or $2x + 1 = 0$.

$$3x = 5 \quad \text{or} \quad 2x = -1$$
$$x = \frac{5}{3} \quad \text{or} \quad x = -\frac{1}{2}$$

Thus the x-intercepts are $\frac{5}{3}$ and $-\frac{1}{2}$.

b. The x-coordinate of the vertex is the mean of the x-intercepts.

$$\frac{\frac{5}{3} + \frac{-1}{2}}{2} = \frac{\frac{10}{6} - \frac{3}{6}}{2} = \frac{\frac{7}{6}}{2} = \frac{7}{12}$$

When $x = \frac{7}{12}$, $y = \left(3 \cdot \frac{7}{12} - 5\right)\left(2 \cdot \frac{7}{12} + 1\right) = \left(\frac{21}{12} - \frac{60}{12}\right)\left(\frac{7}{6} + \frac{6}{6}\right)$

$$= -\frac{39}{12} \cdot \frac{13}{6} = -\frac{169}{24}.$$

So the vertex of the parabola is $\left(\frac{7}{12}, -\frac{169}{24}\right) = \left(\frac{7}{12}, -7\frac{1}{24}\right)$.

Questions

COVERING THE IDEAS

1. Give the x-intercepts of the graph of $y = 3(x - 8)(x + 4)$. 8; –4

2. If the product of two numbers is zero, what must be true of at least one of those numbers? **At least one of the numbers must be zero.**

In 3–5, solve the equation. 3. $x = 32$ or $x = -89.326$

3. $0 = -5(x - 32)(x + 89.326)$ 4. $777(n + 198)(2n - 10) = 0$

5. $p(p + 19) = 0$ $p = 0$ or $p = -19$

4. $n = -198$ or $n = 5$

6. Consider the equations $y = 3(x - 20)(x + 80)$ and $y = -2(x - 20)(x + 80)$.

   a. What two points do the graphs of these equations have in common? (20, 0) and (–80, 0)

   b. What is the x-coordinate of the vertex of both graphs? –30

   c. What is the y-coordinate of the vertex for each graph? –7,500; 5,000

The Factored Form of a Quadratic Function **733**

Accommodating the Learner ⬆

Help students practice finding the easiest way to graph the equation of a parabola. Create a set of equations in a variety of forms. Include some in each form: standard form, vertex form, and factored form. Make sure some of the equations in standard form are factorable over the integers. Then, ask students to find the easiest way to graph each equation. For equations already in vertex or factored form, this will become simply a matter of recognizing the form.

For the equations in standard form, students will need to identify if the equation is factorable or if they will need to complete the square to obtain vertex form.

Additional Example

Example 2

a. Find the x-intercepts of the graph of $y = (2x + 3)(4x - 1)$.
The x-intercepts are $-\frac{3}{2}$ and $\frac{1}{4}$.

b. Find the vertex of the parabola.
The vertex is $\left(-\frac{5}{8}, -\frac{49}{8}\right)$.

3 Assignment

Recommended Assignment

- Questions 1–20
- Question 21 (extra credit)
- Reading Lesson 12-4
- Covering the Ideas 12-4

Notes on the Questions

Questions 3–5 The numbers here are different from those students normally see, but the arithmetic is still very easy. Emphasize that the product must equal 0. Give the equation $0 = -5 + (x - 32) + (x + 89.326)$ for students to solve. $x = -52.326$

Question 6 Because these graphs intersect the x-axis at the same points (20, 0) and (–80, 0), and the vertex lies on the perpendicular bisector of the segment connecting these points, the vertices of the two parabolas have the same x-coordinate. But the vertices have to have different y-coordinates, because these are different parabolas.

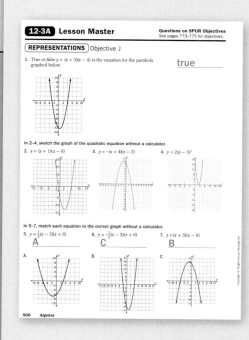

12-3

Notes on the Questions

Question 12 There is a great deal of reading here, and there is a purposeful alliteration of cannon, canyon, cantaloupe, and Candice. The problem is to separate what is important in this situation and what is not. Present it as an enjoyable problem and instruct students to draw a picture of the situation.

7c.

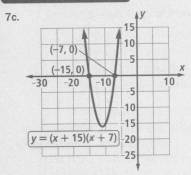

7d. $y = x^2 + 22x + 105$

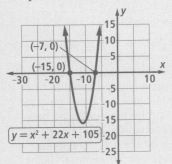

8c.

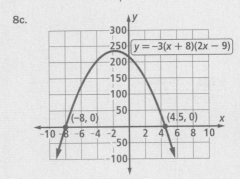

8d. $y = -6x^2 - 21x + 216$

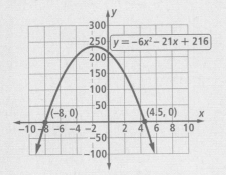

In 7–10, an equation for a function is given.
  a. Find the *x*-intercepts of the graph of the function.
  b. Find the vertex of the graph of the function.
  c. Sketch a graph of the function.
  d. Check your work by writing the equation in standard form and graphing that equation. 7–10c–d. See margin.

7. $y = (x + 15)(x + 7)$

8. $y = -3(x + 8)(2x - 9)$

9. $f(x) = -x(4x + 11)$

10. $g(x) = (x - 3)^2$

10a. 3
10b. (3, 0)

11. A quadratic function is graphed at the right.
  a. Give an equation for the axis of symmetry of the parabola.
  b. Give 3 possible equations in factored form for the graph.
  11a. $x = -6.5$

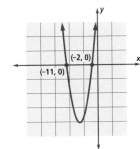

APPLYING THE MATHEMATICS

12. Down in a canyon there is a cannon that shoots cantaloupes straight up. Candice is standing on a cliff above the cannon. The cliff is at ground level or a height of 0 feet, so that the cantaloupes are fired from a negative starting height. The cantaloupe is shot up into the air higher than the cliff (on which Candice is standing) and then comes back down past the cliff back into the canyon. The cantaloupe passes by Candice 1 second after it is fired on the way up and 2 seconds after it was fired on the way down.
  a. What part of the situation represents the *x*-intercepts (or where the cantaloupe has a height of 0 feet)?
  b. In projectile problems where the units are in feet and seconds, $a = -16$. Write an equation for the situation in factored form.
  c. Give the axis of symmetry for this graph. $x = 1.5$
  d. Give the coordinates of the vertex of the graph. (1.5, 4)
  e. What does the vertex represent in the scenario about the cantaloupe?

13. The vertex of a parabola is (–2, –18) and one of the *x*-intercepts is 1.
  a. Give the other *x*-intercept. –5
  b. Write an equation for the parabola in factored, vertex, and standard forms. $y = 2(x - 1)(x + 5)$; $y + 18 = 2(x + 2)^2$; $y = 2x^2 + 8x - 10$

734 More Work With Quadratics

7a. –15 and –7
7b. (–11, –16)
8a. –8 and 4.5
8b. $\left(-\frac{7}{4}, \frac{1,875}{8}\right)$
9a. 0 and $-\frac{11}{4}$
9b. $\left(-\frac{11}{8}, \frac{121}{16}\right)$

11b. Answers vary. Sample answer: $y = 3(x + 11) \cdot (x + 2)$, $y = (x + 11)(x + 2)$, $y = 50(x + 11) \cdot (x + 2)$

12a. when the cantaloupe passes Candice on the way up and on the way down
12b. $y = -16(x - 1)(x - 2)$
12e. The *x*-coordinate represents the time in seconds when the cantaloupe reaches its maximum height, and the *y*-coordinate represents that height.

9c.

9d. $f(x) = -4x^2 - 11x$

10c.

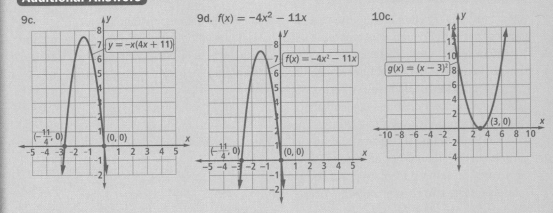

14. A formula that describes how many diagonals d that can be drawn in a polygon with n sides is $d = \frac{1}{2}n(n-3)$.

Number of sides	3	4	5	6	...
Number of diagonals	0	2	5	9	...

a. What are the n-intercepts of the formula's graph? **0 and 3**

b. Why does the point $(2, -1)$ not make sense in this situation?

c. The graph of the formula is part of a parabola. Find its vertex. **(1.5, -1.125)**

14b. A polygon cannot have exactly 2 sides and be a closed figure, nor have -1 diagonals.

REVIEW

15. Consider the equation $y = -x^2 + 10x - 20$. (**Lessons 12-2, 12-1**)

a. Rewrite the equation in vertex form. $y - 5 = -(x - 5)^2$

b. Give the vertex of the parabola. **(5, 5)**

c. Graph the parabola.

In 16 and 17, multiply the expression. (**Lessons 11-6, 11-5**)

16. $(4a - 1)(3a + 6)$

17. $(5n + 8)(5n - 8)$ $25n^2 - 64$

18. If the cost of 15 pads of paper is \$12.30, how many pads can be purchased with \$3.75? (**Lesson 5-5**) **4 pads**

19. Give the coordinates of the point of intersection of the two lines. (**Lesson 4-2**) 19a. $(2, -4)$

a. $x = 2, y = -4$ b. $x = a, y = 0$ $(a, 0)$ c. $x = r, y = s$ (r, s)

20. A class of 34 students contains 2.5% of all the students in the school. How many students are in the school? (**Lesson 4-1**)
1,360 students

EXPLORATION

21. Consider the equation $y_1 = (x - 5)(x - 2)(x + 1)$.

a. Graph this equation using a graphing calculator.

b. Identify the x-intercepts of the graph. **5, 2, and -1**

c. Use the results of Parts a and b to graph $y_2 = -(x - 5)(x - 2)(x + 1)$ without a graphing calculator.

d. Use the results of Parts a and b to graph $y_3 = 3(x - 5)(x - 2)(x + 1)$ without a graphing calculator. **See margin.**

e. Write a few sentences generalizing Parts a through d. **See margin.**

15c.

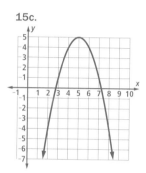

16. $12a^2 + 21a - 6$

21a.

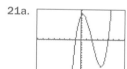

21c.

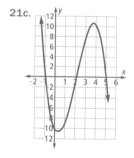

The Factored Form of a Quadratic Function **735**

Notes on the Questions

Question 14 Use this question to review the idea of "domain." The formula is meaningful only if n is an integer greater than 3, but a graphing utility will usually consider the domain to be the set of all real numbers. The domain does not contain points on both sides of the vertex of the parabola.

Question 21 This question foreshadows Lesson 12-7.

4 Wrap-Up

Ongoing Assessment

Organize students into pairs, and provide each student with a quadratic equation in standard form, factorable over the integers. After students do each step listed have them switch, check each other's work, and then do the next step on the problem they just checked.

Step 1: Factor the equation.

Step 2: Find the x-intercepts for the equation.

Step 3: Find the vertex.

Step 4: Sketch the parabola.

Project Update

If you have not had students look over the projects on pages 768 and 769, you might want to do so now. Project 1, Combining Solutions, on page 768, relates to the content of this lesson.

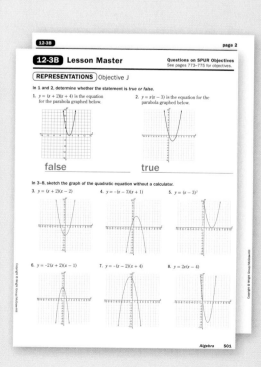

Additional Answers

10d. $g(x) = x^2 - 6x + 9$

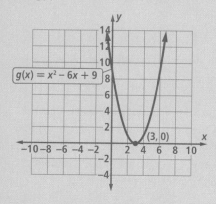

21d.

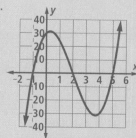

21e. Answers vary. Sample answer: A graph $y = a(x - r_1)(x - r_2)(x - r_3)$ has x-intercepts r_1, r_2, and r_3. When $a = -1$, the graph is reflected about the x-axis. When $a = 3$, the graph of $y = (x - r_1)(x - r_2)(x - r_3)$ stretches by a factor of 3.

Lesson 12-4

Lesson 12-4

Factoring $x^2 + bx + c$

GOAL

Factor quadratic expressions when the coefficient of the square term is 1.

SPUR Objectives

B Factor quadratic expressions of the form $x^2 + bx + c$ and $ax^2 + bx + c$.

E Determine whether a quadratic polynomial can be factored over the integers.

Materials/Resources

· Lesson Master 12-4A or 12-4B
· Resource Masters 2, 187, and 188
· Graphing calculator
· Computer Algebra System (CAS)

HOMEWORK

Suggestions for Assignment

• Questions 1–28
• Question 29 (extra credit)
• Reading Lesson 12-5
• Covering the Ideas 12-5

Local Standards

1 Warm-Up

You may wish to do the Activity in this lesson as a Warm-Up. Here is a shorter Warm-Up.

In 1–4, find two integers whose sum is b and whose product is c.

1. $b = 18$, $c = 45$ 3 and 15
2. $b = 36$, $c = 203$ 29 and 7
3. $b = -2$, $c = -3$ −3 and 1
4. $b = 1$, $c = -72$ 9 and −8
5. Find two numbers whose sum is 0 and whose product is 10.
$\sqrt{10}$ and $-\sqrt{10}$

▶ **BIG IDEA** Some quadratic trinomials of the form $x^2 + bx + c$ can be factored into two linear factors.

In Lesson 12-3 you saw the advantage of the factored form $y = a(x - r_1)(x - r_2)$ in finding the x-intercepts r_1 and r_2 of the graph of a quadratic function. In this lesson you will see how to convert quadratic expressions from the form $x^2 + bx + c$ into factored form.

Notice the pattern that results from the multiplication of the binomials of the forms $(x + p)$ and $(x + q)$. After combining like terms, the product is a trinomial.

	square term	linear term	constant term
$(x + 4)(x + 3) = x^2 + 3x + 4x + 12 =$	x^2	$+ \quad 7x$	$+ \quad 12$
$(x - 6)(x + 8) = x^2 + 8x - 6x - 48 =$	x^2	$+ \quad 2x$	$- \quad 48$
$(x + p)(x + q) = x^2 + qx + px + pq =$	x^2	$+ (p + q)x$	$+ \quad pq$

Examine the trinomials above. Their constant term pq is the product of the constant terms of the binomials. The coefficient $p + q$ of the linear term is the sum of the constant terms of the binomials. This pattern suggests a way to factor trinomials in which the coefficient of the square term is 1.

Mental Math

Use the discriminant to determine the number of real solutions to

a. $-5y^2 + 6y + 7 = 0$.

b. $3h^2 + 10 - h = 0$.

c. $-9x^2 - 12x - 4 = 0$.

a. two

b. none

c. one

Example 1

Factor $x^2 + 11x + 18$.

Solution To factor, you need to identify two binomials, $(x + p)$ and $(x + q)$, whose product equals $x^2 + 11x + 18$. You must find p and q, two numbers whose product is 18 and whose sum is 11. Because the product is positive and the sum is positive, both p and q are positive. List the positive pairs of numbers whose product is 18. Then calculate their sums.

Product is 18	Sum of Factors
1, 18	19
2, 9	11
3, 6	9

The sum of the numbers 2 and 9 is 11. So $p = 2$ and $q = 9$.

Thus, $x^2 + 11x + 18 = (x + 2)(x + 9)$.

Check Factoring can always be checked by multiplication.
$(x + 2)(x + 9) = x^2 + 9x + 2x + 18 = x^2 + 11x + 18$; it checks.

Background

There are two questions to consider about the factorization of $x^2 + bx + c$. First, is it factorable? Then, if it is factorable, what are the factors? When we ask the first question, we understand that we mean *factorable over the set of polynomials with integer coefficients*, because in the set of polynomials with real coefficients, any quadratic of the form $x^2 + bx + c$ is factorable.

Specifically, for all b and c,
$$x^2 + bx + c = \left(x + \frac{b + \sqrt{b^2 - 4c}}{2}\right)\left(x + \frac{b - \sqrt{b^2 - 4c}}{2}\right).$$ More generally, for all a, b, and c, $ax^2 + bx + c =$
$$a\left(x + \frac{b + \sqrt{b^2 - 4c}}{2a}\right)\left(x + \frac{b - \sqrt{b^2 - 4ac}}{2a}\right).$$

In Lesson 12-6, students will learn that the value of the discriminant $b^2 - 4ac$ is critical in determining if the quadratic expression is factorable over the set of polynomials with integer coefficients.

(continued on next page)

GUIDED

Example 2

Factor $x^2 - x - 30$.

Solution Think of this trinomial as $x^2 + -1x + -30$. You need two numbers whose product is -30 and whose sum is -1. Since the product is negative, one of the factors is negative. List the possibilities.

Product is -30		Sum of Factors	
-1, 30		29	
-2, _?_	15	_?_	13
-3, _?_	10	_?_	7
-5, _?_	6	_?_	1
-6, _?_	5	_?_	-1
-10, _?_	3	_?_	-7
_?_ , _?_	-15; 2	_?_	-13
_?_ , _?_	-30; 1	_?_	-29

The only pair of factors of -30 whose sum is -1 is _?_ and _?_. −6; 5
So $x^2 - x - 30 = (x - \underline{?})(x + \underline{?})$. 6; 5

Check 1 Multiply $(x - \underline{?})(x + \underline{?}) = x^2 + \underline{?}x - \underline{?}x - 30 = x^2 - x - 30$. It checks. 6; 5; 5; 6

Check 2 Graph $y = x^2 - x - 30$ and $y = (x - \underline{?})(x + \underline{?})$. The graphs should be identical. Below we show the output from a graphing calculator, with the window $-10 \le x \le 10$, $-35 \le y \le 35$. 6; 5

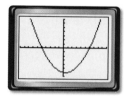

$y = x^2 - x - 30$

$y = (x - 6)(x + 5)$

The graphs appear to be identical.

As you know, some trinomials are perfect squares. You can use the method from Examples 1 and 2 to solve perfect square trinomials.

CAS technology enables us to factor polynomials automatically, thus putting into question whether one should spend a significant amount of time on factoring. Yet the ease with which CAS technology factors also enables students to see patterns in the factoring of polynomials that they would not be expected to see in the past. In this activity, students should have reinforced the idea that when $x^2 + bx + c = (x + p)(x + q)$, then $p + q = b$ and $pq = c$. They also should see that if b and c are small integers, most

of the time the quadratic expression does not factor over the integers.

Activity If you have never done an activity like this one, you should definitely look at the answer in these notes before you begin. You may be surprised at how few of these quadratic expressions factor over the integers.

2 Teaching

Notes on the Lesson

If you used algebra tiles to explain completing the square, you might want to use them here. To factor $x^2 + bx + c$, begin with one square, b lengths, and c units. Try to arrange these tiles into a rectangle. If a rectangle can be formed, its dimensions are $x + p$ and $x + q$. Therefore, $p + q$ must equal b and pq must equal c. Question 12 exemplifies this idea.

Even though the idea is the same, students need practice on the four different combinations of additions and subtractions in $x^2 \pm bx \pm c$. Every time one of the factorizations is done, students should check it by multiplication. The practice of factoring and checking by multiplication should lead to these generalizations:

1. When c is positive in $x^2 + bx + c$, the numbers p and q in the factorization $(x + p)(x + q)$ must have the same sign, and that sign is determined by the sign of b.
2. When c is negative in $x^2 + bx + c$, the numbers p and q must have different signs, and the sign of b will be that of whichever number has the greater absolute value.

Example 1 Because the only sums of factors are 19, 11, and 9, the only quadratic expressions of the form $x^2 + bx + 18$ that are factorable with b positive are $x^2 + 19x + 18$, $x^2 + 11x + 18$, and $x^2 + 9x + 18$. The Activity in the lesson alerts students to the rarity of a quadratic being factorable.

Example 2 You could look at the solution and ask students for the quadratic expression where the product is -30 and the sum is 29: $x^2 + 29x - 30 = (x + 30)(x - 1)$. By doing this with the solutions that fail, students can better see how to obtain correct factors.

Additional Example
Example 1 Factor $x^2 + 7x + 12$.
$(x + 3)(x + 4)$

12-4

Notes on the Lesson

Example 3 Notice that we do not do anything special to factor perfect square trinomials. They can be factored in the same manner as other quadratic trinomials, with the result being two identical factors.

Additional Examples

Example 2 Factor $x^2 - 17x + 42$.

Solution

Think of this trinomial as $x^2 + -17x + 42$.

You need two numbers whose product is 42 and whose sum is -17. Because the product is positive, either both of the numbers must be negative or both must be positive. Their sum is negative, so we can conclude that both numbers are negative.

Product is 42	Sum of Factors
$-1, -42$	-43
$-2, -21$	$\underline{}$ -23
$\underline{}, \underline{}$ $-3, -14$	$\underline{}$ -17
$\underline{}, \underline{}$ $-6, -7$	$\underline{}$ -13

The only pair of factors of 42 whose sum is -17 is $\underline{}_{-3}$ and $\underline{}_{-14}$.

So, $x^2 + -17x + 42 = (x - \underline{}_3)(x - \underline{}_{14})$.

Example 3 Factor $x^2 - 4x - 12$.

$(x - 6)(x + 2)$

Example 4 Factor $p^2 + 6p - 7$.

1. Find factors of $\underline{}$ whose sum is $\underline{}$.
   $-7, 6$

2. Because the product is negative, how many factors are negative? **1**

3. $p^2 + 6p - 7 = (\underline{})(\underline{})$. $p - 1$;
   $p + 7$

Example 3

Factor $t^2 - 8t + 16$.

Solution Find factors of 16 whose sum is -8. Because the product is positive and the sum is negative, both numbers are negative. You need only to consider negative factors of 16.

Product is 16	Sum of Factors
$-1, -16$	-17
$-2, -8$	-10
$-4, -4$	-8

So $t^2 - 8t + 16 = (t - 4)(t - 4) = (t - 4)^2$.

Check Use a CAS to factor $t^2 - 8t + 16$.

Not all trinomials of the form $x^2 + bx + c$ can be factored into polynomials with integer coefficients. For example, to factor $t^2 - 12t + 16$ as two binomials $(t + p)(t + q)$, where p and q are integers, the product of p and q would have to be 16 and their sum would have to be -12. The table in Example 3 shows that there are no such pairs of numbers. We say that $t^2 - 12t + 16$ is *prime over the integers*. A **prime polynomial over the integers** is one that cannot be factored into factors of lower degree with integer coefficients.

GUIDED

Example 4

Factor $m^2 + 5m - 24$.

Solution

1. Think of factors of $\underline{}$ whose sum is $\underline{}$. -24; 5
2. Because the product is negative, how many of the factors are negative? **1**
3. $m^2 + 5m - 24 = (\underline{})(\underline{})$ $m + 8$; $m - 3$

   Check Check your solution by graphing $y = x^2 - 5x - 24$ and $y = (\underline{})(\underline{})$. $x + 8$; $x - 3$

Check

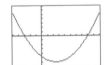

Activity

Use a CAS and the FACTOR command to complete this Activity. Work with a partner, a team, or your entire class.

The entries in the table on the next page are quadratic expressions of the form $x^2 + bx + c$. We want to factor them into polynomials with integer coefficients.

Accommodating the Learner ⬇

Require students to check their work for homework, quizzes, and tests. It is important for students to practice connecting the idea of multiplying binomials to the sum and product pattern they use to factor trinomials. This will also help students when they begin factoring $ax^2 + bx + c$.

b	c = 1	c = 2	c = 3	c = 4	c = 5	c = 6	c = 7	c = 8	c = 9	c = 10
1	$x^2 + x + 1$	$x^2 + x + 2$	$x^2 + x + 3$	$x^2 + x + 4$	$x^2 + x + 5$	$x^2 + x + 6$	$x^2 + x + 7$	$x^2 + x + 8$	$x^2 + x + 9$	$x^2 + x + 10$
2	$x^2 + 2x + 1$	$x^2 + 2x + 2$	$x^2 + 2x + 3$	$x^2 + 2x + 4$	$x^2 + 2x + 5$	$x^2 + 2x + 6$	$x^2 + 2x + 7$	$x^2 + 2x + 8$	$x^2 + 2x + 9$	$x^2 + 2x + 10$
3	$x^2 + 3x + 1$	$x^2 + 3x + 2$	$x^2 + 3x + 3$	$x^2 + 3x + 4$	$x^2 + 3x + 5$	$x^2 + 3x + 6$	$x^2 + 3x + 7$	$x^2 + 3x + 8$	$x^2 + 3x + 9$	$x^2 + 3x + 10$
4	$x^2 + 4x + 1$	$x^2 + 4x + 2$	$x^2 + 4x + 3$	$x^2 + 4x + 4$	$x^2 + 4x + 5$	$x^2 + 4x + 6$	$x^2 + 4x + 7$	$x^2 + 4x + 8$	$x^2 + 4x + 9$	$x^2 + 4x + 10$
5	$x^2 + 5x + 1$	$x^2 + 5x + 2$	$x^2 + 5x + 3$	$x^2 + 5x + 4$	$x^2 + 5x + 5$	$x^2 + 5x + 6$	$x^2 + 5x + 7$	$x^2 + 5x + 8$	$x^2 + 5x + 9$	$x^2 + 5x + 10$
6	$x^2 + 6x + 1$	$x^2 + 6x + 2$	$x^2 + 6x + 3$	$x^2 + 6x + 4$	$x^2 + 6x + 5$	$x^2 + 6x + 6$	$x^2 + 6x + 7$	$x^2 + 6x + 8$	$x^2 + 6x + 9$	$x^2 + 6x + 10$
7	$x^2 + 7x + 1$	$x^2 + 7x + 2$	$x^2 + 7x + 3$	$x^2 + 7x + 4$	$x^2 + 7x + 5$	$x^2 + 7x + 6$	$x^2 + 7x + 7$	$x^2 + 7x + 8$	$x^2 + 7x + 9$	$x^2 + 7x + 10$
8	$x^2 + 8x + 1$	$x^2 + 8x + 2$	$x^2 + 8x + 3$	$x^2 + 8x + 4$	$x^2 + 8x + 5$	$x^2 + 8x + 6$	$x^2 + 8x + 7$	$x^2 + 8x + 8$	$x^2 + 8x + 9$	$x^2 + 8x + 10$
9	$x^2 + 9x + 1$	$x^2 + 9x + 2$	$x^2 + 9x + 3$	$x^2 + 9x + 4$	$x^2 + 9x + 5$	$x^2 + 9x + 6$	$x^2 + 9x + 7$	$x^2 + 9x + 8$	$x^2 + 9x + 9$	$x^2 + 9x + 10$
10	$x^2 + 10x + 1$	$x^2 + 10x + 2$	$x^2 + 10x + 3$	$x^2 + 10x + 4$	$x^2 + 10x + 5$	$x^2 + 10x + 6$	$x^2 + 10x + 7$	$x^2 + 10x + 8$	$x^2 + 10x + 9$	$x^2 + 10x + 10$

Step 1 Make a table like the one above with the same row and column headings, but keep the other cells blank. Steps 1 and 2. See Additional Answers on page T89.

Step 2 Factor each of the 100 entries in the table. Put the factored form in your table. If the quadratic cannot be factored over the integers, write "P," for prime, in the box. The expressions $x^2 + x + 1$ and $x^2 + 2x + 1$ have been done for you below.

b	c = 1
1	P
2	$(x + 1)(x + 1)$

Step 3 In your table, circle the factored expressions.

Step 4 For which values of c is there only one factorization of $x^2 + bx + c$ in that column? What type of numbers are these c values?

Step 5 When c = 6, there are two factorizations of $x^2 + bx + 6$. The factorizations occur when b = 5 and b = 7.

$$x^2 + 5x + 6 = (x + 2)(x + 3)$$

How are the 2 and 3 related to the 6? $2 \cdot 3 = 6$

How are the 2 and 3 related to the 5? $2 + 3 = 5$

$$x^2 + 7x + 6 = (x + 1)(x + 6)$$

How are the 1 and 6 related to the 6? $1 \cdot 6 = 6$

How are the 1 and 6 related to the 7? $1 + 6 = 7$

Step 6 If $x^2 + bx + c$ factors into $(x + p)(x + q)$ then $p + q =$? and $pq =$? . b; c

Step 7 For how many integer values of b is the expression $x^2 + bx + 20$ factorable? Explain. Give the values of b that allow $x^2 + bx + 20$ to be factored.

For how many integer values of b is the expression $x^2 + bx + 37$ factorable? Explain. Give the values of b that allow $x^2 + bx + 37$ to be factored.

Step 4. c = 1, 2, 3, 5, 7, 10; Except for 1 and 10, the numbers are all prime.

Step 7. Three positive values of b make $x^2 + bx + 20$ factorable. 20 has 3 pairs of positive integer factors, 1 and 20, 2 and 10, and 4 and 5, so the sum of each of these pairs makes $x^2 + bx + 20$ factorable; b = 21, b = 12, or b = 9. One positive integer value of b makes $x^2 + bx + 37$ factorable. 37 is prime and has only one positive integer pair of factors, 1 and 37, so, b = 38.

Factoring $x^2 + bx + c$ **739**

Notes on the Lesson

Activity This activity should not be skipped. The work should be split among students or groups. Because there are 79 cells to fill in, divide the cells among the class so that each student is responsible for 3, 4, or 5 cells, or each group of 3 or 4 students is responsible for two rows or one row and one column. Point out that some quadratics do not factor over the integers. This is a major reason why we introduced the Quadratic Formula before this chapter. While factoring is an interesting way to solve quadratics and has some nice graphical properties, it is not as widely applicable as the Quadratic Formula.

Notes on the Activity

Notice, for Step 4, that b and c are always positive, so when c is prime, the only factors of c are c and 1. Thus, for all of the columns where c is prime, students will only have one factorization, which is $(x + c)(x + 1) = x^2 + (c + 1) \cdot x + c$. You may eventually wish to refer back to this Activity to point out that assuming b and c are both positive narrows us down to many fewer cases.

12-4

3 **Assignment**

Recommended Assignment

- Questions 1–28
- Question 29 (extra credit)
- Reading Lesson 12-5
- Covering the Ideas 12-5

Notes on the Questions

We suggest going through Questions 1–12 in order.

Question 1 A check different than that given in the answers is to graph $y =$ the expression and $y =$ the factored form and see whether the graphs are identical. This is the subject of Question 13.

Question 15 Commutativity does not affect the factorization, but changing the order of the terms in a quadratic expression can confuse students. You might show two ways of finding the factors, one keeping the order as is, and the other rewriting the expression as $-(x^2 - 13x + 40)$.

Question 22 This shortcut is particularly easy when the bases of the squares differ by a small whole number. For example, $2{,}007^2 - 2{,}006^2 = (2{,}007 + 2{,}006)(2{,}007 - 2{,}006) = 4{,}013 \cdot 1 = 4{,}013$.

Questions

COVERING THE IDEAS

1. **a.** In order to factor $x^2 + 10x + 24$, list the possible integer factors of the last term and their sums.
   b. Factor $x^2 + 10x + 24$. **c.** Check your work.
   $(x + 4)(x + 6)$
2. Suppose $(x + p)(x + q) = x^2 + bx + c$.
   a. What must pq equal? c **b.** What must $p + q$ equal? b
3. Sandra, Steve, and Simona each attempted to factor $n^2 + 2n - 48$. Which student's factorization is correct? Explain what mistake the other two students made.

Sandra's	**Steve's**	**Simona's**
$(n + 6)(n - 8)$	$(n - 6)(n - 8)$	$(n - 6)(n + 8)$

In 4–9, write the trinomial as the product of two binomials.

4. $x^2 + 22x + 40$ 5. $q^2 + 20q + 19$ 6. $z^2 - z - 56$
7. $v^2 - 102v + 101$ 8. $r^2 + 10r + 16$ 9. $m^2 + 17m - 38$

10. Explain why the trinomial $x^2 + 6x + 4$ cannot be factored over the integers. No pair of factors of 4 sum to 6.

11. **a.** Factor $x^2 - 8x + 15$. $(x - 3)(x - 5)$
    b. What are the x-intercepts of the graph of $y = x^2 - 8x + 15$? 3, 5

APPLYING THE MATHEMATICS

12. The diagram at the right uses tiles to the factorization of
    $x^2 + 4x + 3 = (x + 1)(x + 3)$.

    Make a drawing to show the factorization of $x^2 + 7x + 10$.

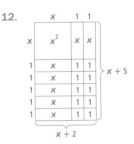

13. **a.** Find an equation of the form
    $y = (x + p)(x + q)$ whose graph is identical to the graph of
    $y = x^2 - 18x + 32$. $y = (x - 2)(x - 16)$
    b. Check your work by graphing both equations on the same set of axes. See margin.

14. **a.** Find the vertex of the parabola with equation $y = x^2 + 2x - 35$ by factoring to find the x-intercepts. $(-1, -36)$
    b. Check Part a by completing the square to put the equation in vertex form. $y + 36 = (x + 1)^2$

15. Factor $-40 + 13x - x^2$. $-(x - 8)(x - 5)$

16. If $m^2 + 13mn + 22n^2 = (m + pn)(m + qn)$, what are p and q?
    $p = 2, q = 11$ or $p = 11, q = 2$

1a. factors: 1, 24; 2, 12; 3, 8; 4, 6
sums: 25, 14, 11, 10

1c. $(x + 4)(x + 6) = x^2 + 6x + 4x + 24 = x^2 + 10x + 24$

3. Simona's factorization is correct. The b term in Sandra's factorization is $6 - 8 = -2$, not 2 as desired. The c term in Steve's factorization is $(-6)(-8) = 48$, not -48 as desired.

4. $(x + 2)(x + 20)$
5. $(q + 1)(q + 19)$
6. $(z - 8)(z + 7)$
7. $(v - 1)(v - 101)$
8. $(r + 2)(r + 8)$
9. $(m - 2)(m + 19)$

12.

12-4A Lesson Master

Questions on SPUR Objectives
See pages 773–775 for objectives.

SKILLS Objective B

In 1–4, factor completely.

1. $x^2 + 9x + 20$ $(x + 4)(x + 5)$ 2. $m^2 - 5m - 14$ $(m - 7)(m + 2)$
3. $a^2 - 11a + 24$ $(a - 8)(a - 3)$ 4. $-2n^2(2n^2 + 3n + 8)$ $-4n^4 - 6n^3 - 16n^2$

5. **a.** Factor $a^2 - 11a + 18$. $(a - 9)(a - 2)$
   b. What are the x-intercepts of the graph of $y = a^2 - 11a + 18$? 9; 2

6. Fill in the blanks.
   a. $x - 3$
   b. $a - 8$

PROPERTIES Objective E

In 7 and 8, an expression is given.
a. For how many integer values of b is the expression factorable?
b. Give the value(s) of b that allow(s) the expression to be factored.

7. $m^2 + bm + 13$
   a. 2
   b. ± 14

8. $y^2 + by - 24$
   a. 8
   b. $\pm 2, \pm 5, \pm 10, \pm 23$

9. Which expression(s) below is/are prime polynomials? B, C
   A $x^2 + 8x + 15$ B $m^2 - 4m + 2$ C $a^2 + 10a - 21$

10. Find a value of c for which the expression $n^2 + 8n + c$ is factorable over the integers. Answers vary. Sample: 7

Additional Answers

13b.

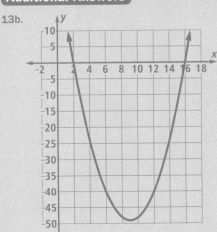

REVIEW

17. Solve and check $(n - 10)\left(\frac{1}{2}n + 6\right) = 0$. (**Lesson 12-3**)
$n = 10$ or $n = -12$

In 18 and 19, find the value of c that makes each trinomial a perfect square. (**Lesson 12-2**)

18. $x^2 - 14x + c$ 49

19. $x^2 + 9x + c$ 20.25

In 20 and 21, expand the expression. (**Lesson 11-6**)

20. $(4 - x)(4 + x)$ $16 - x^2$

21. $(5a - 3)(5a + 3)$ $25a^2 - 9$

22. Explain how $37^2 - 35^2$ can be calculated in your head.
(**Lesson 11-6**) $37^2 - 35^2 = (37 - 35)(37 + 35) = 2 \cdot 72 = 144$

In 23 and 24, simplify the expression. (**Lessons 11-5, 11-4**)

23. $\frac{9z^3 + 10z}{z}$ $9z^2 + 10, z \neq 0$

24. $(n^2 + m^2) - (n - m)^2$ $2mn$

25. Factor $28b^4 + 8b^2 + 40$ completely. (**Lesson 11-4**) $4(7b^4 + 2b^2 + 10)$

26. A certain type of glass allows 85% of the light hitting it to pass through 1 centimeter of glass. The fraction y of light passing through x centimeters of glass is then $y = (0.85)^x$. (**Lesson 7-3**)

   a. Draw a graph of this equation for $0 \leq x \leq 10$. See margin.

   b. Use the graph to estimate the thickness of this glass you would need to allow only a quarter of the light hitting it to pass through. about 8.5 cm

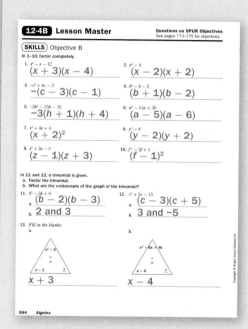

Light is shining through tinted glass.

In 27 and 28, give the slope and y-intercept for each line. (**Lessons 6-8, 6-4**)

27. $y = \frac{1}{4}x$
slope $= \frac{1}{4}$, y-intercept $= 0$

28. $12x - 3y = 30$
slope $= 4$, y-intercept $= -10$

EXPLORATION

29. Using a CAS, make a table like that in the Activity but with integer values of c from -1 to -10. (Row 1 of the table is $x^2 + x - 1$, $x^2 + x - 2$, and so on.)

   a. Repeat Steps 1–3 from the Activity. See Additional Answers on page T89.

   b. How many of these 100 quadratic expressions can be factored over the integers? 12

   c. Describe a pattern in the table that could enable you to extend the table to more factors without doing any calculations.

   Answers vary. Sample answer: The trinomial $x^2 + bx + c$ can be factored as $(x - c)(x - 1)$ if $b = -c - 1$ (for $c < -1$). So, $x^2 + 10x - 11 = (x + 11)(x - 1)$. Also, when $b = \frac{-c}{2} - 2$, $x^2 + bx + c = (x + b + 2)(x - 2)$. For example, $x^2 + 4x - 12 = (x + 6)(x - 2)$.

Factoring $x^2 + bx + c$ **741**

---

17. Check:
If $n = 10$,
$(n - 10)\left(\frac{1}{2}n + 6\right) = 0 \cdot 11 = 0.$
If $n = -12$,
$(n - 10)\left(\frac{1}{2}n + 6\right) = -22 \cdot 0 = 0$

4 Wrap-Up

Ongoing Assessment

Ask students to write down any two numbers, and then compute their sum and product. Finally, ask them to use those four numbers to write a trinomial and its factored form.

Project Update

Project 3, Prime Numbers, Prime Polynomials, on page 768 and Project 4, Public-Key Cryptography, on page 769 relate to the content of this lesson.

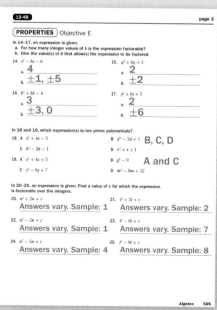

12-4B Lesson Master Questions on SPUR Objectives
See pages 773–775 for objectives.

SKILLS Objective B

In 1–10, factor completely.

1. $x^2 - x - 12$ $(x + 3)(x - 4)$
2. $x^2 - 4$ $(x - 2)(x + 2)$
3. $-c^2 + 4c - 3$ $-(c - 3)(c - 1)$
4. $b^2 - b - 2$ $(b + 1)(b - 2)$
5. $-3h^2 - 15h - 12$ $-3(h + 1)(h + 4)$
6. $a^2 - 11a + 30$ $(a - 5)(a - 6)$
7. $x^2 + 4x + 4$ $(x + 2)^2$
8. $y^2 - 4$ $(y - 2)(y + 2)$
9. $z^2 + 2z - 3$ $(z - 1)(z + 3)$
10. $f^2 - 2f + 1$ $(f - 1)^2$

In 11 and 12, a trinomial is given.
a. Factor the trinomial.
b. What are the x-intercepts of the graph of the trinomial?

11. $b^2 - 5b + 6$
a. $(b - 2)(b - 3)$
b. 2 and 3

12. $c^2 + 2c - 15$
a. $(c - 3)(c + 5)$
b. 3 and -5

13. Fill in the blanks.
a.
b.

$x + 3$ $x - 4$

504 Algebra

12-4B page 2

PROPERTIES Objective E

In 14–17, an expression is given.
a. For how many integer values of b is the expression factorable?
b. Give the value(s) of b that allow(s) the expression to be factored.

14. $x^2 - bx - 6$
a. 4
b. $\pm1, \pm5$

15. $q^2 + bq + 1$
a. 2
b. ±2

16. $k^2 + bk - 4$
a. 3
b. $\pm3, 0$

17. $y^2 + by + 5$
a. 2
b. ±6

In 18 and 19, which expression(s) is/are prime polynomials?

18. A $x^2 + 4x - 5$ B $d^2 - 3d + 1$ B, C, D
C $h^2 - 2h - 1$ D $r^2 + r + 1$

19. A $x^2 + 4x + 5$ B $g^2 - 9$ A and C
C $y^2 - 6y + 7$ D $m^2 - 8m + 12$

In 20–25, an expression is given. Find a value of c for which the expression is factorable over the integers.

20. $n^2 + 2n + c$ Answers vary. Sample: 1
21. $t^2 + 3t + c$ Answers vary. Sample: 2
22. $n^2 - 2n + c$ Answers vary. Sample: 1
23. $t^2 - 8t + c$ Answers vary. Sample: 7
24. $n^2 - 5n + c$ Answers vary. Sample: 4
25. $t^2 - 9t + c$ Answers vary. Sample: 8

Algebra 505

Additional Answers

26a.

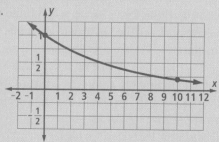

Lesson 12-5

Lesson 12-5

Factoring $ax^2 + bx + c$

▶ **BIG IDEA**   Some quadratic trinomials of the form $ax^2 + bx + c$ can be factored into two linear factors.

You have seen that some trinomials of the form $x^2 + bx + c$ can be factored into a product of two binomials.

$$x^2 + 0x - 100 = (x + 10)(x - 10)$$
$$x^2 + 12x + 36 = (x + 6)(x + 6)$$
$$x^2 - 9x + 14 = (x - 7)(x - 2)$$
$$x^2 + 7x - 8 = (x - 1)(x + 8)$$

In this lesson, we consider quadratic trinomials in which the coefficient of the square term is not 1. Again, we seek to factor the trinomial into binomials with integer coefficients.

In factoring such a trinomial, first check for a common factor of the three terms.

Mental Math

Find the greatest common factor of

a. $16t$ and 32. **16**

b. $9a$, $6b$, and $10ab$. **1**

c. x^2 and $4x^3$. x^2

Example 1

Factor $50x^5 + 200x^4 + 200x^3$.

Solution $50x^3$ is a common factor of the three terms.

$$50x^5 + 200x^4 + 200x^3 = 50x^3(x^2 + 4x + 4)$$

To factor $x^2 + 4x + 4$, we need a binomial whose constant terms have a product of 4 and a sum of 4.

$$x^2 + 4x + 4 = (x + 2)(x + 2)$$

So, $50x^5 + 200x^4 + 200x^3 = 50x^3(x + 2)(x + 2)$.

The original polynomial is said to be factored completely.

Check

$$50x^3(x + 2)(x + 2) = (50x^4 + 100x^3)(x + 2)$$
$$= 50x^5 + 100x^4 + 100x^4 + 200x^3$$
$$= 50x^5 + 200x^4 + 200x^3$$

The factorization checks.

When the coefficient of the square term is not 1 and there is no common factor of the three terms, a different process is applied. Suppose $ax^2 + bx + c = (dx + e)(fx + g)$.

GOAL

Factor a quadratic expression in which the coefficient of the square term is not 1.

SPUR Objectives

B Factor quadratic expressions of the form $x^2 + bx + c$ and $ax^2 + bx + c$.

E Determine whether a quadratic polynomial can be factored over the integers.

Materials/Resources

· Lesson Master 12-5A or 12-5B
· Resource Masters 2 and 189
· Graphing calculator

HOMEWORK

Suggestions for Assignment

• Questions 1–24
• Question 25 (extra credit)
• Reading Lesson 12-6
• Covering the Ideas 12-6

Local Standards

---

1 Warm-Up

1. Suppose that $8x^2 - 27x - 20 = (dx + e)(fx + g)$ for all values of x. How are d, e, f, and g related to the coefficients 8, −27, and −20?
   $df = 8$, $eg = -20$, $dg + ef = -27$

2. Use the information in Question 1 to determine the values of d, e, f, and g.
   $d = 8$, $f = 1$, $e = 5$, $g = -4$ or
   $d = 1$, $f = 8$, $e = -4$, and $g = 5$

Background

A study of advanced algebra, precalculus, and calculus textbooks indicates that factoring is seldom used except in simplifying and operating with rational expressions and in finding limits of rational functions. The difference of squares and the factoring of perfect squares are seen in many contexts.

The trial-and-error method of the examples in this lesson frustrates many people who want an automatic algorithm. One

such algorithm for factoring a quadratic expression uses the Quadratic Formula. Consider the equation of Examples 3 and 4: $15y^2 - 16y - 7 = 0$. Use the Quadratic Formula to find the solutions $\frac{7}{5}$ and $-\frac{1}{3}$. Now reverse the steps to obtain the factorization of $15y^2 - 16y - 7$. An advantage of this algorithm is that it works for factorizations of polynomials with any coefficients.

(continued on next page)

The product of d and f, from the first terms of the binomials, is a. The product of e and g, the constant terms of the binomials, is c. The task is to find d, e, f, and g so that the rest of the multiplication and addition gives b.

Example 2

Factor $5x^2 + 32x + 12$.

Solution

Step 1 Rewrite the expression as a product of two binomials.
$$5x^2 + 32x + 12 = (dx + e)(fx + g)$$
You need to find integers d, e, f, and g.

Step 2 The coefficient of $5x^2$ is 5, so $df = 5$. Assume either d or f is 5, and the other is 1. Now write the following.
$$5x^2 + 32x + 12 = (5x + e)(x + g)$$
The product of e and g is 12, so $eg = 12$. Because the middle term $32x$ is positive, e and g must be positive. Thus, e and g might equal 1 and 12, or 2 and 6, or 3 and 4, in either order. Try all six possibilities.
Can e and g be 1 and 12?
$$(5x + 1)(x + 12) = 5x^2 + 61x + 12$$
$$(5x + 12)(x + 1) = 5x^2 + 17x + 12$$
No, we want $b = 32$, not 61 or 17.
Can e and g be 3 and 4?
$$(5x + 3)(x + 4) = 5x^2 + 23x + 12$$
$$(5x + 4)(x + 3) = 5x^2 + 19x + 12$$
No. Again the middle term is not what we want.
Can e and g be 2 and 6?
$$(5x + 2)(x + 6) = 5x^2 + 32x + 12$$
Yes; here $b = 32$. This is what we want.
$$5x^2 + 32x + 12 = (5x + 2)(x + 6)$$

Check 1 The multiplication $(5x + 2)(x + 6) = 5x^2 + 32x + 12$ is a check.

Check 2 Graph $y = 5x^2 + 32x + 12$ and $y = (5x + 2)(x + 6)$ on the same set of axes. The graphs should be identical. It checks.

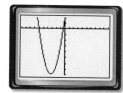

$y = 5x^2 + 32x + 12$
and
$y = (5x + 2)(x + 6)$

(continued on next page)

Factoring $ax^2 + bx + c$ 743

A second algorithm that students will see in later mathematics courses involves the Rational Root Theorem. That theorem enables a person to find all the rational roots of a polynomial with integer coefficients. A third algorithm for factoring uses graphing. To factor $ax^2 + bx + c$, graph $y = ax^2 + bx + c$ and estimate the x-intercepts r and s by tracing along the graph.

Accommodating the Learner

Help students find a pattern that will help them list all possible choices. Students who have a consistent manner of checking for choices will be less likely to be intimidated by a problem that has many factorizations.

2 Teaching

Notes on the Lesson

The questions students should ask themselves as they attempt to factor the expressions in this lesson are the same as those in previous lessons.

1. Is there a common monomial factor? (See Example 1.)
2. Can the quadratic expression be factored over the integers? (See Example 2.)
3. How does a person obtain the factors? (The method used is sophisticated trial and error; the same method is found in both Examples 2 and 3. The strategy is to consider first all the possibilities based on the factors of a and c and then to check each possibility by multiplying until the desired factors are found.)
4. How is this procedure applied when solving equations? (See Example 4.)

In all the examples, the text contains both what a student might write and what a student might think. You might want to take the material in the writing font and display it without the intervening notes.

Emphasize to students that before they try to factor a trinomial, the first question they should ask themselves is whether the trinomial is factorable. Why waste time trying to factor if it is not factorable? Also point out that multiplying is not a good way to check a problem solved by factoring. Substituting a value for the variable in the original expression and the factored expression is a better way to check.

Additional Examples

Example 1 Factor $35x^4 + 35x^3 - 420x^2$.
$35x^2(x - 3)(x + 4)$

Example 2 Factor $7x^2 - 33x - 10$.
$(7x + 2)(x - 5)$

Note-Taking Tips

Now that students have several methods for factoring trinomials, ask them to summarize in their notes when to use each method. Students often mistakenly use the sum and product method to try to factor trinomials of the form $ax^2 + bx + c$. Show them an example of why this is wrong, and ask them to include the example and explanation in their notes.

Additional Example

Example 3 Factor $6z^2 + 13z - 5$.

Solution

First, write the form $(az + b)(cz + d)$.

So $ac = \underline{\ ?\ }$. Thus either a and c are 1 and 6 or they are $\underline{\ ?\ }$ and $\underline{\ ?\ }$. The product $bd = -5$. So b and d are either $\underline{\ ?\ }$ and $\underline{\ ?\ }$, or $\underline{\ ?\ }$ and $\underline{\ ?\ }$. 6; 2; 3; −1; 5; 1; −5

List all the possible factors with $a = 1$ and $c = 6$, and multiply.

$(z + 5)(6z - 1) = \underline{\qquad ?\qquad}$
$6z^2 + 29z - 5$

$(z - 5)(6z + 1) = \underline{\qquad ?\qquad}$
$6z^2 - 29z - 5$

$(z - 1)(6z + 5) = \underline{\qquad ?\qquad}$
$6z^2 - z - 5$

$(z + 1)(6z - 5) = \underline{\qquad ?\qquad}$
$6z^2 + z - 5$

List all the possible factors with $a = 3$ and $c = 2$, and multiply.

$(\underline{\ ?\ }z + 5)(\underline{\ ?\ }z - 1) = \underline{\qquad ?\qquad}$
3; 2; $6z^2 + 7z - 5$

$(\underline{\ ?\ }z - 5)(\underline{\ ?\ }z + 1) = \underline{\qquad ?\qquad}$
3; 2; $6z^2 - 7z - 5$

$(\underline{\ ?\ }z - 1)(\underline{\ ?\ }z + 5) = \underline{\qquad ?\qquad}$
3; 2; $6z^2 + 13z - 5$

$(\underline{\ ?\ }z + 1)(\underline{\ ?\ }z - 5) = \underline{\qquad ?\qquad}$
3; 2; $6z^2 - 13z - 5$

At most, you need to do these eight multiplications. If one of them gives $6z^2 + 13z - 5$, then that is the correct factoring. So $6z^2 + 13z - 5 = \underline{\qquad ?\qquad}$. $(3z - 1)(2z + 5)$

Check 3 Another check is to substitute a value for x, say 4.

Does $5x^2 + 32x + 12 = (5x + 2)(x + 6)$?
$5 \cdot 4^2 + 32 \cdot 4 + 12 = (5 \cdot 4 + 2)(4 + 6)$
$80 + 128 + 12 = 22 \cdot 10$
Yes. Each side equals 220.

In Example 2, there are not many possible factors because the coefficient of x^2 is 5 and all numbers are positive. Example 3 has more possibilities, but the idea is still the same. Try factors until you find the correct ones.

GUIDED

Example 3

Factor $15y^2 - 16y - 7$.

Solution First write down the form. $(ay + b)(cy + d)$. So $ac = \underline{\ ?\ }$. Thus either a and c are 3 and 5 or they are $\underline{\ ?\ }$ and $\underline{\ ?\ }$. The product $bd = -7$. So b and d are either $\underline{\ ?\ }$ and $\underline{\ ?\ }$, or $\underline{\ ?\ }$ and $\underline{\ ?\ }$. 15; 15; 1; −7; 1; 7; −1

List all the possible factors with $a = 3$ and $c = 5$, and multiply.

$(3y + 7)(5y - 1) = \underline{\quad ?\quad}$ $15y^2 + 32y - 7$
$(3y - 7)(5y + 1) = \underline{\quad ?\quad}$ $15y^2 - 32y - 7$
$(3y - 1)(5y + 7) = \underline{\quad ?\quad}$ $15y^2 + 16y - 7$
$(3y + 1)(5y - 7) = \underline{\quad ?\quad}$ $15y^2 - 16y - 7$

List all the possible factors with $a = 1$ and $c = 15$.

$(\underline{\ ?\ }y + 7)(\underline{\ ?\ }y - 1) = \underline{\quad ?\quad}$ 1; 15; $15y^2 + 104y - 7$
$(\underline{\ ?\ }y - 7)(\underline{\ ?\ }y + 1) = \underline{\quad ?\quad}$ 1; 15; $15y^2 - 104y - 7$
$(\underline{\ ?\ }y - 1)(\underline{\ ?\ }y + 7) = \underline{\quad ?\quad}$ 1; 15; $15y^2 - 8y - 7$
$(\underline{\ ?\ }y + 1)(\underline{\ ?\ }y - 7) = \underline{\quad ?\quad}$ 1; 15; $15y^2 + 8y - 7$

At most, you need to do these eight multiplications. If one of them gives $15y^2 - 16y - 7$, then that is the correct factoring.

So $15y^2 - 16y - 7 = \underline{\quad ?\quad}$. $(3y + 1)(5y - 7)$

In Example 3, notice that each choice of factors gives a product that differs only in the coefficient of y (the middle term). If the original problem were to factor $15y^2 - 40y - 7$, this process shows that no factors with integer coefficients will work. The quadratic $15y^2 - 40y - 7$ is a prime polynomial over the set of integers.

Once a quadratic trinomial $f(x)$ has been factored, then solving $f(x) = 0$ is easy using the Zero Product Property.

Accommodating the Learner ⬆

Once students have mastered listing all possible options, they should use educated guessing to decide which option to check first. For example, if the coefficient of x, the linear term, is very large, then they should look for which option will yield greater numbers. Students can often find the correct factorization within the first two or three tries if they think ahead.

12-5

GUIDED

Example 4

Solve $15y^2 - 16y - 7 = 0$.

Solution Use the factorization of $15y^2 - 16y - 7$ in Example 3.

$15^2 - 16y - 7 = 0$

$(\underline{\ ?\ })(\underline{\ ?\ }) = 0$ $3y + 1; 5y - 7$

$\underline{\ \ ?\ \ } = 0$ or $\underline{\ \ ?\ \ } = 0$ $3y + 1; 5y - 7$

$y = \underline{\ ?\ }$ or $y = \underline{\ ?\ }$ $-\frac{1}{3}; \frac{7}{5}$

Questions

COVERING THE IDEAS

1. Perform the multiplications in Parts a–d.

   a. $(2x + 3)(4x + 5)$

   b. $(2x + 5)(4x + 3)$

   c. $(2x + 1)(4x + 15)$

   d. $(2x + 15)(4x + 1)$

   e. Explain how these multiplications are related to factoring $8x^2 + 26x + 15$.

2. Suppose $ax^2 + bx + c = (dx + e)(fx + g)$ for all values of x.

   a. The product of d and f is $\underline{\ ?\ }$. a

   b. The product of $\underline{\ ?\ }$ and $\underline{\ ?\ }$ is c. $e; g$

3. Factor the trinomials completely.

   a. $2x^2 + 14x + 2$ $2(x^2 + 7x + 1)$

   b. $5n^2 + 35n - 50$ $5(n^2 + 7n - 10)$

In 4–9, factor the trinomial, if possible.

4. $5A^2 + 7A + 2$ $(A + 1)(5A + 2)$

5. $-3x^2 + 11x - 6$ $-(x - 3)(3x - 2)$

6. $y^2 - 10y + 16$ $(y - 8)(y - 2)$

7. $14w^2 - 9w - 1$ prime

8. $-4x^2 - 11x + 3$ $-(x + 3)(4x - 1)$

9. $17k^2 - 36k + 19$ $(x - 1)(17x - 19)$

10. Check the solutions to Example 1 by substitution.

11. Solve $20x^2 + 11x - 3 = 0$ by factoring. $x = -\frac{3}{4}$ or $x = \frac{1}{5}$

1a. $8x^2 + 22x + 15$

1b. $8x^2 + 26x + 15$

1c. $8x^2 + 34x + 15$

1d. $8x^2 + 62x + 15$

1e. All of these would be found in the process of trying to factor the trinomial.

10. Let $x = 2$. Then
$50x^2 + 200x^4 + 200x^3 = 1{,}600 + 3{,}200 + 1{,}600 = 6{,}400$ and
$50x^3(x + 2)(x + 2) = 50 \cdot 8 \cdot 4 \cdot 4 = 6{,}400$.

Additional Example

Example 4 Solve $6z^2 + 13z - 5 = 0$.

Solution

Use the factoring of $6z^2 + 13z - 5$ in Example 3.

$6z^2 + 13z - 5 = 0$
$(3z - 1)(2z + 5) = 0$
So $\underline{\ ?\ } = 0$ or $\underline{\ ?\ } = 0$.
$z = \underline{\ ?\ }$ or $z = \underline{\ ?\ }$.

$3z - 1; 2z + 5; \frac{1}{3}; -\frac{5}{2}$

3 Assignment

Recommended Assignment

- Questions 1–24
- Question 25 (extra credit)
- Reading Lesson 12-6
- Covering the Ideas 12-6

Notes on the Questions

Questions 4–9 In Lesson 12-6, students will learn to use the discriminant to test whether a quadratic trinomial of the form $ax^2 + bx + c$ can be factored. Thus you might want to use these questions as motivation for that lesson. Students can check their factorings by graphing or by using a CAS.

12-5

Notes on the Questions

Question 14c Poll your class to see which method is preferred. Expect that students will not necessarily agree. There is no correct answer.

Question 19 Students have to think of x^8 as $(x^4)^2$. Some students are surprised that a factorization of the type in Part b is possible.

Question 20 The idea is not to use arithmetic, but to start with the equation $n(n + 2) = 360$ and then complete the square or use the Quadratic Formula.

Question 25 Students can check using a CAS.

APPLYING THE MATHEMATICS

12. Jules solved the equation $2x^2 - 5x + 3 = 7$ in the following way.

Step 1 He factored $2x^2 - 5x + 3$ into $(2x - 3)(x - 1)$.

Step 2 He substituted the factored expression back into the equation $(2x - 3)(x - 1) = 7$.

Step 3 He considered all the possibilities: $2x - 3 = 7$ and $x - 1 = 1$, in this case $x = 5$ or $x = 2$; or $2x - 3 = 1$ and $x - 1 = 7$, in this case $x = 2$ or $x = 8$.

Step 4 He checked his work and found that none of these values of x check in the original equation.

What did Jules do wrong?

13. Find the vertex of the parabola with equation $y = 8x^2 - 6x + 1$ by first factoring to obtain the x-intercepts.

14. Consider the equation $6t^2 + 7t - 24 = 0$.
    a. Solve the equation by using the Quadratic Formula. $t = -\frac{8}{3}$ or $t = \frac{3}{2}$
    b. Solve the equation by factoring. $t = -\frac{8}{3}$ or $t = \frac{3}{2}$
    c. Which method do you prefer to solve this problem? Why?

15. a. Solve the equation $3n^2 = 2 - 5n$ using the Quadratic Formula.
    b. Check your solution to Part a by solving the same equation using factoring. The solution works.

16. a. Factor $14x^3 - 21x^2 - 98x$ into the product of a monomial and a trinomial. $x(14x^2 - 21x - 98)$ or $7x(2x^2 - 3x - 14)$
    b. Give the complete factorization of $14x^3 - 21x^2 - 98x$. $7x(x + 2)(2x - 7)$

In 17 and 18, find the complete factorization.

17. $9p^2 + 30p^3 + 25p^4$ $p^2(5p + 3)^2$

18. $-2x^2 + 23xy - 30y^2$ $-(x - 10y)(2x - 3y)$

REVIEW

19. Rewrite $x^8 - 16$ as the product of
    a. two binomials. $(x^4 - 4)(x^4 + 4)$
    b. three binomials. (Lessons 12-4, 11-6) $(x^2 - 2)(x^2 + 2)(x^4 + 4)$

20. Find two consecutive positive even integers whose product is 360. (Lessons 12-4, 12-2) 18, 20

21. Find the x-intercepts of $y = x^2 - 8x + 3$ by completing the square. (Lessons 12-3, 12-2) $4 - \sqrt{13}, 4 + \sqrt{13}$

12. Answers vary. Sample answer: He should have subtracted 7 from both sides and then solved for x.

13. $\left(\frac{3}{8}, -\frac{1}{8}\right)$

14c. Answers vary. Sample answer: Factoring, because this quadratic was easy to factor.

15a. $n = -2$ or $n = \frac{1}{3}$

Extension

Students will find it helpful if they are able to recognize that trinomials such as $6x^2 + x - 2 = (2x - 1)(3x + 2)$ and $6x^2 - x - 2 = (2x + 1)(3x - 2)$ have a significant relationship. Take time to consider several such examples with students. This will help them with both factoring and remembering to check the sign of their answer.

22. **a.** Here are three instances of a pattern. Describe the general pattern using two variables, x and y. (**Lessons 11-6, 1-2**)

$$(48 + 32)(24 - 16) = 2(24^2 - 16^2)$$
$$(10 + 20)(5 - 10) = 2(5^2 - 10^2)$$
$$(4 + 1)(2 - 0.5) = 2(2^2 - 0.5^2)$$

b. Does your general pattern hold for all real values of x and y? Justify your answer.

23. **Multiple Choice** Which equation is graphed below?

(**Lesson 9-1**) A

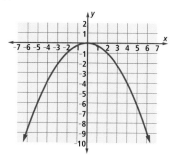

A $y = -\frac{1}{4}x^2$	**B** $y = 4x^2$
C $y = -4x^2$	**D** $y = \frac{1}{4}x^2$

24. When a fair, six-sided die is tossed, the probability of getting a 1 is $\frac{1}{6}$. If the die is tossed twice, the probability of getting a 1 both times is $\frac{1}{6} \cdot \frac{1}{6} = \left(\frac{1}{6}\right)^2$. (**Lessons 8-2, 8-1**)

a. Write an expression to represent the probability of rolling a die m times and getting a 1 each time. $\left(\frac{1}{6}\right)^m$

b. Write your answer to Part a as a power of 6. 6^{-m}

EXPLORATION

25. The polynomial $6x^3 + 47x^2 + 97x + 60$ can be factored over the integers into $(3x + a)(2x + b)(x + c)$. Find a, b, and c. (*Hint:* What is $a \cdot b \cdot c$?) $a = 4, b = 3, c = 5$

22a. $(2x + 2y)(x - y) = 2(x^2 - y^2)$

22b. Yes, because $(2x + 2y)(x - y) = 2(x + y)(x - y) = 2(x^2 - y^2)$, which is the right side.

12-5

4 Wrap-Up

Ongoing Assessment

Ask students to factor the trinomial $8c^2 + 2c - 3$ and to show all of their work. This may be done on paper, or in pairs at the board. Walk around the room and check and correct as they work. Once the trinomial is factored, ask students to solve the equation $8c^2 + 2c - 3 = 0$.

$(4c + 3)(2c - 1); \frac{-3}{4}; \frac{1}{2}$

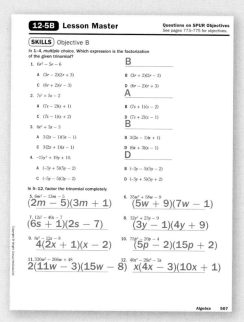

Lesson 12-6

Lesson 12-6

Which Quadratic Expressions Are Factorable?

GOAL

Use the discriminant $b^2 - 4ac$ and the fact that when a, b, and c are integers, the discriminant must be a perfect square or 0 in order for $ax^2 + bx + c$ to be factorable over the integers.

SPUR Objective

E Determine whether a quadratic polynomial can be factored over the integers.

Materials/Resources

· Lesson Master 12-6A or 12-6B
· Resource Master 190
· Scientific or graphing calculator
· Computer Algebra System (CAS)
· Quiz 2

HOMEWORK

Suggestions for Assignment
• Questions 1–19
• Questions 20–21 (extra credit)
• Reading Lesson 12-7
• Covering the Ideas 12-7

Local Standards

1 Warm-Up

A quadratic expression of the form $ax^2 + bx + c$ is given. Determine the value of $\sqrt{b^2 - 4ac}$ and tell whether that value is rational, irrational, or not real. If the value is rational, factor the quadratic.

1. $3x^2 + 4x + 5$ $\sqrt{-44}$; not real
2. $17 - 2n^2 + 15n$ 19; rational;
   $(17 - 2n)(1 + n)$
3. $9y^2 + 12y + 4$ 0; rational;
   $(3y + 2)(3y + 2)$
4. $25z^2 - 25z - 25$ $\sqrt{3,125}$; irrational

> ▶ **BIG IDEA** A quadratic expression with integer coefficients is factorable over the integers if and only if its discriminant is a perfect square.

This lesson connects two topics you have seen in this chapter: factoring and solutions to quadratic equations. These topics seem quite different. Their relationship to each other is an example of how what you learn in one part of mathematics is often useful in another part.

You have seen four ways to find the real-number values of x that satisfy $ax^2 + bx + c = 0$.

1. You can graph $y = ax^2 + bx + c$ and look for its x-intercepts.

2. You can use the Quadratic Formula.

3. You can factor $ax^2 + bx + c$ and use the Zero Product Property.

4. You can set $f(x) = ax^2 + bx + c$ to 0 and look for values of x such that $f(x) = 0$.

The first two ways can always be done. But you know that it is not always possible to factor $ax^2 + bx + c$ over the integers, so it useful to know when it is possible.

Mental Math

Match each function graphed below with its type.

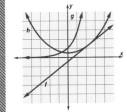

a. exponential growth g

b. linear f

c. quadratic h

A Quadratic Equation with Rational Solutions

Consider the equation $9x^2 + 14x - 8 = 0$. Use the Quadratic Formula.

Step 1 $x = \dfrac{-14 \pm \sqrt{14^2 - 4 \cdot 9 \cdot (-8)}}{2 \cdot 9}$

Step 2 $= \dfrac{-14 \pm \sqrt{484}}{18}$

Step 3 $= \dfrac{-14 \pm 22}{18}$

Step 4 So $x = \dfrac{-14 + 22}{18} = \dfrac{4}{9}$ or $x = \dfrac{-14 - 22}{18} = -2$

Notice that the solutions $\frac{4}{9}$ and -2 have no visible radical sign. This is because the number 484 under the square root sign is a perfect square (Step 2). So, after calculating the square root (Step 3), one integer is divided by another, and the solutions are rational numbers.

748 More Work with Quadratics

Background

Most of this chapter has laid the foundation for this lesson. Students have factored by trial and error and with technology. They have seen that most randomly chosen quadratic trinomials are not factorable. By this time, students have done so much factoring that they want a simple criterion that will tell them when a quadratic expression is factorable.

The logic of the development is given in the Discriminant Theorem. Here are the three if-and-only-if statements which lead

to that theorem. For integers a, b, and c with $a \neq 0$:

1. The quadratic equation $ax^2 + bx + c = 0$ has rational solutions if and only if $ax^2 + bx + c = (dx + e)(fx + g)$, where d, e, f, and g are integers.

2. The quadratic equation $ax^2 + bx + c = 0$ has rational solutions if and only if $b^2 - 4ac$ is a perfect square.

3. The quadratic expression $ax^2 + bx + c$ is factorable if and only if $b^2 - 4ac$ is a perfect square.

In general, for quadratic equations with integer coefficients, if the *discriminant* $b^2 - 4ac$ in the quadratic equation $ax^2 + bx + c = 0$ is a perfect square, then the solutions are rational. The square root of an integer that is not a perfect square is irrational. So the square root will remain in the solutions, and the solutions will be irrational. These results can be summarized in one sentence: *When a, b, and c are integers, the solutions to $ax^2 + bx + c = 0$ are rational numbers if and only if $b^2 - 4ac$ is a perfect square.*

Relating the Solving of $ax^2 + bx + c = 0$ to the Factoring of $ax^2 + bx + c$

Now we connect this with factoring. Consider the same equation as before: $9x^2 + 14x - 8 = 0$.

Factor the left side.

$$(9x - 4)(x + 2) = 0$$

Use the Zero Product Property.

$$9x - 4 = 0 \quad \text{or} \quad x + 2 = 0$$
$$x = \frac{4}{9} \quad \text{or} \quad x = -2$$

You can see from the equation above that when a quadratic equation in standard form is factorable, the solutions are rational numbers. Combining this observation with the facts on the previous page leads us to the following conclusion, which we call the *Discriminant Theorem*. A formal proof of this theorem is given in Chapter 13.

Discriminant Theorem

When a, b, and c are integers, with $a \neq 0$, either all three of the following conditions hold, or none of these hold.

1. $b^2 - 4ac$ is a perfect square.

2. $ax^2 + bx + c$ is factorable over the set of polynomials with integer coefficients.

3. The solutions to $ax^2 + bx + c = 0$ are rational numbers.

Example 1

Is $8x - 5x^2 + 21$ factorable into polynomials with integer coefficients?

Solution First rewrite this expression in the standard form of a polynomial.

$$-5x^2 + 8x + 21$$

Thus $a = -5$, $b = 8$, and $c = 21$.

(continued on next page)

Which Quadratic Expressions Are Factorable? **749**

Accommodating the Learner ⬇

Students who like to mimic an earlier problem as they do their homework will take a lot longer to remember the Quadratic Formula. Suggest that students keep their notes closed during the first attempt of every problem in the homework and do not look back. Students should also try to write the Quadratic Formula from memory every time they begin a problem that uses it. They can then check to see if they remembered it correctly.

2 Teaching

Notes on the Lesson

This lesson has many ideas, so you may wish to organize them. The Discriminant Theorem will help you. When a quadratic equation has integer coefficients, rational solutions to the quadratic mean the quadratic is factorable and its discriminant is a perfect square.

You might want to put a specific case and the general form side by side so that students see the connection between them. Start with an equation such as $2x^2 + 5x - 12 = 0$. It has the rational solutions $\frac{3}{2}$ and -4. This means that the quadratic can be factored as $(2x - 3)(x + 4) = 0$. Then use the equation $ax^2 + bx + c = 0$ where a, b, and c are integers. It has rational solutions $\frac{-b \pm \sqrt{b^2 - 4ac}}{2a}$ if and only if $b^2 - 4ac$ is a perfect square. Calculate the discriminant of $2x^2 + 5x - 12$ to verify that it is a perfect square ($121 = 11^2$).

Some students may think $\sqrt{b^2 - 4ac}$ is the discriminant. Indicate that it is the number *under* the radical sign that does the discriminating. It is that number that is or is not a perfect square.

Unless students know that a quadratic can be factored, we strongly urge them to calculate the discriminant before they engage in any sort of trial-and-error process to find the factors. If the discriminant is not a perfect square, students will have saved valuable time that would have been wasted otherwise. If the discriminant is a perfect square, then the quadratic can be factored, and the students are halfway toward the calculation of the solutions to the quadratic equation.

Examples 1–4 are straightforward.

Additional Example

Example 1 Is $10x^2 - x - 24$ factorable into polynomials with integer coefficients? Yes, because $b^2 - 4ac = 961$, which is a perfect square.

12-6

Additional Examples

Example 2 Is the polynomial $5x^2 - 1 - 3x$ factorable?

Solution

1. Write the polynomial in standard form: _?_ $5x^2 - 3x - 1$

2. Identify a, b, and c. $a = $ _?_ , $b = $ _?_ , $c = $ _?_ . 5; –3; –1

3. Calculate $b^2 - 4ac$. _?_ 29

4. Is $b^2 - 4ac$ a perfect square? _?_ no

5. What is your conclusion? ___?___ $5x^2 - 1 - 3x$ is not factorable with integer coefficients.

Example 3 What can be learned by applying the Discriminant Theorem to the quadratic equation $x^2 - 8 = 0$? $x^2 - 8$ cannot be factored into linear factors with integer coefficients.

Note-Taking Tips

As students write the Discriminant Theorem in their notes, encourage them to include a justification in their own words of why the theorem works. They should use the Quadratic Formula for their explanation.

Then $b^2 - 4ac = (8)^2 - 4 \cdot (-5) \cdot 21 = 64 + 420 = 484$.

Since $484 = 22^2$, 484 is a perfect square. So the expression is factorable.

🛑 QY

> ▶ QY
>
> Verify Example 1 by finding the factorization of $8x - 5x^2 + 21$.

GUIDED

Example 2

Is the polynomial $2x^2 - 10 + 5x$ factorable?

Solution

Step 1 Write the polynomial in standard form. __?__ $2x^2 + 5x - 10$

Step 2 Identify a, b, and c. $a = $ _?_ , $b = $ _?_ , and $c = $ _?_ 2; 5; –10

Step 3 Calculate $b^2 - 4ac$. _?_ 105

Step 4 Is $b^2 - 4ac$ a perfect square? ___?___ no

Step 5 What is your conclusion? The expression is not factorable with integer coefficients.

The phrase "with integer coefficients" is necessary in Example 1 because every quadratic expression is then factorable if noninteger coefficients are allowed.

Example 3

What can be learned by applying the Discriminant Theorem to the quadratic equation $x^2 - 29 = 0$?

Solution In this case, $a = 1$, $b = 0$, and $c = -29$, so $b^2 - 4ac = 0^2 - 4 \cdot 1 \cdot (-29) = 116$. Since 116 is not a perfect square, the solutions to $x^2 - 29 = 0$ are irrational and the polynomial $x^2 - 29$ cannot be factored into linear factors with integer coefficients.

Yet the polynomial $x^2 - 29$ in Example 3 can be factored as the difference of two squares.

$$x^2 - 29 = x^2 - \left(\sqrt{29}\right)^2 = \left(x - \sqrt{29}\right)\left(x + \sqrt{29}\right)$$

The factors do not have integer coefficients, so we say that $x^2 - 29$ is prime over the set of polynomials with integer coefficients, but not over the set of all polynomials. It is just like factoring 7 into $3 \cdot \frac{7}{3}$. The integer 7 is prime over the integers but can be factored into rational numbers.

Accommodating the Learner ⬆

Discuss relating solving $ax^2 + bx + c = 0$ to factoring $ax^2 + bx + c$ in greater detail. What will happen if the discriminant indicates that a trinomial is not factorable into polynomials with integer coefficients? Does that mean the related equation is not solvable? Ask students to discuss this using the problem from Example 3.

Applying the Discriminant Theorem

Knowing whether an expression is factorable can help determine what methods are available to solve an equation.

Example 4

Solve $m^2 - 9m + 24 = 0$ by any method.

Solution Because the coefficient of m^2 is 1, it is reasonable to try to factor the left side. But first evaluate $b^2 - 4ac$ to see whether this is possible.

$a = 1$, $b = -9$, and $c = 24$. So, $b^2 - 4ac = (-9)^2 - 4 \cdot 1 \cdot (24) = -15$. This is not a perfect square, so the equation does not factor over the integers.

In fact, because $b^2 - 4ac$ is negative, there are no real solutions to this equation.

Check Graph $y = x^2 - 9x + 24$. You will see that the graph does not intersect the x-axis. There are no x-intercepts.

What percent of quadratic expressions are factorable? Try the following activity.

Activity

This activity can be done with a partner if a CAS is available, or as a whole-class activity otherwise.

There are infinitely many quadratic expressions of the form $ax^2 + bx + c$, but there are only 8,000 of these in which a, b, and c are nonzero integers from –10 to 10. What percent of these are factorable? There are too many to try to factor by hand, even with a CAS. It is possible to determine this number by programming a computer to factor all of them. But it is also possible to estimate the percent by sampling.

Step 1 Set a calculator to generate random integers from –10 to 10.

Step 2 Generate three such nonzero integers. Call them a, b, and c. Record them and the expression $ax^2 + bx + c$ in a table like the one shown below. **Answers vary. Sample answer:**

Trial	a	b	c	$ax^2 + bx + c$	Factorable?
1	2	–3	7	$2x^2 - 3x + 7$	Prime
2	? 5	? 8	? 3	?	?
3	? 1	? –5	? 6	?	?

$5x^2 + 8x + 3$; $(x + 1)(5x + 3)$

$x^2 - 5x + 6$; $(x - 3)(x - 2)$

(continued on next page)

Notes on the Lesson

Activity This activity shows that only a small percent of quadratics with integer coefficients from –10 to 10 are factorable over the integers. In this activity, the range of coefficients is enlarged to include coefficients of x^2 other than 1 and to include any integers from –10 to 10 as coefficients.

We exclude situations in which one or more of the coefficients a, b, and c are 0. If $a = 0$, then the polynomial is no longer quadratic. If $c = 0$, the trinomial can always be factored with x as one factor. If $b = 0$, then the trinomial may be able to be factored into two binomials. However, there are not many instances of this. Excluding common monomial factors, here are the only expressions of the form $ax^2 + c$ with nonzero coefficients in the range –10 to 10 that are factorable into binomials. In parentheses following each expression is the number of multiples of the expression that lie in the range and thus can be factored. For example, the multiples of $x^2 - 1$ include $3x^2 - 3$ and $-x^2 + 1$. But only thirty-four of the 400 expressions of the form $ax^2 + c$ with nonzero integer coefficients between –10 and 10 are not prime.

This means that only a small percent of quadratic equations with these coefficients have rational solutions. The simplest quadratic equations with integer coefficients are those of the form $x^2 = n$, where n is an integer. If n is negative, the solutions are never real, let alone rational.

Additional Example

Example 4 Solve $p^2 - 4p + 7 = 0$ by any method. Because $b^2 - 4ac = -12$, the equation does not factor over the integers. In fact, because the discriminant is negative, there are no real solutions to this equation.

Notes on the Activity

If students are not using a CAS, suggest they include an extra column in their table after the column $ax^2 + bx + c$ that they title $b^2 - 4ac$. For Step 1, if using a TI calculator, you can generate random numbers by going to MATH, PRB, randInt, and typing (–10, 10, 3) into randInt to obtain three random integer numbers between –10 and 10.

12-6

3 Assignment

Recommended Assignment

- Questions 1–19
- Questions 20–21 (extra credit)
- Reading Lesson 12-7
- Covering the Ideas 12-7

Notes on the Questions

Question 8 Any quadratic whose discriminant is not a perfect square is acceptable.

Question 9 You might caution students to first determine if the sum is possible by using the discriminant.

Question 10 This is an easier way to prove that a number is irrational than a method to be used in Chapter 13. However, it is more sophisticated.

Question 12 This question emphasizes the domain of the Discriminant Theorem. Solving the equation $x^2 + 10x + 23 = 0$ shows the relationship between the solutions to the quadratic equation and the factors of the quadratic expression. The result is a good example of the Factor Theorem to be discussed in Lesson 12-7. This question is a good way to introduce the next lesson.

Question 21c This is the same question as asked in Question 12c, but in a more general setting.

Step 3 If you have a CAS, try to factor $ax^2 + bx + c$ over the integers. If you are working by hand, calculate $b^2 - 4ac$. If the expression is factorable, record the factors. If not, record the word *Prime*.

Step 4 Repeat Steps 2 and 3 at least 20 times. What percent of your quadratic expressions are factorable?
Answers vary. Sample answer: 15%

Step 5 Combine your results with those of others in the class. What is your class's estimate of the percent of these quadratic expressions that are factorable? **Answers vary. Sample answer: 15%**

Questions

COVERING THE IDEAS

In 1–5, a quadratic expression is given. Calculate $b^2 - 4ac$ to determine if the quadratic is factorable or prime over the integers. If possible, factor the expression.

1. $x^2 - 9x - 22$
2. $36 - y^2$
3. $4n^2 - 12n + 9$
4. $-3 + m^2 + 2m$
5. $7x^2 - 13x - 6$ 337; prime

6. Consider the equation $ax^2 + bx + c = 0$ where a, b, and c are integers. If $b^2 - 4ac$ is a perfect square, explain why x is rational.

7. Suppose a, b, and c are integers. When will the x-intercepts of $y = ax^2 + bx + c$ be rational numbers?

8. Give an example of a quadratic expression that can be factored only if noninteger coefficients are allowed.
Answers vary. Sample answer: $x^2 + 6x + 3$

APPLYING THE MATHEMATICS

9. The sum of the integers from 1 to n is $\frac{1}{2}n(n + 1)$. Find n if the sum of the integers from 1 to n is 499,500. $n = 999$

10. What in this lesson tells you that the solutions to the quadratic equation $x^2 - 3 = 0$ are irrational? (This provides a way of showing that $\sqrt{3}$ is irrational.) $b^2 - 4ac = 12$, which is not a perfect square.

11. Find a value of k such that $4x^2 + kx - 5$ is factorable over the integers. **Answers vary. Sample answer: $k = 8$**

12. **a.** By multiplying, verify that $(x + 5 + \sqrt{2})(x + 5 - \sqrt{2}) = x^2 + 10x + 23$.
    b. Verify that the discriminant of the expression $x^2 + 10x + 23$ is not a perfect square. $b^2 - 4ac = 8$
    c. Parts a and b indicate that $x^2 + 10x + 23$ is factorable, yet its discriminant is not a perfect square. Why doesn't this situation violate the Discriminant Theorem?

1. 169; factorable; $(x - 11)(x + 2)$
2. 144; factorable; $(6 + y)(6 - y)$
3. 0; factorable; $(2n - 3)(2n - 3)$
4. 16; factorable; $(m + 3)(m - 1)$
6. If $b^2 - 4ac$ is a perfect square, then the expression $\sqrt{b^2 - 4ac}$ in the Quadratic Formula is an integer, so $-b \pm \sqrt{b^2 - 4ac}$ will be integers and the values of x will be rational.
7. The x-intercepts will be rational numbers when the expression is factorable. This occurs when $b^2 - 4ac$ is a perfect square.
12a. $x^2 + 5x - \sqrt{2}x + 5x + 25 - 5\sqrt{2} + \sqrt{2}x + 5\sqrt{2} - 2 = x^2 + 10x + 23$
12c. The factorization shown is not done over the integers, so the Discriminant Theorem does not apply.

12-6A Lesson Master

PROPERTIES Objective E

1. *Multiple Choice.* If a quadratic polynomial is factorable over the integers, then the discriminant must be __?__. **D**

   A positive   B negative
   C an integer   D a perfect square

In 2–5, a quadratic expression is given. Calculate $b^2 - 4ac$ to determine whether the quadratic is factorable over the integers or prime. If possible, factor the expression.

2. $4x^2 - x - 3$ 49; factorable; $(4x + 3)(x - 1)$

3. $3m^2 + 2m + 5$ −56; prime

4. $n^2 - 30n + 225$ 0; factorable; $(n - 15)(n - 15)$

5. $9p^2 - 20$ 720; prime

6. Which of the expressions below are factorable over the integers? **A, C**

   A $2x^2 + 9x - 5$ C $9x^2 - 25$
   B $5x^2 + 10x - 2$ D $x^2 + 5x + 7$

7. If the following numbers are values of discriminants, which would allow $ax^2 + bx + c$ to be factorable over the integers? **A, D, E**

   A 121   D 1
   B 55   E 0
   C −49   F 8,000

REVIEW

In 13 and 14, factor the polynomial completely. (Lessons 12-5, 12-4)

13. $r^2 - 5r + 4$ $(r - 4)(r - 1)$ 14. $-2x^2 + 5x + 12$ $-(2x + 3)(x - 4)$

15. Consider $w^2 + 9w + c$. (Lesson 12-2)

   a. Complete the square to find the value of c. $c = 20.25$

   b. Express the perfect square trinomial in factored form.
   $(w + 4.5)(w + 4.5)$

16. The surface area S of a cylinder with radius r and height h is
   given by the formula $S = 2\pi r^2 + 2\pi rh$. (Lesson 11-4) 16a. $2\pi r(r + h)$

   a. Factor the right hand side of this formula into prime factors.

   b. Calculate the exact surface area of a cylinder with a diameter
   of 12 cm and a height of 9 cm using either the given formula
   or its factored form. Which form do you think is easier for this
   purpose? 180π; The factored form may be easier.

In 17–19, rewrite the expression with no negative exponents and each
variable mentioned no more than once. (Lessons 8-5, 8-4, 8-3)

17. $\dfrac{8n^{-3}m^2}{6m^{-5}} \cdot \dfrac{4m^7}{3n^3}$ 18. $\left(\dfrac{a^2b}{4a^5}\right)^2 \cdot \dfrac{b^2}{16a^6}$ 19. $\left(\dfrac{3x^4y^{-1}}{15x^3y^0}\right)^2 \cdot \dfrac{x^2}{25y^2}$

EXPLORATION

20. Look back at Question 11. Find *all* integer values of k such that
   $4x^2 + kx - 5$ is factorable in the set of polynomials over the
   integers. Explain how you know that you have found all values.

21. Use a CAS to factor the general expression $ax^2 + bx + c$. (You
   will likely have to indicate that x is the variable.)

   a. What factorization does the CAS give?

   b. Explain how you know that this factorization is correct.

   c. Why doesn't the existence of factors for any quadratic
   expression violate the Discriminant Theorem? The solutions
   are not necessarily rational numbers.

20. $k = -1, k = 1,$
$k = -19, k = 19,$
$k = -8, k = 8.$
The numbers -5
and 4 only have a
few factors. These
values of k were
formed by trying all
possibilities.

21a.
$$a\left(x - \left(\dfrac{-b + \sqrt{b^2 - 4ac}}{2a}\right)\right) \cdot$$
$$\left(x - \left(\dfrac{-b - \sqrt{b^2 - 4ac}}{2a}\right)\right)$$

21b. If you set the
expression equal
to 0, the solutions
to this equation
are
$$x = \dfrac{-b + \sqrt{b^2 - 4ac}}{2a}$$
and
$$x = \dfrac{-b - \sqrt{b^2 - 4ac}}{2a},$$
which are the
solutions given by
the Quadratic
Formula.

QY ANSWER

$-(5x + 7)(x - 3)$

Which Quadratic Expressions Are Factorable? **753**

---

4 **Wrap-Up**

Ongoing Assessment

Ask students to write a clear description
of what the discriminant is and how
they can use it to describe a quadratic
equation. Students should also describe
what the discriminant tells us about the
solutions to a quadratic equation.

Lesson 12-7

Graphs of Polynomial Functions of Higher Degree

Vocabulary

cubic polynomial

GOAL

Make a connection between the x-intercepts of the graphs and factors of quadratic expressions to polynomials of degree higher than 2.

SPUR Objectives

C Find the product of three or more binomials.

F Apply the Factor Theorem.

Materials/Resources

· Lesson Master 12-7A or 12-7B
· Resource Masters 2 and 191–194
· Graphing calculator
· Computer Algebra System (CAS)

HOMEWORK

Suggestions for Assignment

• Questions 1–22
• Question 23 (extra credit)
• Reading Lesson 12-8
• Covering the Ideas 12-8

Local Standards

1 Warm-Up

Activity 1 in the lesson may be used as a Warm-Up. Here is another possible Warm-Up.

The quadratic equation $8x^2 - 14x - 15 = 0$ has rational solutions.

1. Find the solutions. $-\frac{3}{4}$ and $\frac{5}{2}$
2. Use the solutions to indicate, without graphing, where the graph of $y = 8x^2 - 14x - 15$ intersects the x-axis. at the points $\left(-\frac{3}{4}, 0\right)$ and $\left(\frac{5}{2}, 0\right)$
3. Check your answer to Question 2 by graphing. The graph is a parabola that contains the points $\left(-\frac{3}{4}, 0\right)$ and $\left(\frac{5}{2}, 0\right)$.

▶ **BIG IDEA**   The factored form of a polynomial is useful in graphing and solving equations.

Some of the ideas that you have seen in earlier lessons of this chapter extend to the graphs of polynomial functions of degrees 3 and higher. In particular, factoring a polynomial can be a powerful tool to uncover interesting features of graphs of polynomial functions.

How Are Factors and x-Intercepts Related?

Activity 1

In 1–6, a polynomial function is given in factored form. 1–6. See margin
a. Graph the function with a graphing calculator.   on pages 755
b. Identify the x-intercepts of the graph.   and 756.
c. How are the x-intercepts of the graph related to the factors?

1. $f(x) = 5(x - 1)$
2. $g(x) = (x - 1)(x + 2)$
3. $h(x) = (x - 1)(x + 2)(x - 4)$
4. $k(x) = 3(x - 1)(x + 2)(x - 4)$
5. $m(x) = (x - 1)^2(x + 2)^2$
6. $q(x) = (x - 1)(x + 2)(x - 4)(2x + 15)$
7. Look back at your work. Make a conjecture about the factors of a polynomial and the x-intercepts of its graph. Test your conjecture with a different polynomial function than those above.

A graph of the function P with $P(x) = x(x - 8)(x + 6)$ is shown at the right, along with a table of values. Notice how the factors and the x-intercepts are related.

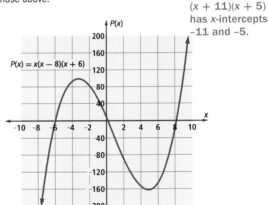

$P(x) = x(x - 8)(x + 6)$

x	P(x)	x	P(x)	x	P(x)
−9	−459	−1	45	7	−13
−8	−256	0	0	8	0
−7	−105	1	−49	9	135
−6	0	2	−96	10	320
−5	65	3	−135	11	561
−4	96	4	−160	12	864
−3	99	5	−165		
−2	80	6	−144		

Mental Math

A baseball player has a batting average of .245. State whether his batting average goes up or down if he plays a game where he goes

a. 1 for 4. up
b. 1 for 5. down
c. 2 for 6. up
7. Answers vary. Sample answer: The factors of a polynomial are of the form $(x - a)$, where a is an x-intercept of the function. For example, the function $f(x) = (x + 11)(x + 5)$ has x-intercepts −11 and −5.

Background

The three ideas introduced in this lesson are multiplying three or more binomials, factoring a product of three or more binomials, and applying the Factor Theorem. Students have already seen the connection between factors of a quadratic expression and x-intercepts. The Factor Theorem is a generalization of polynomials of higher degree. If $P(x) = a(x - r_1)(x - r_2)$ ... $(x - r_n)$, then the graph of $y = P(x)$ intersects the x-axis at $r_1, r_2, \ldots,$ and r_n.

If n linear expressions in x are multiplied, the result is a polynomial of degree n in x. For instance, the product $(ax + b)(cx + d) \cdot (ex + f)(gx + h)$ is a polynomial in x of degree 4. If all the coefficients are integers, then the coefficients of the 4th-degree polynomial will also be integers. Conversely, a polynomial in x of degree 4 with integer coefficients, $a_4x^4 + a_3x^3 + a_2x^2 + a_1x + a_0$ may be able to be factored into linear expressions with integer coefficients.

The graph of the function P has three x-intercepts: 0, 8, and –6. Would your conjecture from Activity 1 have predicted this result? Whether or not you predicted this, there is a simple but elegant relationship between factors and x-intercepts that holds for any polynomial function.

Factor Theorem

Let r be a real number and $P(x)$ be a polynomial in x.

1. If $x - r$ is a factor of $P(x)$, then $P(r) = 0$; that is, r is an x-intercept of the graph of P.

2. If $P(r) = 0$, then $x - r$ is a factor of $P(x)$.

The Factor Theorem is true because the x-intercepts of the graph of the function P are the values of x such that $P(x) = 0$. For the polynomial $P(x) = x(x - 8)(x + 6)$ graphed on the previous page, the equation $P(x) = 0$ means $x(x - 8)(x + 6) = 0$.

By the Zero Product Property, this is a true statement when $x = 0$ or $x - 8 = 0$ or $x + 6 = 0$.
$$x = 8 \text{ or } \qquad x = -6$$

So, because x, $x - 8$, and $x + 6$ are factors of $P(x)$, 0, 8, and –6 are the x-intercepts of the graph of P.

GUIDED

Example 1

A polynomial function P has x-intercepts 5, 7.8, –46, and –200. What is a possible equation for the function?

Solution The polynomial must have at least four factors.

Because 5 is an x-intercept, $x - 5$ is a factor of the polynomial.

Because 7.8 is an x-intercept, ___?___ is a factor of the polynomial. $(x - 7.8)$

Because –46 is an x-intercept, ___?___ is a factor of the polynomial. $(x + 46)$

Because –200 is an x-intercept, ___?___ is a factor of the polynomial. $(x + 200)$

Possibly, $P(x) = (x - 5)(\underline{\ ?\ })(\underline{\ ?\ })(\underline{\ ?\ })$. $x - 7.8$; $x + 46$; $x + 200$

Converting from Factored Form to Standard Form

The polynomial $P(x) = x(x - 8)(x + 6)$ is the product of three factors. To convert this polynomial to standard form, multiply any two of its factors. Then multiply the product of those factors by the third factor. Because multiplication is associative, it does not make any difference which two factors you multiply first.

Graphs of Polynomial Functions of Higher Degree   **755**

 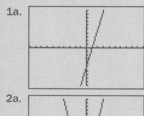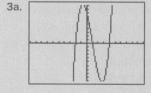
---

2 Teaching

Notes on the Lesson

Activity 1 Whether or not you use Activity 1 as a Warm-Up, it is an appropriate way to begin discussion of the lesson. There are two patterns to be seen. The first pattern is that the x-intercepts and the factors are related (when $x - r$ is a factor, then r is an intercept). Question 6 of Activity 1 is critical for seeing this pattern. The graph of $y = q(x)$ intersects the x-axis at $(-7.5, 0)$, a point whose x-coordinate may not be immediately apparent because it is not an integer. Because the other intercepts are easy to connect with factors, it should be clear that this point is associated with the factor $2x + 15$. Then students may realize that when $2x + 15 = 0$, $x = -7.5$. You may wish to note that $2x + 15 = 2(x + 7.5)$ to make the relationship clearer.

The second pattern is that as the degree of the polynomial increases by 1 in Questions 1–3 of Activity 1, the graph gains a turn. Students have seen that as x increases, the values of a quadratic polynomial function $f(x) = ax^2 + bx + c$ with $a > 0$ decrease (until the vertex of the parabola) and then increase. Or, if $a < 0$, they increase until the vertex and then decrease. When the polynomial function is of degree 3, its leading coefficient is positive and it has three distinct x-intercepts. This is the case for the polynomial graphed following Activity 1: the function increases, then decreases, and then increases. So it changes direction twice. In general, the graph of every polynomial function of degree n with n distinct x-intercepts changes direction $n - 1$ times.

Notes on the Activity

Activity 1 Ask students to start the activity by defining the x-intercept. Then, after they complete the activity, students should be able to justify their results by using the Zero-Product Property.

Additional Example

Example 1 A polynomial function P has x-intercepts at –2, 4, 3, 21 and –30. What is a possible equation for the function?

Answers vary. Sample answer: $P(x) = (x + 2)(x - 4)(x - 3)(x - 21)(x + 30)$

12-7

Notes on the Lesson

Example 2 The direction "rewrite in standard form" is accomplished by the word "expand" in the language of many CAS utilities. Emphasize that to expand the product of more than two polynomials, any two of the polynomials can be selected to be multiplied first. Thus, for example, to expand $(x - 1)(x - 2)(x + 1)(x + 2)$, one might be tempted to multiply the first two and the last two together first to get $(x^2 - 3x + 2)(x^2 + 3x + 2)$ and then multiply these trinomials, but it is easier to multiply the 1st and 3rd binomials together and the 2nd and 4th binomials to obtain $(x^2 - 1)(x^2 - 4)$ and then multiply these to obtain the final product $x^4 - 5x^2 + 4$.

Additional Example

Example 2 Rewrite the polynomial $r(x) = (x - 3)(3x + 2)(x + 2)^2$ in standard form.
$3x^4 + 5x^3 - 22x^2 - 52x - 24$

Additional Answers

Activity 1

4a.
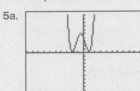

4b. $x = 1$; $x = -2$; $x = 4$

4c., 5c., 6c. The x-intercept(s) make the factor equal to zero.

5a.
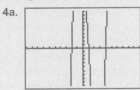

5b. $x = 1$; $x = -2$

6a.
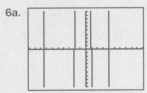

6b. $x = 1$; $x = -2$; $x = 4$; $x = -7.5$

$$P(x) = x(x - 8)(x + 6)$$
$$= (x^2 - 8x)(x + 6)$$
$$= (x^2 - 8x) \cdot x + (x^2 - 8x) \cdot 6$$
$$= x^3 - 8x^2 + 6x^2 - 48x$$
$$= x^3 - 2x^2 - 48x$$

The standard form shows clearly that $P(x)$ is a polynomial of degree 3. It is a **cubic polynomial.** Just as a quadratic function has at most two x-intercepts, a cubic function has at most three x-intercepts.

The following example involves the function q from Activity 1. It is a polynomial function of 4th degree.

Example 2

Rewrite the polynomial $q(x) = (x - 1)(x + 2)(x - 4)(2x + 15)$ in standard form.

Solution There are four factors in the polynomial. Any two can be multiplied first. We multiply the first two and the last two.

$q(x) = (x - 1)(x + 2)(x - 4)(2x + 15)$
    $= (x^2 + x - 2)(2x^2 + 7x - 60)$

Now use the Extended Distributive Property. Each term of the left factor must be multiplied by each term of the right factor. There are nine products.

$= x^2(2x^2 + 7x - 60) + x(2x^2 + 7x - 60) - 2(2x^2 + 7x - 60)$
$= 2x^4 + 7x^3 - 60x^2 + 2x^3 + 7x^2 - 60x - 4x^2 - 14x + 120$
$= 2x^4 + 9x^3 - 57x^2 - 74x + 120$

Check 1 In factored form it is easy to see that $q(1) = 0$. So substitute 1 for x in the standard form to see if the value of the polynomial is 0. The value is $2 + 9 - 57 - 74 + 120 = 0$. It checks.

Check 2 Use a CAS to factor the answer. See if the original factored form appears. Our CAS gives $q(x) = (x - 1)(x + 2)(x - 4)(2x + 15)$.

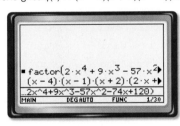

In Activity 2, you are asked to explore what happens when the same factor appears twice in a polynomial.

Accommodating the Learner

Discuss why the directions in Example 1 phrase the question "What is a possible equation for this function," instead of "What is the equation of the function."

Additional Answers

Activity 2

Step 1a. $f(x) = x(x - 3)(x + 7)$
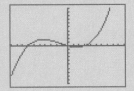

$g(x) = x(x - 3)(x + 7)^2$
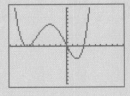

$h(x) = x(x - 3)^2(x + 7)^2$
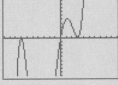

$j(x) = x^2(x - 3)^2(x + 7)^2$
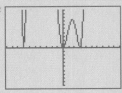

Activity 2

Step 1 **a.** Graph the following polynomial functions on the window
$-10 \leq x \leq 10, -500 \leq y \leq 500$. Make a sketch of each graph.

$f(x) = x(x - 3)(x + 7)$ $g(x) = x(x - 3)(x + 7)^2$
$h(x) = x(x - 3)^2(x + 7)^2$ $j(x) = x^2(x - 3)^2(x + 7)^2$

b. What are the x-intercepts of these graphs?

c. What is different about the graphs around the point $(-7, 0)$ when $(x + 7)^2$ is a factor rather than just $(x + 7)$?

Step 2 **a.** Multiply each polynomial by -1 and graph the resulting functions.

b. Describe what happens to the x-intercepts.

Step 3 Multiplying $P(x)$ by -1 means graphing $-P(x)$. The graph wiggles in the middle. But in all these functions, as you go farther to the right, the graph heads either up or down. As you go farther to the left, the graph also heads either up or down.

a. Copy and complete the table.

Polynomial	Far Right: Up or Down?	Far Left: Up or Down?	Polynomial	Far Right: Up or Down?	Far Left: Up or Down?
$f(x) = x(x - 3)(x + 7)$	?	?	$-f(x)$	?	?
$g(x) = x(x - 3)(x + 7)^2$	?	?	$-g(x)$	?	?
$h(x) = x(x - 3)^2(x + 7)^2$	?	?	$-h(x)$	?	?
$j(x) = x^2(x - 3)^2(x + 7)^2$	?	?	$-i(x)$	?	?

b. Describe the general pattern.

Step 4 **a.** Experiment to find what happens to the graph of
$P(x) = ax(x - 3)(x + 7)$ as values of a change from positive to negative.

b. Does the same situation hold for the graph of
$j(x) = ax^2(x - 3)^2(x + 7)^2$? **yes**

The Importance of Polynomial Functions

In this course, you have studied polynomial functions of degrees 1 and 2 in detail. A polynomial function of degree 1 has an equation of the form $y = mx + b$. Its graph is a line. A polynomial function of degree 2 has an equation of the form $y = ax^2 + bx + c$. Its graph is a parabola. The graphs of polynomial functions of degrees 3 and 4 have more varied shapes and graphs of higher degrees have still more varied shapes. This makes polynomial functions very useful in approximating data of many kinds and very useful in approximating other functions. Polynomials also appear as formulas in a number of situations, a few of which are mentioned in the Questions for this lesson.

Graphs of Polynomial Functions of Higher Degree **757**

1a. See margin.
1b. 0; 3; −7
1c. Instead of crossing the x-axis, the graph just touches it.
2a. See margin.
2b. They are unchanged.
3a. Row 1: up; down; down; up
Row 2: up; up; down; down
Row 3: up; down; down; up
Row 4: up; up; down; down
3b. Polynomial functions with an odd number of factors and a positive coefficient of the highest degree term go down on the far left and functions with an even number of factors go up on the far left. The negative sign reflects the graph over the x-axis.
4a. The graph is reflected over the x-axis.

Notes on the Lesson

Activity 2 This activity deals with the *local behavior* of polynomials around the points where there are multiple x-intercepts and the *end behavior* of those polynomials. These topics were discussed in calculus before the existence of graphing technology. Now they can be explored much earlier. You should treat this activity as optional.

Notes on the Activity

Activity 2 To help students answer Step 1c, encourage them to zoom in around the key point to see what is happening. Remind students that for Step 2, because of the Commutative Property of Multiplication, they can simply multiply the functions at the end by (-1).

Additional Answers

Activity 2

Step 2a. $f(x) = -x(x - 3)(x + 7)$

$g(x) = -x(x - 3)(x + 7)^2$

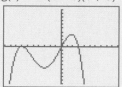

$h(x) = -x(x - 3)^2(x + 7)^2$

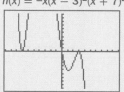

$j(x) = -x^2(x - 3)^2(x + 7)^2$

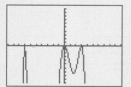

Accommodating the Learner

Draw a random squiggle on a coordinate grid on the board. Ask students to discuss key qualities of the graph. These could include the x-intercepts, y-intercepts, areas where the function is increasing or decreasing, or positive or negative. These might include maximum and minimum areas on the graph. Ask students if we can use the Factor Theorem here. They should learn that we do not know if this is a polynomial function, so we cannot automatically apply the Factor Theorem.

This is a good opportunity to discuss the fact that it is far easier to describe the graph of a random equation than it is to take a random sketch and use an equation to describe it. Remind students that an equation is a general rule, and unless we can clearly identify the shape, we cannot predict any part of the graph that we cannot see.

12-7

3 Assignment

Recommended Assignment

- Questions 1–22
- Question 23 (extra credit)
- Reading Lesson 12-8
- Covering the Ideas 12-8

Notes on the Questions

Questions 1 and 2 These are quadratic functions, and students should remember the connection between graphs and factors from preceding lessons.

Question 4 Because the expression is a product of four different linear factors, students should look for four intercepts.

Questions

COVERING THE IDEAS

In 1–4, an equation for a function is given.

   a. Identify the x-intercepts of the graph of the function.

   b. Check your answer to Part a by graphing the function. Draw a rough sketch of the graph.

   c. Write the equation in standard form.

1. $f(x) = (x + 5)(2x - 3)$

2. $y = (x + 5.8)(2x - 3.4)$

3. $y = -3(x - 1)(2x + 1)^2$

4. $g(x) = x(8x + 5)(10x + 2)(x - 1)$

5. Give an equation for a polynomial function whose graph intersects the x-axis at $(-9, 0)$, $(4, 0)$, and nowhere else.

6. Suppose the graph of a polynomial function has three x-intercepts: 1, –4, and 5.

   a. Give an equation in factored form for the polynomial function.

   b. Rewrite your equation from Part a in standard form.

7. a. Give an equation in factored form for a polynomial function with four x-intercepts: 2, –2, 5, and –5.

   b. Rewrite your equation from Part a in standard form.

8. Match the following equations with their possible graphs.

   a. $a(x) = (x + 2)(x - 4)^2(x - 6)$ iii

   b. $b(x) = -1(x + 2)(x - 4)(x - 6)$ i

   c. $c(x) = -1(x + 2)^2(x - 4)(x - 6)$ ii

   d. $d(x) = -(x + 2)(x - 4)^2(x - 6)$ iv

i.
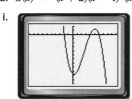

ii.

iii.
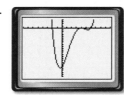

iv.
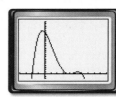

1a. –5, 1.5

1b.
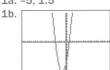

1c. $f(x) = 2x^2 + 7x - 15$

2a. –5.8, 1.7

2b.

2c. $y = 2x^2 + 8.2x - 19.72$

3a. 1; –0.5

3b.

3c. $y = -12x^3 + 9x + 3$

4a. 0, –0.625, –0.2, 1

4b.

4c. $g(x) = 80x^4 - 14x^3 - 56x^2 - 10x$

5. Answers vary.
Sample answer:
$y = (x + 9)(x - 4)$

6a. Answers vary.
Sample answer:
$y = (x + 4)(x - 1) \cdot (x - 5)$

6b. $y = x^3 - 2x^2 - 19x + 20$

7a. Answers vary.
Sample answer:
$y = (x - 2)(x + 2) \cdot (x - 5)(x + 5)$

7b. $y = x^4 - 29x^2 + 100$

In 9–12, give a possible equation in factored form for each graph.

9.

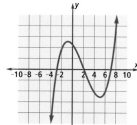

10.

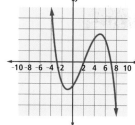

11.

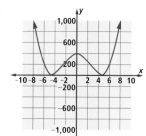

12.

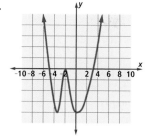

13. Let $S(n)$ = the sum of the squares of the integers from 1 to n. It is known that $S(n) = \frac{1}{6}n(n + 1)(2n + 1)$.

   a. Find $S(5)$ using the formula and verify your answer by using the definition of $S(n)$. **55; 1 + 4 + 9 + 16 + 25 = 55**

   b. What is the value of $S(n + 1) - S(n)$? **$(n + 1)^2$**

   c. Write the formula for $S(n)$ in standard form.

14. Explain what you know about each of the following aspects of the graph of the function $h(x) = -8(x - 11)^2(x + 5)(x + 10)^2$.

   a. x-intercepts **11; –5; –10**

   b. when the graph changes direction at an x-intercept

   c. the direction of the far right side of the graph **down**

APPLYING THE MATHEMATICS

15. a. Graph $y_1 = (x - 2)(x + 4)(x - 5)$ and $y_2 = (x - 2)^3(x + 4)(x - 5)$.

   b. Use the results of Part a to predict a characteristic of the graph of $y_3 = (x - 2)(x + 4)(x - 5)^3$.

   c. Use the results of Parts a and b to predict a characteristic of the graph of $y_4 = (x - 2)^3(x + 4)(x - 5)^3$.

   d. Generalize the results of Parts a, b, and c.

9. Answers vary.
   Sample answer: $y = (x + 3)(x - 2)(x - 7)$

10. Answers vary.
   Sample answer: $y = -(x + 3)(x - 2)(x - 7)$

11. Answers vary.
   Sample answer: $y = (x + 5)^2(x - 4)^2$

12. Answers vary.
   Sample answer: $y = (x + 2)^2(x + 5) \cdot (x - 3)$

13c. $S(n) = \frac{1}{3}n^3 + \frac{1}{2}n^2 + \frac{1}{6}n$

14b. $x = 11$ and $x = -10$

15a.

15b. Answers vary.
   Sample answer: The graph crosses the x-axis at the x-intercept 5.

15c. Answers vary.
   Sample answer: The graph crosses the x-axis at the x-intercept 5.

15d. Answers vary.
   Sample answer: If a polynomial in factored form has a term of the form $(x - a)^3$, then the graph will cross the x-axis at $(a, 0)$.

Notes on the Questions

Question 13 The answer should be found in two ways: by multiplying the factors in $S(n + 1)$ and $S(n)$ and doing the subtraction, and by realizing from the definition of $S(n)$ that the difference between the sum of the first $n + 1$ squares and the sum of the first n squares is going to be the $(n + 1)$th square.

Question 15 Expect students to have to try more examples before a generalization can be made.

Question 22 There are six possible equations of best fit in this table, because any one of the three columns could be the independent variable and then either of the other two columns could be the dependent variable. Thus the calculation of the number of possible equations is a simple example of a permutation.

Graphs of Polynomial Functions of Higher Degree   **759**

Extension

Extend the activity by comparing the degree of the polynomial with the number of x-intercepts. Students may initially think that there are always the same number of x-intercepts as the degree of the polynomial, but ask them to consider the polynomial $m(x) = (x - 1)^2(x + 2)^2$. They will see that this is of degree 4 but it has only two distinct x-intercepts, which are 1 and –2. Ask students to predict whether it is possible for a polynomial of degree n to have more than n x-intercepts.

12-7

4 Wrap-Up

Ongoing Assessment

Provide students with several sketches of polynomials, and ask them to call out the *x*-intercepts and the corresponding factors of the polynomial. If there is time, connect the final answer for each to the results of Activity 2 to see if this could be the correct polynomial based on the end behavior.

Project Update

Project 5, Using Polynomials to Approximate, and Project 6, The Bisection Method, on page 769 relate to the content of this lesson.

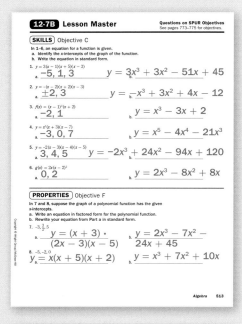

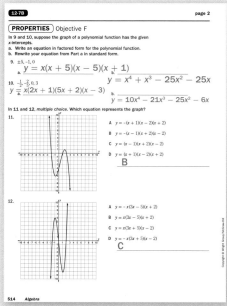

REVIEW

In 16–18, factor the polynomial. (Lessons 12-5, 11-4)

16. $9x^2y^2 - 27x^3y + 19xy$ $xy(9xy - 27x^2 + 19)$

17. $4a^2 - 16b^2$ $4(a + 2b)(a - 2b)$

18. $15n^2 + 1 - 8n$ $(3n - 1)(5n - 1)$

19. $a = -11$ or $a = 5$

20. $w = \dfrac{-7 \pm \sqrt{181}}{6}$

In 19–22, solve by using any method. (Lessons 12-5, 12-2, 9-5)

19. $a^2 + 6a = 55$

20. $-3w^2 - 7w + 11 = 0$

21. **Multiple Choice** Which system of inequalities is graphed at the right? (Lesson 10-9) B

A $\begin{cases} y \ge -2x - 8 \\ y \ge 0 \\ x \le -9 \end{cases}$ B $\begin{cases} y \le -2x - 8 \\ y \ge 0 \\ x \ge -9 \end{cases}$ C $\begin{cases} y \ge -2x - 8 \\ y \le 0 \\ x \le -9 \end{cases}$ D $\begin{cases} y \le -2x - 8 \\ y \ge -9 \\ x \ge 0 \end{cases}$

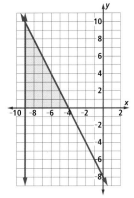

22. According to the U.S. Department of Labor, the following percentages of the adult population were employed in the particular years shown in the table at the right. Assume these trends continue. (Lesson 6-7)

   a. Use linear regression to find a line that fits the pairs (year, male). Write the equation of a line of best fit.

   b. Repeat Part a for the pairs (year, female). Write the equation of a line of best fit. $y = 0.481x - 905$

   c. Using your equation from Part b, predict what percentage of adult women will be employed in the year 2010. $\approx 61.8\%$

   d. Using your equations from Parts a and b, predict when, if ever, the same percentage of adult men and adult women will be employed. 2019

Year	Male	Female
1974	74.9	42.6
1979	73.8	47.5
1984	70.7	49.5
1989	72.5	54.3
1995	70.8	55.6
2001	70.9	57.0
2002	69.7	56.3

22a. $y = -0.151x + 371$

EXPLORATION

23. a. Explore the graphs of $y_1 = x^3$, $y_2 = x^4$, $y_3 = x^5$, and $y_4 = x^6$ and make a generalization about the graph of $f(x) = x^n$, when n is a positive integer.

   b. If x is replaced by $x - 5$ in each of the graphs of Part a, what happens to the graphs?

   c. Generalize the result in Part b.

23a. When n is even, the graph is bowl-shaped, with $x = 0$ at the bottom. When n is odd, the graph moves up at different levels of steepness, appearing flat near $x = 0$.

23b. The graphs are shifted 5 units to the right.

23c. Answers vary. Sample answer: When x is replaced by $x - a$ in a function, the graph of the function is shifted a units to the right.

Lesson
12-8
Factoring and Rational Expressions

Vocabulary

rational expression

lowest terms

▶ **BIG IDEA** The factored form of a polynomial is useful in writing rational expressions in lowest terms and in performing operations on rational expressions.

In Lesson 12-7, you saw how factoring can help find the solutions to polynomial equations. Factoring can also help in working with fractions that have polynomials in their numerators and denominators.

Activity

Step 1 Before reading Step 2, perform the addition of these fractions and write your answer in lowest terms. Do not use a calculator.

$$\frac{75}{100} + \frac{66}{99} \quad \frac{17}{12}$$

Step 2 Describe how you did the addition. Did you find a common denominator? If so, then you probably worked with fractions with denominator 9,900. Or, did you put each fraction in lowest terms first? Then you could do the addition with a common denominator of 12. Compare the way you added these fractions with the ways that others in your class added them.

Writing Rational Expressions in Lowest Terms

In the addition of fractions above, it is useful to write each fraction in lowest terms. As you know, this is done by dividing both the numerator and denominator of the fraction by one of their factors. Because 25 is a common factor of the numerator and denominator of the first fraction, $\frac{75}{100} = \frac{25 \cdot 3}{25 \cdot 4}$. Similarly, $\frac{66}{99} = \frac{33 \cdot 2}{33 \cdot 3} = \frac{2}{3}$.

The same idea can be used with *rational expressions*. A **rational expression** is the written quotient of two polynomials. Here are five examples of rational expressions.

$$\frac{0.7819}{x + y} \qquad \frac{3x^3 y}{x^2 y^4}$$

$$\frac{a + \pi}{b - \pi} \qquad \frac{4n^2 + 4n + 1}{4n^2 - 1}$$

$$\frac{6k^3 - 12k^2 + 42k - 210}{3k^3 - 6k^2 + 21k - 105}$$

Mental Math

Estimate to the nearest dollar the interest earned in one year in a savings account with 2.02% annual interest rate containing

a. $501. $10

b. $4,012. $81

c. $9,998. $202

Step 2. Answers vary. Sample answer: I simplified each fraction and then found the common denominator of 12 and added the two fractions.

Factoring and Rational Expressions   **761**

Background

Both rational expressions and simple fractions are indicated divisions. The operations with simple fractions extend well to rational expressions. We add, subtract, multiply, divide, and take powers of rational expressions just as we do these operations with simple fractions. We can also put rational expressions in lowest terms as we do with simple fractions, by dividing both numerator and denominator by factors they have in common. A simple fraction cannot have 0 in its denominator. A rational

expression is undefined for those values of the variable(s) that would lead to a 0 in the denominator.

Although there is work with addition and subtraction of rational expressions in this lesson, the only skill with rational expressions that is expected in this course is the ability to rewrite a rational expression in lowest terms. For most students, it is too much to expect them to gain facility with operations with rational expressions in their first full year of a study of algebra.

GOAL

Apply factoring to operations with, and simplifications of, rational expressions.

SPUR Objective

D Use factoring to write rational expressions in lowest terms.

Materials/Resources

· Lesson Master 12-8A or 12-8B
· Resource Masters 2 and 195
· Graphing calculator
· Computer Algebra System (CAS)

HOMEWORK

Suggestions for Assignment
• Questions 1–24
• Question 25 (extra credit)
• Reading Lesson 13-1
• Covering the Ideas 13-1

Local Standards

1 **Warm-Up**

Write the fraction in lowest terms. Assume variables do not have values that would make the denominator 0.

1. $\frac{23 \cdot 19}{19 \cdot 24}$ $\frac{23}{24}$

2. $\frac{mp}{pq}$ $\frac{m}{q}$

3. $\frac{(2x - 7)(x + 4)}{(x + 4)(3x - 1)}$ $\frac{2x - 7}{3x - 1}$

4. $\frac{ab^2}{bcd}$ $\frac{ab}{cd}$

5. $\frac{3x - 6}{2x^2 - 3x - 2}$ $\frac{3}{2x + 1}$

12-8

2 Teaching

Notes on the Lesson

Each idea of this lesson can be considered a generalization of work with fractions that students have known for years. You might wish to take the ideas in order of their appearance.

Activity The fractions to be added are equal to $\frac{3}{4}$ and $\frac{2}{3}$, so it is far more efficient to put the fractions in lowest terms before adding than to find a common denominator of 9,900.

Writing rational expressions in lowest terms. To put a rational expression in lowest terms, look for common factors of the numerator and denominator, just as you would do with fractions. The Warm-Up can lead you into this part of the lesson. Then work through Example 1. QY reminds students to look for obvious relationships between the numerator and denominator before doing anything else. Explain to students that the reason this expression can be simplified is that the numerator can be factored into 2 times the denominator, and not because term-by-term simplification works.

Additional Example

Example 1 Write $\frac{6x^2 - x - 2}{3x^2 + x - 2}$ in lowest terms.

Solution

1. Factor the numerator and the denominator.

2. From Step 1, fill in the blanks. $\frac{(?x + 2)(?x - 2)}{(?x + 2)(?x + 2)}$ 2; 1; 3; 2   3; 2; 1; 1

3. The numerator and denominator in Step 2 have a factor in common.

   Divide them by that factor. $\frac{6x^2 - x - 2}{3x^2 + x - 2} = \frac{(?x + ?)}{(?x + ?)}$ 2; 1   1; 1

Because the resulting numerator and denominator have no common factors, the fraction is in lowest terms.

A rational expression is in **lowest terms** when there is no polynomial that is a factor of its numerator and denominator. The second rational expression on the previous page is not in lowest terms because x^2y is a common factor of the numerator and denominator.

$$\frac{3x^3y}{x^2y^4} = \frac{x^2y \cdot 3x}{x^2y \cdot y^3} = \frac{3x}{y^3}$$

Technically, $\frac{3x}{y^3}$ is not exactly equivalent to $\frac{3x^3y}{x^2y^4}$ because the x in $\frac{3x}{y^3}$ can equal 0 while the x in $\frac{3x^3y}{x^2y^4}$ cannot equal 0. Often this is taken for granted, but sometimes people will write $x \neq 0$ and $y \neq 0$ because fractions do not allow 0 as the denominator.

The rational expressions $\frac{4n^2 + 4n + 1}{4n^2 - 1}$ and $\frac{6k^3 - 12k^2 + 42k - 210}{3k^3 - 6k^2 + 21k - 105}$ look more complicated than the others on page 761. But each expression can be put in lowest terms by factoring out the common factors.

GUIDED

Example 1

Write $\frac{4n^2 + 4n + 1}{4n^2 - 1}$ in lowest terms. Assume the denominator does not equal 0.

Solution

Step 1 Factor the numerator $4n^2 + 4n + 1$. $(2n + 1)^2$

Step 2 The denominator $4n^2 - 1$ is the difference of two squares. Use this information to factor it. $(2n + 1)(2n - 1)$

Step 3 From Steps 1 and 2, fill in the blanks.

$$\frac{4n^2 + 4n + 1}{4n^2 - 1} = \frac{(\underline{?}n + \underline{?})(\underline{?}n + \underline{?})}{(\underline{?}n + \underline{?})(\underline{?}n - \underline{?})}$$ 2; 1; 2; 1   2; 1; 2; 1

Step 4 The numerator and denominator in Step 3 have a factor in common. Divide them by that factor.

$$\frac{4n^2 + 4n + 1}{4n^2 - 1} = \frac{(\underline{?}n + \underline{?})}{(\underline{?}n - \underline{?})}$$ 2; 1   2; 1

Because the numerator and denominator on the right have no common factor, the fraction is in lowest terms.

Check Check your answer by substituting 3 for n in the original rational expression and in the expression of Step 4.

STOP **QY**

A graphing calculator and CAS technology can be of great assistance when writing a fraction in lowest terms.

▶ QY

Explain why

$$\frac{6k^3 - 12k^2 + 42k - 210}{3k^3 - 6k^2 + 21k - 105}$$

is not in lowest terms.

Accommodating the Learner 🔽

Take extra time to practice finding roots and writing polynomials in factored form using the calculator. You may wish to create additional examples. Remind students to always factor out the greatest common factor before they begin the more complicated factoring. Students can use a CAS to check their work.

Example 2

Simplify the expression $\dfrac{x^3 - 2x^2 - 23x + 60}{x^3 + 8x^2 - 3x - 90}$.

Solution 1 To factor the numerator, graph $f(x) = x^3 - 2x^2 - 23x + 60$ with a graphing calculator. The graph has three x-intercepts: -5, 3, and 4, indicating that $(x - 4)$, $(x - 3)$, and $(x - -5)$ are factors of the numerator. To factor the denominator, graph $g(x) = x^3 + 8x^2 - 3x - 90$. This graph has x-intercepts 3, -5, and -6, indicating that $(x - 3)$, $(x - -5)$, and $(x - -6)$ are factors of the denominator. Thus,

$$\frac{x^3 - 2x^2 - 23x + 60}{x^3 + 8x^2 - 3x - 90} = \frac{(x + 5)(x - 4)(x - 3)}{(x - 3)(x + 5)(x + 6)} = \frac{x - 4}{x + 6}.$$

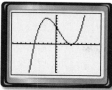

$-10 \le x \le 10, -100 \le y \le 100$

Solution 2 Use a CAS. If you enter the given rational expression into a CAS, you may immediately see the expression in lowest terms.

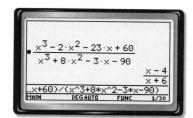

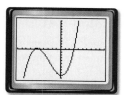

$-10 \le x \le 10, -100 \le y \le 100$

Solution 3 Use a CAS to show the steps of Solution 1. Factor the numerator and the denominator.

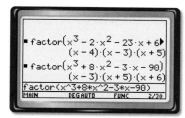

Thus $\dfrac{x^3 - 2x^2 - 23x + 60}{x^3 + 8x^2 - 3x - 90} = \dfrac{(x - 4)(x - 3)(x + 5)}{(x - 3)(x + 5)(x + 6)}.$

Divide numerator and denominator by the common factors.

The solution is $\dfrac{x - 4}{x + 6}$.

Caution: Notice that you *cannot* simplify $\dfrac{x - 4}{x + 6}$ by dividing by x because the x's are terms, not factors.

(continued on next page)

Factoring and Rational Expressions   **763**

Notes on the Lesson

Example 2 This example, involving polynomials of degree 3, requires the use of the Factor Theorem. With a graphing calculator, an efficient strategy is to graph f and g on the same axes and look to see if the graphs intersect on the x-axis. Since they intersect at $(3, 0)$, $(-5, 0)$, and one other point not on the x-axis, $x - 3$ and $x + 5$ are common factors. With a CAS, the work is even simpler because most machines will automatically rewrite the expression in lowest terms even as you enter it.

Additional Example

Example 2 Simplify the expression.
$\dfrac{2x^4 - 6x^3 - 20x^2 + 48x}{4x^4 - 4x^3 - 88x^2 + 160x}$
$\dfrac{x + 3}{2x + 10}$

ENGLISH LEARNERS
Vocabulary Development

Review the definition of a rational number, and transition students from that definition to the definition of a rational expression. Compare the use of lowest terms for each.

Notes on the Lesson

Examples 3 and 4 These examples involve the addition and subtraction of rational expressions. Again the work proceeds in analogy with what is done with numerical fractions. That is, the usual strategy is to find a common denominator, rewrite each fraction with that denominator, and then perform the operations on the numerators. In Example 4, the common error is for students to subtract $3k$ but not 7 in the second-to-last step of the hand calculation. Again, a CAS can do these operations automatically.

Additional Example

Example 3 Write $\frac{2}{x} - \frac{3}{y}$ as a single rational expression.

Solution

Because x and y have no common factors, their least common multiple is xy. This is the common denominator.

$\frac{2}{x} - \frac{3}{y} = \frac{2 \cdot ?}{x \cdot y} - \frac{3 \cdot ?}{x \cdot y}$ $y; x$

Fraction Multiplication Property

$= \frac{?}{x \cdot y}$ Distributive Property $2y - 3x$

Check Graph Y1 $= \frac{x^3 - 2x^2 - 23x + 60}{x^3 + 8x^2 - 3x - 90}$ and Y2 $= \frac{x - 4}{x + 6}$ to see whether they appear to be equivalent expressions. Use the WINDOW $-25 \leq x \leq 25$, $-6 \leq y \leq 6$.

 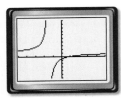

The two appear to form the same graph, so the result checks.

Adding and Subtracting Rational Expressions

To add $\frac{1}{9} + \frac{7}{15}$, you can either look for a calculator or look for a common denominator. If you do not have a calculator that does fractions, the least common denominator can be found by factoring each denominator and finding a product that will be a multiple of each denominator. Since $9 = 3 \cdot 3$ and $15 = 3 \cdot 5$, the least common denominator is $3 \cdot 3 \cdot 5$, or 45.

$$\frac{1}{9} + \frac{7}{15} = \frac{1}{3 \cdot 3} + \frac{7}{3 \cdot 5}$$

$$= \frac{1 \cdot 5}{3 \cdot 3 \cdot 5} + \frac{7 \cdot 3}{3 \cdot 5 \cdot 3}$$

$$= \frac{5}{45} + \frac{21}{45}$$

$$= \frac{26}{45}$$

You may have done most of this process in your head. We show the steps because you can add or subtract rational expressions in the same way.

GUIDED

Example 3

Write $\frac{a}{b} + \frac{c}{d}$ as a single rational expression.

Solution Since b and d have no common factors, their least common multiple is bd. This is the common denominator.

$\frac{a}{b} + \frac{c}{d} = \frac{a \cdot ?}{b \cdot d} + \frac{? \cdot c}{b \cdot d}$ Fraction Multiplication Property $d; b$

$= \frac{?}{b \cdot d}$ Distributive Property $ad + bc$

Check You can check by substituting numbers for a, b, c, and d. Try $a = 1$, $b = 9$, $c = 7$, and $d = 15$, since you already know the sum is $\frac{26}{45}$. The rest is left as a question in the Questions section.

Example 4

Write $\frac{6}{k + 1} - \frac{3k + 7}{k^2 - 1}$ as a single rational expression.

Solution 1 Use a CAS. You must be careful to include parentheses to identify numerators and denominators of the fractions. In one calculator, we entered `6/(k+1) - (3*k+7)/(k^2-1)`. The calculator returned the expression $\frac{3k - 13}{(k - 1)(k + 1)}$.

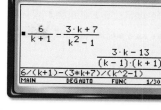

Solution 2 Work by hand. Find the least common denominator. The denominator $k + 1$ is prime. The denominator $k^2 - 1$ equals $(k + 1)(k - 1)$. So the least common denominator is $(k + 1)(k - 1)$. Rewrite the first fraction with that denominator.

$$\frac{6}{k + 1} - \frac{3k + 7}{k^2 - 1} = \frac{6k - 1}{(k + 1)(k - 1)} - \frac{3k + 7}{(k + 1)(k - 1)}$$

Subtract the fractions as you would any fractions with the same denominator. But notice that the subtracted numerator must be treated as a quantity.

$$= \frac{6(k - 1) - (3k + 7)}{(k + 1)(k - 1)}$$

$$= \frac{6k - 6 - 3k - 7}{(k + 1)(k - 1)}$$

$$= \frac{3k - 13}{(k - 1)(k + 1)}$$

Check You can check by substitution or by graphing. We leave these checks to you in the Questions section.

Questions

COVERING THE IDEAS

1. What is the definition of *rational expression*? A rational expression is the written quotient of two polynomials.

2. **Multiple Choice** Which of the following are *not* rational expressions? D

   A $\frac{2x}{3}$ B $\frac{4y^0}{5y^{15}}$ C $\frac{z\sqrt{6}}{7}$ D $\frac{8\sqrt{w}}{9w}$

In 3 and 4, simplify the rational expression and indicate all restrictions on values of the variables.

3. $\frac{30a^4b^2c^3}{12a^4bc^5} \cdot \frac{5b}{2c^2}, a \neq 0, b \neq 0, c \neq 0$ 4. $\frac{28x - 21x}{7xy} \cdot \frac{1}{y}, x \neq 0, y \neq 0$

5. a. By factoring the numerator and denominator, write $\frac{2x^2 - 7x + 6}{x^2 - 4}$ in lowest terms. $\frac{2x - 3}{x + 2}$

   b. What values can x not have in this expression? 2 and –2

   c. Check your answer by letting $x = 10$. $\frac{2(10) - 3}{(10) + 2} = \frac{17}{12} = \frac{2(10)^2 - 7(10) + 6}{(10)^2 - 4}$

Additional Example

Example 4 Write $\frac{3}{x^2 + x} + \frac{4 + x}{x^2 - 1}$ as a single rational expression.

$\frac{x^2 + 7x - 3}{x(x + 1)(x - 1)}$ or $\frac{x^2 + 7x - 3}{x^3 - x}$

Accommodating the Learner

Students may notice that, just as one does not have to use the least common multiple as the common denominator for traditional fractions, it is possible to use the denominator $(k + 1)(k^2 - 1)$ for Example 4. Ask students to compare the simplification using this denominator, and discuss why it is important to factor first to find the least common denominator.

12-8

3 Assignment

Recommended Assignment

- Questions 1–24
- Question 25 (extra credit)
- Reading Lesson 13-1
- Covering the Ideas 13-1

Notes on the Questions

Question 6 You might want to ask for restrictions on x. Some students may think the denominator is never negative. When finding the restrictions $x \neq -10$ and $x \neq -3$, the Factor Theorem implies that $x + 10$ and $x + 3$ are factors of the denominator, so finding restrictions is not at all a waste of time.

Question 9 Students are reluctant to use substitution to check work with complicated expressions, but the benefit of substitution is that it corroborates the fact that these expressions have equal values for every value in the domain of the variable, and it is good arithmetic practice.

Questions 10–13 Use a variety of checks: graphing, substitution, CAS.

Question 25 This question can be answered either with a CAS or with a graphing calculator. If students have neither, we suggest not assigning the question.

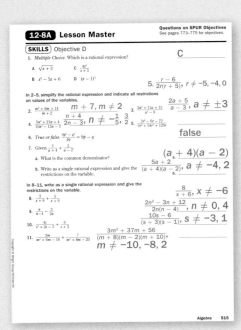

---

6. **a.** Write $\dfrac{7x^2 + 161x + 910}{14x^2 + 182x + 420}$ in lowest terms. $\dfrac{x + 13}{2(x + 3)}$

   b. Check your answer by graphing, as was done in Example 2.

7. Complete the check of Guided Example 3.

8. Check the answer to Example 4 by graphing.

9. Check the answer to Example 4 by substitution.

In **10–13**, write as a single rational expression. Check your answer.

10–13. See margin.

10. $\dfrac{a}{b} - \dfrac{c}{d}$

11. $\dfrac{3}{2n} + \dfrac{3}{8n}$

12. $\dfrac{z + 1}{4z - 3} + \dfrac{3z}{8z^2 - 18z + 9}$

13. $\dfrac{8x^2 + 16x + 8}{5x + 5} - \dfrac{x + 1}{3x^2 - 3}$

APPLYING THE MATHEMATICS

In **14** and **15**, use a CAS or graphing calculator to write the expression in lowest terms.

14. $\dfrac{-3x^3 - 15x^2 - 24x - 12}{x^2 + 3x + 2}$ $-3(x + 2)$

15. $\dfrac{x^5 - 4x^4 - 37x^3 + 124x^2 + 276x - 720}{x^5 + 20x^4 + 155x^3 + 580x^2 + 1{,}044x + 720}$ $\dfrac{(x - 6)(x - 4)(x - 2)}{(x + 2)(x + 4)(x + 6)}$

In **16** and **17**, the sum F of the integers from 1 to n is given by the formula $F = \dfrac{n^2 + n}{2}$. The sum S of the squares of the integers from 1 to n is given by the formula $S = \dfrac{2n^3 + 3n^2 + n}{6}$. The sum C of the cubes of the integers from 1 to n is given by the formula $C = \dfrac{n^4 + 2n^3 + n^2}{4}$.

16. **a.** Find the values of C, F, and $\dfrac{C}{F}$ when $n = 13$.

    b. Show that $\dfrac{C}{F} = F$ for all values of n.

17. **a.** Find the values of S, F, and $\dfrac{S}{F}$ when $n = 13$.

    b. Find a rational expression for $\dfrac{S}{F}$ in lowest terms. $\dfrac{S}{F} = \dfrac{2n + 1}{3}$

    c. Explain why there are values of n for which $\dfrac{S}{F}$ is not an integer. See margin.

18. Generalize the following pattern and use addition of rational expressions to show why your generalization is true.

$$\frac{1}{2} - \frac{1}{3} = \frac{1}{6}, \quad \frac{1}{3} - \frac{1}{4} = \frac{1}{12}, \quad \frac{1}{4} - \frac{1}{5} = \frac{1}{20}$$

$$\frac{1}{n} - \frac{1}{n + 1} = \frac{1(n + 1)}{n(n + 1)} - \frac{n}{n(n + 1)} = \frac{n + 1 - n}{n(n + 1)} = \frac{1}{n(n + 1)};$$

For any two consecutive integers, the difference of their reciprocals is the reciprocal of their product.

6b.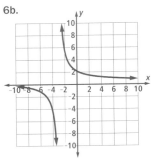

7. $\dfrac{1 \cdot 15 + 9 \cdot 7}{9 \cdot 15}$

   $= \dfrac{78}{135} = \dfrac{26}{45}$

8.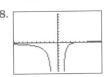

9. Answers vary.
   Sample answer:
   Let $k = 2$; then
   $\dfrac{6}{2 + 1} - \dfrac{3(2) + 7}{4 - 1} =$
   $-\dfrac{7}{3} = \dfrac{3(2) - 13}{(2 - 1)(2 + 1)}$

16a. $C = 8{,}281$,
   $F = 91$, $\dfrac{C}{F} = 91$

16b. $\dfrac{C}{F} = \dfrac{n^4 + 2n^3 + n^2}{4} \div$
   $\dfrac{n^2 + n}{2} =$
   $\dfrac{n^4 + 2n^3 + n^2}{4} \cdot \dfrac{2}{n^2 + n}$
   $= \dfrac{(n^2 + n)^2}{4} \cdot \dfrac{2}{n^2 + n}$
   $= \dfrac{n^2 + n}{2} = F$

17a. $S = 819$,
   $F = 91$, $\dfrac{S}{F} = 9$

Additional Answers

10. $\dfrac{ad - cb}{bd}$; let $a = b = c = d = 1$
    Then $\dfrac{1}{1} - \dfrac{1}{1} = 0 = \dfrac{1 - 1}{1}$

11. $\dfrac{15}{8n}$; let $n = 1$, $\dfrac{3}{2} + \dfrac{3}{8} = \dfrac{12}{8} + \dfrac{3}{8} = \dfrac{15}{8}$

12. $\dfrac{2z^2 + 2z - 3}{(2z - 3)(4z - 3)}$; $z = 1$, then we have
    $\dfrac{1 + 1}{4 - 3} + \dfrac{3}{8 - 18 + 9} = -1 = \dfrac{2 + 2 - 3}{(2 - 3)(4 - 3)}$

13. $\dfrac{24x^2 - 29}{15(x - 1)}$; $x = 0$, then we have
    $\dfrac{8}{5} - \dfrac{1}{-3} = \dfrac{29}{15} = \dfrac{-29}{-15}$

17c. $\dfrac{S}{F}$ will only be an integer if $2n + 1$ is a multiple of 3. However, we know for some n, such as $n = 2$, $2n+1$ will not be a multiple of 3, so $\dfrac{S}{F}$ is not an integer for that n.

REVIEW

19. If an object is thrown upward from a height of 0 meters at a speed of $v \frac{\text{meters}}{\text{second}}$, then its height after t seconds is $vt - 4.9t^2$ meters. **(Lesson 12-6)**

   a. If an object is thrown upward with speed v, how long will it take it to hit the ground? $t = \frac{v}{4.9}$

   b. What must be true about v if the time it takes the object to hit the ground in seconds is an integer? Give an example of a v for which this happens and a v for which it does not happen.

20. Is $3x^2 - 2x + 5$ a prime polynomial? How do you know? **(Lesson 12-6)** Yes; The descriminant is not a perfect square.

21. Gerardo is cutting a shape out of paper. He begins with a square piece of paper, and cuts out the upper right corner, as in the figure at the right. What is the area of the piece he cut out? **(Lesson 12-2)** $0.09x^2$

22. Nikki wants to call her friend Adelaide. She remembers that the last three digits of her number are 3, 4, and 7, but she doesn't remember the correct order. If she guesses an order at random, what is the probability that she will get the right number? **(Lesson 11-7)** $\frac{1}{6}$

23. Marcus took a test in which there were 20 questions. In this test, every correct answer gave 6 points, and every incorrect answer subtracted 3 points from the grade. If Marcus got a 93 on the test, how many questions did he get right? **(Lesson 10-5)** 17 questions right

24. Is there a convex polygon with exactly 43 diagonals? Explain how you know. **(Lesson 9-7)**

EXPLORATION

25. A teacher, wanting to show students that their ideas could be used with very complicated rational expressions, used the following expression.

$$\frac{x^9 + 11x^8 - 84x^7 - 1{,}660x^6 - 4{,}874x^5 + 44{,}082x^4 + 400{,}140x^3\,1{,}347{,}300x^2 + 2{,}156{,}625x + 1{,}366{,}875}{x^8 - 22x^7 + 90x^6 + 882x^5 - 5{,}508x^4 - 10{,}530x^3 + 74{,}358x^2 + 39{,}366x - 295{,}245}$$

However, the teacher forgot the operation sign between x^3 and $1{,}347{,}300$.

   a. If the numerator was meant to be factored, what is the operation? addition

   b. Use the answer to Part a to write the expression in lowest terms. $\frac{(x+5)^3(x+3)}{(x-9)(x-3)^2}$

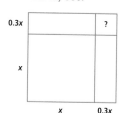

0.3x | ?
x |
x   0.3x

24. No there isn't. Answers vary. Sample answer: when 43 is substituted for d into the equation $d = \frac{n(n+1)}{2}$, and solved for the number of sides n, the result is a non-integer n. It is impossible to have a polygon with a non-integer number of sides.

19b. v is a multiple of 4.9. Answers vary. Sample answer: t is an integer if $v = 4.9$ m/sec and t is not an integer if $v = 10$ m/sec.

QY ANSWER

The numerator and denominator have common factors.

$$\frac{6k^3 - 12k^2 + 42k - 210}{3k^3 - 6k^2 + 21k - 105} =$$

$$\frac{6(k^3 - 2k^2 + 7k - 35)}{3(k^3 - 2k^2 + 7k - 35)} = 2$$

Factoring and Rational Expressions **767**

12-8

4 Wrap-Up

Ongoing Assessment

Organize students into groups of 4. Create several problems you would like to assess.

Some possible problems could include writing each of the following as a single rational expression.

a. $\frac{3}{s} + \frac{3t}{r}$ $\frac{3r+3st}{sr}$

b. $\frac{4-x}{2} + \frac{1}{3}$ $\frac{14-3x}{6}$

c. $\frac{4x^2-9}{(x-3)(2x+3)} + \frac{1}{x+3}$ $\frac{2x^2+4x-12}{x^2-9}$

d. $\frac{4}{4+x} - \frac{4}{4+4x}$ $\frac{3x}{x^2+5x+4}$

Ask students to complete each of the following steps. After they finish one step, ask them to pass the paper to the left and check the previous student's work.

Step 1: Students factor both the numerator and denominator of each term of their expression.

Step 2: Students find a common denominator (if necessary) and write each term using the common denominator.

Step 3: Students add or subtract the rational expressions and simplify the numerator.

Step 4: Students attempt to factor the numerator to see if any cancellation occurs between numerator and denominator.

Project Update

Project 2, Infinite Repeating Continued Fractions, on page 768, relates to the content of this lesson.

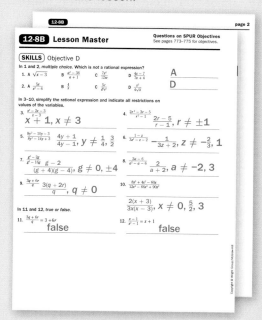

Chapter 12

12 Projects

The projects relate to the content of the lessons of this chapter as follows:

Project	Lesson(s)
1	12-3
2	12-8
3	12-4
4	12-4
5	12-7
6	12-7

1 Combining Solutions

If students are struggling to find the pattern, suggest that they write the numbers out in full after multiplying, instead of simplifying. For example, when they consider $(x - 1)(x - 2)(x - 3)$ in Part c, they can leave this as $(x^2 + (-1 - 2)x + (-1)(-2))(x - 3) = x^3 + (-1 - 2 - 3)x^2 + [(-1 - 2)(-3) + (-1)(-2)]x + (-1)(-2)(-3)$. This can help them see the patterns.

2 Infinite Repeating Continued Fractions

Remind students that order of operations requires them to work from the inside of nested grouping symbols out, and that the fraction bar acts as a grouping symbol. So, in order to find Part b, they will have to nest their current answer inside another $\frac{1}{5 + ?}$. They will have to approximate the value of x by looking at longer and longer strings of the pattern.

3 Prime Numbers, Prime Polynomials

To help students answer Part b, recommend that they start with a binomial, and look at multiples of that binomial. They can start with integer multiples, then multiply by powers of x, and finally begin to multiply by other binomials. Ask them to justify their answer.

1 Combining Solutions

a. Choose an equation of the form $x^2 + bx + c = 0$ and call its two solutions: r and s. Calculate $r + s$ and $r \cdot s$. How are these related to your original equation? Do the same thing for three more equations, and write a short description of what you found.

b. Repeat Part a, but this time with equations of the form $ax^2 + bx + c = 0$.

c. The solutions to $x^3 - 6x^2 + 11x - 6 = 0$ are 1, 2, and 3. The solutions to $x^3 - 10x^2 + 24x = 0$ are 0, 4, and 6. How are these solutions related to the results you found in Part a? Can you find how the coefficient of x is related to the solutions?

d. Repeat Part c, but this time use equations of the form $ax^3 + bx^2 + cx + d = 0$.

2 Infinite Repeating Continued Fractions

Consider this sequence of complex fractions: $\frac{1}{5}, \dfrac{1}{5 + \frac{1}{5}}, \dfrac{1}{5 + \frac{1}{5 + \frac{1}{5}}}, \dfrac{1}{5 + \frac{1}{5 + \frac{1}{5 + \frac{1}{5}}}} \ldots$

a. Calculate the values of the first five terms of this sequence.

b. As you calculate more and more terms of this sequence, the sequence approaches the value of x, where

$$x = \cfrac{1}{5 + \cfrac{1}{5 + \cfrac{1}{5 + \cfrac{1}{5 + \frac{1}{5 + \frac{1}{5 + \cdots}}}}}} .$$ This x satisfies $x = \frac{1}{5 + x}$. Find the value of x.

c. Complete Parts a and b, this time with a 4 replacing each 5.

3 Prime Numbers, Prime Polynomials

One of the most famous discoveries of the Greek mathematician and astronomer Eratosthenes (276 BCE–194 BCE) is an algorithm to check if a number is a prime, called the sieve of Eratosthenes.

a. Look up the sieve of Eratosthenes. Write a description of how it works. If you can, write a computer (or calculator) program that checks if an integer is a prime.

b. Do you think a similar algorithm could be invented to check if a polynomial is prime over the integers? Why, or why not?

ERATOSTHENES

Project Rubric

Advanced	Student correctly provides all of the details asked for in the project as well as additional correct independent conclusions.
Proficient	Student correctly provides all of the details asked for in the project.
Partially proficient	Student correctly provides some of the details asked for in the project or provides all details with some inaccuracies.
Not proficient	Student correctly provides few of the details asked for in the project or provides all details with many inaccuracies.
No attempt	Student makes little or no attempt to complete the project.

4 Public-Key Cryptography

The use of codes based on prime numbers to protect information is called *public-key cryptography*. Do research in your library or on the Internet and write an essay describing how public-key cryptography works.

5 Using Polynomials to Approximate

The graphs of polynomials of higher degree can have interesting shapes. Using a graphing calculator, to make graphs of polynomials that look like the letters of the English alphabet (both lower case and upper case).

a. For each letter you successfully create, write down the polynomial and the appropriate window.

b. Write some letters which you think cannot be drawn well this way. Why do you think this is so?

c. Which are harder to draw, lower case letters or upper case letters? Why?

6 The Bisection Method

For higher degree polynomials, there are no simple formulas that allow you to find the x-intercepts of the graphs. Nevertheless, in real life, it is often important to find those x-intercepts. One method in which approximate values can be found is called the *bisection method*.

a. Look up the bisection method in other books or on the Internet. Write a description of how it works. Include pictures to illustrate your explanation.

b. Suppose you know that there is an x-intercept of a graph between 0 and 1. How many times would you need to apply the bisection method to get an approximation with an accuracy of at least 0.01?

c. Use the bisection method to find the value of one of the x-intercepts of $y = x^5 - 2x + 5$ with an accuracy of at least 0.01.

4 Public-Key Cryptography

Include a rubric for the essay that details your expectations. You may want to require a certain length or number of examples, or ask them to include a specific definition.

5 Using Polynomials to Approximate

Remind students to consider the patterns of end behavior discussed during the activity in Lesson 12-7 while they work instead of just randomly guessing.

6 The Bisection Method

Remind students that they can use their calculator to check their answers. Consider asking students to use their solution to Part c to demonstrate their explanation in Part a.

Notes

Summary and Vocabulary

Summary and Vocabulary

The Summary gives an overview of the entire chapter and provides an opportunity for students to consider the material as a whole. Thus, the Summary can be used to help students relate and unify the concepts presented in the chapter.

Terms and symbols are listed by lesson to provide a checklist of concepts that students must know. Emphasize to students that they should read the vocabulary list carefully before starting the Self-Test on the next page. If students do not understand the meaning of a term, they should refer back to the indicated lesson.

Theorems and Properties covered in the chapter are listed below the Summary, with page references included to lead students back to the location in the chapter where the theorem or property is stated.

○ From the **standard form of a quadratic equation,** $y = ax^2 + bx + c$, the vertex of the parabola is not visible, but if the form is converted to $y - k = a(x - h)^2$, then the vertex is (h, k). The process of converting is called **completing the square.**

○ The x-intercepts of this parabola are the solutions to the equation $ax^2 + bx + c = 0$. These can be found using the Quadratic Formula: $x = \frac{-b \pm \sqrt{b^2 - 4ac}}{2a}$. Letting $r_1 = \frac{-b + \sqrt{b^2 - 4ac}}{2a}$ and $r_2 = \frac{-b - \sqrt{b^2 - 4ac}}{2a}$, then $y = a(x - r_1)(x - r_2)$. This **factored form** is a special case of a more general theorem about polynomials: If $P(x)$ is a polynomial and $P(r) = 0$, then $x - r$ is a factor of $P(x)$.

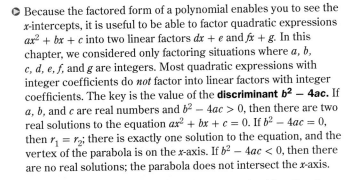

○ Because the factored form of a polynomial enables you to see the x-intercepts, it is useful to be able to factor quadratic expressions $ax^2 + bx + c$ into two linear factors $dx + e$ and $fx + g$. In this chapter, we considered only factoring situations where $a, b, c, d, e, f,$ and g are integers. Most quadratic expressions with integer coefficients do *not* factor into linear factors with integer coefficients. The key is the value of the **discriminant $b^2 - 4ac$.** If $a, b,$ and c are real numbers and $b^2 - 4ac > 0$, then there are two real solutions to the equation $ax^2 + bx + c = 0$. If $b^2 - 4ac = 0$, then $r_1 = r_2$; there is exactly one solution to the equation, and the vertex of the parabola is on the x-axis. If $b^2 - 4ac < 0$, then there are no real solutions; the parabola does not intersect the x-axis.

○ The factoring of polynomials also helps in work with **rational expressions.** By dividing out common factors from the numerator and denominator, you can write rational expressions in **lowest terms** and can be added or subtracted.

Theorems and Properties

Parabola Vertex Theorem (p. 716)	Discriminant Theorem (p.749)
Factor Theorem for Quadratic Functions (p. 731)	Factor Theorem (p. 755)

Vocabulary

12-1
vertex form of an equation for a parabola

12-2
complete the square

12-3
factored form (of a quadratic function)

12-4
square term
linear term
constant term
prime polynomial over the integers

12-7
cubic polynomial

12-8
rational expression
lowest terms

Chapter 12 Self-Test

Take this test as you would take a test in class. You will need a calculator. Then use the Selected Answers section in the back of the book to check your work.

In 1–3, factor completely. 1–3. See margin.

1. $x^2 + 3x - 40$

2. $m^2 - 17m + 72$

3. $-9h^2 + 9h - 2$

4. **Multiple Choice** Which of the following can be factored over the integers? **B**

   A $x^2 + 22x - 9$ **B** $x^2 + 9x - 22$

   C $x^2 - 9x + 22$ **D** $x^2 - 22x + 9$

5. Determine what number must be added to $z^2 - 12z$ to complete the square.

6. Simplify the expression $\frac{3x^2 - 75}{2x^2 - 7x - 15}$ and indicate all restrictions on x.

7. **Multiple Choice** Which equation is graphed below? **D**

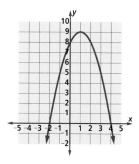

   A $y = (x + 2)(x - 4)$

   B $y = (x - 2)(x + 4)$

   C $y = (-x - 2)(x + 4)$

   D $y = -(x + 2)(x - 4)$

8. **a.** Give an equation in factored form for a polynomial function with 3 x-intercepts: 0, –3, and 9. See margin.

   b. Rewrite your equation from Part a in standard form. $y = x^3 - 6x^2 - 27x$

9. A square frame is x feet on each side. The painting it holds is 1 foot shorter and 2 feet narrower than the frame. If the area of the painting is 12 square feet, what are the dimensions of the frame? See margin.

In 10 and 11, determine the vertex of the parabola with the given equation.

10. $y = x^2 - 2x - 3$ See margin.

11. $y = 7 - 4x - 2x^2$ See margin on page 772.

In 12 and 13, sketch the graph of the equation without a calculator. 12–13. See margin on page 772.

12. $y - 4 = 2(x - 3)^2$

13. $y = (x - 5)(x + 4)$

14. Factor $3n^4 - 15n^3 + 18n^2$ completely over the integers. See margin.

15. Suppose a rectangle has an area of 486 cm², and one side is 9 cm longer than the other side. Find the dimensions of the rectangle.

16. **True or False** A quadratic expression with a positive discriminant is always factorable over the integers. Justify your answer. See margin.

15. Let x be the length of the shorter side. Then $x(x + 9) = 486$, which gives $x^2 + 9x = 486$. Solving this equation gives x to be −27 or 18, but since length is positive, $x = 18$, so the dimensions are 18 cm by 27 cm.

5. To complete the square, we add $\left(\frac{1}{2}b\right)^2$, so because $(-6)^2 = 36$, add 36.

6. $\frac{3x^2 - 75}{2x^2 - 7x - 15} = \frac{3(x^2 - 25)}{(2x + 3)(x - 5)} = \frac{3(x + 5)(x - 5)}{(2x + 3)(x - 5)} = \frac{3(x + 5)}{2x + 3}$, $x \neq 5$; $x \neq -\frac{3}{2}$

1. The product is −40, so possible factors include 10 and −4, −10 and 4, 8 and −5, and because $8 + -5 = 3$, the two factors are 8 and −5. Thus, $(x + 8)(x - 5)$.

2. The product is 72, and the sum is negative. Therefore, possible factors include −18 and −4, −24 and −3, and −8 and −9, and since $-8 + -9 = -17$, the two factors are −8 and −9. Thus, $(m - 8)(m - 9)$.

3. $a = -9$, so possible factors are 3 and −3, 9 and −1, or −9 and 1. $c = -2$, so the factors are either 2 and −1 or −2 and 1. Because $dg + ef = 9$, $d = -3$, $e = 2$, $f = 3$, and $g = -1$ as this is the only combination that works. Thus, $(-3h + 2)(3h - 1)$.

8a. By the Factor Theorem, the polynomial must have the factors $(x - 0) = x$, $(x + 3)$, and $(x - 9)$. One such polynomial is $y = x(x + 3)(x - 9)$.

Self-Test

For the development of mathematical competence, feedback and correction, along with the opportunity for practice, are necessary. The Self-Test provides the opportunity for feedback and correction; the Chapter Review provides additional opportunities for practice. We cannot overemphasize the importance of these end-of-chapter materials. It is at this point that the material gels for many students, allowing them to solidify skills and understanding. In general, student performance should improve after they complete these pages.

Assign the Self-Test as a one-night assignment. Worked-out solutions for all questions are in the Selected Answers section of the student book. Encourage students to take the Self-Test honestly, grade themselves, and then be prepared to discuss the test in class.

Advise students to pay special attention to those Chapter Review questions (pages 773–775) which correspond to the questions they missed on the Self-Test.

9. Let x be the length of a side of the frame. Since the area of the painting is 12 square feet, we can write $(x - 1)(x - 2) = 12$. We then put the equation in standard form, so $x^2 - 3x + 2 = 12$, which gives $x^2 - 3x - 10 = 0$. This factors as $(x - 5)(x + 2)$, so we have $(x - 5)(x + 2) = 0$. We cannot have a frame with length −2, so the side length must be 5 feet.

10. Put the equation in $y - k = a(x - h)^2$ form by completing the square. Thus, since $\left(\frac{1}{2}b\right)^2 = 1$, we add 4 to both sides to get $y + 4 = x^2 - 2x + 1$. This factors as $y + 4 = (x - 1)^2$, so the vertex is at $(1, -4)$.

Additional Answers

11. Put the equation in $y - k = a(x - h)^2$ form by completing the square. First, we move the 7 to the other side and factor -2 out of the righthand side, which gives $y - 7 = -2(x^2 + 2x)$. Thus, because $\left(\frac{1}{2}b\right)^2 = 1$, we must add 1 into the $(x^2 + 2x)$ quantity. This gives $y - 9 = -2(x^2 + 2x + 1)$, $y - 9 = -2(x + 1)^2$. Thus, the vertex is at $(-1, 9)$.

12. By the equation, the vertex is at $(3, 4)$ and a is positive, so the graph opens up.

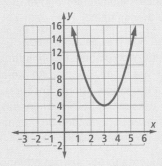

13. By the equation, the zeros of the function are at $x = 5$ and $x = -4$. Also, the axis of symmetry is $x = 0.5$, so the vertex is at $(0.5, -20.25)$.

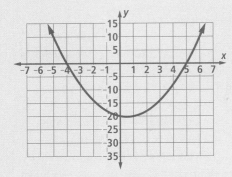

14. First, factor out $3n^2$ to get $3n^2(n^2 - 5n + 6)$. Now deal with what is in the parentheses. Because $c = 6$, possible factors include 3 and 2, -3 and -2, 6 and 1, and -6 and -1. Because $-3 + -2 = -5$, we have $3n^2(n - 3)(n - 2)$.

17. Write a possible equation for the polynomial graphed below.

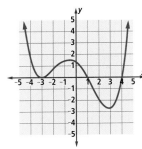

Answers vary. Sample answer: $y = 0.04(x + 3)^2(x - 1)(x - 4)$

18. For the graph of the parabola, Marie wrote $y = (x + 3)(x + 1)$. Anthony wrote $y = (x + 2)^2 - 1$.

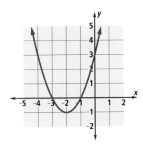

a. Are Marie and Anthony's equations equivalent? Explain. See margin.

b. What is Anthony's equation useful for finding on the graph? the vertex of the parabola

Additional Answers

16. False. A quadratic expression is only factorable over the integers when the discriminant is a perfect square, and not all positive numbers are perfect squares.

18a. Yes, they are equivalent because expanding each equation gives $x^2 + 4x + 3$.

Chapter 12 Chapter Review

SKILLS Procedures used to get answers

OBJECTIVE A Complete the square on a quadratic expression. (Lesson 12-2)
1b–4b. See margin.
In 1–4, a quadratic expression is given.

a. Determine what number must be added to the expression to complete the square.

b. Complete the square.

1. $x^2 + 4x$ a. 4
2. $t^2 - 5t$ a. 6.25
3. $z^2 + bz$ a. $\left(\frac{1}{2}b\right)^2$
4. $w^2 - \frac{3}{4}w$ a. $\frac{9}{64}$

OBJECTIVE B Factor quadratic expressions of the form $x^2 + bx + c$ and $ax^2 + bx + c$. (Lessons 12-4, 12-5)

In 5–8, factor the quadratic expression.
5–8. See margin.

5. $x^2 - x - 6$
6. $y^2 + 60y + 800$
7. $m^2 - 2m - 24$
8. $n^2 + 4n - 12$

In 9–12, factor the trinomial. 9–12. See margin.

9. $3x^2 - 2x - 8$
10. $5x^2 + 16x + 3$
11. $6d^2 - 8d - 8$
12. $8n^2 + 21 + 34n$

OBJECTIVE C Find the product of three or more binomials. (Lesson 12-7)
13–16. See margin.
In 13–16, an equation of a function is given.

a. Identify the x-intercepts of its graph.

b. Put the equation into standard form.

13. $y = 6(x + 1)(x - 3)(2x - 11)$
14. $y = x(x - 5)(x + 2)$
15. $f(x) = (x - 4)(2x - 7)(x + 2)$
16. $g(x) = (3 - x)(4x - 1)(x + 3)(x + 1)$

SKILLS
PROPERTIES
USES
REPRESENTATIONS

17. $4(n - 2m)$; $n \neq 0$, $m \neq 0$
18. $\frac{-7rstq^3}{s+1}$; $t \neq 0$, $q \neq 0$, $s \neq -1$

OBJECTIVE D Use factoring to write rational expressions in lowest terms. (Lesson 12-8)

In 17 and 18, simplify the rational expression and indicate all restrictions on values of the variables.

17. $\frac{4n^2m - 8nm^2}{nm}$
18. $\frac{-7rst^2q^4}{(s+1)tq}$

In 19–21, write as a single rational expression. You may need a calculator or a CAS.

19. $\frac{-4n^2 + 23n - 15}{n^2 - 8n + 15}$ $\frac{3 - 4n}{n - 3}$

20. $\frac{3}{x + 4} - \frac{3x - 7}{x^2 + 3x - 4}$ $\frac{4}{(x-1)(x+4)}$

21. $\frac{-m^3 + 5m^2 - 2m - 8}{2m^3 - 9m^2 + 3m + 14}$ $\frac{-(m - 4)}{2m - 7}$

PROPERTIES Principles behind the mathematics

OBJECTIVE E Determine whether a quadratic polynomial can be factored over the integers. (Lessons 12-4, 12-5, 12-6)

22. **True or False** Every quadratic polynomial whose discriminant is an integer is factorable over the integers. false

23. For what values of the discriminant is a quadratic polynomial factorable? perfect squares

In 24–27, determine whether the quadratic polynomial is factorable over the integers. If it is not, label it *prime*. If it is, factor the polynomial.

24. $5x^2 + 33x + 12$
25. $15x^2 + 69x + 72$
24–25. See margin.
26. $4c^2 - 14c + 8$
27. $8x^2 + 34x + 182$
    $2(2c^2 - 7c + 4)$ $2(4x^2 + 17x + 91)$

Chapter Review

The main objectives for the chapter are organized in the Chapter Review under the four types of understanding this book promotes—Skills, Properties, Uses, and Representations.

Whereas end-of-chapter material may be considered optional in some texts, in *UCSMP Algebra* we have selected these objectives and questions with the expectation that they will be covered. Students should be able to answer these questions with about 85% accuracy after studying the chapter.

You may assign these questions over a single night to help students prepare for a test the next day, or you may assign the questions over a two-day period. If you work the questions over two days, then we recommend assigning the *evens* for homework the first night so that students get feedback in class the next day, and then assigning the *odds* the night before the test because the answers are provided to the odd-numbered questions in the Selected Answers at the back of the book.

It is effective to ask students which questions they still do not understand and use the day as a total class discussion of the material which the class finds most difficult.

Resources

- Assessment Resources: Chapter 12 Test, Forms A–D; Chapter 12 Test, Cumulative Form

Technology Resources

Teacher's Assessment Assistant, Ch 12
Electronic Teacher's Edition, Ch.12

Additional Answers

1b. $(x + 2)^2 - 4$
2b. $(t - 2.5)^2 - 6.25$
3b. $\left(z + \frac{1}{2}b\right)^2 - \left(\frac{1}{2}b\right)^2$
4b. $v\left(w - \frac{3}{8}\right)^2 - \frac{9}{64}$
5. $(x - 3)(x + 2)$
6. $(y + 20)(y + 40)$
7. $(m - 6)(m + 4)$
8. $(n + 6)(n - 2)$
9. $(3x + 4)(x - 2)$
10. $(5x + 1)(x + 3)$
11. $2(3d + 2)(d - 2)$

12. $(2n + 7)(4n + 3)$
13a. $x = 3, x = -1, x = \frac{11}{2}$
13b. $y = 12x^3 - 90x^2 + 96x + 198$
14a. $x = 0, x = 5, x = -2$
14b. $y = x^3 - 3x^2 - 10x$
15a. $x = 4, x = \frac{7}{2}, x = -2$
15b. $f(x) = 2x^3 - 11x^2 - 2x + 56$
16a. $x = 3, x = \frac{1}{4}, x = -3, x = -1$
16b. $g(x) = -4x^4 - 3x^3 + 37x^2 + 27x - 9$
24. prime
25. $3(x + 3)(5x + 8)$

Chapter **12** Review

29a. Answers vary. Sample answer:

$f(x) = (x - 2)(x + 2)$

29b. $f(x) = (x - 2)(x + 2) = x^2 - 4$

30a. Answers vary. Sample answer:

$g(x) = x(x - 7)(x + 10)$

30b. $g(x) = x(x - 7)(x + 10) =$

$x^3 + 3x^2 - 70x$

31. Answers vary. Sample answer:

$y = 4(x + 4)(x - 1)(x - 2)$

32. Answers vary. Sample answer:

$y = 3x(x + 2)^2 (x - 2)$

39.

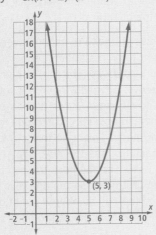

40.

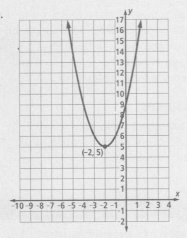

41.

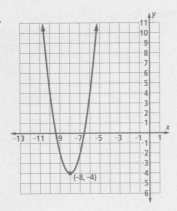

29–30. See margin.

OBJECTIVE F Apply the Factor Theorem.
(Lesson 12-7) 28a. $f(x) = 3x(x - 7)(x + 2)$

28. $f(x) = 3x^3 - 15x^2 - 42x$.

   a. Write $f(x)$ in factored form.

   b. What does the Factor Theorem tell you
     about the graph of $f(x)$?
     The x-intercepts are 0, 7, and −2.

In 29 and 30, x-intercepts are given.

a. Give an equation in factored form for a polynomial
   function with the given x-intercepts.

b. Rewrite your equation in standard form.

29. 2 and –2   30. 0, 7, and –10

In 31 and 32, give a possible equation, in factored
form, for the graph. 31–32. See margin.

31.

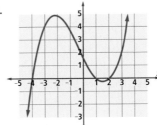

32.

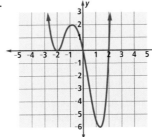

USES Applications of mathematics in
real-world situations

OBJECTIVE G Solve problems involving
areas and perimeters of rectangles
that lead to quadratic functions or
equations. (Lesson 12-1)

In 33 and 34, a rectangle is given.

a. Find its area A and perimeter P.

b. Determine the dimensions of the rectangle so that
   the perimeter and area are numerically equal.

33.

33a. $A = 10x - x^2$;
$P = 20$
33b. $5 - \sqrt{5}$ units
by $5 + \sqrt{5}$
units

34.

34a. $A = x^2 - x - 6$;
$P = 4x - 2$
34b. $\dfrac{9 + \sqrt{41}}{2}$ units by
$\dfrac{\sqrt{41} - 1}{2}$ units

35. A rectangular soccer field has a perimeter
of 390 yards.

   a. Write a formula for the area of the field
     in terms of its length x. $A = x(195 - x)$

   b. If the width of the field must be at least
     50 yards and at most 75 yards, what is
     the maximum area of the field? 9,000 yd²

36. A dairy cow is walking around the outside
of her rectangular pasture at an average
speed of 2 feet per second.

   a. If it takes the cow 20 minutes to
     walk around the pasture, what is the
     perimeter of the pasture? 2,400 ft

   b. Write a formula for the area A of the
     pasture in terms of the length of one
     side L, and determine the dimensions
     of the rectangle that will maximize the
     cow's pasture.
     $A = L(1,200 - L)$; 600 ft by 600 ft

42.

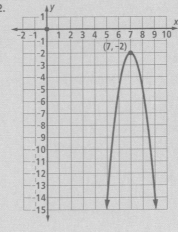

51.

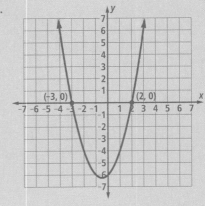

37. The Irish sport of hurling can be played on a rectangular field with an area of 12,600 m². If the longer side of a hurling field is 50 m longer than the shorter side, what are the dimensions of the field? **90 m by 140 m**

38. The perimeter of a rectangle is 24 cm.

   a. Write a formula for the area A of the rectangle in vertex form in terms of the length x of one of its sides.
   $A - 36 = -(x - 6)^2$

   b. What is the meaning of the vertex in this scenario? **The area is maximized when the sides are of length 6 cm, and the maximum area is 36 cm².**

REPRESENTATIONS Pictures, graphs, or objects that illustrate concepts

OBJECTIVE H Graph quadratic functions whose equations are given in vertex form. (Lesson 12-1)

In 39–42, sketch the graph of the equation without a calculator. **39–42. See margin.**

39. $y - 3 = (x - 5)^2$

40. $y - 5 = (x + 2)^2$

41. $y + 4 = 2(x + 8)^2$

42. $y + 2 = -3(x - 7)^2$

OBJECTIVE I Find the vertex of a parabola whose equation is given in standard form. (Lesson 12-2)

In 43–46, match the graph with one of the equations i. through iv. below.

i. $y = -x^2 + 6x - 14$ ii. $y = x^2 - 6x + 14$

iii. $y = -x^2 - 6x - 4$ iv. $y = x^2 + 6x + 9$

43.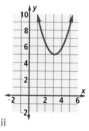

ii

44.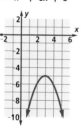

i

45. iii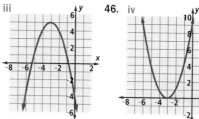

46. iv

In 47–50, find the vertex of the parabola.

47. $y = 2x^2$ (0, 0)

48. $y = x^2 + 3x - 2$ (−1.5, −4.25)

49. $y = -3x^2 + 2x - 5$ $\left(\frac{1}{3}, \frac{-14}{3}\right)$

50. $y = -x^2 + 6x + 4$ (3, 13)

OBJECTIVE J Graph quadratic functions whose equations are given in factored form. (Lesson 12-3)

In 51–54, sketch the graph of the equation without using a calculator. **51–54. See margin.**

51. $y = (x - 2)(x + 3)$

52. $y = (x + 4)(x - 6)$

53. $y = (2x - 1)(x + 4)$

54. $y = (3x + 7)(x + 8)$

Assessment

Evaluation The *Assessment Resources* provide four forms of the Chapter 12 Test. Forms A and B present parallel versions of a short-answer format. Form C consists of four to six short-response questions that cover the SPUR objectives from Chapter 12. Form D offers performance assessment that covers a subset (or even just one) of the SPUR objectives for the chapter.

Feedback After students have taken the test for Chapter 12 and you have scored the results, return the tests to students for discussion. Class discussion on the questions that caused trouble for most students can be very effective in identifying and clarifying misunderstandings. You might want to have them note the items they missed and work either in groups or at home to correct them. It is important for students to receive feedback on every chapter test, and we recommend that students see and correct their mistakes before proceeding too far into the next chapter.

Additional Answers

54.

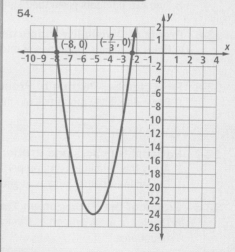

Additional Answers

52.

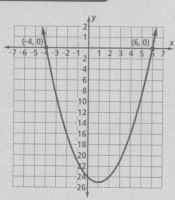

53.

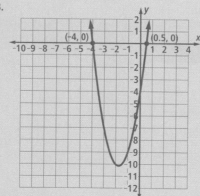

Chapter
13 Using Algebra to Prove

Chapter Overview

	Local Standards	Pacing (in days)		
		Average	Advanced	Block
13-1 If-Then Statements **C** Identify the antecedent and consequent of an if-then statement not necessarily given in if-then form. **D** Determine whether if-then and if-and-only-if statements in algebra or geometry are true or false. **G** Determine whether if-then and if-and-only-if statements in real-world contexts are true or false.		1	0.5	0.5
13-2 The Converse of an If-Then Statement **D** Determine whether if-then and if-and-only-if statements in algebra or geometry are true or false. **G** Determine whether if-then and if-and-only-if statements in real-world contexts are true or false.		1	0.5	0.5
13-3 Solving Equations as Proofs **A** Show and justify the steps in solving an equation.		1	1	0.75
QUIZ 1		0.5	0.5	0.25
13-4 A History and Proof of the Quadratic Formula **B** Find two numbers given their sum and product.		1	1	0.5
13-5 Proofs of Divisibility Properties **E** Prove divisibility properties of integers.		1	1	0.5
13-6 From Number Puzzles to Properties of Integers **E** Prove divisibility properties of integers.		1	0.5	0.75
QUIZ 2		0.5	0.5	0.25
13-7 Rational Numbers and Irrational Numbers **F** Apply the definitions and properties of rational and irrational numbers. **I** Determine whether lengths in geometric figures are rational or irrational.		1	0.5	0.5
13-8 Proofs of the Pythagorean Theorem **H** Display or prove properties involving multiplication using areas of polygons or squares.		1	1	0.5
Self-Test		1	1	0.5
Chapter Review		2	2	1
Test		1	1	0.5
TOTAL		**13**	**11**	**7.0**

Technology Resources
Teacher's Assessment Assistant, Ch. 13
Electronic Teacher's Edition, Ch. 13

Differentiated Options Universal Access

	Accommodating the Learner	Vocabulary Development	Ongoing Assessment	Materials
13-1	pp. 779, 780		oral, p. 783	**scientific or graphing calculator**
13-2	p. 785		group, p. 787	**scientific or graphing calculator**
13-3	pp. 790, 791	p. 790	written, p. 794	**scientific or graphing calculator**
13-4	pp. 797, 798		group, p. 801	**scientific or graphing calculator**
13-5	pp. 803, 804		written, p. 808	**scientific or graphing calculator**
13-6	pp. 810, 812		oral, p. 815	**scientific or graphing calculator**
13-7	pp. 818, 819	p. 818	written, p. 822	**scientific or graphing calculator**
13-8	p. 824		written, p. 828	**scientific or graphing calculator**

Objectives

	Lessons	Self-Test Questions	Chapter Review Questions
Skills			
A Show and justify the steps in solving an equation.	13-3	1	1–4
B Find two numbers given their sum and product.	13-4	8	5–10
Properties			
C Identify the antecedent and consequent of an if-then statement not necessarily given in if-then form.	13-1	2, 5	11–14
D Determine whether if-then and if-and-only-if statements in algebra or geometry are true or false.	13-1, 13-2	3, 10	15–18
E Prove divisibility properties of integers.	13-5, 13-6	6, 12	19–22
F Apply the definitions and properties of rational and irrational numbers.	13-7	4	23–28
Uses			
G Determine whether if-then and if-and-only-if statements in real-world contexts are true or false.	13-1, 13-2	11	29–32
Representations			
H Display or prove properties involving multiplication using areas of polygons or squares.	13-8	7	33–36
I Determine whether lengths of geometric figures are rational or irrational.	13-7	9	37–41

Resource Masters Chapter 13

Resource Master 1, Graph Paper (page 2), can be used as needed. **Resource Master 2, Four-Quadrant Graph Paper** (page 3), can be used with Lessons 13-4 and 13-7. **Resource Master 5, Spreadsheet** (page 6), can be used with Lesson 13-7.

Resource Master 196 Lesson 13-1

Warm-Up

Give a counterexample to each statement.

1. If a word is correctly spelled in English, then it has "i before e, except after c".
2. If n is positive, then $n^4 > n$.
3. If you are in Birmingham, then you are in Alabama.
4. If a figure is quadrilateral $ABCD$, then its diagonals $\overline{AC}$ and $\overline{BD}$ intersect inside the quadrilateral.

Additional Examples

1. **True or False** If C is a horse, then C has four legs.
2. **True or False** If b is a bird, then b can fly.
3. Draw a Venn diagram for the statement: If A is a garbage truck, then A is a sports car.

Resource Master for Lesson 13-1

Resource Master 197 Lesson 13-1

Additional Examples

4. Fill in the blanks.

If-Then Statement	True or False	Explanation
a. If $2x - 3 = 27$, then $x = 15$.	true	If $2x - 3 = 27$, then $2x =$ ___?___ If $2x =$ ___?___, then $x = 15$.
b. If a figure is a rhombus, then it is a rectangle.		definition of a rhombus: A rhombus is a ___?___.
c. If x is a negative real number, then $x^3 > 0$.		-2 is a negative real number and $(-2)^3$ is not greater than 0.
d. If a triangle has at least two congruent sides, then it is equilateral.	false	

5. Rewrite each statement in if-then form.

Statement	If-then form with variables
a. Every whole number is an integer.	If x is a whole number, then ___?___.
b. A polygon with six sides is a hexagon.	If ___?___, then P is a hexagon.
c. The square root of a negative number is not a real number.	If B is a negative number, then ___?___.

Resource Master for Lesson 13-1

Resource Master 198 Lesson 13-1

Example 4

If-Then Statement	True or False	Explanation
a. If $3n + 5 = 65$, then $n = 20$.	true	If $3n + 5 = 65$, then $3n =$ ___?___ If $3n =$ ___?___, then $n = 20$.
b. If a figure is a square, then it is a rectangle.		Definition of square: a square is a ___?___.
c. If x is a real number, then $x^2 > 0$.		0 is a real number and 0^2 is not greater than 0.
d. If a quadrilateral has 3 right angles, then it is a square.	false	

Example 5

Statement	If-Then Form with Variables
a. Every whole number is a real number.	If x is a whole number, then ___?___.
b. All people born in the United States are U.S. citizens.	If ___?___, then P is a U.S. citizen.
c. No power of a positive number is negative.	If p is a positive number and g is any real number, then ___?___.

Resource Master for Lesson 13-1

Resource Master 199 Lesson 13-2

Warm-Up

A statement is given. (a) Tell whether or not it is true. (b) Give its converse. (c) Tell whether or not its converse is true.

1. If $5x + x^2 = -4$, then $(x + 4)(x + 1) = 0$.
2. If the 7th power of a number is less than the 6th power of the number, then the number must be negative.
3. If a figure is a rectangle, then it is a parallelogram.

Additional Examples

1. The given statement is true. Write its converse and explain why the converse is not true.
   a. If the length of each side of a triangle is 15, then the perimeter of the triangle is 45.
   b. If you live in San Diego, then you live in California.
2. The given statement is true and so is its converse. Write the converse and then combine the statement and its converse in one if-and-only-if statement.
   a. Statement: If a triangle has 3 congruent sides, then it is an equilateral triangle.

Question 24

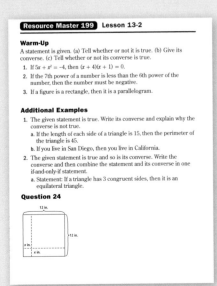

Resource Master for Lesson 13-2

Resource Master 200 Lesson 13-3

Warm-Up

Two steps in solving an equation or inequality are given.
(a) Indicate what was done to get from the first step to the second.
(b) Name the general property that justifies what was done.
(c) Describe the general property with variables.

1. **Step 1:** $40\% \cdot x = 75$ **Step 2:** $x = 187.5$
2. **Step 1:** $3y + 2x < 5$ **Step 2:** $3y < 5 - 2x$.

Additional Examples

1. Prove that if $7p + 11 = -101$, then $p = -16$.
2. Prove that if $-3a - 7 = 20$, then $a = -9$.
3. Find all solutions to $\sqrt{x} = x - 2$.

Questions 31–32

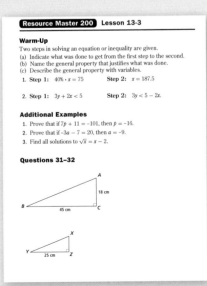

Resource Master for Lesson 13-3

Resource Master 201 Lesson 13-4

Warm-Up

1. There are two whole numbers whose sum is 80 and whose product is 1,591.
   a. Find these numbers.
   b. Show that the numbers you found in Part a are the solutions to $x^2 - 80x + 1{,}591 = 0$.
   c. Use the information in Parts a and b to factor $x^2 - 80x + 1{,}591$.
2. There are two integers whose sum is −5 and whose product is −84.
   a. Find these numbers.
   b. Find a quadratic equation whose solutions are the numbers you found in Part a.

Additional Example

1. Find the dimensions of a rectangular field whose perimeter is 160 feet and whose area is 1,500 square feet.

Resource Master for Lesson 13-4

Resource Master 202 Lesson 13-5

Warm-Up

1. Find two numbers between 100 and 500 that are divisible by 4. Add them.
   a. Is the sum divisible by 2?
   b. Is the sum divisible by 4?
   c. Is the sum divisible by 8?
   d. Will the answers to Parts a–c be the same no matter what numbers you chose to begin with?
2. Use the same numbers as Question 1. Subtract the smaller from the larger.
   a. Is the difference divisible by 2?
   b. Is the difference divisible by 4?
   c. Is the difference divisible by 8?
   d. Will the answers to Parts a–c be the same no matter what numbers you chose to begin with?
3. Multiply the two numbers you used in Question 1.
   a. Is the product divisible by 4?
   b. Is the product divisible by 8?
   c. Is the product divisible by 16?
   d. Will the answers to Parts a–c be the same no matter what numbers you chose to begin with?

Resource Master for Lesson 13-5

Resource Master 203 Lesson 13-5

Additional Examples

1. Prove that the sum of three even numbers is an even number.
2. Prove that the sum of three odd numbers is an odd number.
3. Prove that the product of three odd numbers is an odd number.
4. Prove that if n is a positive integer, $n^2 + n$ is divisible by 2.

Activity 1

m	n	m + n	m − n	mn
even	even			
even	odd			
odd	even			
odd	odd			

Activity 2

n	1	3	5	7	9	11	13	15	17
n^2									
$n^2 - 1$									

Resource Master for Lesson 13-5

Resource Master 204 Lesson 13-5

Question 27

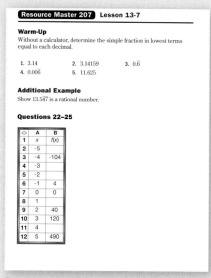

3n + 1 dots   3n + 2 dots

Resource Master for Lesson 13-5

Resource Master 205 Lesson 13-6

Warm-Up

Step 1: Pick a 3-digit number m with no repeating digits, and let r be the number formed by reversing the digits of m. Calculate $|r - m|$ and write it as a 3-digit number n with a 0 in the front if the number has only 2 digits.

Step 2: Let s be the number formed by reversing the digits of n. Calculate $s + n$. Did you get 1089?

Step 3: If you pick m in Step 1 at random, what is the relative frequency that 1,089 will result at the end of Step 2? Try different numbers to see.

Additional Examples

1. Prove that if the unit digit of a number in base 10 is zero, then the number is divisible by 10.
2. Prove that if the sum of the digits of a 3-digit integer written in base 10 is divisible by 9, then the number is divisible by 9.
3. Prove that if the sum of the digits of a 5-digit integer written in base 10 is divisible by 3, then the number is divisible by 3.
4. Prove that if a 3-digit number is subtracted from the number formed by reversing its digits, then the difference is divisible by 11.

Resource Master for Lesson 13-6

Resource Master 206 Lesson 13-6

Question 21

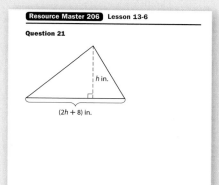

h in.

(2h + 8) in.

Resource Master for Lesson 13-6

Resource Master 207 Lesson 13-7

Warm-Up

Without a calculator, determine the simple fraction in lowest terms equal to each decimal.

1. 3.14 2. 3.14159 3. $0.\overline{6}$
4. $0.00\overline{6}$ 5. 11.625

Additional Example

Show $13.5\overline{47}$ is a rational number.

Questions 22–25

	A	B
1	x	f(x)
2	-5	
3	-4	-104
4	-3	
5	-2	
6	-1	4
7	0	0
8	1	
9	2	40
10	3	120
11	4	
12	5	490

Resource Master for Lesson 13-7

Resource Master 208 Lesson 13-7

Question 30

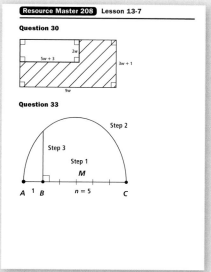

2w
5w + 3
3w + 1
9w

Question 33

Step 2
Step 3
Step 1
M

A 1 B   n = 5   C

Resource Master for Lesson 13-7

Resource Master 209 Lesson 13-8

Warm-Up

1. If two sides of a right triangle have lengths 3 and 5, what are the two possible lengths for the third side?
2. Consider the diagram of squares drawn on the three sides of a right triangle as on the first page of the lesson. If the squares on sides a and b have areas of 171 and 93, what is the area of the square on side c?
3. A trapezoid has vertices at (0, 0), (10, 0), (7, 8), and (0, 8). What is its area?

Question 10   Question 11

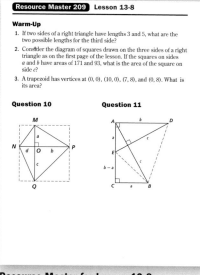

Resource Master for Lesson 13-8

Pacing

This chapter is meant to be taken at a lesson-a-day pace. However, given the nature of proof, you may wish to spend more time, particularly in Lessons 13-5 and 13-6. With 1 day for the Self-Test, 1–2 days for Review, and 1 day for the Chapter Test, this chapter should take 13–15 days.

Using Pages 776–777

This opener should be read and discussed in class, as it sets the stage for the entire chapter. Students should be able to recognize the difference between inductive and deductive reasoning, but providing and asking for examples will help create a more obvious contrast of the two ideas. Reinforce the idea that although you can make true generalizations with inductive reasoning, you have not provided a proof unless you use deduction. Point out that although many of the properties that have been studied in previous lessons have been stated and assumed to be true, there are others that were proved (for example, the Multiplication Property of −1, the Equal Fractions Property, or the Power of a Product Property).

Chapter 13 Projects

At the end of each chapter, you will find projects related to the chapter. At this time you might want to have students look over the projects on pages 829 and 830. Have each student tentatively select a project on which to work. Then, as students read and progress through the chapter, they can finalize their project choices.

In previous chapters, you looked at instances and made generalizations about patterns. For example, the instances $3 \cdot 5 + 3 = 3 \cdot 6$, $7.4 \cdot 5 + 7.4 = 7.4 \cdot 6$, and $\left(-\frac{8}{99}\right) \cdot 5 + \left(-\frac{8}{99}\right) = \left(-\frac{8}{99}\right) \cdot 6$ can be described by the general pattern $n \cdot 5 + n = n \cdot 6$. In making this generalization, you have used *inductive reasoning*. **Inductive reasoning** is the process of arriving at a general conclusion (not necessarily true) from specific instances. You use inductive reasoning quite often in everyday situations. For example, if every single family house you see on a block is yellow, you may want to conclude that every house in a city is also yellow. That conclusion is wrong. There are houses in a neighborhood or city that are not yellow. But the general

Chapter 13 Overview

This is the fourth chapter of this book whose title begins "Using Algebra to... ." Each of these chapters is designed to give students experience with an important aspect of algebra. Here, in using algebra "to prove," we go beyond using algebra "to explain." An *explanation* is a convincing argument and may use pictures or inductive reasoning. In mathematics, a *proof* is a formal argument that follows particular rules and is definitive.

Lessons 13-1 and 13-2 deal with the fundamental type of statement in a proof, the *if-then* statement. Understanding the difference between an if-then statement and its converse is critical, and sets the stage for Lesson 13-3, which views solving an equation as an example of a proof.

(continued on next page)

pattern $n \cdot 5 + n = n \cdot 6$ does happen to be true for all real numbers. We know this because we can *prove* it mathematically.

To prove a generalization, you must use *deductive reasoning*. Deductive reasoning starts from properties that are assumed to be true. For example, we assumed the Distributive Property of Multiplication over Addition to be true: If a, b, and c, are any real numbers, then $ab + ac = a(b + c)$.

If this is true for all real numbers, then it is true when $a = n$, $b = 5$, and $c = 1$. Substituting these values for a, b, and c, $n \cdot 5 + n \cdot 1 = n(5 + 1)$.

Using another assumed property, that if n is any real number, then $n \cdot 1 = n$. Adding 5 and 1 then gives $n \cdot 5 + n = n \cdot 6$.

This string of justified if-then statements has *proved* that for all real numbers n, $n \cdot 5 + n = n \cdot 6$.

You may not have written the words *if* and *then*, but in this course you have often strung if-then statements to follow each other.

A string of justified statements that follow from each other like these is a *proof*. In this chapter, you will see many examples of proofs that use the algebra that you have studied. These proofs involve the solving of equations, divisibility properties of arithmetic, and geometric figures. They comprise one of the most important uses of algebra: showing that a statement is true when there are infinitely many cases to consider.

777

Proofs of two of the most important theorems in high school mathematics are found in Lessons 13-4 and 13-8, the Quadratic Formula and the Pythagorean Theorem. But if we were to have only those two examples, students might think that we only prove things we already "know." Lessons 13-5 and 13-6 show how proof can be used to establish some very nice properties of integers. Lesson 13-7 shows how we can prove that particular numbers are irrational.

Taken as a whole, the chapter is designed to show students the power of proof in a nonthreatening way, thus setting the stage for the proofs they will see in *Geometry* and in later courses. Its broad reach also provides an opportunity to review many of the ideas from all the preceding chapters.

Lesson 13-1

GOAL

Understand the language of if-then statements.

SPUR Objectives

(The SPUR Objectives for all of Chapter 13 are found in the Chapter Review on pages 833–835.)

C Identify the antecedent and consequent of an if-then statement not necessarily given in if-then form.

D Determine whether if-then and if-and-only-if statements in algebra or geometry are true or false.

G Determine whether if-then and if-and-only-if statements in real-world contexts are true or false.

Materials/Resources

· Lesson Master 13-1A or 13-1B
· Resource Masters 196–198
· Scientific or graphing calculator

HOMEWORK

Suggestions for Assignment

• Questions 1–28
• Question 29 (extra credit)
• Reading Lesson 13-2
• Covering the Ideas 13-2

Local Standards

1 Warm-Up

In 1–4, give a counterexample to each statement.

1. If a word is correctly spelled in English, then it has "i before e except after c". **Counterexamples: weird, height, weight**

2. If n is positive, then $n^4 > n$. **Counterexample: any value of n between 0 and 1**

(continued on next page)

Lesson 13-1   If-Then Statements

Vocabulary

if-then statement
antecedent
consequent
generalization

▶ **BIG IDEA**   Statements that are of the form *if . . . then* are the basis of mathematcial logic, so it is important to know how to determine if they are true or false.

If is one of the most important words in mathematics. (The words *given, when, whenever,* and *suppose* often have the same meaning.) The word *if* is often followed by the word *then*, which may or may not be written. The result is an **if-then statement.** Here are some examples.

1. If a bug is an insect, it has six legs.

2. Suppose a person likes outdoor football. Then the person will like arena football.

3. Every animal on land grows leaves.

In an if-then statement, the clause following *if* is called the **antecedent.** The clause following *then* is the **consequent.** Below we have underlined the antecedent once and the consequent twice.

If a <u>bug is an insect</u>, then <u>it has six legs</u>.
    antecedent   consequent

Some if-then statements are *generalizations*. A **generalization** is an if-then statement in which there is a variable in the antecedent and consequent. In Statements 1–3 above, the variable is not seen but each statement can be thought of as an if-then statement with a variable.

> If B is an insect, (then) B has six legs.

> If P likes outdoor football, then P will like arena football.

 QY

When Is an If-Then Statement True?

An if-then statement is true if its consequent is true for *every* value in the domain of the variables in its antecedent.

Mental Math

A 28-page newspaper consists of a News section, a Classifieds section, and a Sports section. The News section is twice as long as the Sports section, and the Classifieds section is half as long as the Sports section. How long is

a. the News section?

b. the Sports section?

c. the Classifieds section? **4 pages**

a. **16 pages**

b. **8 pages**

▶ **QY**

Write Statement 3 above using a variable.

Background

An if-then statement is true if and only if every time the "if" part is true, then so is the "then" part. We do not care what happens if the "if" part is not true. For example, consider this sentence:

> If a person is in Chicago, then that person is in Illinois.

This is true for everyone in Chicago. It says nothing about people who are not in Chicago. For this reason, equivalent statements are:

Everyone who is in Chicago is in Illinois. All people in Chicago are in Illinois. If x is in Chicago, then x is in Illinois.

It also explains why the Venn diagram for this if-then statement has one circle inside another.

Example 1

True or False If *B* is an insect, (then) *B* has six legs.

Solution The statement is true because every insect has six legs. (Having six legs is one of the defining characteristics of insects.)

An if-then statement with a variable describes a pattern. As in any pattern, a value of the variable for which both the antecedent and consequent of an if-then statement is true is an instance of the statement. A beetle is an insect and a beetle has six legs. So a beetle is an instance of Statement 1.

Situations in which the antecedent is false do not affect whether an if-then statement is true. A dining room table might have six legs, but a table is not an insect. So a dining room table is not an instance of Statement 1.

A true if-then statement can be represented with a Venn diagram. The set of insects is placed inside the set of things with six legs.

Beetles are the largest group in the animal kingdom, representing one-fourth of all animals.

Source: San Diego Zoo

If A, then B.

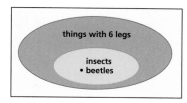

Example 2

True or False If *x* is a month of the year, then *x* has 31 days.

Solution This statement is not true because there are some months that have fewer than 31 days.

If there is a value of the variable for which the antecedent of an if-then statement is true and the consequent is not true, then the if-then statement is *false*. This value is a *counterexample* to the statement. The month of November has only 30 days, so it is a counterexample to the if-then statement. One counterexample is enough to cause an if-then statement to be false.

Even though there are values of the variable for which the statement of Example 2 is true, because there is a counterexample, the generalization is false.

If A, then sometimes (but not always) B.

If-Then Statements   779

How do we know that an if-then statement is true? It may be because of categories or a definition—if something is an *x*, then it is a *y*. It may be because of a property— if something is an *x*, then it has a *y*.

Accommodating the Learner ⬆

The table shows the final team standings in the East and North divisions of the National Football Conference (NFC) in 2005. Ask your students to write 3 or 4 true if-then statements using this information.

NFC East		
Team	**Wins**	**Losses**
N. Y. Giants	11	5
Washington	10	6
Dallas	9	7
Philadelphia	6	10
NFC North		
Team	**Wins**	**Losses**
Chicago	11	5
Minnesota	9	7
Detroit	5	11
Green Bay	4	12

3. If you are in Birmingham, then you are in Alabama. Counterexample: you could be in England (the original Birmingham), Iowa, Michigan, New Jersey, Ohio, or Pennsylvania.

4. If a figure is quadrilateral *ABCD*, then its diagonals $\overline{AC}$ and $\overline{BD}$ intersect inside the quadrilateral. Counterexample: any nonconvex quadrilateral such as the one drawn here.

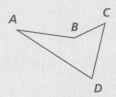

2 Teaching

Notes on the Lesson

Some of this lesson should be review for students who have studied *Transition Mathematics*.

Examples 1–3 You might wish to go through each of these examples, making sure that students understand how the Venn diagrams relate the antecedent and consequent. In Example 3, we need to refer to "land animal" because there are sea animals that look very much like they have leaves.

Additional Examples

Example 1 **True or False** If *C* is a horse, (then) *C* has four legs. The statement is true because every horse has four legs.

Example 2 **True or False** If *b* is a bird, then *b* can fly. This statement is not true because there are birds, such as penguins, that cannot fly.

13-1

Notes on the Lesson

Guided Example 4 Ensure that students understand why the statements are true or false.

Example 3

Draw a Venn diagram for the statement: If *G* is a land animal, *G* grows leaves.

Solution A tiger is a land animal and a tiger does not grow leaves, so the statement is false. In fact, no land animals grow leaves. So if *G* is a land animal, *G* never grows leaves. The Venn diagram has two circles that do not overlap.

If A, then not B.

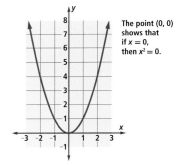

If-Then Statements in Mathematics

If-then statements occur throughout mathematics because they clarify what is given information and what are conclusions.

GUIDED

Example 4

Fill in the blanks.

If-Then Statement	True or False	Explanation
a. If $3n + 5 = 65$, then $n = 20$.	true	If $3n + 5 = 65$, then $3n = \underline{\ ?\ }$. **60** If $3n = \underline{\ ?\ }$, then $n = 20$. **60**
b. If a figure is a square, then it is a rectangle.	true **?**	Definition of square: a square is $\underline{\ ?\ }$. **a rectangle**
c. If *x* is a real number, then $x^2 > 0$.	false **?**	0 is a real number and 0^2 is not greater than 0.
d. If a quadrilateral has 3 right angles, then it is a square.	false	?

A rectangle has 3 right angles, but it does not have to be a square.

Counterexamples to the two false statements in Guided Example 4 can be pictured. For Statement c, graph $y = x^2$. Notice that the graph is not always above the *x*-axis, so it is not the case that $x^2 > 0$ for every value of *x*. For Statement d, show a quadrilateral that has 3 right angles but is not a square.

This quadrilateral has 3 right angles and is not a square.

The point (0, 0) shows that if $x = 0$, then $x^2 = 0$.

Accommodating the Learner ⬇

Using the Venn diagram below, ask your students to write several true if-then statements. Students should also explain how the diagram illustrates each of their conditional statements.

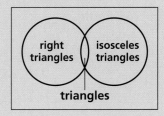

Putting Statements into If-Then Form

Statements with the words "all," "every," and "no" can be rewritten in if-then form without changing their meaning.

GUIDED

Example 5

Rewrite each statement in if-then form.

Statement	If-then Form with Variables	
a. Every whole number is a real number.	If x is a whole number, then ___?___.	x is a real number
b. All people born in the United States are U.S. citizens.	If ___?___, then P is a U.S. citizen.	P is a person born in the United States
c. No power of a positive number is negative.	If p is a positive number and g is any real number, then ___?___.	p^g is not negative

Questions

COVERING THE IDEAS

In 1 and 2, identify the antecedent and the consequent of the if-then statement.

1. If the sun shines this afternoon, I will be happy.

2. The world would be a better place if people did not litter.
   people did not litter; the world would be a better place

In 3 and 4, rewrite the statement as an if-then statement with a variable in it. Underline the antecedent once and the consequent twice.

3. Every integer greater than 1 is either a prime number or a product of prime numbers.

4. When a person drives over 35 miles per hour on that street, that person is speeding. If <u>n is a person driving over 35 miles per hour on that street</u>, then <u><u>n is speeding</u></u>.

5. Explain why this if-then statement is true.
   If $3x + 16 > 10$, then $x > -2$. See margin.

6. Explain why this if-then statement is false.
   If $3x + 16 > 10$, then $x > 0$. See margin.

In 7–9, an antecedent is given. Complete the statement with two consequents that make it true. 7–8. See margin.

7. If L and W are the length and width of a rectangle, then ___?___.

8. If $x^m \cdot x^n = x^{m+n}$, then ___?___.

9. If n is divisible by 10, then ___?___. Answers vary. Sample answer: n is a multiple of 10; n is an integer

1. the sun shines this afternoon; I will be happy

3. If <u>x is an integer greater than 1</u>, then <u><u>x is a prime number or the product of prime numbers</u></u>.

Interstate highways nationwide usually have posted speed limits between 55 and 75 mi/h.

Source: Federal Highway Administration

Notes on the Lesson

Example 5 Ask students to give other sentences that begin with "Every," "No," and "All" and put them into if-then form.

Additional Example

Example 5 Rewrite each statement in if-then form.

Statement	If-then form with variables
a. Every whole number is an integer.	If x is a whole number, then ___?___.
b. A polygon with six sides is a hexagon.	If ___?___, then P is a hexagon.
c. The square root of a negative number is not a real number.	If B is a negative number, then ___?___.

x is an integer; P is a polygon with six sides; the square root of B is not a real number

3 Assignment

Recommended Assignment

- Questions 1–28
- Question 29 (extra credit)
- Reading Lesson 13-2
- Covering the Ideas 13-2

Notes on the Question

Question 2 It is important for students to realize that the "if" part of a statement does not always come first.

Additional Answers

5. Solving the inequality for x gives $x > -2$, so if the original inequality is true, then $x > -2$ must also be true.

6. If the inequality is true, then $x > 0$ does not need to be true. For example, if $x = -1$, then $3x + 16 = 13 > 10$, but $x < 0$.

7. Answers vary. Sample answer: LW is the area of the rectangle; $2L + 2W$ is the perimeter of the rectangle.

8. Answers vary. Sample answer:
   $x^m \cdot x^{-n} = x^{m-n}$; $x^{2m} \cdot x^{2n} = x^{2m+2n}$

Notes on the Questions

Question 11 If it were true that the only Chattanooga in the U.S. were in Tennessee, then the statement would be true. But there is a Chattanooga in Oklahoma, too. The word *chattanooga* is a word in the language of the Muskegon Indians, a Creek tribe, meaning "rock coming to an end" or "mountains looking at each other."

Question 12 There is only one even number that is not a counterexample.

Question 13 Every value of x that satisfies the antecedent does not satisfy the consequent. This statement is never true. Notice that 0 is not a counterexample because 0 does not satisfy the antecedent.

Questions 15 and 18 0 is the only counterexample to each. Students should be on the lookout for situations where 0, negative numbers, or numbers between 0 and 1 are the only counterexamples.

Additional Answers

17a. Answers vary. Sample answer:
Let $x = -\frac{1}{2}$. Then $x^2 + x = \left(-\frac{1}{2}\right)^2 + \left(-\frac{1}{2}\right) = \frac{1}{4} - \frac{1}{2} = -\frac{1}{4}$, so $y < 0$.

18.

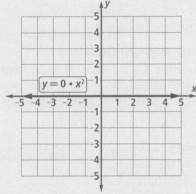

19. Answers vary. Sample answer:

$m\angle CAB = 90.00°$
$m\angle ABC = 12.59°$
$m\angle BCA = 77.41°$

In 10–13, an if-then situation is given.

a. Tell whether the statement is true or false.

b. Draw a Venn diagram picturing the situation.

10. If a figure is a rectangle, then the figure is a square. a. false

11. If you are in the United States and in Chattanooga, then you are in Tennessee. a. false

12. If a number is an even number, then it is a prime number. a. false

13. If $x > 0$, then $-x > 0$. a. false

APPLYING THE MATHEMATICS

In 14–17, a false statement is given.

a. Find a counterexample that shows it is false.

b. Find the largest domain of the variable for which the statement is true.

14. If w is a real number, then w^3 is positive. b. $w > 0$

15. If t is a real number, then t^4 is positive.
b. Answers vary. Sample answer: t can be any real number except 0.

16. If r is a real number, then $2r \geq r$. b. $r \geq 0$

17. If x is a real number and $y = x^2 + x$, then $y \geq 0$. 17a. See margin.
b. $x \geq 0$ or $x \leq -1$

In 18 and 19, draw a counterexample to the statement.

18. For all real numbers a, the graph of $y = ax^2$ is a parabola.

19. A triangle cannot have two angles each with measure over $75°$.

20. Draw the following four true statements in one Venn diagram.

a. Every rhombus is a parallelogram. 20. See margin.

b. Every rectangle is a parallelogram.

c. If a figure is both a rhombus and a rectangle, then it is a square.

d. Every square is both a rhombus and a rectangle.

In 21 and 22, rewrite the statement as an if-then statement and indicate why each statement is false. 21–22. See margin.

21. All sentences have a subject, verb, and object.

22. Every president of the United States has served fewer than three terms.

REVIEW

23. **Skill Sequence** Factor each expression. (**Lesson 12-4**)

a. $a^2 - 36$ $(a - 6)(a + 6)$

b. $n^2 - 5n - 36$ $(n - 9)(n + 4)$

c. $x^2 - 5xy - 36y^2$ $(x - 9y)(x + 4y)$

Additional Answers

20.

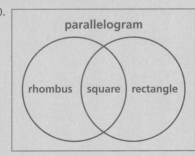

21. If something is a sentence, then it has a subject, verb, and object; Answers vary. Sample answer: The sentence "He went." has no object.

22. If someone has been president of the United States, then he has served fewer than three terms. Franklin Roosevelt served three full terms and part of a fourth.

10b.

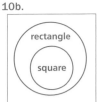

11b.

12b.

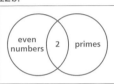

13b.

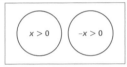

14a. Answers vary. Sample answer: Let $w = -1$. Then $w^3 = -1$, and -1 is not positive.

15a. Answers vary. Sample answer: Let $t = 0$. Then $t^4 = 0$, and 0 is not positive.

16a. Answers vary. Sample answer: Let $r = -1$. Then $2r = -2$, and $-2 < -1$, so $2r < r$.

18–19. See margin.

24. **Fill in the Blank** Do this problem in your head. Because one thousand times one thousand equals one million, then $1{,}005 \cdot 995 = \underline{\quad?\quad}$. (**Lesson 11-6**) **999,975**

25. Tickets to a hockey game cost \$22 for adults and \$16 for children. The total attendance at one game was 3,150 and the total revenue from ticket sales for the game was \$66,258. How many of each kind of ticket were sold for the game? (**Lesson 10-5**)

26. Write $2^{-3} + 4^{-3}$ as a simple fraction. (**Lesson 8-4**) $\frac{9}{64}$

27. Let $g(x) = \frac{3}{4}x - 7$. (**Lesson 7-6**)
    a. Calculate $g(80)$. **53**
    b. Calculate $g(-80)$. **-67**
    c. Describe the graph of g.

28. **True or False** The slope of the line through (x_1, y_1) and (x_2, y_2) is the opposite of the slope of the line through (x_2, y_2) and (x_1, y_1). (**Lesson 6-6**) **false**

The Carolina Hurricanes won hockey's 2006 Stanley Cup.

EXPLORATION

29. Consider this statement: No four points in a plane can all be the same distance from each other.
    a. Write the statement in if-then form.
    b. Is the statement true or false? **The statement is true.**
    c. If "in a plane" is deleted from the statement, show that the resulting statement is false. **Answers vary. Sample answer: On a sphere, four noncoplanar points can be found such that the distance between them along the sphere is the same.**

25. **2,643 adult tickets and 507 child tickets**

27c. **Answers vary. Sample answer: The graph is the line with slope $\frac{3}{4}$ and y-intercept -7.**

29a. **If four points are in a plane, then they cannot all be the same distance from each other.**

---

4 Wrap-Up

Ongoing Assessment

Call on different students to identify the antecedent and consequent in each of the following if-then statements.

a. If a polygon has four sides, then it is a rectangle.
b. All people who live in Sacramento live in California.
c. A number cannot be −2 if the number is greater than 13.
d. If it is raining outside, the sidewalk is wet.

Project Update

If you have not had students look over the projects on pages 829 and 830, you might want to do so now. Project 1, Squares Surrounding Triangles, on page 829 relates to the content of this lesson.

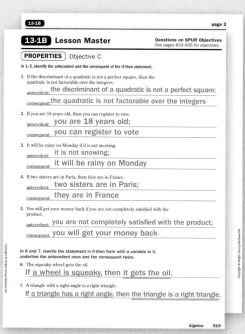

Lesson

13-2

GOAL

Emphasize the idea that the truth of the converse of an if-then statement does not depend on the truth of the original statement.

SPUR Objectives

D Determine whether if-then and if-and-only-if statements in algebra or geometry are true or false.

G Determine whether if-then and if-and-only-if statements in real-world contexts are true or false.

Materials/Resources

· Lesson Master 13-2A or 13-2B
· Resource Master 199
· Scientific or graphing calculator

HOMEWORK

Suggestions for Assignment

• Questions 1–28
• Question 29 (extra credit)
• Reading Lesson 13-3
• Covering the Ideas 13-3

Local Standards

---

1 ⟩ Warm-Up

In 1–3, a statement is given. **a.** Tell whether or not it is true; **b.** Give its converse; and **c.** Tell whether or not its converse is true.

1. If $5x + x^2 = -4$, then $(x + 4)(x + 1) = 0$. a. true; b. If $(x + 4)(x + 1) = 0$, then $5x + x^2 = -4$; c. true.

2. If the 7th power of a number is less than the 6th power of the number, then the number must be negative. a. false; b. If a number is negative, then its 7th power is less than its 6th power. c. true

3. If a figure is a rectangle, then it is a parallelogram. a. true; b. If a figure is a parallelogram, then it is a rectangle; c. false.

Lesson

13-2 The Converse of an If-Then Statement

Vocabulary

converse
equivalent statements
if and only if

▶ **BIG IDEA** The converse of the statement, "If A, then B." is the statement, "If B, then A."

You might have heard of the question, "Which came first, the chicken or the egg?" This question is difficult because: If there is a chicken, then there must have been an egg. If there is an egg, then there must have been a chicken.

These two if-then statements are *converses*. The *converse* of the statement, "If p, then q" is the statement, "If q, then p." Another way of stating this is: the **converse** of an if-then statement is found by switching the antecedent and the consequent of the statement.

STOP **QY**

Converses of True Statements

Often the converse of a true statement is not true. Here is an example.

Statement If $x = 8$, then $x^2 = 64$. (true)

Converse If $x^2 = 64$, then $x = 8$. (False; x could also be -8.)

> GUIDED

Example 1

The given statement is true. Write its converse and explain why the converse is not true.
a. If a quadrilateral has 4 sides of the same length and its diagonals have the same length, then the quadrilateral is a rectangle.
b. If you live in the state of North Dakota, then you live in the United States.

> Solutions

a. Converse: If a quadrilateral is ___?___, then ___?___. This statement is false because ___?___.

b. Converse: If ___?___, then ___?___ The statement is false because ___?___.

784 Using Algebra to Prove

Mental Math

Evaluate when $a = 2$ and $b = -2$.

a. $(a + b)^2$ 0
b. $a^2 + b^2$ 8
c. $a^2 + 2ab + b^2$ 0

▶ **QY**

Give the converse of the statement: If $\sqrt{2x} = 10$, then $x = 50$.

1a. a rectangle; it has 4 sides of the same length and its diagonals have the same length; a rectangle can have different width and length

1b. you live in the United States; you live in the state of North Dakota; you could live in any of the other 49 states

---

Background

Related syntactically to the statement "If p, then q" are three other statements:
the converse: If q, then p.
the inverse: If not p, then not q.
the contrapositive: If not q, then not p.

A statement and its contrapositive are either both true or both false. Similarly, the converse and inverse of a statement are either both true or both false.

Even when the if-then statement is true, the converse may not be true. When both

a statement and its converse are true, then the statements are equivalent.

There is evidence that some students find it difficult to distinguish between a statement and its converse. The word "if" often means "if and only if." When a parent says, "If you finish your homework, you can watch television," the intended meaning is usually the converse: "In order to watch television, then you must have finished your homework," or equivalently, the inverse: "If you don't finish your homework, then you can't watch television."

Sometimes the converse of a true statement is true. When a statement and its converse are both true, then the antecedent and consequent are **equivalent statements.** Equivalent statements can be connected by the phrase *if and only if.* Here is an example.

Statement If $x = 6$, then $2^x = 64$. (true)

Converse If $2^x = 64$, then $x = 6$. (true)

Because the statement and its converse are both true, you can write:
$x = 6$ **if and only if** $2^x = 64$.

GUIDED

Example 2

The given statement is true and so is its converse. Write the converse and then combine the statement and its converse into one if-and-only-if statement.
a. If a quadrilateral has 4 sides of the same length and its diagonals have the same length, then the quadrilateral is a square.
b. If you live in the largest country in South America, then you live in Brazil.

Solution

a. Converse: If a quadrilateral ___?___, then ___?___. You can write: A quadrilateral has 4 sides of the same length and diagonals of the same length *if and only if* ___?___.

b. Converse: If you live in Brazil, then you live in the largest country in South America. You can write: ___?___ *if and only if* ___?___.

Brazil is the fourth most populous country in the world with about 190 million people.

Source: *The World Factbook*

Example 2
a. is a square; it has 4 sides of the same length and its diagonals have the same length; it is a square
b. You live in Brazil; you live in the largest country in South America

When you see the phrase "if and only if," then you can separate the sentence into two if-then statements.

In Hardnox High School, a student is on the honor roll if and only if his or her grade point average is at least 3.75.

means

In Hardnox High School, if a student's grade point average is at least 3.75, then the student is on the honor roll.

and

If a student in Hardnox High School is on the honor roll, then his or her grade point average is at least 3.75.

Questions

COVERING THE IDEAS

1. State the converse of the statement: If there is smoke, then there is fire. If there is fire, then there is smoke.

Accommodating the Learner ⬆

Ask students to consider what they might conclude after reading the following two true statements: If Clarissa behaves, then her mom is happy; If Clarissa's mom is happy, then her dad is happy. They should conclude the following: If Clarissa behaves, then her dad is happy. This is an example of a chain of reasoning. Ask students to create several examples to illustrate their understanding about the idea of a chain of reasoning.

Accommodating the Learner ⬇

Students should write the converse of each of the following true statements.

• If Willie stands on a chair, then he is taller than his sister.
• If a bottle holds 32 ounces, then it holds a quart.

Once they have written the converse of each correctly, ask them to identify which of the converses is true and which one could be false.

13-2

2 Teaching

Notes on the Lesson

Emphasize that for an if-then statement to be true, the consequent must be true for all possible instances for which the antecedent is true. So, for example, to determine the truth of the statement, "If $x^2 = 9$, then $x > -5$," we need to check only two values of x, 3 and -3. And because $3 > -5$ and $-3 > -5$, the statement is true. Now examine the converse: "If $x > -5$, then $x^2 = 9$", there are infinitely many values of x for which the antecedent is true, and it is easy to find some for which the consequent is not true. Any value of x other than 3 or -3 will do.

Additional Examples

Example 1 The given statement is true. Write its converse and explain why the converse is not true.

a. If the length of each side of a triangle is 15, then the perimeter of the triangle is 45.

b. If you live in San Diego, then you live in California.

Solution

a. Converse: If the perimeter of a triangle is ___?___, then ___?___. This statement is false because ___?___.
45; each side length is 15; the side lengths may be 10, 15, and 20

b. Converse: If ___?___, then ___?___. The statement is false because ___?___.
you live in California; you live in San Diego; many people who live in California do not live in San Diego

Example 2 The given statement is true and so is its converse. Write the converse and then combine the statement and its converse in one if-and-only-if statement.

Statement: If a triangle has 3 congruent sides, then it is an equilateral triangle.

Solution

Converse: If a triangle is ___?___, then ___?___. You can write: A triangle has three congruent sides *if and only if* ___?___.
equilateral; it has 3 congruent sides; it is equilateral

13-2

3 Assignment

Recommended Assignment

- Questions 1–28
- Question 29 (extra credit)
- Reading Lesson 13-3
- Covering the Ideas 13-3

Notes on the Questions

Question 3d Allow a variety of answers. Students may have to alter some parts significantly so that they would be true.

Question 12 Point out that the answer assumes that the domain of y is the set of real numbers. If the domain of y is the set of positive real numbers, then the statements are equivalent.

Question 16 This question provides an opportunity to review terminology from geometry: pentagon, hexagon, heptagon, octagon, nonagon, and decagon.

Question 21 Some students have been known to complain that they shouldn't have to know an idea from social studies in a mathematics class. Point out that not only should they know this as an educated citizen, but it is an example of how the mathematical skills of logic are used outside mathematics.

Question 29 Students have been known to be very inventive. Have students share their answers.

2. **Multiple Choice** If a statement is true, then its converse B
   A must be true.   B may be true.   C must be false.

In 3–5, a statement is given.
   a. Is it true?
   b. State its converse.
   c. Is its converse true?
   d. If either the statement or its converse is not true, correct them so that they are both true.

3. If an integer is divisible by 3 and by 4, then it is divisible by 24.

4. If both the units and tens digits of an integer written in base 10 equal 0, then the integer is divisible by 100.

5. If $7u < 56$, then $u > 8$.

In 6–8, write the two if-then statements that are meant by the if-and-only-if statement. 6–8. See margin.

6. You will receive full credit for this question if and only if you get both parts correct.

7. A quadrilateral is a rectangle if and only if it has four right angles.

8. $5x + 4y = 20$ if and only if $y = -1.25x + 5$.

In 9 and 10, rewrite the definition as an if-and-only-if statement.

9. Every linear function has an equation of the form $f(x) = ax + b$.

10. The reciprocal of a nonzero number x is the number y such that $xy = 1$.

In 11–14, are statements (1) and (2) equivalent? If not, why not?

11. (1) $x = 3$ yes
    (2) $2x = 6$

12. (1) $y = 15$
    (2) $y^4 = 50,625$

13. (1) $z = 8$
    (2) $z^2 + 48 = 14z$

14. (1) $a + b = c$ yes
    (2) $c - b = a$

APPLYING THE MATHEMATICS

In 15–18, a statement is given. 15b, d., 16b, d. See margin.
   a. Is it true?
   b. State its converse.
   c. Is its converse true?
   d. If either the statement or its converse is not true, correct them so that they are both true.

15. If $(x - 5)(2x + 3) = 45$, then $2x^2 - 7x + 30 = 90$. a. yes c. yes

13. No, the statement "If $z^2 + 48 = 14z$, then $z = 8$" is not true because $z^2 + 48 = 14z$ is also true for $z = 6$.

3a. no
3b. If an integer is divisible by 24, then it is divisible by 3 and 4.
3c. yes
3d. Answers vary. Sample answer: If an integer is divisible by 3 and 4, then it is divisible by 12. If an integer is divisible by 24, then it is divisible by 3 and 8.
4a. yes
4b. If an integer is divisible by 100, then both the units and tens digits of the integer written in base 10 equal 0.
4c. yes
4d. Both are true.
5a. no
5b. If $u > 8$, then $7u < 56$.
5c. no
5d. If $7u > 56$, then $u > 8$; If $u > 8$, then $7u > 56$.
9. A function is a linear function if and only if it has an equation of the form $f(x) = ax + b$.
10. A number y is the reciprocal of a nonzero number x if and only if $xy = 1$.
12. No, the statement "If $y^4 = 50,625$, then $y = 15$" is not true because $y^4 = 50,625$ is also true for $y = -15$.

Additional Answers

6. If you get both parts correct, then you will receive full credit for this question; If you receive full credit for this question, then you got both parts correct.

7. If a quadrilateral has four right angles, then it is a rectangle; If a quadrilateral is a rectangle, then it has four right angles.

8. If $y = -1.25x + 5$, then $5x + 4y = 20$. If $5x + 4y = 20$, then $y = -1.25x + 5$.

15b. If $2x^2 - 7x + 30 = 90$, then $(x - 5)(2x + 3) = 45$.

15d. n/a

16b. If a polygon is a hexagon, then it has 7 sides.

16d. If a polygon has 7 sides, then it is a heptagon; If a polygon is a hexagon, then it has 6 sides.

17b. If the x-intercepts of a parabola are -5 and 3, then it has an equation of the form $y = (x - 5)(x + 3)$.

17d. If a parabola has an equation of the form $y = a(x - 5)(x + 3)$, then its x-intercepts are 5 and -3; If the x-intercepts of a parabola are -5 and 3, then it has an equation of the form $y = a(x + 5)(x - 3)$.

---

16. If a polygon has 7 sides, then it is a hexagon. **a. no c. no**

17. If a parabola has an equation of the form $y = (x - 5)(x + 3)$, then its x-intercepts are –5 and 3. **a. no c. no; b, d. See margin.**

18. If $3x + 4y = 6$ and $2x - 5y = 7$, then $x = 6$ and $y = -3$. **a. no c. no b, d. See margin.**

In 19–21, a statement is given. **19b., 20b., 21b. See margin.**

   a. Tell whether the statement is true.

   b. If the statement is true, give an example. If it is not true, modify it so that it is true.

19. A line is a vertical line if and only if its slope is undefined. **a. true**

20. $x^a \cdot x^b = x^{a + b}$ if and only if a and b are positive integers. **a. false**

21. A person can be a U.S. citizen if and only if the person was born in the United States. **a. false**

A valid U.S. passport is required for U.S. citizens to enter and leave most foreign countries.

Source: U.S. Department of State

REVIEW

In 22 and 23, tell whether the given if-then statement is true or false. If it is false, provide a counterexample to the statement. (Lessons 13-1, 9-1) **22–23. See margin.**

22. If a dining room table seats 8 people, then it seats 6 people. **true**

23. If n is even, the graph of $y = ax^n$ crosses the x-axis twice.

24. **Multiple Choice** Rectangles of width x are cut off from two adjacent sides of a 12 in.-by-12 in. sheet of wrapping paper, as shown at the right. What is the area, in square inches, of the square region that remains? (Lesson 11-6) **D**

   A $12 - x^2$ B $144 + x^2$

   C $144 - x^2$ D $144 - 24x + x^2$

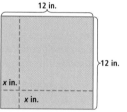

12 in.

12 in.

x in.

x in.

25. If 8 pencils and 5 erasers cost \$4.69 and 3 pencils and 4 erasers cost \$2.80, find the cost of 2 pencils. (Lesson 10-5) **\$0.56**

In 26–28, simplify the expression. (Lessons 8-6, 8-5)

26. $5(3\sqrt{x})^2$ **45x**   27. $(6 \cdot 2^{-2})^3$ $\frac{27}{8}$ 28. $\frac{9 \pm \sqrt{18}}{3}$ $3 \pm \sqrt{2}$

EXPLORATION

29. Write two statements from outside of mathematics that are true but whose converses are false. **Answers vary. Sample answer: If it has rained, then the sidewalk is wet. If the light bulb is broken, then the room is dark.**

QY ANSWER

If $x = 50$, then $\sqrt{2x} = 10$.

The Converse of an If-Then Statement   **787**

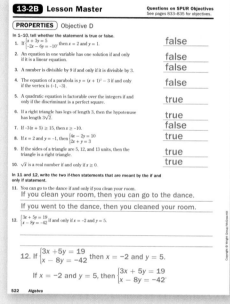

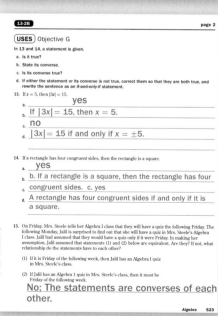

Additional Answers

18b. If $x = 6$ and $y = -3$, then $3x + 4y = 6$ and $2x - 5y = 7$.

18d. If $3x + 4y = 6$ and $2x - 5y = 7$, then $x = \frac{58}{23}$ and $y = -\frac{9}{23}$; If $x = 6$ and $y = -3$, then $3x + 4y = 6$ and $2x - 5y = 27$.

19b. Answers vary. Sample answer: $x = 10$.

20b. $x^a \cdot x^b = x^{a + b}$ for any real values of a and b and all nonzero x.

21b. A person can be a U.S. citizen if and only if the person was born in the United States or the person was naturalized.

23. False; the graph of $y = ax^2$ crosses the x-axis only once at $(0, 0)$ for all $a \neq 0$.

GOAL

Relate the solving of equations to the if-then statements and their converses, and to the idea of proof.

SPUR Objective

A Show and justify the steps in solving an equation.

Materials/Resources

· Lesson Master 13-3A or 13-3B
· Resource Master 200
· Scientific or graphing calculator
· Quiz 1

HOMEWORK

Suggestions for Assignment

* Questions 1–33
* Question 34 (extra credit)
* Reading Lesson 13-4
* Covering the Ideas 13-4

Local Standards

1 Warm-Up

In 1 and 2, two steps in solving an equation or inequality are given.
a. Indicate what was done to get from the first step to the second; **b.** Name the general property that justifies what was done; and **c.** Describe the general property with variables.

1. Step 1: $40\% \cdot x = 75$;
   Step 2: $x = 187.5$ Solution 1:
   a. Both sides were divided by 0.40.
   b. Division Property of Equality
   c. If $a = b$ and $c \neq 0$, then $\frac{a}{c} = \frac{b}{c}$.
   Solution 2:
   a. Both sides were multiplied by $\frac{1}{0.4}$.
   b. Multiplication Property of Equality
   c. If $a = b$, then $ac = bc$.
2. Step 1: $3y + 2x < 5$;
   Step 2: $3y < 5 - 2x$. a. $-2x$ was added to both sides. b. Addition Property of Inequality c. If $a < b$, then $a + c < b + c$.

Vocabulary

justifications
proof argument
deduction

▶ **BIG IDEA**   Writing the steps in solving an equation and then checking the solutions together prove that you have found the only solutions to the equation.

An Example of a Proof Argument

Every time you solve an equation, you are proving or deducing something true. Consider solving the equation $8x + 19 = 403$. The solution is 48. You may write the steps as we show here.

i. $8x + 19 = 403$
ii. $8x + 19 + -19 = 403 + -19$
iii. $8x + 0 = 384$
iv. $8x = 384$
v. $\frac{1}{8} \cdot 8x = \frac{1}{8} \cdot 384$
vi. $1 \cdot x = 48$
vii. $x = 48$

If you include the statements that show why each step follows from the previous steps, then you have written a *proof*. These statements are called **justifications.** They indicate why you can do what you have done to solve the equation.

	Conclusion	What Was Done	Justification
i.	$8x + 19 = 403$	Given	Given
ii.	$8x + 19 - 19 = 403 + -19$	Add −19 to both sides.	Addition Property of Equality
iii.	$8x + 0 = 384$	$19 + -19 = 0$	Additive Inverse Property
iv.	$8x = 384$	$8x + 0 = 8x$	Additive Identity Property
v.	$\frac{1}{8} \cdot 8x = \frac{1}{8} \cdot 384$	Multiply both sides by $\frac{1}{8}$.	Multiplication Property of Equality
vi.	$1x = 48$	$\frac{1}{8} \cdot 8 = 1,$ $\frac{1}{8} \cdot 384 = 48$	Multiplicative Inverse Property
vii.	$x = 48$	$1 \cdot x = x$	Multiplicative Identity Property

Mental Math

Solve for *n*.

a. $5^n \cdot 5^4 = 5^{20}$ $n = 16$
b. $(5^n)^4 = 5^{20}$ $n = 5$

Background

A proof is a sequence of justified statements, starting with some given information or information assumed to be true and using principles known to be true, to obtain other statements. In this lesson, the equation $8x + 19 = 403$ is solved four times. The first would generally not be called a proof because it has no justifications. The second is like the first but with justifications. The third and the fourth are proofs with varying amounts of detail. Each of these four arguments

proves: If $8x + 19 = 403$, then $x = 48$. But it does not finish the solution to the equation because it does not provide the "only if."

Most students will think that the check is only for themselves, to show that they got the right answer. But in this lesson, they learn that the check is to show everyone else that the answer they got checks.

(continued on next page)

With this argument, you have proved: *If 8x + 19 = 403, then x = 48.* In this if-then statement, *8x + 19 = 403* is the antecedent and *x = 48* is the consequent. A **proof argument** in mathematics is a sequence of justified conclusions, starting with the antecedent and ending with the consequent. The use of a proof to show that one statement follows from another is called **deduction**.

A Justification Is Different from What Was Done

What you *do* to solve an equation is different from the justification. What was done applies to the specific equation being solved. The justification is the general property. In proofs, some people prefer to see what was done. Other people prefer the justification.

GUIDED

Example 1

Prove if −6x − 14 = 118, then x = −22.

ii. Addition Property of Equality; iii. −6x = 118 + 14; v. Multiply both sides by −$\frac{1}{6}$; vi. Multiplicative Inverse Property; vii. −$\frac{1}{6}$(132) = −22; Identity

Solution

	Conclusion	What Was Done	Justification
i.	−6x − 14 = 118	Given	Given
ii.	−6x − 14 + 14 = 118 + 14	14 was added to both sides.	?
iii.	?	−14 + 14 = 0, 118 + 114 = 132	Additive Inverse Property
iv.	−6x = 132	−6x + 0 = −6x	Arithmetic
v.	−$\frac{1}{6}$(−6x) = −$\frac{1}{6}$(132)	?	Multiplication Property of Equality
vi.	1 · x = −$\frac{1}{6}$(132)	−$\frac{1}{6}$(−6) = 1	?
vii.	x = −22	?	? Property

An Abbreviated Proof

Because work with additive and multiplicative inverses and identities is so automatic, some people prefer abbreviated proofs that do not show these steps. Here is an abbreviated proof of the statement: If 8x + 19 = 403, then x = 48.

	Conclusion	Justification
i.	8x + 19 = 403	Given
ii.	8x + 19 + −19 = 403 + −19	Addition Property of Equality
iii.	8x = 384	Arithmetic
iv.	$\frac{1}{8}$ · 8x = $\frac{1}{8}$ · 384	Multiplication Property of Equality
v.	x = 48	Multiplicative Inverse Property

The first three "proofs" of the statement 'If 8x + 19 = 403 then x = 48.' have seven steps. But a more rigorous proof would include a minimum of several additional steps. Such a proof would begin:

i.   8x + 19 = 403   Given

ii. (8x + 19) + −19 = 403 + −19
          Addition Property of Equality

iii. 8x + (19 + −19) = 403 + −19
          Associative Property of Addition

iv.   8x + 0 = 384
          Additive Inverse Property, arithmetic

v.   8x = 384
          Additive Identity Property

We see little reason to be so rigorous at this level.

Justifications and properties. Students will be confused as to what can be a justification. Properties are of three types: definitions, postulates, and theorems. Here we do not use the technical term "postulate" for "assumption," or "theorem" for a previously proved property, but you might want to introduce these two terms.

Notes on the Activity

The four solutions of the equation 8x + 19 = 403 may be described as follows:

First solution: (page 788) steps only (no justifications)

Second solution: (page 788) major and minor steps with names of properties as justifications

Third solution: (Example 1): major and minor steps with names of properties and what was done in each step

Fourth solution: (p. 789) major steps with names of properties.

These are not the only possibilities. Some teachers prefer the following even more abbreviated proof than the fourth solution:

i.	8x + 19 = 403	Given
ii.	8x = 384	Addition Property of Equality
iii.	x = 48	Multiplication Property of Equality

Additional Example

Example 1 Prove that if 7p + 11 = −101, then p = −16.

Solution

	Conclusion	What Was Done	Justification
i.	7p + 11 = −101	Given	Given
ii.	7p + 11 + −11 = −101 + −11	−11 was added to both sides.	Addition Property of Equality
iii.	?	11 + −11 = 0	Additive Inverse Property
iv.	7p = −112	7p + 0 = 7p	?
v.	$\frac{1}{7}$(7p) = $\frac{1}{7}$(−112)	?	Multiplication Property of Equality
vi.	1 · p = $\frac{1}{7}$(−112)	$\frac{1}{7}$(7) = 1	Multiplicative Inverse Property
vii.	p = −16	?	?

iii. 7p + 0 = −112; iv. Additive Identity Property; v. Multiply both sides by $\frac{1}{7}$.; vii. $\frac{1}{7}$(−112) = −16; Arithmetic

13-3

13-3

Additional Example

Example 2 Prove that if $-3a - 7 = 20$, then $a = -9$.

Solution

Supply the justifications for the following conclusions.

Conclusion	Justification
i. $-3a - 7 = 20$	___?___ Given
ii. $-3a - 7 + 7$ $= 20 + 7$	___?___ Addition Property of Equality
iii. $-3a = 27$	___?___ Additive Identity Property, Arithmetic
iv. $-\frac{1}{3}(-3a)$ $= -\frac{1}{3}(27)$	___?___ Multiplication Property of Equality
v. $a = -9$	___?___ Multiplicative Inverse Property, Arithmetic

Vocabulary Development

This would be a good time to suggest to your students that they go back and review the many properties that have been introduced in this course. These properties should be found in their notebooks along with examples illustrating each property. If their notes are not complete, suggest they review chapters 1, 2, and 8, which introduce many of the properties. Help students realize that when they want to review the course, it is essential that their notebook is complete.

GUIDED

Example 2

Prove that if $2x - 9 = 37$, then $x = 23$.

Solution Supply the justifications for the following conclusions.

Conclusion	Justification
i. $2x - 9 = 37$	___?___ Given
ii. $2x - 9 + 9 = 37 + 9$	___?___ Addition Property of Equality
iii. $2x = 46$	___?___ Additive Inverse Property and arithmetic
iv. $\frac{1}{2}(2x) = \frac{1}{2}(46)$	___?___ Multiplication Property of Equality
v. $x = 23$	___?___ Multiplicative Inverse Property and arithmetic

Justifications and Properties

In solving an equation or inequality, every justification is one of the following:

1. *Given* information (the given equation or inequality to be solved)

2. A property, of which there are three types:
   a. a *defined property*, such as the definition of slope, absolute value, or square root
   b. an *assumed property* of numbers, such as the Product of Powers Property or the Distributive Property
   c. a *previously-proved property*, such as the Means-Extremes Property or the Power of a Product Property, that were not assumed but proved using definitions or other known properties

3. *Arithmetic* (a catch-all term for all the properties you have learned that help you compute results of operations)

The Check Is a Converse

On the previous page you saw the proof of the statement: *If 8x + 19 = 403, then x = 48.* When you check your work by substitution, you are proving: *If x = 48, then 8x + 19 = 403.* The check is the converse of the solution. Together, the solution and the check mean *8x + 19 = 403 if and only if x = 48.*

Another way of saying this is: *8x + 19 = 403 exactly when x = 48.*

This means that 48 is a solution and no other numbers are solutions. Solving an equation means proving both a statement (to find the possible solutions) and its converse (to check that the possible solutions do work). Example 3 illustrates the importance of the check.

790 Using Algebra to Prove

Accommodating the Learner ⬇

Present students with the following proof and ask them to identify any incorrect justifications.

Conclusion	Justification
i. $11 = 3(-1 + x)$	Given
ii. $11 = -3 + 3x$	Multiplication Property of Equality
iii. $3 + 11 = 3 + -3 + 3x$	Addition Property of Equality
iv. $14 = 0 + 3x$	Additive Inverse Property
v. $14 = 3x$	Additive Identity Property
vi. $\frac{1}{3} \cdot 14 = \frac{1}{3} \cdot 3x$	Multiplication Property of Equality
vii. $\frac{14}{3} = 1 \cdot x$	Multiplicative Identity Property
viii. $\frac{14}{3} = x$	Multiplicative Identity Property

Example 3

Find all solutions to $\sqrt{x} = x - 6, x > 0$.

Solution

$\sqrt{x} = x - 6$	Given
$\sqrt{x} \cdot \sqrt{x} = (x - 6)(x - 6)$	Multiplication Property of Equality
$x = (x - 6)(x - 6)$	Definition of square root
$x = x^2 - 12x + 36$	Extended Distributive Property
$0 = x^2 - 13x + 36$	Addition Property of Equality
$x = \dfrac{13 \pm \sqrt{(-13)^2 - 4 \cdot 1 \cdot 36}}{2}$	Quadratic Formula
$x = \dfrac{13 \pm 5}{2}$	Simplify.
$x = 9$ or $x = 4$	Simplify.

This argument proves: If $\sqrt{x} = x - 6$, then $x = 9$ or $x = 4$. So, 9 and 4 are possible values of x. To see if they are solutions, a check is necessary.

Check When $x = 9$: Does $\sqrt{9} = 9 - 6$? Yes, $\sqrt{9} = 3$ and $9 - 6 = 3$. It checks.

When $x = 4$: Does $\sqrt{4} = 4 - 6$? No, $\sqrt{4} = 2$ and $4 - 6 = -2$. It does not check.

Consequently, $x = 9$ is the only solution to $\sqrt{x} = x - 6$. Putting it another way, $\sqrt{x} = x - 6$ if and only if $x = 9$.

In Example 3, the solution has proved: *If $\sqrt{x} = x - 6$, then $x = 9$ or $x = 4$.* The check has shown *If $x = 4$, then $\sqrt{x} \neq x - 6$ and if $x = 9$, then $\sqrt{x} = x - 6$.* So, $\sqrt{x} = x - 6$ if and only if $x = 9$.

Questions

COVERING THE IDEAS

1. Here is part of a proof argument. Explain what was done to get to Steps a–e and supply the missing justification.

$$40x + 12 = 3(6 + 13x)$$

  a. $\qquad 40x + 12 = 18 + 39x$
  b. $40x + 12 + -12 = 18 + 39x + -12$
  c. $\qquad 40x + 0 = 18 + 39x + -12$
  d. $\qquad 40x = 18 + 39x + -12$
  e. $\qquad 40x = 6 + 39x$ $18 + -12 = 6$; arithmetic
  f. The argument in Steps a–e proves what if-then statement?

1a. $3(6) = 18$, $3(13x) = 39x$; Distributive Property

1b. Add −12 to both sides; Addition Property of Equality

1c. $12 + -12 = 0$; Additive Inverse Property

1d. $40x + 0 = 40x$; Additive Identity Property

1f. If $40x + 12 = 3(6 + 13x)$, then $40x = 6 + 39x$.

Notes on the Lesson

Example 3 In this example, 4 is sometimes called an *extraneous solution*. The reason that solving yields a possible solution that does not satisfy the original sentence is due to the application of the Multiplication Property of Equality on the second line to square both sides of the equation. It is true that if $x = y$, then $x^2 = y^2$. But if $x^2 = y^2$, it is possible that $x \neq y$. So the solution shows that if $\sqrt{x} = x - 6$, then $x = 9$ or $x = 4$. But it does not necessarily mean that both values 4 and 9 will work.

Additional Example

Example 3 Find all solutions to $\sqrt{x} = x - 2$. $x = 4$

3   Assignment

Recommended Assignment

- Questions 1–33
- Question 34 (extra credit)
- Reading Lesson 13-4
- Covering the Ideas 13-4

Notes on the Questions

Question 1 Part f is critical.

Accommodating the Learner

Students often think that every equation has a real solution. Ask students to solve the equation $\sqrt{x} = x + 2$.

If students utilize the technique illustrated in this chapter they will square both sides and get $x = x^2 + 4x + 4$.

Solving this equation will yield the answers $x = -1$ and $x = -4$. Upon checking each possible solution students should find that neither value works. This is a good time to revisit the idea of domain.

Extension

Have students graph $Y1 = \sqrt{x}$ and $Y2 = x - 6$ on their calculators and find the point of intersection. Ask them to relate the graphs to Example 3. Then have them graph $Y3 = -\sqrt{x}$ in the same window. Ask them how the three graphs relate to the solutions provided by the Quadratic Formula.

13-3

Notes on the Questions

Question 2 Even though the example in the lesson is an equation, students should be able to transfer the ideas to the solving of inequalities. We do not discuss an inequality in detail because the check is more complicated than for an equation.

Question 7 You might ask students for an example of each kind of justification. Examples are given in the middle part of page 790.

Question 8 The check is essential unless students realize from the start that any solution must satisfy both $2n + 1 \geq 0$ and $n - 7 \geq 0$, which means that $n \geq 7$ is necessary.

Additional Answers

7a. i. $12m + -3m = 3m + -3m + 5$;
Addition Property of Equality

ii. $9m = 0 + 5$; Additive Inverse Property and Arithmetic

iii. $m = \frac{5}{9}$; Additive Identity Property and Multiplication Property of Equality

12. Multiply both sides by equal values $\sqrt{t}$ and 400, $\sqrt{t} \cdot \sqrt{t} = 400 \cdot 400$; Multiplication Property of Equality

---

2. Steps a–c are the conclusions in an abbreviated proof argument. Write what was done to get to each step and provide the justifications.

$$29 - 3y \leq 44$$
a. $-29 + 29 - 3y \leq -29 + 44$
b. $\qquad -3y \leq 15$
c. $\qquad y \geq -5$

2a. Add −29 to both sides; Addition Property of Inequality

2b. −29 + 29 = 0; Additive Inverse Property and arithmetic

d. The argument in Steps a–c proves what if-then statement?

3. Explain the difference between inductive reasoning and deduction.

4. Give another example of inductive reasoning that is not written in this book.

5. After a month of timing her walks to school, Sula told her friend Lana, "It takes me 5 minutes less to get to school if I walk at a constant pace diagonally through the rectangular park than if I walk around two edges of its perimeter!" Lana replied, "That's a result of the Pythagorean Theorem!"
a. Who used inductive reasoning? **Sula**
b. Who used deduction? **Lana**

6. What five kinds of justifications are allowed in solving an equation or inequality?

7. a. Provide conclusions and justifications to prove that if $12m = 3m + 5$, then $m = \frac{5}{9}$. See margin.
b. What else do you need to do in order to prove that $12m = 3m + 5$ if and only if $m = \frac{5}{9}$.

8. Find all solutions to the equation $\sqrt{2n + 1} = n - 7$. You do not have to give justifications. $n = 12$

APPLYING THE MATHEMATICS

In 9–14, two consecutive steps of a proof are shown as an if-then statement. State what was done and state the justification.

9. If $d = rt$, then $r = \frac{d}{t}$.

10. If $3x + 5x = 80$, then $8x = 80$.

11. If $gn^2 + hn + k = 0$, then $n = \frac{-h \pm \sqrt{h^2 - 4gk}}{2g}$.

12. If $\sqrt{t} = 400$, then $t = 160{,}000$. See margin.

13. If $3x + 4y = 6$ and $3x - 4y = -18$, then $6x = -12$. See margin.

14. If $\frac{8}{3}b = 12$, then $8b = 36$. See margin.

15. Prove: If $ax + b = c$ and $a \neq 0$, then $x = \frac{c - b}{a}$. (*Hint:* Follow the steps of the solution to the first equation in the lesson.) See margin.

16. Show that if $x = \frac{c - b}{a}$, then $ax + b = c$. See margin.

2c. Divide both sides by −3, change the direction of the inequality; arithmetic, Multiplication Property of Inequality (part 2)

2d. If $29 - 3y \leq 44$, then $y \geq -5$.

3. Inductive reasoning is used to make a general conclusion out of specific instances, while deduction is used to prove a specific instance of a general case, using known facts.

4. Answers vary. Sample answer: Because 3, 33, and 63 are all divisible by 3, any number with units digit 3 is divisible by 3.

6. given information, a defined property, an assumed property, a previously-proved property, arithmetic

7b. Show that if $m = \frac{5}{9}$, then $12m = 3m + 5$.

9. Multiply both sides by $\frac{1}{t}$ (Multiplication Property of Equality), and $t \cdot \frac{1}{t} = 1$ by the Multiplicative Inverse Property.

10. Add $3x + 5x$ to get $8x$ by the Distributive Property.

11. Because the equation is quadratic, the Quadratic Formula can be applied to solve for n.

Additional Answers

13. $3x - 4y = -18$ can be added to $3x + 4y = 6$ to get $6x = -12$; Addition Property of Equality

14. Multiply both sides by 3; Multiplication Property of Equality

15. i. $ax + b = c$　Given

ii. $ax + b - b = c - b$　Addition Property of Equality

iii. $ax + 0 = c - b$　Additive Inverse Property

iv. $ax = c - b$　Additive Identity Property

v. $\frac{1}{a} \cdot ax = \frac{1}{a} \cdot (c - b)$　Multiplication Property of Equality

vi. $x = \frac{(c - b)}{a}$　Multiplicative Inverse Property, Multiplicative Identity Property

17. Together, what do the statements in Questions 15 and 16 prove?

18. Use the definition of absolute value to find all values of x satisfying $|500x - 200| = 800$. $x = 2$ or $x = -\frac{6}{5}$

19. In Parts a and b, give abbreviated proofs. **See margin.**
   a. Prove: If a and k are both positive and $a(x - h)^2 = k$, then $x = h \pm \sqrt{\frac{k}{a}}$.
   b. Prove: If a and k are both positive and $x = h \pm \sqrt{\frac{k}{a}}$, then $a(x - h)^2 = k$.
   c. What has been proved in Parts a and b?

20. Prove: The slope of the line with equation $Ax + By = C$ is the reciprocal of the slope of the line with equation $Bx + Ay = D$.
   See margin.

REVIEW

21. Consider the following statement to be true: Every person under 8 years of age receives a reduced fare on the metro city bus.
   (Lessons 13-2, 13-1)
   a. Write this as an if-then statement.
   b. Write the converse.
   c. Is the converse true? Why or why not?

22. What value(s) can z not have in the expression $\frac{(2 - z)(1 + z)}{(4 + z)(3 - z)}$?
   (Lessons 12-8, 5-2) −4, 3

23. a. Factor $3x^2 + 9x - 12$. $3(x - 1)(x + 4)$
   b. Find a value for x for which $3x^2 + 9x - 12$ is a prime number.
   (Lesson 12-5)

24. a. Solve the system $\begin{cases} 2y + 3x = 7 \\ y = 6x - 1 \end{cases}$. $x = \frac{3}{5}, y = \frac{13}{5}$
   b. Are the lines in Part a coincident, parallel, or intersecting?
   (Lessons 10-6, 10-2) Intersecting

In 25–30, a property is stated. **Describe the property using variables.**

25. Product of Square Roots Property **(Lesson 8-7)** $\sqrt{ab} = (\sqrt{a})(\sqrt{b})$

26. Quotient of Square Roots Property **(Lesson 8-7)** $\sqrt{\frac{a}{b}} = \frac{\sqrt{a}}{\sqrt{b}}$

27. Power of a Power Property **(Lesson 8-2)** $(a^x)^y = a^{xy}$

28. Zero Product Property **(Lesson 2-8)**

29. Multiplication Property of −1 **(Lesson 2-4)** $-1 \cdot a = -a$

30. Distributive Property of Multiplication over Subtraction
   (Lesson 2-1) $a(b - c) = ab - ac$

17. $x = \frac{c - b}{a}$ if and only if $ax + b = c$ and $a \neq 0$.

21a. If you are under 8 years of age, then you receive a reduced fare on the metro city bus.

21b. If you receive a reduced fare on the metro city bus, then you are under 8 years of age.

21c. No. Answers vary. Sample answer: Other groups of people might receive a reduced fare as well.

23b. Answers vary. Sample answer: $-\frac{3}{2} + \frac{\sqrt{29}}{2}$

28. If $a \cdot b = 0$, then $a = 0$, $b = 0$, or both $a = b = 0$.

Notes on the Questions

Question 18 The definition of absolute value is: If $x \geq 0$, then $|x| = x$; if $x < 0$, then $|x| = -x$. So the proof has two parts, when $500x - 200 \geq 0$ and when $500x - 200 < 0$.

Question 20 Have students verify this general theorem with specific lines, such as showing that the slope of the line with equation $5x - 8y = 20$ is the reciprocal of the slope of the line with equation $-8x + 5y = 47$.

19b. i. $x = h \pm \sqrt{\frac{k}{a}}$ Given
   ii. $x - h = \pm\sqrt{\frac{k}{a}}$ Addition Property of
            $+ h - h$ Equality
   iii. $x - h = \pm\sqrt{\frac{k}{a}}$ Additive Inverse
                                Property
   iv. $(x - h)^2$ Multiplication Property
         $= \left(\sqrt{\frac{k}{a}}\right)^2$ of Equality
   v. $(x - h)^2 = \frac{k}{a}$ Definition of square root
   vi. $a \cdot (x - h)^2$ Multiplication Property
         $= \frac{k}{a} \cdot a$ of Equality
   vii. $a(x - h)^2 = k$ Multiplicative Inverse
                              and Identity Properties

20. i. $Ax + By = C$ Given
   ii. $Ax + By -$ Addition Property of
          $Ax = C - Ax$ Equality
   iii. $By = C - Ax$ Additive Inverse
                          Property
   iv. $\frac{1}{B} \cdot By =$ Multiplication Property
          $\frac{1}{B} \cdot (C - Ax)$ of Equality
   v. $y = \frac{C}{B} - \frac{A}{B}x$ Multiplicative Inverse
                          and Identity Properties,
                          Distributive Property
   vi.   Slope $= -\frac{A}{B}$ Definition of slope
   vii. $Bx + Ay = D$ Given
   viii. $Bx + Ay - Bx$ Addition Property of
          $= D - Bx$ Equality
   ix. $Ay = D - Bx$ Additive Inverse Property
   x. $\frac{1}{A} \cdot Ay$ Multiplication Property
          $= \frac{1}{A} \cdot (D - Bx)$ of Equality
   xi. $y = \frac{D}{A} - \frac{B}{A}x$ Multiplicative Inverse
                          Identity Property,
                          Distributive Property
   xii. Slope $= -\frac{B}{A}$ Definition of slope
   xiii. $-\frac{B}{A}$ is the   Definition of reciprocal
          reciprocal of $-\frac{A}{B}$

Additional Answers

16. i. $x = \frac{(c - b)}{a}$ Given
   ii. $ax = a \cdot \frac{(c - b)}{a}$ Multiplication Property
                                of Equality
   iii. $ax = 1(c - b)$ Multiplicative Inverse
                          Property
   iv. $ax = c - b$ Multiplicative Identity
                        Property
   v. $ax + b =$ Addition Property of
         $c - b + b$ Equality
   vi. $ax + b = c + 0$ Additive Inverse
                           Property
   vii. $ax + b = c$ Additive Identity
                        Property

19a. i. $a(x - h)^2 = k$ Given
   ii. $\frac{1}{a} \cdot a(x - h)^2 =$ Multiplication Property
         $\frac{1}{a} \cdot k$ of Equality
   iii. $\sqrt{(x - h)^2} =$ Definition of square root
         $\sqrt{\frac{k}{a}}$
   iv. $x - h = \pm\sqrt{\frac{k}{a}}$ Definition of square root
   v. $x - h + h =$ Addition Property of
         $\pm\sqrt{\frac{k}{a}} + h$ Equality
   vi. $x = h \pm \sqrt{\frac{k}{a}}$ Additive Inverse
                                Property

19c. $a(x - h)^2 = k$ if and only if a and k are both positive and $x = h \pm \sqrt{\frac{k}{a}}$.

Notes on the Questions

Question 32 The measure of $\angle Y$ is determined by the given information; $m\angle Y = \tan^{-1}(0.4)$.

Question 33 You may wish to use a CAS to expand the product to verify the result before beginning the proof.

4 Wrap-Up

Ongoing Assessment

Prove $5r = \dfrac{7r + 3}{2}$ if and only if $r = 1$. Give conclusions and justifications.

In 31 and 32, $\triangle ACB$ is similar to $\triangle XZY$. (Lesson 5-10, Previous Course)

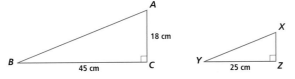

31. Find the missing lengths.

32. **Fill in the Blank** If $m\angle Y \approx 22°$, then $m\angle B \approx \underline{\ ?\ }$. 22°

33. Two cards are drawn at random from a standard 52-card deck, without replacement. What is the probability of drawing an ace and a jack, in that order? (**Lesson 5-8**) $\dfrac{4}{663} \approx 0.006033$

31. $AB = 9\sqrt{29}$ cm, ≈ 48.47 cm; $XZ = 10$ cm; $XY = 5\sqrt{29}$ cm, ≈ 26.93 cm.

EXPLORATION

34. Use the Extended Distributive Property and other properties you have learned in this course to prove:
$(a + b + c)(a + b - c)(b + c - a)(c + a - b) = 2(a^2b^2 + b^2c^2 + c^2a^2) - (a^4 + b^4 + c^4)$. See margin.

The earliest playing cards are believed to have originated in Central Asia.

Source: The International Playing-Card Society

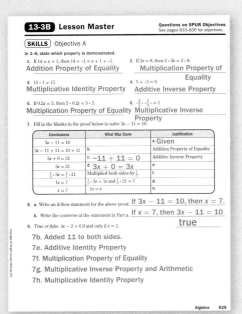

Additional Answers

34. $(a + b + c)(a + b - c)(b + c - a)(c + a - b)$
$= (a(a + b - c) + b(a + b - c) + c(a + b + c))(b(c + a - b) + c(c + a - b) - a(c + a - b)) = (a^2 + ab - ac + ab + b^2 - bc + ac - c^2)(bc + ab - b^2 + c^2 + ac - bc - ac - a^2 + ab) = (a^2 + 2ab + b^2 - c^2)(2ab - b^2 + c^2 - a^2) = a^2(2ab - b^2 + c^2 - a^2) + 2ab(2ab - b^2 + c^2 - a^2) + b^2(2ab - b^2 + c^2 - a^2) - c^2(2ab - b^2 + c^2 - a^2) = 2a^3b - a^2b^2 + a^2c^2 - a^4 + 4a^2b^2 - 2ab^3 + 2abc^2 - 2a^3b + 2ab^3 - b^4 + b^2c^2 - a^2b^2 - 2abc^2 + b^2c^2 - c^4 + a^2c^2 = 2a^2b^2 + 2a^2c^2 + 2b^2c^2 - a^4 - b^4 - c^4 = 2(a^2b^2 + b^2c^2 + c^2a^2) - (a^4 + b^4 + c^4)$

A History and Proof of the Quadratic Formula

> **BIG IDEA** The Quadratic Formula can be proved using the properties of numbers and operations.

The Quadratic Formula $x = \dfrac{-b \pm \sqrt{b^2 - 4ac}}{2a}$ is quite complicated. You may wonder how people used to solve quadratic equations before they had this formula, and how they discovered the Quadratic Formula in the first place. Here is some of the history.

What Problem First Led to Quadratics?

Our knowledge of ancient civilizations is based only on what survives today. The earliest known problems that led to quadratic equations are on Babylonian tablets dating from 1700 BCE. In these problems, the Babylonians were trying to find two numbers x and y that satisfy the system $\begin{cases} x + y = b \\ xy = c \end{cases}$.

This suggests that some Babylonians were interested in finding the dimensions x and y of a rectangle with a given area c and a given perimeter $2b$. The historian Victor Katz suggests that maybe there were some people who believed that if you knew the area of a rectangle, then you knew its perimeter. In solving these problems, these Babylonians may have been trying to show that many rectangles with different dimensions have the same area.

Mental Math

Use the graph below to find each length.

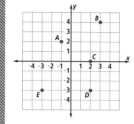

a. ED 5

b. CD 3

c. BC $\sqrt{17}$

d. AD $\sqrt{34}$

GUIDED

Example

Find the dimensions of a rectangular field whose perimeter is 300 meters and whose area is 4,400 square meters.

Solution Let L and W be the length and width of this rectangle.

Then $\begin{cases} \underline{} + \underline{} = 300 \quad 2L;\ 2W \\ \underline{} \cdot \underline{} = 4{,}400 \quad L;\ W \end{cases}$.

This system can be solved by substitution. First solve the top equation for W.

$\underline{} = 300 - \underline{} \quad 2W;\ 2L$

$W = 150 - \underline{} \quad L$

(continued on next page)

Background

The lesson begins with the problem of finding two numbers whose sum is b and whose product is c. The Babylonian procedure was to work from the mean $\frac{b}{2}$ of the numbers rather than the sum. Graphically, the procedure is equivalent to moving the graph of the quadratic so that the axis of the parabola is the y-axis, which makes the roots of the quadratic symmetric to the y-axis. For example, suppose we want to find two numbers whose sum is 10 and whose product is 13. Call the numbers

$5 + x$ and $5 - x$. Now the product $(5 + x)(5 - x) = 13$, so $25 - x^2 = 13$, from which $x^2 = 12$ and $x = \pm\sqrt{12} = \pm 2\sqrt{3}$. So the two numbers are $5 + 2\sqrt{3}$ and $5 - 2\sqrt{3}$.

Mathematicians of the 16th century considered the following problem: Find two numbers whose sum is 10 and whose product is 40. They solved the quadratic equation $(5 + x)(5 - x) = 40$. The two numbers are $5 \pm \sqrt{-15}$. What we today call complex numbers first arose in this way.

GOAL

Discuss the type of problem leading to the first known solutions of quadratics, a general description of the process used to solve quadratics, and a proof of the Quadratic Formula.

SPUR Objective

B Find two numbers given their sum and product.

Materials/Resources

· Lesson Master 13-4A or 13-4B
· Resource Masters 2 and 201
· Scientific or graphing calculator

HOMEWORK

Suggestions for Assignment

• Questions 1–21
• Question 22 (extra credit)
• Reading Lesson 13-5
• Covering the Ideas 13-5

Local Standards

---

1 **Warm-Up**

1. There are two whole numbers whose sum is 80 and whose product is 1,591.

   a. Find these numbers. **37 and 43**

   b. Show that the numbers you found in Part a are the solutions to $x^2 - 80x + 1{,}591 = 0$.
   $37^2 - 80 \cdot 37 + 1{,}591 = 0;$
   $43^2 - 80 \cdot 43 + 1{,}591 = 0$

   c. Use the information in Parts a and b to factor $x^2 - 80x + 1{,}591$.
   $(x - 37)(x - 43)$

2. There are two integers whose sum is −5 and whose product is −84.

   a. Find these numbers. **−12 and 7**

   b. Find a quadratic equation whose solutions are the numbers you found in Part a. $x^2 + 5x - 84 = 0$

13-4

2 Teaching

Additional Example

Example Find the dimensions of a rectangular field whose perimeter is 160 feet and whose area is 1,500 square feet.

Solution

Let L and W be the length and width of the rectangle.

Then $\begin{cases} \underline{}\, + \underline{}\, = 160 \\ \underline{}\, \cdot\, \underline{}\, = 1{,}500 \end{cases}$. **2L; 2W** **L; W**

This system can be solved by substitution. First, solve the top equation for W.

$\underline{} = 160 - \underline{}$ **2W; 2L**

$W = 80 - \underline{}$ **L**

Now substitute for W in the second equation.
$L(\underline{\;?\;}) = 1{,}500$ **80 − L**

This is a quadratic equation and it can be solved using either the Quadratic Formula or factoring to get $L = \underline{\;?\;}$ or $L = \underline{\;?\;}$. **30; 50**

Now substitute these values for L in either of the original equations to get $W = \underline{\;?\;}$ or $W = \underline{\;?\;}$. **50; 30**

So the dimensions of the field are $\underline{\;?\;}$ ft by $\underline{\;?\;}$ ft. **30; 50**

Now, substitute $\underline{\;?\;}$ for W in the second equation. **150 − L**

$L(\underline{\;?\;}) = 4{,}400$ **150 − L**

This is a quadratic equation and so it can be solved by using either the Quadratic Formula or factoring to get $L = \underline{\;?\;}$ or $L = \underline{\;?\;}$. Now substitute these values for L in either of the original equations to get $W = \underline{\;?\;}$ or $W = \underline{\;?\;}$. So, the dimensions of the field are $\underline{\;?\;}$ m by $\underline{\;?\;}$ m.
40; 110; 110; 40; 40; 110

How the Babylonians Solved Quadratics

The Babylonians, like the Greeks who came after them, used a geometric approach to solve problems like these. Using today's algebraic language and notation, here is what they did. It is a sneaky way to solve this sort of problem. Look back at the Example.

Because $L + W = 150$, the average of L and W is 75. This means that L is as much greater than 75 as W is less than 75. So let $L = 75 + x$ and $W = 75 - x$. Substitute these values into the second equation.

$$L \cdot W = 4{,}400$$
$$(75 + x)(75 - x) = 4{,}400$$
$$5{,}625 - x^2 = 4{,}400$$
$$x^2 = 1{,}225$$

Taking the square root, $x = 35$ or $x = -35$.

If $x = 35$:
$L = 75 + x$, so $L = 75 + 35 = 110$
$W = 75 - x$, so $W = 75 - 35 = 40$

If $x = -35$:
$L = 75 + -35 = 40$
$W = 75 - -35 = 110$

This tablet contains 14 lines of a mathematical text in cuneiform script and a geometric design.

Source: Iraq Museum

Either solution tells us that the field is 40 meters by 110 meters.

STOP QY

Notice what the Babylonians did. They took a complicated quadratic equation and, with a clever substitution, reduced it to an equation of the form $x^2 = k$. That equation is easy to solve. Then they substituted the solution back into the original equation.

> ▶ QY
>
> Use the Babylonian method to find two numbers whose sum is 72 and whose product is 1,007. (*Hint:* Let one of the numbers be $36 + x$, the other $36 - x$.)

The Work of Al-Khwarizmi

The work of the Babylonians was lost for many years. In 825 CE, about 2,500 years after the Babylonian tablets were created, a general method that is similar to today's Quadratic Formula was authored by the Arab mathematician Muhammad bin Musa al-Khwarizmi in a book titled *Hisab al-jabr w'al-muqabala*. Al-Khwarizmi's techniques were more general than those of the Babylonians. He gave a method to solve any equation of the form $ax^2 + bx = c$, where a, b, and c are positive numbers. His book was very influential. The word "al-jabr" in the title of his book led to our modern word "algebra." Our word "algorithm" comes from al-Khwarizmi's name.

Muhammad bin Musa al-Khwarizmi

A Proof of the Quadratic Formula

Neither the Babylonians nor al-Khwarizmi worked with an equation of the form $ax^2 + bx + c = 0$, because they considered only positive numbers, and if a, b, and c are positive, this equation has no positive solutions.

In 1545, a Renaissance scientist, Girolamo Cardano, blended al-Khwarizmi's solution with geometry to solve quadratic equations. He allowed negative solutions and even square roots of negative numbers that gave rise to complex numbers, a topic you will study in Advanced Algebra. In 1637, René Descartes published *La Géometrie* that contained the Quadratic Formula in the form we use today.

Now we prove why the formula works. Examine the argument in the following steps closely. See how each equation follows from the preceding equation. The idea is quite similar to the one used by the Babylonians, but a little more general. We work with the equation $ax^2 + bx + c = 0$ until the left side is a perfect square. Then the equation has the form $t^2 = k$, which you know how to solve for t.

Given the quadratic equation: $ax^2 + bx + c = 0$ with $a \neq 0$. We know $a \neq 0$ because otherwise the equation is not a quadratic equation.

Step 1 Multiply both sides of the equation by $\frac{1}{a}$. This makes the left term equal to $x^2 + \frac{b}{a}x + \frac{c}{a}$. The right side remains 0 because $0 \cdot \frac{1}{a} = 0$.

$$x^2 + \frac{b}{a}x + \frac{c}{a} = 0$$

Step 2 Add $-\frac{c}{a}$ to both sides in preparation for completing the square on the left side.

$$x^2 + \frac{b}{a}x = -\frac{c}{a}$$

A History and Proof of the Quadratic Formula   **797**

The area of an *ellipse* can be found by the formula $A = \pi ab$, where a and b are the lengths of the line segments shown in the diagram.

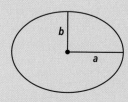

Have the students find a and b if $a + b = 10$ and $a \cdot b = 17$. Ask them to provide a geometric interpretation for their answers.

$a = 10 - b$; $(10 - b) \cdot b = 17$;

$10b - b^2 = 17$; $b^2 - 10b + 17 = 0$;

$b = \dfrac{10 \pm \sqrt{(-10)^2 - 4 \cdot 17}}{2 \cdot 1} = \dfrac{10 \pm \sqrt{32}}{2} =$

$5 \pm 2\sqrt{2}$; $x \approx 7.28$ or $x = 2.72$; which are the lengths of the two segments.

Notes on the Lesson

Students should not be expected to memorize the proof, but they should be able to see what was done to get from one step to the next. You might ask for the name of the property that justifies each step.

Step 1: Multiplication Property of Equality

Step 2: Addition Property of Equality

Step 3: Addition Property of Equality

Step 4: Extended Distributive Property (factoring a perfect square)

Step 5: Multiplication of Fractions Property

Step 6: Equal Fractions Property

Step 7: Distributive Property (adding like terms)

Step 8: Definition of Square Root

Step 9: Quotient of Square Roots Property

Step 10: Addition Property of Equality

Step 11: Distributive Property (adding like terms).

This will cover Question 10 (page 799) but in a different way.

Step 3 To complete the square add the square of half the coefficient of x to both sides. (See Lesson 12-2.)

$$x^2 + \frac{b}{a}x + \left(\frac{b}{2a}\right)^2 = -\frac{c}{a} + \left(\frac{b}{2a}\right)^2$$

Step 4 The left side is now the square of a binomial.

$$\left(x + \frac{b}{2a}\right)^2 = -\frac{c}{a} + \left(\frac{b}{2a}\right)^2$$

Step 5 Take the power of the fraction to eliminate parentheses on the right side.

$$\left(x + \frac{b}{2a}\right)^2 = -\frac{c}{a} + \frac{b^2}{4a^2}$$

Step 6 To add the fractions on the right side, find a common denominator.

$$\left(x + \frac{b}{2a}\right)^2 = -\frac{4ac}{4a^2} + \frac{b^2}{4a^2}$$

Step 7 Add the fractions.

$$\left(x + \frac{b}{2a}\right)^2 = \frac{b^2 - 4ac}{4a^2}$$

Step 8 Now the equation has the form $t^2 = k$, with $t = x + \frac{b}{2a}$ and $k = \frac{b^2 - 4ac}{4a^2}$. This is where the discriminant $b^2 - 4ac$ becomes important. If $b^2 - 4ac \geq 0$, then there are real solutions. They are found by taking the square roots of both sides.

$$x + \frac{b}{2a} = \pm\sqrt{\frac{b^2 - 4ac}{4a^2}}$$

Step 9 The square root of a quotient is the quotient of the square roots.

$$x + \frac{b}{2a} = \pm\frac{\sqrt{b^2 - 4ac}}{2a}$$

Step 10 This is beginning to look like the formula. Add $-\frac{b}{2a}$ to each side.

$$x = -\frac{b}{2a} \pm \frac{\sqrt{b^2 - 4ac}}{2a}$$

Step 11 Adding the fractions results in the Quadratic Formula.

$$x = \frac{-b \pm \sqrt{b^2 - 4ac}}{2a}$$

What if $b^2 - 4ac < 0$? Then the quadratic equation has no real number solutions. The formula still works, but you have to take square roots of negative numbers to get solutions. You will study these nonreal solutions in a later course.

Accommodating the Learner ⬇

The proof of the Quadratic Formula is not an easy proof to understand. Many students simply get confused and stop listening or thinking as the proof unfolds. Before proving it, consider illustrating the proof using actual quadratic equations. In sequence, solve each of the following quadratic equations by the process of completing the square.

i. $x^2 + 2x - 24 = 0$

ii. $2x^2 - 8x - 10 = 0$

iii. $2x^2 - 3x - 2 = 0$

Questions

COVERING THE IDEAS

1. **Multiple Choice** The earliest known problems that led to the solving of quadratic equations were studied about how many years ago? **D**

   A 1,175

   B 1,700

   C 2,500

   D 3,700

2. In what civilization do quadratic equations first seem to have been considered and solved? **Babylonian**

3. What is the significance of the work of al-Khwarizmi in the history of the Quadratic Formula?

In 4 and 5, suppose two numbers sum to 53 and have a product of 612. Show your work in finding the numbers. 4–5. See margin.

4. Use the Quadratic Formula.

5. Use the Babylonian Method.

6. Suppose a rectangular room has a floor area of 54 square yards. Find two different lengths and widths that this floor might have.

In 7 and 8, suppose a rectangular room has a floor area of 144 square yards and that the perimeter of its floor is 50 yards. 7–8. See margin.

7. Find its length and width by solving a quadratic equation using the Quadratic Formula or factoring.

8. Find its length and width using a more ancient method.

9. Find two numbers whose sum is 15 and whose product is 10.

10. In the proof of the Quadratic Formula, each of Steps 1–11 tells what was done but does not name the property of real numbers. For each step, name the property (or properties) from the following list.

   i. Addition Property of Equality

   ii. Multiplication Property of Equality

   iii. Distributive Property of Multiplication over Addition

   iv. Equal Fractions Property

   v. Power of a Quotient Property

   vi. Quotient of Square Roots Property

   vii. Definition of square root

3. Al-Khwarizmi created a general method similar to today's Quadratic Formula.

6. Answers vary. Sample answer: 6 ft by 9 ft, 18 ft by 3 ft

9. $\dfrac{15 + \sqrt{185}}{2}$ and $\dfrac{15 - \sqrt{185}}{2}$

10. Step 1. ii; Step 2. i; Step 3. i; Step 4. iii; Step 5. v; Step 6. iv; Step 7. iii; Step 8. vii; Step 9. vi; Step 10. i; Step 11. iii

A History and Proof of the Quadratic Formula   **799**

13-4

3 Assignment

Recommended Assignment

- Questions 1–21
- Question 22 (extra credit)
- Reading Lesson 13-5
- Covering the Ideas 13-5

Additional Answers

5. $x + y = 53$ so their average is 26.5.

   Let $M = 26.5 + x$ and $N = 26.5 - x$.

   $MN = 612$,

   so $(26.5 + x)(26.5 - x) = 612$;

   $702.25 - x = 612$, $x^2 = 90.25$,

   $x = 9.5$ or $x = -9.5$. If $x = 9.5$,

   $M = 26.5 + 9.5 = 36$,

   $N = 26.5 - 9.5 = 17$.

   If $x = -9.5$, $M = 26.5 - 9.5 = 17$,

   $N = 26.5 + 9.5 = 36$. The two numbers are 17 and 36.

7. $L = 25 - W$

   $W(25 - W) = 144$, $25W - W^2 = 144$,

   $W^2 - 25W + 144 = 0$

   $(W - 16)(W - 9) = 0$

   16 yards by 9 yards

8. $(12.5 + x)(12.5 - x) = 144$

   $156.25 - x^2 = 144$

   $x^2 = 12.25$

   $x = 3.5$

   $L = 12.5 + x = 12.5 + 3.5 = 16$

   $L = 12.5 - x = 12.5 - 3.5 = 9$

   16 yards by 9 yards

Additional Answers

4. $x + y = 53$ and $xy = 612$,

   so $y = 53 - x$. Then $x(53 - x) = 612$

   so $-x^2 + 53x = 612$. $x^2 - 53x + 612 = 0$,

   so by the Quadratic Formula,

   $x = \dfrac{53 \pm \sqrt{(-53)^2 - 4(1)(612)}}{2} = \dfrac{53 \pm \sqrt{361}}{2}$
   $= \dfrac{53 \pm 19}{2}$. So $x = 36$ or $x = 17$. If $x = 36$,

   $y = 17$ and if $x = 17$, $y = 36$ so the numbers are 17 and 36.

13-4

Notes on the Questions

Question 13 We have left the wording of this question as close to the original as possible. Because the problem asks for the dimensions of the door, the corners refer to opposite vertices of a rectangle. The problem is from a book that is famous in Chinese mathematical history, *Jiuzhang suanshu* (*Nine Chapters of the Mathematical Art*) that was probably completed around 200 BCE. However, it is believed that some of the material in the book was in existence before that date.

Question 14 This version of the proof of the Quadratic Formula avoids fractions for as long as possible.

APPLYING THE MATHEMATICS

11. Solve the equation $7x^2 - 6x - 1 = 0$ by following the steps in the derivation of the Quadratic Formula. $x = -\frac{1}{7}$ or $x = 1$

12. Explain why there are no real numbers x and y whose sum is 10 and whose product is 60.

13. In a Chinese text that is thousands of years old, the following problem is given: The height of a door is 6.8 more than its width. The distance between its corners is 10. Find the height and width of the door. **The door is 9.6 units high and 2.8 units wide.**

14. Here is an alternate proof of the Quadratic Formula. Tell what was done to get each step.

$$ax^2 + bx + c = 0$$

a. $\quad 4a^2x^2 + 4abx + 4ac = 0$ Multiply both sides by $4a$.

b. $4a^2x^2 + 4abx + 4ac + b^2 = b^2$ Add b^2 to both sides.

c. $\quad 4a^2x^2 + 4abx + b^2 = b^2 - 4ac$ Subtract $4ac$ from both sides.

d. $\quad (2ax + b)^2 = b^2 - 4ac$ Factor the left side.

e. $\quad 2ax + b = \pm\sqrt{b^2 - 4ac}$

f. $\quad 2ax = -b \pm \sqrt{b^2 - 4ac}$

g. $\quad x = \dfrac{-b \pm \sqrt{b^2 - 4ac}}{2a}$

12. If x and y sum to 10, then $y = 10 - x$, so $x(10 - x) = 60$. Therefore, $10x - x^2 = 60$, and $x^2 - 10x + 60 = 0$. If you substitute these coefficients, you find that $b^2 - 4ac = -149$, which means that there are no real solutions to this equation.

14e. Take the square root of both sides.

14f. Subtract b from both sides.

14g. Divide both sides by $2a$.

REVIEW

15. Consider the following statement. (**Lessons 13-2, 13-1**)

    A number that is divisible by 8 is also divisible by 4.

    a. Write the statement in if-then form.

    b. Decide whether the statement you wrote in Part a is true or false. If it is false, find a counterexample. **true**

    c. Write the converse of the statement you wrote in Part a.

    d. Decide whether the statement you wrote in Part c is true or false. If it is false, find a counterexample.

16. Solve $x^2 + 5x = 30$. (**Lesson 12-6**) $x = \dfrac{-5 \pm \sqrt{145}}{2}$

In 17–19, an open soup can has volume $V = \pi r^2 h$ and surface area $S = \pi r^2 + 2\pi rh$, where r is the radius and h is the height of the can.

17. Use common monomial factoring to rewrite the formula for S. (**Lesson 11-4**) $S = \pi r(r + 2h)$

18. Find each of the following. (**Lesson 11-2**)

    a. the degree of V 3

    b. the degree of S 2

15a. If a number is divisible by 8, then it is also divisible by 4.

15c. If a number is divisible by 4, then it is also divisible by 8.

15d. false; Answers vary. Sample answer: 12 is divisible by 4, but not by 8.

19. If the can has a diameter of 8 cm and a height of 12 cm, about how many milliliters of soup can it hold? ($1\text{ L} = 1,000\text{ cm}^3$) (Lesson 5-4) about 603 mL

20. Solve this system by graphing. $\begin{cases} y = |x| \\ y = \frac{1}{4}x^2 \end{cases}$ (Lessons 10-1, 4-9)

21. **Skill Sequence** Simplify each expression. (Lessons 8-7, 8-6)

   a. $\dfrac{\sqrt{8} + \sqrt{5}}{2\sqrt{2} + \sqrt{5}}$ b. $\sqrt{8} \cdot \sqrt{5}$ $2\sqrt{10}$ c. $\dfrac{\sqrt{8} \cdot \sqrt{5}}{\sqrt{2}}$ $2\sqrt{5}$

EXPLORATION

22. In a book or on the Internet, research al-Khwarizmi and find another contribution he made to mathematics or other sciences. Write a paragraph about your findings. Answers vary. Sample answer: He wrote a geography book listing coordinates of cities and other places. It was used to help find the latitude and longitude of certain places, and maps were able to be created from the lists.

20.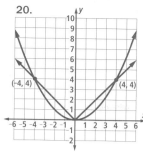

(4, 4), (−4, 4), and (0, 0)

Extension

The Babylonians did more than just work with quadratic equations. For example, they had an advanced number system, constructed tables to aid in calculations, and worked in the areas of algebra and geometry. These are just a few of the topics in mathematics pursued by the Babylonians. Consider having students do similar research on mathematics in other cultures, such as Greek, Indian, and Mayan.

13-4

4 Wrap-Up

Ongoing Assessment

Form groups of three students. Instruct the students to solve the equation $2x^2 + 12x + 16 = 0$ by following the steps used in the derivation of the Quadratic Formula. Then use the Quadratic Formula to see if the new answers agree with the earlier answer. Challenge the students to use yet another method, such as factoring, to solve the equation. $x = -2$ or $x = -4$

Project Update

Project 2, Can Everything be Proved?, on page 829, relates to the content of this lesson.

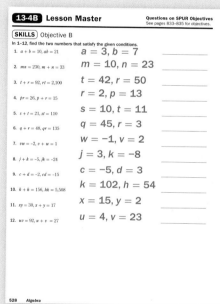

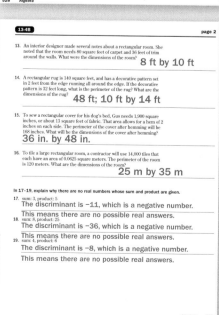

Lesson

13-5

GOAL

Show how algebra can be used to prove properties of divisibility of integers.

SPUR Objective

E Prove divisibility properties of integers.

Materials/Resources

· Lesson Master 13-5A or 13-5B
· Resource Masters 202–204
· Scientific or graphing calculator

HOMEWORK

Suggestions for Assignment

• Questions 1–26
• Questions 27–28 (extra credit)
• Reading Lesson 13-6
• Covering the Ideas 13-6

Local Standards

1 Warm-Up

1. Find two numbers between 100 and 500 that are divisible by 4. Add them.
   a. Is the sum divisible by 2? yes
   b. Is the sum divisible by 4? yes
   c. Is the sum divisible by 8?
      Answers will vary.
   d. Will the answers to Parts a–c be the same no matter what numbers you chose to begin with?
      yes, yes, no
2. Use the same numbers as Question 1. Subtract the smaller from the larger.
   a. Is the difference divisible by 2? yes
   b. Is the difference divisible by 4? yes
   c. Is the difference divisible by 8?
      Answers will vary.
   d. Will the answers to Parts a–c be the same no matter what numbers you chose to begin with?
      yes, yes, no

(continued on next page)

Lesson

13-5   Proofs of Divisibility Properties

▶ **BIG IDEA**   Using algebra, you can prove that even and odd numbers have certain general properties.

In this lesson, the following statements are assumed to be true.

> The sum of two integers is an integer.
>
> The difference of two integers is an integer.
>
> The product of two integers is an integer.

The three properties above are examples of *closure properties*. A set is **closed under an operation** if the results of that operation always lies in that set. So another way of saying the above statements is:

> The set of integers is closed under addition.
>
> The set of integers is closed under subtraction.
>
> The set of integers is closed under multiplication.

But the set of integers is *not* closed under division. For example, $8 \div 3$ is not an integer. When the quotient $a \div b$ is an integer, then we say that a is divisible by b, or that a is a multiple of b.

From the closure properties and other properties of real numbers that you know, it is possible to prove criteria that describe when one number is divisible by another.

Divisibility by 2

An **even integer** (or **even number**) E is an integer that is twice another integer; that is, it is an integer that can be written as $2n$, where n is an integer. As you know, the integers are the numbers $0, 1, -1, 2, -2, 3, -3, \ldots$. So, if you multiply these numbers by 2, the results are the *even integers* $0, 2, -2, 4, -4, 6, -6, 8, -8, \ldots$.

Geometrically, a positive even number of dots can be arranged in two rows of the same length. For example, 14 dots can be split into two rows of 7.

Vocabulary

closed under an operation
even integer, even number
odd integer, odd number
semiperimeter

Mental Math

A function contains
$\{(-16, 4.5), (-7, 4.5),$
$(0, 2), (1, -5), (5.5, 10)\}$.

a. State the domain.

b. State the range.
$\{4.5, 2, -5, 10\}$

a. $\{-16, -7, 0, 1, 5.5\}$

Background

In this lesson, the properties of divisibilty are independent of how the number is written—it could be in scientific notation, in base 10, in exponential notation, in base 2, etc.

Four proofs are given in this lesson. The first is a special case of the theorem that if two numbers are multiples of the same number, so is their sum. The second and third proofs involve odd numbers and the operations of subtraction and multiplication. The fourth proof involves the square of

an odd number and is quite a bit more complicated because it has a substitution in the middle of the proof.

To tell whether a large number is even, you cannot draw a pattern of dots. You must be able to show that it is twice another integer. For example, you can show that 5,734 is an even integer because $5{,}734 = 2 \cdot 2{,}867$, and 2,867 is an integer. How did we find 2,867? We divided 5,734 by 2. The number 0 is an even integer because $0 = 2 \cdot 0$. The negative number –88 is an even integer because $-88 = 2 \cdot -44$.

Odd Integers

An integer that is not even is called *odd*. Geometrically, an odd number of dots cannot be arranged in two rows of the same length. An example of this is shown with 15 dots. Notice below that there are two rows of 7 dots plus an additional dot.

You can see that an odd integer is one more than an even integer. So we define an **odd integer** (or **odd number**) as an integer that can be written as $2n + 1$, where n is an integer. For example, $2 \cdot (-54) + 1 = -107$, so –107 is odd.

 QY

If two numbers m and n are positive, you know that their sum $m + n$ and their product mn are positive. But the difference $m - n$ might be positive or negative. What happens if you know whether m and n are even or odd?

By trying some numbers, fill in the following table with one of the words "odd" or "even."

> **QY**
>
> Let $m = 87{,}654$ and $n = 3{,}210$. Tell whether these numbers are even or odd.
>
> a. $m + n$
> b. $m - n$
> c. mn

Activity 1

m	n	$m + n$	$m - n$	mn
even	even	? even	? even	? even
even	odd	? odd	? odd	? even
odd	even	? odd	? odd	? even
odd	odd	? even	? even	? odd

Testing pairs of numbers is not enough to show that a statement is true for *all* odd or even integers. Proofs are needed.

Consider presenting the following problem to your students. Prove the sum of any three consecutive positive integers is divisible by 3. Students may need assistance with the notation for consecutive integers. Let n be any positive integer. Then represent three consecutive positive integers as n, $n + 1$, and $n + 2$. So $n + (n + 1) + (n + 2) = 3n + 3 = 3(n + 1)$ which is divisible by 3.

3. Multiply the two numbers you used in Question 1.
   a. Is the product divisible by 4? yes
   b. Is the product divisible by 8? yes
   c. Is the product divisible by 16? yes
   d. Will the answers to Parts a–c be the same no matter what numbers you chose to begin with? yes, yes, yes

2 Teaching

Notes on the Lesson

There is a style to writing a proof that involves many details, such as the use of the words "so" and "by" or "then" and "consequently" and "because." The properties are used in a different way from their uses before to solve problems or find equivalent expressions. The goal of this lesson and the next is to give students a taste of proof that will help to make them want to learn more. When in the Questions section, students are asked to write a proof, they should be encouraged to find an example in the lesson and try to imitate it to obtain their proof.

The basic idea in starting these proofs is to represent the kind of number involved (odd, even, multiple of 35) in some algebraic way. Specifically, we use the following definitions: 1. A number is **even** if and only if it can be represented as $2n$, where n is an integer; 2. A number is **odd** if and only if it can be represented as $2n + 1$, where n is an integer; and 3. A number is **divisible by k** if and only if it can be written as kn where n is an integer.

Notes on the Activity

Activity 1 Several times in this lesson it is stated that testing numbers is not enough to show that a statement is true. Students who read this statement may not completely understand what "it" means. Consider providing your students with an example that illustrates the point. For example, ask them if $\sqrt{x^2} = x$ for all integers. Keep in mind that students may square a negative number incorrectly, especially if they enter -3^2 in their calculators rather then $(-3)^2$.

Additional Examples

Example 1 Prove that the sum of three even numbers is an even number.
Solution: Let a, b, and c be even numbers. Then, by the definition of even number, there are integers p, q, and r with $a = 2p$, $b = 2q$, and $c = 2r$. So $a + b + c = 2p + 2q + 2r$. By the Distributive Property of Multiplication over Addition, $a + b + c = 2(p + q + r)$. Because the sum of two integers is an integer, $p + q$ is an integer. Likewise $(p + q) + r$ is an integer. So $a + b + c$, being 2 times an integer, is even.

Example 2 Prove that the sum of three odd numbers is an odd number.

Solution: Let a, b, and c be odd numbers. Then by the definition of odd number, there are integers p, q, and r with $a = 2p + 1$, $b = 2q + 1$, and $c = 2r + 1$. So $a + b + c = (\underline{?}) + (\underline{?}) + (\underline{?}) = 2p + 2q + 2r + 3$. Now $2p + 2q + 2r + 3 = (2p + 2q + 2r + 2) + 1 = 2(p + q + r + 1) + 1$. So $a + b + c = 2(p + q + r + 1) + 1$. Because $2(p + q + r)$ is even, then $2(p + q + r + 1) + 1$ is odd. Consequently $a + b + c$ is an $\underline{?}$ number. $2p + 1, 2q + 1, 2r + 1$: odd

Example 3 Prove that the product of three odd numbers is an odd number.
Solution: Let a, b, and c be odd numbers. Then by the definition of odd number, there are integers p, q, and r with $a = 2p + 1$, $b = 2q + 1$, and $c = 2r + 1$. Now multiply these numbers.

$$abc = (2p + 1)(2q + 1)(2r + 1)$$
$$= 8pqr + 4pq + 4pr + 4qr + 2p + 2q + 2r + 1$$
$$= 2(4pqr + 2pq + 2pr + 2qr + p + q + r) + 1$$

Because the product of two integers is an integer; pq, pr, and qr are integers. Because pq and r are integers, then pqr is an integer. So their sum $4pqr + 2pq + 2pr + 2qr + p + q + r$ is an integer. This means that abc is 1 more than twice an integer, so abc is odd.

Example 1
Prove that the sum of two even numbers is an even number.

Solution To prove this statement, we think of it as an if-then statement: If two even numbers are added, then their sum is an even number.

Let m and n be the even numbers. Then, by the definition of even number, there are integers p and q with m = 2p and n = 2q. So m + n = 2p + 2q.

By the Distributive Property of Multiplication over Addition, m + n = 2(p + q).

Since the sum of two integers is an integer, p + q is an integer.

So m + n, equal to 2 times an integer, is even.

Example 1 shows that the set of even numbers is closed under addition.

Using the idea of Example 1, you can prove that the difference of two even numbers is an even number. That is, the set of even numbers is closed under subtraction. (You are asked to write a proof of this in one of the questions at the end of the lesson.) Also, the product of two even numbers is an even number.

> **GUIDED**
>
> ### Example 2
> **Prove that the difference of two odd numbers is an even number.**
>
> **Solution** Let m and n be odd numbers. Then, by the definition of odd number, there are integers p and q with m = 2p + 1 and n = 2q + 1.
>
> So m − n = ($\underline{?}$) − ($\underline{?}$) = 2p − 2q. $2p + 1; 2q + 1$
>
> Thus m − n = 2($\underline{?}$). $p - q$
>
> Since the difference of integers is an integer, $\underline{?}$ is an integer. $p - q$
>
> Consequently, m − n is $\underline{?}$ times an integer, so m − n is even. 2

You can similarly prove that the sum of two odd numbers is an even number. The set of odd integers is *not* closed under addition or subtraction.

Example 3 deals with products.

> ### Example 3
> **Prove that the product of two odd numbers is an odd number.**

Accommodating the Learner

Some students have difficulty visualizing integers represented by p, q, or r. Place the following proof for the sum of two odd integers on the board. $(2p + 1) + (2q + 1) = 2p + 2q + 2 = 2(p + q + 1) = 2r$ where $r = (p + q + 1)$. Next have them substitute integers for p and q and work through the proof and verbalize each step as they verify the proof.

Solution Let m and n be odd numbers. Then, by the definition of odd number, there are integers p and q with m = 2p + 1 and n = 2q + 1.

Now multiply these numbers.

$$mn = (2p + 1)(2q + 1)$$
$$= 4pq + 2p + 2q + 1 \quad \text{Extended Distributive Property}$$
$$= 2(2pq + p + q) + 1 \quad \text{Distributive Property}$$
$$\text{(Common monomial factoring)}$$

Since the product of two integers is an integer, 2pq is an integer. Since p and q are integers, the sum 2pq + p + q is an integer. This means that mn is 1 more than twice an integer, so mn is odd.

Divisibility by Other Numbers

A number is *divisible by 3* if and only if it can be written as 3n, where n is an integer. Similarly, a number is *divisible by 4* if and only if it can be written as 4n, where n is an integer. In general, a number is divisible by m if and only if it can be written as mn, where n is an integer.

Activity 2

Step 1 Let n be an odd positive integer. Fill in the table.

n	1	3	5	7	9	11	13	15	17
n^2	? 1	? 9	? 25	? 49	? 81	? 121	? 169	? 225	? 289
$n^2 - 1$	? 0	? 8	? 24	? 48	? 80	? 120	? 168	? 224	? 288

Step 2 **a.** What is the greatest common factor of the integers in the bottom row? **8**

b. Is this number a factor of $n^2 - 1$ for all odd integers?

Step 2b. Probably, but we cannot say for sure according to the table.

You cannot answer the last question in Activity 2 by just writing down more odd integers, squaring them, and subtracting 1. You can never show by examples that the statement is true for all odd integers. A proof is needed.

Example 4

Prove that the square of an odd integer is always 1 more than a multiple of 4.

Solution First find the square of an odd integer.

(continued on next page)

Notes on the Activity

Activity 2 Students may not recognize that 0 has 8 as a factor. This may throw them off a bit and you may need to provide some help. Also note that there is a second pattern that exists in the factoring of the bottom row. The products are $0 \cdot 8$, $1 \cdot 8$, $3 \cdot 8$, $6 \cdot 8$, $10 \cdot 8$, $15 \cdot 8$, $21 \cdot 8$, $28 \cdot 8$, and $36 \cdot 8$. Ask students to identify the next two products, extending the table to $n = 19$ and $n = 21$ without evaluating $n^2 - 1$. $45 \cdot 8 = 360$; $55 \cdot 8 = 440$

Additional Example

Example 4 Prove that if n is a positive integer, $n^2 + n$ is divisible by 2.
Proof: The proof can be done in cases. First let n be even which implies that $n = 2k$ for some integer k. Now $n^2 + n = (2k)^2 + 2k = 4k^2 + 2k = 2k(2k + 1)$. Because 2 is a factor in the product, $n^2 + n$ is divisible by 2 when n is even. Now let n be odd which implies that $n = 2k + 1$ for some integer k. Now $n^2 + n = (2k + 1)^2 + (2k + 1) = (4k^2 + 4k + 1) + (2k + 1) = 4k^2 + 6k + 2 = 2(2k^2 + 3k + 1)$. Because 2 is a factor in the product, $n^2 + n$ is divisible by 2 when n is odd.

Here is an alternative proof:
$n^2 + n = n(n + 1)$. Because n and n + 1 are consecutive integers, one of them must be even. That means that their product is even, so the product is divisible by 2.

13-5

3 Assignment

Recommended Assignment
- Questions 1–26
- Questions 27–28 (extra credit)
- Reading Lesson 13-6
- Covering the Ideas 13-6

Notes on the Questions

Questions 11–13 Before beginning these proofs, make sure students understand what is being proved. They should write down at least one example. Then, when students get to Questions 14 and 15, they will better understand what is meant by *finding a counterexample*.

Additional Answers

5b. No. Answers vary. Sample answer: From Part a, the sum of two odd integers is an even integer, not an odd integer.

6.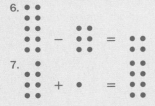

7.

8. Answers vary. Sample answer: Let m and n be even numbers. Then by definition, there are integers p and q such that $m = 2p$ and $n = 2q$. Then $mn = (2p)(2q)$, so by the Commutative and Associative Properties of Multiplication, $2(2pq) = mn$. Since 2, p, and q are all integers, their product $2pq$ is an integer. Thus mn is an even number.

Let n be an odd integer. By definition of an odd integer, there is an integer k such that $n = 2k + 1$.

$$\text{So } n^2 = (2k + 1)^2$$
$$= (2k + 1)(2k + 1)$$
$$= 4k^2 + 4k + 1$$
$$n = 4k(k + 1) + 1$$

This shows that n^2 is 1 more than a multiple of 4.

Questions

COVERING THE IDEAS

1. State the definition of *even integer*.

2. State the definition of *odd integer*.

3. Find a counterexample to show that this statement is not always true: *If two numbers are each divisible by 2, then their sum is divisible by 4.*

In 4 and 5, use Example 1 or Guided Example 2 as a guide to write a proof.

4. Prove: The difference of two even integers is an even integer.

5. a. Prove: The sum of two odd integers is an even integer.
   b. Is the set of odd integers closed under addition? Why or why not? **See margin.**

6. Use rows of dots to explain why the statement of Question 4 is true. **See margin.**

7. Use rows of dots to explain why the statement of Question 5 is true. **See margin.**

8. Prove that the set of even numbers is closed under multiplication. (*Hint:* Use Example 3 as a guide.) **See margin.**

APPLYING THE MATHEMATICS

In 9 and 10, complete the fact triangle. Then state the related facts.

9.

10.

9–10. See margin for the facts.

11. Prove: If a number is even, then its square is a multiple of 4. **See margin.**

12. Prove: If a number is divisible by 3, then its square is divisible by 9. **See margin.**

Additional Answers

9. even + odd = odd; odd + even = odd; odd − even = odd; odd − odd = even

10. odd + odd = even; even − odd = odd

11. Answers vary. Sample answer: Let m be an even number. Then there is an integer p such that $m = 2p$, so $m^2 = (2p)^2$. Thus $m^2 = 4p^2$, and since p is an integer, p^2 is an integer. Thus m^2 is a multiple of 4.

12. Answers vary. Sample answer: Let m be a number divisible by 3. Then $m = 3n$, where n is an integer, and $m^2 = (3n)^2 = 9n^2$. Since n is an integer, n^2 is an integer. Thus, m^2 is divisible by 9.

---

1. an integer that can be written as $2n$, where n is an integer

2. an integer that can be written as $2n + 1$, where n is an integer

3. Answers vary. Sample answer: 6 and 4 are both divisible by 2, but 10 is not divisible by 4.

4. Answers vary. Sample answer: Let p and q be two even integers such that $p = 2m$ and $q = 2n$, where m and n are integers. Then $p - q = 2m - 2n$, which gives $2(m - n) = p - q$ by the Distributive Property of Multiplication. We know that since m and n are integers, $m - n$ is an integer. Thus $p - q$ is even.

5a. Answers vary. Sample answer: Let p and q be odd integers such that $p = 2m + 1$ and $q = 2n + 1$, where m and n are integers. Then $p + q = 2m + 1 + 2n + 1 = 2m + 2n + 2 = 2(m + n + 1)$. Since m, n, and 1 are integers, $m + n + 1$ is an integer. Thus $p + q$ is an even integer.

13. Prove: If the sum of two numbers is divisible by 35 and one of the two numbers is divisible by 70, then the other number is divisible by 35. **See margin.**

14. Prove or find a counterexample: If one number is divisible by 20 and a second number is divisible by 30, then their sum is divisible by 50.

15. Prove or find a counterexample: If one number is divisible by 4 and a second number is divisible by 6, then their product is divisible by 24. **See margin.**

REVIEW

16. Find two numbers whose sum is 562 and whose product is 74,865. (**Lesson 13-4**) **345 and 217**

17. Find a value of b so that the quadratic expression $2x^2 - bx + 20$ is factorable over the integers. (**Lesson 12-6**)

In 18–23, solve the sentence. (**Lessons 12-5, 9-5, 8-6, 4-5, 4-4, 3-4**)

18. $100x^2 + 100x - 100 = 0$

19. $x^2 - 11x + 28 = 0$ $x = 7$ or $x = 4$

20. $\frac{26}{N} = \frac{N}{0.5}$ $N = \pm\sqrt{13}$

21. $a \cdot 11^{\frac{1}{2}} = 99^{\frac{1}{2}}$ $a = 3$

22. $4p - 12 \leq 60 - 5p$ $p \leq 8$

23. $9.5 = 6x + 23.3$ $x = -2.3$

24. Consider the system of equations $\begin{cases} 2x - 2y = 10 \\ -3x + 8y = -6 \end{cases}$. (**Lesson 10-8**)
   a. Write the system in matrix form.
   b. Use technology to find the inverse of the coefficient matrix.
   c. Solve the system. $x = \frac{34}{5}, y = \frac{9}{5}$

25. The **semiperimeter** of a triangle is half the perimeter of the triangle. Heron's formula (also called Hero's formula) shown below can be used to calculate the area A of a triangle given the lengths of the three sides a, b, and c. (**Lesson 8-6**)

   $A = \sqrt{s(s-a)(s-b)(s-c)}$, where $s = \frac{1}{2}(a+b+c)$

   a. If the side lengths of a triangle are 15, 9, and 12 inches, calculate the semiperimeter s of the triangle. **18 units**
   b. Find the area of the triangle in Part a. **54 units²**

26. If Emily reads 20 pages of a 418-page novel in 42 minutes, about how many hours will it take her to read the entire novel? (**Lesson 5-9**) **about 14.6 hr**

Statue of Hero of Alexandria

14. Answers vary.
Sample answer:
Let $m = 40$ and $n = 30$. Then m is divisible by 20 and n is divisible by 30, but $m + n = 70$, which is not divisible by 50.

17. Answers vary.
Sample answer:
$b = 13$

18. $x = \frac{-1 \pm \sqrt{5}}{2}$

24a. $\begin{bmatrix} 2 & -2 \\ -3 & 8 \end{bmatrix} \begin{bmatrix} x \\ y \end{bmatrix} = \begin{bmatrix} 10 \\ -6 \end{bmatrix}$

24b. See margin.

Notes on the Questions

Question 16 Do not let students be intimidated by the large numbers. You might point out that these are small compared to the gross national product.

Question 25 The prefix "semi-" comes from the Latin word meaning "half." Semiperimeter is half the perimeter, just as a semicircle is half a circle. "Semester," meaning half a year, comes from the same root. The word "semi" referring to a truck originally only meant the trailer part of the tractor-trailer combination, and thus referred to half the truck. The triangle in Part a is a right triangle, so its area can be found in a different manner; this can be used to check the calculations in Heron's formula. When the sides and the area of a triangle are whole numbers, the calculation in Heron's formula can be greatly simplified by the repeated use of $\sqrt{x^2 y} = x\sqrt{y}$ when x is positive.

Question 27 Students can build fact triangles like those in Questions 9 and 10 with numbers of the forms $3n + 1$ and $3n + 2$.

Additional Answers

13. Answers vary. Sample answer: Let m and n be numbers such that $m + n = 35a$ and $n = 70b$, where a and b are integers. Then $m + n = m + 70b = 35a$, so $m = 35a - 70b$, and by the Distributive Property, $m = 35(a - 2b)$. Because a and $2b$ are integers, their difference is an integer, so m is divisible by 35.

15. Answers vary. Sample answer: Let m and n be numbers such that $m = 4p$ and $n = 6q$, where p and q are integers. Then $mn = (4p)(6q) = 24pq$ by the Commutative and Associative Properties of Multiplication. Because p and q are integers, pq is an integer.

24b. $\begin{bmatrix} \frac{4}{5} & \frac{1}{5} \\ \frac{3}{10} & \frac{1}{5} \end{bmatrix}$

13-5

4 Wrap-Up

Ongoing Assessment

On a piece of paper, have students prove or write down counterexamples to each of the following.

i.   If two integers are divisible by 3, then their sum is divisible by 6.
ii. If two integers are divisible by 3, then the sum of their squares is divisible by 9.
iii. The product of an even integer and an odd integer is an even integer.

i. $3 + 6 = 9$; 9 is not divisble by 6.
ii. $(3m)^2 + (3n)^3 = 9m^2 + 9n^2 = 9(m^2 + n^2)$; $9(m^2 + n^2)$ is divisible by 9.
iii. $(2m)(2n + 1) = 4mn + 2m = 2(2mn + m)$; $2(mn + m)$ is an even integer.

Project Update

Project 3, Divisibility Tests, on page 829, and Project 6, Euclidean Algorithm, on page 830, relate to the content of this lesson.

EXPLORATION

27. The numbers 1, 4, 7, 10, ..., which increase by 3, can be pictured as 3 equal rows of dots with 1 left over. These numbers are of the form $3n + 1$. The numbers 2, 5, 8, 11, ..., which increase by 3, can be pictured as 3 equal rows of dots with 2 left over. These numbers are of the form $3n + 2$.

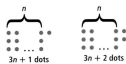

What happens if you add, subtract, and multiply numbers of these forms? Are the answers all of the same form? Try to prove any results you find. See margin.

28. In Activity 2, you found that, for the first 9 odd positive integers, the square of the odd number is 1 more than a multiple of 8. Prove that the result is true for all odd integers. $n = 8$;
    Answers vary. Sample answer: Let n be an integer. By the definition of an odd integer, there is an integer k such that $n = 2k + 1$. From Example 4, $n^2 = (2k + 1)^2 = 4k(k + 1) + 1$. There are 2 cases to consider.
    Case 1: k is even. Then $k = 2m$, where m is an integer, and $n^2 = 4(2m)(k + 1) + 1 = 8m(k + 1) + 1$, so n^2 is 1 more than a multiple of 8.
    Case 2: k is odd. Then $k + 1$ is even, so $k + 1 = 2m$, where m is an integer, and $n^2 = 4k(2m) + 1 = 8km + 1$. So again, n^2 is 1 more than a multiple of 8.

808   Using Algebra to Prove

Additional Answers

27. Answers vary. Sample answer: If numbers of the form $3n + 1$ are added, then the new number will be of the form $3m + 2$. If numbers of the form $3n + 2$ are added, then the new number will be of the form $3m + 1$. If one number of each form is added, then the new number will be of the form $3n$. If numbers of the form $3n + 1$ are multiplied, then the new number will be of the form $3m + 1$. If numbers of the form $3n + 2$ are multiplied, then the new number will be of the form $3m + 1$. If one number of each form is multiplied, then the new number will be of the form $3m + 2$.

Lesson 13-6

From Number Puzzles to Properties of Integers

▶ **BIG IDEA** Using algebra, you can show why divisibility tests and tricks relating to divisibility work.

In Lesson 2-3, you saw some number puzzles. In this lesson, you will see some unusual properties of divisibility that are like puzzles. Algebra shows why they work.

Activity 1

Step 1 Write down a 3-digit whole number, such as 175 or 220.

Step 2 Reverse the digits and subtract the new number from your original number. $175 - 571 = -396$; $220 - 022 = 198$.

$$
\begin{array}{cc}
175 & 220 \\
-\,571 & -\,022
\end{array}
$$

Step 3 Repeat Steps 1 and 2 with a few different numbers. You should find that the differences you get are always divisible by a large 2-digit number. What is that number? **99**

Activity 2

1. Repeat Activity 1 with a few 4-digit numbers. Does the result you got in Activity 1 work for 4-digit numbers? **See margin on page 810.**

2. Does the result you got in Activity 1 work for 5-digit numbers? **The result from Activity 1 seems to hold for 5-digit numbers.**

Activity 3

Step 1. Answers vary. Sample answer: 749

Step 1 Write down a 3-digit whole number.

Step 2 Next to your number from Step 1 write the same 3 digits, creating a 6-digit number. **749,749**

Step 3 The 6-digit number you get is always divisible by 3 different small prime numbers. What are those numbers? **7, 11, and 13**

Mental Math

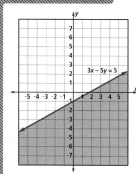

a. Describe the shaded region of the graph with an inequality. $3x - 5y \geq 5$

b. Describe the unshaded region of the graph with an inequality. $3x - 5y < 5$

From Number Puzzles to Properties of Integers **809**

Background

All of the properties discussed in this lesson are properties related to divisibility. These properties are of two types: number curiosities and divisibility tests. Divisibility tests can be sorted into two groups: those that involve the digits of a number, and those that are independent of digits. For example, testing a number for divisibility by 9 by adding its digits is of the first type; while knowing that if two numbers are divisible by k, so is their sum, is of the second type.

Do not expect mastery of these kinds of proofs after even a couple of days. It is wisest to spread them out over as many days as you can afford until the chapter is finished. Start by making certain that students understand the difference between the number and the *value of the number* and the *digits*. The next consideration is to know the definition in algebraic terms of what is meant for a number to be even, odd, or divisible by k.

Lesson 13-6

Lesson
13-6

GOAL

Prove some divisibility properties of integers that depend on the digits of numbers.

SPUR Objective

E Prove the divisibility properties of integers.

Materials/Resources

- Lesson Master 13-6A or 13-6B
- Resource Masters 205 and 206
- Scientific or graphing calculator
- Quiz 2

HOMEWORK
Suggestions for Assignment

- Questions 1–27
- Question 28 (extra credit)
- Reading Lesson 13-7
- Covering the Ideas 13-7

Local Standards

1 Warm-Up

Step 1. Pick a 3-digit number m with no repeating digits, and let r be the number formed by reversing the digits of m. Calculate $|r - m|$ and write it as a 3-digit number n with a 0 in the front if the number has only 2 digits. **Answers will vary.**

Step 2. Let s be the number formed by reversing the digits of n. Calculate $s + n$. Did you get 1,089? **$s + n$ should always be 1,089.**

Step 3. If you pick m in Step 1 at random, what is the relative frequency that 1,089 will result at the end of Step 2? Try different numbers to check. **The relative frequency is 1; the result always happens.**

2 Teaching

Notes on the Activities

Activities 1 through 5 display examples of five unusual divisibility properties involving the digits of numbers written in base 10.

Activity 1 Ask what differences students found in Step 2. If one has not been found, ask students what number might get that difference? (Samples: $534 - 435 = 99$, $200 - 002 = 198$, etc.) Example 4 proves why the differences are always divisible by 99.

Activity 2 Consider proving the conjecture made in Activity 1. Let *abc* represent a 3-digit whole number where $abc = 100a + 10b + c$. Now subtract: $abc - cba = (100a + 10b + c) - (100c + 10b + a) = 100(a - c) - (a - c) = 99(a - c)$. Therefore 99 is the greatest common factor of $abc - cba$.

Activity 3 If you write the same digit next to itself, as in 88, the number is always divisible by 11. If you begin with a 2-digit number and write it next to itself, as in 4,747, then it will always be divisible by 101. Beginning with a 3-digit number and writing it next to itself, the result will always be divisible by 1,001. Since $1,001 = 7 \cdot 11 \cdot 13$, the result is always divisible by three small prime numbers. Of course, if the original 3-digit number is divisible by another prime, the resulting 6-digit number also will be divisible by that prime. For example, $483 = 7 \cdot 3 \cdot 23$, so 483,483 is divisible not only by 7, 11, and 13, but also by 3 and 23. Students are asked to prove part of the result of Activity 3 in Question 15 of this lesson.

Activity 4

Step 1 Write down spaces for the digits of an 8-digit number. Answers vary. Sample answer: 1; 8; 4; 3; 5; 3; 6; 2

$$\underline{\ ?\ }\ \underline{\ ?\ },\underline{\ ?\ }\ \underline{\ ?\ }\ \underline{\ ?\ },\underline{\ ?\ }\ \underline{\ ?\ }\ \underline{\ ?\ }$$

Step 2 Choose numbers for these digits so that the sum of the 1st, 3rd, 5th, and 7th digits equals the sum of the 2nd, 4th, 6th, and 8th digits. Answers vary. Sample answer: 18,435,362

Step 3 Try this with a few numbers. Find a 2-digit number less than 25 that divides the 8-digit number. You may want to use the FACTOR feature of a CAS. **22**

Activity 5 Step 1. Answers vary. Sample answer: 8,046,759,231

Step 1 Create a 10-digit number using each of the digits 0, 1, 2, 3, 4, 5, 6, 7, 8, and 9 once. For example, one such number is 8,627,053,914.

Step 2 Tell whether the statement is true or false.

    a. Every number created in Step 1 will be divisible by 3. **true**

    b. Every number created in Step 1 will be divisible by 6. **false**

    c. Every number created in Step 1 will be divisible by 9. **true**

    d. Every number created in Step 1 will be divisible by 18. **false**

    e. Every number created in Step 1 will be divisible by 27. **false**

Divisibility Properties Depending on the Rightmost Digits of Numbers

You have known for a long time that in the base-10 number system the 4-digit number 5,902 is a shorthand for $5 \cdot 1,000 + 9 \cdot 100 + 0 \cdot 10 + 2 \cdot 1$ or, using exponents, it is a shorthand for $5 \cdot 10^3 + 9 \cdot 10^2 + 0 \cdot 10^1 + 2 \cdot 10^0$.

We say that 2 is the units digit, or the digit in the units place, 0 is the tens digit, 9 is the hundreds digit, and 5 is the thousands digit for the number 5,902. In general, if u is the units digit, t is the tens digit, h is the hundreds digit, and T is the thousands digit, then the value of the 4-digit number is

$$1,000T + 100h + 10t + u.$$

You can extend this idea using more variables to give the value of any integer written in base 10 in terms of its digits.

By representing the value of a number in terms of its digits, you can prove some divisibility tests that you have known for a long time. The proofs are quite similar to those used in Lesson 13-5.

Accommodating the Learner ⬆

Challenge students to prove that 5-digit integers ending in 00, 25, 50, and 75 are divisible by 25. (*Hint:* The following is an outline of the proof for an integer ending in 75. Let $N = 10,000a + 1,000T + 100h + 75 = 25(400a + 40T + 4h + 3)$. Since $400a + 40T + 4h + 3$ is an integer, N is divisible by 25.)

Additional Answers

Activity 2

Step 1. Answers vary. Sample answer: 1,673 gives a difference of 2,088, and 5,792 gives a difference of 2,817. Neither of these numbers is divisible by 99.

Example 1

Prove that if the units digit of a number in base 10 is even, then the number is even.

Solution The proof here is for a 4-digit number N. The proof for numbers with fewer or more digits is very similar. A 4-digit number in base 10 with digits as named above has the value

$$N = 1{,}000T + 100h + 10t + u.$$

If the units digit u is even, then u = 2k, where k is an integer. Substituting 2k for u, N = 1,000T + 100h + 10t + 2k.

Notice that 2 is a common monomial factor of the polynomial on the right side. Factor out the 2.

$$N = 2(500T + 50h + 5t + k)$$

Since 500T + 50h + 5t + k is an integer, N is twice an integer, so it must be even.

In a similar way, you can prove divisibility tests for 4, 5, 8, and 10.

Divisibility Tests Based on the Sum of the Digits

There is a different type of divisibility test for 9: just add the digits of the number. The number is divisible by 9 if and only if the sum of its digits is divisible by 9. Proving this involves a variation of the approach taken in Example 1.

Example 2

Prove that if the sum of the digits of a 4-digit integer written in base 10 is divisible by 9, then the number is divisible by 9.

Solution Call the number N. Suppose N has digits T, h, t, and u as named above. (The same idea holds for any number of digits.)

$$N = 1{,}000T + 100h + 10t + u$$

Now separate the sum of the digits from the value of the number.

$$N = (T + h + t + u) + (999T + 99h + 9t)$$

If the sum of the digits is divisible by 9, then there is an integer k with T + h + t + u = 9k. Substitute 9k for T + h + t + u.

$$N = 9k + (999T + 99h + 9t)$$
$$N = 9(k + 111T + 11h + t)$$

Since k + 111T + 11h + t is an integer, N is divisible by 9.

Notes on the Activities

Activity 4 If the students work carefully they will soon discover that the correct answer is 11. This same rule works for 2-digit, 4-digit, 6-digit, and 8-digit numbers. In fact, if the number of digits is even, the rule will always work. Encourage students to do some research as to why this works.

Activity 5 This activity applies the common divisibility test for 9. Regardless of the permutation of the digits 0 through 9, the sum of the digits remains 45, which is divisible by 9. So the number is divisible by 9.

Additional Examples

Example 1 Prove that if the unit digit of a number in base 10 is zero, then the number is divisible by 10. Proof: The proof here is for a 4-digit number N. The proof for numbers with fewer or more digits is very similar. The number N can be expressed as follows where T is the thousands digit, h is the hundreds digit, and t is the tens digit:
$N = 1{,}000T + 100h + 10t + 0$
Factoring N you get $N = 1{,}000T + 100h + 10t + 0 = 10(100T + 10h + t)$. Because 10 is a factor of N, N is divisible by 10.

Example 2 Prove that if the sum of the digits of a 3-digit integer written in base 10 is divisible by 9, then the number is divisible by 9. Proof: Call the number N. Suppose h is the hundreds digit, t is the tens digit, and u is the units digit. Then $N = 100h + 10t + u$. Now separate the sum of the digits from the value of the number.
$N = (h + t + u) + (99h + 9t)$
If the sum of the digits is divisible by 9, then there is an integer k with $h + t + u = 9k$. Substituting 9k for $h + t + u$, $N = 9k + (99h + 9t)$
$N = 9(k + 11h + t)$
Since $k + 11h + t$ is an integer, N is divisible by 9.

Additional Examples

Example 3 Prove that if the sum of the digits of a 5-digit integer written in base 10 is divisible by 3, then the number is divisible by 3.

Solution

1. Call the number N. Suppose N has digits a, T, h, t, and u. Then

   $N = 10,000a + \underline{} + \underline{} + \underline{} + \underline{}$
   1,000T; 100h; 10t; u

2. Now separate the sum of the digits from the value of the number.

   $N = (a + T + h + t + u) + (\underline{} + \underline{} + \underline{} + \underline{})$ 9,999a; 999T; 99h; 9t

3. If the sum of the digits is divisible by 3, then there is an integer k with $a + T + h + t + u = 3k$.

4. Substitute into Step 2,

   $N = 3k + (\underline{} + \underline{} + \underline{} + \underline{})$
   9,999a; 999T; 99h; 9t

   $N = 3(\underline{}) k + 3,333a + 333T + 33h + 3t$

   Because $\underline{}$ is an integer, N is divisible by 3. $k + 3,333a + 333T + 33h + 3t$

Example 4 Prove that if a 3-digit number is subtracted from the number formed by reversing its digits, then the difference is divisible by 11. Proof: Suppose the original number has the value $100h + 10t + u$. Then the number with its digits reversed has value $100u + 10t + h$. Subtracting the reversed number from the original yields the difference D:

$D = 100h + 10t + u - (100u + 10t + h)$
$D = 100h + 10t + u - 100u - 10t - h$
$D = 99h - 99u$
$D = 11(9h - 9u)$

Because $9h - 9u$ is an integer, the difference D is divisible by 11.

Example 3

Prove that if the sum of the digits of a 4-digit integer written in base 10 is divisible by 3, then the number is divisible by 3.

Solution Use Example 2 as a model for your solution.

1. Call the number N. Suppose N has digits T, h, t, and u.

   $N = 1,000T + \dfrac{\underline{}}{100h} + \dfrac{\underline{}}{10t} + \dfrac{\underline{}}{u}$

2. Now separate the sum of the digits from the value of the number.

   $N = (T + h + t + u) + (\dfrac{\underline{}}{999T} + \dfrac{\underline{}}{99h} + \dfrac{\underline{}}{9t})$

3. If the sum of the digits is divisible by 3 then there is an integer k with $T + h + t + u = 3k$.

4. Substitute into Step 2.

   $N = 3k + (\underline{} + \underline{} + \underline{})$ 999T; 99h; 9t
   $N = 3(\underline{}) k + 333T + 33h + 3t$

   Because $\underline{}$ is an integer, N is divisible by 3. $k + 333T + 33h + 3t$

Reversing Digits of a Number

Consider the 3-digit number $581 = 5 \cdot 100 + 8 \cdot 10 + 1$.

Reversing the digits of this number results in the number $185 = 1 \cdot 100 + 8 \cdot 10 + 5$.

So if a number has hundreds digit h, tens digit t, and units digit u, the number with the digits reversed has hundreds digit u, tens digit t, and units digit h. Whereas the first number has value $100h + 10t + u$, the number with its digits reversed has value $100u + 10t + h$.

Working with these numbers yields some surprising properties.

Example 4

Prove that if a 3-digit number is subtracted from the number formed by reversing its digits, then the difference is divisible by 99.

Solution Suppose the original number has the value $100h + 10t + u$.

Then the number with its digits reversed has value $100u + 10t + h$.

Subtracting the reversed number from the original yields the difference D.

Accommodating the Learner ⬇

How do you know if a 3-digit number is divisible by 3? The divisibility rule of 3 says to add the digits and check to see if the sum is divisible by 3. If the sum is divisible by 3, the original number is divisible by 3. Help students try to prove this conjecture. The proof goes something like the following: Given a 3-digit number abc, rewrite it as $100a + 10b + c$. Now $100a + 10b + c = (99 + 1)a + (9 + 1)b + c = 99a + 9b + a + b + c$. Because 3 divides $99a$ and $9b$, 3 need only divide the remaining expression $a + b + c$ to be a divisor of the original number. Thus 3 must divide the sum of the digits.

$D = 100h + 10t + u - (100u + 10t + h)$

$D = 100h + 10t + u - 100u - 10t - h$

$D = 99h - 99u$

$D = 99(h - u)$

Since $h - u$ is an integer, the difference D is divisible by 99.

Questions

COVERING THE IDEAS

In 1–4, what is the value of the number?

1. The units digit of this 2-digit number is 7 and the tens digit is 5.

2. The units digit of this 2-digit number is u and the tens digit is t.

3. The thousands digit of the 4-digit number is A, the hundreds digit is B, the tens digit is C, and the units digit is D.

4. The millions digit of this 7-digit number is M, the thousands digit of this number is T, the units digit is 3, and all other digits are 0. $1{,}000{,}000M + 1{,}000T + 3$

5. A 4-digit number has thousands digit T, hundreds digit h, tens digit t, and units digit u. 5b. $1{,}000u + 100t + 10h + T$
   a. What is the value of the number? $1{,}000T + 100h + 10t + u$
   b. What is the value of the number with its digits reversed?

6. Use Example 1 as a guide to prove: If the units digit of a 4-digit number in base 10 is 5, then the number is divisible by 5. *See margin.*

7. The proof in Example 2 is given for a 4-digit number. Adapt this proof for a 5-digit number, letting D be the ten-thousands digit. *See margin.*

8. **Fill in the Blanks** A number is divisible by 3 if and only if it can be written as __?__, where __?__ is an integer. $3k; k$

In 9–12, an integer is given.
   a. Tell whether the integer is divisible by 2 and state a reason why.
   b. Tell whether the integer is divisible by 5 and state a reason why.
   c. Tell whether the integer is divisible by 9 and state a reason why.

9. 259,259,259

10. 225

11. 522

12. $522 - 225$

1. 57

2. $10t + u$

3. $1{,}000A + 100B + 10C + D$

9a. No, the units digit is odd.

9b. No, the units digit is neither 5 nor 0.

9c. No, the digits do not sum to a number divisible by 9.

10a. No, the units digit is odd.

10b. Yes, the units digit is 5.

10c. Yes, the digits sum to 9.

11a. Yes, the units digit is even.

11b. No, the units digit is neither 5 nor 0.

11c. Yes, the digits sum to 9.

12a. No, the units digit is odd, since the difference of an even and an odd number is odd.

12b. No, the units digit is neither 5 nor 0.

12c. Yes, since by Activity 1, this is divisible by 99, which is itself divisible by 9.

From Number Puzzles to Properties of Integers **813**

3 Assignment

Recommended Assignment
- Questions 1–27
- Question 28 (extra credit)
- Reading Lesson 13-7
- Covering the Ideas 13-7

Notes on the Questions

Questions 1–5 Knowing the answers to these questions is critical for students' being able to begin the proofs in later questions.

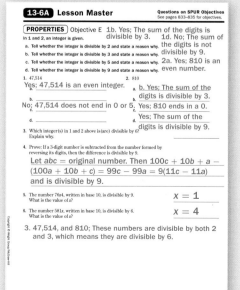

13-6

Notes on the Questions

Question 16 Given the divisibility test for 11 that students might have ascertained from Activity 4 in this lesson, you could also ask for the value of x if $46x3$ is divisible by 11. (Answer: 11)

Question 17 This question can be answered rather easily without algebra. Because the tens digit is 4 times the hundreds digit, the only possibilities for the number are 14 and 28. No multiple of 19 is from 140 to 149, since $19 \cdot 7 = 133$. But $19 \cdot 15 = 285$. So the number is 285. Then why use algebra? As usual, the answer is that in more complicated problems, a solution without algebra might not be available.

Question 28 We encourage discussion of this question, as it points out a nice connection between the factoring of polynomials and the factoring of integers.

Additional Answers

13a. Answers vary. Sample answer:
$2,346 - 6,432 = -4,086$, which, when divided by 99 gives about -41.28, which is not an integer.

13b. A 4-digit number in base 10 can be written as $N = 1,000T + 100h + 10t + u$, where T, h, t, u are all digits. Moreover, the number with reversed digits is $1000u + 100t + 10h + T$. The difference between these two numbers is $1,000T + 100h + 10t + u - (1,000u + 100t + 10h + T) = 999T + 90h - 90t - 999u = 9(111T + 10h - 10t - 111u)$. Since $111T + 10h - 10t - 111u$ is an integer we know that this difference is divisible by 9.

15. A 6-digit number in base 10 can be written as $N = 100,000H + 10,000D + 1,000T + 100h + 10t + u$, where H, D, T, h, t, u are all digits. Our given conditions mean $H = h$, $D = t$ and $T = u$, and so our number can be rewritten as $100,000h + 10,000t + 1,000u + 100h + 10t + u = 100,100h + 10,010t + 1,001u$. We can factor 13 from this expression to get $N = 13(7,700h + 770t + 77u)$, and since $7,700h + 770t + 77u$ is an integer, N is 13 times an integer, and thus divisible by 13.

APPLYING THE MATHEMATICS

13. **a.** Find a counterexample: If a 4-digit number is subtracted from the number formed by reversing its digits, then the difference is divisible by 99. **See margin.**

   b. Prove: If a 4-digit number is subtracted from the number formed by reversing its digits, then the difference is divisible by 9. **See margin.**

14. **a.** Give an example of this statement and then prove it: If the units digit of a 5-digit number is 5 and the tens digit is 2, then the number is divisible by 25.

   b. Is the converse of the statement in Part a true? **no**

15. In a certain 6-digit number, the hundred-thousands and hundreds digits are equal, the ten-thousands and tens digits are equal, and the thousands and units digits are equal. Prove that this number is divisible by 13. **See margin.**

16. The number $46x3$, written in base 10, is divisible by 9. What is the value of x? $x =$ **any integer in the form 3k**

17. The tens digit of a 3-digit number is 4 times the hundreds digit and the number is divisible by 19. Find the number. **285**

REVIEW

In **18** and **19**, a statement is given. Prove the statement to show that it is true or provide a counterexample to show that it is false. (**Lesson 13-5**) **18–19. See margin.**

18. If a number is divisible by 5, then its square is divisible by 25.

19. If one number is divisible by 3, and a second number is divisible by 4, then the product of the two numbers is divisible by 7.

20. Give an example of an if-then statement that is false but whose converse is true. (**Lessons 13-2, 13-1**) **See margin.**

21. The triangle below has an area of 45 square inches. Find the height h of the triangle if the base is $2h + 8$ inches. (**Lesson 12-4**) $h = 5$

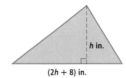

h in.

$(2h + 8)$ in.

14a. Answers vary. Sample answer $23,425 = 937 \cdot 25$, so 23,425 is divisible by 25. A 5-digit number in base-10 can be written as $N = 10,000D + 1,000T + 100h + 10t + u$, where D, T, h, t, u are all digits. Having the units digits be 5 means $u = 5$, and having the tens digit equal 2 means $t = 2$; so our number can be written as $10,000D + 1,000T + 100h + 25$, from which we can factor 25, resulting in $N = 25(400D + 40T + 4h + 1)$. Since $400D + 40T + 4h + 1$ is an integer, N is 25 times an integer, which means N is divisible by 25.

Additional Answers

18. If n is divisible by 5, then $n = 5k$, where k is an integer. Then, $n^2 = (5k)^2 = 25k^2$, and so n^2 is divisible by 25, since k^2 is an integer.

19. Answers vary. Sample answer: As a counterexample, consider 6 and 8, where $6 \cdot 8 = 48$ which is not divisible by 7.

20. Answers vary. Sample answer: If it is precipitating, then it is snowing.

22. A rectangular box has dimensions a, $a + 3$, and $2a + 1$.
   (Lessons 11-5, 11-2)

   a. Find a polynomial expression in standard form for the volume of the box. $2a^3 + 7a^2 + 3a$ units^3

   b. What is the degree of the polynomial in Part a? 3

23. Consider the quadratic equation $4m^2 - 20m + 25 = 0$. (Lesson 9-6)

   a. Find the value of the discriminant. 0

   b. Use your answer to Part a to determine the number of real solutions to the equation. 1

In 24–26, solve the sentence. (Lessons 8-6, 5-9, 4-5)

24. $\sqrt{m - 10} = 3$
   $m = 19$

25. $5y - 2 > y$
   $y > 0.5$

26. $\frac{w + 27}{9} = \frac{w}{3}$ $w = 13.5$

27. What is the value of x in the equation $\frac{(h^5)^{10} \cdot h^{15}}{h^{20}} = h^x$?
   (Lessons 8-4, 8-3, 8-2) $x = 45$

EXPLORATION

28. Let h, t, and u be the hundreds, tens, and units digits of a 3-digit number in base 10.

   a. Find values of h, t, and u so that $hx^2 + tx + u$ is factorable over the integers. Answers vary. Sample answer: $h = 1, t = 2, u = 1$

   b. For your values of h, t, and u, is it true that $100h + 10t + u$ is factorable over the integers? yes

   c. **True or False** If h, t, and u are digits, and $hx^2 + tx + u$ is factorable over the set of polynomial with integer coefficients, then $100h + 10t + u$ is factorable over the integers. true

   d. Explore this statement to decide whether it is true or false: If h, t, and u are digits, and $100h + 10t + u$ is a prime number, then $hx^2 + tx + u$ is a prime polynomial over the integers. true

From Number Puzzles to Properties of Integers   **815**

13-6

4 Wrap-Up

Ongoing Assessment

On a sheet of paper, ask students to prove that a 3-digit integer ending in 0 or 5 is divisible by 5. Call on students to explain how the proof works. Ask them to extend the proof to integers with 4 or more digits. If students understand the proof, they should be able verbalize how to extend the idea to integers with 4 or more digits.

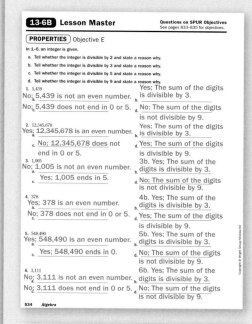

Lesson
13-7

Lesson
13-7
Rational Numbers and Irrational Numbers

Vocabulary

irrational number

GOAL

Provide students with the criteria to distinguish rational numbers from irrational numbers, to show them how to draw some irrational lengths, and to demonstrate a proof that certain numbers are irrational.

SPUR Objectives

F Apply the definitions and properties of rational and irrational numbers.

I Determine whether lengths in geomtric figures are rational or irrational.

Materials/Resources

· Lesson Master 13-7A or 13-7B
· Resource Masters 2, 5, 207, and 208
· Scientific or graphing calculator

HOMEWORK

Suggestions for Assignment

- Questions 1–31
- Questions 32–33 (extra credit)
- Reading Lesson 13-8
- Covering the Ideas 13-8

Local Standards

---

1 Warm-Up

Without a calculator, determine the simple fraction in lowest terms equal to each decimal.

1. 3.14 $\frac{157}{50}$
2. 3.14159 $\frac{314,159}{100,000}$
3. $0.\overline{6}$ $\frac{2}{3}$
4. $0.00\overline{6}$ $\frac{1}{150}$
5. 11.625 $\frac{93}{8}$

> ▶ **BIG IDEA** The Distributive Property enables you to prove that repeating decimals represent rational numbers, and divisibility properties enable you to prove square roots of certain integers are irrational.

A number that can be represented by a decimal is a real number. All the real numbers are either rational or irrational. In this lesson, you will see how we know that some numbers are not rational numbers.

What Are Rational Numbers?

Recall that a *simple fraction* is a fraction with integers in its numerator and denominator. For example, $\frac{2}{3}$, $\frac{5,488}{212}$, $\frac{10}{5}$, $\frac{-7}{-2}$, and $\frac{-43}{1}$ are simple fractions.

Some numbers are not simple fractions, but are *equal* to simple fractions. Any mixed number equals a simple fraction. For example, $3\frac{2}{7} = \frac{23}{7}$. Also, any integer equals a simple fraction. For example, $-10 = \frac{-10}{1}$. And any finite decimal equals a simple fraction. For example, $3.078 = 3\frac{78}{1,000} = \frac{3,078}{1,000}$. All these numbers are *rational numbers*. A *rational number* is a number that can be expressed as a simple fraction.

All repeating decimals are also rational numbers. The Example below shows how to find a simple fraction that equals a given repeating decimal.

Example

Show that $18.4\overline{23}$ is a rational number.

Solution Let $x = 18.4\overline{23}$. Multiply both sides by 10^n, where n is the number of digits in the repetend $\overline{23}$. Here there are two digits in the repetend, so we multiply by 10^2, or 100.

$$x = 18.4\overline{23}$$
$$100x = 1,842.3\overline{23}$$

Mental Math

A school enrolled 120 freshmen, 110 sophomores, 125 juniors, and 100 seniors. What is the probability that

a. a student at the school is a sophomore? $\frac{22}{91}$

b. a student at the school is a junior or senior? $\frac{45}{91}$

c. a student is not a junior? $\frac{66}{91}$

Background

This lesson is divided into two parts. The first part deals with the definition and the identification of rational numbers. The second part deals with these same ideas as they apply to irrational numbers. By treating these ideas together, we attempt to show students that both kinds of numbers are important and that both must be considered in algebra and geometry.

What are rational numbers? The Example shows how a repeating decimal represents a rational number. Because calculators more often give answers as decimals than in any other form, the skill of rewriting a repeating decimal as a rational number is more important today than it might have been a generation ago.

How do we know that certain numbers are irrational? When n is not a perfect square, one can mimic the proof in the lesson to show that $\sqrt{n}$ is irrational. For example, consider $\sqrt{6}$. If there were integers a and b with $\sqrt{6} = \frac{a}{b}$ and the fraction were in lowest

(continued on next page)

Subtract the top equation from the bottom equation. The key idea here is that the result is no longer an infinite repeating decimal; in this case, after the first decimal place the repeating parts subtract to zero.

$$100x = 1{,}842.3\overline{23}$$
$$- x = \phantom{1{,}84}18.4\overline{23}$$
$$\overline{99x = 1{,}823.900}$$

Divide both sides by 99.

$$x = \frac{1{,}823.9}{99} = \frac{18{,}239}{990}$$

Since $x = \frac{18{,}239}{990}$, x is a rational number.

 QY1

▸ QY1

a. Divide 18,239 by 990 to check the result of the Example.

b. Write $4.\overline{123}$ as a simple fraction.

Rational numbers have interesting properties. They can be added, subtracted, multiplied, and divided; and they give answers that are also rational numbers.

What Are Irrational Numbers?

The ancient Greeks seem to have been the first to discover that there are numbers that are not rational numbers. They called them *irrational*. An **irrational number** is a real number that is not a rational number. Some of the most commonly found irrational numbers in mathematics are the square roots of integers that are not perfect squares. That is, numbers like $\sqrt{2}, \sqrt{3}, \sqrt{5}, \sqrt{6}, \sqrt{7}, \sqrt{8}, \sqrt{10}$, and so on, are irrational. But notice that $\sqrt{4}$ is rational not irrational, because $\sqrt{4} = 2 = \frac{2}{1}$. All these numbers can arise from situations involving right triangles. Examine the array of right triangles shown below.

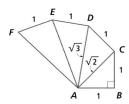

$\triangle ABC$ is a right triangle with legs of 1 and 1. Use the Pythagorean Theorem to find the side lengths AC and AD.

$$AC^2 = AB^2 + BC^2$$
$$AC^2 = 1 + 1$$
$$AC^2 = 2$$
$$AC = \sqrt{2}$$

2 Teaching

Notes on the Lesson

If you think the Example is new to students, go over it carefully. Note that it is important to write quite a few decimal places for each repeating decimal so that students understand how to pick the number by which to multiply both sides of the equation. Point out that they multiply $\frac{1}{3}$ by 2 to get $\frac{2}{3}$; likewise, they can multiply 0.3333... by 2 to get 0.6666... .

What are rational numbers? Remind students that a number can *look* irrational but still be rational. For example, $\frac{\sqrt{72}}{\sqrt{8}}$ is rational because it is equal to 3.

Drawing segments with (theoretical) lengths $\sqrt{n}$ gives a concreteness to irrational numbers that is helpful to many students.

Additional Example

Example Show that $13.5\overline{47}$ is a rational number. If $N = 13.54747...$, then $100N - N = 1{,}354.74747...$ $- 13.54747...$. So $99N = 1{,}341.2$ and $N = \frac{1{,}341.2}{99} = \frac{13{,}412}{990} = \frac{6{,}706}{495}$.

terms, then these integers would satisfy $6b^2 = a^2$. This means that a^2 is divisible by 2 and 3, so a would also be divisible by 2 and 3. So let $a = 6m$. Then $a^2 = 36m^2$, so, by the Transitive Property of Equality, $6b^2 = 36m^2$ and, dividing both sides by 6, $b^2 = 6m^2$. Consequently b^2 is divisible by 6, and so b is divisible by both 2 and 3. Thus $\frac{a}{b}$ is not in lowest terms.

Notes on the Lesson

How do we know that certain numbers are irrational? You should go over the proof of the theorem in the lesson carefully with your students. It relies on the fact that if the square of a number is even, the number has to be even. You may want to begin by making certain your students believe that.

$\triangle ACD$ is drawn with leg $\overline{AC}$, and another leg $CD = 1$. Use the Pythagorean Theorem.

$$AD^2 = AC^2 + CD^2$$
$$AD^2 = (\sqrt{2})^2 + 1^2$$
$$AD^2 = 2 + 1$$
$$AD^2 = 3$$
$$AD = \sqrt{3}$$

 QY2

> ▶ **QY2**
>
> Find *AE* and *AF* in the figure on the previous page.

How Do We Know That Certain Numbers Are Irrational?

If you evaluate $\sqrt{2}$ on a calculator, you will see a decimal approximation. One calculator shows 1.414213562. Another shows 1.41421356237. No matter how many decimal places the calculator shows, it is not enough to show the entire decimal because the decimal for $\sqrt{2}$ is infinite and does not repeat.

Is it possible the decimal could repeat after 1,000 decimal places, or after 1 million or 1 billion decimal places? How do we know that the decimal does not repeat? The answer is that we can *prove* the decimal does not repeat, because we can prove that $\sqrt{2}$ is not a rational number. The proof uses some of the ideas of divisibility you have seen in Lessons 13-5 and 13-6. In particular, we use the fact that if a number is even, then its square is divisible by 4. The idea of the proof is to show that there is no simple fraction in lowest terms equal to $\sqrt{2}$.

Here is the proof: Suppose $\sqrt{2}$ is rational. Then there would be two whole numbers a and b with $\sqrt{2} = \frac{a}{b}$ (with the fraction in lowest terms). Then, multiply each side of this equality by itself.

$$\sqrt{2} \cdot \sqrt{2} = \frac{a}{b} \cdot \frac{a}{b} \quad \text{Multiplication Property of Equality}$$
$$2 = \frac{a^2}{b^2} \quad \text{Definition of square root;}$$
$$\qquad\qquad \text{Multiplication of Fractions}$$
$$2b^2 = a^2 \quad \text{Multiply both sides by } b^2.$$

So if you could find two numbers a and b with twice the square of b equal to the square of a, then $\sqrt{2}$ would be a rational number. (You can come close. 7^2 or 49 is one less than twice 5^2 or 25.)

Notice that since a^2 would be twice an integer, a^2 would be even. This means that a would be even (because the square of an odd number is odd). Because a would be even, there would be an integer m with $a = 2m$. This means that $a^2 = (2m)^2 = 4m^2$. Substitute in the bottom equation.

818 Using Algebra to Prove

Vocabulary Development

It is very important that students have a clear understanding of the definition of rational numbers and irrational numbers. Instruct your students to identify these definitions in the lesson and include them together with examples in their notebooks.

Accommodating the Learner ⬆

Challenge the students to consider whether there exist two irrational numbers that do not have a rational number between them. Ask them to find a rational number between $\sqrt{2}$ and $\sqrt{1.9}$. Repeat the question for $\sqrt{2}$ and $\sqrt{1.99}$, and again for $\sqrt{2}$ and $\sqrt{1.999}$. Have them make a conjecture. You may use a similar procedure to explore irrational numbers between rational numbers.

$2b^2 = 4m^2$ Substitute $4m^2$ for a^2.

$b^2 = 2m^2$ Divide both sides by 2.

Now we repeat the argument used above. Because b^2 would be twice an integer, b^2 would be even. This means that b would have to be even. And because a and b would both be even, the fraction $\frac{a}{b}$ could not be in lowest terms. This shows that what we supposed at the beginning of this proof is not true.

For this reason, it is impossible to find two whole numbers a and b with $\sqrt{2} = \frac{a}{b}$ and with the fraction in lowest terms. Since any simple fraction can be put in lowest terms, it is impossible to find any two whole numbers a and b with $\sqrt{2} = \frac{a}{b}$.

Arguments like this one can be used to prove the following theorem.

Irrationality of $\sqrt{n}$ Theorem

If n is an integer that is not a perfect square, then $\sqrt{n}$ is irrational.

Johann Lambert

Today, we now know that there are many irrational numbers. For example, every number that has a decimal expansion that does not end or repeat is irrational. Among the irrational numbers is the famous number π. But the argument to show that π is irrational is far more difficult than the argument used above for some square roots of integers. It requires advanced mathematics, and was first done by the German mathematician Johann Lambert in 1767, more than 2,000 years after the Greeks had first discovered that some numbers were irrational.

There is a practical reason for knowing whether a number is rational or irrational. When a number is rational, arithmetic can be done with it rather easily because it can be represented as a simple fraction. Just work as you do with fractions. But if a number is irrational, then it is generally more difficult to do arithmetic with it. Rather than use its infinite decimal, we often leave it alone and just write π or $\sqrt{3}$, for example.

Questions

COVERING THE IDEAS

In 1–3, find an example of each.

1. a simple fraction   Answers vary. Sample answer: $\frac{1}{3}$

2. a fraction that is not a simple fraction   Answers vary. Sample answer: $\frac{\sqrt{2}}{3}$

3. a rational number   Answers vary. Sample answer: 2

Rational Numbers and Irrational Numbers   **819**

13-7

Notes on the Questions

Question 8 This question can help in a discussion of the proof of the theorem of this lesson.

Questions 12 and 17 Refer students to the diagram on page 817 for a method of constructing a segment whose length is irrational.

Question 15 Many students look for complicated possibilities and miss the easy examples, such as $\sqrt{5} + (-\sqrt{5})$ and $\pi + (3 - \pi)$.

Question 19 Some people believe that because all measurements are estimates, none of them are really irrational. However, measurements are estimates whether they are rational or irrational. In mathematics, when we speak of *the* length of an object, we are always idealizing that length. Here we are asking for that idealized length for the perimeter of a square; we could just as well be asking for the idealized length of half the diagonal of the square.

12. $\sqrt{5}$ units

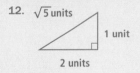

In 4–6, write the number as a simple fraction.

4. $98.\overline{6}$ $\frac{493}{5}$ 5. $0.\overline{84}$ $\frac{28}{33}$ 6. $14.0\overline{327}$ $\frac{46,729}{3,330}$

7. **Multiple Choice** Which *cannot* stand for a rational number? D

  A a terminating decimal

  B a simple fraction

  C a repeating decimal

  D an infinite nonrepeating decimal

8. Refer to the proof that $\sqrt{2}$ is irrational.

  a. If $\sqrt{2}$ were rational, what would $\sqrt{2}$ have to equal?

  b. **True or False** If the square of an integer is even, then the integer is even. true

  c. **True or False** If an integer is divisible by 2, then its square is divisible by 4. true

  d. In the proof, what characteristic of both a and b shows that the fraction $\frac{a}{b}$ is not in lowest terms? They are both divisible by 2.

In 9–11, tell whether the number is a rational or an irrational number.

9. π irrational   10. –220 rational   11. $\sqrt{121}$ rational

12. Draw a segment whose length is $\sqrt{5}$ units. See margin.

13. Draw a square whose diagonal has length $\sqrt{338}$ cm.

APPLYING THE MATHEMATICS

14. Is 0 a rational number? Why or why not?

15. Is it possible for two irrational numbers to have a sum that is a rational number? Explain why or why not.

16. Using the proof in this lesson as a guide, prove that $\sqrt{3}$ is irrational. See margin.

17. a. Draw a segment whose length is $1 + \sqrt{3}$ units. See margin.
  b. Is $1 + \sqrt{3}$ rational or irrational? irrational

18. If a circular table has a diameter of 4 cm, is its circumference rational or irrational? irrational

19. A diagonal of a square has a length of 42 cm. Find the perimeter of the square. Is the perimeter rational or irrational?

20. Determine whether the solutions to the equation $x^2 - 8x - 1 = 0$ are rational or irrational. irrational

21. Refer to the right triangle at the right.
  a. Find the exact value of a. $a = \sqrt{1,606}$
  b. Is a rational or irrational? irrational

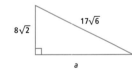

820   Using Algebra to Prove

8a. $\frac{a}{b}$, where a and b are whole numbers.

13.

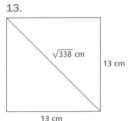

$\sqrt{338}$ cm

13 cm

13 cm

14. Yes, it is rational because $0 = \frac{0}{1}$, which is a simple fraction.

15. Yes, Answers vary. Sample answer: $\sqrt{2} + (-\sqrt{2}) = 0$, and both of them are irrational, while 0 is rational.

19. $84\sqrt{2}$ cm; irrational

16. Suppose $\sqrt{3}$ is rational and write $\sqrt{3} = \frac{a}{b}$ with a, b, whole numbers and $\frac{a}{b}$ in lowest terms. Then $3b^2 = a^2$. Then a^2 is divisible by 3, so a must be divisible by 3. If a is divisible by 3, then a^2 is divisible by 9. Let $a^2 = 9p$. Because $3b^2 = a^2 = 9p$, $b^2 = 3p$ so b^2 must be divisible by 3. Because a is divisible by 3 and b is divisible by 3, and then $\frac{a}{b}$ is not in lowest terms. It is impossible to find whole numbers a and b with $\sqrt{3} = \frac{a}{b}$ and $\frac{a}{b}$ in lowest terms.

17a.

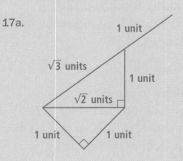

1 unit

$\sqrt{3}$ units

1 unit

$\sqrt{2}$ units

1 unit   1 unit

REVIEW

In 22–25, consider the spreadsheet below, which was used to compute the value of $f(x) = 3x^3 + 5x^2 - 2x$ for integer values of x from −5 to 5. (Lessons 12-7, 12-6, 11-4)

22. Complete the spreadsheet.

23. Graph the function f for $-5 \le x \le 5$.

24. Identify all x-intercepts. −2, 0, $\frac{1}{3}$

25. Rewrite the equation in factored form.
$f(x) = x(x + 2)(3x - 1)$

◇	A	B
1	x	f(x)
2	-5	
3	-4	-104
4	-3	
5	-2	
6	-1	4
7	0	0
8	1	
9	2	40
10	3	120
11	4	
12	5	490

22. See margin.

23.

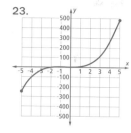

26. Solve $x^3 - 10x^2 + 16x = 0$. (Lessons 12-6, 12-5, 11-4)

27. Suppose $20x^2 + 9xy - 20y^2 = (ax + b)(cx + d)$. (Lesson 12-5)
   a. Find the value of $ad + bc$. 9y
   b. Find b, c, and d if $a = 5$. $b = -4y$, $c = 4$, $d = 5y$

28. Find two numbers whose sum is 30 and whose product is 176. (Lessons 12-4, 11-6, 10-2) 8, 22

29. Expand the expression $\left(\sqrt{25} - \sqrt{x^2}\right)\left(\sqrt{25} + \sqrt{x^2}\right)$.
   (Lessons 11-6, 8-6) $25 - x^2$

30. Calculate the area of the shaded region. (Lesson 11-3) $17w^2 + 3w$

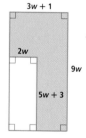

3w + 1

2w

9w

5w + 3

31. With a stopwatch and a stone, you can estimate the depth of a well. If the stone takes 2.1 seconds to reach the bottom, how deep is the well? Use Galileo's equation, $d = 16t^2$. (Lesson 9-1)
   70.56 ft

26. $x = 0$ or $x = 2$ or $x = 8$

Dug wells typically used for drinking water are 10 to 30 feet deep.

Source: U.S. Environmental Protection Agency

Rational Numbers and Irrational Numbers   **821**

Notes on the Questions

Question 29 Some students may simplify the square roots before multiplying. Even though $\sqrt{x^2} \ne x$ for all x, that error will not cause the final answer to be incorrect since $\left(\sqrt{x^2}\right)^2 = x^2$ for all x.

Question 32 The sequence of rational numbers $\frac{3}{2}, \frac{7}{5}, \frac{17}{12}, \frac{41}{29}, \frac{99}{70}, \dots$, where the fraction after $\frac{a}{b}$ is $\frac{a + 2b}{a + b}$, converges to $\sqrt{2}$. Notice that the square of the numerator of each term is one more or one less than twice the square of the denominator. The numerators and denominators of these fractions are the only pairs of numbers with this property.

Question 33 As in Question 19 and the drawing of right triangles in the lesson, these are idealized lengths. This construction utilizes the theorem from geometry that the altitude to the hypotenuse of a right triangle is the mean proportional between the segments of the hypotenuse that it forms. The right triangle is not drawn here, but has hypotenuse $\overline{AC}$ and a right angle at the unnamed endpoint of the vertical segment. (A triangle inscribed in a semicircle is a right triangle.)

22.

◇	A	B
1	x	f(x)
2	−5	−240
3	−4	−104
4	−3	−30
5	−2	0
6	−1	4
7	0	0
8	1	6
9	2	40
10	3	120
11	4	264
12	5	490

13-7

4 Wrap-Up

Ongoing Assessment

Ask students to consider the equation $\frac{a}{b} = c$. If possible, give an example of the following; if not, write *none*.

i.   *a* is rational, *b* is rational, *c* is irrational.

ii. *a* is irrational, *b* is irrational, *c* is rational.

iii. *a* is rational, *b* is irrational, *c* is rational.

iv. *a* is irrational, *b* is rational, *c* is irrational.

i.   none

ii. Answers vary. Sample answer:

$$\frac{\sqrt{8}}{\sqrt{2}} = \sqrt{\frac{8}{2}} = \sqrt{4} = 2$$

iii. none

iv. Answers vary. Sample answer:

$$\frac{\sqrt{2}}{2} = 0.5\sqrt{2}$$

Project Update

Project 7, Rationals vs. Irrationals, on page 830 relates to the content of this lesson.

EXPLORATION

32. Because $2 \cdot 5^2$ is one away from 7^2, 2 is close to $\frac{7^2}{5^2}$. That means that $\sqrt{2}$ is close to $\frac{7}{5}$, or 1.4. Find two other numbers *c* and *d* such that $2 \cdot c^2$ is one away from d^2. (*Hint:* There is a pair of such numbers with both of them greater than 2 less than 20.) What rational number estimate does that pair give for $\sqrt{2}$?

33. Shown here is a different way to draw a segment with length $\sqrt{n}$ from the one given in the lesson.

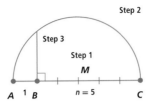

Step 1 Draw a segment $\overline{AB}$ with length 1, and then next to it, a segment BC with length *n*. (In the drawing here, $n = 5$.)

Step 2 Find the midpoint *M* of segment $\overline{AC}$. Draw the circle with center *M* that contains *A* and *C*. ($\overline{AC}$ will be a diameter of this circle.)

Step 3 Draw a segment perpendicular to $\overline{AC}$ from *B* to the circle. This segment has length $\sqrt{n}$. (In our drawing it should have length $\sqrt{5}$.)

  a. Try this algorithm to draw a segment with length $\sqrt{7}$.
  b. Measure the segment you find. **2.647**
  c. How close is its length to $\sqrt{7}$? $2.647 - \sqrt{7} = 0.001249$

32. Answers vary. Sample answer: $c = 12$, $d = 17$; $\frac{17}{12} = 1.41\overline{6}$

Step 3a: See students' work.

Extension

On one side of an index card write a number. On the back of the card write descriptors of the number found on the front of the card. For example, if the number is $2.\overline{58}$, the descriptors on the card should be rational number and repeating decimal. If the number is $\sqrt{9}$, the descriptors should be natural number, whole number, integer, rational number, and finite. Create one card using different numbers for each student in your class. Pass the cards out to your students. Have each student show his or her number to another student. Each student should try to list all of the terms found on the back of his or her partner's card.

13-7B   page 2

13-7B Lesson Master   Questions on SPUR Objectives
See pages 833–835 for objectives.

SKILLS Objective F
In 1–18, tell whether the number is rational or irrational.

1. $20.\overline{4}$ — rational
2. 3.2 — rational
3. $\sqrt{15}$ — irrational
4. $\sqrt{32}$ — irrational
5. $0.\overline{8}$ — rational
6. $\frac{4}{51}$ — rational
7. $3\sqrt{19}$ — irrational
8. 0 — rational
9. $\sqrt{9}$ — rational
10. $\frac{413}{3{,}214}$ — rational
11. $3\frac{4}{32}$ — rational
12. $\frac{\sqrt{3}}{3}$ — irrational
13. 9.123 — rational
14. $\frac{\pi}{3}$ — irrational
15. $3\sqrt{3}$ — irrational
16. $123.\overline{2}$ — rational
17. $-4\sqrt{600}$ — irrational
18. -3 — rational

In 19–21, write the number as a simple fraction.
19. $3\frac{35}{66}$ $\frac{39}{11}$
20. $0.9\overline{3}$ $\frac{14}{15}$
21. $4.\overline{789}$ $\frac{1{,}595}{333}$

Algebra   537

Lesson 13-8 — Proofs of the Pythagorean Theorem

▶ **BIG IDEA** There are many ways to deduce the Pythagorean Theorem using algebra.

In this book you have seen how areas of rectangles can picture various forms of the Distributive Property. The idea is to calculate the area of a figure in two different ways. Here is a picture of $(a + b)(c + d + e) = ac + ad + ae + bc + bd + be$.

	c	d	e
a	ac	ad	ae
b	bc	bd	be

You could also say that this reasoning uses area to prove that $(a + b)(c + d + e) = ac + ad + ae + bc + bd + be$.

We close this book by showing how areas of figures provide proofs of the most famous theorem in geometry, the Pythagorean Theorem. If a and b are the lengths of the legs of a right triangle, and c is the length of its hypotenuse, then $a^2 + b^2 = c^2$.

For these proofs, you need to think of a^2, b^2, and c^2 as the areas of squares whose sides are a, b, and c. This is the form in which the theorem was discovered over 2,500 years ago in many different parts of the world.

These proofs assume that you are familiar with the definitions and area formulas for some common figures. They are:

square: $A = s^2$ rectangle: $A = \ell w$

right triangle: $A = \frac{1}{2}ab$ triangle: $A = \frac{1}{2}bh$

trapezoid: $A = \frac{1}{2}h(b_1 + b_2)$

The proofs also use the properties of real numbers that you have seen in this course.

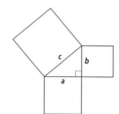

Mental Math

Tell whether the three numbers can be lengths of sides in a triangle.

a. 5, 13, 5   no

b. 2, 14, 15   yes

c. 1, 2, 3   no

Background

We think it is quite appropriate to end this book by discussing proofs of the Pythagorean Theorem. Most, if not all, students next year will take a geometry course in which proof plays a significant role.

There are hundreds of proofs of the Pythagorean Theorem. In most high school geometry courses, students see a proof using similarity. In this lesson, we show proofs involving area.

The basic idea in an area proof is to combine smaller figures to form a larger one, individually calculate the areas of the smaller figures and equate it to the area of the larger figure; then do some algebraic manipulation that winds up with the equation known as the Pythagorean Theorem.

Lesson

13-8

GOAL

Present several algebraic proofs of the Pythagorean Theorem, applying the area model for multiplication.

SPUR Objective

H Display or prove properties involving multiplication using areas of polygons or squares.

Materials/Resources

· Lesson Master 13-8A or 13-8B
· Resource Master 209
· Scientific or graphing calculator

HOMEWORK

Suggestions for Assignment

• Questions 1–17
• Question 18 (extra credit)

Local Standards

1   **Warm-Up**

1. If two sides of a right triangle have lengths 3 and 5, what are the two possible lengths for the third side? If the two sides are the legs of the right triangle, the third side has length $\sqrt{34}$. If the two sides are the hypotenuse and a leg, then the third side has length 4.

2. Consider the diagram of squares drawn on the three sides of a right triangle as on the student page. If the squares on sides a and b have areas of 171 and 93, what is the area of the square on side c? 264

3. A trapezoid has vertices at (0, 0), (10, 0), (7, 8), and (0, 8). What is its area? 68 square units

Bhaskara's Proof

Bhaskara's proof is a generalization of the idea that you saw in Lesson 8-6. Begin with right triangle DHK with side lengths a, b, and c. Make three copies of the triangle and place them so that quadrilateral $DEFG$ is a square, as shown at the right. In $\triangle DHK$, $\angle DHK$ and $\angle DKH$ are complementary. Since corresponding parts of congruent triangles are congruent, m$\angle GKJ = $ m$\angle DHK$. So m$\angle DKH + $ m$\angle GKJ = 90°$. Thus, m$\angle JKH = 180° - 90° = 90°$. Likewise the other three angles of $HIJK$ are right angles. So, the inside quadrilateral $HIJK$ formed by the four hypotenuses has four right angles and four sides of length c, so it is also a square.

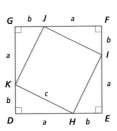

Let A be the area of quadrilateral $DEFG$. Each side of quadrilateral $DEFG$ has length $a + b$. So $A = (a + b)^2$. But the area of $DEFG$ can also be found by adding up the areas of the four right triangles $\left(4 \cdot \frac{1}{2}ab\right)$ and the square in the middle (c^2). So $A = 4 \cdot \frac{1}{2}ab + c^2$. The two values of A must be equal.

$$(a + b)^2 = 4 \cdot \frac{1}{2}ab + c^2$$

Now use the formula for the square of a binomial on the left side and simplify the right side.

$$a^2 + 2ab + b^2 = 2ab + c^2$$

Add $-2ab$ to each side of the equation.

$$a^2 + b^2 = c^2$$

This is the Pythagorean Theorem.

President Garfield's Proof

This proof of the Pythagorean Theorem was discovered by James Garfield in 1876 while he was a member of the U.S. House of Representatives. Five years later he became the 20th President of the United States.

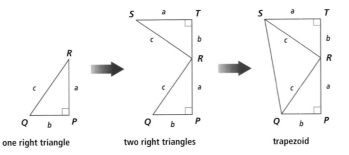

one right triangle   two right triangles   trapezoid

Major General James Garfield won the 1880 Presidential election by only 10,000 popular votes, defeating Gen. Winfield Scott Hancock.

Source: The White House

Accommodating the Learner ⬆

Have students sketch a right triangle with legs a and b, and the hypotenuse c. Have them write down an expression for the area of this triangle. Then tell them to make three copies of the triangle by rotating it 90°, 180°, and 270°, respectively. Place the figure at the right on an overhead and have the students put their 4 triangles together as in the figure. Have the students find an expression for the area of the inner square formed. The area of the larger square is the sum of the areas of the four triangles and the inner square.

Have the students represent this algebraically so that the result is the Pythagorean Theorem.

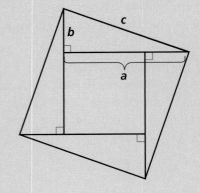

---

2 Teaching

Notes on the Lesson

An important idea to emphasize is that we cannot use the Pythagorean Theorem to prove itself. The proof has to depend on properties that we have already proved. Students should realize that all those formulas can be traced back logically to the area formula for a rectangle, $A = \ell w$, which is assumed to be true.

Bhaskara's proof is special for its simplicity. Only the area formulas for a right triangle and square are needed. President Garfield's proof uses half the figure of Bhaskara's proof and, as a result, needs to involve the area of a trapezoid. Questions 3, 4, and 7 will help you discuss these proofs.

President Garfield's proof uses half the figure of the preceding proof. Begin with right triangle PQR as shown on the previous page. With one copy of $\triangle PQR$, create a trapezoid $PQST$ with bases a and b and height $a + b$. The area of any trapezoid is $\frac{1}{2}h(b_1 + b_2)$. Here the height $h = a + b$.

$$\text{Area of } PQST = \tfrac{1}{2}(a + b)(a + b)$$

But the area of $PQST$ is also the sum of the areas of three right triangles: PQR, RST, and QRS. Look at $\triangle QRS$. Because the sum of the measures of the angles of a triangle is $180°$, $m\angle QRP + m\angle RQP = 90°$. Consequently, $m\angle QRP + m\angle SRT = 90°$. This means that $\angle QRS$ is a right angle and so $\triangle QRS$ is a right triangle. Now add the areas of the three right triangles.

$$\text{Area of } PQST = \tfrac{1}{2}ab + \tfrac{1}{2}ab + \tfrac{1}{2}c^2$$

The area of the entire trapezoid must be the same regardless of how it is calculated.

$$\tfrac{1}{2}(a + b)(a + b) = \tfrac{1}{2}ab + \tfrac{1}{2}ab + \tfrac{1}{2}c^2.$$

Now multiply both sides of the equation by 2.

$$(a + b)(a + b) = ab + ab + c^2$$

Multiply the binomials on the left side and collect terms on the right side.

$$a^2 + 2ab + b^2 = 2ab + c^2$$

Subtract $2ab$ from each side of the equation and the result is the Pythagorean Theorem.

$$a^2 + b^2 = c^2$$

Other Proofs

It takes only one valid proof of a theorem to make it true. Yet in mathematics you will often see more than one proof of a statement, just as you often see more than one way to solve a problem. Alternate methods can help you to understand better how the various parts of mathematics are related. In this lesson, you have seen how areas of triangles, trapezoids, and squares are put together with binomials to prove a statement about the lengths of the three sides of any right triangle. In your next course, likely to be more concerned with geometry than this one, you will see how this theorem is related to similar triangles. Later you will learn how important this theorem is in the study of trigonometry. The algebra you have learned this year is fundamental in these and every other area of mathematics.

Proofs of the Pythagorean Theorem **825**

Have students sketch a right triangle. Then ask them to draw three equilateral triangles using the legs and hypotenuse as bases.

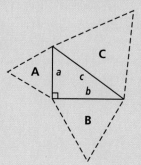

Tell them that the height of each triangle is equal to $\sqrt{3}$ times half its base and remind them that the area of a triangle is $\frac{1}{2}b \cdot h$. Ask them to demonstrate that the area of triangle A plus the area of triangle B equals the area of triangle C.

$$\text{Area } \triangle A = \frac{a}{2} \cdot \frac{a\sqrt{3}}{2} = \frac{a^2\sqrt{3}}{4}$$

$$\text{Area } \triangle B = \frac{b}{2} \cdot \frac{b\sqrt{3}}{2} = \frac{b^2\sqrt{3}}{4}$$

$$\text{Area } \triangle C = \frac{c}{2} \cdot \frac{c\sqrt{3}}{2} = \frac{c^2\sqrt{3}}{4} = \frac{(a^2 + b^2)\sqrt{3}}{4}$$

$$\text{Area } \triangle A + \text{Area } \triangle B = \frac{(a^2 + b^2)\sqrt{3}}{4} = \text{Area } \triangle C$$

13-8

3) Assignment

Recommended Assignment

- Questions 1–17
- Question 18 (extra credit)

Notes on the Questions

We suggest going through all the Questions in order.

Questions 3 and 4 These questions can be used to explain Bhaskara's proof.

Question 7 This question can be used to explain President Garfield's proof.

Questions

COVERING THE IDEAS

1. Picture the property that for all positive numbers a, b, and c, $a(b + c) = ab + ac$.

2. Picture the property that for all positive numbers a and b, $a(a + b) = a^2 + ab$.

In 3 and 4, refer to Bhaskara's proof of the Pythagorean Theorem.

3. **a.** Draw the figure of Bhaskara's proof when $a = 6$ and $b = 2$.
   b. What is the area of $DEFG$? **64 units²**
   c. Explain how to get the area of $HIJK$.
   d. What is the value of c? **$2\sqrt{10}$**

4. $DH = a$ and $DK = b$ in the figure of Bhaskara's proof.
   a. What is the length of EF? **$a + b$**
   b. What is the area of $EFGD$? **$(a + b)^2 = a^2 + 2ab + b^2$**
   c. What is the area of triangle IJF? **$\frac{1}{2}ab$**
   d. What is the area of $HIJK$? **c^2**
   e. What is the length of HK in terms of a and b? **$\sqrt{a^2 + b^2}$**

5. **a.** Draw a trapezoid whose bases have lengths 1 in. and 2 in., and whose height is 1 in. **See margin.**
   b. What is the area of this trapezoid? **1.5 in²**

6. Draw a trapezoid with bases b_1 and b_2 and height h. Explain why the area of this trapezoid is $\frac{1}{2}hb_1 + \frac{1}{2}hb_2$. **See margin.**

7. Refer to President Garfield's proof of the Pythagorean Theorem. Let $a = 28$ and $b = 45$.
   a. Find the area of trapezoid $PQST$. **2,664.5 units²**
   b. Explain how to get the area of $\triangle RQS$. **See margin.**
   c. What is the value of c? **53**
   d. Does the value of c agree with what you would get using the Pythagorean Theorem? **yes**

APPLYING THE MATHEMATICS

8. **a.** Find two expressions for the shaded region in the figure below. **$xy - xz$; $x(y - z)$**
   b. What property is illustrated by the answer to Part a?

Distributive Property of Multiplication over Subtraction

826 Using Algebra to Prove

---

1. Answers vary. Sample answer:

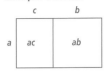

2. Answers vary. Sample answer:

3a.

3c. Answers vary. Sample answer: Subtract four times the area of a triangle with base 6 and height 2 from the total area of 64.

Additional Answers

5a. Answers vary. Sample answer:

6.

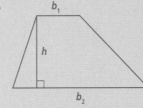

Answers vary. Sample answer: Let b_1 be the shorter base. Then the area of the trapezoid

is $b_1 \cdot h$ plus the area of the two (or possibly one) triangles remaining after removing the rectangle of area $b_1 \cdot h$. These triangles have height h and bases that sum to $b_2 - b_1$. Therefore, the area of the trapezoid is $b_1 \cdot h + \frac{1}{2}h(b_2 - b_1) = \frac{1}{2}hb_1 + \frac{1}{2}hb_2$.

7b. Subtract twice the area of a rectangle with base a and height b from the total area, i.e., the trapezoid with bases a and b and height $a + b$.

---

9. The square below has been split into two smaller squares and two rectangles. What property is pictured? **The Extended Distributive Property**

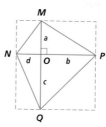

10. Quadrilateral $MNQP$ at the right has perpendicular diagonals. Add the areas of the four triangles to show that the area of $MNQP$ is one-half the product of the lengths of its diagonals. **See margin.**

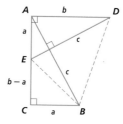

11. A proof of the Pythagorean Theorem published by W.J. Dobbs in 1916 uses the figure at the right. $\triangle ACB$ and $\triangle DAE$ are right triangles, and $AC = b$, $BC = a$, and $AB = c$. Complete each step to show the proof.

   a. What is the length of $\overline{EB}$ in terms of a and b?

   b. Find the area of $\triangle EBC$. $\frac{1}{2}(ab - a^2)$

   c. Find the area of $AEBD$, a quadrilateral with perpendicular diagonals, using the formula from Question 10. $\frac{1}{2}c^2$

   d. Add the areas in Parts b and c to find an expression for the area of $ACBD$. $\frac{1}{2}(ab - a^2 + c^2)$

   e. Use the formula for the area of a trapezoid to express the area of $ACBD$.

   f. Set the formulas from Parts d and e equal to each other to show that $c^2 = a^2 + b^2$. **See margin.**

11a. $\sqrt{2a^2 + b^2 - 2ab}$

11e. $\frac{1}{2}(ba + b^2)$

REVIEW

12. Prove that if the last three digits of a 4-digit number form a number divisible by 8, then the entire number is divisible by 8. **(Lesson 13-6) See margin.**

13. **Multiple Choice** Consider the following statement. If the cost of 5 pounds of ice is $2.15, then at the same rate, the cost of 32 ounces of ice is 86 cents. **(Lessons 13-2, 13-1, 5-9) A**

   A The statement and its converse are both true.

   B The statement and its converse are both false.

   C The statement is true but its converse is false.

   D The statement is false but its converse is true.

14. a. Find a value of c to complete the square for $4x^2 - 12x + c$. $c = 9$

   b. Use your answer to Part a to solve the equation $4x^2 - 2x = -9 + 10x$. **(Lessons 12-3, 12-2)** $x = 1.5$

Proofs of the Pythagorean Theorem **827**

Additional Answers

10. Answers vary. Sample answer: $A = \frac{1}{2}ab + \frac{1}{2}bc + \frac{1}{2}cd + \frac{1}{2}ad = \frac{1}{2}a(b + d) + \frac{1}{2}c(b + d) = \frac{1}{2}(a + c)(b + d)$

11f. $\frac{1}{2}(ab - a^2 + c^2) = \frac{1}{2}(ba + b^2)$; $ab - a^2 + c^2 = ba + b^2$; $c^2 = a^2 + b^2$

12. We can write $N = 1{,}000T + 100h + 10t + u = 1{,}000T + 8k$. Since $1{,}000 = 8 \cdot 125$, $N = 8(125T + k)$, so N is divisible by 8.

Notes on the Questions

Question 10 Because kites and rhombuses (rhombi) have perpendicular diagonals, their areas can be found using this formula.

Question 11 Dobbs's proof relies on the result of Question 10. Because it was proved rather recently, within the last 100 years, this suggests that there are still other proofs of the Pythagorean Theorem to be discovered. However, these do not make the Pythagorean Theorem *more true* than it already is. A theorem needs only one proof.

Additional Answers

18. (continued)

   The diagram shows a proof of the Pythagorean Theorem via dissection. Here is an explanation of why it works. Triangles 1 and 5 were cut such that they are congruent to the original triangle and thus have side lengths a, b, and c. Then square 3 was constructed in the bottom left corner, and thus has a side length of $b - a$. Then, 2 and 4 were constructed by connecting the corner of square 3 and the corner of the larger square, giving them one side length of $a - b$, another of length c, and the third side (along the diagonal) length of $a\sqrt{2}$. This is because the diagonal of the large square has a length of $b\sqrt{2}$, the diagonal of square 3 is $(b - a)\sqrt{2}$, so by subtracting these lengths we get $a\sqrt{2}$. The square with length a is simply cut in half to form 7 and 6. From pieces 4 and 7 and pieces 6 and 2 we are able to create two more copies of the original triangle. This is because the hypotenuse of 7 (or 6) is the same length as the side along the diagonal of 4 (or 2), and the large angle in 4 (or 2) is $135°$ which is supplementary with the $45°$ angle of 7 (or 6). Now by arranging these four copies of the original triangle as shown in the diagram it remains to be shown that the area of the remaining square is congruent to 3. This is true by the simple observation that its side length has to $b - a$. Thus the areas are equivalent and $a^2 + b^2$.

13-8

4 Wrap-Up

Ongoing Assessment

For each problem students should draw a figure that represents the following properties.

i. $(a + b)^2 = a^2 + 2ab + b^2$

ii. $a(a + b + c) = a^2 + ab + ac$

iii. $(a + b + c)(a + b + c) =$
$a^2 + b^2 + c^2 + 2ab + 2ac + 2bc$

Project Update

Project 4, Conjectures on page 830 relates to the content of this lesson.

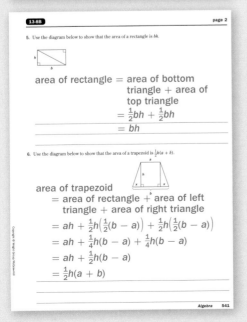

15. Leonardo and Miranda are at an amusement park and are trying to decide in which order they want to ride the 9 roller coasters in the park. **(Lesson 11-7)**
  a. How many different orders can they ride all 9 roller coasters if they ride each coaster one time? **362,880 orders**
  b. If they only have time to ride six of the roller coasters, how many ways can they do this? **60,480 ways**

16. Consider the following number puzzle. **(Lessons 8-6, 2-3)**
  Step 1 Choose any whole number. **5**
  Step 2 Square that number. **25**
  Step 3 Add 4 times your original number. **45**
  Step 4 Add 4 to the result of Step 3. **49**
  Step 5 Take the square root of the result of Step 4. **7**
  Step 6 Subtract your original number. **2**

  a. Follow the number puzzle with any whole number. What is your result? **2**
  b. Let x represent the number chosen. Write a simplified expression to represent each step of the puzzle and to show why your result will always be what you found in Part a. **See margin.**

17. A piece of landscaping machinery is valued at $15,000. If the machinery depreciates at a constant rate of 8% per year, what will be its value in 6 years? **(Lesson 7-3)** about $9,095.32

Out of the 710 roller coasters in North America, 628 are in the United States.

Source: Roller Coaster Database

EXPLORATION

18. A different kind of proof of the Pythagorean Theorem is called a *dissection proof*. Dissection means cutting the squares on the legs of the right triangle shown on page 823 into pieces and then rearranging these pieces together to fill up the square on the hypotenuse. Find such a proof in a book or on the Internet and explain why it works. **See margin.**

Additional Answers

16b. Step 1: x; Step 2: x^2; Step 3: $x^2 + 4x$;
  Step 4: $x^2 + 4x + 4 = (x + 2)^2$;
  Step 5: $x + 2$; Step 6: 2

18. Answers vary. Sample answer:

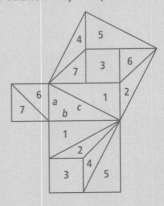

Chapter 13 Projects

1 Squares Surrounding Triangles

Step 1 On a piece of grid paper, draw ten squares of different sizes. (*Note:* They don't *all* have to be different from one another.) Then, carefully cut them out.

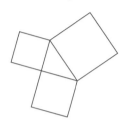

Step 2

a. Lay three of the squares on the table to form a triangle, as shown above. Refer to the longest side as c and the shorter sides as a and b.

b. Add the areas of the two smaller squares, and write down the sum. Is the sum $(a^2 + b^2)$ equal to the area of the largest square (c^2)? If not, is the sum greater or less?

c. Use a protractor to measure the angle across from the longest side of the triangle. Does it have the largest measure? Is it a right angle? If not, is it acute or obtuse?

Step 3 Repeat this procedure for at least ten different triangles. Record your information in a table, and look for any patterns in the data.

Step 4 Write a brief report about what you have learned about triangles, their largest angles, and the lengths of their sides.

2 Can Everything Be Proved?

At the beginning of the 20th century, a widespread belief among mathematicians was that any mathematical statement could either be proved, if it were true, or disproved, if it were false. But nobody knew for certain if this were true or not. In 1931, the mathematician Kurt Gödel settled the issue with his Incompleteness Theorems. Research to find out what Gödel discovered and how it impacted the world of mathematics.

3 Divisibility Tests

In this chapter, you saw several divisibility rules. These were just the tip of the iceberg. There are a great many known divisibility rules.

a. Find properties to check if a number is divisible by 4, by 8, by 25, and by 125. Explain how these rules work.

b. Look up a rule that can check if a number is divisible by 7, and one that can be used to check if a number is divisible by 11. Show why these methods work.

Project Rubric

Advanced	Student correctly provides all of the details asked for in the project as well as additional correct independent conclusions.
Proficient	Student correctly provides all of the details asked for in the project.
Partially proficient	Student correctly provides some of the details asked for in the project or provides all details with some inaccuracies.
Not proficient	Student correctly provides few of the details asked for in the project or provides all details with many inaccuracies.
No attempt	Student makes little or no attempt to complete the project.

The projects relate to the content of the lessons of this chapter as follows:

Project	Lesson
1	13-1
2	13-4
3	13-5
4	13-8
5	13-2
6	13-5
7	13-7

1 Squares Surrounding Triangles

This is an excellent project for students who learn best by doing. The students who choose this project must draw and cut out the squares necessary to form the triangles. They must measure the angle opposite the longer side. Once all of the data are gathered and organized, the students must analyze the data and make conjectures. This is a good project for "learning by discovery."

2 Can Everything Be Proved?

The student who chooses Project 2 will most likely be introduced to an area of mathematics not within the realm of their experiences. Gödel's Incompleteness Theorem is one of the most important theorems proven in the twentieth century. You can pique your students' interest in this project by asking them if computers will ever be as smart as or smarter than a human being. Gödel's Incompleteness Theorem is used in arguments which attempt to answer this question.

3 Divisibility Tests

After completing Lesson 13-5, students have seen a number of divisibility rules and their proofs. Most of the rules are easy to understand, use, and prove. The divisibility rules for 7 and 11 are a bit more complicated to use and prove. This is an excellent project to challenge students' algebraic skills and extend their algebraic knowledge.

4 Conjectures

Fermat's Last Theorem is one of the most famous theorems in the history of mathematics. It states the following: If an integer n is greater than 2, then $a^n + b^n = c^n$ has no integer solutions for a, b, and c other than zero. It took 357 years before a mathematician was able to prove it. During our lifetime, the theorem has been mentioned in a number of modern venues such as in two episodes of *Star Trek*, in an episode of *The Simpsons*, and in a scene from the movie *Bedazzled*.

5 If-Then Statements in Games

One almost can't open a newspaper today without finding the daily Sudoku puzzle. It offers unique challenges using numbers to fill a grid while following predefined rules. Many of your students have already tried a Sudoku puzzle and if they haven't, they should. To motivate students to attempt this project, why not bring a Sudoku puzzle into class and let the students work on it.

6 The Euclidean Algorithm

The Euclidian Algorithm is one of the oldest known to mankind. It appeared in Euclid's *Elements* around 300 BCE. History indicates that Euclid may not have been the first to discover the algorithm. Students should make sure they explore the possibility that while the algorithm has Euclid's name, it may have been known to others. Who were these other mathematicians, how long before Euclid did they know the algorithm, and how did they use it?

7 Rationals vs. Irrationals

This might be a good whole-class project. Consider forming three panels of students. One panel would research and weigh in on the side of the rational numbers, and the second panel would research and weigh in on the side of the irrational numbers. The third panel would do research on both and prepare questions to ask the other two competing panels.

4 Conjectures

A mathematical statement may be easy to write down and understand yet still be very difficult to prove. A statement that a mathematician believes to be true but is not yet proved is called a *conjecture* or a *hypothesis*. Sometimes conjectures remain unproved for many years. One of the most famous problems in mathematics is Fermat's Last Theorem. Research to learn about Fermat and his famous theorem, and about Andrew Wiles, the man who finally proved it. Finally, find at least two conjectures in mathematics that are still unproved today.

5 If-Then Statements in Games

When solving problems in life, you use many if-then statements.

a. Start with a single Sudoku puzzle. Write the first 5 if-then statements you can use to solve it. Estimate how many if-then statements it would take for you to solve the whole puzzle.

b. In 1997, the IBM supercomputer Deep Blue won 1 out of 3 matches against world Chess champion Garry Kasparov (above at the right). Find out how many different possible chess moves Deep Blue could consider each second. Given this number, how do you think that Kasparov was able to win 2 out of the 3 matches?

6 The Euclidean Algorithm

Given two positive integers m and n, the greatest common divisor of m and n is the greatest integer that divides both of them. For example, the greatest common divisor of 8 and 12 is 4; the greatest common divisor of 12 and 15 is 3. The ancient Greek mathematicians knew an algorithm, today called the Euclidean algorithm, to find the greatest common divisor of two numbers. Look up the Euclidean algorithm and write a description of how it works.

7 Rationals vs. Irrationals

When they were first discovered, irrational numbers were an oddity. As you saw in this chapter, there are many irrational numbers. One natural question to ask is which kind of number is more common: rational or irrational? Together with a friend, prepare a debate about this question. One side should present the position that rational numbers are more common and the other side should present that irrational numbers are more common. You may use any material you can find on the subject. Be sure to include a discussion about what you mean by "more common." Present your debate before the class.

Notes

Chapter 13 — Summary and Vocabulary

○ Generalizations in mathematics include **assumptions** (assumed properties), **definitions** (meanings of terms or phrases), and **theorems** (statements deduced from assumptions, definitions, or other theorems). These generalizations are often presented as **if-then statements.** For example, one assumed property of real numbers is the Distributive Property of Multiplication over Addition. It can be written in if-then form as: If a, b, and c are real numbers, then $a(b + c) = ab + ac$.

○ The **converse** of the statement, "If a, then b" is the statement, "If b, then a." The converse of a true statement is not necessarily true. When the converse is true, then the statement "a if and only if b" is true. Definitions are **if-and-only-if statements.** For example, x is an even number if and only if x can be written as $2n$, where n is an integer.

○ By putting together if-then statements of assumptions and definitions, a **mathematical proof** can be created. From the definition of even number, you can prove that if the square of an integer is even, then the integer is even. You can also prove that $\sqrt{2}$ and square roots of other nonzero integers that are not perfect squares are **irrational numbers.** Using the definition of divisibility by any number and what it means for a number to be in base 10, you can prove divisibility tests and other interesting properties of numbers.

○ Every equation or inequality that you solve showing steps and justifications can be thought of as a **proof.** Suppose you solve $8x + 50 = 2$ and obtain $x = -6$. If you can justify the steps that you used in your solution, you have proved: "If $8x + 50 = 2$, then $x = -6$." The check is the converse: "If $x = -6$, then $8x + 50 = 2$."

○ Mathematical knowledge grows by deducing statements from those that are assumed to be true or have been proved earlier to be true. Among the oldest and most important theorems in all of mathematics are the **Quadratic Formula** and the **Pythagorean Theorem.** Proofs of the Quadratic Formula use the properties that are most associated with solving equations. The proofs of the Pythagorean Theorem that we show in this chapter use area formulas for triangles, squares, and trapezoids.

Vocabulary

13-1
if-then statement
antecedent
consequent
generalization

13-2
converse
equivalent statements
if and only if

13-3
justifications
proof argument
deduction

13-5
closed under an operation
even integer, even number
odd integer, odd number
semiperimeter

13-7
irrational number

Theorems and Properties

Irrationality of $\sqrt{n}$ Theorem (p. 819)

Chapter 13

Summary and Vocabulary

The Summary gives an overview of the entire chapter and provides an opportunity for students to consider the material as a whole. Thus, the Summary can be used to help students relate and unify the concepts presented in the chapter.

Terms and symbols are listed by lesson to provide a checklist of concepts that students must know. Emphasize to students that they should read the vocabulary list carefully before starting the Self-Test on the next page. If students do not understand the meaning of a term, they should refer back to the indicated lesson.

Theorems and Properties covered in the chapter are listed below the Summary, with page references included to lead students back to the location in the chapter where the theorem or property is stated.

Additional Answers

(Self-Test)

2. The antecedent is $8(2y - 1) = y + 37$ and the consequent is $y = 3$.

3a. If $xy = 0$, then both x and y equal 0; If both x and $y = 0$, then $xy = 0$.

3b. No, Amalia is not correct. Answers may vary. Sample: The statement "If $xy = 0$, then both x and y equal 0" is not true because, for example, when $x = 1$ and $y = 0$, $xy = 0$ but x does not equal 0.

4a. $\sqrt{7^2 + 8^2} = \sqrt{49 + 64} = \sqrt{113}$ in.

4b. $\sqrt{113}$ is an irrational number, so its decimal is infinite and does not repeat. Marcus's ruler is not accurate for the smallest length that it measures.

Additional Answers

Self-Test, p. 832

1.

Conclusions	Justifications
$8(2y - 1) = y + 37$	Given
$16y - 8 = y + 37$	Distributive Property
$16y - 8 - y =$ $y + 37 - y$	Addition Property of Equality
$15y - 8 = 0 + 37$	Arithmetic, Additive Inverse Property
$15y - 8 = 37$	Additive Identity Property
$15y - 8 + 8 =$ $37 + 8$	Addition Property of Equality
$15y + 0 = 45$	Arithmetic, Additive Inverse Property
$15y = 45$	Additive Identity Property
$\frac{1}{15} \cdot 15y = \frac{1}{15} \cdot 45$	Multiplication Property of Equality
$1y = 3$	Arithmetic, Multiplicative Inverse Property
$y = 3$	Multiplicative Identity Property

Self-Test

For the development of mathematical competence, feedback and correction, along with the opportunity for practice, are necessary. The Self-Test provides the opportunity for feedback and correction; the Chapter Review provides additional opportunities and practice. We cannot overemphasize the importance of these end-of-chapter materials. It is at this point that the material gels for many students, allowing them to solidify skills and understanding. In general, student performance should improve after they complete these pages.

Assign the Self-Test as a one-night assignment. Worked-out solutions for all questions are in the Selected Answers section of the student book. Encourage students to take the Self-Test honestly, grade themselves, and then be prepared to discuss the test in class.

Advise students to pay special attention to those Chapter Review questions (pages 833–835) that correspond to the questions they missed on the Self-Test.

13 Self-Test

Take this test as you would take a test in class. You will need a calculator. Then use the Selected Answers section in the back of the book to check your work.

1. State conclusions and justifications to prove that if $8(2y - 1) = y + 37$, then $y = 3$. **See margin.**

2. Determine the antecedent and consequent of the statement proved in Question 1. **See margin.**

3. Amalia says that xy equals 0 if and only if both x and y equal 0.

   a. Write the two if-then statements that are equivalent to Amalia's if-and-only-if statement. **3a–b. See margin.**

   b. Is Amalia correct? Explain your answer.

4. Marcus is measuring the diagonal across a piece of paper. The paper is 7 in. by 8 in.

   a. What is the exact length of a diagonal of the paper? **4a–b. See margin.**

   b. Explain why Marcus' ruler will not give him an exact measurement of the diagonal.

5. Consider the following statement: All algebra students can solve quadratic equations. **5a–d. See margin.**

   a. Write the statement in if-then form.

   b. Identify the antecedent and consequent for Part a.

   c. Write the converse of the statement you wrote in Part a.

   d. Decide whether the statement you wrote in Part c is true. Explain your answer.

6. Prove or find a counterexample to the statement: If the tens digit of a 4-digit number is 4 and the units digit is 8, then the number is divisible by 4. **See margin.**

7. What algebraic relationship is pictured by the rectangles, given that $b < a$? **See margin.**

8. The product of two numbers is 717, and their sum is –242. What are the numbers? **See margin.**

9a. Find the value of x in the diagram at the right. **See margin.**

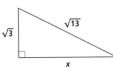

   b. Is x rational or irrational? **x is irrational**

10. **True or False** Determine whether each of the following is true or false. Explain your answers.

   a. If a triangle is formed by cutting a square in half along one of its diagonals, then the triangle is isosceles.

   b. If a triangle is formed by cutting a square in half along one of its diagonals, then the triangle is equilateral.
   10a–b. See Additional Answers on page T89.

11. **True or False** Determine whether the following statement is true or false and explain your answer: A person can be President of the United States if and only if he or she was born in the United States. **See margin.**

12. If a number is divisible by 3 and another number is divisible by 4, then their product is divisible by 12. Illustrate this statement with a picture and explain why your picture shows that the statement is true. **See margin.**

Additional Answers

1–4. See answers on page 831.

5a. If a student is taking algebra, then the student can solve quadratic equations.

5b. The antecedent is a student is taking algebra, the consequent is the student can solve quadratic equations.

5c. If a student can solve quadratic equations, then the student is taking algebra.

5d. The statement is not true. For example, a student who knows how to solve quadratic equations could be a student in geometry.

Additional Answers

6. True. Answers vary. Sample answer: If the tens digit of a four-digit number is 4 and the units digit is 8, then the number can be written as $1,000n + 48$, where n is a whole number. Then $1,000n + 48 = 4(250n + 12)$, and because $250n$ and 12 are integers, $250n + 12$ is an integer, so 4 divides $100n + 48$.

7. The rectangles picture the equation
$(a - b)(a + b) = (a - b)a + (a - b)b = a^2 - b^2$.

8. $ab = 717$ and $a + b = -242$. Then $a = -242 - b$, so substitution gives $(-242 - b)b = 717$, so $b^2 + 242b + 717 = 0$. This is a quadratic equation, so solving for b gives $b = -239$ or $b = -3$. Thus, the numbers are -239 and -3.

9a. $x^2 + (\sqrt{3})^2 = (\sqrt{13})^2$, so $x^2 + 3 = 13$. $x^2 = 10$ so $x = \sqrt{10}$.

Chapter 13 Chapter Review

SKILLS
PROPERTIES
USES
REPRESENTATIONS

SKILLS Procedures used to get answers

OBJECTIVE A Show and justify the steps in solving an equation. (Lesson 13-3)

In 1 and 2, fill in the table for the proof.
1. See margin.
1.

Conclusions	What Was Done	Justifications
$4x + 5 = 17$	?	?
$4x + 5 + -5 = 17 + -5$	?	?
$4x + 0 = 12$	?	?
$4x = 12$	?	?
$\frac{1}{4} \cdot 4x = 12 \cdot \frac{1}{4}$	?	?
$1 \cdot x = 3$	?	?
$x = 3$	?	?

2. 2-4. See Additional Answers on page T89-T90.

Conclusions	What Was Done	Justifications
$2n + 5 = 4n + 3$	?	?
$2n + 2 = 4n$	?	?
$2 = 2n$	?	?
$1 = n$	?	?

3. Prove: If $3t - 15 = 4t + 2$, then $t = -17$.

4. Prove: $\sqrt{16y - 16} = 2y$ if and only if $y = 2$.

OBJECTIVE B Find two numbers given their sum and product. (Lesson 13-4)

5. There are 26 students in a dancing class. If you know there are 165 possible boy-girl couples from this group, how many boys and how many girls are in the class? **15 boys, 11 girls or 11 boys, 15 girls**

7. $\dfrac{5.6 + \sqrt{22.16}}{2}, \dfrac{5.6 - \sqrt{22.16}}{2}$

In 6-9 find the two numbers that satisfy the given conditions.

6. $n + m = 10$, $nm = 24$ **4 and 6**

7. $xy = 2.3$, $x + y = 5.6$

8. $uv = 35$, $u + v = 12$ **5 and 7**

9. $p + q = -46$, $pq = 529$ **−23 and −23**

10. Mrs. Violet doesn't know the dimensions of her rectangular garden, but she knows it has an area of 23.52 square meters. She also remembers that she needs 19.6 meters of fencing for her garden. Find the dimensions of Mrs. Violet's garden. **5.6 m by 4.2 m**

PROPERTIES The principles behind the mathematics

OBJECTIVE C Identify the antecedent and consequent of an if-then statement not necessarily given in if-then form. (Lesson 13-1)

In 11-14 identify the antecedent and the consequent. **11-14. See margin.**

11. If an animal has feathers then it is a bird.

12. It is spring if the trees are blooming.

13. No irrational number can be represented as the ratio of two integers.

14. James doesn't listen to music when he studies.

OBJECTIVE D Determine whether if-then and if-and-only-if statements in algebra or geometry are true or false. (Lessons 13-1, 13-2)

Chapter Review

The main objectives for the chapter are organized in the Chapter Review under the four types of understanding this book promotes—Skills, Properties, Uses, and Representations.

Whereas end-of-chapter material may be considered optional in some texts, in *UCSMP Algebra* we have selected these objectives and questions with the expectation that they will be covered. Students should be able to answer these questions with about 85% accuracy after studying the chapter.

You may assign these questions over a single night to help students prepare for a test the next day, or you may assign the questions over a two-day period. If you work the questions over two days, then we recommend assigning the *evens* for homework the first night so that students get feedback in class the next day, and then assigning the *odds* the night before the test because the answers are provided to the odd-numbered questions in the Selected Answers at the back of the book.

It is effective to ask students which questions they still do not understand and use the day as a total class discussion of the material that the class finds most difficult.

Resources

- Assessment Resources: Chapter 13 Test, Forms A–D; Chapter 13 Test, Cumulative Form; Comprehensive Test, Chapters 1–13

Additional Answers

1.

	Conclusions	What Was Done	Justifications
i.	$4x + 5 = 17$	Given	Given
ii.	$4x + 5 + -5 = 17 + -5$	Added −5 to both sides.	Addition Property of Equality
iii.	$4x + 0 = 12$	$5 + -5 = 0$; $17 + -5 = 12$	Additive Inverse Property; Arithmetic
iv.	$4x = 12$	$4x + 0 = 4x$	Additive Identity Property
v.	$\frac{1}{4} \cdot 4x = 12 \cdot \frac{1}{4}$	Multiplied both sides by $\frac{1}{4}$.	Multiplication Property of Equality
vi.	$1 \cdot x = 3$	$\frac{1}{4} \cdot 4 = 1$; $12 \cdot \frac{1}{4} = 3$	Multiplicative Inverse Property; Arithmetic
vii.	$x = 3$	$1 \cdot x = x$	Multiplicative Identity Property

Additional Answers

11. antecedent: an animal has feathers; consequent: it is a bird

12. antecedent: the trees are blooming; consequent: it is spring

13. antecedent a number is irrational; consequent: it cannot be represented as the ratio of two integers

14. antecedent: when James studies; consequent: he doesn't listen to music

Chapter 13 Review

Additional Answers

19. Suppose that $2a + 3b + c$ is not divisible by 7. Then $2a + 3b + c + (14)(7a) + 7b$ is not divisible by 7. Hence, $100a + 10b + c$ is also not divisible by 7. So the three-digit number abc is not divisible by 7.

20. Let n be even. So $n = 2k$, where k is an integer. Thus, $n^3 = (2k)^3 = 2^3k^3 = 8m$, where $m = k^3$. So if n is even, then n^3 is divisible by 8.

21. Consider a six-digit integer of the form $xyzxyz$. This is equal to $100{,}000x + 10{,}000y + 1{,}000z + 100x + 10y + z$. And equivalently, this is $(7{,}692)(13x) + 4x + (769)(13y) + 3y + (76)(13z) + 12z + (7)(13x) + 9x + 10y + z$. Combining and factoring, we obtain $xyzxyz = (13)(7{,}700x + 770y + 77z)$. So all six-digit integers of the form $xyzxyz$ are divisible by 13.

22. Let a 4-digit number $abcd$ be divisible by 11. So $1{,}000a + 100b + 10c + d = 11k$, where k is an integer. Hence, $(90)(11a) + 10a + (9)(11b) + b + 10c + d = 11k$. Equivalently, we also have $(91)(11a) - a + (9)(11b) + b + (1)(11c) - c + d = 11k$. Factoring, we obtain $11(91a + 9b + c) + b + d - (a + c) = 11k$. Hence, $b + d - (a + c)$ must also be divisible by 11.

28. No. If one rational number is $\frac{a}{b}$ and another $\frac{c}{d}$, then $\frac{a}{b} \cdot \frac{c}{d} = \frac{ac}{bd}$ must be a rational number.

29a. yes

29b. yes

29c. n/a

30a. no

30b. yes

30c. Answers vary. Sample answer: You live in Paris, France, if and only if you live within approximately 10 km of the Eiffel Tower.

31a. yes

31b. no

31c. You are in high school if and only if you are in grades 9–12.

32a. yes

32b. no

32c. Answers vary. Sample answer: An animal is a quadruped if and only if it is four-legged.

In 15–18, is the statement true or false?

15. A number is divisible by 3 if it is divisible by 9. **true**

16. If $x = 7$ or $x = 3$, then $x^2 + 10x + 21 = 0$. **false**

17. A triangle is equilateral if and only if two of its sides are equal and it has one 60° angle. **true**

18. If only two outcomes are possible and they are equally likely, then the probability of each is 50%. **true**

OBJECTIVE E Prove divisibility properties of integers. (Lessons 13-5, 13-6)

19. Prove that a 3-digit number abc is divisible by 7 only if the number $2a + 3b + c$ is divisible by 7. **19–22. See margin.**

20. Show that if n is even then n^3 is divisible by 8.

21. Show that all 6-digit integers of the form $xyzxyz$ are divisible by 13.

22. Show that if the 4-digit number $abcd$ written in base 10 is divisible by 11, then $b + d - (a + c)$ is divisible by 11.

OBJECTIVE F Apply the definitions and properties of rational and irrational numbers. (Lesson 13-7)

In 23–26, tell whether the number is rational or irrational.

23. $\sqrt{6}$ **irrational**

24. $0.\overline{142857}$ **rational**

25. $\sqrt{169}$ **rational**

26. $2\pi - 3$ **irrational**

27. Is it possible for two irrational numbers to have a product that is rational? Explain why or why not. **Yes, for example $\sqrt{2} \cdot \sqrt{2} = 2$.**

28. Is it possible for two rational numbers to have a product that is irrational? Explain why or why not. **See margin.**

USES Applications of mathematics in real-world situations

OBJECTIVE G Determine whether if-then and if-and-only-if statements in real-world contexts are true or false. (Lessons 13-1, 13-2)

In 29–32, a statement is given.

a. Is the statement true?   **29–32. See margin.**

b. Is the converse true?

c. If either the statement or the converse is not true, change the statement so that both are true. Rewrite the new statement in if-and-only-if form.

29. A year with 366 days is a leap year.

30. If you live in France, you live within 10 kilometers of the Eiffel Tower.

31. If you are an eleventh grader, you are in high school.

32. All horses are four-legged animals.

REPRESENTATIONS Pictures, graphs, or objects that illustrate concepts

OBJECTIVE H Display or prove properties involving multiplication using areas of polygons or squares. (Lesson 13-8)

33. Picture the property that for all positive numbers a and b, $(a + b)^2 = a^2 + b^2 + 2ab$. **See margin.**

34. Square $ABCD$ is pictured below. Show that the area of $ABCD$ is equal to the sum of the areas of the four small triangles. **See margin.**

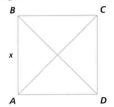

Additional Answers

33.

	a	b
a	a^2	ab
b	ab	b^2

34. Each of the triangles has an area of $\frac{1}{2}(x)\left(\frac{x}{2}\right) = \frac{1}{4}x^2$. Since there are 4 identical triangles, the aggregate area of the triangles must be $(4)\frac{1}{4}x^2 = x^2$. Note also that the side length of the square is x. And hence the area of the square is x^2. So the sum of the areas of the four triangles is equal to the area of $ABCD$.

35. Draw a rectangle with dimensions a and b, and draw a diagonal from one corner to the other, making two triangles. Prove that the diagonal cuts the area of the rectangle in half. **See margin.**

36. Use the isosceles trapezoid below to show that $\frac{1}{2}(2b + 2x)h = xh + bh$. **See margin.**

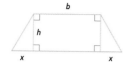

OBJECTIVE I Determine whether lengths of geometric figures are rational or irrational. (Lesson 13-7)

37. Consider the circle below. Its circumference is 32 inches.

37a. $\frac{16}{\pi}$ in.

a. What is the exact radius of the circle?

b. Is this number rational or irrational?
   irrational

In 38–40,

a. determine the missing length, and

b. determine whether your answer to Part a is rational or irrational.

38.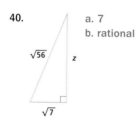
   a. $10\sqrt{5}$
   b. irrational

39.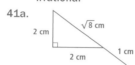
   a. 0.15
   b. rational

40.
   a. 7
   b. rational

41. a. Draw a segment whose length is $1 + \sqrt{8}$ centimeters.
   b. Is that length rational or irrational?
      irrational

41a.

Assessment

Evaluation The *Assessment Resources* provide four forms of the Chapter 13 Test. Forms A and B present parallel versions of a short-answer format. Form C consists of four to six short-response questions that cover the SPUR objectives from Chapter 13. Form D offers performance assessment that covers a subset (or even just one) of the SPUR objectives for the chapter.

Feedback After students have taken the test for Chapter 13 and you have scored the results, return the tests to students for discussion. Class discussion on the questions that caused trouble for most students can be very effective in identifying and clarifying misunderstandings. You might want to have them note the items they missed and work either in groups or at home to correct them. It is important for students to receive feedback on every chapter test, and we recommend that students see and correct their mistakes.

Technology Resources

Teacher's Assessment Assistant, Ch 13
Electronic Teacher's Edition, Ch. 13

Additional Answers

35. The area of each triangle is $\frac{1}{2}ab$. Because the area of the entire rectangle is ab, and $\frac{1}{2}ab + \frac{1}{2}ab = ab$, each of the triangles must occupy exactly half the area of the rectangle. So the diagonal cuts the area of the rectangle in half.

36. Consider two trapezoids overlaid side-by-side with one rotated 180 degrees. The total area of the parallelogram formed is $(2b + 2x)h$. Hence, the area of one trapezoid is $\frac{1}{2}(2b + 2x)h$. Also, note that the trapezoid is comprised of one rectangle whose area is bh and two triangles, each with an area of $\frac{1}{2}xh$. So the total area of the trapezoid must also be $\frac{1}{2}xh + \frac{1}{2}xh + bh = xh + bh$. Hence, $\frac{1}{2}(2b + 2x)h = xh + bh$ as desired.

Selected Answers

Chapter 7

Lesson 7-1 (pp. 398-403)
Guided Example 3: 2,000; 0.054; 18; 2000; 1.054; 18; 5154.196734; $5,154.19; $5,154.19

Questions: 1. "4 to the 10th power" or "4 to the 10th"
3. a. 343 **b.** 343; ⑦⌷③⌷ENTER **5.** $18 \cdot (-3)^4$
7. a. 100,000 people **b.** 250,000 people **c.** about 269,159 people **9.** $1.02P$ **11. a.** $A = P(1 + r)^t$ **b.** total amount including interest **c.** starting principal **d.** annual yield **e.** number of years **13.** $2,529.55 **15. a.** Susana earns $20.40; Jake earns $41.60 **b.** No. After the first year, he has more money on which to earn interest than Susana does.
17. a. $A = 100 \cdot 1.1^t$

b.

Time since investment (in years)	Danica's account ($)
0	100.00
2	121.00
4	146.41
6	177.16
8	214.36
10	259.37
12	313.84
14	379.75
16	459.50
18	555.99
20	672.75

19. around year 15 **21. a.** $3W + T > 3$
b.

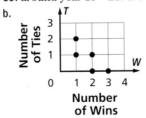

23. $\frac{5}{6}$ **25.** all real numbers
27. $t = 5$

Lesson 7-2 (pp. 404-410)
1. a. $y = 11 \cdot 3^x$, where y is the population and x is the number of years after 1995. **b.** 99 round gobies **c.** 2,673 trillion round gobies **d.** about 2,265 trillion round gobies **3. a.** 1.045 **b.** $3,276.07 **5. a.** 1 **b.** 17 **c.** 1
7. $(-5)^0 = 1$, but $-5^0 = -1$, by the order of operations

9. a.

x	y
0	0.5
1	1
2	2
3	4
4	8

b.

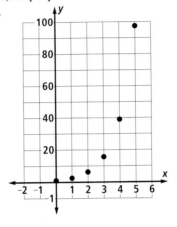

11. a. by about 3.585 million people **b.** about 56.190 million people **13. a.** 1.04 is the growth rate; 34,277 is the 1860 population **b.** 1,731,158 people; 22,789 people **c.** about 26,956,933 people
15. a.

b. 1.5 **c.** 58.59375 **d.** This graph is not a line. Its rate of change increases as x increases. **17. a.** $\frac{1}{31}$ **b.** $\frac{9}{31}$
19. 25.74

Lesson 7-3 (pp. 411-418)
Guided Example 3: a. 10; 0.97; 10; 0.97 **b.** 23; 23 **c.** 240; 240; 10; 0.97; 240
Questions: 1. 0.83 **3.** 1 **5. a.** $27,200 **b.** $25,600 **c.** $32,000 \cdot (1 - 0.01d)$ dollars **7.** about 6 units; $15 \cdot 0.97^x$ units **9.** constant **11.** decay
13. a. $y = 2,500 \cdot 0.98^x$ **b.** about 2,043 students

15. a.

Light-Panes Relation

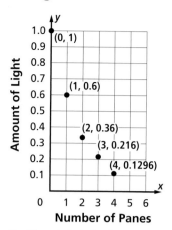

b. No, it will get infinitely close to zero.

17. a.

x	Decimals	Fractions
0	1	1
1	0.5	$\frac{1}{2}$
2	0.25	$\frac{1}{4}$
3	0.125	$\frac{1}{8}$
10	0.000976563	$\frac{1}{1,024}$
20	0.0000009536	$\frac{1}{1,048,576}$

b. no solutions

19. a.

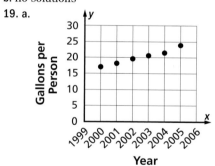

b. Answers vary. Sample answer: $y = 1.7x - 3,359.8$
c. Answers vary. Sample answer: $y = 1.7x - 3,359.8$
d. about 29.1 gal of bottled water per person

Lesson 7-4 (pp. 419–424)

Guided Example: a. $2.241 \cdot 1.218^x$ **b.** $2.241 \cdot 1.218^{24} \approx 255$; 255; 165; 165 MHz **c.** 2.241; 1.218; 44; 13,150
Questions: 1. a. 6 ft **b.** 55% **3.** 8.4 ft; about 0.83 ft **5.** about 80,817 MB **7.** c **9.** a

11. a.

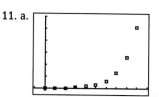

b. Let p be the number of pennies and t be the trial number. $p = 1.57 \cdot 1.49^t$ **13.** Answers vary. Sample answer: If 35% of a 14-kg block of ice melts every day, how much ice, y, remains after x weeks?

15.

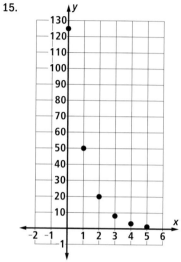

17. \$23 **19. a.** \$270 **b.** \$225 **c.** \$200

Lesson 7-5 (pp. 425–431)

Guided Example 2: all real numbers; all real numbers
Questions: 1. a. 9 **b.** 4 is the input and 16 is the output.
c. 4 is the independent variable and 16 is the dependent variable. **d.** {1, 4, 9, 16, 25} **3. a.** −1 **b.** $\frac{2}{7}$ **5.** No real number has 0 as its reciprocal because if $0 = \frac{1}{x}$, then $x = \frac{1}{0}$, which is undefined. **7. a.** {x: −5 ≤ x ≤ 5}
b. {y: 0 ≤ y ≤ 5} **9.** C **11.** No; The input $x = 3$ corresponds to both outputs $y = 1$ and $y = 4$. **13. a.** false
b. 5 **c.** the set of all real numbers **d.** {y: $y > 0$} **e.** 4

15. Answers vary. Sample answer: time is input and height is output

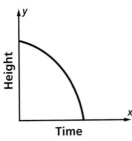

17. $\{y: 0 \leq y \leq 2\}$ **19.** domain: the set of all real numbers; range: the set of all real numbers **21. a.** Answers vary. Sample answer: As the value of the input increases, that of the output decreases. **b.** Khalid Khannouchi is associated with two record-setting times; that is, one input produces two outputs. **23.** $\frac{21}{160}$ **25.** $pw \leq 1{,}500; p \leq \frac{1{,}500}{w}$

Lesson 7-6 (pp. 432–438)

Guided Example 2: 10; 121,899; 100,000 + 3,000(10); 130,000; 10; constant; 100,000

Questions: 1. f of x **3. a.** $E(25) \approx 164{,}061; L(25) = 175{,}000;$ $C(25) = 100{,}000$ **b.** They are the population estimates for 25 yr from the present. **5.** 12,800 **7. a.** $45 **b.** $135 **c.** 20 **9. a.** 506.25; It is the estimated value of the computer in four years.

b.

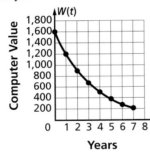

c. $t > 1.63$. This means after about 1.63 years the computer's value is less than $1,000.
11. a. about 325°
b. The temperature of the oven after it was on for 25 minutes was 325°.
c. $t \approx 6$ **d.** The oven reached 200° after being on for about 6 minutes.
13. No. Answers vary. Sample answer: $x = 1$ results in both $y = -2$ and $y = 0$. **15. a.** $5x - 4y = -12$
b. $y = \frac{5}{4}x + 3$

Lesson 7-7 (pp. 439–446)

Guided Example: Option 1: $60; $110; Option 2: $15; $22.50
Questions: 1. Answers vary. Sample answer: The rate of change varies in an exponential growth situation, but remains constant in a constant increase situation.

3.

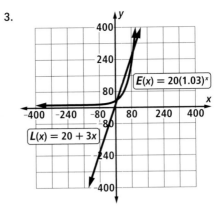

5. Answers vary. Sample answer: $E(x)$ could represent the value of a $20 investment in a bank account with an annual yield of 3% after x years. $L(x)$ could represent the amount in a bank account after x years if $20 is initially invested and $3 is added each year. **7. a.** A2 + 13; A3 + 13
b. 54; 67 **c.** They will decrease to 21 and 34. **d.** constant increase; The outputs are represented by the linear function $f(x) = 13x + 28$. **9. a.** Next = Now + 270
b. Next = Now · 1.15 **c.** $L(x) = 85{,}000 + 270x$
d. $E(x) = 85{,}000(1.15)^x$ **e.** Answers vary. Sample answer: Yes, $L(8) = 87{,}160$. **11. a.** Constant increase. Answers vary. Sample answer: Reading at 25 pages per hour is a constant rate increase. **b.** $f(x) = 67 + 25x$ **c.** 33.32 hr
13. a **15.** d
17. a.

	Constant	Exponential
0	2,410	2,410
1	2,270	2,270
2	2,130	2,138
3	1,990	2,014
4	1,850	1,897
5	1,710	1,787
6	1,570	1,683
7	1,430	1,585
8	1,290	1,493
9	1,150	1,406
10	1,010	1,325
11	870	1,248
12	730	1,175
13	590	1,107
14	450	1,043
15	310	982

b. 1,570, approximately 1,683; by 113 **c.** 170, approximately 925; by 755 **19.** true **21.** $24x + 5y = -3$ **23.** $\frac{24}{73}$

Self-Test (pp. 450–451)

1. $\left(\frac{1}{5}\right)^2 + \left(\frac{1}{5}\right)^0 = \frac{1}{25} + 1 = \frac{26}{25}$ **2.** $8^4 d^6$ **3.** $f(1,729) = 3(1,729)^0 = 3 \cdot 1 = 3$ **4.** $g(-2) = 3(-2) - (-2)^2 = -6 - 4 = -10$ **5.** $400(1.044)^7 \approx 540.70$ **6.** Tyrone will have $400(1.044)^{10} \approx 615.26$ dollars and Oleta will have $400 + 22(10) = 620$ dollars, so Oleta will have more.
7. After 25 years, Tyrone will have $400(1.044)^{25} \approx 1,173.74$ dollars, and Oleta will have $400 + 22(25) = 950$ dollars, so Tyrone will have more money. **8.** The value of the car is depreciating 16%, so the growth factor is $1 - 0.16 = 0.84$.
9. $m(x) = 34,975(0.84)^x, x \geq 0$. Because x represents years, it cannot be negative. **10.** $m(5) = 34,975(0.84)^5 \approx 14,626.96$ dollars **11.** $f(1) = 5 \cdot 0.74^1 = 3.7$
12. $f(5) = 5 \cdot 0.74^5 \approx 1.11$ **13.** $f(7) = 5 \cdot 0.74^7 \approx 0.61$
14. $f(12) = |-12 - 3| = |-15| = 15$ **15.** From the graph and knowledge of the absolute value function, you can see only positive values and 0 are in the range. The range is all nonnegative numbers. **16.** From the graph you can see the only values in the range are those greater than or equal to $f(5)$. $f(5) = |5 - 3| = 2$ so the range is all real numbers ≥ 2.

17.

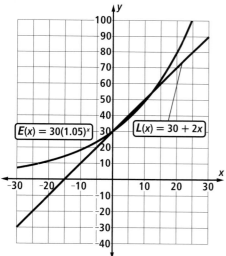

$E(x) = 30(1.05)^x$ $L(x) = 30 + 2x$

18. $L(9) = 30 + 2 \cdot 9 = 48$, $E(9) = 30(1.05)^9 \approx 46.5$; $L(9)$ is greater. **19.** Answers vary. Sample answer: $x = 20$; $E(20) \approx 79.60$, $L(20) = 70$, $70 < 79.60$ **20.** An increase of 2.5% tells you that the growth factor is 1.025. The beginning population is 76 million, so the population p, in millions, k years after 1980, is $p(k) = 76(1.025)^k$.

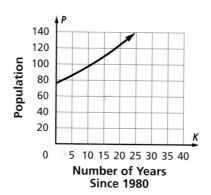

Number of Years Since 1980

21. A decrease of 1% tells you that the growth factor is 0.99. The beginning circulation is 880,000, so the circulation is $c(x) = 880,000(0.99)^x$.

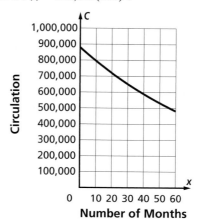

Number of Months Since Jan. 2000

22.

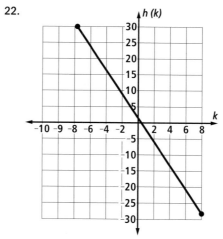

23.

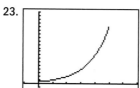

24. a. f is a linear function with negative slope, so it describes a constant decrease situation, ii. **b.** g is an exponential function with growth factor 5. Since $5 > 1$, g describes an exponential growth situation, iii. **c.** h is an exponential function with growth factor 0.4. Since $0.4 < 1$, h describes an exponential decay situation, iv. **d.** m is a linear function with positive slope, so it describes a constant increase situation, i. **25. a.** The year increases by 1, so add 1 to the value in A2. Input "=A2 + 1". **b.** Answers vary. Sample answer: In cell B3, input "=1.04*B2", and then replicate the formula from B3 to B4 through B22.

The chart below keys the **Self-Test** questions to the objectives in the **Chapter Review** on pages 452–455 or to the **Vocabulary (Voc)** on page 449. This will enable you to locate those **Chapter Review** questions that correspond to questions missed on the **Self-Test.** The lesson where the material is covered is also indicated on the chart.

Question	1	2	3	4	5	6	7	8	9	10
Objective	A	A	A	A	D	G	G	E	C	E
Lesson(s)	7-6	7-6	7-6	7-6	7-1	7-7	7-7	7-2, 7-3, 7-4	7-5, 7-6	7-2, 7-3, 7-4

Question	11	12	13	14	15	16	17	18	19	20
Objective	A	A	A	A	C	C	I	G	G	H
Lesson(s)	7-6	7-6	7-6	7-6	7-5, 7-6	7-5, 7-6	7-5, 7-6	7-7	7-7	7-2, 7-3

Question	21	22	23	24	25
Objective	H	I	H	F	B
Lesson(s)	7-2, 7-3	7-5, 7-6	7-2, 7-3	7-4	7-7

Chapter Review (pp. 452–455)

1. 4 **3.** 17 **5.** $\frac{121}{36}$ **7.** -4 **9. a.** Answers vary. Sample answer: "= B2*1.05" **b.** 1,050 **c.** Replicate the formula in B3 down to B12. **11. a.** x **b.** f **13. a.** {2, 4, 5, 10} **b.** {200, 400, 500, 1,000} **c.** $f(x) = 100x$; $x = 2, 4, 5, 10$ **15.** \$918.66 **17.** (b), $1.04^8 > 1.08^4$ **19. a.** $20^5 = 3{,}200{,}000$ **b.** C **21.** constant increase **23.** exponential growth **25.** neither **27. a.** $A(n) = 10{,}000{,}000\,(1.02)^n$ **b.** $B(n) = 20{,}000{,}000 + 1{,}000{,}000n$ **c.** country B; $B(30) = 50{,}000 > A(30) = 18{,}113{,}616$ **d.** country B; $B(100) > A(100)$

29.

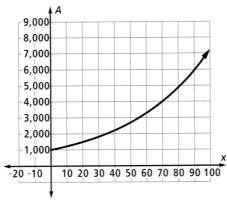

Answers vary. Sample answer: \$1,000 is invested at 2% interest per year.

31.

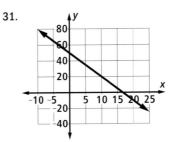

Answers vary. Sample answer: You have \$50 in a bank account, and each day you take out \$3.

33.

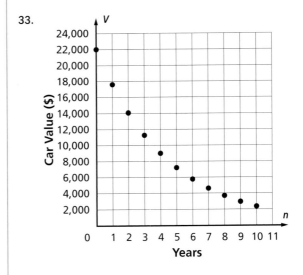

35.

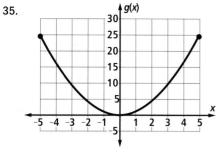

37.

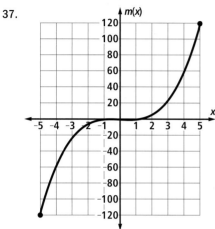

39. **a.** 1 **b.** 2 **c.** $\{x: 0 \le x \le 4\}$ **d.** $\{y: 0 \le y \le 2\}$

Chapter 8

Lesson 8-1 (pp. 458–463)

Guided Example 3: 4^{20}; 5^{10}; $(4^{20})(5^{10})$; $\frac{1}{10,737,418,240,000,000,000}$

Questions: 1. a. AA, AE, AI, AO, AU, EA, EE, EI, EO, EU, IA, IE, II, IO, IU, OA, OE, OI, OO, OU, UA, UE, UI, UO, UU **b.** 2; 5 **3.** 15,625; $1.5625 \cdot 10^4$ **5. a.** 90 **b.** To label each cell, we choose each cell among 15 columns and 6 rows, so there are $6 \cdot 15$ choices, thus 90 cells. **7. a.** 2^{10}; 1,024; $1.024 \cdot 10^3$ **b.** $\frac{1}{1,024}$ **c.** 2^Q; $\frac{1}{2^Q}$ **9. a.** $10^3 = 1,000$ **b.** $10^{-12} = 0.000000000001$ **11.** $\frac{1}{32}$ **13.** 17,069 people **15.** No, because for each value of x, there are several values of y. **17.** 108 units^2 **19.** $x = 6$ **21.** $2.8 \cdot 10^9$

Lesson 8-2 (pp. 464–468)

1. 18^9 **3.** w^7; $2^4 \cdot 2^3 = 16 \cdot 8 = 128$; $2^7 = 128$ **5.** 2^7 **7.** m^8 **9.** m^{10} **11.** $15a^6$ **13.** d^{14} **15.** a^8b^3 **17.** 65,536 sequences **19.** $x = 1$ **21. a.** $P \cdot 3^4$ **b.** 16 days **23. a.** 30 ways **b.** 6 more choices **25. a.** $y = -51.6x + 3,058$ **b.** 2,026 tickets **27.** 3.24×10^{-3}

Lesson 8-3 (pp. 469–473)

1. 2^3 **3.** 3^{m-n} **5.** 1 **7.** $6ab^5$ **9.** $4a^6$ **11.** The bases differ. **13.** 1 **15.** 2^{-3} **17.** $7 + 3m$ **19.** $4a$

21. a. about 12,410.8 barrels of oil per person per day **b.** about 158,547,936 gallons **23.** $3x^3$ **25.** $24h^7$ **27. a.** $\frac{1}{4^5}$ **b.** $\frac{243}{1,024}$ **29. a.** \$23.92 **b.** \$52.50

Lesson 8-4 (pp. 474–480)

Guided Example 2: a. $\left(\frac{4}{5}\right)^2$; $\frac{16}{25}$; **b.** $\left(\frac{m^2}{1}\right)^3$; $(m^2)^3$; m^6

Guided Example 4: -7; 2; -1; 2; 7; -1; $\frac{b^2}{3a^7c}$

Questions: 1. $\frac{1}{3}, \frac{1}{9}, \frac{1}{27}, \frac{1}{81}, \frac{1}{243}$ **3.** $\frac{1}{125}$ **5.** $\frac{1}{y^{24}}$ **7.** 3^{-4} **9.** 10^{-4}

11. a. $\frac{1}{w}$ **b.** $\frac{1}{wx^2}$ **c.** $\frac{y^3}{w}$ **d.** $\frac{5y^3}{wx^2}$ **13.** 1 **15.** $\frac{4a^2c^2}{b^3}$

17. The values of y seem to get extremely close to 0.

19. $x^{-2}(x^{-3} + x^4) = x^{-2}(x^{-3}) + x^{-2}(x^4) = x^{(-2 + -3)} + x^{(-2 + 4)} = x^{-5} + x^2 = x^2 + \frac{1}{x^5}$ **21.** $m = -1$; $5^{-1} \cdot \frac{1}{25} = 5^{-1} \cdot 5^{-2} = 5^{-3}$ **23.** a^6; 64 **25.** $2^a b^{3a}$; 62,500 **27. a.** $m(x) = 8x + 25$ **b.** whole numbers less than 13 **c.** 121 and 25

Lesson 8-5 (pp. 481–487)

Guided Example 2: 3; 3; 3; 3; 3; 6; 9; 3; $-125x^6y^9z^3$

Questions: 1. a. $216x^3$ **b.** $(6 \cdot 2)^3 = 1,728$; $216(2)^3 = 1,728$ **3.** $-2,744x^3y^3$ **5.** $-t^{93}$ **7.** $\frac{16}{81}$ **9.** $\frac{6,859}{8y^3}$ **11.** The area is multiplied by 36. **13.** $\frac{x^5}{y}$ **15.** $144w^{10}$ **17.** 0 **19.** 225

21. $\frac{17}{3,125r^2s^2}$; $\frac{17}{7,031.25}$ **23.** $-\frac{1}{5} < p$

Lesson 8-6 (pp. 488–496)

1. a. 256 units^2 **b.** 4 units **3.** 6 **5.** 7.07 **7.** 31.623 **9.** 5 **11. a.** 3.31662 **b.** 11 **c.** Square of the Square Root Property **13.** 52 **15.** 1; 8; 27; 64; 125; 216; 343; 512; 729; 1,000 **17. a.** $\sqrt[3]{1,700}$ **b.** 11.935 **19.** 45 **21.** 100,995; Answers vary. Sample answer: The population 6 months from the original date **23. a.** Answers vary. Sample answer: The scarecrow's statement is an incorrect statement about isosceles triangles, while the Pythagorean Theorem is a true statement about right triangles. The statement is about the square roots of the sides, while the Pythagorean Theorem is about the squares of the lengths of the sides. **b.** No, Answers vary. Sample answer: Let an isosceles triangle with $a = 9$, $b = 9$ and $c = 4$ cm. Then $\sqrt{a} + \sqrt{b} = \sqrt{9} + \sqrt{9} = 3 + 3 = 6$; while $\sqrt{c} = \sqrt{4} = 2$, so $\sqrt{a} + \sqrt{b} \ne \sqrt{c}$. **25.** $(x^2)(y^2) = (xy)^2$ **27.** 8 **29.** 865,177 yr

Lesson 8-7 (pp. 497–504)

Guided Example 2: a. 7; 7; $\sqrt{98}$ **b.** 49; 49; 2; 7; $7\sqrt{2}$

Guided Example 3: 16; 4; 4 Check 6,912; 48

Questions: 1. 4 **3.** 2 **5.** $x = 18$, $y = 3$, $z = 2$ **7.** B **9.** $3\sqrt{2}$ **11.** $5\sqrt{2}$ **13. a.** $5m\sqrt{6n}$ **b.** $4m^2$ **15.** Quotient of Square Roots Property **17.** $3\sqrt{3}$, 5.20 **19.** $x = \sqrt{81 - y^2}$, $y = \sqrt{81 - x^2}$ **21.** Answers vary. Sample answer: Because $\sqrt{49} = 7$ **23.** $-8\sqrt{3}$ **25.** $29\sqrt{2}$ **27.** (250, 100) **29.** x^5 **31.** $(6^4)^2$ **33.** Slope $= -1.5$, y-intercept $= 46$; The slope describes how many floors it descends per second, and the y-intercept is where the elevator is at 0 sec.

Lesson 8-8 (pp. 505–510)

Guided Example 2: 23; 16; 31; –11; 31; 23; –11; 16; 8; –27; 64; 729; 793; 28.160

Questions: 1. a. 2 **b.** 6 **c.** $\sqrt{40} \approx 6.325$ **3.** 7 **5.** 22 **7.** $\sqrt{29} \approx 5.385$ **9.** 13 **11.** $\sqrt{65} \approx 8.062$ **13.** $\sqrt{0.0833} \approx 0.288617$ **15.** $\sqrt{11.25} \approx 3.35$ miles **17.** $\sqrt{b^2 + d^2}$ **19.** $[(x_2 - x_1)^2 + (y_2 - y_1)^2]^{\frac{1}{2}}$ **21.** 12 **23.** 40 **25.** $f(x) = \frac{8}{5}x - 10$

Lesson 8-9 (pp. 511–516)

Guided Example 4: Solution 1 –7; 35; –7; 21; –7; 14; –7; 7; 14; 7; 7; 14; 7; 14; 7; 14 **Solution 2 1.** $(9q^{-5}) = \left(\frac{9}{6}q^{-2}\right)^{-7}$ **2.** $\left(\frac{3}{2}q^{-2}\right)^{-7}$ **3.** $\left(\frac{3}{2}\right)^{-7}q^{-2 \cdot -7} = \left(\frac{2}{3}\right)^{-7} \cdot q^{14}$

Questions: 1. B **3.** C **5.** A special case for which the answer is false **7.** true **9.** no **11.** yes **13.** Product of Powers **15.** Negative Exponent **17.** $\frac{y^6}{9x^4}$ **19.** 6

21. Answers vary. Sample answer: $\left(\frac{x^6}{x^3}\right)^{-2} = \frac{x^{12}}{x^6} = x^{-6} = \frac{1}{x^6}$; $\left(\frac{x^6}{x^3}\right)^{-2} = (x^3)^{-2} = x^{-6} = \frac{1}{x^6}$ **23.** $2^{75}3^{50}5^{25}$ **25.** 66.7

27. Yes, Answers vary. Sample answer: In an isosceles right triangle with legs of length s and a hypotenuse of length h, $h^2 = s^2 + s^2 = 2s^2$. So, $h = \sqrt{2s^2} = \sqrt{2}\sqrt{s^2} = s \cdot \sqrt{2}$.

29. $-\frac{5}{4}x + 15$

Self-Test (p. 520)

1. A, $x^{4+7} = x^{11}$ **2.** $5^{-3} = \frac{1}{5^3} = \frac{1}{125}$ **3.** $(-4)(-3) = 12$; $(-4)^{-3} = -\frac{1}{64}$; $(-3)^4 = 81$.; So, from least to greatest: $(-4)^{-3}$, $(-4)(-3)$, $(-3)^4$ **4.** $\sqrt{600} = \sqrt{100 \cdot 6} = \sqrt{100} \cdot \sqrt{6} = 10\sqrt{6}$
5. $\sqrt{25x} = \sqrt{25 \cdot x} = \sqrt{25} \cdot \sqrt{x} = 5\sqrt{x}$
6. $2^{\frac{1}{2}} \cdot 50^{\frac{1}{2}} = (2 \cdot 50)^{\frac{1}{2}} = 100^{\frac{1}{2}} = 10$ **7.** $y^4 \cdot y^2 = y^{4+2} = y^6$
8. $(10m^2)^3 = 10^3(m^2)^3 = 10^3 m^6 = 1{,}000m^6$

9. $\frac{a^{15}}{a^3} = a^{15-3} = a^{12}$ **10.** $\left(\frac{m}{6}\right)^3 = \frac{m^3}{6^3} = \frac{m^3}{216}$
11. $g^4 \cdot g \cdot g^0 = g^{4+1+0} = g^5$
12. $\frac{6n^2}{4n^3 \cdot 2n} = \frac{6n^2}{8n^4} = \frac{3}{4}n^{2-4} = \frac{3}{4}n^{-2} = \frac{3}{4n^2}$ **13.** $\frac{4w^2}{y^3}$, by the Negative Exponent Property **14.** $\frac{2}{x^2} \cdot \frac{5}{x^5} = \frac{2 \cdot 5}{x^2 x^5}$ Multiplication of fractions $= \frac{10}{x^{(2+5)}}$ Arithmetic and Product of Powers Property $= \frac{10}{x^7}$ Arithmetic **15.** The prime factorization of $10(288)^2$ is $2 \cdot 5 \cdot (2^5 \cdot 3^2)^2 = 2 \cdot 5 \cdot (2^5)^2 \cdot (3^2)^2 = 2 \cdot 5 \cdot 2^{10} \cdot 3^4 = 5 \cdot 2^{11} \cdot 3^4$ **16.** $\left(\frac{3}{y^2}\right)^{-3}\left(\left(\frac{3}{y^2}\right)^{-1}\right)^3 = \left(\frac{y^2}{3}\right)^3 = \frac{(y^2)^3}{3^3} = \frac{y^6}{27}$ **17.** 3.107 **18.** $1{,}000(1.06)^{-3} = 1{,}000 \cdot 0.84 \approx 840$ **19. a.** Power of a Quotient Property **b.** Power of a Power Property **c.** Quotient of Powers Property **d.** Negative Exponent Property **20.** Answers vary. Sample answer: $\frac{1}{4}$ **21.** $\sqrt{(1-9)^2 + (-10-5)^2} = \sqrt{289} = 17$ **22.** The upper right corner of the paper has coordinates $(297, 210)$, the lower left corner has coordinates $(0, 0)$ so using the distance formula gives $\sqrt{(297-0)^2 + (210-0)^2} = \sqrt{132{,}309} \approx 363.7$ mm. **23.** $V = s^3$, so $s = \sqrt[3]{v}$. Therefore $s = \sqrt[3]{30} \approx 3.107$ in. **24.** The diagonal and two consecutive sides of the square form an isoscels triangle. The Pythagorean Theorem gives $s^2 + s^2 = 12^2$, where s is the length of a side of the square. So, $2s^2 = 144$ or $s^2 = 72$. Since the area of the square is s^2, the area is 72 m². **25.** $26^2 \cdot 10^4 = (676) \cdot (10{,}000) = 6{,}760{,}000$

The chart below keys the **Self-Test** questions to the objectives in the **Chapter Review** on pages 521–523 or to the **Vocabulary (Voc)** on page 519. This will enable you to locate those **Chapter Review** questions that correspond to questions missed on the **Self-Test**. The lesson where the material is covered is also indicated on the chart.

Question	1	2	3	4	5	6	7	8	9	10
Objective	A	B	B	D	D	D	A	C	A	C
Lesson(s)	8-2, 8-3, 8-4, 8, 5	8-4, 8-5	8-4, 8-5	8-6, 8-7	8-6, 8-7	8-6, 8-7	8-2, 8-3, 8-4, 8-5	8-5, 8-9	8-2, 8-3, 8-4, 8-5	8-5, 8-9

Question	11	12	13	14	15	16	17	18	19	20
Objective	A	A	G	G	A	C	E	B	G	F
Lesson(s)	8-2, 8-3, 8-4, 8-5	8-2, 8-3, 8-4, 8-5	8-2, 8-3, 8-4, 8-5	8-2, 8-3, 8-4, 8-5	8-2, 8-3, 8-4, 8-5	8-5, 8-9	8-6	8-4, 8-5	8-2, 8-3, 8-4, 8-5	8-9

Question	21	22	23	24	25
Objective	J	U	I	I	H
Lesson(s)	8-8	8-8	8-8	8-8	8-1

Chapter Review (pp. 521–523)

1. $24m^9$ **3.** $\frac{7y^4}{3x}$ **5.** $\frac{1}{v^{24}}$ **7.** $5a^{20} - 7a^{13}$ **9. a.** approximately 1.33x^4 **b.** $\frac{4}{3}x^4$ **11.** $\frac{42}{x^7y^3}$ **13.** $\frac{1}{36}$ **15.** $\frac{243}{32}$ **17.** \$129,000 **19.** $n = -3$ **21. a.** negative **b.** negative **23.** $3,600m^4n^6$ **25.** $\frac{2,187}{16,384}$ **27.** $\frac{t^8}{4,096s^4}$ **29.** $\frac{9z^{14}}{y^{10}}$ **31.** $8\sqrt{2}$ **33.** $10\sqrt{21}$ **35.** $\frac{2x}{y}$ **37.** -2 **39.** 5.848 **41.** 0.368; $0.368^3 \approx 0.0498 \approx$ 0.05 **43. a.** yes **b.** yes **c.** no **d.** It is not always true. Part c is a counterexample. **45.** Answers vary. Sample answer: $a = 1$ **47.** Power of a Quotient Property **49.** Power of a Power Property or Zero Exponent Property **51.** Product of Powers Property **53.** Answers vary. Sample answer: By first applying the Negative Exponent Property for Fractions and then the Power of a Quotient Property, $\left(\frac{12}{13}\right)^{-4} = \left(\frac{13}{12}\right)^4 = \frac{13^4}{12^4} = \frac{28,561}{20,736}$. By applying the Power of Quotient Property and then the Negative Exponent Property, $\left(\frac{12}{13}\right)^{-4} = \frac{12^{-4}}{13^{-4}} = \frac{13^4}{12^4} = \frac{28,561}{20,736}$. **55. a.** 243 answer sheets **b.** $\frac{1}{243}$ **c.** $\frac{32}{243}$ **57.** 54 different pizzas **59.** $2\sqrt{2}$ units **61.** x^2y^2 **63.** 1 m **65. a.** 5 **b.** 3 **c.** $\sqrt{34}$ **67.** $9\sqrt{2}$ **69.** $\sqrt{(a+1)^2 + (b-4)^2}$ **71. a.** yes **b.**

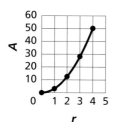

Chapter 9

Lesson 9-1 (pp. 526–531)

Guided Example 1: Step 1

A and r can only assume positive values

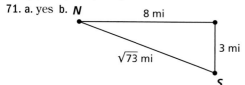

Step 2

r	A
1	3.14
2	12.57
3	28.27
4	50.27

Steps 3 and 4

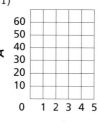

Step 5: about 2 units

Questions: 1. a.

x	$g(x) = \frac{1}{2}x^2$
-4	8
-3	4.5
-2	2
-1	0.5
0	0
1	0.5
2	2
3	4.5
4	8

b.

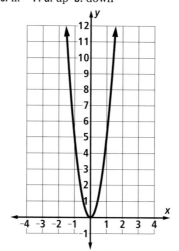

c. up

3. a. down **b.** maximum value **c.** $(0, 0)$ **d.** $x = 0$ **5. a.** iii. **b.** i. **c.** ii. **7. a.** up **b.** down

9. a.

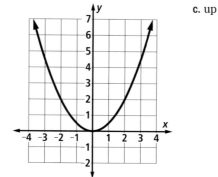

b.

x	$y = 5x^2$
-2	20
-1.5	11.25
-1	5
-0.5	1.25
0	0
0.5	1.25
1	5
1.5	11.25
2	20

c.

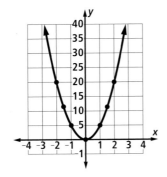

d. ≈ 1.7 and –1.7   **11. a.** $y = 0$ **b.** $x = 1$ and $x = -1$
c. $x = 2$ and $x = -2$ **13. a.** negative **b.** zero **c.** negative
d. The graph is has vertex $(0, 0)$ and opens down.   **15.** 0
17. $a = -1.5$ **19. a.** $t = 5$ **b.** about 3.5 sec
21. $\sqrt{244} \approx 15.6$ in.   **23.** $2,250

Lesson 9-2 (pp. 532–536)
1. $x = \pm 5$ **3.** $x = \sqrt{40} \approx \pm 6.32$ **5.** $v = \sqrt{5} \approx \pm 2.24$
7. $a = -3$ or $a = -7$ **9. a.** about 92 ft **b.** about 2 sec
11. 5.64 units   **13.** $v \pm 2.5$ **15.** about 8.50 in.
17. $m^5 n^6$ **19.** $\frac{9}{25a^2}$ **21. a.** the set of all real numbers
b. the set of nonnegative real numbers
23. a. $6x + 4y \geq 975$

b.

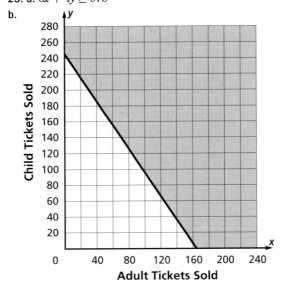

c. 121 tickets   **25.** B

Lesson 9-3 (pp. 537–543)
1. the total distance traveled in the time it takes for a car to
stop   **3.** 206.25 ft   **5.** $a = 0.05; b = 1; c = 0$

7. a.

x	y
–3	3
–2	–2
–1	–5
0	–6
1	–5
2	–2
3	3

b.

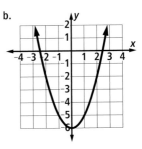

c. y-intercept: –6; x-intercepts: $\pm\sqrt{6}$; vertex: $(0, -6)$
d. $y \geq -6$
9. a.

x	y
–3	31
–2	16
–1	7
0	4
1	7
2	16
3	31

b.

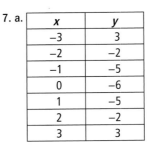

c. y-intercept: 4; x-intercepts: none; vertex: $(0, 4)$ **d.** $y \geq 4$
11. a. $(-4, 36)$ **b.** $(-2, 20), (-1, 0), (0, -28)$ **13.** B; Answers
vary. Sample answer: When $x = 2, y = 0$. Only graph B
intersects the x-axis at $x = 2$.   **15.** d   **17.** b
19. a. $t = \sqrt{\frac{350}{16}} \approx 4.68$ **b.** Answers vary. Sample answer: If
you drop a stone off of a 350-ft cliff, how long will it take
for the stone to hit the ground?   **21. a.** 288 **b.** 352 **c.** $4\sqrt{22}$
or about 18.76

Lesson 9-4 (pp. 544–551)
Guided Example 2: a. 0; 90; 90 **b.** 90; 90; 18.37; 4.3
Guided Example 3: a. $-4.9t^2 + 22t + 2$ **b.** 1.1, 3.4; 1.1; 3.4
Questions: 1. Answers vary. Sample answer: A projectile is
an object that is dropped or launched and travels through
the air to get to a target. Cannonballs, baseballs, and tennis
balls can all be considered projectiles.   **3. a.** $h = -16t^2 +$
$30t + 5$ **b.** 1 ft   **c.** 19.1 ft   **5. a.** 0 ft/sec; 40 ft **b.** $h =$
$-16t^2 + 40$ **c.** about 1.6 sec   **7.** No; at 40 yards from the
kicker, the ball is only 8.6 ft high.
9. a.

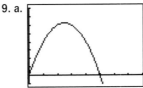

b. 31.25 m **c.** 20 m
d. between 1 and 4 sec after
launch **e.** –30 m **f.** 5 sec

11. a.

x	−3	−2	−1	0	1	2	3
y	2.25	1	0.25	0	0.25	1	2.25

b.

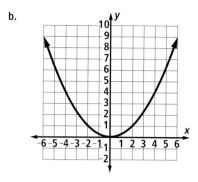

13. $A = (2, 2), B = (3, 5)$ **15.** D

Lesson 9-5 (pp. 552–557)

Guided Example 2: 4.3; –; –4.9; 10; –4.9; 214.49; 214.49; 214.49; 14.65; 14.65

Questions: 1. If $ax^2 + bx + c = 0$ and $a \neq 0$, then $x = \frac{-b \pm \sqrt{b^2 - 4ac}}{2a}$
3. 3 and –6 **5.** $t = -2$; Check: Does $(-2)^2 + 4(-2) + 4 = 0$? $4 + -8 + 4 = 0$ Yes, it checks. **7.** $y = -4$ or $y = \frac{25}{3}$; Check: Does $3(-4)^2 = 13(-4) + 100$? $3(16) = -52 + 100$ Yes, it checks; Does $3\left(\frac{25}{3}\right)^2 = 13\left(\frac{25}{3}\right) + 100$? $3\left(\frac{625}{9}\right) = \frac{325}{3} + 100$; Yes, it checks. **9.** $p = -5.48$ or $p = -0.85$

11. a. $x = -3$ or $x = 5$

b.

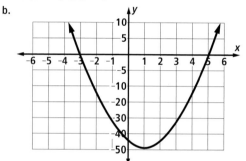

c.

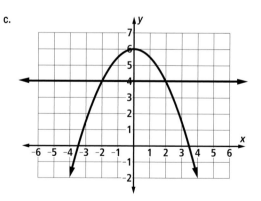

13. a. $t = 1.91$ sec and $t = 13.09$ sec **b.** 15 sec **15.** 2
17. 5 units **19. a.** 2 **b.** 3 **c.** $\frac{5x-1}{x+1}$

Lesson 9-6 (pp. 558–564)

Guided Example 1: b. 1, 1, 1 **c.** 0, 0
Guided Example 3: 2; 16; 32; $(16)^2 - 4(2)(32)$; 256 –256; zero; 1

Questions: 1. a. $-x^2 + 2x = 0$ **b.** yes, twice **3. a.** 0 **b.** 1 **c.** 2
5. a. 1 **b.** 0 **c.** 2 **d.** 2 **7. a.** 0 **b.** There is one real solution.
c. $n = 7$ **9. a.** 120 **b.** 2 **c.** $x = \frac{6 - \sqrt{30}}{2}$ or $x = \frac{6 + \sqrt{30}}{2}$
11. negative **13. a.** 25 **b.** 2 **15.** 1 **17.** No; All parabolas of the form $y = ax^2 + bx + c$ contain the point $(0, c)$.
19. $x = \frac{-2\sqrt{5}}{3}$ or $x = \frac{2\sqrt{5}}{3}$ **21. a.** 48 ft **b.** about 3.5 ft
23. down

Lesson 9-7 (pp. 565–570)

1. The cable can be placed either 87.87 ft away or 512.13 ft away from the left side of the bridge. **3.** No, a polygon cannot have exactly 21 diagonals. **5.** 120 **7. a.** $x + 7$ **b.** 9
9. 5.7 units **11.** It is equal to 0. **13.** 1 **15.** 0
17. a. $a = 36$ **b.** $b = 28$ **c.** $c = 10.25$ **19.** 26 ft
21. a. Answers vary. Sample answer:

$$m = \frac{1 + 24}{2 - 7} = -5$$
$$y - 1 = -5(x - 2)$$
$$(31) - 1 = -5((-4) - 2)$$
$$30 = 30$$

Since we can find the slope of the line between $(2, 1)$ and $(7, -24)$, we can find an equation for the line containing those two points. We then check to make sure that $(-4, 31)$ is also on the line, which it is. **b.** $5x + y = 11$

Self-Test (pp. 574–575)

1. $x^2 = 81; \sqrt{x^2} = \sqrt{81}; x = 9, -9$
2. $n^2 - 8n - 10 = 0$

$$n = \frac{-b \pm \sqrt{b^2 - 4ac}}{2a}$$
$$n = \frac{-(-8) \pm \sqrt{(-8)^2 - 4(1)(-10)}}{2(1)}$$
$$n = \frac{8 \pm \sqrt{64 + 40}}{2}$$
$$n = \frac{8 \pm \sqrt{104}}{2}$$
$$n = \frac{8 \pm 2\sqrt{26}}{2}$$
$$n = 4 + \sqrt{26}, 4 - \sqrt{26}$$
$$n \approx 9.10, n \approx -1.10$$

3. $5y^2 - 11y - 1 = 0$

$$y = \frac{-b \pm \sqrt{b^2 - 4ac}}{2a}$$

$$y = -(-11) \pm \frac{\sqrt{(-11)^2 - 4(5)(-1)}}{2(5)}$$

$$y = \frac{11 \pm \sqrt{121 + 20}}{10}$$

$$y = \frac{11 + \sqrt{141}}{10}, \frac{11 - \sqrt{141}}{10}$$

$$y \approx 2.29, y \approx -0.09$$

4. $24 = \frac{1}{6}z^2$

$6 \cdot 24 = \frac{6 \cdot 1}{6z^2}$

$144 = z^2$

$z = 12, -12$

5. $v^2 - 16v + 64 = 0$

$(v - 8)(v - 8) = 0$

$v = 8$

6. $3p^2 - 9p + 7 = 0$ If there are any real solutions, then $b^2 - 4ac$ must be greater than or equal to 0.

$b^2 - 4ac = (-9)^2 - 4(3)(7)$

$= 81 - 84$

$= -3$ There are no real solutions. **7.** 2 because the discriminant is positive **8.** A

9. a.

x	$2x^2$
−3	18
−2	8
−1	2
0	0
1	2
2	8
3	18

b.

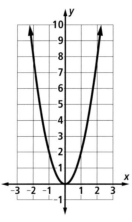

10. a.

x	$-x^2 + 4x - 3$
−3	−24
−2	−15
−1	−8
0	−3
1	0
2	1
3	0

b.

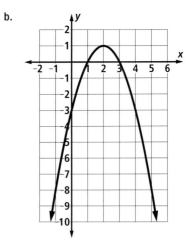

11. $h = 0.049(20)^2$; 19.6 m **12.** $44 = 0.049v^2$; $897.96 = v^2$; 29.97 m/sec **13.** $h = 0.049(35)^2$; 60 m

14. $n(n + 1) = 1,722$; $n^2 + n = 1,722$; $n^2 + n - 1,722 = 0$; $n = 41$ or $n = -42$; $n = -42$ or $n + 1 = -41$

15. $2x + 2(x + 6) = 24$; $4x = 12$; $x = 3$; $A = 3 \cdot 9 = 27$; πr^2; $8.59 \approx r^2$; $2.93 \approx r$ **16.** −1.6 **17.** −3, 1 **18.** $x = -1$

19. $0 = -16t^2 + 40t + 50$;

$$t = \frac{-b \pm \sqrt{b^2 - 4ac}}{2a};$$

$$t = \frac{-40 \pm \sqrt{(40)^2 - 4(-16)(50)}}{2(-16)};$$

$$t = \frac{-40 \pm \sqrt{1,600 + 3,200}}{-32};$$

$$t = \frac{-40 \pm \sqrt{4,800}}{-32};$$

$$t = \frac{-40 \pm 40\sqrt{3}}{-32}$$

$t = -0.92, t = 3.42$

$t = 3.42$ sec

20. $0 = -16t^2 + 40t - 20$

$$t = \frac{-b \pm \sqrt{b^2 - 4ac}}{2a}$$

$$t = \frac{-40 \pm \sqrt{(40)^2 - 4(-16)(-20)}}{2(-16)}$$

$$t = \frac{-40 \pm \sqrt{1,600 - 1,280}}{-32}; t = \frac{-40 \pm \sqrt{320}}{-32}$$

$$t = \frac{-40 \pm 8\sqrt{5}}{-32}$$

$t = 0.69, t = 1.81$

21. false **22.** $b^2 - 4ac = 1$; $(-5)^2 - 4(a)(3) = 1$

$25 - 12a = 1$

23. $b^2 - 4ac$; $12a = 24$; $a = 2$

$= (12)^2 - 4(-3)(-7)$

$= 144 - 84$

$= 60$; There are two real solutions since the discriminant has a value greater than 0.

24. $b^2 - 4ac$;
$= (-4)^2 - 4(1)(4)$
$= 16 - 16$
$= 0$; There is one real solution since the discriminant has a value of 0.

The chart below keys the **Self-Test** questions to the objectives in the **Chapter Review** on pages 576–579 or to the **Vocabulary (Voc)** on page 573. This will enable you to locate those **Chapter Review** questions that correspond to questions missed on the **Self-Test**. The lesson where the material is covered is also indicated on the chart.

Question	1	2	3	4	5	6	7	8	9	10
Objective	A	B	B	A	B	B	C	G	G	H
Lesson(s)	9-2	9-5, 9-6	9-5, 9-6	9-2	9-5, 9-6	9-5, 9-6	9-6	9-1	9-1	9-3

Question	11	12	13	14	15	16	17	18	19	20
Objective	F	F	F	F	E	H	H	H	D	D
Lesson(s)	9-7	9-7	9-7	9-7	9-2, 9-7	9-3	9-3	9-3	9-2, 9-4	9-2, 9-4

Question	21	22	23	24
Objective	C	C	C	C
Lesson(s)	9-6	9-6	9-6	9-6

Chapter Review (pp. 576-579)

1. $x = 13, x = -13$ **3.** $k = \pm\sqrt{85}$ **5.** $m = 3, m = -9$
7. $v = 4.75, v = 3.25$ **9.** $m = -3, m = -4$ **11.** $y = -0.46$, $y = 6.46$ **13.** $p = -5$ **15.** $n = -2, n = 0.2$ **17.** $b = -7.9$, $b = 2.5$ **19.** $x = \frac{-b \pm \sqrt{b^2 - 4ac}}{2a}$ **21.** 48 **23.** $b = 4$ or $b = -4$
25. 0 **27.** 0 **29. a.** 3,600 ft **b.** about 19 sec
31. a. 15.1 m **b.** about 1.0 sec and 3.1 sec **c.** 4.1 sec
33. a. $A = 60x - x^2$ **b.** $x = 30$
35. about 98°C **37. a.** Yes, the company's profits will exceed $100 million. **b.** 4.8 yr after 2005, or in late 2009
39. a.

x	$\frac{3}{5}x^2$
-2	2.4
-1	0.6
0	0
1	0.6
2	2.4

b.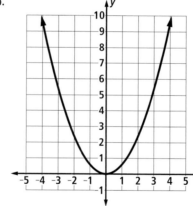

41. B **43. a.** 5
b. $x = 8$
c. $A = (6, 1)$, $B = (7, 4)$
45. true
47. $(24, -50)$

49. a.

x	$-x^2 - 4x + 3$
-5	-2
-4	3
-3	6
-2	7
-1	6
0	3
1	-2

b.

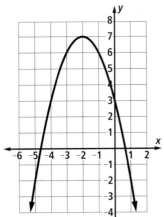

c. maximum

50. A

13. a. Answers vary. Sample answer: men: $y = -0.1235x + 522.17$; women: $y = -0.311x + 680.23$ Yes; both times will be equal in 2074. In 2076, the women's time will pass the men's time.

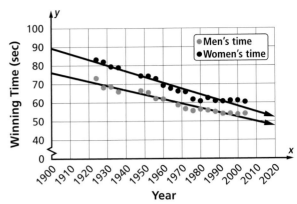

15. a. $-\frac{3}{5}$ **b.** -1 **c.** $-\frac{1}{2}, 3$ **d.** $-1.137, 2.637$ **17.** $625x^{28}y^{36}$
19. **21.** 3 days

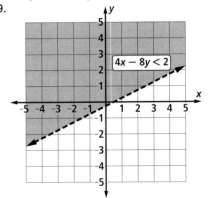

Chapter 10

Lesson 10-1 (pp. 582–588)

Guided Example 3: 1. zero **2.** -1 **3.** parallel **4.** no
Questions: 1. true **3. a.** $-8 = 4(-2)$ and $2(8) + 3(-2) = 16 + -6 = 10$ **b.** Answers vary. Sample answer: $x = 8$ and $y = -2$; $(x, y) = (8, -2)$

5. a. $\begin{cases} 3x - y = 3 \\ y = -2x + 7 \end{cases}$ **b.** $(2, 3)$ **c.** $3(2) - 3 = 3$ and $2(2) + 3 = 7$

7. a. $(6, 6)$

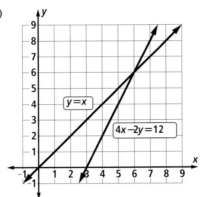

b. $6 = 6$; $24 - 12 = 12$ **9. a.** $\begin{cases} y = 3{,}800 + 4.25x \\ y = 12.5x \end{cases}$

b. Answers vary. Sample answer: $x\min = 400$, $X\max = 800$; $Y\min = 3{,}800$, $Y\max = 8{,}000$ **c.** about $(461, 5{,}758)$ **d.** yes
$(5, 15)$

11.

X	Y₁	Y₂
0	5	0
1	7	3
2	9	6
3	11	9
4	13	12
5	15	15
6	17	18

X=5

Lesson 10-2 (pp. 589–593)

Guided Example 3: $4t$; $10 + 3t$; $4t$; 10; $3t$; 10
Questions: 1. a. $(3, 5)$ **b.** $3(3) - 4 = 5$; $5(3) - 10 = 5$
3. a. $(-18, 8)$ **b.** $-\frac{1}{9}(-18) + 6 = 8$; $\frac{5}{3}(-18) + 38 = 8$
5. a. $(-144.6, -22.2)$ **b.** $8(-22.2) + 33 = -144.6$;
$3(-22.2) - 78 = -144.6$ **7.** $d = 15 + 3t$, $d = 4t$; The solution is $(15, 60)$, so Bart's sister will win.

9. a. $\begin{cases} d = 60t \\ d = 65\left(t - \frac{1}{10}\right) \end{cases}$ **b.** $(1.3, 78)$; after 1.3 hours

c. 78 miles **11. a.** about 8.42 yr before 2000 (1991)
b. about 4,189,474 people **13.** $2\frac{1}{2}$ hr **15. a.** $(1, 4)$ and $(-8, 85)$ **b.** $2(1^2) + 5(1) - 3 = 4$ and $1^2 - 2(1) + 5 = 4$; $2(-8)^2 + 5(-8) - 3 = 85$ and $(-8)^2 - 2(-8) + 5 = 85$

17. (–18, 8)

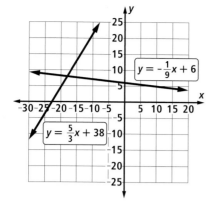

19. a. $y^2 - 5y + 1$ **b.** $y = -0.076$ and $y = 13.076$
21. $18x + 25y$ dollars

Lesson 10-3 (pp. 594–600)

Guided Example 3: $100 - x$; $100 - x$; $100 - x$; 3,000; 30x; 10x; –10x

Questions: 1. 1,190 adults, 2,380 children **3.** $56.00 by the drama club, $224 by the service club **5. a.** $n = 16$, $w = -2$
b. $16 + 5(-2) = 6$ and $-8(-2) = 16$ **7. a.** $x = 6$, $y = 5$
b. $6 - 1 = 5$ and $4(6) - 5 = 19$ **9. a.** (–4, 12)
b.

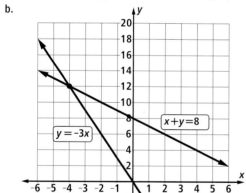

11. (40, –50) **13.** $T = \$870,000$, $L = \$750,000$

15. a. $\begin{cases} m = v + 40 \\ m + v = 1{,}230 \end{cases}$ **b.** $m = 635$, $v = 595$

17. no solution **19.** $x = -2$
21. a.

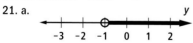

b.

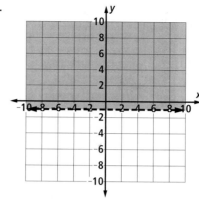

Lesson 10-4 (pp. 601–607)

Guided Example 3: $3N + 2M = 488$; $-3N - 2M = -488$; $4M = 76$; 19; 150; 19; $150; $19

Questions: 1. a. when the coefficients of the same variable are opposites **b.** to eliminate one variable from a system **3. a.** $x = \frac{-35}{4}$, $y = \frac{45}{4}$ **b.** $3\left(-\frac{35}{4}\right) + 9\left(\frac{45}{4}\right) = 75$;
$-3\left(-\frac{35}{4}\right) - \frac{45}{4} = 15$ **5.** 1,634 and 142 **7.** when one of the coefficients for a variable in one equation is the same as the variable's coefficient in another equation
9. $(x, y) = (6, 15)$ **11.** $3(150) + 6(19) = 564$,
$3(150) + 2(19) = 488$ **13.** $(x, y) = \left(12, -\frac{5}{3}\right)$ **15. a.** Yes; by the Generalized Addition Property of Equality **b.** Answers vary. Sample answer: Yes; because $\frac{3}{5} = 60\%$, they are simply different ways of writing the same value.
17. $(x, y) = (0.9, -1.2)$ **19. a.** $x = -7$, $x = 4$ **b.** –7, 4
21. a. $\left\{x: x \geq \frac{9}{2}\right\}$ **b.** All nonnegative numbers **23.** $-\frac{b}{a}$
25. $x = 212$

Lesson 10-5 (pp. 608–615)

1. a. Answers vary. Sample answer: second; –3, d
b. $(x, d) = (69, -112)$ **3. a.** Answers vary. Sample answer: The first equation can be multiplied by 2 and the second equation can be multiplied by –7. **b.** The first equation can be multiplied by 5 and the second equation can be multiplied by 3. **c.** $(r, s) = (3, 4)$ **5. a.** 31 musicians and 26 flag bearers **b.** No, it is not possible. **7.** $(x, y) = \left(-\frac{5}{4}, \frac{10}{3}\right)$
9. $(x, y) = \left(-\frac{13}{5}, -\frac{3}{5}\right)$ **11.** $(x, y) = (-5.\overline{1}, -8.47\overline{2})$ **13.** 5 ER, 30 MC **15. a.** 11 cows, 16 chickens **b.** Answers vary. Sample answer: By assuming there will be 14 chickens and 13 cows, a person would count 80 legs. For every cow replaced by a chicken, we lose 2 legs. Therefore, someone could conclude that there were 16 chickens and 11 cows.
17. $(x, y) = (12, 4)$ **19. a.** 15 weeks **b.** $1,050 **21.** $-\frac{1}{4}$
23. a. true **b.** true **c.** true

Lesson 10-6 (pp. 616-621)

Guided Example 2: 1. $36x - 30y = 6$ **2.** $-36x + 30y = -6$
3. $0 = 0$
Questions: 1. They are equal.

3. a.

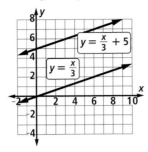

b.

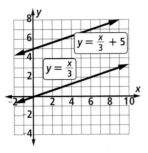

c. $y = \frac{1}{3}x$ **5.** Answers vary. Sample answer:
$\begin{cases} y = 2x + 3 \\ 2y = 4x + 6 \end{cases}$ **7. a.** coincident

b.

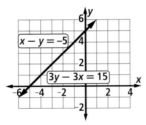

9. a. none **b.** Answers vary. Sample answer: The system
$\begin{cases} x + y = -2 \\ \frac{x+y}{2} = 1 \end{cases}$ has no solution. **11.** coincident lines
13. two intersecting lines **15.** Yes, she got her
15% discount. **17. a.** $t + u = 16, t + 3u = 28$
b. $t = 10, u = 6$ **c.** $6 + 10 = 16, 10 + 18 = 28$ **19. a.** $2d^4$
b. $\sqrt{2^8 + 3(2)^8} = 32 = 2(2)^4$ **21. a.** $x = -6$ **b.** $y = 18$

Lesson 10-7 (pp. 622-628)

1. a. 2×3 **b.** a, b, c **c.** f **3. a.** $\begin{bmatrix} 5 & -2 \\ 3 & 4 \end{bmatrix}$ **b.** $\begin{bmatrix} -4 \\ 34 \end{bmatrix}$

5. -4 **7.** $\begin{bmatrix} 18.5 & -32 \\ -20 & 44 \end{bmatrix}$ **9.** Answers vary.

Sample answer: $\begin{bmatrix} 2 & -1 \\ 1 & 2 \end{bmatrix} \cdot \begin{bmatrix} 3 & -1 \\ -3 & 2 \end{bmatrix} = \begin{bmatrix} 9 & -4 \\ -3 & 3 \end{bmatrix}$,

$\begin{bmatrix} 3 & -1 \\ -3 & 2 \end{bmatrix} \cdot \begin{bmatrix} 2 & -1 \\ 1 & 2 \end{bmatrix} = \begin{bmatrix} 5 & -5 \\ -4 & 7 \end{bmatrix}$ **11.** -10 **13.** Answers

vary. Sample answer: $M = \begin{bmatrix} 1 & 1 \\ 1 & 1 \end{bmatrix}, N = \begin{bmatrix} 2 & 1 \\ 1 & 2 \end{bmatrix}$,

$P = \begin{bmatrix} 0 & -1 \\ 3 & 1 \end{bmatrix}$ **a.** $MN = \begin{bmatrix} 3 & 3 \\ 3 & 3 \end{bmatrix}$ **b.** $MN(P) = \begin{bmatrix} 9 & 0 \\ 9 & 0 \end{bmatrix}$

c. $NP = \begin{bmatrix} 3 & -1 \\ 6 & 1 \end{bmatrix}$ **d.** $M(NP) = \begin{bmatrix} 9 & 0 \\ 9 & 0 \end{bmatrix}$

e. It might be associative. **15.** two intersecting lines, by
comparing the slopes and y-intercepts **17.** $(2.5, 0)$
19. a. $(0.5, 3), (5, 3), (5, -6)$ **b.** $4.5, 9$, and approximately
10.06 **c.** 20.25 units^2 **21.** approximately 27.9%

Lesson 10-8 (pp. 629-634)

1. $(7, -3)$ **3.** $\begin{bmatrix} 1 & 0 \\ 0 & 1 \end{bmatrix} \begin{bmatrix} x \\ y \end{bmatrix} = \begin{bmatrix} 7 \\ -3 \end{bmatrix}$

5. $\begin{bmatrix} 1 & -2 \\ 5 & 4 \end{bmatrix} \cdot \begin{bmatrix} \frac{2}{7} & \frac{1}{7} \\ -\frac{5}{14} & \frac{1}{14} \end{bmatrix} = \begin{bmatrix} \frac{2}{7} & \frac{1}{7} \\ -\frac{5}{14} & \frac{1}{14} \end{bmatrix} \cdot \begin{bmatrix} 1 & -2 \\ 5 & 4 \end{bmatrix} = \begin{bmatrix} 1 & 0 \\ 0 & 1 \end{bmatrix}$

7. a. $\begin{bmatrix} 3 & 5 \\ 2 & 3 \end{bmatrix} \begin{bmatrix} x \\ y \end{bmatrix} = \begin{bmatrix} 27 \\ 17 \end{bmatrix}$ **b.** $\begin{bmatrix} -3 & 5 \\ 2 & -3 \end{bmatrix}$

c. $(x, y) = (4, 3)$ **9. a.** $\begin{bmatrix} 2 & -6 \\ 7.5 & -15 \end{bmatrix} \begin{bmatrix} m \\ t \end{bmatrix} = \begin{bmatrix} -6 \\ -37.5 \end{bmatrix}$

b. $\begin{bmatrix} -1 & 0.4 \\ -0.5 & 0.13 \end{bmatrix}$ **c.** $(m, t) = (-9, -2)$ **11. a.** $\begin{bmatrix} 0.992 & -.413 \\ -1.281 & 0.950 \end{bmatrix}$

$\begin{bmatrix} -5.5 \\ -1.1 \end{bmatrix}$ **b.** $(x, y) = (-5, 6)$ **c.** $2.3(-5) + 6 = -5.5; 3.1(-5) +$

$2.4(6) = -1.1$ **13. a.** III; $\begin{bmatrix} 4 & -5 \\ 12 & -15 \end{bmatrix}$ **b.** Answers vary.

Sample answer: Error: Singular matrix. **15.** $\begin{bmatrix} -20 & 17 \\ -8 & -4 \end{bmatrix}$

17. $a = 8$ **19.** intersecting at only one point
21. a. $x = 12, x = -12$ **b.** $x = 10, x = -10$ **c.** $x = 5, x = -5$
d. $x = -5.5$ **23.** $2,154.76

Lesson 10-9 (pp. 635–639)

Guided Example 3: 1. parallel

2.
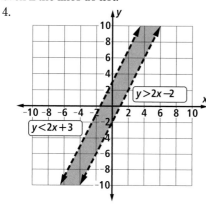

3. below; above. No, because the half-planes can intersect even if the lines do not.

4.
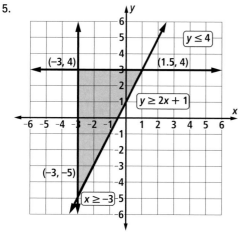

Questions: 1. IV **3. a.** It is the intersection of the half-planes below or on the line $y = 4x + 1$ and above $y = 2x + 1$. **b.** half-plane **c.** Because $\leq$ means less than or equal to, not just less than **d.** No, it is not because it is on the boundary line $y = 2x + 1$.

5.
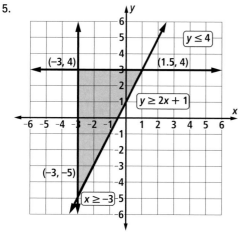

7. Yes it is possible. If there are no solutions satisfying both conditions, then the solution is Ø.

9. $\begin{cases} y \leq 0 \\ 3x + 7y < 10 \end{cases}$ **11. a.** $\begin{cases} 10L + 8P \leq 60 \\ P \geq 0 \\ L \geq 0 \end{cases}$

b.
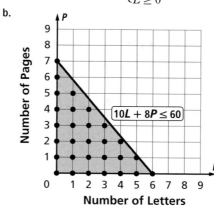

13. a.
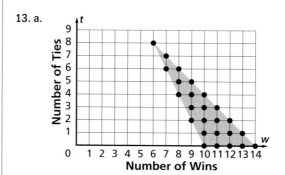

b. 25 **15. a.** $\begin{bmatrix} 6 & 4 \\ -2 & -3 \end{bmatrix} \cdot \begin{bmatrix} x \\ y \end{bmatrix} = \begin{bmatrix} 14 \\ -18 \end{bmatrix}$

b. $\begin{bmatrix} \frac{3}{10} & \frac{2}{5} \\ -\frac{1}{5} & -\frac{3}{5} \end{bmatrix}$ **c.** $(-3, 8)$ **17.** $(6.5, -10.25)$ **19. a.** -10 ft

b. The rocket has already landed.

Lesson 10-10 (pp. 640–644)

Guided Example 1: 7; 12; –2, 7; 3, 12

Questions: 1. (–3, –1)   **3.** (0, 0)   **5.** (4, 61), (–3, –2)

7.

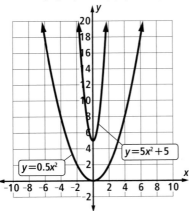

no solution

9. (3, 0)

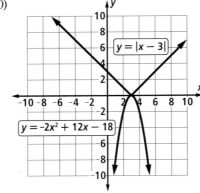

11. $\begin{cases} y = x^2 + 6x + 11 \\ y = -x^2 + 6x - 9 \end{cases}$; multiply the second equation

by –1: $\begin{cases} y = x^2 + 6x + 11 \\ -y = x^2 - 6x + 9 \end{cases}$; then add: $0 = 2x^2 + 20$.

So, $2x^2 = -20, x^2 = -10$ which there is no solution.

13. a. The system must have exactly one solution.
b. 0.41 sec **c.** about 2.76 ft **d.** Answers vary. Sample answer: No, the graph represents the height with respect to time; if the graph were of height with respect to distance traveled, then the graph would be of the ball's flight. **15.** $n = 5$ **17.** $45,604

Self-Test (pp. 648–649)

1. $(x, y) = (-18, -25); x - 7 = 1.5x + 2 - 0.5x = 9; x = -18;$ $y = -25$ **2.** $(d, f) = (6, 3); 4f = 12; f = 3; d = 6$

3. $(g, h) = \left(\frac{-6}{13}, \frac{10}{13}\right); \begin{cases} 7h + 3g = 4 \\ 6h - 3g = 6 \end{cases}$ $13h = 10; h = \frac{10}{13}; g = -\frac{6}{13}$

4. (15, 7)

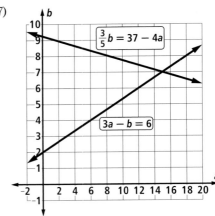

5. (1, –1) and (2, 5). Answers vary. Sample answer: $6x - 7 = x^2 + 3x - 5, x^2 - 3x + 2 = 0, x = 1$ or $x = 2$. When $x = 1, y = -1$. When $x = 2, y = 5$. **6.** This is a linear system of 2 lines with different slopes. Thus there is one solution.

7. $\begin{bmatrix} 2 \cdot 3 + 7 \cdot 4 \\ 1 \cdot 3 + 0 \cdot 4 \end{bmatrix} = \begin{bmatrix} 34 \\ 3 \end{bmatrix}$

8. $\begin{bmatrix} 3 \cdot 2 + 5 \cdot 1 & 3 \cdot 8 + 5 \cdot 7 \\ 4 \cdot 2 + 6 \cdot 1 & 4 \cdot 8 + 6 \cdot 7 \end{bmatrix} = \begin{bmatrix} 11 & 59 \\ 14 & 74 \end{bmatrix}$

9. $\begin{bmatrix} 3 & 5 \\ 1 & -1 \end{bmatrix}\begin{bmatrix} p \\ q \end{bmatrix} = \begin{bmatrix} 5 \\ 7 \end{bmatrix}$

$\begin{bmatrix} \frac{1}{8} & \frac{5}{8} \\ \frac{1}{8} & -\frac{3}{8} \end{bmatrix}\begin{bmatrix} 3 & 5 \\ 1 & -1 \end{bmatrix}\begin{bmatrix} p \\ q \end{bmatrix} = \begin{bmatrix} \frac{1}{8} & \frac{5}{8} \\ \frac{1}{8} & -\frac{3}{8} \end{bmatrix}\begin{bmatrix} 5 \\ 7 \end{bmatrix}$

$\begin{bmatrix} p \\ q \end{bmatrix} = \begin{bmatrix} 5 \\ -2 \end{bmatrix}$

10. $\begin{cases} 3d + 6t = 6{,}795 \\ 4d + 4t = 4{,}860 \end{cases}, \begin{cases} -6d - 12t = -13{,}590 \\ 12d - 12t = 14{,}580 \end{cases}, 6d = 990,$ $d = 165, t = 1{,}050$; DVD players cost $165 each; high-definition televisions cost $1,050 each. **11.** Answers vary. Sample answer: $m = n = 5, c = d = 4$ **12.** All points with integer coordinates in the shaded region below.

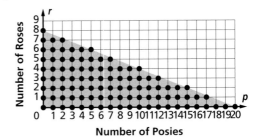

Number of Posies

13. $(0.4, 6.2)$

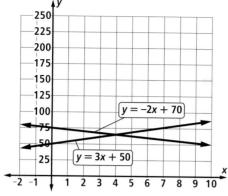

$y = -2x + 70$

$y = 3x + 50$

14. $\begin{cases} 2j + 2w = 1{,}000 \\ 2.5j - 2.5w = 1{,}000 \end{cases} \begin{cases} 2j + 2w = 1{,}000 \\ 2.5j - 2.5w = 1{,}000 \end{cases}$

$j = 500 - w, 2.5(500 - w) - 2.5w = 1{,}000, 1{,}250 - 2.5w - 2.5w = 1{,}000, 5w = 250, w = 50, j = 450$ airplane's speed: 450 mph; speed of jet stream: 50 mph

15. a.

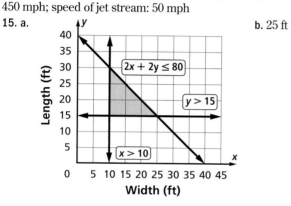

$2x + 2y \le 80$

$y > 15$

$x > 10$

Width (ft)

b. 25 ft

16.

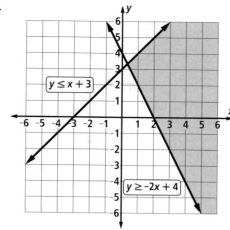

$y \le x + 3$

$y \ge -2x + 4$

17. $\begin{cases} q + d = 15 \\ 0.25q + 0.10d = 2.40 \end{cases}$

$q = 15 - d, 0.25(15 - d) + 0.10d = 2.40, 3.75 - 0.25d + 0.10d = 2.40, -0.15d = -1.35, d = 9, q = 6$; 9 dimes and 6 quarters

18. $\begin{cases} y < 7 \\ y \ge 2x - 7 \\ y \ge -\frac{3}{4}x + 4 \end{cases}$

The chart below keys the **Self-Test** questions to the objectives in the **Chapter Review** on pages 650–653 or to the **Vocabulary (Voc)** on page 647. This will enable you to locate those **Chapter Review** questions that correspond to questions missed on the **Self-Test**. The lesson where the material is covered is also indicated on the chart.

Question	1	2	3	4	5	6	7	8	9	10
Objective(s)	A	B	B	I	E	F	C	C	D	G
Lesson(s)	10-2, 10-3	10-4, 10-5	10-4, 10-5	10-1, 10-6, 10-10	10-10	10-6	10-7	10-7	10-8	10-2, 10-3, 10-4, 10-5, 10-6

Question	11	12	13	14	15	16	17	18
Objective(s)	F	J	I	H	J	J	G	K
Lesson(s)	10-6	10-9	10-1, 10-6, 10-10	10-9	10-9	10-9	10-2, 10-3, 10-4, 10-5, 10-6	10-9

Chapter Review (pp. 650–653)

1. $m = 2, n = 2$ **3.** $(-0.2, 4.6)$ **5.** $(a, b) = \left(-\frac{1}{3}, -\frac{13}{9}\right)$

7. $(f, g) = \left(\frac{102}{7}, -\frac{19}{7}\right)$ **9.** $(v, w) = \left(-\frac{29}{27}, \frac{44}{27}\right)$ **11.** $\begin{bmatrix} -2 \\ 41 \end{bmatrix}$

13. $\begin{bmatrix} 26 & -2 \\ 19 & -13 \end{bmatrix}$ **15. a.** $\begin{bmatrix} 3 & 2 \\ 5 & 7 \end{bmatrix}\begin{bmatrix} x \\ y \end{bmatrix} = \begin{bmatrix} 7 \\ 9 \end{bmatrix}$

b. $\begin{bmatrix} \frac{7}{11} & -\frac{2}{11} \\ -\frac{5}{11} & \frac{3}{11} \end{bmatrix}$ **c.** $\begin{bmatrix} x \\ y \end{bmatrix} = \begin{bmatrix} \frac{31}{11} \\ -\frac{8}{11} \end{bmatrix}$ **17. a.** $\begin{bmatrix} 5 & -7 \\ 4 & -8 \end{bmatrix} \begin{bmatrix} p \\ q \end{bmatrix} = \begin{bmatrix} 20 \\ 14 \end{bmatrix}$

b. $\begin{bmatrix} \frac{2}{3} & -\frac{7}{12} \\ \frac{1}{3} & -\frac{5}{12} \end{bmatrix}$ **c.** $\begin{bmatrix} p \\ q \end{bmatrix} = \begin{bmatrix} \frac{31}{6} \\ \frac{5}{6} \end{bmatrix}$ **19.** $(-1, -2), (1, -2)$

21. 0 solutions **23.** 1 solution **25.** When $a \neq b$, since equating y and subtracting mx from both sides yields $a = b$. **27.** slope **29.** Austin: 280 mi, Antonio: 70 mi **31.** after the fourth year **33.** $\frac{8}{3}$ pints of the 15% solution and $\frac{16}{3}$ pints of the 30% solution

35.

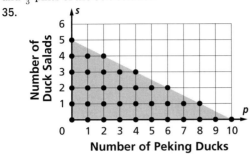

37. a.

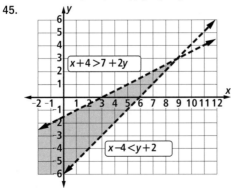

b. 650 ft **c.** 670 ft **39.** $(5, -4.5)$ **41.** infinitely many solutions **43.** $(-4.2, -2.8), (2.7, 7.6)$

45.

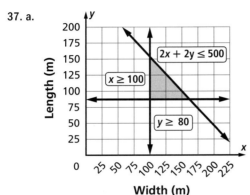

47.

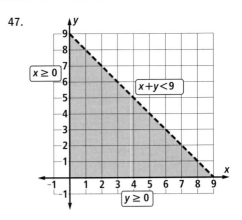

49.

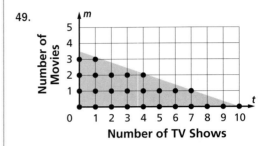

51. $\begin{cases} y \leq 0 \\ y \geq -5 \\ y \leq -2x + 7 \\ y \geq -2x - 5 \end{cases}$

Chapter 11

Lesson 11-1 (pp. 656–662)
Guided Example 2: $100; 100; 3; $120; $120x^2$; $140; 140x^1$ $160
Questions: 1. a. $4,071 **b.** $125.90 **3. a.** $75x^3 + 85x^2 + 95x + 105$ **b.** $225x^3 + 255x^2 + 285x + 315$ **5.** Kelsey is correct. **7.** $84,267 = 8 \cdot 10^4 + 4 \cdot 10^3 + 2 \cdot 10^2 + 6 \cdot 10^1 + 7 \cdot 10^0$
9. $515 **11. a.** $200x^2 + 300x + 250$ **b.** $200x^3 + 300x^2 + 250x + 300$ **c.** $200x^4 + 300x^3 + 250x^2 300x$ **d.** $200x^5 + 300x^4 + 250x^3 + 300x^2$ **13.** D **15.** $54n^2 + 65n - 21$
17. $6x^3 + 2x^2 - 2x + 2$ **19.** $x = \frac{2}{9}$ **21.** $7y^2 + 4y - 22$
23. $0.56 **25. a.** $h = \frac{1}{2}$ **b.** h can be any real number but $\frac{1}{2}$.
27. a. cross-fertilized: skewed left; self-fertilized: symmetric **b.** Cross-fertilize the plants because the mean is greater than that of self-fertilized plants.

Lesson 11-2 (pp. 663–668)
Guided Example: 1. $22w + 8$ **2.** 2 **3.** $x^3 - x^2 - 12; 3$
4. $2x - 2; 1$ **Questions: 1.** $3x^2 + 4$ is a sum of monomials, while $\frac{3}{x^2} + 4$ includes a quotient of monomials.
3. a. a monomial **b.** 11 **5. a.** a monomial **b.** 2 **7.** xyz is not a trinomial, it is a monomial because there is only one term. **9.** $-3x^5 + 8x^2 - 4x + 12$ **11.** $3x^2 + 2x + 5$

13. never; Polynomials with the same degree are like terms; to find their sum you add the coefficients. Thus, the degrees of the sum may be less than or equal to, but will never be greater than the degree of either addend.
15. a. $-140x^2$ **b.** 2   **17. a.** $2xy$ **b.** 2   **19. a.** 3 **b.** 3 **c.** 3
d. 3   **21.** 1   **23.** 2 **25. a.** Answers vary. Sample answer:
x^{70} **b.** Answers vary. Sample answer: $x^{35}y^{35}$
27. a. Answers vary. Sample answer: $x^5 + x + 1, x^5 + x + 6$
b. Answers vary. Sample answer: $x^5 + 6x + 8, -x^5 + 4x + 2$
29. a. $1{,}000x^{18}$ **b.** $2,406.61   **31.** 2 m   **33.** $n^2 + 52n$

Lesson 11-3 (pp. 669-674)

1. $55x^2$ **3. a.** $3h^2 + 15h$

b.

	h	1	1	1	1	1
h	h^2	h	h	h	h	h
h	h^2	h	h	h	h	h
h	h^2	h	h	h	h	h

5. a. $4x^2 + 2x$ **b.** $2x(2x + 1)$
c. $4x^2 + 2x = 2x(2x + 1)$
7. $ab - ac + ad$
9. $-25x^3 - 5x^2 + 31x$
11. $-2ab^2 + a^2b - 5ab$

13. a. $(2 + h)C + (2 + h)B + (2 + h)E$ **b.** $h(C + B + E) + 2(C + B + E)$ **c.** $(2 + h)(C + B + E)$ **15.** $4x^2$
17. $2m^4 + 2m^3 + 6m^2$ **19.** $4xy$ **21.** $20n^2 + 9n - 10$
23. a. not a polynomial **b.** The term $2a^{-2}$ is not a monomial and polynomials are all monomials or sums of monomials.   **25.** Answers vary. Sample answer: $x^4 + x + 1$
27. $c > \frac{4}{3}$ **29.** $\frac{10}{9m}$ **31.** $y = \frac{1}{2}(x - 1)$

Lesson 11-4 (pp. 675-679)

Guided Example 3: 4; a; $4a$; $5a^2b$; 2; $-3a^4b^2$; $5a^2b$; 2; $3a^4b^2$
Questions: 1. $1, 3, 11, 33, x, x^2, x^3, x^4, 3x, 3x^2, 3x^3, 3x^4,$
$11x, 11x^2, 11x^3, 11x^4, 33x, 33x^2, 33x^3, 33x^4$ **3.** a^2b
5. a. The greatest common factor of $15c^2 + 5c$ is $5c$.
So $15c^2 + 5c = 5c(3c + 1)$.

b.

	c	c	c	1
c	c^2	c^2	c^2	c
c	c^2	c^2	c^2	c
c	c^2	c^2	c^2	c
c	c^2	c^2	c^2	c
c	c^2	c^2	c^2	c

7. The factor of both x^2 and xy is x and thus, it is factorable.   **9.** $6n^4 + 5n^2$
11. $33(a - b + ab)$
13. $4v^9(3 + 4v)$ **15.** $7rh$

17. a. 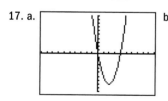 **b.**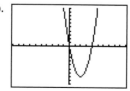

c. The two graphs are the same because $2x(x - 4)$ is a factored form of $2x^2 - 8x$, so the two equations describe the same graph.   **19.** $2\pi r(r + h)$

21. $-50n^{98} - 40n^{78} + 30n^{58}$ for $n \neq 0$
23. $2k^3 - kn + 4n^2$ **25.** B   **27.** 121

Lesson 11-5 (pp. 680–684)

Guided Example 1: $5x$; (-3); $5x$; (-3); $5x$; (-3); $5x^3$; $(-3x^2)$;
$(-20x^2)$; $12x$; $40x$; (-24); $5x^3$; $-23x^2$; $52x$; -24
Questions: 1. a. $(y + 12) \cdot (y^2 + 5y + 7)$ **b.** $y^3 + 17y^2 + 67y + 84$ **3. a.** $12x^2 - 22x - 20$ **b.** $(2(10) - 5) \cdot (6(10) + 4)$
$= 960$; $12(10)^2 - 22(10) - 20 = 960$

c.

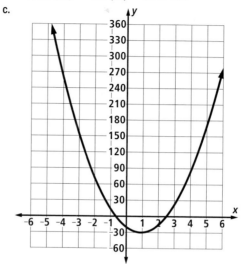

5. $2n^3 + 5n^2 + 2n - 1$ **7.** $4x^4 + 16$ **9.** $5c^2 + 28d^2 - 39cd$
$+ c - 7d$ **11. a.** $12x^2 + 26x + 10$ **b.** $12x^2 - 26x + 10$
c. The expansion of $(a - b)(c - d)$ is the same as the expansion of $(a + b)(c + d)$, except the second term has the opposite sign.   **13.** $\frac{1}{25}x^2 - 1.08x + 7.29$ **15.** $n = 5$ or
$n = -\frac{31}{2}$ **17.** $-5x^2 - 8$ **19. a.** $\frac{33}{16}$ **b.** 6 **c.** 69

Lesson 11-6 (pp. 685–690)

Guided Example 2: Solution 1: $2 \cdot 7c \cdot 5$; 5^2; 49; 70; 25
Solution 2: $7c$; 5; $7c$; $7c$; 5; 5; 49; 70; 25
Solution 3:

	7c	5
7c	$49c^2$	$35c$
5	$35c$	25

$49c^2 + 70c + 25$
Check: 26; 676; 49; 70; 25; 49; 70; 25; 676

Questions: 1. $g^2 + 2gh + h^2$ **3.** $g^2 - h^2$ **5.** Answers vary. Sample answer: $x^2 + 2x + 1$

7. a.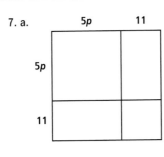

b. $(5p + 11)^2$ c. $25p^2 + 110p + 121$ 9. $x^2 - 10x + 25$ 11. $n^4 - 16$ 13. $81 - 36x + 4x^2$ 15. $9x^2 - y^2z^2$ 17. a. 900; Answers vary. Sample answer: $30^2 = (3 \cdot 10)^2 = 3^2 \cdot 10^2 = 900$ b. 899;

Answers vary. Sample answer: $29 \cdot 31 = (30 - 1)(30 + 1) = 30^2 - 1^2 = 899$ c. 896; Answers vary. Sample answer: $28 \cdot 32 = (30 - 2)(30 + 2) = 30^2 - 2^2 = 896$ d. 891; Answers vary. Sample answer: $27 \cdot 33 = (30 - 3)(30 + 3) = 30^2 - 3^2 = 891$ 19. 40,401; Answers vary. Sample answer: $201^2 = (200 + 1)(200 + 1) = 200^2 + 2 \cdot 200 \cdot 1 + 1^2 = 40,401$ 21. perfect square trinomial 23. perfect square trinomial 25. difference of squares 27. If the sum is 100, the two numbers can be written as $(50 + x)$ and $(50 - x)$, and the product is $2{,}500 - x^2$. That value is greatest when $x^2 = 0$, or $x = 0$, so the numbers are 50 and 50. 29. $18x^2 + 2y^2$ 31. a. $2{,}000$ b. 800 c. Answers vary. Sample answer: $x = 1.03$; $10{,}453.31$ 33. Answers vary. Sample answer: the volume of a cube with side e 35. Answers vary. Sample answer: the area of the region between a circle with radius s that is inside a circle with radius r

Lesson 11-7 (pp. 691-696)

Guided Example 2: without; 11; 10; 9; 11; 10; 9; 990
Questions: 1. a. Answers vary. Sample answer: ABCD, ABCE b. 360 permutations 3. $n(n - 1)$ 5. a. Answers vary. Sample answer: VWXYZ, ZYXWV b. 120 permutations 7. $n!$ 9. 56 11. $\frac{1}{272}$ 13. Yes, $n! = n \cdot (n - 1)!$, for $n \geq 1$ 15. a. 24 b. 3157; 3159; 3175; 3179; 3195; 3197; 3517; 3519; 3571; 3579; 3591; 3597; 3715; 3719; 3751; 3759; 3791; 3795; 3915; 3917; 3951; 3957; 3971; 3975

17. ABCD, ABDC, ACBD, ACDB, ADBC, ADCB 19. The smaller circle has $8\pi(r - 2)$ square units less area.
21. $6x^4 + 2x + 4, x \neq 0$ 23. Answers vary. Sample answer: $-3x^3 + 4x^2 + 7$

Lesson 11-8 (pp. 697-702)

1. how different a set of actually observed scores is from a set of expected scores 3. for expected frequencies less than 5 5. a. 23.7 b. Yes, the chi-square value of 23.7 for 7 events occurs with probability less than 0.001. 7. The spinner seems to be fair. 9. The chi-square value of 44.9 for 4 events occurs with probability less than 0.001, so there is evidence for the view that more tornadoes occur at certain times of the year (spring) than at others. 11. a. 120 b. 720 13. a. $4x^2 + 4xy + y^2$ b. $4x^2 - 4xy + y^2$ c. $4x^2 - y^2$ 15. $9k^4 - 36k^3m + 54k^2m^2 - 36m^3k + 9m^4$ 17. a. 3.6 cm/day b. 25.2 cm/wk

Self-Test (pp. 706-707)

1. $3x(10 - 4x + x^3) = 30x - 12x^2 + 3x^4 = 3x^4 - 12x^2 + 30x$
2. $(2b - 5)^2 = (2b - 5)(2b - 5) = (2b)^2 - 2(2b)(5) + 5^2 = 4b^2 - 20b + 25$ 3. $(8z + 3)(8z - 3) = (8z)^2 - 3^2 = 64z^2 - 9$
4. $6a(2a^2 + 9a - 1) = 12a^3 + 54a^2 - 6a$ 5. $(5a^2 - a)$ $(5a^2 - a) = (5a^2)^2 - 2(5a^2)(a) + a^2 = 25a^4 - 10a^3 + a^2$
6. $(2 - 6c)(4 + 3c) = 2(4 + 3c) - 6c(4 + 3c) = 8 + 6c - 24c - 18c^2 = -18c^2 - 18c + 8$ 7. 3 8. In standard form the polynomial is $19x^3 - 9x^2 + 2x - 5$ and has four terms, so it is not a monomial, binomial, nor a trinomial.
9. $6x^2y^2(2x - 4y + 5y^2)$ 10. $(20n^2 - 8n - 12) + (16n^3 - 7n^2 + 5) = 16n^3 + (20n^2 - 7n^2) - 8n + (5 - 12) = 16n^3 + 13n^2 - 8n^2 - 7$ 11. $9p^4 + p^2 - 5 - p(3p^3 + p - 2) = 9p^4 + p^2 - 5 - 3p^4 - p^2 + 2p = 6p^4 + 2p - 5$ 12. False; the expression has three terms so it is a trinomial, but the highest power of a variable term is 2 so it has degree 2.
13. $\frac{28w^3 - 18w}{2w} = \frac{28w^3}{2w} - \frac{18w}{2w} = 14w^2 - 9$ 14. area of rectangle: $(2n + 2)(2n - 2)$; area of triangle: $\frac{1}{2}(n + 3)(n - 1)$; area of shaded region $= 4n^2 - 4 - \frac{1}{2}n^2 - n + \frac{3}{2} = \frac{7}{2}n^2 - n - \frac{5}{2}$ 15. 840; There are 7 swimmers to choose from to swim first, then 6 left to choose the second swimmer, 5 left to choose the third swimmer, and 4 swimmers left to pick the final racer. Thus, there are $7 \cdot 6 \cdot 5 \cdot 4 = 840$ possible orders. 16. 13,800; There are 25 students who could get 1st place, then 24 remaining who could get 2nd place, and 23 remaining to get 3rd place. $25 \cdot 24 \cdot 23 = 13{,}800$ different permutations. 17. For each year that she has had a certain amount of money she receives interest on that amount at the rate of x, thus M dollars received n years ago will be worth Mx^n dollars. So on her 21st birthday she will have $200x^5 + 150x^4 + 300x^3 + 300x^2$ dollars. 18. $200(1.03)^5 + 150(1.03)^4 + 300(1.03)^3 + 300(1.03)^2 = 1{,}046.77$; she would have $1{,}046.77 on her 21st birthday. 19. a. $9x^2 + 18x$ b. $3x(3x + 6)$ c. No, 3 can be factored out of the parentheses and it can be factored completely to get $9x(x + 2)$.

20.

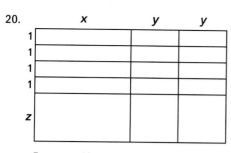

$5x + xz + 10y + 2yz$

21. The probability of the chi-square value of 11.03 for 6 events is between 0.10 and 0.05, so the results aren't very far from a random distribution; the die is probably not weighted. **22.** $x^2 + 8x + 16$; See students' work.

The chart below keys the **Self-Test** questions to the objectives in the **Chapter Review** on pages 708–711 or to the **Vocabulary (Voc)** on page 705. This will enable you to locate those **Chapter Review** questions that correspond to questions missed on the **Self-Test.** The lesson where the material is covered is also indicated on the chart.

Question	1	2	3	4	5	6	7	8	9	10
Objective	B	D	B	B	D	B	E	E	C	A
Lesson(s)	11-3, 11-5, 11-6	11-6	11-3, 11-5, 11-6	11-3, 11-5, 11-6	11-6	11-3, 11-5, 11-6	11-2	11-2	11-4	11-1, 11-2

Question	11	12	13	14	15	16	17	18	19	20
Objective	A, B	E	C	I	G	G	F	F	C, I	I
Lesson(s)	11-1, 11-2, 11-3	11-2	11-4	11-3, 11-5, 11-6	11-7	11-7	11-1	11-1	11-3, 11-4, 11-5	11-3, 11-5, 11-6

Question	21	22
Objective	H	I
Lesson(s)	11-8	11-3, 11-5, 11-6

Chapter Review (pp. 708–711)

1. $4k^3 - 17k$ **3.** $5.4s^4 + 3.7x^3 + 9.8s^2 - 5.2s - 4$ **5.** -21
7. $9p^4 + 9p^3 - 54p^2 + 45p$ **9.** $\frac{1}{7}q^{11} - 2q^{10} + 16q^9 - \frac{5}{7}q^8$
11. $b^2 - 9$ **13.** $-72w^2 + 2$ **15.** $n^3 - 9n^2 + 26n - 24$
17. $\frac{51}{2}x^2 - \frac{11}{2}x - 1$ **19.** $uv(u - v)$ **21.** $15a^3b^2(3a^6b^3 + 4a^3b^2 - a^2b + 28)$ **23.** $p^2 + 12p + 36$ **25.** $2{,}025z^2 - 990z + 121$ **27.** B **29.** Answers vary. Sample answer: $xy^3z + 3y + 9$ **31.** b and c **33.** c **35. a.** $1{,}200x^3 + 700x^2 + 500x$ **b.** \$373.05 **37.** 2,520 different ways
39. 10,000 different ways **41.** 4,536 different ways
43. 504 different ways **45. a.** The company expected 36 pieces of mail each day Tuesday through Friday and 109 pieces on Monday. **b.** 5.523 **c.** There is no evidence for the belief that there was too much mail coming on Monday. The probability of a chi-square value of 5.523 for 5 events is greater than 0.1, so it is likely the deviation from the expected amount of mail was due to random chance.
47. a. $ab + 2a + 6b + 12$ **b.** $(a + 6)(b + 2)$ **c.** Yes, the answers are equal. **49. a.** $3x(2x + 1)$ **b.** $6x^2 + 3x$

51.

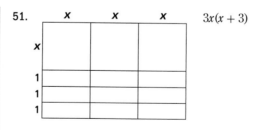

$3x(x + 3)$

Chapter 12

Lesson 12-1 (pp. 714–722)

Guided Example 4: a. $24 - 2L$; $12 - L$; $12 - L$; $(12 - L)$
c. 9 units; $3 \cdot 9$; 27 units^2; 2 units; $10 \cdot 2$; 20 units^2; 36 units^2; 6 units; 6 units
Questions: 1. a. $(-8, -16)$ **b.** $x = -8$ **3.** because $(x - 5)^2$ is never negative, $-4(x - 5)^2$ is never positive, and the greatest nonpositive number is 0, and so the greatest value of $-4(x - 5)^2 + 7$ is 7. **5. a.** $(15, 21)$ **b.** $x = 15$ **c.** up
7. a. $(-6, -0.5)$ **b.** $x = -6$ **c.** down **9.** All 3 graphs have $(4, -8)$ as their vertex, c opens up wider than a, and a opens up wider than b. **11.** $y - 9 = -(x + 12)^2$

13. $y + 6 = -0.5x^2$ **15.** Answers may vary. Sample:
$y + 18 = -(x - 5)^2$ and $y + 18 = -2(x - 5)^2$ **17.** (23, 5)
19. Answers may vary. Sample:

	a	8
a		
a		
a		

21. $m = \pm\sqrt{3}$ or $m = \pm 2\sqrt{3}$ **23.** 5:20 P.M.   **25. a.** $x = 0$
b. $x < 0$

Lesson 12-2 (pp. 723–728)

1. $x^2 + 14x + 49$ **3.** $100; x + 10$ **5. a.** 1 **b.** $x + 1$
7. a. 12.25 **b.** $r - 3.5$ **9. a.** $\frac{1}{4}b^2$ **b.** $w - \frac{1}{2}b$
11. a. $y + 1.25 = (x - 1.5)^2$ **b.** -1.25 **13. a.** (1, 22)
b. maximum   **15.** No, because the minimum value of y is
0.75 since the vertex is (0.5, 0.75).   **17.** $x = \sqrt{137} - 12$ or
$x = -\sqrt{137} - 12$ **19.** The data do support the hypothesis.
The chi-square statistic yielded a value of approximately 4.
For $n = 3$, this occurs with a probability greater than 0.10.
So there is no reason to question the expected values of
the hypothesis.   **21.** 7.5   **23.** $120.83

Lesson 12-3 (pp. 729–735)

1. 8; –4   **3.** $x = 32$ or $x = -89.326$ **5.** $p = 0$ or $p = -19$
7. a. –15 and –7 **b.** (–11, –16)
c.

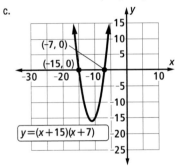

d.

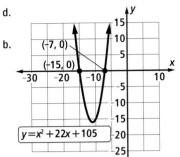

$y = x^2 + 22x + 105$
9. a. 0 and $-\frac{11}{4}$
$\left(-\frac{11}{8}, \frac{121}{16}\right)$

b.

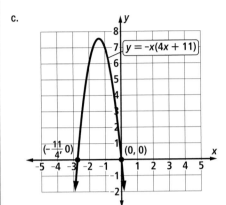

c.

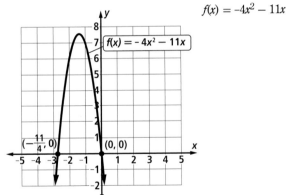

$f(x) = -4x^2 - 11x$

d.

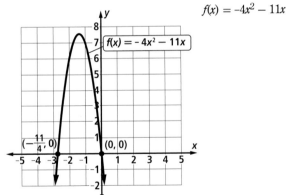

11. a. $x = -6.5$ **b.** Answers may vary. Sample: $y = 3(x + 11) \cdot$
$(x + 2), y = (x + 11)(x + 2), y = 50(x + 11) \cdot (x + 2)$
13. a. –5 **b.** $y = 2(x - 1)(x + 5); y + 18 = 2(x + 2)^2;$
$y = 2x^2 + 8x - 10$ **15. a.** $y - 5 = -(x - 5)^2$ **b.** (5, 5)

c.

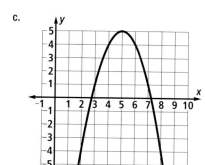

b.

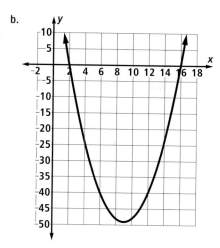

17. $25n^2 - 64$ **19. a.** $(2, -4)$ **b.** $(a, 0)$ **c.** (r, s)

Lesson 12-4 (pp. 736–741)

Guided Example 2:

Product is −30	Sum of Factors
−1, 30	20
−2, 15	13
−3, 10	7
−5, 6	1
−6, 5	−1
−10, 3	−7
−15, 2	−13
−30; 1	−29

−6; 5; 6; 5 **Check 1:** 6; 5; 5; 6 **Check 2:** 6; 5

Guided Example 4: 1. −24; 5 **2.** 1 **3.** $m + 8$; $m - 3$
Check: $x + 8$; $x - 3$

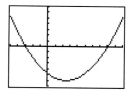

Questions: 1. a. factors: 1, 24; 2, 12; 3, 8; 4, 6; sums: 25, 14,
11, 10 **b.** $(x + 4)(x + 6)$ **c.** $(x + 4)(x + 6) = x^2 + 6x + 4x +$
$24 = x^2 + 10x + 24$ **3.** Simona's factorization is correct.
The b term in Sandra's factorization is $6 - 8 = -2$, not 2 as
desired. The c term in Steve's factorization is $(-6)(-8) = 48$,
not −48 as desired. **5.** $(q + 1)(q + 19)$ **7.** $(v - 1)(v - 101)$
9. $(m - 2)(m + 19)$ **11. a.** $(x - 3)(x - 5)$ **b.** 3, 5
13. a. $y = (x - 2)(x - 16)$

15. $-(x - 8)(x - 5)$ **17.** $n = 10$ or $n = -12$. Check:
If $n = 10$, $(n - 10)(\frac{1}{2}n + 6) = 0 \cdot 11 = 0$. If $n = -12$,
$(n - 10)(\frac{1}{2}n + 6) = -22 \cdot 0 = 0$.   **19.** 20.25
21. $25a^2 - 9$ **23.** $9z^2 + 10$, $z \neq 0$ **25.** $4(7b^4 + 2b^2 + 10)$
27. slope $= \frac{1}{4}$, y-intercept $= 0$

Lesson 12-5 (pp. 742–747)

Guided Example 3: 15; 15; 1; −7; 1; 7; −1; $15y^2 + 32y - 7$;
$15y^2 - 32y - 7$; $15y^2 + 16y - 7$; $15y^2 - 16y - 7$; 1; 15;
$15y^2 + 104y - 7$; 1; 15; $15y^2 - 104y - 7$; 1; 15; $15y^2 - 8y - 7$;
1; 15; $15y^2 + 8y - 7$; $(3y + 1)(5y - 7)$
Guided Example 4: $3y + 1$; $5y - 7$; $3y + 1$; $5y - 7$; $-\frac{1}{3}$; $\frac{7}{5}$
Questions: 1. a. $8x^2 + 22x + 15$ **b.** $8x^2 + 26x + 15$
c. $8x^2 + 34x + 15$ **d.** $8x^2 + 62x + 15$ **e.** All of these would
be found in the process of trying to factor the trinomial.
3. a. $2(x^2 + 7x + 1)$ **b.** $5(n^2 + 7n - 10)$ **5.** $-(x - 3)(3x - 2)$
7. prime **9.** $(x - 1)(17x - 19)$ **11.** $x = -\frac{3}{4}$ or $x = \frac{1}{5}$
13. $\left(\frac{3}{8}, -\frac{1}{8}\right)$ **15. a.** $n = -2$ or $n = \frac{1}{3}$ **b.** The solution works.
17. $p^2(5p + 3)^2$ **19. a.** $(x^4 - 4)(x^4 + 4)$ **b.** $(x^2 - 2)(x^2 + 2)$
$(x^4 + 4)$ **21.** $4 - \sqrt{13}, 4 + \sqrt{13}$ **23.** A

Lesson 12-6 (pp. 748–753)

Guided Example 2: 1. $2x^2 + 5x - 10$ **2.** 2; 5; −10 **3.** 105
4. no **5.** The expression is not factorable with integer
coefficients.
Questions: 1. 169; factorable, $(x - 11)(x + 2)$ **3.** 0;
factorable; $(2n - 3)(2n - 3)$ **5.** 337; prime

7. The x-intercepts will be rational numbers when the expression is factorable. This occurs when $b^2 - 4ac$ is a perfect square. **9.** $n = 999$ **11.** Answers vary. Sample answer: $k = 8$ **13.** $(r - 4)(r - 1)$ **15. a.** $c = 20.25$ **b.** $(w + 4.5)(w + 4.5)$ **17.** $\frac{4m^7}{3n^3}$ **19.** $\frac{x^2}{25y^2}$

Lesson 12-7 (pp. 754–760)

Guided Example 1: $(x - 7.8)$; $(x + 46)$; $(x + 200)$; $x - 7.8$; $x + 46$; $x + 200$

Questions: 1. a. -5; 1.5

b.

c. $f(x) = 2x^2 + 7x - 15$ **3. a.** 1; -0.5

b.

c. $y = -12x^3 + 9x + 3$ **5.** Answers vary. Sample answer: $y = (x + 9)(x - 4)$ **7. a.** Answers vary. Sample answer: $y = (x - 2)(x + 2) \cdot (x - 5)(x + 5)$ **b.** $y = x^4 - 29x^2 + 100$ **9.** Answers vary. Sample answer: $y = (x + 3)(x - 2)(x - 7)$ **11.** Answers vary. Sample answer: $y = (x + 5)^2(x - 4)^2$ **13. a.** 55; $1 + 4 + 9 + 16 + 25 = 55$ **b.** $(n + 1)^2$ **c.** $S(n) = \frac{1}{3}n^3 + \frac{1}{2}n^2 + \frac{1}{6}n$

15. a.

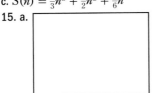

b. Answers vary. Sample answer: The graph crosses the x-axis at the x-intercept 5. **c.** Answers vary. Sample answer: The graph crosses the x-axis at the x-intercept 5. **d.** Answers vary. Sample answer: If a polynomial in factored form has a term of the form $(x - a)^3$, then the graph will cross the x-axis at $(a, 0)$. **17.** $4(a + 2b)(a - 2b)$ **19.** $a = -11$ or $a = 5$ **21.** B

Lesson 12-8 (pp. 761–767)

Guided Example 1: 1. $(2n + 1)^2$ **2.** $(2n + 1)(2n - 1)$ **3.** 2; 1; 2; 1; 2; 1; 2; 1 **4.** 2; 1; 2; 1

Guided Example 3: d; b; $ad + bc$

Questions: 1. A rational expression is the written quotient of two polynomials. **3.** $\frac{5b}{2c^2}$, $a \neq 0$, $b \neq 0$, $c \neq 0$ **5. a.** $\frac{2x - 3}{x + 2}$ **b.** 2 and -2 **c.** $\frac{2(10) - 3}{(10) + 2} = \frac{17}{12} = \frac{2(10)^2 - 7(10) + 6}{(10)^2 - 4}$ **7.** $\frac{1 \cdot 15 + 9 \cdot 7}{9 \cdot 15} = \frac{78}{135} = \frac{26}{45}$ **9.** Answers vary. Sample answer: Let $k = 2$; then $\frac{6}{2 + 1} - \frac{3(2) + 7}{4 - 1} = -\frac{7}{3} = \frac{3(2) - 13}{(2 - 1)(2 + 1)}$ **11.** $\frac{15}{8n}$; let $n = 1$, $\frac{3}{2} + \frac{3}{8} = \frac{12}{8} + \frac{3}{8} = \frac{15}{8}$. **13.** $\frac{24x^2 - 29}{15(x - 1)}$; $x = 0$, then we have $\frac{8}{5} - \frac{1}{-3} = \frac{29}{15} = \frac{-29}{-15}$. **15.** $\frac{(x - 6)(x - 4)(x - 2)}{(x + 2)(x + 4)(x + 6)}$ **17. a.** $S = 819$, $F = 91$, $\frac{S}{F} = 9$ **b.** $\frac{S}{F} = \frac{2n + 1}{3}$ **c.** $\frac{S}{F}$ will only be an integer if $2n + 1$ is a multiple of 3. However, we know for some n, such as $n = 2$, $2n + 1$ will not be a multiple of 3 so $\frac{S}{F}$ is not an integer for that n. **19. a.** $t = \frac{v}{4.9}$ **b.** v is a multiple of 4.9. Answers vary. Sample answer: t is an integer if $v = 4.9$ m/sec and t is not an integer if $v = 10$ m/sec. **21.** $0.09x^2$ **23.** 17 questions right

Self-Test (pp. 771–772)

1. The product is -40, so possible factors include 10 and -4, -10 and 4, 8 and -5, and because $8 + -5 = 3$, the two factors are 8 and -5. Thus, $(x + 8)(x - 5)$ **2.** The product is 72, and the sum is negative. Therefore, possible factors include -18 and -4, -24 and -3, and -8 and -9, and since $-8 + -9 = -17$, the two factors are -8 and -9. Thus, $(m - 8)(m - 9)$ **3.** $a = -9$, so possible factors are 3 and -3, 9 and -1, or -9 and 1. $c = -2$, so the factors are either 2 and -1 or -2 and 1. Because $dg + ef = 9$, $d = -3$, $e = 2$, $f = 3$, and $g = -1$ as this is the only combination that works. Thus, $(-3h + 2)(3h - 1)$ **4.** B **5.** To complete the square, we add $\left(\frac{1}{2}b\right)^2$, so because $(-6)^2 = 36$, add 36.

6. $\frac{3x^2 - 75}{2x^2 - 7x - 15} = \frac{3(x^2 - 25)}{(2x + 3)(x - 5)} = \frac{3(x + 5)(x - 5)}{(2x + 3)(x - 5)} = \frac{3(x + 5)}{2x + 3}$, $x \neq 5$; $x \neq -\frac{3}{2}$ **7.** D **8. a.** By the Factor Theorem, the polynomial must have the factors $(x - 0) = x$, $(x + 3)$, and $(x - 9)$. One such polynomial is $y = x(x + 3)(x - 9)$. **b.** $y = x^3 - 6x^2 - 27x$ **9.** Let x be the length of a side of the frame. Since the area of the painting is 12 square feet, we can write $(x - 1)(x - 2) = 12$. We then put the equation in standard form, so $x^2 - 3x + 2 = 12$, which gives $x^2 - 3x - 10 = 0$. This factors as $(x - 5)(x + 2)$, so we have $(x - 5)(x + 2) = 0$. We cannot have a frame that has length -2, so the frame must have side length 5 feet. **10.** To put the equation in $y - k = a(x - h)^2$ form, we must complete the square. Thus, since $\left(\frac{1}{2}b\right)^2 = 1$, we must add 4 to both sides to get $y + 4 = x^2 - 2x + 1$. This then factors as $y + 4 = (x - 1)^2$, so the vertex is at $(1, -4)$. **11.** To put the equation in $y - k = a(x - h)^2$ form, we must complete the square. First, we move the 7 to the other side and factor a -2 out of the right hand side, which gives $y - 7 = -2(x^2 + 2x)$. Thus, because $\left(\frac{1}{2}b\right)^2 = 1$, we must add 1 into the $(x^2 + 2x)$ quantity. This gives $y - 9 = -2(x^2 + 2x + 1)$, which factors as $y - 9 = -2(x + 1)^2$.

Thus, the vertex is at $(-1, 9)$.   **12.** By the equation, the vertex is at $(3, 4)$ and a is positive, so the graph opens up.

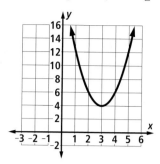

13. By the equation, the zeros of the function are at $x = 5$ and $x = -4$. Also, the axis of symmetry is $x = 0.5$, so the vertex is at $(0.5, -20.25)$.

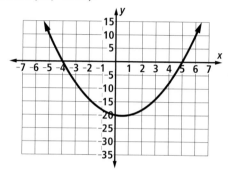

14. First, factor out $3n^2$ to get $3n^2(n^2 - 5n + 6)$. Now deal with what is in the parentheses. Because $c = 6$, possible factors include 3 and 2, –3 and –2, 6 and 1, and –6 and –1. Because $-3 + -2 = -5$, we have $3n^2(n - 3)(n - 2)$.
15. Let x be the length of the shorter side. Then $x(x + 9) = 486$, which gives $x^2 + 9x = 486$. Solving this equation gives x to be –27 or 18, but because length is positive, $x = 18$, so the dimensions are 18 cm by 27 cm.   **16.** False. A quadratic expression is only factorable over the integers when the discriminant is a perfect square, and not all positive numbers are perfect squares.   **17.** Answers vary. Sample answer: $y = 0.04(x + 3)^2(x - 1)(x - 4)$
18. a. Yes, they are equivalent because expanding each equation gives $x^2 + 4x + 3$. **b.** the vertex of the parabola

The chart below keys the **Self-Test** questions to the objectives in the **Chapter Review** on pages 773–775 or to the **Vocabulary (Voc)** on page 770. This will enable you to locate those **Chapter Review** questions that correspond to questions missed on the **Self-Test**. The lesson where the material is covered is also indicated on the chart.

Question	1	2	3	4	5	6	7	8	9	10
Objective	B	B	B	E	A	D	J	F	G	I
Lesson(s)	12-4, 12-5	12-4, 12-5	12-4, 12-5	12-4, 12-5, 12-6	12-2	12-8	12-3	12-7	12-1	12-2

Question	11	12	13	14	15	16	17	18
Objective	I	H	J	C	G	E	F	H
Lesson(s)	12-2	12-1	12-3	12-7	12-1	12-4, 12-5, 12-6	12-7	12-1

Chapter Review (pp. 773–775)

1. a. 4 **b.** $(x+2)^2 - 4$ **3. a.** $\left(\frac{1}{2}b\right)^2$ **b.** $\left(\frac{z+1}{2}b\right)^2 - \left(\frac{1}{2}b\right)^2$

5. $(x-3)(x+2)$ **7.** $(m-6)(m+4)$ **9.** $(3x+4)(x-2)$

11. $2(3d+2)(d-2)$ **13. a.** $x=3, x=-1, x=\frac{11}{2}$

b. $y = 12x^3 - 90x^2 + 96x + 198$ **15. a.** $x=4, x=\frac{7}{2}, x=-2$

b. $f(x) = 2x^3 - 11x^2 - 2x + 56$ **17.** $4(n-2m); n \neq 0,$

$m \neq 0$ **19.** $\frac{3-4n}{n-3}$ **21.** $\frac{-(m-4)}{(2m-7)}$ **23.** perfect squares

25. $3(x+3)(5x+8)$ **27.** $2(4x^2 + 17x + 91)$

29. a. Answers vary. Sample answer: $f(x) = (x-2)(x+2)$

b. $f(x) = (x-2)(x+2) = x^2 - 4$ **31.** Answers vary.

Sample answer: $y = 4(x+4)(x-1)(x-2)$

33. a. $A = 10x - x^2; P = 20$ **b.** $5 - \sqrt{5}$ units by $5 + \sqrt{5}$

units **35. a.** $A = x(195 - x)$ **b.** 9,000 yd^2

37. 90 m by 140 m

39.

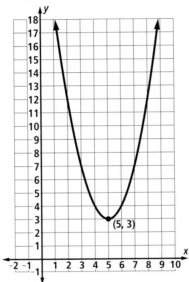

(5, 3)

41.

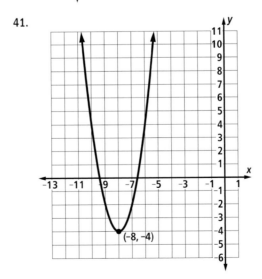

(-8, -4)

43. ii **45.** iii **47.** (0, 0) **49.** $\left(\frac{1}{3}, -\frac{14}{3}\right)$

51.

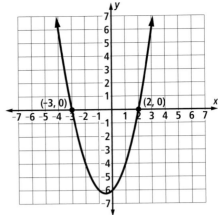

(-3, 0) (2, 0)

53.

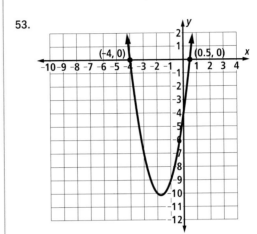

(-4, 0) (0.5, 0)

Chapter 13

Lesson 13-1 (pp. 778–783)

Guided Example 4: a. 60; 60 **b.** true, a rectangle **c.** false
d. A rectangle has 3 right angles, but it does not have to
be a square.

Guided Example 5: a. x is a real number **b.** P is a person
born in the United States **c.** p^g is not negative.

Questions: 1. the sun shines this afternoon; I will be
happy **3.** If x is an integer greater than 1, then x is a prime
number or the product of prime numbers. **5.** Solving the
inequality for x gives $x > -2$, so if the original inequality
is true, then $x > -2$ must also be true. **7.** Answers vary.
Sample answer: LW is the area of the rectangle; $2L + 2W$
is the perimeter of the rectangle. **9.** Answers vary.
Sample answer: n is a multiple of 10; n is an integer.

11. a. false **b.**

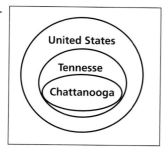

13. a. false **b.**

15. a.
Answers vary. Sample answer: Let $t = 0$. Then

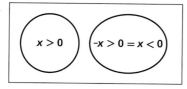

$t^4 = 0$, and 0 is not positive.
b. Answers vary. Sample answer: t can be any real number except 0. **17. a.** Answers vary. Sample answer: Let $x = -\frac{1}{2}$. Then $x^2 + x = \left(-\frac{1}{2}\right)^2 + \left(-\frac{1}{2}\right) = \frac{1}{4} - \frac{1}{2} = -\frac{1}{4}$, so $y < 0$. **b.** $x \geq 0$ or $x \leq -1$
19. Answers vary. Sample answer:

$m\angle CAB = 90.00°$
$m\angle ABC = 12.59°$
$m\angle BCA = 77.41°$

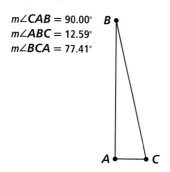

21. If something is a sentence, then it has a subject, verb, and object; Answers vary. Sample answer: The sentence "He went." has no object. **23. a.** $(a - 6)(a + 6)$ **b.** $(n - 9)(n + 4)$ **c.** $(x - 9y)(x + 4y)$ **25.** 2,643 adult tickets and 507 child tickets **27. a.** 53 **b.** –67 **c.** Answers vary. Sample answer: The graph is the line with slope $\frac{3}{4}$, y-intercept –7.

Lesson 13-2 (pp. 784–787)
Guided Example 1: a. a rectangle; it has 4 sides of the same length and its diagonals have the same length; a rectangle can have different width and length. **b.** you live in the United States; you live in the state of North Dakota; you could live in any of the other 49 states **Guided Example 2: a.** is a square; it has 4 sides of the same length and its diagonals have the same length; it is a square. **b.** You live in Brazil; you live in the largest country in South America **Questions: 1.** If there is fire, then there is smoke. **3. a.** no **b.** If an integer is divisible by 24, then it is divisible by

3 and 4. **c.** yes **d.** Answers vary. Sample answer: If an integer is divisible by 3 and 4, then it is divisible by 12. If an integer is divisible by 24, then it is divisible by 3 and 8. **5. a.** no **b.** If $u > 8$, then $7u < 56$. **c.** no **d.** If $7u > 56$, then $u > 8$; If $u > 8$, then $7u > 56$. **7.** If a quadrilateral has four right angles, then it is a rectangle; If a quadrilateral is a rectangle, then it has four right angles. **9.** A function is a linear function if and only if it has an equation of the form $f(x) = ax + b$. **11.** yes **13.** No, the statement "If $z^2 + 48 = 14z$, then $z = 8$" is not true, because $z^2 + 48 = 14z$ is also true for $z = 6$. **15. a.** yes **b.** If $2x^2 - 7x + 30 = 90$, then $(x - 5)(2x + 3) = 45$. **c.** yes **d.** n/a **17. a.** no **b.** If the x-intercepts of a parabola are –5 and 3, then it has an equation of the form $y = (x - 5)(x + 3)$. **c.** no **d.** If a parabola has an equation of the form $y = a(x - 5)(x + 3)$, then its x-intercepts are 5 and –3; If the x-intercepts of a parabola are –5 and 3, then it has an equation of the form $y = a(x + 5)(x - 3)$. **19. a.** true **b.** Answers vary. Sample answer: $x = 10$. **21. a.** false **b.** A person can be a U.S. citizen if and only if the person was born in the United States or the person was naturalized. **23.** False; the graph of $y = ax^2$ crosses the x-axis only once at $(0, 0)$ for all $a \neq 0$. **25.** $0.56 **27.** $\frac{27}{8}$

Lesson 13-3 (pp. 788–794)
Guided Example 1: 1. ii. Addition Property of Equality; **iii.** $-6x = 118 + 14$; **v.** both sides multiplied by $-\frac{1}{6}$; **vi.** Multiplicative Inverse Property; **vi.** $-\frac{1}{6}(132) = -22$; Identity **Guided Example 2: i.** Given; **ii.** Addition Property of Equality; **iii.** Additive Inverse Property and arithmetic; **iv.** Multiplication Property of Equality; **v.** Multiplicative Inverse Property and arithmetic
Questions: 1. a. $3(6) = 18$, $3(13x) = 39x$; Distributive Property **b.** Add –12 to both sides; Addition Property of Equality **c.** $12 + -12 = 0$; Additive Inverse Property **d.** $40x + 0 = 40x$; Additive Identity Property **e.** $18 + -12 = 6$; arithmetic **f.** If $40x + 12 = 3(6 + 13x)$, then $40x = 6 + 39x$. **3.** Inductive reasoning is used to make a general conclusion out of a specific instances, while deduction is used to prove a specific instance of a general case, using known facts. **5. a.** Sula **b.** Lana **7. a. (i.)** $12m + -3m = 3m + -3m + 5$; Addition Property of Equality **(ii.)** $9m = 0 + 5$; Additive Inverse Property and arithmetic **(iii.)** $m = \frac{5}{9}$; Additive Identity Property and Multiplication Property of Equality **b.** Show that if $m = \frac{5}{9}$, then $12m = 3m + 5$. **9.** Multiply both sides by $\frac{1}{t}$ (Multiplication Property of Equality), and $t \cdot \frac{1}{t} = 1$ by the Multiplicative Inverse Property. **11.** Because the equation is quadratic, the Quadratic Formula can be applied to solve for n. **13.** $3x - 4y = -18$ can be added to $3x + 4y = 6$ to get $6x = -12$; Addition Property of Equality **15. (i.)** $ax + b = c$ Given **(ii.)** $ax + b - b = c - b$ Addition

Property of Equality (iii.) $ax + 0 = c - b$ Additive Inverse Property (iv.) $ax = c - b$ Additive Identity Property (v.) $\frac{1}{a} \cdot ax = \frac{1}{a} \cdot (c - b)$ Multiplication Property of Equality (vi.) $x = \frac{(c-b)}{a}$ Multiplicative Inverse Property, Multiplicative Identity Property **17.** $x = \frac{c-b}{a}$ if and only if $ax + b = c$ and $a \neq 0$. **19. a.** (i.) $a(x - h)^2 = k$ Given (ii.) $\frac{1}{a} \cdot a(x - h)^2 = \frac{1}{a} \cdot k$ Multiplication Property of Equality (iii.) $\sqrt{(x - h)^2} = \sqrt{\frac{k}{a}}$ Definition of square root (iv.) $x - h = \pm\sqrt{\frac{k}{a}}$ Definition of square root (v.) $x - h + h = \pm\sqrt{\frac{k}{a}} + h$ Addition Property of Equality (vi.) $x = h \pm\sqrt{\frac{k}{a}}$ Additive Inverse Property **b.** (i.) $x = h \pm\sqrt{\frac{k}{a}}$ Given (ii.) $x - h = \pm\sqrt{\frac{k}{a}} + h - h$ Addition Property of Equality (iii.) $x - h = \pm\sqrt{\frac{k}{a}}$ Additive Inverse Property (iv.) $(x - h)^2 = \left(\sqrt{\frac{k}{a}}\right)^2$ Multiplication Property of Equality (v.) $(x - h)^2 = \frac{k}{a}$ Definition of square root (vi.) $a \cdot (x - h)^2 = \frac{k}{a} \cdot a$ Multiplication Property of Equality (vii.) $a(x - h)^2 = k$ Multiplicative Inverse and Identity Properties **c.** $a(x - h)^2 = k$ if and only if a and k are both positive and $x = h \pm\sqrt{\frac{k}{a}}$. **21. a.** If you are under 8 years of age, then you receive a reduced fare on the metro city bus. **b.** If you receive a reduced fare on the metro city bus, then you are under 8 years of age. **c.** No. Answers vary. Sample answer: Other groups of people might receive a reduced fare as well. **23. a.** $3(x - 1)(x + 4)$ **b.** Answers vary. Sample answer: $-\frac{3}{2} + \sqrt{\frac{119}{12}}$ **25.** $\sqrt{ab} = (\sqrt{a})(\sqrt{b})$ **27.** $(a^x)^y = a^{xy}$ **29.** $-1 \cdot a = -a$ **31.** $AB = 9\sqrt{29}$ cm $\approx$ 48.47 cm, $XZ = 10$ cm, $XY = 5\sqrt{29}$ cm ≈ 26.93 cm **33.** $\frac{4}{663} \approx 0.006033$

Lesson 13-4 (pp. 795-801)

Guided Example: $2L$; $2W$; L; W; $2W$; $2L$; L; $150 - L$; $150 - L$; 40; 110; 110; 40; 40; 110

1. D **3.** Al-Khwarizmi created a general method similar to today's Quadratic Formula. **5.** $x + y = 53$ so their average is 26.5. Let $M = 26.5 + x$ and $N = 26.5 - x$. $MN = 612$, so $(26.5 + x)(26.5 - x) = 612$; $702.25 - x = 612$; $x^2 = 90.25$, $x = 9.5$ or $x = -9.5$. If $x = 9.5$, $M = 26.5 + 9.5 = 36$, $N = 26.5 - 9.5 = 17$. If $x = -9.5$, $M = 26.5 - 9.5 = 17$, $N = 26.5 + 9.5 = 36$. The two numbers are 17 and 36. **7.** $L = 25 - W$; $W(25 - W) = 144$, $25W - W^2 = 144$, $W^2 - 25W + 144 = 0$; $(W - 16)(W - 9) = 0$; 16 yards by 9 yards **9.** $\frac{15 + \sqrt{185}}{2}$ and $\frac{15 - \sqrt{185}}{2}$ **11.** $x = -\frac{1}{7}$ or $x = 1$ **13.** The door is 9.6 units high and 2.8 units wide. **15. a.** If a number is divisible by 8, then it is also divisible by 4. **b.** true **c.** If a number is divisible by 4, then it is also divisible by 8. **d.** false; Answers vary. Sample answer: 12 is divisible by 4, but not by 8. **17.** $s = \pi r(r + 2h)$ **19.** about 603mL **21. a.** $2\sqrt{2} + \sqrt{5}$ **b.** $2\sqrt{10}$ **c.** $2\sqrt{5}$

Lesson 13-5 (pp. 802-808)

Guided Example 2: $2p + 1$; $2q + 1$; $p - q$; $p - q$; 2

Questions: 1. an integer that can be written as $2n$, where n is an integer **3.** Answers vary. Sample answer: 6 and 4 are both divisible by 2, but 10 is not divisible by 4. **5. a.** Answers vary. Sample answer: Let p and q be odd integers such that $p = 2m + 1$ and $q = 2n + 1$, where m and n are integers. Then $p + q = 2m + 1 + 2n + 1 = 2m + 2n + 2 = 2(m + n + 1)$. Since m, n, and 1 are integers, $m + n + 1$ is an integer. Thus $p + q$ is an even integer. **b.** No. Answers vary. Sample answer: From Part a, the sum of the two odd integers is an even integer, not an odd one. **7.**

9. even + odd = odd; odd + even = odd; odd − even = odd; odd − odd = even

11. Answers vary. Sample answer: Let m be an even number. Then there is an integer p such that $m = 2p$, so $m^2 = (2p)^2$. Thus $m^2 = 4p^2$, and since p is an integer, p^2 is an integer. Thus m^2 is a multiple of 4. **13.** Answers vary. Sample answer: Let m and n be numbers such that $m + n = 35a$ and $n = 70b$, where a and b are integers. Then $m + n = m + 70b = 35a$, so $m = 35a - 70b$, and by the Distributive Property, $m = 35(a - 2b)$. Because a and $2b$ are integers, their difference is an integer, so m is divisible by 35. **15.** Answers vary. Sample answer: Let m and n be numbers such that $m = 4p$ and $n = 6q$, where p and q are integers. Then $mn = (4p)(6q) = 24pq$ by the Commutative and Associative Properties of Multiplication. Because p and q are integers, pq is an integer. **17.** Answers vary. Sample answer: $b = 13$ **19.** $x = 7$, $x = 4$ **21.** $a = 3$ **23.** $x = -2.3$ **25. a.** 18 units **b.** 54 units^2

Lesson 13-6 (pp. 809-815)

Guided Example 3: 1. $100h$; $10t$; u **2.** $999T + 99h + 9t$ **4.** $999T$; $99h$; $9t$; $k + 333T + 33h + 3t$; $k + 333T + 33h + 3t$

Questions: 1. 57 **3.** $1{,}000A + 100B + 10C + D$ **5. a.** $1{,}000T + 100h + 10t + u$ **b.** $1{,}000u + 100t + 10h + T$ **7.** A five digit number in base 10 can be written as $N = 10{,}000D + 1{,}000T + 100h + 10t + u$, where D, T, h, t, u are all digits. Separate the sum of the digits from the value of the number. $N = (D + T + h + t + u) + (9{,}999D + 999T + 99h + 9t)$. The sum of the digits is divisible by 9, so there is an integer k with $D + T + h + t + u = 9k$. Substituting, $N = 9k + (9999D + 999T + 99h + 9t) = 9(k + 1{,}111D + 111T + 11h + t)$. Since $k + 1{,}111D + 111T + 11h + t$ is an integer, N is divisible by 9. **9. a.** No, the units digit is odd. **b.** No, the units digit is neither 5 nor 0. **c.** No, the digits do not sum to a number divisible by 9. **11. a.** Yes, the units digit is even. **b.** No, the units digit is neither 5 nor 0. **c.** Yes, the digits sum to 9. **13. a.** Answers vary. Sample answer: $2{,}346 - 6{,}432 = -4{,}086$, which, when divided by 99 gives about -41.28, which is not an integer. **b.** A four digit number in base 10 can be written as $N = 1{,}000T + 100h + 10t + u$, where T, h, t, u are all digits. Moreover, the number with reversed digits is $1{,}000u + 100t + 10h + T$. The difference between these two numbers is $1{,}000T + 100h + 10t + u - (1{,}000u + 100t + 10h + T) = 999T + 90h - 90t - 999u = 9(111T + 10h - 10t - 111u)$. Since $111T + 10h - 10t - 111u$ is an integer we know that this difference is divisible by 9. **15.** A six digit number in base 10 can be written as $N = 100{,}000H + 10{,}000D + 1{,}000T + 100h + 10t + u$, where H, D, T, h, t, u are all digits. Our given conditions mean $H = h$, $D = t$ and $T = u$, and so our number can be rewritten as $100{,}000h + 10{,}000t + 1{,}000u + 100h + 10t + u = 100{,}100h + 10{,}010t + 1{,}001u$. We can factor 13 from this expression to get $N = 13(7{,}700h + 770t + 77u)$, and since $7{,}700h + 770t + 77u$ is an integer, N is 13 times an integer, and thus divisible by 13. **17.** 285 **19.** Answers vary. Sample answer: As a counterexample, consider 6 and 8, where $6 \cdot 8 = 48$ which is not divisible by 7. **21.** $h = 5$ **23. a.** 0 **b.** 1 **25.** $y > 0.5$ **27.** $x = 45$

Lesson 13-7 (pp. 816–822)

1. Answers vary. Sample answer: $\frac{1}{3}$ **3.** Answers vary. Sample answer: 2 **5.** $\frac{28}{33}$ **7.** D **9.** irrational **11.** rational

13.

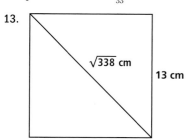

15. Yes, Answers vary. Sample answer: $\sqrt{2} + (-\sqrt{2}) = 0$, and both of them are irrational, while 0 is rational.

17. a.

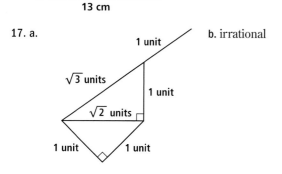

b. irrational

19. $84\sqrt{2}$ cm; irrational **21. a.** $a = \sqrt{1{,}606}$ **b.** irrational

23.

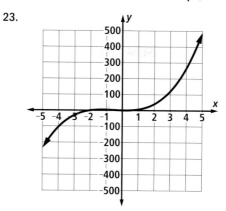

25. $f(x) = x(x + 2)(3x - 1)$ **27. a.** $9y$ **b.** $b = -4y$, $c = 4$, $d = 5y$ **29.** $25 - x^2$ **31.** 70.56 ft

Lesson 13-8 (pp. 823–828)

1. Answers vary. Sample answer:

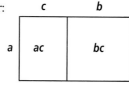

3. a.

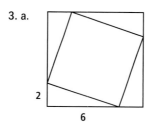

b. 64 units^2 **c.** Answers vary. Sample answer: Subtract four times the area of a triangle with base 6 and height 2 from the total area of 64. **d.** $2\sqrt{10}$

5. a. Answers vary. Sample answer: **b.** 1.5 in.^{2} **7. a.** 2,664.5 units^2 **b.** Subtract twice the area of a rectangle with base a and height b from the total area, i.e., the trapezoid with bases a and b and height $a + b$. **c.** 53 **d.** yes **9.** The Extended Distributive Property **11. a.** $\sqrt{2a^2 + b^2 - 2ab}$ **b.** $\frac{1}{2}(ab - a^2)$ **c.** $\frac{1}{2}c^2$ **d.** $\frac{1}{2}(ab - a^2 + c^2)$ **e.** $\frac{1}{2}(ba + b^2)$ **f.** $\frac{1}{2}(ab - a^2 + c^2) = \frac{1}{2}(ba + b^2)$; $ab - a^2 + c^2 = ba + b^2$; $c^2 = a^2 + b^2$ **13.** A **15 a.** 362,880 orders **b.** 60,480 ways **17.** about \$9,095.32

Self-Test (p. 832)

1.

Conclusions	Justifications
$8(2y - 1) = y + 37$	Given
$16y - 8 = y + 37$	Distributive Property
$16y - 8 - y = y + 37 - y$	Addition Property of Equality
$15y - 8 = 0 + 37$	Arithmetic, Additive Inverse Property
$15y - 8 = 37$	Additive Identity Property
$15y - 8 + 8 = 37 + 8$	Addition Property of Equality
$15y + 0 = 45$	Arithmetic, Additive Inverse Property
$15y = 45$	Additive Identity Property
$\frac{1}{15} \cdot 15y = \frac{1}{15} \cdot 45$	Multiplication Property of Equality
$1y = 3$	Arithmetic, Multiplicative Inverse Property
$y = 3$	Multiplicative Identity Property

2. The antecedent is $8(2y - 1) = y + 37$ and the consequent is $y = 3$. **3. a.** If $xy = 0$, then both x and y equal 0; If both x and $y = 0$, then $xy = 0$. **b.** No, Amalia is not correct. Answers vary. Sample answer: The statement "If $xy = 0$, then both x and y equal 0" is not true because, for example, when $x = 1$ and $y = 0$, $xy = 0$ but x does not equal 0. **4. a.** $\sqrt{7^2 + 8^2} = \sqrt{49 + 64} = \sqrt{113}$ in. **b.** $\sqrt{113}$ is an irrational number, so its decimal is infinite and does not repeat. Marcus's ruler is not accurate for the smallest length that it measures. **5. a.** If a student is taking algebra, then the student can solve quadratic equations.

b. The antecedent is a student is taking algebra, the consequent is the student can solve quadratic equations. **c.** If a student can solve quadratic equations, then the student is taking algebra. **d.** The statement is not true. For example, a student who knows how to solve quadratic equations could be a student in geometry. **6.** True. Answers vary. Sample answer: If the tens digit of a four-digit number is 4 and the units digit is 8, then the number can be written as $1,000n + 48$, where n is a whole number. Then $1,000n + 48 = 4(250n + 12)$, and because $250n$ and 12 are integers, $250n + 12$ is an integer, so 4 divides $100n + 48$. **7.** The rectangles picture the equation $(a - b)(a + b) = (a - b)a + (a - b)b = a^2 - b^2$. **8.** $ab = 717$ and $a + b = -242$. Then $a = -242 - b$, so substitution gives $(-242 - b)b = 717$, so $b^2 + 242b + 717 = 0$. This is a quadratic equation, so solving for b gives $b = -239$ or $b = -3$. Thus, the numbers are -239 and -3. **9. a.** $x^2 + (\sqrt{3})^2 = (\sqrt{13})^2$, so $x^2 + 3 = 13$. $x^2 = 10$ so $x = \sqrt{10}$ **b.** x is irrational **10. a.** True. Because the sides of a square are all equal, two of the sides of the triangle will have equal length, so the triangle will be isosceles. **b.** False. If the length of one side of the square is a, then the length of the diagonal will be $a\sqrt{2}$, so the lengths of the sides are not all equal. **11.** False. Any person born in the United States cannot necessarily become president, since the person also needs to be at least 35 years old and have lived in the United States for at least 14 years.

12. ••• Answers may vary. Sample: If a number is ••• divisible by 3 and 4, then it can be ••• represented as such and broken up into rectangles of 12 dots each. Thus, it is divisible by 12.

The chart below keys the **Self-Test** questions to the objectives in the **Chapter Review** on pages 833–835 or to the **Vocabulary (Voc)** on page 831. This will enable you to locate those **Chapter Review** questions that correspond to questions missed on the **Self-Test**. The lesson where the material is covered is also indicated on the chart.

Question	1	2	3	4	5	6	7	8	9	10
Objective	B	B	B	E	A	E	H	B	A	D
Lesson(s)	13-3	13-1	13-1, 13-2	13-4	13-1, 13-2	13-5, 13-6	13-8	13-4	13-3	13-1, 13-2

Question	11	12	13	14
Objective	G	E	F	I
Lesson(s)	13-1, 13-2	13-5, 13-6	13-7	13-7

Chapter Review (pp. 833–835)

1.

	Conclusions	What Was Done	Justifications
i.	$4x + 5 = 17$		Given
ii.	$4x + 5 + {-5} = 17 + {-5}$	-5 added to both sides.	Addition Property of Equality
iii.	$4x + 0 = 12$	$5 + {-5} = 0$; $17 + {-5} = 12$	Additive Inverse Property; Arithmetic
iv.	$4x = 12$	$4x + 0 = 4x$	Additive Identity Property
v.	$\frac{1}{4} \cdot 4x = 12 \cdot \frac{1}{4}$	Both sides were multiplied by $\frac{1}{4}$.	Multiplication Property of Equality
vi.	$1 \cdot x = 3$	$\frac{1}{4} \cdot 4 = 1$; $12 \cdot \frac{1}{4} = 3$	Multiplicative Identity Property; Arithmetic
vii.	$x = 3$	$1 \cdot x = x$	Multiplicative Identity Property

3.

	Conclusions	What Was Done	Justifications
i.	$3t - 15 = 4t + 2$	Given	Given
ii.	$3t - 17 = 4t$	-2 added to both sides.	Addition Property of Equality
iii.	$-17 = t$	$-3t$ added to both sides.	Addition Property of Equality

5. 15 boys, 11 girls or 11 boys, 15 girls   **7.** $\frac{5.6 + \sqrt{22.16}}{2}$, $\frac{5.6 - \sqrt{22.16}}{2}$ **9.** –23 and –23   **11.** antecedent: an animal has feathers: consequent: it is a bird   **13.** antecedent a number is irrational; consequent: it cannot be represented as the ratio of two integers   **15.** true   **17.** true   **19.** Suppose that $2a + 3b + c$ is not divisible by 7. Then $2a + 3b + c + (14)(7a) + 7b$ is not divisible by 7. Hence, $100a + 10b + c$ is also not divisible by 7. So the three-digit number abc is not divisible by 7.   **21.** Consider a six-digit integer of the form $xyzxyz$. This is equal to $100{,}000x + 10{,}000y + 1{,}000z + 100x + 10y + z$. And equivalently, this is $(7{,}692)(13x) + 4x + (769)(13y) + 3y + (76)(13z) + 12z + (7)(13x) + 9x + 10y + z$. Combining and factoring, we obtain $xyzxyz = (13)(7{,}700x + 770y + 77z)$. So all six-digit integers of the form $xyzxyz$ are divisible by 13.

23. irrational   **25.** rational   **27.** Yes, for example $\sqrt{2} \cdot \sqrt{2} = 2$.   **29. a.** yes **b.** yes **c.** n/a   **31. a.** yes **b.** no **c.** You are in high school if and only if you are in grades 9–12.   **33.**

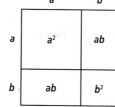

35. The area of each triangle is $\frac{1}{2}ab$. Because the area of the entire rectangle is ab, and $\frac{1}{2}ab + \frac{1}{2}ab = ab$, each of the triangles must occupy exactly half the area of the rectangle. So the diagonal cuts the area of the rectangle in half.   **37. a.** $\frac{16}{\pi}$ in. **b.** irrational   **39. a.** 0.15 **b.** rational **b.** irrational   **41 a.**

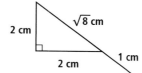

Additional Answers

Chapter 12

Lesson 12-1
Activity 1 Page 714

1.
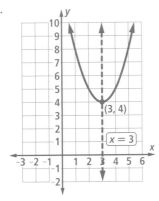

2.
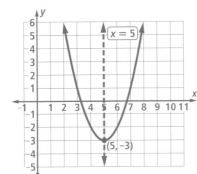

3.
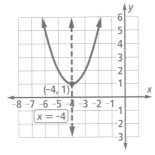

4.
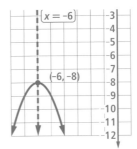

5.
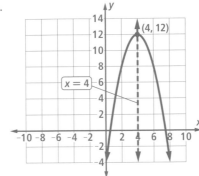

6.
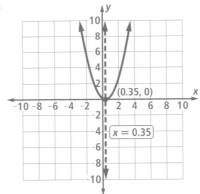

Lesson 12-4
Activity Page 739

Steps 1, 2

b	c = 1	c = 2	c = 3	c = 4	c = 5	c = 6	c = 7	c = 8	c = 9	c = 10
1	P	P	P	P	P	P	P	P	P	P
2	$(x+1)(x+1)$	P	P	P	P	P	P	P	P	P
3	P	$(x+1)(x+2)$	P	P	P	P	P	P	P	P
4	P	P	$(x+1)(x+3)$	$(x+2)(x+2)$	P	P	P	P	P	P
5	P	P	P	$(x+1)(x+4)$	P	$(x+2)(x+3)$	P	P	P	P
6	P	P	P	P	$(x+1)(x+5)$	P	P	$(x+2)(x+4)$	$(x+3)(x+3)$	P
7	P	P	P	P	P	$(x+1)(x+6)$	P	P	P	$(x+2)(x+5)$
8	P	P	P	P	P	P	$(x+1)(x+7)$	P	P	P
9	P	P	P	P	P	P	P	$(x+1)(x+8)$	P	P
10	P	P	P	P	P	P	P	P	$(x+1)(x+9)$	P

Lesson 12-4
Questions Page 741

29a.

b	c = -1	c = -2	c = -3	c = -4	c = -5	c = -6	c = -7	c = -8	c = -9	c = -10
1	P	$(x+2)(x-1)$	P	P	P	$(x+3)(x-2)$	P	P	P	P
2	P	P	$(x+3)(x-1)$	P	P	P	P	$(x+4)(x-2)$	P	P
3	P	P	P	$(x+4)(x-1)$	P	P	P	P	P	$(x+5)(x-2)$
4	P	P	P	P	$(x+5)(x-1)$	P	P	P	P	P
5	P	P	P	P	P	$(x+6)(x-1)$	P	P	P	P
6	P	P	P	P	P	P	$(x+7)(x-1)$	P	P	P
7	P	P	P	P	P	P	P	$(x+8)(x-1)$	P	P
8	P	P	P	P	P	P	P	P	$(x+9)(x-1)$	P
9	P	P	P	P	P	P	P	P	P	$(x+10)(x-1)$
10	P	P	P	P	P	P	P	P	P	P

Chapter 13

Self-Test Page 832

10a. True. Because the sides of a square are all equal, two of the sides of the triangle will have equal length, so the triangle will be isosceles.

10b. False. If the length of one side of the square is a, then the length of the diagonal will be $a\sqrt{2}$, so the lengths of the sides are not all equal.

11. False. Any person born in the United States cannot necessarily become president, since the person also needs to be at least 35 years old and have lived in the United States for at least 14 years.

12.
```
• • •
• • •
• • •
```

Answers vary. Sample answer: If a number is divisible by 3 and 4, then it can be represented as such and broken up into rectangles of 12 dots each. Thus, it is divisible by 12.

Chapter Review Page 833

2.

Conclusions	What Was Done	Justifications
$2n + 5 = 4n + 3$	Given	Given
$2n + 2 = 4n$	Added -3 was to both sides.	Addition Property of Equality
$2 = 2n$	Added $-2n$ to both sides.	Addition Property of Equality
$1 = n$	Multiplied both sides by $\frac{1}{2}$.	Multiplication Property of Equality

3.

Conclusions	What Was Done	Justifications
$3t - 15 =$ $4t + 2$	Given	Given
$3t - 17 =$ $4t$	Added -2 to both sides.	Addition Property of Equality
$-17 = t$	Added $-3t$ to both sides.	Addition Property of Equality

4.

Conclusions	What Was Done	Justifications
$\sqrt{16y - 16} = 2y$	Given	Given
$16y - 16 = 4y^2$	Multiplied the left side by $\sqrt{16y - 16}$, the right side by $2y$.	Multiplication Property of Equality
$0 = 4y^2 - 16y + 16$	Added $-16y$ and 16 to both sides	Addition Property of Equality
$0 = y^2 - 4y + 4$	Multiplied both sides by $\frac{1}{4}$.	Multiplication Property of Equality
$y = \dfrac{4 \pm \sqrt{(4)^2 - 4(1)(4)}}{2}$	Solved for y.	Quadratic Formula
$y = \frac{4 \pm 0}{2}$	$\sqrt{4^2 - 4(1)(4)} = 0$	Arithmetic
$y = 2$	$\frac{4}{2} = 2$	Definition of $\pm$, Arithmetic
$\sqrt{16(2) - 16} = 4$ $= 2(2)$		Arithmetic

Glossary

A

absolute value (A) The distance a number x is from 0 written $|x|$. (B) $|x| = x$ if $x \geq c$; $|x| = -x$ if $x < c$. (**43**)

addition method for solving a system Given two equations in a system, applying the Addition Property if $a = b$ and $c = d$, then $a + c = b + d$, to obtain another equation that is satisfied by the solution to the system. (**602**)

Addition Property of Equality For all real numbers a, b, and c, if $a = b$, then $a + c = b + c$. (**106**)

Addition Property of Inequality For all real numbers a, b, and c, if $a < b$, then $a + c < b + c$. (**162**)

Additive Identity Property For any real number a, $a + 0 = 0 + a = a$. (**108**)

Additive Inverse Property For any real number a, $a + -a = -a + a = 0$. (**109**)

additive inverses Two numbers whose sum is zero; also called opposites. (**85**)

Algebraic Definition of Division For all real numbers a and b with $b \neq 0$, $a \div b = \frac{a}{b} = a \cdot \frac{1}{b}$. (**7**)

Algebraic Definition of Subtraction For all real numbers a and b, $a - b = a + -b$. (**7**)

algebraic expression An expression that includes one or more variables. (**6**)

algebraic fraction A fraction with a variable in the numerator, in the denominator, or in both. (**252**)

annual yield The percent of interest that money on deposit earns per year. (**398**)

antecedent The clause following *if* in an if-then statement. (**778**)

Arrangements Theorem If there are n ways to select each object in a sequence of length L, then n^L different sequences are possible. (**459**)

Associative Property of Addition For any real numbers a, b, and c, $(a + b) + c = a + (b + c)$. (**10**)

Associative Property of Multiplication For any real numbers a, b, and c, $(ab)c = a(bc)$. (**9**)

B

axis of symmetry Given a figure, a line over which the reflection image of the figure is the figure itself. (**526**)

base The number x in the power x^n. (**398**)

binomial A polynomial that has two terms. (**663**)

boundary line A line that separates two sets, e.g., solutions from nonsolutions in the graph of a linear inequality. (**381**)

boundary A point or number that separates solutions from nonsolutions on a number line. (**155**)

C

capture-recapture method The use of proportions to estimate the total number of objects in a set (e.g., the number of deer in a forest or the number of fish in a pond). (**303**)

Celsius scale The temperature scale of the metric system, developed by Anders Celsius, in which the freezing point of water is $0°$ and the boiling point of water is $100°$; also known as the *centigrade scale*. (**221**)

centigrade scale See *Celsius scale*. (**221**)

chi-square statistic A member calculated from data to determine whether the difference in two frequency distributions is greater than that expected by chance. (**698**)

circular permutation An ordering of objects around a circle. (**695**)

clearing fractions Multiplying each side of an equation or inequality by a constant to get an equivalent equation without fractions as coefficients. (**170**)

closed under an operation A set is closed under an operation if the result of the operation always lies within the particular set. (**802**)

coefficient A number that is a factor in a term containing a variable. (**73**)

coefficient matrix In the matrix equation $\begin{bmatrix} a & b \\ c & d \end{bmatrix} \cdot \begin{bmatrix} x \\ y \end{bmatrix} = \begin{bmatrix} e \\ f \end{bmatrix}$, the coefficient matrix is $\begin{bmatrix} a & b \\ c & d \end{bmatrix}$. (**622**)

coincident Two or more lines or other sets of points that are identical. (**618**)

collinear points Points that all lie on the same line. (**130**)

Commutative Property of Addition For all real numbers a and b, $a + b = b + a$. (**16**)

Commutative Property of Multiplication For all real numbers a and b, $ab = ba$. (**16**)

complementary events Two events that have no elements in common, but together they contain all the possible outcomes. (**283**)

complete factorization The representation of a polynomial as a product of prime polynomials. (**676**)

completing the square Converting a quadratic equation in standard form to one in vertex form. (**724**)

complex fraction A fraction that has a fraction in the numerator or a fraction in the denominator, or both. (**259**)

compound interest The money a bank pays on the principal and earned interest in an account. (**399, 400**)

compound sentence A single sentence consisting of two or more sentences linked by the words *and* or *or*. (**227**)

conditional probability The probability that an event will occur given that another event has occurred. (**283**)

consequent The clause following *then* in an if-then statement. (**778**)

constant-decrease situation A quantity that decreases at a constant amount in a period of time. (**130**)

constant-increase situation A quantity that increases at a constant amount in a period of time. (**130**)

constant matrix In the matrix equation $\begin{bmatrix} a & b \\ c & d \end{bmatrix} \cdot \begin{bmatrix} x \\ y \end{bmatrix} = \begin{bmatrix} e \\ f \end{bmatrix}$, the constant matrix is $\begin{bmatrix} e \\ f \end{bmatrix}$. (**622**)

constant term A term in a polynomial without a variable. (**736**)

converse An if-then statement in which the antecedent and the consequent of the statement have been switched. (**784**)

conversion rate A rate determined from an equality between two quantities with different units. (**269**)

coordinates The numbers x and y that locate a point (x, y) in the coordinate plane. (**27**)

counterexample An instance for which a general statement is not true. (**23**)

cube The third power of a number x, or x^3. (**493**)

Cube of the Cube Root Property For any nonnegative number x, $\sqrt[3]{x} \cdot \sqrt[3]{x} \cdot \sqrt[3]{x} = \sqrt[3]{x^3} = x$. (**493**)

cube root If $V = s^3$, then s is a cube root of V. (**493**)

cubic polynomial A polynomial of degree 3. (**756**)

D

deduction Using a proof to show that one if-then statement follows from another. (**789**)

define a variable The process of describing the quantity a variable represents. (**14**)

degree of a monomial The sum of the exponents of the variables in the monomial. (**664**)

degree of a polynomial The highest degree of any of the monomial terms of a polynomial. (**664**)

dependent variable A variable (y) whose value is determined by the value of at least one other variable in a given function. (**426**)

deviation (A) The difference between a member of a data set and the mean of that data set. (**42**) (B) The difference between an expected number and an actual observed number. (**697**)

difference of squares An expression of the form $x^2 - y^2$. For all real numbers x and y, $x^2 - y^2 = (x + y)(x - y)$. (**687–688**)

dimensions (of a matrix) The number of rows and columns in a matrix. (**622**)

direct variation A number y varies directly with a number x if y is a constant multiple of x. (**353**)

discount The amount by which the original price of an item is lowered. (**184**)

discount rate The ratio of the discount to the original price. (**275**)

discriminant The value of $b^2 - 4ac$ in the quadratic equation $ax^2 + bx + c = 0$. (**561**)

Discriminant Property Suppose $ax^2 + bx + c$ and a, b, and c are real numbers with $a \neq 0$. Let $D = b^2 - 4ac$. Then when $D > 0$, the equation has two real solutions. When $D = 0$, the equation has exactly one real solution. When $D < 0$, the equation has no real solutions. (**561**)

Discriminant Theorem When a, b, and c are integers, with $a \neq 0$, either all three of the following conditions are true or none are true. **1.** $b^2 - 4ac$ is a perfect square. **2.** $ax^2 + bx + c$ is factorable over the set of polynomials with integer coefficients. **3.** The solutions to $ax^2 + bx + c = 0$ are rational numbers. **(749)**

Distance between Two Points in a Coordinate Plane The distance AB between the points $A = (x_1, y_1)$ and $B = (x_2, y_2)$ in a coordinate plane is
$$AB = \sqrt{(x_2 - x_1)^2 + (y_2 - y_1)^2}.$$ **(507)**

Distributive Property of Multiplication over Addition For all real numbers a, b, and c, $c(a + b) = ca + cb$. **(66)**

Distributive Property of Multiplication over Subtraction For all real numbers a, b, and c, $c(a - b) = ca - cb$. **(67)**

Dividing Fractions Property For all real numbers a, b, c, and d, with $b \neq 0$, $c \neq 0$, and $d \neq 0$, $\frac{a}{b} \div \frac{c}{d} = \frac{a}{b} \cdot \frac{d}{c}$. **(258)**

Division Property of Equality For all real numbers a, b, and all real nonzero numbers c, if $a = b$, then $\frac{a}{c} = \frac{b}{c}$. **(113)**

domain of a function The set of possible values of the first (independent) variable. **(426)**

domain of a variable All the values that may be meaningfully substituted for a variable. **(28)**

double inequality An inequality of the form $a < x < b$. (The $<$ may be replaced with $>$, $\leq$, or $\geq$.) **(156, 227)**

E

elements (of a matrix) The objects in a rectangular array. **(622)**

empty set A set that has no elements in it, written as $\{\ \}$ or $\varnothing$. **(584)**

endpoints (A) The points A and B in the segment $\overline{AB}$. (B) The coordinates of those points on a number line. **(156)**

Equal Fractions Property For all real numbers a, b, and k, if $b \neq 0$ and $k \neq 0$, then $\frac{a}{b} = \frac{ak}{bk}$. **(253)**

equivalent equations Equations with exactly the same solutions. **(139)**

equivalent expressions Expressions that have the same value for *every* number that can be substituted for the variable(s). **(22)**

equivalent formulas Two or more formulas in which every set of values that satisfies one of the formulas also satisfies the others. **(222)**

equivalent statements When an if-then statement and its converse are both true, then the antecedent and consequent are equivalent. **(784)**

equivalent systems Systems with exactly the same solutions. **(608)**

evaluating an expression The process of finding the numerical value of an expression. **(6)**

even integer (even number) An integer that can be written as $2n$, where n is an integer. **(802)**

event A set of possible outcomes. **(280)**

expected number The mean frequency of a given event that is predicted by a probability. **(697)**

exponent The number n in the power x^n. **(398)**

exponential decay A situation in which $y = bg^x$ and $0 < g < 1$. **(411)**

exponential growth A situation in which $y = bg^x$ and $g > 1$. **(404)**

exponential growth equation If the amount at the beginning of the growth period is b, the growth factor is g, and y is the amount after x time periods, then $y = b \cdot g^x$. **(405)**

exponential regression A method to determine an equation of the form $y = b \cdot g^x$ for modeling a set of ordered pairs. **(419)**

Extended Distributive Property To multiply two sums, multiply each term in the first sum by each term in the second sum, and then add the products. **(680)**

extremes The numbers a and d in the proportion $\frac{a}{b} = \frac{c}{d}$. **(301)**

F

factors (A) A number or expression that is multiplied. (B) If $ab = c$, then a and b are factors of c. **(15)**

factored form of a quadratic function A quadratic function $y = ax^2 + bx + c$ is in factored form when it is written as $y = a(x - r_1)(x - r_2)$. **(730)**

factoring The process of expressing a given number or expression as a product. **(75, 675)**

factorization The result of factoring a number or polynomial. **(676)**

Factor Theorem Let r be a real number and $P(x)$ be a polynomial in x. If $x - r$ is a factor of $P(x)$, then $P(r) = 0$; that is, r is an x-intercept of the graph of P. If $P(r) = 0$, then $x - r$ is a factor of $P(x)$. **(755)**

Factor Theorem for Quadratic Functions The x-intercepts of the graph of $y = a(x - r_1)(x - r_2)$ are r_1 and r_2. **(731)**

fact triangle A triangle in which any pair of numbers in the triangle can be added, subtracted, multiplied, or divided to produce the third number. **(105, 112)**

Fahrenheit scale A temperature scale, developed by Gabriel Fahrenheit, in which the freezing point of water is 32° and the boiling point of water is 212°. **(221)**

fair A situation in which each outcome has the same probability; also called *unbiased*. **(281)**

Fundamental Property of Similar Figures If two polygons are similar, then the ratios of corresponding lengths are equal. **(309)**

function A set of ordered pairs in which each first coordinate corresponds to *exactly one* second coordinate. **(426)**

function notation Notation to indicate a function, such as $f(x)$, and read "f of x." **(435)**

$f(x)$ notation Notation indicating the value of a function f at x. When a function f contains the ordered pair (x, y), then y is the value of the function at x, and we may write $y = f(x)$. **(435)**

G

general formula for the height of a projectile over time Let h be the height (in feet) of a projectile launched from Earth's surface with an initial upward velocity v feet per second and an initial height of s feet. Then, after t seconds, $h = -16t^2 + vt + s$. **(546)**

generalization An if-then statement in which there is a variable in the antecedent and in the consequent. **(778)**

Generalized Addition Property of Equality For all numbers or expressions a, b, c, and d: If $a = b$ and $c = d$, then $a + c = b + d$. **(601)**

general linear equation An equation of the form $ax + b = cx + d$, where $a \neq 0$. **(202)**

greatest common factor (GCF) For two or more integers, the greatest integer that is a common factor. For two or more monomials, the GCF is the product of the greatest common factor of the coefficients and the greatest common factor of the variables. **(675)**

growth factor In exponential growth or decay, the positive number which is repeatedly multiplied by the original amount. **(404)**

growth model for powering If a quantity is multiplied by a positive number g (the growth factor) in each of x time periods, then, after the x periods, the quantity will be multiplied by g^x. **(405)**

H

half-life The time it takes for one half the amount of an element to decay. **(414)**

half-plane In a plane, the region on either side of a line. **(381)**

horizontal line A line with the equation $y = k$, where k is a real number. **(189)**

I

if and only if A phrase used to connect equivalent if-then statements. **(785)**

if-then statement A statement that contains an antecedent and a consequent. **(778)**

independent variable A variable whose value does not rely on the values of other variables. **(426)**

inductive reasoning The process of arriving at a general conclusion (not necessarily true) from specific instances. **(776)**

inequality A mathematical sentence with one of the verbs < (is less than), > (is greater than), ≤ (is less than or equal to), ≥ (is greater than or equal to), or ≠ (is not equal to). **(155)**

initial height The starting height of a projectile. **(545)**

initial upward velocity The velocity of a projectile when it is first launched, assuming no gravity effects. **(545)**

input A number substituted for the independent variable in a function. **(221, 426)**

instance A special case of a general pattern. **(13)**

interest The amount that a bank or other financial institution pays on money in an account, based on a percentage of the principal. **(398)**

intersection of sets The set of elements in both set A and set B and written as $A \cap B$. **(227)**

interval The set of numbers between two numbers a and b, possibly containing a or b. **(156)**

inverse (of a matrix) For a matrix A, the matrix B such that AB and BA are the identity matrix. (**629**)

Irrationality of $\sqrt{n}$ Theorem If n is an integer that is not a perfect square, then $\sqrt{n}$ is irrational. (**819**)

irrational number A real number that is not a rational number. For example, the square roots of integers that are not perfect squares are irrational. (**817**)

J

justification A statement explaining why each step in a proof follows from preceding statements. (**787**)

L

least squares line The line whose squares of deviations from data set points are least. Also called the *line of best fit*. (**370**)

like terms Two or more terms in which the variables and corresponding exponents are the same. (**72**)

linear combination An expression of the form $Ax + By$, where A and B are fixed numbers. (**375**)

linear inequalities Inequalities of the form $Ax + By < C$ or $Ax + By \le C$, where A, B, and C are constants. ($>$ and $\ge$ can be substituted for $<$ and $\le$.) (**383**)

linear polynomial A polynomial of degree one. (**664**)

linear regression The fitting of a straight line through a given set of points according to specific criteria, such as least squares. (**369**)

linear term A term containing one variable with a power equal to 1. (**736**)

line of best fit A line whose equation is determined by the method of least squares and represents a linear relationship between data values. (**369**)

lowest terms (A) A fraction whose numerator and denominator have no common factors other than 1. (**761**) (B) A rational expression with no polynomial being a factor of both its numerator and denominator. (**762**)

M

markup A percent by which the original price of an item is raised. (**184**)

matrix (matrices) A rectangular array, such as $\begin{bmatrix} 3 & -4 \\ 15 & 0 \end{bmatrix}$. (**622**)

matrix form A way of expressing a system of equations using matrices. The matrix form for $\begin{cases} ax + by = e \\ cx + dy = f \end{cases}$ is $\begin{bmatrix} a & b \\ c & d \end{bmatrix} \cdot \begin{bmatrix} x \\ y \end{bmatrix} = \begin{bmatrix} e \\ f \end{bmatrix}$. The coefficient matrix is $\begin{bmatrix} a & b \\ c & d \end{bmatrix}$, the variable matrix is $\begin{bmatrix} x \\ y \end{bmatrix}$, and the constant matrix is $\begin{bmatrix} e \\ f \end{bmatrix}$. (**623**)

mean absolute deviation (m.a.d.) The average difference between individual measurements and the mean. (**48**)

means The numbers b and c in the proportion $\frac{a}{b} = \frac{c}{d}$. (**301**)

Means-Extremes Property For all real numbers a, b, c, and d (with $b \ne 0$ and $d \ne 0$), if $\frac{a}{b} = \frac{c}{d}$, then $ad = bc$. (**302**)

monomial A polynomial with 1 term. (**663**)

Multiplication Counting Principle If one choice can be made in m ways and a second choice can be made in n ways, then there are mn ways of making the first choice followed by the second choice. (**459**)

multiplication method for solving a system Given two equations in a system, applying the Multiplication Property of Equality to obtain another equation that is satisfied by the solution to the system. (**609**)

Multiplication Property of Zero For any real number a, $a \cdot 0 = 0 \cdot a = 0$. (**115**)

Multiplication Property of –1 For any real number a, $a \cdot -1 = -1 \cdot a = -a$. (**86**)

Multiplication Property of Equality For all real numbers a, b, and c, if $a = b$, then $ca = cb$. (**113**)

Multiplication Property of Inequality If $x < y$ and a is positive, then $ax < ay$. If $x < y$ and a is negative, then $ax > ay$. (**157**)

Multiplicative Identity Property of 1 For any real number a, $a \cdot 1 = 1 \cdot a = a$. (**116**)

Multiplicative Inverse Property For any real number a, where $a \ne 0$, $a \cdot \frac{1}{a} = \frac{1}{a} \cdot a = 1$. (**116**)

Multiplying Fractions Property For all real numbers a, b, c, and d, with $b \ne 0$ and $d \ne 0$, $\frac{a}{b} \cdot \frac{c}{d} = \frac{ac}{bd}$. (**252**)

N

n factorial ($n!$) The product of the integers from 1 to n. (693)

Negative Exponent Property For any nonzero b and all n, $b^{-n} = \frac{1}{b^n}$, the reciprocal of b^n. (474)

Negative Exponent Property for Fractions For any nonzero x and y and all n, $\left(\frac{x}{y}\right)^{-n} = \left(\frac{y}{x}\right)^n$. (475)

nonlinear system A system of equations or inequalities in which at least one of the equations or inequalities is nonlinear. (640)

nth power The number x^n is the nth power of x. (398)

null set See *empty set*. (584)

O

oblique A line that is neither horizontal nor vertical. (377)

odd integer (odd number) An integer that can be written as $2n + 1$, where n is an integer. (803)

odds of an event The ratio of the probability that an event will not occur to the probability that an event will occur. (284)

Opposite of a Difference Property For all real numbers a and b, $-(a - b) = -a + b$. (87)

Opposite of a Sum Property For all real numbers a and b, $-(a + b) = -a + -b = -a - b$. (86)

Opposite of Opposites Property For any real number a, $-(-a) = a$. (85)

opposites Two numbers that add to zero; also called additive inverses. (85)

order of operations The correct order of evaluating numerical expressions: perform operations within parentheses or other grouping symbols. Then evaluate powers from left to right. Next multiply or divide from left to right. Then add or subtract from left to right. (6)

origin The point $(0, 0)$ on a coordinate graph. (44)

outcomes A result of an experiment. (280)

output A number that is returned by a function after it is evaluated. (221, 426)

P

parabola The curve that is the graph of an equation of the form $y = ax^2 + bx + c$, where $a \neq 0$. (526)

Parabola Vertex Theorem The graph of all ordered pairs (x, y) satisfying the equation $y - k = a(x - h)^2$ is a parabola with vertex (h, k). (716)

pattern A general idea for which there are many instances. (13)

P(E) The probability of event E or "P of E." (280)

percent (%) A number times $\frac{1}{100}$ or "per 100." (182)

percentile The pth percentile of a data set is the smallest data value that is greater than or equal to p percent of the data values. (292)

perfect square trinomial A trinomial that is the square of a binomial. $a^2 + 2ab + b^2 = (a + b)^2$ and $a^2 - 2ab + b^2 = (a - b)^2$. (687)

period of a pendulum The time it takes a pendulum to complete one swing back and forth. On Earth, the formula $p = 2\pi \sqrt{\frac{L}{32}}$ gives the time p in seconds for one period in terms of the length L (in feet) of the pendulum. (501)

permutation An ordered arrangement of letters, names, or objects. (691)

$\pm$ notation (A) $\pm x$ means (x or $-x$). (B) $a \pm b$ means $(a + b$ or $a - b)$. (553)

point-slope form An equation of a line in the form $y - k = m(x - h)$, where m is the slope and (h, k) is a point on the line. (357)

polynomial An expression that is either a monomial or a sum of monomials. (663)

polynomial in x A sum of multiples of powers of x. (657)

population The set of individuals or objects to be studied. (302)

power An expression written in the form x^n. (398)

Power of a Power Property For all m and n, and all nonzero b, $(b^m)^n = b^{mn}$. (466)

Power of a Product Property For all nonzero a and b, and for all n, $(ab)^n = a^n b^n$. (481)

Power of a Quotient Property For all nonzero a and b, and for all n, $\left(\frac{a}{b}\right)^n = \frac{a^n}{b^n}$. (482)

prime polynomial A polynomial that cannot be factored into polynomials of lower degree. (676)

polynomial over the integers A polynomial with integer coefficients. **(738)**

principal Money deposited in an account. **(398)**

probability of an event A number from 0 to 1 that measures the likelihood that an event will occur. **(280)**

probability distribution The set of ordered pairs of outcomes and their probabilities. **(281)**

Probability Formula for Geometric Regions Suppose points are selected at random in a region and some of that region's points represent an event E of interest. The probability $P(E)$ of the event is given by $\frac{\text{measurement of region in event}}{\text{measure of entire region}}$. **(296)**

Product of Powers Property For all m and n, and all nonzero b, $b^m \cdot b^n = b^{m+n}$. **(465)**

Product of Square Roots Property For all nonnegative real numbers a and b, $\sqrt{a} \cdot \sqrt{b} = \sqrt{ab}$. **(498)**

proof argument A sequence of justified conclusions, starting with the antecedent and ending with the consequent. **(789)**

proportion A statement that two fractions are equal. **(301)**

Pythagorean Theorem In any right triangle with legs of lengths a and b and hypotenuse of length c, $a^2 + b^2 = c^2$. **(492)**

Q

quadratic equation An equation that can be written in the form $ax^2 + bx + c = 0$ with $a \neq 0$. **(552)**

Quadratic Formula If $ax^2 + bx + c = 0$ and $a \neq 0$, then $x = \frac{-b \pm \sqrt{b^2 - 4ac}}{2a}$. **(553)**

quadratic polynomial A polynomial of degree 2. **(664)**

Quotient of Powers Property For all m and n, and all nonzero b, $\frac{b^m}{b^n} = b^{m-n}$. **(469)**

Quotient of Square Roots Property For all positive real numbers a and c, $\frac{\sqrt{c}}{\sqrt{a}} = \sqrt{\frac{c}{a}}$. **(499)**

R

radical sign (A) ($\sqrt{}$) The symbol for square root. **(489)** (B) ($\sqrt[3]{}$) The symbol for cube root. **(493)**

radicand The quantity under the radical sign. **(499)**

randomly (chosen) Every member of a population has an equal chance of being chosen. **(302)**

range (A) The difference between the maximum value M and minimum value m of a data set. **(48)** (B) The set of possible values of the second (dependent) variable. **(426)**

rate The quotient of two quantities with different units. **(263)**

rate of change The difference of values of a quantity divided by the amount of time between the values. The rate of change between points (x_1, y_1) and (x_2, y_2) is $\frac{y_2 - y_1}{x_2 - x_1}$. **(328)**

rate unit The unit of a rate. **(328)**

ratio A quotient of two quantities with the same units. **(274, 275)**

rational expression A quotient of two polynomials. **(761)**

rational number A number that can be expressed as a simple fraction. **(816)**

ratio of similitude The ratio of the lengths of corresponding sides of two similar figures. **(309)**

reciprocal rates Two rates in which the quantities are compared in both orders. **(264)**

reflection-symmetric The property held by a figure that coincides with its image under a reflection over a line. **(526)**

Related Facts Property of Addition and Subtraction For all real numbers a, b, and c, if $a + b = c$, then $b + a = c$, $c - b = a$, and $c - a = b$. **(106–107)**

Related Facts Property of Multiplication and Division For all nonzero real numbers a, b, and c, if $ab = c$, then $ba = c$, $\frac{c}{b} = a$, and $\frac{c}{a} = b$. **(113–114)**

relation Any set of ordered pairs. **(428)**

relative frequency The ratio of the number of times an event occurs to the total number of possible occurrences. **(280, 289)**

Repeated Multiplication Property of Powers When n is a positive integer, $x^n = x \cdot x \cdot \ldots \cdot x$ for n factors. **(398)**

S

sample A subset taken from a set of people or things. **(302)**

scatterplot A two-dimensional coordinate graph of individual points. (**27**)

scientific notation A number represented as $x \cdot 10^n$, where n is an integer and $1 \le x < 10$. (**460**)

semiperimeter Half the perimeter of a figure. (**807**)

sequence A collection of numbers or objects in a specific order. (**20**)

simple fraction A fraction with integers in its numerator and denominator. (**816**)

skewed left A distribution in which the lower half of the values extends much farther to the left than the upper half, leaving a tail on the left. (**51**)

skewed right A distribution in which the upper half of the values extends much farther to the right than the lower half, leaving a tail on the right. (**51**)

slope The rate of change between points on a line. The slope of the line through (x_1, y_1) and (x_2, y_2) is $\frac{y_2 - y_1}{x_2 - x_1}$. (**334**)

slope-intercept form An equation of a line in the form $y = mx + b$, where m is the slope and b is the y-intercept. (**350**)

Slopes and Parallel Lines Property If two lines have the same slope, then they are parallel. (**616**)

solution to an equation Any value of a variable that makes an equation true. (**135**)

solution to a system In a system of equations with two variables, the solution is all ordered pairs (x, y) that satisfy all equations in the system. (**582**)

square The second power of a number x, or x^2. (**488**)

Square of the Square Root Property For any nonnegative number x, $\sqrt{x} \cdot \sqrt{x} = \sqrt{x^2} = x$. (**490**)

square root If $A = s^2$, then s is a square root of A. (**489**)

square term The terms containing a variable with a power equal to 2. (**736**)

squaring function A function defined by $y = x^2$. (**426**)

standard form of an equation of a line An equation in the form $Ax + By = C$, where A, B, and C are constants. (**375**)

standard form for a polynomial A polynomial written with the terms in descending order of the exponents of its terms. (**658**)

standard form of a quadratic equation An equation of the form $ax^2 + bx + c = 0$, where $a \ne 0$. (**555**)

standard window The common view on a graphing calculator. (**34**)

Subtraction Property of Equality For all real numbers a, b, and c, if $a = b$, then $a - c = b - c$. (**106**)

symmetric distribution Data that are centered around one point and in which the values on the left and right sides are roughly mirror images. (**51**)

system A set of equations or inequalities separated by the word *and* that together describe a single situation. (**582**)

T

tax rate The ratio of the tax to the amount being taxed. (**275**)

term A number, variable, or product of numbers and variables. (**15, 20, 663**)

Transitive Property of Equality For any real numbers a, b, and c, if $a = b$ and $b = c$, then $a = c$. (**10**)

trinomial A polynomial that has three terms. (**663**)

trivial factors In every expression, the factors 1 and the expression itself. (**675**)

2 × 2 identity matrix The matrix $\begin{bmatrix} 1 & 0 \\ 0 & 1 \end{bmatrix}$. (**626**)

U

unbiased A situation in which each outcome has the same probability; also called *fair*. (**281**)

uniform distribution A distribution that has roughly the same quantity for all events. (**51**)

union of sets The set of elements in either set A or set B (or in both) and written as $A \cup B$. (**228**)

Unique Factorization Theorem for Polynomials Every polynomial can be represented as a product of prime polynomials in exactly one way, disregarding order and integer multiples. (**677**)

V

value of a function The output of a function obtained for a given first variable. (**426**)

variable A letter or other symbol that can be replaced by any number (or other object) from a set. **(6)**

variable matrix In the matrix equation $\begin{bmatrix} a & b \\ c & d \end{bmatrix} \cdot \begin{bmatrix} x \\ y \end{bmatrix} = \begin{bmatrix} e \\ f \end{bmatrix}$, the variable matrix is $\begin{bmatrix} x \\ y \end{bmatrix}$. **(622)**

vertex The point of intersection of a parabola with its axis of symmetry. **(526)**

vertex form of an equation for a parabola An equation of the form $y - k = a(x - h)^2$, where (h, k) is the vertex. **(716)**

vertical line A line with the equation $x = h$, where h is a real number. **(189)**

W

window The part of a coordinate grid that is visible on a graphing calculator. **(33)**

X

x-intercept The x-coordinate of a point where a graph intersects the x-axis. **(357)**

Xmax The greatest x-value (right edge) displayed on the window screen of a graphing calculator. **(34)**

Xmin The least x-value (left edge) displayed on the window screen of a graphing calculator. **(34)**

Xscl The x-scale of a graphing calculator. **(34)**

Y

y-intercept The y-coordinate of a point where a graph intersects the y-axis. **(350)**

Ymax The greatest y-value (top edge) displayed on the window screen of a graphing calculator. **(34)**

Ymin The least y-value (bottom edge) displayed on the window screen of a graphing calculator. **(34)**

Yscl The y-scale of a graphing calculator. **(34)**

Z

Zero Exponent Propery If x is any nonzero real number, then $x^0 = 1$. **(405)**

Zero Product Property For any real numbers a and b, if $ab = 0$, then either $a = 0$, $b = 0$, or both a and b equal 0. **(115)**

Index

Index

Cayley, Arthur, 622
Celsius, Anders, 221
Celsius scale, 221-222, 224
    linear relationship with Fahrenheit, 366
centigrade scale, 221
central tendency, measures of, 47
Chamberlain, Wilt, 394
change, See *rate of change*.
Chapter Review, 60-63, 125-127, 178-179,
    245-249, 320-323, 392-395, 452-455,
    521-523, 576-579, 650-653, 708-711,
    773-775, 833-835, See also *Review
    questions*.
Chapter Test, 60, 63, 125, 127, 178, 179, 245,
    249, 320, 323, 392, 452, 455, 521, 523,
    576, 579, 650, 653, 708, 711, 773, 775,
    833, 835
check, of a proof, 790-791
Chinese mathematicians, 492
chi-square statistic, 697-700
    calculating, 698
    reading table, 699
choosing from *n* objects repeatedly, 459-460
chunking, 532, 533
circle
    circumference, 835
    equation, 644
circular permutation, 695
clearing decimals, 170-171
clearing fractions to solve equations, 167-170
closed under an operation, 802
closure properties, 802
codes, encoding and decoding using
    formulas, 56
coefficient, 73
    distinguished from exponents, 74
    negative, solving inequalities with, 164
    positive, solving inequalities with, 163
coefficient matrix, 622
    inverse of, 629
coincide, 618
coincident lines, 617-618
Cole, Joe, 403
collinear points, 130
common denominator, 74
Commutative Property of Addition, 16, 113
Commutative Property of Multiplication, 16,
    113, 252, 669
Comparison Model for Subtraction, 42
complementary events, 283
complements, 283
complete factorization, 677
completing the square, 723-725
complex fractions, 259-260
    infinite repeating continued, 768
complex numbers, 797
    polynomials over, 663
compound inequalities, 227-231
    intersection and union of sets, 227-228
    intervals, 229

    solving with *and* and *or*, 230
compound interest, 398-399
    calculation of, 399-400
    formula, 405
    formula, with negative
        exponents, 476
    and polynomials, 656, 659
Compound Interest Formula, 400
compound sentences, 227-231
computer algebra system (CAS), 98
    EXPAND command, 168, 203
    EXPAND feature, 681
    factoring polynomials with, 737
    multiplying both sides of an
        equation, 167
    quadratic equations and, 712
    SIMPLIFY command, 168
    slope-intercept form vs. standard
        equation, 375
    SOLVE command, 597, 612
    solving general linear equations, 202-203
    solving linear equations, 140
    solving systems of equations, 597-598, 612
    string variable, 435
    substitution, 435
    testing for equivalence, 100-102
    value of, 525
computers
    memory, 422
    processing speed, 420-421
    value of, 436
conditional probability, 283
cone, volume of, 222, 667
conjectures, 830
consequent, 778
consistency, 511
    measuring with mean absolute deviation,
        53
consistent system, 616
constant function, 432
constant growth, graph of, 396-397, 415
constant matrix, 622
constant of variation, 353
constant slope of line, 334-335
constant term, 736
constant-decrease situations, 333, See also
    exponential decay.
    compared to exponential decay, 439-442
    patterns in, 130
constant-increase situations, 356-357, See
    also *exponential growth*.
    compared to exponential growth, 439-443
    patterns in, 130
continuous graph, 130
contrapositive, 784
converse, as check of proof, 790-791
converses of true statements, 784-785
conversion of temperatures, 221-222
conversion rates, 269-270
coordinate plane
    distance between two points in, 506-507

    moving in, 518
coordinates, 27
cord of wood, 661
cosine, 279
cost equation, 584-585
counterexample, 23, 512, 779
counting
    diagonals in convex polygon, 567
    multiplication principle, 458-459
crossword puzzles, and mathematics, 518
cryptography, public-key, 769
Cube of the Cube Root Property, 489, 493
cube of *x*, 493
cube roots, 488, 489, 493, 498
cubic polynomial, 663, 756
curve-fitting, See *line(s) of fit*.
Cyclopedia of Puzzles (Loyd), 209
cylinders
    surface area of, 667, 753, 800
    volume of, 486, 800

D

Darwin, Charles, 662
data, fitting a line to, 368-370
data set
    mean absolute deviation of, 48-50
    mean of, 47-48
    range of, 48
De La Cruz, Ulises, 403
Death Valley, California, 143
decay, See *exponential decay*.
decimal expansion, 819
decimals
    clearing, 170-171
    finite, 816
    multiplying by power of 10, 671-672
    ratios as, 275
    rational numbers vs. irrational, 816, 818
    repeating
        finding simple fractions for, 607
decreasing function, 431
deduction, 789
define a variable, 14
defined property, 790
degree of a monomial, 664
degree of a polynomial, 664
    checking operations with, 665
degrees of freedom, 697
density of object, calculation of, 316
dependent variable, 425, 426
depreciation, 412
Descartes, René, 144, 797
descriptive statistics, 697
deviation
    between actual and predicted, 370
    in altitude, 43
    of *a* from *e*, 697
    from the mean, 191-192
    mean absolute, 48
diagonal game, 388
diagonals, in polygons, 567, 735

jewelry and precious materials, 313
landscaping, 31, 828
military, 89
Olympic games, 379, 394
    swimming, 207, 580-581, 582, 587
radio stations, 462
rental of property, 219
rocket technology, 11
space, 577
    distances in, 496
    golf ball on the moon, 556
    planets, volumes of, 513
space industry, 159, 232
sports
    baseball, 195, 306, 599, 643
    basketball, 208, 290-291, 378, 385, 551, 606, 722, 727
    football, 169, 549, 643, 701
    golf, 90, 192, 722
    hockey, 638, 783
    hurling, 774
    soccer, 32, 305, 403, 550
    softball, 50
    swimming and diving, 371, 554, 556, 558, 562
    tennis, 531
    track and field, 364, 379, 431, 576, 590
    volleyball, 385, 694
stocks and dividends, 172
transportation, 28, 240
    airports and airplanes, 279, 602, 605, 621
    car and computer numbers, 645
    car purchases, 468
    car trips, 536
    driver age and accidents, 542
    school buses, 446
    speed limits, 781
    traffic lights, 537
    trains, 133
zookeeping, 145
matrices (matrix), 622
    2 × 2 identity, 626, 629-630
    3 × 3 identity, 628
    inverse 2 × 2, 631
    inverse 2 × 2, formula for, 634
    multiplication of 2 × 2, 623-624
    solving a system, 629-632
    types of, 622
matrix form of a system, 623
matrix method
    solving a system, 629-632
    summary of, 631-632
matrix multiplication, 623-625
McNabb, Donovan, 643
mean
    of a data set, 47-48
    deviation from, 191-192
mean absolute deviation (m.a.d.), 47, 48
    algorithm for finding, 50
    of a data set, 48-50

measuring consistency, 53
means, in proportions, 301-302
Means-Extremes Property, 301, 302
median, and percentiles, 291, 292
method of testing a point, 382
midpoint of a segment, 227
miles per hour, 264
mixed number, 816
models
    exponential decay, 411, 419-420
    exponential growth, 420-421
    growth for powering, 405
    of life expectancy, 370
    population, See *population models.*
    for weather forecasting, 284
monomial, 663, See also *binomials.*
    degree of, 664
    factoring, 675-678
    multiplication by polynomial, 669-671
Moore, Gordon, 690
Morton, J. Sterling, 210
most likely outcome, 281-282
mu (mean), 47
multiplication
    of algebraic fractions, 252-253
    counting principle, 458-459
    of decimal by power of 10, 671-672
    fact triangle, 112
    by growth factor, 404
    of inequalities, 156-157, 211
    matrices, 2 × 2, 624-625
    matrix, 623-624
    of polynomial by monomial, 669-671
    of polynomials, 680-682
    power of a power, 466
    power of a product, 481-482
    of powers with different bases, 466
    of powers with same base, 464-465
    properties
        of -1, 84, 86
        associative, 9, 113, 252, 669
        commutative, 16, 113, 252, 669
        distributive, over addition, 66
        distributive, over subtraction, 67
        of equality, 113, 139, 167
        identity, 113, 252
        of inequality, 155, 156-157, 159, 210, 211, 230
        multiplying fractions, 252-253
        power of a power, 466
        power of a product, 481-482
        product of powers, 465
        product of square roots, 498
        related facts, of multiplication and division, 113-114

repeated, of powers, 398
of rates, 269-270
solving a system of equations, 608-612
of square roots, 497-502
of sum and difference of two numbers, 687-688
of two odd numbers, 804-805
by zero, 114-115
Multiplication Counting Principle, 458-459
    in permutations, 691
    in polynomials, 680, 681
multiplication method for solving a system, 608, 609
Multiplication Property of -1, 84, 86
Multiplication Property of Equality, 113, 139
    clearing fractions with, 167
Multiplication Property of Inequality, 155, 156-157, 159, 210, 211, 230
Multiplication Property of Zero, 115
Multiplicative Identity Property, 113, 116, 252
multiplicative inverse, 113, 252
Multiplicative Inverse Property, 116
multiplier, for clearing fractions, 167-168
Multiplying Fractions Property, 252-253
multiplying through (process), 167

N

n factorial, 691, 693-694
n! symbol, 693
Nash, Steve, 208
National Center for Health Statistics, 280
negative coefficients, solving inequalities with, 164
Negative Exponent Property, 474
Negative Exponent Property for Fractions, 475, 481
negative exponents
    applying power of a power property, 477-478
    for fractions, 475-476
    value of power with, 474-475
negative first power, 475
negative fractions, 265
negative rate of change, 327, 330
negative root, 489
negative slopes, 335
never true, 216-218
nonintersecting parallel lines, 616-617
nonlinear systems, 640-642
nonnegative real numbers, 29
± notation, 229
notation, scientific, See *scientific notation.*
Note-Taking Tips, 7, 17, 86, 131, 141, 146, 164, 170, 185, 190, 212, 230, 282, 311, 329, 335, 352, 363, 377, 400, 427, 466, 471, 482, 506, 529, 545, 546, 560, 618, 631, 670, 682, 698, 717, 744, 750
Now/Next method, 406, 439
Noyce, Robert, 420
*n*th power, 398
null set, 584, 638

Index

Index

Z

zero
    division by, 113, 114-115, 265, 761
    getting closer and closer, 241
    multiplication properties, 112, 115
    as power, 470
    as special number for addition, 108-109
Zero Exponent Property, 405
zero power, 470
    of any number, 405
    of zero, 405, 410
Zero Product Property, 115
    used in factored form, 729, 731
zero rate of change, 329, 330
zero slope, 335, 343
zero the dive, 346
zooming in and out, *Powers of Ten* (movie),
    448

Photo Credits

Chapters 7–13

Cover: ©Scott McDermott/Corbis, cover **front**, **back**. ©AFP/Getty Images. p. **830** *right*; ©age fotostock/SuperStock, p. **v** *right*; ©Mike Agliolo/Photo Researchers, Inc., p. **420**; ©Altrendo Images/Getty Images, pp. **viii** *left*, **424-425**; ©AP/ Wide World Photos, pp. **403, 549, 554, 558, 582, 621, 643, 694, 727, 783**; ©BananaStock/Jupiterimages, p. **586**; ©BananaStock/PunchStock, p. **480**; ©Jean Louis Batt/Taxi/Getty Images, p. **472**; ©Charles Bowman/Robert Harding, p. **785**; ©Tom Brakefield/Getty Images, p. **444**; ©Jiri Castka/Shutterstock, p. **404**; ©Creatas/PunchStock, p. **543**; ©Alfredo Dagli Orti/Corbis, p. **517**; ©Gianni Dagli Orti/Corbis, p. **627** *bottom*; ©Phil Degginger/Alamy, p. **572**; ©Phil Degginger/Stone/Getty Images, p. **408**; ©Digital Vision Ltd., p. **722**; ©Digital Vision/Getty Images, p. **442**; ©Digital Vision/PunchStock, p. **661**; ©Digital Vision/SuperStock, p. **692**; ©Hadi Djunaedi/iStockphoto, p. **504**; ©Dynamic Graphics Group/IT Stock Free/Alamy, p. **646**; ©Wayne Eardley/Masterfile, p. **424**; ©Sean Ellis/Stone/Getty Images, p. **695**; ©Enigma/Alamy, pp. **vii** *left*, **396-397**; ©Don Farrall/Photodisc/Getty Images, p. **v**, *left*; ©Arlene Jean Gee/Shutterstock, p. **741**; ©Getty Images/Steve Allen, p. **599**; ©Getty Images/SW Productions, p. **409**; ©Philip Gould/Corbis, p. **417**; ©The Granger Collection, N.Y., p. **824**; ©Tomasz Gulla/Shutterstock, p. **658**; ©Tom Hahn/iStockphoto, p. **496**; ©Toru Hanai/Reuters/Corbis, p. **505**; ©Gavin Hellier/Robert Harding World Imagery, Getty Images, p. **vi**, *left*; ©Hemera Technologies/Jupiterimages, p. **638**; ©Walter Hodges/Brand X Pictures/Jupiterimages, p. **590**; ©Jenny Horne/Shutterstock, p. **769**; ©Image Ideas, Inc./Indexstock, p. **627** *hammer, right*; ©INTERFOTO Pressebildagentur/Alamy, p. **819**; ©Iraq Museum, Baghdad/Bridgeman Art Library, p. **796**; ©Pekka Jaakkola/ Shutterstock, p. **794**; ©Jupiterimages Corporation, p. **531**; ©Robb Kendrick/Aurora/Getty Images, p. **588**; ©Nick Koudis/ Getty Images, p. **447**; ©Art Kowalsky/Alamy, pp. **x** *left*, **776-777**; ©Matthias Kulka/Corbis, p. **830** *left*; ©Lana Langlois/ Shutterstock, p. **592**; ©Eric Lessing/Art Resource, NY, pp. **ix** *right*, **712-713**; ©Library of Congress, Prints and Photographs Division [LC-USZ62-117122], p. **700**; ©Jim Linna/Photodisc/Getty Images, p. **779**; ©Jim Lopes/Shutterstock, p. **604**; ©Dennis MacDonald/PhotoEdit, pp. **446, 564**; ©Will & Deni McIntyre/Corbis, p. **583**; ©Ian Mckinnell/Getty Images, p. **iv** *right*; ©mdd/Shutterstock, pp. **ix** *left*, **654-655**; ©Simon Marcus/Corbis, p. **571** *bottom*; ©Jeffrey Markowitz/Corbis Sygma, p. **463**; ©Lori Martin/Shutterstock, p. **518**; ©Doug Menuez/Getty Images, p. **585**; ©Tan Wei Ming/Shutterstock, p. **620**; ©Marvin Nauman/FEMA News Photo, p. **569**; Courtesy NBA Photos, p. **606** *top, bottom*; ©Michael Newman/PhotoEdit, pp. **458, 460, 614**; ©Greg Nicholas/iStockphoto, p. **412**; ©Oleg Nikishin/Getty Images Sport/Getty Images, p. **611**; ©Phillip Novess/ Shutterstock, p. **633**; ©Shawn Pecor/Shutterstock, p. **550**; ©Photodisc/PunchStock, p. **468**; ©PhotoSpin, Inc., p. **428**; ©Frederic Pitchal/Corbis Sygma, p. **510**; ©Plush Studios/Bill Reitzel/Blend Images/Getty Images, p. **594**; ©Siede Preis/ Getty Images, p. **627** *wrench, right*; ©Adam Pretty/Reportage/Getty Images, pp. **viii** *right*, **580-581**; ©Purestock/SuperStock, p. **828**; ©Ken Reid/Taxi/Getty Images, p. **487**; ©Elena Rooraid/PhotoEdit, p. **436**; ©Deborah Roundtree/The Image Bank/ Getty Images, pp. **vii** *right*, **456-457**; ©Royalty-Free/Corbis, pp. **470, 536, 660**; ©Rubberball/Getty Images, p. **551**; ©Len Rubenstein/Index Stock Imagery, Inc., p. **462**; ©Carol Schultz/Painet, p. **537**; ©SGC/Shutterstock, p. **571** *top*; ©C. Sherburne/ PhotoLink/Getty Images, p. **787**; ©Dwight Smith/Shutterstock, p. **602**; ©Johnathan Smith/Cordaiy Photo Library/Corbis, p. **807**; ©Joseph Sohm/VisionsofAmerica.com/Photodisc/Getty Images, p. **vi**, *right*; ©Space Frontiers/Taxi/Getty Images, p. **704**; ©SSPL/The Image Works, p. **645**; ©Doug Steley/Alamy, p. **702**; ©Stockbyte/PunchStock Images, p. **781**; ©Stockdisc/ PunchStock, p. **501**; ©Rudy Sulgan/Corbis, p. **565**; ©SW Productions/Getty Images, p. **821**; ©ThinkStock LLC/Index Stock Imagery, Inc., p. **516**; ©Trip/Alamy, p. **797**; ©US Navy via CNP/CNP/Corbis, p. **448**; ©Visual Arts Library (London)/Alamy, p. **768**; ©Drazen Vukelic/Shutterstock, p. **430**; ©Stuart Westmorland/Corbis, p. **407**; ©Ross Woodhall/Taxi/Getty Images, p. **iv**, *left*; ©Yellow Dog Productions/The Image Bank/Getty Images, p. **598**; ©Kenneth C. Zirkel/iStockphoto, p. **400**;

Illustrations: Ron Carboni

Acknowledgements: It is impossible for UCSMP to thank all the people who have helped create and test these books. We wish particularly to thank Carol Siegel, who coordinated the use of the test materials in the schools; Kathleen Andersen, Aisha Bradshaw, Paul Campbell, Jena Dropela, Meri Fohran, Lisa Hodges, Rachel Huddleston, Evan Jenkins, Nurit Kirshenbaum, Lindsay Knight, Nathaniel Loman, Matthew McCrea, Jadele McPherson, Erin Moore, Dylan Murphy, Gretchen Neidhardt, Jennifer Perton, Daniel Rosenthal, Luke I. Sandberg, Sean Schulte, Andrew L. Shu, Emily Small, John Stevenson, James Thatcher, Alex Tomasik, Erica Traut, Alex Yablon, and Melissa Yeung.

We wish to acknowledge the generous support of the Amoco Foundation and the Carnegie Corporation of New York in helping to make it possible for the first edition of these materials to be developed, tested, and distributed, and the additional support of the Amoco Foundation for the second edition.

We wish to acknowledge the contribution of the text *Algebra Through Applications with Probability and Statistics*, by Zalman Usiskin (NCTM, 1979), developed with funds from the National Science Foundation, to some of the conceptualizations and problems used in this book.